CT M

PHYSICS
in FOCUS

PHYSICS
in FOCUS

Michael Brimicombe

Nelson

Thomas Nelson and Sons Ltd
Nelson House   Mayfield Road
Walton-on-Thames   Surrey
KT12 5PL   UK

51 York Place
Edinburgh
EH1 3JD   UK

Thomas Nelson (Hong Kong) Ltd
Toppan Building 10/F
22A Westlands Road
Quarry Bay   Hong Kong

Distributed in Australia by

Thomas Nelson Australia
480 La Trobe Street
Melbourne   Victoria 3000
and in Sydney, Brisbane, Adelaide and Perth

© Michael Brimicombe 1990
First published by Thomas Nelson and Sons Ltd 1990
ISBN 0–17–448174–8
NPN 987654321
Printed in Hong Kong

Acknowledgement is due to the following for permission
to use photographs:

Fig. 6.59, Allsport;
Fig. 27.31, Orville Andrews/Science Photo Library;
Fig. 21.54, Atomic Energy Authority;
Fig. 31.12, Automobile Association;
Figs 7.4 (right), 32.8, Alex Bartel/Science Photo Library;
Fig. 32.13, Beamish, The North of England Open Air
Museum, County Durham;
Figs 21.12, 22.20, 23.30, Lawrence Berkeley/Science
Photo Library;
Fig. 23.53, R de Blois, C. D. Graham;
Fig. 4.36, Martin Bond/Science Photo Library;
Fig. 9.27, British Aerospace;
Fig. 1.2, Dr Jeremy Burgess/Science Photo Library;
Figs 6.49, 6.58, 26.37 (right), 27.22 J. Allan Cash;
Fig. 25.4, CEGB;
Fig. 23.21, CERN;
Figs. 7.28, 7.37, 7.38, 7.51, 21.5, 21.6, 21.7, 23.13, 25.31,
26.17, 26.18, 26.31, 27.43, 30.24, 31.18, 32.19, 32.31, John
Clark;
Fig. 32.9, Dr Ray Clark/Science Photo Library;
Fig. 32.21, Andrew Clarke/Science Photo Library;
p. 39 (both), Bruce Coleman;
Figs 15.48, 17.34, 26.15, Simon James Collier;
Fig. 26.14, Adam Hart Davis/Science Photo Library;
Fig. 20.6, Dr Espenar/Science Photo Library;
Fig. 5.53, Ford Motor Company;
Fig. 2.1, Lowell Georgin/Science Photo Library;
Fig. 27.41, Ronald Grant Archive;
Figs 4.33, 5.66, 10.13, 15.23, 23.15, Griffin and George;
Fig. 6.45, C. M. Guy/Robert Harding;
Figs 6.46, 7.4 (middle left), 20.20, 20.21, 27.2, 27.49,
Robert Harding Picture Library;
Fig. 15.22 (both), Property Services Agency/HMSO
Publications;
Fig. 18.26, Holt Studios;
Fig. 6.21, E. Hummel/Zefa;
Fig. 28.29, Dr. M. B. Hursthouse/Science Photo Library;
Fig. 17.38, Institute of Civil Engineers;
Fig. 22.28, Joint European Torus (JET) Laboratory;
Fig. 29.28, Claus Jonsson;
Fig. 12.10, John Kyle;
Figs 27.46, 27.58, E. Leitz (Instruments) Ltd;
Fig. 21.42, Will and Deni Macintyre/Science Photo
Library;
Fig. 1.1, The Mansell Collection;
Fig. 32.22, Tom McHugh/Science Photo Library;
Fig. 11.6, Mike McNamee/Science Photo Library;
Fig. 32.14 (asbestos suit), A De Menil/Science Photo
Library;

Fig. 17.11, Directorate of Public Affairs/Metropolitan
Police;
Figs 20.5, 20.8 (all), 32.17, NASA/Science Photo Library;
Fig. 27.6, National Museum of Photography;
Figs 2.4, 2.17, 10.17, National Physical Laboratory;
Fig. 27.56, Olympus;
Fig. 24.17, David Parker/Science Photo Library;
Fig. 3.6, Permaquip;
Fig. 27.33, Phillips;
Fig. 23.27, Professor G. Piragino/Science Photo Library;
Fig. 22.29, Philippe Plailly/Science Photo Library;
Fig. 7.56, Axel Poignant;
Fig. 21.53, Popperfoto;
Figs 2.3, 6.51, 7.4 (top left, bottom left), 7.28, 7.42, 10.9,
15.34, 15.46, 26.23, 32.14 (teapot), Stuart Powles;
Figs 12.19, 14.62, 29.5, Radiospares;
Fig. 26.22, Mikki Rain/Science Photo Library;
Figs 4.22, 5.31, Rolls Royce;
Fig. 25.9, Ann Ronan;
Fig. 5.3, Rev. Ronald Royers/Science Photo Library;
Figs 1.3, 21.11, Science Museum;
Figs 5.15, 7.29, 7.30, 7.39, 10.23, 19.33, 20.18, 20.19,
21.21, 29.30, Science Photo Library;
Figs 11.38, 11.39, 13.1, 14.55, Solex;
Fig. 4.38, Sinclair Stammers/Science Photo Library;
Figs 18.16, 32.29, Thomas Nelson and Sons Ltd;
Fig. 2.28, Tony Stone Worldwide;
Figs 9.23, 15.44, Topham Picture Library;
Figs 5.35, Transport and Road Research Laboratory;
Fig. 10.6, Alexander Tsiaras/Science Photo Library;
Figs 4.7, 4.8, 4.9, 4.28, 4.29, 4.30, 4.31, 5.10, 7.60, 7.65,
10.1, 10.4, 10.5, 10.14, 10.15, 10.46, 11.20, 12.2, 13.2,
14.1, 16.2, 17.43, 21.15, 22.4, 23.1, 23.2, 23.22, 24.9,
24.20, 24.21, 24.24, 24.32, 24.48, 25.5, 26.25, 26.26, 26.27,
27.8, 27.45, 27.48, 28.3, 32.7, 32.13 (marathon man), John
Walmsley;
Fig. 19.17, John Walsh/Science Photo Library;
Figs. 5.42, 6.47, 7.22, Zefa;

The publishers would also like to thank the following for
all their help and cooperation:

Emilie Bell (Science Photo Library), Griffin and George,
Texas Instruments, Comet, Supervision TV, Solex, R.S.
Components, Vinten, Joint European Torus, E. Leitz
(Instruments), Klochner Moeller, Rolls Royce, Ford,
CEGB, Gavin M. Rees (Science Museum), Michael John
Collier and the Staff and Pupils of The Cedars Upper
School.

P R E F A C E

This book has been written with the needs of today's sixth-form students firmly in mind. It provides complete coverage of all the areas of physics mentioned in A-level syllabuses and similar courses. A graduated approach has been adopted, which will ease the transition from physics or 'broad-and-balanced' science at GCSE to the narrower and more demanding in-depth style of A-level physics and similar syllabuses.

The recent introduction of GCSE poses problems for students taking A-level courses. They launch themselves into sixth form studies from a smaller knowledge base than their predecessors, yet they have to reach the same target at the end of the course. However, GCSE aims to foster skills and attitudes to science which are traditionally part of good sixth-form teaching. Providing that an A-level course takes account of their lack of specialist knowledge and leads them gradually up to A-level standard, today's sixth form students should be successful.

In order to help the student, each chapter in this book is divided into two or three sections, each of a digestible length. Within each section, there is mainstream text which introduces the ideas, plus 'boxes' which deal with applications, advanced derivations and references to other chapters in the book. At the end of each section there is a list of learning objectives. This should help the students to realise what they should have learnt from their study, as well as providing guidance for note-making. The questions (of which there are about 450 in total) have been carefully designed and graduated to test and reinforce the student's understanding of that section. Some of the early questions are similar to worked examples to boost the confidence of weak students, whereas later questions are at full A-level standard. Comprehensive hints and answers to all of the numerical problems are provided at the end of the book . A large appendix summarises the mathematical tools which are introduced and explained at appropriate points in the text.

The 32 chapters are grouped into 11 blocks according to their common theme. Summaries at the end of each block provide a useful focus for revision, as well as a reference source during the study of subsequent blocks. The order of presentation of material is such that later chapters build on the knowledge and skills imparted by study of earlier chapters. In particular, the book makes no assumptions about which areas of physics the student has studied at GCSE: complete and thorough coverage of basic concepts is provided at the start of each block. Of course, no student need study all of the material in this book — different exam boards have different syllabus requirements. We have tried to group the material into chapters in such a way that students following any particular syllabus can easily omit whole chapters or sections which are irrelevant to their course of study.

The book contains no details for the laboratory work which is an indispensible part of any A-level physics course. Nevertheless, wherever possible it discusses the importance of measurement and exploration using apparatus commonly to be found in a sixth-form laboratory. The book attempts to supplement the practical aspects of physics, guiding the student in easy stages from GCSE science to A-level physics.

Just as no man is an island, no author works alone. This is especially true of a book of this size and complexity. It could not have been produced without the active support and encouragement of many people. Foremost among these must be the staff at Thomas Nelson and Sons Ltd. My grateful thanks must also go to my colleagues in the science department at the Cedars Upper School for their patience and understanding, especially when I took half a term off to concentrate on this book. Dr Virginia Stacey has done a very thorough job of reading the text and tackling all of the problems; along with my wife Jane, she has probably corrected most of my errors of physics. Any errors which remain are my own.

No A-level physics book can be truly original. Any writer will be heavily influenced by the style and approach of what he regards as the successful predecessors of his own attempt. My own attitudes and approaches to physics teaching have been dominated by two books in particular. Eric Rogers' *Physics for the Inquiring Mind*, although not written as a school textbook, helped me to think out successful strategies for learning physics during the early stages in my teaching career. My question style is inevitably based on that of Wilson and Hackett's *Inquiring into Physics*. This excellent collection of physics problems placed in a real context has been the model for many of the questions in my own book. Finally, the Nuffield A-level physics initiatives of recent years have given me much food for thought.

Michael Brimicombe, 1990

C O N T E N T S

1

INTRODUCTION

This chapter is probably the most important one in the book. Its purpose is two-fold. The first part will try to clarify what advanced level physics is all about and explain the benefits you can expect to gain by studying it. The second part will describe the structure of the book and explain how it will help you learn the skills, knowledge and attitudes that are necessary for success in physics. *Don't be tempted to skip this chapter!* You are probably starting a two-year course of study which will use up many hours of your time — a little thought about the point of the whole exercise and some advice on efficient learning is very valuable at this stage. Physics is certainly challenging and often demanding, but can also be fun and rewarding if you go about it the right way!

PHYSICS

Physics can be thought of as a game for any number of players who take part at a variety of levels. It has its great solo players who make the new moves and take the game into fresh areas of the board. Most professionals who earn their living by physics specialise in practising and perfecting a limited range of moves at one edge of the play area. The majority of players participate at amateur level — they try out moves and tactics away from the advancing edges and derive great satisfaction from following the moves made by the great soloists and teams of the past, discovering patterns and links for themselves along the way. Finally, there is a large contingent of spectators who take a global view of the game and use its discoveries to provide the foundations of the technologies which maintain our civilisation.

Modelling reality

One of the features which makes humans different from animals is their basic need to find out how their environment works and adapt it to their own needs. (Most living organisms appear to adapt to their environment.) At its most fundamental level, physics is about finding out how the Universe works. One of the outcomes is the wide range of technologies which are used to support our lifestyle.

For example, several thousand years ago people realised that the changing positions of the stars in the sky could be used to predict the best time of year to plant their crops. This information was clearly vital to civilisations which relied on organised agriculture for their food. Resources

Figure 1.1 The Dresden Codex, part of an ancient Mayan calendar which could be used to predict, among other things, the positions of Venus and Saturn in the night sky over Central America

were made available for a chosen few (the first professional scientists) to study the stars at night and chart their progress during the year. They watched the planets slowly wander among the stars in complicated cycles and noticed how the Moon and Sun changed their positions against the background of fixed stars in monthly and yearly timescales. These early astronomers invariably did more than just make observations and abstract patterns from them: they tried to make sense of the patterns with the help of **models**. In this way they could extrapolate to the future, building calendars and confidently predicting eclipses of the Sun and Moon (figure 1.1).

Models are the mental pictures that attempt to *explain* what we know, not to just to *describe* it. A typical early model of the Universe is illustrated in figure 1.2 — it is the one suggested by Pythagoras about 2500 years ago. It consists of a number of transparent concentric spheres, each rotating at a different speed and supporting a different part of the Universe. That model fulfilled a basic need among Greek astronomers to make sense of the facts. By thinking about the model, the Greeks felt that they understood why the heavens behaved the way they did. In particular, by applying some mathematics to their model, they could predict (with fairly modest success) how the heavens would change in the future. The Babylonians and Egyptians used models which were more abstract, based on the use of tables of numbers. These models were purely mathematical and more successful at making predictions. However, the Greek style of model, a combination of a mental picture and mathematics, represents the successful way forwards in physics. The right model, such as the one suggested by Copernicus about 400 years ago (figure 1.3), not only allowed a close match between prediction and observation, but sparked off the development of other models (such as Newtonian gravitation) to explain it.

Figure 1.2 The Ptolemaic world system, developed in the third century BC. The Earth is at the centre (with its four 'elements': earth, water, fire and air). The Moon, Mercury, Venus, the Sun, Mars, Jupiter and Saturn move around the Earth in circular orbits of increasing radius

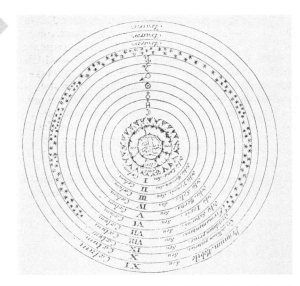

Figure 1.3 The Copernican model of the Solar system. Notice that the Sun is at the centre with the planets moving around it in circular orbits. In practice, the planets follow elliptical (egg-shaped) orbits. Elliptical orbits are difficult to obtain with a mechanical model!

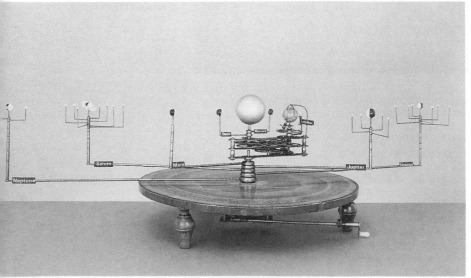

Accumulated experience

The human species is probably unique in the way that it transmits knowledge and understanding from one generation to the next. Education has always been a central feature of human culture. Each generation is taught to understand and use the knowledge and experience gained by all of the previous generations. In particular, the models of physics are passed down through time, being refined and improved at the same time. So you can think of this book as containing some of the distilled wisdom of the ages, describing a limited number of models which have allowed previous generations to successfully explain their environment and use it for their own ends. The number of these models which you will meet as part of your physics course is limited for two reasons. First, the models used at the forefront of physics require the use of very sophisticated mathematical techniques (such as differential calculus and Riemannian geometry). Secondly, many models in physics are like brick walls (figure 1.4)! Each model is based on some other models — unless you have a thorough understanding of the underlying models, a particular model may be incomprehensible! So this book aims to give you a good understanding of the fundamental concepts and models (such as mass, energy, momentum, field, wave and particle) so that you can appreciate how they have been used in the numerous applications described in the text. Along the way you should acquire the important skills of comprehension, abstraction, precision, estimation and clarity of thought. Ultimately you will end up with a clearer understanding of the world you live in.

USING THE BOOK

If you are using this book as a reference source, dipping into it whenever needed, you are probably not reading this paragraph. So what follows assumes that you are using this book as part of your course.

Structure

The book contains 32 chapters, and five appendices near the end of the book provide extra information and help with the maths. The chapters are grouped into eleven blocks, with a summary at the end of each block.

A chapter consists of a number of short sections, each short enough for you to work through in one or two sittings. Within the mainstream text you will find 'boxes' with one of three symbols in their top right-hand corner. These boxes deal with:

applications 🖝

references to other chapters ▶▶ / ◀◀

advanced topics **!**

It is best to stick to the mainstream text on your first read through, returning to the applications boxes once you are familiar with the ideas. This is important — many of the worked examples of ideas presented in the mainstream text are related to these applications.

Don't worry if you have difficulty in understanding advanced topic boxes — this will not prevent you from making progress in subsequent sections.

The forward references will make more sense towards the end of the course; in the meantime they will give you 'food for thought' and an idea of what is to come!

Throughout the book, you will notice some mathematical equations appear on a special grey background. These are key formulae, which you will need to know and understand.

Each section ends with a list of objectives followed by some questions. The objectives should be used as a checklist: they tell you what you should have learnt by studying that section. The questions which follow are designed to reinforce your understanding of the material.

Studying physics is an art that you can only acquire by practice. Each section will present a few new ideas and show how they can be incorporated into the physics you already know. Think carefully as you read, and don't be afraid to re-read anything you don't understand. In particular, make sure that you follow the steps in any piece of algebra or arithmetic presented in the mainstream text or applications 'boxes'. (Whether or not you are mathematical, you need to know your way around Appendix B which deals with mathematics for physics.) This will help you when you get to the questions at the end of the section. In many cases, they are similar to the examples described in that section. Working out the answers to questions is an excellent way of reinforcing your understanding of a model — it forces you to apply the model to an actual situation. If you get the answer right (and they are all listed, with some hints, towards the end of the book) you obviously understand the physics you used.

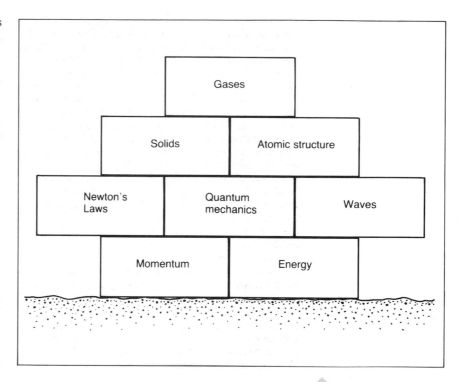

Figure 1.4 Modelling physics as a brick wall!

Each chapter assumes that you understand all of the mainstream material presented in the chapters before it. It is inevitable that you will come across statements or ideas which are unfamiliar or which you have forgotten. If this bothers you (and it may stop you making further progress), don't hesitate to consult the index and find out where the ideas are first explained in the book. Appendix A may also prove to be useful. It contains all of the formulae and definitions of the symbols they contain. Each block of chapters is terminated with a summary of its contents. This acts as a useful point for backwards reference as you move forwards through the book, as well as help during revision for exams.

FORCES

2

SOLIDS UNDER STRESS

Things which can preserve their shape and size are called **solids**. Concrete is a typical solid. It doesn't appear to change its shape when left alone. (Think about all those structures made of concrete which populate our towns and cities (figure 2.1). We rely on them maintaining their shape year after year.) Of course, a swift blow with a sledgehammer can change the shape of a lump of concrete, but this remoulding process never seems to change the total amount of concrete. The size of the bits left after the hammer blow always seems to add up to the size of the original block. Using standard physics jargon, solids appear to **conserve** volume and shape. In fact, as this chapter will explain, the volume and shape of any solid can be changed slightly. Such changes form the basis of instruments which can be used to measure the important properties of mass and weight.

STACKING SOLIDS

We are going to describe a **thought experiment** to illustrate one of the less obvious properties of solids. A thought experiment is one which could be performed in principle; but, in practice, it might be difficult to arrange. By assuming that perfect measuring instruments are available, a thought experiment is a good way of discussing physics. The results of this particular thought experiment will illustrate the general behaviour of solid objects when they are stacked one on top of each other.

Figure 2.1   The Hoover Dam (the highest in the USA) — one of the many important structures made out of concrete whose shape is not supposed to change

The experiment

We will suppose that you have a number of identical blocks made out of the same material. That material has all of the properties of a typical solid (in this case nylon). The experiment is very simple. It involves observing one of the blocks as the others are stacked on top of it to form a column. The arrangement is shown in figure 2.2. To make it easier to visualise, each block will be a cube with sides of length 2.5 cm (toy building-brick size). So the experiment is concerned with finding out what happens to a plastic toy brick when a large number of similar bricks are piled on top of it.

Intuitive results

Your everyday experience of stacking plates or bricks would lead you to expect that the item at the base of the column is exactly the same as the one at the top. (Think of comparing the bricks at the bottom of a house with those at the top.) Your **intuition** (a jargon word for common sense obtained from many years of studying the behaviour of your environment) tells you that the size of a solid is independent of its place in the column. However, your intuition should only be trusted to within the precision of the measuring instruments that you use in everyday life. Your eyes can probably judge the relative size of two objects to (at best) the nearest millimetre. All that intuition tells you is that a 25 mm brick changes by less than 1 mm as other bricks are stacked on top of it (figure 2.3).

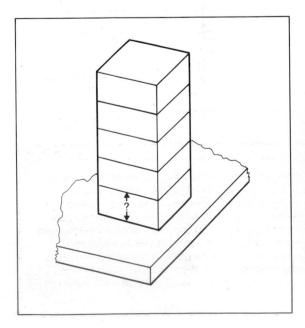

Figure 2.2   A column of blocks

So you ought to observe the brick at the bottom of the column with a **measuring instrument** such as a ruler. This allows you to state the results of your observations in the form of numbers. You can then make **quantitative** statements about the experiment. However, you cannot assume that we can measure the dimensions of the bottom brick to any desired precision. Even though we are dealing with a thought experiment, we must make sure that we stick with the restrictions of the real world. We need to consider how we might set about measuring the height of the bottom brick to a high degree of precision.

Measuring length

We are concerned with measuring the height of a toy brick. This is about 0.025 m, so it will make sense to use a smaller unit, the millimetre (see Appendix E). A ruler marked off in millimetres held against a brick and viewed with the naked eye will allow you to measure the length of the brick with a precision, at best, of ±0.5 mm.

A **vernier gauge** held against the ruler could give you a precision of ±0.05 mm. This is the arrangement used in **calipers** (figure 2.5). The zero mark on the gauge is used to determine the length of the object being measured to the nearest whole millimetre. The mark on the gauge which coincides with a millimetre marking on the ruler then tells you how many tenths of a millimetre you have to add to get the length of the object.

For even greater precision (±0.005 mm) you could use a **micrometer screw gauge**, as shown in figure 2.6. The screw thread inside the gauge is built so that it has a pitch of 1 mm, i.e. one turn of the screw moves it along by one millimetre. The barrel of the screw is marked off into 100 equal intervals, so that movements of the end of the screw by 1/200th of a millimetre (5 μm) can be detected with ease.

Figure 2.3 Can you tell if this photograph of a brick wall has been printed the right way up?

Figure 2.4 A collection of standard gauges as used in manufacturing industry for checking the calibration of their measuring instruments. Each block of metal has end faces which are polished flat and are accurately parallel. The distance between those faces has been accurately measured in a standards laboratory

Figure 2.5 Vernier calipers

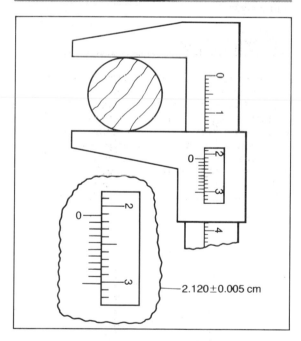

2.120±0.005 cm

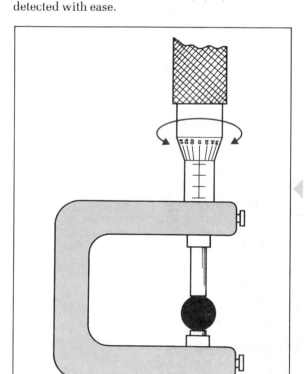

Figure 2.6 Micrometer screw gauge

STANDARD LENGTH ▶▶ 26

The international standard unit for measuring length is the **metre**. The speed of light in a vacuum is defined to be *exactly* 299 792 458 metres per second (m s^{-1}). So the length of an object can, in principle, be measured by finding out how long it takes light to get from one end of it to the other. This precise (but cumbersome) definition (the **primary standard**) ensures that everybody agrees exactly what one metre means. It allows **secondary standards**, which are carefully built rulers, to be checked against the primary standard from time to time. Commercial measuring instruments can then be calibrated with these secondary standards. Some examples of secondary standards are shown in figure 2.4.

The most precise method which can be easily used in a laboratory is illustrated in figure 2.7. The apparatus is known as an **interferometer**: it can detect movements with a precision of about 0.5 μm. Although an interferometer is good at measuring small changes in the height of the brick, it is not very convenient for measuring its absolute height. So we are going to measure the height of the brick with a pair of calipers before it has other bricks placed on it. This gives 25.2 ± 0.1 mm for the initial height of the brick. We can then use the interferometer to measure how that height changes with a precision of ±0.000317 mm.

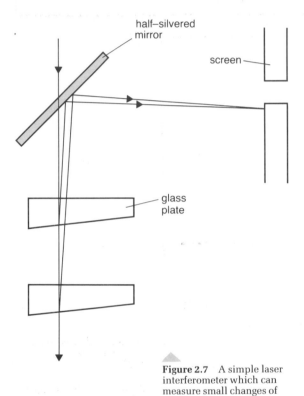

half–silvered mirror

screen

glass plate

Figure 2.7 A simple laser interferometer which can measure small changes of distance between the two glass plates

INTERFEROMETERS ▶▶ 28

An interferometer of the type shown in figure 2.7 can measure changes of length as little as 0.32 μm. This is how it works.

The red light from the helium−neon laser has a well-defined wavelength of 633 nm. The thin beam of light which emerges from the laser is first expanded by a couple of lenses. It then passes through a pair of glass plates, each one firmly attached to one end of the brick. Each time that the beam passes from one medium to another (air to glass, or glass to air) 4% of it is reflected. The plates have to be carefully adjusted so that the two inner faces of the interferometer are almost parallel to each other. Then the beams reflected from those faces will overlap at the screen after reflection off the half-silvered mirror.

The two overlapping beams will have a set of dark stripes running across them, as shown in figure 2.8. These **fringes** are due to destructive interference between the two beams. (The extra distance covered by one of the beams is almost exactly twice the distance between the interferometer plates; there will be destructive interference at the screen if this equals a whole number of wavelengths of the laser light.) As the plates of the interferometer move towards or away from each other, the pattern of stripes moves across the spot on the screen. A photodiode placed in the centre of the screen can detect the movement of the dark and bright stripes. The signal from the photodiode is sent to an electronic counter so that the number of fringes which pass across the photodiode can be recorded. Each fringe going past the photodiode corresponds to a displacement of half a wavelength (317 nm) of the plates. So if the counter reading changes by 6 when a brick is placed on the pile, the bottom brick must have shrunk by 6 × 317 = 1902 ± 317 μm.

Figure 2.8 The red fringes on the screen where the two reflected beams overlap

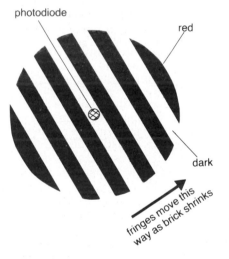

photodiode

red

dark

fringes move this way as brick shrinks

PRESSURE ▶▶ 8

Atmospheric pressure is 1.01×10^5 Pa and varies by less than 5% from day to day. So the pressure on the brick from the atmosphere above it might vary by about $0.05 \times 101\,000 \approx 5 \times 10^3$ Pa. Unless this is much smaller than the pressure exerted by one brick placed on another, variations in atmospheric pressure might affect our results. A nylon brick which has sides of length 25 mm will have a weight of about 0.20 N. If one brick is placed on another, the area of contact will be 25×10^{-3} m × 25×10^{-3} m = 6.25×10^{-4} m^2. The pressure this exerts on the bottom brick is easily calculated, as follows (the formula and symbols are explained in Appendix A):

$$P = ?$$
$$F = 0.20 \text{ N}$$
$$A = 6.25 \times 10^{-4} \text{ m}^2$$

$$P = \frac{F}{A}$$

$$\therefore P = \frac{0.20}{6.25 \times 10^{-4}}$$

$$\therefore P = 0.32 \times 10^3 \text{ Pa}$$

Therefore one brick will exert a pressure of roughly 0.3×10^3 Pa, about ten times smaller (an order of magnitude) than fluctuations in atmospheric pressure. So we will either have to do the experiment in a vacuum (without an atmosphere at all) or keep a careful eye on atmospheric pressure during the experiment.

Controlling variables

When you perform an experiment to explore how one **variable** of a system (the height of a brick) depends on another (the number of bricks in the pile), you must ensure that all of the other variables are kept constant. You have to think about all of the things which could affect the variable you are trying to measure and ensure that they do not change during your experiment. The variables which are most likely to affect the height of our brick are air pressure and temperature.

Specimen Data

Table 2.1 gives some results which might be obtained if you attempted our thought experiment, i.e. measuring the height of the bottom brick for different numbers of other bricks on top of it.

Table 2.1

Number of bricks	Height of bottom brick/mm
0	25.200000
1	25.198415
2	25.196830
3	25.194928
4	25.193343
5	25.191441
6	25.189856
7	25.188271
8	25.186369
9	25.184784

The table presents the data in a clear, but indigestible, format. All it tells you directly is that the bottom brick is compressed slightly each time an extra brick is added to the pile. What we really want to know is how the compression is related to the number of bricks in the pile.

Graphical representation

To get any more information from the data in table 2.1, the numbers need to be presented in a different format. One alternative way of presenting data, much used in physics, is as a graph. Of course, for the graph to display the information efficiently, the scales of its axes need to be chosen carefully. For example, figure 2.9 shows what you get if you start both axes at zero: this graph contains even less information than the original table!

The graph in figure 2.10 has a more sensible choice of axes. A pattern in the data is now visible, since it is clear that all of the points very nearly fit onto a straight line. Furthermore, if we use **error bars** to show the uncertainty of ±0.000317 mm in each measurement of height, a straight line can be drawn through all of the points. There is clearly a **linear** relationship between the two variables: the addition of a single brick to the pile always compresses the bottom brick by the same amount. In other words, the compression is **proportional** to the number of bricks in the column.

The pattern

Table 2.2 shows how the compression c of the bottom brick is related to the number of bricks n in the pile. The values for c are calculated from the data in table 2.1 using the following formula:

$$\text{compression} = \frac{\text{original}}{\text{height}} - \frac{\text{actual}}{\text{height}}$$
$$\text{of brick} \quad \text{of brick}$$

Table 2.2

n	$c/\mu m$
0	0.000
1	1.585
2	3.170
3	5.072
4	6.657
5	8.559
6	10.144
7	11.729
8	13.631
9	15.216

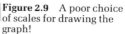

TEMPERATURE ▶▶ 4

The **expansivity** of nylon has a value of about $8.0\times10^{-5}°C^{-1}$. If the nominal height of the brick is 25 mm, we can calculate (with the help of a formula from Appendix A) how much this changes for a temperature rise of 1 °C.

$e = ?$　　　　　　$e = \alpha l T$　　$\therefore\ e = 8.0\times10^{-5} \times 25\times10^{-3} \times 1$

$l = 25\times10^{-3}$m　　　　　　　　　　$\therefore\ e = 2.0\times10^{-6}$ m

$T = 1$ °C

$\alpha = 8.0\times10^{-5}$ °C^{-1}

Therefore we expect the brick to extend by 2 μm for every degree centigrade rise in temperature. The precision of the interferometer is 0.317 μm, so we shall also have to be careful to keep the environment around the experiment at a constant temperature.

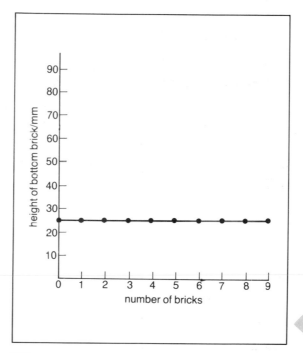

Figure 2.9 A poor choice of scales for drawing the graph!

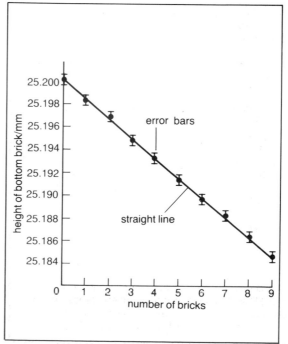

Figure 2.10 Displaying the information from the experiment by means of a graph

The data in table 2.2 have been used to draw the graph in figure 2.11. The **best straight line** has been drawn through the points by eye. The slope of the line can be calculated by finding out how much c changes for a known change of n:

$$\text{slope} = \frac{\text{change of } c}{\text{change of } n} = \frac{\Delta c}{\Delta n} \simeq \frac{15.2}{9} = 1.69$$

(The prefix Δ (delta) in front of a symbol always means a change in the quantity represented by the symbol. Thus if x represents a distance, then Δx represents a change of distance.) The slope of the graph of figure 2.11 is therefore 1.69. Thus c increases by 1.69 μm when an extra brick is added to the pile.

Conclusions

Where has all this analysis of data led us? A straight line through the origin can be drawn within all of the error bars of the graph of c against n. This means that our brick's compression is proportional to the number of bricks placed on top of it. This can be expressed with the following piece of algebra:

$$c = Kn \qquad \text{where } K = 1.69 \times 10^{-6} \text{ m} \qquad \textbf{(2.1)}$$

The formula is a very concise statement of our knowledge of the behaviour of one brick in a pile of bricks. It can be used to make calculations of the compression of bricks in various situations. The following example shows how the results of our experiment can be **extrapolated** to make a prediction of the total compression of a large pile of blocks.

The height of a pile

We want to calculate the actual height of a column of 160 cubic nylon blocks. Each block is 25 mm high, and is compressed by 1.7 μm for every block placed on top of it. We shall start by working out an expression for the height h of a column of n blocks.

The situation is shown in figure 2.12. Let the blocks be labelled from 1 to n, with block 1 being at the bottom. Each block will obey an equation like equation (2.1) above: its compression will be proportional to the number of blocks above it. Consider the block labelled m. Its original height is h. It will have $n - m$ blocks on top of it. So its compression $(-\Delta h)$ will be given by

$$-\Delta h = K(n - m) \qquad \textbf{(2.2)}$$

(The minus sign is included because h gets smaller.) The constant K has the value of 1.7×10^{-6} m. So the height h_m of the mth block in the column is given by

$$h_m = h + \Delta h = h - K(n - m) \qquad \textbf{(2.3)}$$

The total height of the column will be the sum of the height of each block in the column. We therefore have to find the sum of h_m for all values of m between 1 and n.

$$\begin{aligned}
\Sigma h_m &= \Sigma(h - K(n - m)) \\
&= \Sigma(h - Kn + Km) \\
&= \Sigma h - \Sigma Kn + \Sigma Km \\
&= nh - nKn + K\Sigma m \qquad \textbf{(2.4)}
\end{aligned}$$

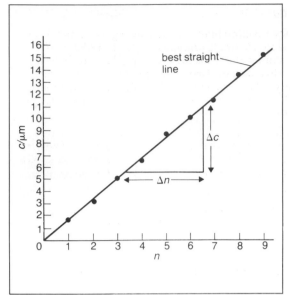

Figure 2.11 The compression c plotted as a function of the number of bricks n

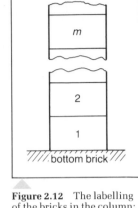

Figure 2.12 The labelling of the bricks in the column: m can be any number between 1 (the bottom brick) and n (the top brick)

The sum of all the integers between 1 and n is $\frac{1}{2}n(n + 1)$. (Standard mathematical formulae are given in Appendix B.) So equation (2.4) becomes

$$\begin{aligned}
\Sigma h_m &= nh - Kn^2 + \tfrac{1}{2}Kn(n + 1) \\
&= nh - \tfrac{1}{2}Kn^2 + \tfrac{1}{2}Kn \qquad \textbf{(2.5)}
\end{aligned}$$

The first term in equation (2.5) is the height of the column of blocks if there was no compression. Substituting $n = 160$ and $h = 25 \times 10^{-3}$ m, that term is equal to 4.00 m. The other two terms give the compression. $K = 1.7 \times 10^{-6}$ m, so the compression term is equal to $(0.5 \times 1.7 \times 10^{-6} \times 160^2) - (0.5 \times 1.7 \times 10^{-6} \times 160) = 0.022$ m. This is close to 25 mm, the height of one block. So if you plan to build a 4 m wall of nylon bricks and forget to take account of the compression, you could end up a layer of bricks short!

OBJECTIVES

After studying this section you should be able to do the following.

Describe different methods for measuring the length of an object.

State approximate precisions for different length-measuring instruments.

Understand the importance of controlling variables in an experiment.

Know that if two variables are proportional to each other, their graph is a straight line through the origin.

Be able to measure the slope of the line on a graph.

Understand the meaning of the prefix Δ.

Be able to express the proportionality of two variables with an algebraic formula.

QUESTIONS

1 Imagine that you have been given a metal bar which is exactly 50 cm long (a secondary standard). Describe how you would go about using it to construct two other metal bars which are exactly 25 cm and 1 m long. Estimate the precision that your methods would give for the lengths of the two bars.

2 It is usual practice for workshop rulers to be made of stainless steel. The expansivity of steel is 1.6×10^{-5}°C^{-1}. A 25 cm ruler is taken from a warm workshop (+30°C) to a cold outside yard (−10°C).

a By how much will the ruler shrink?

b Is this going to really affect the accuracy of a measurement made with the ruler?

c Suppose that a pair of stainless steel calipers, about 25 cm long, is taken from the workshop to the yard. Will this seriously affect its accuracy?

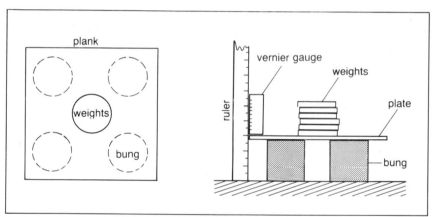

Figure 2.13

3 A student has investigated how rubber bungs shrink when weights are piled on top of them. Her apparatus is shown in figure 2.13: four of the bungs support the weight between them. The vernier gauge allows her to measure the compression of the bung with a precision of ± 0.05 mm. Her results are given in table 2.3: she has assumed that the plate has no weight at all.

Table 2.3

Vernier gauge reading/mm	Weight on the bung/N
2.55	0.0
2.45	5.0
2.40	10.0
2.30	15.0
2.25	20.0

a Draw up a table to show how the compression of a *single* bung depends on the weight it is supporting.

b Use the data to draw a graph which shows how the compression c of a bung depends on the weight W it is supporting. Make sure that each point has error bars. Draw the best straight line through the points and measure its slope.

c Write down a formula linking the compression of a bung with the weight it is supporting. (Use the standard units of length and weight.)

4 Figure 2.14 shows a schematic diagram of part of a skyscraper. Each floor is supported by concrete pillars, one at each corner. Measurements during the construction of the building show that each time an extra floor is added to the building, the four pillars on the ground floor shrink by 0.1 mm.

a The finished building has 40 floors, all identical. By how much does this compress the ground floor pillars?

b How much have the 20th floor pillars been compressed?

c How much shorter is the whole building because of the compression of the pillars?

5 In an idle moment a student suspends two identical spring balances from a clamp stand, as shown in figure 2.15. He notices that the top spring balance is 11 cm long and the bottom spring balance is 10 cm long, so their total length is 21 cm.

a Suppose that the top spring balance is supporting n spring balances. Write down an expression for its length. What assumptions are you making?

b Five of the spring balances are suspended from each other. Work out their total length.

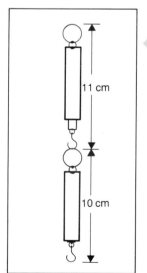

Figure 2.15

Figure 2.14

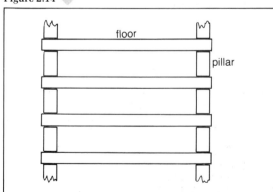

MASS, WEIGHT AND DENSITY

The experiment described in the last section established a relationship between the compression of a brick and the number of similar bricks that it was supporting. The cause of that compression is intuitively obvious. The **weight** of the brick column must be squashing the brick at its base. What the experiment really gave us was a relationship between the compression of a brick and the weight it is supporting. It told us that the compression of a typical solid is proportional to the weight on top of it.

Weight

Weight is a very familiar concept because it is so important in our everyday lives. It is a commonplace experience that almost every object on Earth appears to be tugged downwards. (Hot air balloons are one exception!) Every time that you let something rest on your hand, you can feel its weight pushing down. Your own weight even keeps your feet firmly on the ground. However, the very familiarity of weight means that you have to be very careful about exactly what it means in physics. The word 'weight' has a rather restricted meaning for a scientist compared with the normal everyday usage. The weight of an object is just the gravitational force acting on it.

Figure 2.17 A high precision lever balance at a standards laboratory. This balance is capable of comparing the weight of two objects with a precision of 1 part in 10^9

The fact that the weight of an object depends on its location has been known as long as international commerce has existed. An object has least weight when at the Equator; it will increase by about 0.5% if taken to either of the poles (figure 2.16). Furthermore, smaller variations occur as an object is moved about, due to changes in the density of the ground underneath or the height above the ground. At first sight, such small variations may not seem to be very important, but consider this example. Suppose that you purchase some gold at the Equator and then transport it to the North Pole. £1000 will buy enough gold to have a weight of one newton at the Equator. Then your investment will grow by 0.5%, or £5 on its way from the Equator to the North Pole!

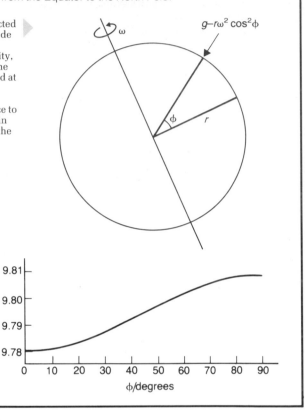

Figure 2.16 The predicted variation of g with latitude for a spherical Earth of uniform density. In reality, the Earth bulges out at the equator and it is flattened at the poles. Furthermore, there are small local variations from one place to another due to changes in the type of rocks under the surface

Mass

Clearly, weight is not a fundamental property of an object if it depends on where the object is. Weight is a function of both the object itself and its surroundings. So you cannot be sure of its weight unless you know exactly where it is. Furthermore, a change in the environment will cause a change in the weight of an otherwise unchanged object. So it is convenient to express the weight of something as the product of two other quantities, known as **mass** and **g**. The mass of an object is supposed to be **invariant**, a property of the object whose value is independent of the object's surroundings. The strength of the local gravitational field is given by g (known affectionately as 'little gee' by physicists). Its value is supposed to be unaffected by the presence of the object, depending only on the location.

$W = mg$

W is the weight of the object (N)

m is the mass of the object (kg)

g is the local gravitational field strength (N kg^{-1})

Measuring mass

The mass of an object can, in principle, be determined by comparing it with the international prototype kilogram. This is a lump of platinum−iridium, kept near Paris, which has a mass of exactly 1 kg. In practice, the international prototype is used to check the masses of secondary standard kilograms, by exploiting the idea that objects with the same mass should have the same weight as each other at the same location.

A lever balance, similar to that shown in figure 2.17, can be used as follows. The prototype kilogram is placed on the left-hand scale pan, and the right-hand scale pan is loaded up with items (which could be anything) until the lever is accurately horizontal. The weight of the prototype kilogram is then the force needed on the left-hand scale pan to keep the lever horizontal. If the lever remains horizontal when the prototype kilogram is replaced with a secondary standard, then they must both have the same weight. Since the weight of both items is being compared at the same location, they will both have the same value of g. So equal weights also mean equal masses.

Standard masses of any mass can be generated in a similar fashion. For example, suppose that you wanted to generate a set of accurate 100 g secondary standards. You will need ten of them. Start off by checking that they all have the same weight as each other with the help of a lever balance. Then check that all ten of them together have the same weight as the prototype kilogram.

Measuring g

One of the simplest (but time consuming) methods of obtaining a precise value for g at a particular location involves the use of a simple pendulum, like the one shown in figure 2.19. The period T of small amplitude oscillations of a mass suspended a distance l below a fixed pivot by a light string is given by the following formula:

$$T = 2\pi(l/g)^{\frac{1}{2}}$$

Notice that the formula does not contain the mass m of the pendulum. So it can be used to find a value for g which does not involve measuring weight mg. In principle, measuring the time taken for a number of oscillations should allow you to determine g with a high precision. A pendulum with a length of 1 m will have a period of about 2 s. You could easily time 100 oscillations with an electronic stopwatch with an accuracy of 0.1 s, so that T would be known to within 0.05%. However, to get a similar accuracy for g you would need to know the length of the pendulum to this accuracy: this is not so easy. Nevertheless, a simple pendulum can be used to make highly accurate measurements of the *variation* of g from one location to another, provided that you use an accurate clock and make sure that any thermal expansion of the string is accounted for. (Electronic clocks routinely keep good time to 1 s in 100 000 s, so precise time measurement is no problem.) The average value of g in Europe is about 9.81 N kg^{-1}. This is often approximated to 10 N kg^{-1} in calculations where precision is not important.

MASS WITHOUT GRAVITY ▶▶15

It is somewhat irritating that this method of comparing two masses in fact relies on comparing their weights. There are, however, ways of comparing masses which do not involve their weight at all. For instance, the time for one complete oscillation (the **period**) T of a mass m suspended from the end of a spring (figure 2.18) is given by the following formula:

$$T = 2\pi(m/k)^{\frac{1}{2}}$$

k is a property of the spring, and is called the force constant. Its value is independent of the mass hung from the end of the spring. So if two items suspended from the same spring have the same period of oscillation, they must have the same mass.

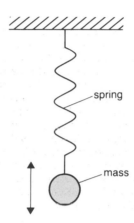

Figure 2.18 A mass suspended by a spring: its period of vertical oscillations depends on its mass but not on the local value of g

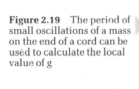

Figure 2.19 The period of small oscillations of a mass on the end of a cord can be used to calculate the local value of g

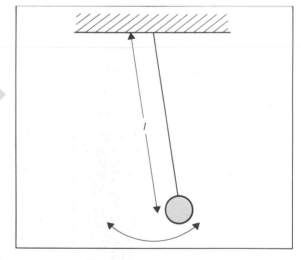

MEASURING TIME !

The standard unit of time used for physics is the second. Until recently (1966), the Earth was supposed to make one complete rotation about its axis in $24 \times 60 \times 60 = 86\,400$ seconds. In other words, the rotation of the Earth with respect to the rest of the Universe was the primary standard of time. However, because of tidal effects and other interactions with the Moon, the rotation of the Earth is imperceptibly, but steadily, slowing down. This can be detected by super-precise clocks. These use the frequency of radiation absorbed by atoms when they change from one energy level to another as their time standard. Today, the second is defined by international agreement by means of one of these atomic clocks based on the element caesium: the frequency of radiation needed to push a caesium atom between its two bottom energy levels is exactly $9\,192\,631\,770$ s^{-1}.

Forcemeters

We are now going to describe how an instrument, which we will call a **forcemeter**, can be constructed and calibrated. It will be able to measure the size of a force in a reproducible fashion. It will make use of the notion that a given deformation of a particular elastic object always requires the same force.

Construction

The forcemeter is shown in figure 2.20. It consists of a light spring (i.e. one whose weight is negligible compared with the forces to be measured) with a pointer attached to it. The position of the pointer can be read off a scale rigidly held to the base of the spring. The force to be measured is applied to the light plate at the other end of the spring. Any force acting on the spring will squash it: the compression of the spring can be read off the scale with the help of the pointer.

The only important property of the spring that we require is for it to be **elastic**. This means that every time a force is removed from the plate the pointer returns to the same place on the scale: the spring is not permanently deformed by the force. The spring is selected so that it deforms a lot over the range of forces we want to measure. This gives a large movement of the pointer along the scale, making the device easy to read.

Calibration

The process of marking off the scale in newtons is known as **calibration**. Suppose that we wanted our forcemeter to measure forces up to 10.0 N with a precision of 0.1 N (1%). We could proceed to calibrate it as follows.

Place the forcemeter on its side, as shown in figure 2.21. Record the pointer reading: this corresponds to a force of 0 N on the plate. Then place a 10.0 g mass on the plate. If the local value of g is 9.81 N kg^{-1} (it could be measured with a pendulum as explained above), that mass will have a weight of 0.0981 N. (Convince yourself!) So the pointer reading will be equivalent to a force of 0.0981 N on the forcemeter. Different masses can then be added to the plate, up to a maximum of 1000 g, with the pointer reading recorded each time. We end up with a series of pointer readings for different known forces acting on the plate. Those readings can be used to plot a **calibration curve** like the one shown in figure 2.22. By drawing a smooth curve which goes through all the points, the graph can be used to convert any pointer reading (within the range) into a measurement of the force acting on the plate.

Density

An accurate forcemeter can be used to study the relationship between the weight of a body and its volume. Consider the following thought experiment. You have a number of blocks, identical in every respect (dimensions, temperature, substance, etc.), which you can weigh with a forcemeter, as shown in figure 2.23. Each block is cubical in shape, with sides of length l so that it has a volume $l \times l \times l = l^3$.

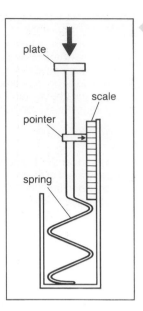

Figure 2.20 A simple forcemeter on its side

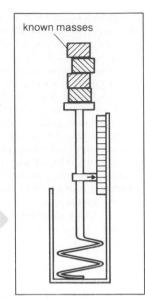

Figure 2.21 Calibrating a forcemeter by letting it support a number of known masses

Figure 2.22 A typical calibration curve for a forcemeter

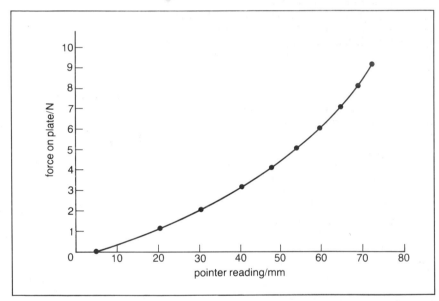

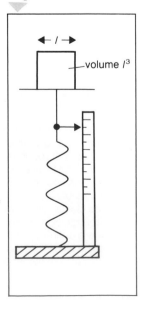

Figure 2.23 Weighing a single block

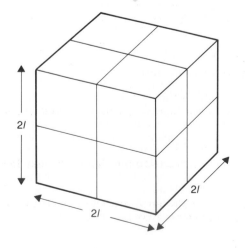

Figure 2.24 The volume of a cube increases by $2^3 = 8$ when the length of each side is doubled

Each block has a weight W. Eight blocks on the forcemeter have a weight of $8\,W$. (This implies that the weight of each block does not depend on the presence of the other blocks — they exert their forces on the plate independently of each other.) But the eight cubes can be arranged to make a larger cube with sides of $2l$ (see figure 2.24). The volume of this larger cube will be $(2l)^3 = 8l^3$.

The fact that eight single cubes have a weight which is eight times as much as that of a single cube means that we can merge the eight cubes into a larger cube without altering their weight. Furthermore, we could alter the shape made up by the eight cubes without altering their weight. The different arrangements shown in figure 2.25 will all exert the same force on the plate of the forcemeter. Convince yourself that all of the arrangements have a volume of $8l^3$.

Mass depends on volume

By making the volume eight times larger we have increased the weight by a factor of eight. Since all of the measurements were made at the same location (g remained the same throughout), we can conclude that the mass of an object made from a particular substance is proportional to its volume. We can express this most succinctly with some algebra:

$$m \propto V$$

We can use a constant of proportionality ρ (rho) to obtain a useful formula linking the mass of an object to its volume.

> $m = \rho V$
>
> m is the mass of the object (kg)
>
> V is the volume of the object (m^3)
>
> ρ is the density of the material (kg m^{-3})

A graph of mass against volume for a given substance will therefore be a straight line through the origin (see figure 2.26). The slope of the line will be equal to the density of that substance. This is shown as follows, starting with the basic equation

$$m = \rho V \qquad (2.6)$$

Suppose that V increases by ΔV, increasing the mass from m to $m + \Delta m$. These two new values for mass and volume must still obey equation (2.6). So we can write down the following equation:

$$m + \Delta m = \rho(V + \Delta V) \qquad (2.7)$$

Multiplying out the brackets:

$$m + \Delta m = \rho V + \rho \Delta V \qquad (2.8)$$

Substituting for m in equation (2.8) with equation (2.6):

$$\rho V + \Delta m = \rho V + \rho \Delta V \qquad (2.9)$$

The terms ρV cancel out on both sides, leaving:

$$\Delta m = \rho \Delta V \qquad (2.10)$$

Equation (2.10) can be rearranged to obtain an expression for the slope of the graph:

$$\frac{\Delta m}{\Delta V} = \rho \qquad (2.11)$$

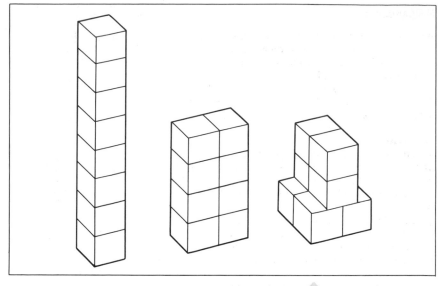

Figure 2.25 Different shapes with the same volume and weight

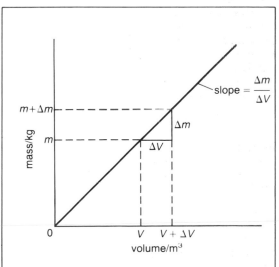

Figure 2.26 How the mass of a substance depends on its volume: the slope of the line is the density of the substance

It is helpful to think of the density of a substance as being the mass of one cubic metre of it: set $V = 1$ in equation (2.6) and you get $m = \rho$. The concept of density is useful because it is a property of a material which is independent of its shape or size. Thus all iron objects have the same density, regardless of what they have been made into.

OBJECTIVES

After studying this section you should be able to do the following.

Explain the distinction between *mass* and *weight*.

Describe how the mass of an object can be measured.

State and use the formula $W = mg$.

Describe a method of measuring g and quote an approximate value for it on Earth.

Describe how a forcemeter can be constructed and calibrated.

State and use the formula $m = \rho V$.

Explain the meaning of *density*.

QUESTIONS

1 An item is transported from the North Pole to the Equator. Bearing in mind that its temperature will change in the process, will the following quantities increase, decrease or stay the same? Explain your answers!

a Mass.
b Weight.
c Volume.
d Density.

2 Piezoelectric materials develop a potential difference (p.d.) when they are subjected to forces. Table 2.4 below shows the results of a test that a student made on a piezoelectric slab. She measured the voltage across the slab for various masses placed on top of it. She then used an array of nine of the piezoelectric slabs to make a set of electronic bathroom scales: this is shown in figure 2.27.

Table 2.4

mass/kg	0.0	2.0	4.0	6.0	8.0	10.0
p.d./μV	0	10	19	27	35	43

a Draw a calibration curve for the scales, showing how the voltmeter reading is related to the weight of the person on the scales. Assume $g = 9.81$ N kg^{-1}.

b The scales read 30 μV when the student steps on them. What is her weight?

c Suppose that the student wants to measure the weight of a table with the scales. What is the easiest way for her to do this?

3 If the pressure exerted on snow exceeds 8000 Pa, it will give way. (The definition of pressure is given in Appendix A). Suppose that a cubic block of concrete is placed on top of some snow. This question is about finding the maximum size of block which will not sink into the snow.

a If the cube has sides of length d and the density of concrete is ρ, write down an expression for the weight of the cube.

b Work out an expression for the pressure P exerted on the snow by the cube in terms of d, ρ and g.

c The density of concrete is 2400 kg m^{-3}. What is the maximum size of concrete block which can sit on snow without sinking in?

d A cube of iron cannot have sides greater than 12 cm without sinking into the snow. What is the density of iron?

4 Anything that has a property which changes with time can be used as a clock. Water drips, pendulums, the human pulse rate, the night–day cycle and candles have all been used as clocks in the past. One overriding requirement for a useful clock is that it ticks at a uniform rate, regardless of how long it has been ticking.

a Galileo used his own pulse to time the swing of the candles in a cathedral (figure 2.28). Discuss the shortcomings of his clock.

b Explain how you would verify that a new type of clock ticked at a uniform rate *without* using any other type of clock. This was the problem faced by early scientists trying to make precise clocks.

5 Imagine that you have managed to make radio contact with an alien civilisation. (They have a computer program which can translate English into their own language, so they have no difficulty in understanding you.) One of the things they want to know is the units by which mass, length and time are measured on Earth. How would you convey the meaning of the words second, metre and kilogram as precisely as possible?

Figure 2.27

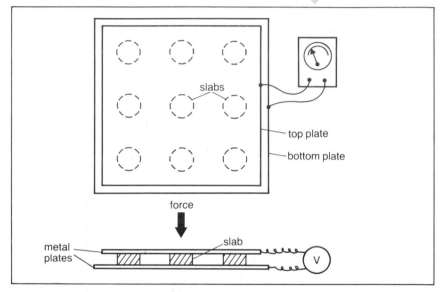

Figure 2.28 A candle holder suspended from the roof of Pisa Cathedral. Galileo is supposed to have noticed (presumably during a boring sermon!) that the period of oscillation of this pendulum was independent of the amplitude of the swing

HOOKE'S LAW

For hundreds of years scientists have been demonstrating that all solid objects get smaller when they are squeezed by an external force. Anything, not just a brick, will be compressed when weights are stacked on top of it. The weights on the top of the object shown in figure 2.29 provide the force on it. Furthermore, all solid objects expand when they are stretched. That is, any solid object will get longer when weights are suspended from it as shown in figure 2.30. What is truly remarkable is the fact that the deformation of an object is proportional to the deforming force (provided that it is not too large). This fact is so all-pervasive and useful that it is given the status of a law, named after the man who first mentioned it in 1676. His name was Robert Hooke.

Observing springs

Robert Hooke discovered his law by doing experiments with springs. He observed how the length of a spring increased when he hung weights from the end of it. Results for a typical steel spring are shown in the graph of figure 2.30. The significant fact is that the graph is a straight line for forces which are smaller than a certain limit. Although different springs have different slopes for the line and different limits at which the line starts to curve, they all share the straight line characteristic for small enough forces. This is not only true for all springs made of metal, but for springs made out of other materials such as glass, ceramics and plastics. In fact, whatever material the spring is made out of and whatever shape the spring has, its force—length graph will be a straight line for small forces.

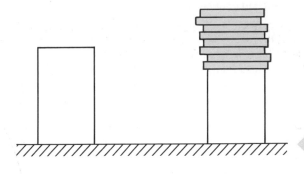

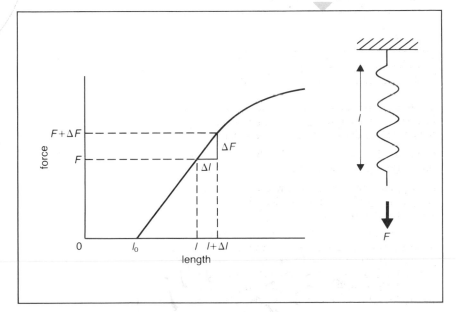

Figure 2.29 All objects shrink when weights are stacked on top of them

Figure 2.30 How the length of a typical spring depends on the force applied to it. The slope of the graph is the value of the spring's force constant

The force constant

Consider the graph drawn in figure 2.30. It shows how the length l of a typical spring depends on the force F applied to it. Because the line is straight we can represent it with the following piece of algebra:

$$F = k(l - l_0) \qquad (2.12)$$

The quantity l_0 is the length of the spring when no forces are acting on it, so $l - l_0$ is the change of length caused by a force. k is the force constant, a measure of how much longer the spring gets for a given force. If you consider the change of length Δl caused by an increase in the force ΔF, it is easily shown that k is just the slope of the line on the graph.

$$F + \Delta F = k(l + \Delta l - l_0) \qquad (2.13)$$

Substitute for F from equation (2.12), multiply out the brackets and do some cancelling:

$$k(l - l_0) + \Delta F = k(l + \Delta l - l_0)$$
$$\therefore kl - kl_0 + \Delta F = kl + k\Delta l - kl_0$$
$$\therefore \Delta F = k\Delta l \qquad (2.14)$$

Finally, rearrange equation (2.14) to get

$$\frac{\Delta F}{\Delta l} = k \qquad (2.15)$$

ADVANCES IN SCIENCE

Hooke's Law is particularly easy to observe with coiled springs as their length can change quite dramatically when forces are applied to them. The extension of a spring is easily measured with a ruler when even a modest force is applied to it. You could not claim that this was true of a brick or of the other solid objects around you! Although a coiled steel spring is a relatively simple piece of technology, Hooke's Law would probably not have been discovered without it. In other words, it could be argued that the availability of coiled steel springs made it possible for Hooke to discover his law. If the technology of the day had not been sufficiently advanced to produce such articles, the discovery of the law would have been delayed. Furthermore, you might also argue that if Hooke had not discovered his law, the easy availability of springs guaranteed that someone else would have found the law quite quickly! In actual fact, Hooke gave his colleagues two years in which to discover his law for themselves before he published it.

So although it would appear that advances in science are closely linked with the advances in technology which make new experiments possible, the importance of the individual enquiring scientist in using that technology to explore nature must not be ignored. The technology does not dictate the experiment to be performed, it simply makes it possible. It is the imagination of the experimenter who thinks of the experiment which really makes the important advances in science possible. Only rarely can a scientist be successful by being simply the right person in the right place at the right time!

Since the value of the force constant is obtained by dividing a force by a length, its units will be N m^{-1}.

Equation (2.12) says that the change of length of the spring is proportional to the force acting on it. So if we represent the change of length (the **deformation**) of the spring by x, we end up with the following simple expression of Hooke's Law:

$$F = kx \qquad\qquad (2.16)$$

Thus a graph of deformation against deforming force will always be a straight line near the origin. This is illustrated in figure 2.31.

Squeezing springs

Hooke's Law does not only apply to forces which make springs longer, i.e. giving them a positive deformation. It also applies to forces which make springs shorter, giving them a negative deformation. If we adopt the convention that a negative force is one which gives a negative deformation (see figure 2.32) then we can use $F = kx$ for both types of deformation. Notice that the graph in figure 2.32 implies that a spring has the same force constant for both types of deformation. As you will find out later, this fact (as well as Hooke's Law itself) is a consequence of the relationship between the force on an object and its energy. This is why Hooke's Law applies to all solid objects: they all obey the same fundamental laws of motion.

Although the force−deformation curve of a spring is always a straight line through the origin, it does not necessarily have mirror symmetry about the F-axis well away from the origin. Most springs get weaker as they get longer, and stronger as they get shorter. This is shown in figure 2.32.

$F = kx$

F is the force applied to the spring (N)

k is the force constant of the spring (N m^{-1})

x is the deformation of the spring (m)

Figure 2.31 The force−deformation curve of a spring for small values of the force

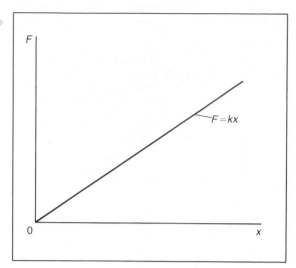

Figure 2.32 Hooke's Law applies to both the compression and the extension of a spring

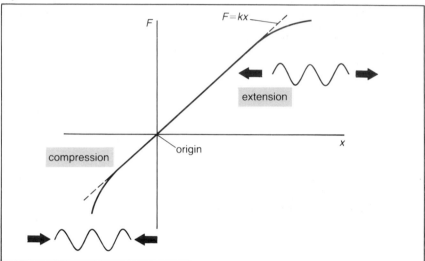

Figure 2.33 Three situations where Hooke's Law is obeyed

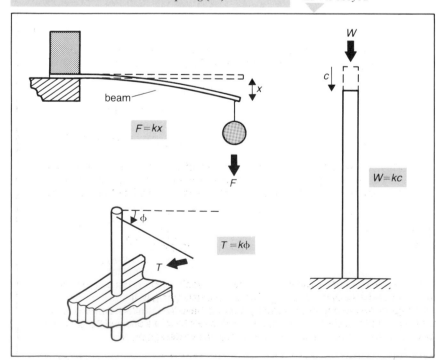

A universal law

Hooke's law is an example of a **universal law**. This means that it applies to everything, everywhere. So it describes more than the behaviour of just springs. Whenever a force is used to deform a solid, then it turns out that the deformation is proportional to the deforming force, at least for small forces. It also works for all types of solid, not only metals. For example, figure 2.33 shows three situations in which Hooke's Law can be used to predict the deformation caused by a given force. The displacement of the end of a beam is proportional to the force pushing down on it. The force needed to twist a rod is proportional to the angle that the rod is twisted round. The compression of a pillar is proportional to the weight it is supporting.

The real usefulness of Hooke's Law lies in the simple form of its algebra and the fact that it applies to *any* substance. This simplicity and universality ensures that it is widely used in engineering to predict the changes in length of objects when forces are applied to them.

LIFT CABLES

Here is an example of Hooke's Law in action. An engineer wants to know how much a lift is going to sink down each time a passenger steps into it. A movement of more than a few millimetres would probably be unacceptable to the lift users, so the engineer has to ensure that a strong enough cable is used to support the lift cage (figure 2.34). Suppose that she has chosen to use a 50 m cable made from 100 strands of steel. She takes a 5.0 m length of a single strand and hangs a 10 N weight on the end of it. This extends the strand by 3.0 mm. This single piece of data allows her to calculate the force constant of the strand.

$F = 10\,\text{N}$ $F = kx$ $\therefore\; 10 = k \times 3.0 \times 10^{-3}$

$k = ?$

$x = 3.0\,\text{mm} = 3.0 \times 10^{-3}\,\text{m}$ $\therefore\; \dfrac{10}{3.0 \times 10^{-3}} = k = 3.3 \times 10^3\,\text{N m}^{-1}$

Now she has to work out the force constant for the whole cable, not just part of one strand. She does this in two steps, arguing as follows.

A 10 m strand will stretch twice as much as a 5 m strand which supports the same weight. This is shown in figure 2.35. The 10 m strand is just like one 5 m strand supporting another identical strand. Both 5 m strands have to support the full weight hung from the bottom strand. So doubling the length of the strand doubles its extension for the same force, if we ignore the weight of the cable itself. Therefore the extension of a 10 × 5 = 50 m strand holding up 10 N would be 10 × 3.0 = 30 mm.

$F = 10\,\text{N}$ $F = kx$ $\therefore\; 10 = k \times 3.0 \times 10^{-2}$

$k = ?$

$x = 30\,\text{mm} = 3.0 \times 10^{-2}\,\text{m}$ $\therefore\; \dfrac{10}{3 \times 10^{-2}} = k = 3.3 \times 10^2\,\text{N m}^{-1}$

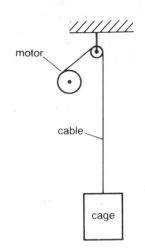

Figure 2.34 The essential parts of a simple lift

Figure 2.36 Doubling the number of strands halves the extension for the same force

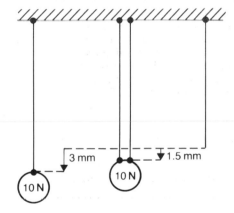

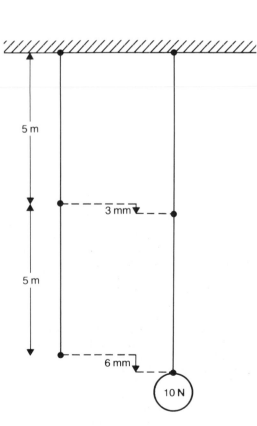

Figure 2.35 Doubling the length of a strand doubles the extension for the same force

Two strands side-by-side (shown in figure 2.36) will each support half of the weight that they are holding up between them. So a cable made of a hundred 50 m strands will need to support 100 × 10 = 1000 N to be stretched by 30 mm. So we can now calculate the force constant of the whole cable.

$F = 1000\,\text{N}$ $F = kx$ $\therefore\; 1000 = k \times 3.0 \times 10^{-2}$

$k = ?$

$x = 30\,\text{mm} = 3.0 \times 10^{-2}\,\text{m}$ $\therefore\; \dfrac{1000}{3.0 \times 10^{-2}} = k = 3.3 \times 10^4\,\text{N m}^{-1}$

So the whole cable should have a force constant of $3.3 \times 10^4\,\text{N m}^{-1}$. An average human being has a weight of about 700 N (a mass of about 70 kg), so we can calculate how much the cable will stretch when someone walks into the lift cage.

$F = 700\,\text{N}$ $F = kx$ $\therefore\; 700 = 3.3 \times 10^4 \times x$

$k = 3.3 \times 10^4\,\text{N m}^{-1}$ $\therefore\; \dfrac{700}{3.3 \times 10^4} = x$

$x = ?$

$\therefore\; x = 2.1 \times 10^{-2}\,\text{m}$

Therefore the lift cage will sink by roughly 2 cm each time someone steps into it on the ground floor of the building. This is obviously going to alarm the passengers, so the engineer is clearly going to have to use either a stiffer cable or several cables side by side. The use of Hooke's Law has allowed her to avoid making an embarrassing and potentially expensive design error.

Limitations of Hooke's Law

Hooke's Law does not state that the deformation is *always* proportional to the deforming force. It only claims that this is true if the deforming force is small enough. So when data gleaned from a small-scale laboratory experiment is used to predict the force constant of a large structure, the result of that calculation must be regarded as only a rough prediction. You can only expect that prediction to hold true if you know that the forces acting will not stretch or squeeze the material beyond the region where its deformation is proportional to the deforming force. Nevertheless, although the equation $F = kx$ only applies accurately to the unshaded area of the graph of figure 2.37, it is not a bad approximation for the shaded areas where the force is large.

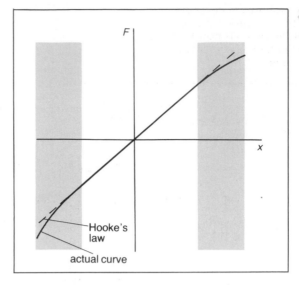

Figure 2.37 Hooke's Law ($F = kx$) is only approximately correct in the shaded regions of the graph

OBJECTIVES

After studying this section you should be able to do the following.

State Hooke's Law in algebraic form.

Know that the force constant of a spring is the slope of its force–deformation curve.

Recognise the limitations and usefulness of Hooke's Law.

Use the formula $F = kx$.

QUESTIONS

1 A student investigates the elastic properties of a nylon climbing rope by taking one strand out of it and hanging weights from its end. His data are shown in table 2.5.

Table 2.5

Mass supported/kg	0	1.0	2.0	3.0	4.0
Extension/mm	0	1.6	3.2	4.6	5.6

a Plot a graph to find out the range of forces over which $F = kx$ is an accurate description. Assume that $g = 9.8 \text{ N kg}^{-1}$.

b Obtain a value for the force constant of the strand.

c The strand used by the student was 2.0 m long. If the rope contains 100 of these strands and is 30 m long, what is the value of its force constant?

d By how much will the rope stretch when it supports the student who weighs 750 N?

2 A woman who has a mass of 50 kg walks along to the end of a diving board, as shown in figure 2.38. Her weight depresses the end of the board by 5.0 cm. When a man steps onto the end of the board as well, its depression becomes 12.0 cm.

a Calculate the force constant of the diving board. Assume $g = 10 \text{ N kg}^{-1}$.

b What is the mass of the man?

3 A car has four wheels in contact with the road. Each wheel supports a quarter of the car's weight via a spring, as shown in figure 2.39.

a When a man of mass 75 kg steps into the car it drops down by 1.5 cm. Assuming that his weight is shared equally by the springs, calculate a value for the force constant of one spring.

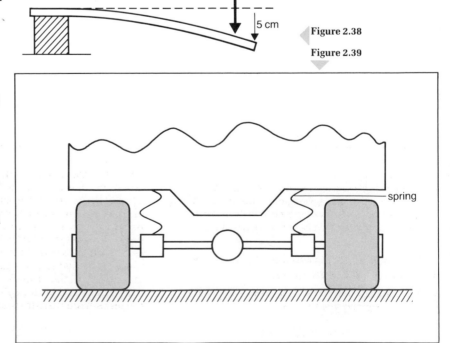

Figure 2.38

Figure 2.39

b The man jacks up the car as shown in figure 2.40 so that it is only supported by two wheels and the jack. If the car weighs 10 000 N, estimate how high the jack will have to lift up the car body before the wheels stop touching the ground.

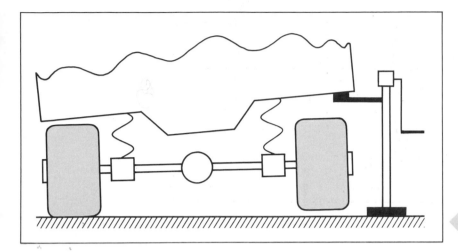

Figure 2.40

Figure 2.41

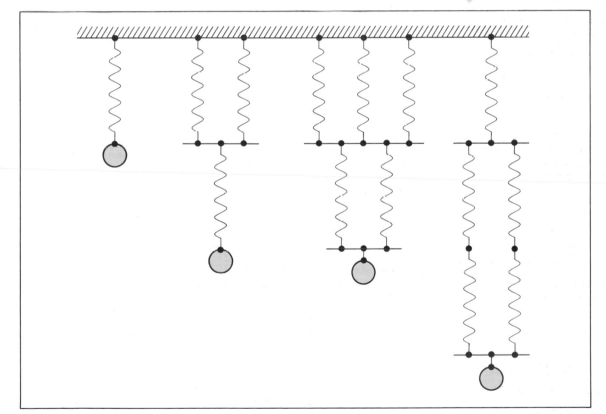

4 Figure 2.41 shows a number of spring assemblies supporting the same load of 8 N. All of the springs have the same force constant, and the springs and connecting bars have a negligible weight.

a If the single spring is extended by 2 cm, calculate the force constant of the spring.

b Calculate the effective force constants of the other three spring assemblies.

5 Joe reckons that Hooke's Law is baloney. His argument goes as follows. 'I agree that when you hang weights on the end of a spring, its extension is proportional to the total weight being supported. But the weights themselves have to be measured with a forcemeter, and that forcemeter is just a spring which obeys Hooke's Law. So the whole thing is circular and not physically significant at all!' Point out the errors in Joe's reasoning and convince him that Hooke's Law is independent of the measuring instruments used.

3

YOUNG'S MODULUS

Although all solid objects obey Hooke's Law, some of them deform much more readily than others. Rubber bands stretch easily but string does not. A cube of jelly deforms easily but a cube of wood does not. Even objects made of the same substance can have widely different stiffnesses — subject a steel piano wire and a steel girder to the same force and one will deform much more than the other. The force constant of an object must therefore depend on both its shape and the material that it is made of. This chapter will help you to unscramble the various factors which decide the value of an object's force constant. It will convince you that it helps to use two new quantities (**stress** and **strain**) in place of force and deformation.

STRESS AND STRAIN

In order to separate out the various factors which affect the stiffness of an object, we need to consider each variable in turn. We will start off with the area over which the deforming force is applied.

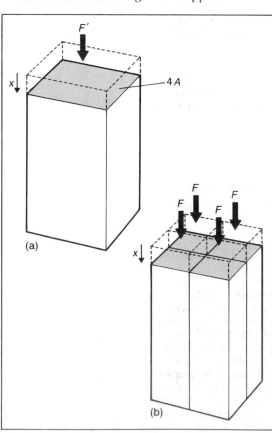

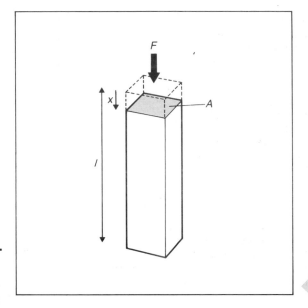

Figure 3.1 A pillar being compressed by a force

Figure 3.2 The force is proportional to the cross-sectional area for a given deformation

Area

Figure 3.1 shows a pillar which is being compressed by a force F. Its deformation will, of course, be given by Hooke's Law:

$$F = kx \tag{3.1}$$

A different pillar is shown in figure 3.2(a). It is made of the same material and has the same height as the one shown in figure 3.1, but its width and depth are doubled. It too will obey Hooke's Law, but it will have a different force constant k'. So a different force F' will be needed to get the same compression as before.

$$F' = k'x \tag{3.2}$$

It should be obvious that the pillar shown in figure 3.2(a) is equivalent to four of those in figure 3.1 placed side-by-side, as shown in figure 3.2(b). So $F' = 4F$. Inserting this into equation (3.2) we get another equation:

$$4F = k'x \tag{3.3}$$

We can now proceed to find out how the two force constants k' and k are related. Start off by shuffling equation (3.3):

$$k' = \frac{4F}{x} \tag{3.4}$$

Then substitute for F from equation (3.1):

$$k' = \frac{4(kx)}{x} \tag{3.5}$$

Finally cancel x top and bottom:

$$k' = 4k \qquad (3.6)$$

Stress

We have shown that the force constant of the thicker pillar is four times larger than that of the thinner pillar. A glance at figure 3.2 will make it obvious that the four-fold increase in force constant coincides with a four-fold increase of cross-sectional area. In other words, the force constant of a pillar must be proportional to its cross-sectional area A. This can be expressed as

$$k = cA \qquad (3.7)$$

(The constant c is the force constant of a pillar with a cross-sectional area of 1 m².) So we can write a version of Hooke's Law which applies to all pillars of the material, regardless of their thicknesses:

$$F = cAx \qquad (3.8)$$

Of course, this equation only applies to pillars of the same length, made out of the same material. (In a moment we will look at what happens when the length is changed.) An alternative version of equation (3.8), giving the deformation, is easily obtained with some shuffling:

$$\frac{F}{A} = cx \qquad (3.9)$$

The left-hand side contains the force divided by the area. This quantity is called the **stress** on the pillar. Equation (3.9) really says that the deformation x is proportional to the stress, with c acting as the constant of proportionality.

Length

In the last section we analysed the dependence of the force constant on cross-sectional area. We compared the behaviour of two systems which were identical in every respect except cross-sectional area. This allowed us to use algebra to show that the force constant is proportional to the cross-sectional area. A similar technique will now be used to show that the force constant is inversely proportional to the length of a system.

Figure 3.3(a) shows a pillar being subjected to a force F. The pillar is twice as long as the one shown in figure 3.1, but both have the same cross-sectional area A. The deformation x″ of the longer pillar is, of course, given by Hooke's Law.

$$\frac{F}{A} = c''x'' \qquad (3.10)$$

Two pillars of length l placed end to end as shown in figure 3.3(b), will behave like a single pillar of length 2l. Each pillar in figure 3.3(b) is subjected to the same force F, so it will be deformed by the same amount x. An expression for x may be obtained by shuffling the contents of equation (3.9):

$$x = \frac{F}{cA} \qquad (3.11)$$

Obviously the total deformation of the two pillars in figure 3.3(b) is the same as the deformation of the pillar in figure 3.3(a). So x″ = 2x. Now we insert this into equation (3.10) and substitute for x from equation (3.11):

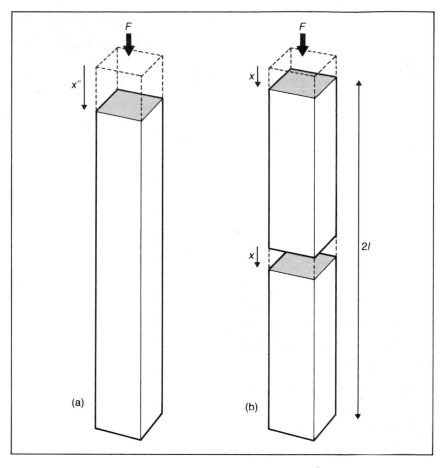

$$\frac{F}{A} = c''2x \qquad \therefore \frac{F}{A} = c''2\frac{F}{cA} \qquad (3.12)$$

After cancelling F and A from both sides and shuffling a bit, we are left with this statement:

$$c'' = \frac{c}{2} \qquad (3.13)$$

Equation (3.13) says that doubling the length has halved the value of c. This means that c is **inversely proportional** to the length l.

$$c \propto \frac{1}{l} \qquad \therefore c = \frac{E}{l} \qquad (3.14)$$

The real significance of the constant of proportionality E becomes evident when we substitute for c from equation (3.14) into equation (3.9).

$$\frac{F}{A} = cx \quad \therefore \frac{F}{A} = \frac{Ex}{l} \quad \therefore \frac{F}{A} = E\frac{x}{l} \quad (3.15)$$

Strain

The quantity x/l is called the **strain**. It is the **fractional deformation** which occurs when the pillar is subjected to a stress F/A. Since the stress and the strain between them contain all of the dependence on the shape and dimensions of the pillar, the value of E must only depend on the material of which the pillar is made. E, **Young's modulus**, is an intrinsic property of a material, similar to its density. All objects made of the same material will have the same value of Young's modulus, regardless of their shape or size.

Figure 3.3 The deformation is proportional to the length for a given force

Our algebraic analysis of the dependence of the force constant upon length and cross-sectional area has led us towards an alternative version of Hooke's Law.

> stress = E × strain
>
> stress is the force per unit area on the object (N m^{-2} or Pa)
>
> E is Young's modulus for the material (N m^{-2} or Pa)
>
> strain is the fractional change in length of the object

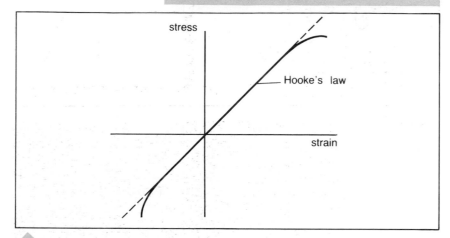

Figure 3.4 Stress is proportional to strain near the origin

This is illustrated with the graph in figure 3.4. Notice the units for stress and strain. Stress is measured in N m^{-2} as it is obtained by dividing a force by an area, but strain has no units as it is a length divided by a length. (The alternative unit for stress is the pascal (Pa); 1 N m^{-2} = 1 Pa.) The stress will only be proportional to the strain near to the origin. The graph will deviate from a straight line for large stresses.

Example
A student hangs a 5.0 kg mass from the end of a 2.0 m length of fine steel wire and notes that this extends the wire by 2.5 mm. If the diameter of the wire is 0.5 mm, calculate a value of Young's modulus for steel.

Start off by calculating the stress on the wire.

stress = ?

$F = 5.0 \times 9.8 = 49 \, \text{N}$

$A = \pi r^2 = \pi \times (0.25 \times 10^{-3})^2 = 1.96 \times 10^{-7} \, \text{m}^2$

$\text{stress} = \dfrac{F}{A}$

$\therefore \text{stress} = \dfrac{49}{1.96 \times 10^{-7}}$

$\therefore \text{stress} = 2.5 \times 10^8 \, \text{Pa}$

Then calculate the strain.

strain = ?

$x = 2.5 \, \text{mm} = 2.5 \times 10^{-3} \, \text{m}$

$l = 2.0 \, \text{m}$

$\text{strain} = \dfrac{x}{l} = \dfrac{2.5 \times 10^{-3}}{2.0} = 1.25 \times 10^{-3}$

Finally, calculate Young's modulus.

$\text{stress} = 2.5 \times 10^8 \, \text{Pa}$

$E = ?$

$\text{strain} = 1.25 \times 10^{-3}$

stress = E × strain

$\therefore 2.5 \times 10^8 = E \times 1.25 \times 10^{-3}$

$\therefore \dfrac{2.5 \times 10^8}{1.25 \times 10^{-3}} = E = 2.0 \times 10^{11} \, \text{Pa}$

QUESTIONS

1 A 3.0 m length of copper wire is suspended from the ceiling. When a 1.0 kg mass is suspended from the bottom of the wire it extends by 1.8 mm. The diameter of the wire is 0.4 mm.

a Calculate the strain of the wire.

b Calculate the stress on the wire.

c Calculate a value of Young's modulus for copper.

2 Young's modulus for wood is about 1.0×10^{10} N m^{-2}. A typical wooden chair has four legs, each of length 40 cm and cross-sectional area 1.0×10^{-3} m^2. The mass of a typical human being is 70 kg.

a Calculate the stress on each leg when you sit on the chair.

b By how much do the chair legs shrink when you sit on the chair?

3 Figure 3.5 shows the cross-sections of a number of different steel girders. Each girder is 10 m long and is going to support part of a large building as shown. Young's modulus for steel is 2.0×10^{11} N m^{-2}.

a Calculate the cross-sectional area of each girder.

b Which of the girders will be compressed the least when it is made part of the building, as shown in the figure?

c If the load on that girder will be 1.0×10^6 N, calculate its compression.

4 When the temperature of an unrestrained bar increases it will expand. On the other hand, if the bar is clamped in place, it will exert a pressure on the clamps when its temperature is raised. This question will help you to work out how that pressure is related to Young's modulus and the expansivity of the bar.

Suppose that a bar of cross-sectional area A and length l is heated from temperature T to temperature $T + \Delta T$. This makes it expand by an amount x. Then it is clamped and squeezed back to its original length without changing its temperature.

a Write down an algebraic expression for the thermal expansion of the bar. Use the symbol α for the expansivity.

b Write down another expression for the force F needed to squeeze the bar back to its original length.

c Combine your answers to parts (a) and (b) to show that the stress produced in a bar which cannot expand is proportional to its temperature rise.

d Young's modulus for steel is 2.0×10^{11} Pa and it has an expansivity of $1.1 \times 10^{-5}\,°C^{-1}$. Calculate the stress required to stop a steel bar expanding when its temperature changes from $-20\,°C$ to $+40\,°C$.

e The lengths of steel used for making continuous welded railway track are laid under tension (see figure 3.6). That is, they are deliberately stretched while they are being fastened to the track. As they warm up during the day and cool down at night, the tension in the rails will change. However, provided that the tension does not become a compression, the rails will not buckle and distort. Suppose that the maximum temperature the rails are ever likely to get to is 50 °C and that they are laid at 15 °C. Estimate the force needed to stretch the rails when they are being laid. You will have to make an educated guess for the cross-sectional area of a typical rail.

5 Show that the stress at the base of a vertical column of height h and density ρ is equal to ρgh.

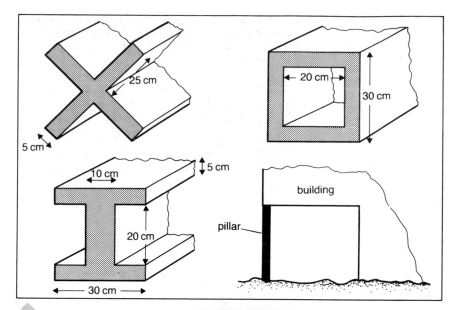

Figure 3.5

Figure 3.6 Hydraulic equipment used to stretch lengths of railway track while they are being laid

Figure 3.7 The stress–strain curve of an ideal solid

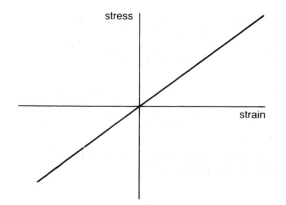

STRESS–STRAIN CURVES

The stress–strain curve of an ideal solid is shown in figure 3.7. It is a straight line through the origin, so it has the same value of Young's modulus for compression and extension. Hooke's Law, however, tells us that the stress–strain curve of a real solid will only be a straight line close to the origin. This section of the chapter is about the acquisition and interpretation of the stress–strain curves of real materials. Not only will it explain how stress and strain data can be obtained in a school laboratory, it will also show how some important properties of a material can be deduced from the shape of its stress–strain curve.

Measuring stress–strain curves

Making measurements which can be used to plot an accurate stress—strain curve for a substance is not particularly straightforward. This is because the maximum strain of most materials is quite small (typically less than 0.05) and the maximum stress is quite large (typically 1×10^{10} Pa). The small value of the strain means that there is a big advantage to using a long sample so that a large extension is obtained. Similarly, if you use a sample with a small cross-sectional area, you can obtain a large stress with relatively small masses hung from the end of the sample.

Measuring extension

The basic experimental set-up is shown in figure 3.8. A long thin sample is suspended from a firm support and its extension measured for different masses hung from its end. The length and diameter of the sample can be measured with a ruler and a micrometer respectively. This allows the stress and strain to be calculated from the values of the suspended mass and the extension. Of course, since the sample is being stretched in the experiment, the data gleaned from it only refer to **tensile** stress and strain. The measurement of **compressive** stress and strain in the laboratory is very much more difficult, mainly because a long thin sample is going to buckle and bend as soon as you compress it. So the samples used for the study of compressive stress have to be short and thick, making the measurement of the change of length more difficult and making the forces required much larger.

Figure 3.8 A simple arrangement of apparatus to obtain data for a stress–strain curve

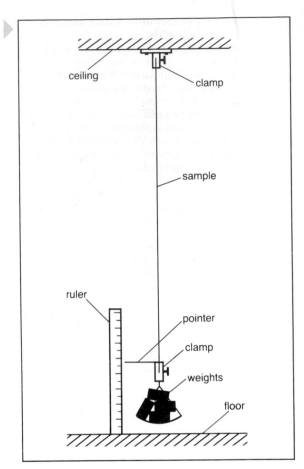

Figure 3.9 Using a spirit level and a micrometer screw to measure small extensions of the sample

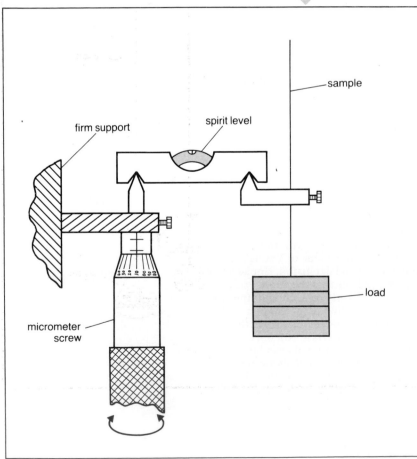
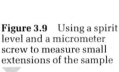

For many samples, the extension is going to be fairly small and difficult to measure directly with a ruler. Figure 3.9 shows how the small extension of a sample which is hung vertically can be measured with a micrometer. As the sample is stressed by hanging weights from its end, the micrometer screw is adjusted so that the spirit level is kept horizontal. The change in reading of the micrometer for a given change of stress is equal to the extension produced by that stress.

Interpreting stress–strain curves

The stress—strain curve of a typical pure metal is shown in figure 3.11. (The curve is drawn for only positive values of the strain, i.e. expansion of the metal under tension.) The shape, slope and extent of the curve all contain information about how the metal behaves when it is stressed. For example, we can infer from the graph that metals are stiff, strong and ductile.

Pure metals

The slope of the graph near the origin is very steep. So the metal has a high value for Young's modulus (stress/strain $\simeq 1 \times 10^{11}$ Pa) and a large stress is required to obtain a small strain. In other words, it will need a large tension to obtain any noticeable extension. So the graph shows that metals are **stiff**. It also shows that metals are **strong**. The sample snaps if the stress exceeds 1.0×10^8 Pa: this is called the **tensile strength** of the material. Unlike Young's modulus, the tensile strength of a material varies from one sample to another and can only be measured once for each sample! So although a precise value can be quoted for Young's modulus, only an approximate (or minimum) value is usually quoted for tensile strength.

Metals are **elastic** provided that they are not stressed beyond the linear portion of the stress–strain curve. This means that when the stress is removed, their strain returns to zero. The **yield stress** is the maximum stress at which elastic behaviour happens. Should the metal be stressed onto the curved portion of the line, it usually exhibits **plastic** behaviour. When the stress is removed, the strain does not return to zero, so the sample remains permanently strained. The graph in figure 3.12 shows what happens. As the stress is increased, the sample follows the curve from O to S. When the stress is removed the sample follows the curve from S to P, rather than going back from S to O. Note how the slope of the line PS is equal to that of OE. The point on the stress–strain curve at which the sample starts to exhibit plastic behaviour is called the **elastic limit**. The fact that metals can have their dimensions permanently changed if sufficient stress is applied means that they are **ductile** — they can be drawn into different shapes.

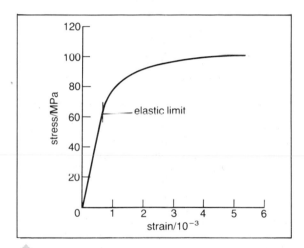

Figure 3.11 The stress–strain curve of a typical pure metal

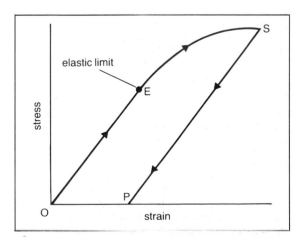

Figure 3.12 Plastic deformation of a sample of metal taken beyond its elastic limit

TEMPERATURE COMPENSATION

There are two reasons why a solid should expand. Its strain can increase because the stress is increased, but it can also change if the temperature changes. So when you do an experiment to plot a stress–strain curve you must ensure that you only measure strain due to stress. For example, the strain of a metal sample will change by approximately $2 \times 10^{-5} \,°\mathrm{C}^{-1}$, so temperature fluctuations of only $\pm 5 \,°\mathrm{C}$ will limit the precision of the strain measurements to $\pm 1 \times 10^{-4}$. Although this appears to be small, it must be compared with the largest strain at which metals still obey Hooke's Law, which is about 1×10^{-3}.

The most obvious strategy is to keep the sample at the same temperature all the way through the experiment. This is no problem if the experiment can be done quickly compared with the time scale of any temperature fluctuations of the room. However, as we shall see later, it is very useful to be able to explore what happens to the strain of a sample when its stress is kept constant. So a better strategy is to arrange matters so that temperature changes are automatically compensated for. This can be done by making the ruler which is used to measure the length of the sample out of the same material, so that they both get longer and shorter by the same amount as the temperature changes.

Figure 3.10 shows how this can be done. Two wires of the material being studied are suspended from a stout support. The thick wire is held taut by a weight hung from its end and a scale is attached to it near the bottom. This wire acts as the ruler; a vernier gauge attached to the thin wire (the sample) can be used to measure its extension as weights are hung from its end. Since both wires are hung in the same environment, they will suffer the same changes of temperature as each other. Therefore, any expansion of the sample caused by a change of temperature will result in an identical expansion of the wire which supports the scale. So any change in the strain of the sample due to thermal expansion will not be detected by the vernier gauge.

Figure 3.10 If the scale is suspended by the same material as the vernier gauge, then thermal expansion of the sample will not affect the measurements of extension

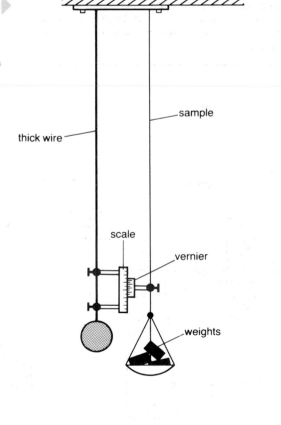

Building materials

The stress–strain curve of a typical building material (such as concrete, brick or glass) is shown in figure 3.13. The curve is steep near the origin, so the material has a high value of Young's modulus ($\approx 1\times 10^{11}$ Pa): it is stiff. However, the tensile strength is relatively low ($\approx 1\times 10^{7}$ Pa) and the material breaks before it reaches its elastic limit. These are the typical characteristics of a **brittle** material. It is very difficult to extend, snaps easily and cannot be permanently stretched.

Elastic and plastic materials

If you have ever tried stretching a rubber band, you will know that it can have a very large strain (at least 3) for a comparatively small stress. So it has a very low value of Young's modulus. On the other hand, a rubber band becomes very stiff when its strain is large and is difficult to snap. Figure 3.14 shows the stress–strain curve of a typical sample of rubber. Note that although rubber is elastic in the sense that its strain returns to zero when the stress is removed, the curves for increasing and decreasing stress are not necessarily identical. Young's modulus for a plastic (such as nylon or polythene) is only about 1×10^{9} Pa. So although they are much less stiff than metals, plastics are considerably stiffer than rubber. Like rubber they can have very large strains before they break, but the large strain only happens in the region beyond the elastic limit. The stress–strain curve of a typical plastic is shown in figure 3.15.

OBJECTIVES

After studying this section you should be able to do the following.

Describe how the stress–strain curve of a material can be measured.

Understand the meaning of the terms *compressive* and *tensile*.

Recognise the shape of stress–strain curves for metals, building materials and plastic materials.

State the meaning of the terms *tensile strength* and *yield stress*.

Explain the meaning of the terms *stiff*, *strong*, *elastic*, *plastic*, *ductile* and *brittle*.

Be able to state the properties of a material from a study of its stress–strain curve.

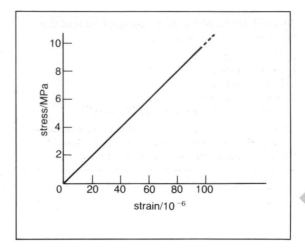

Figure 3.13 The stress–strain curve of a typical brittle building material such as brick, stone or concrete

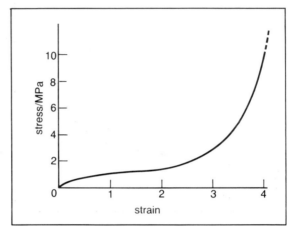

Figure 3.14 The stress–strain curve of a typical sample of rubber

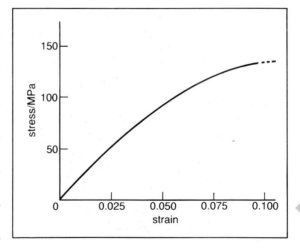

Figure 3.15 The stress–strain curve of a typical man-made plastic such as perspex

QUESTIONS

1 Table 3.1 contains some data for a copper wire whose unstressed length was 1.80 m. It was hung vertically and weights added to its end until it snapped. Its diameter was 0.23 mm.

Table 3.1

Weight/N	0.0	1.0	2.0	3.0	4.0	5.0	6.0
Extension/mm	0.00	0.35	0.70	1.05	1.85	3.25	8.05

a Use the data to prepare a table of the strain of the wire for different stresses.

b Plot a stress–strain graph for the wire.

c Use the graph to calculate Young's modulus for copper.

d Estimate the strain at which the wire reached its elastic limit. Explain your answer.

e Suppose that the wire had been stressed with a 5.5 N weight which was then removed. By how much would the wire have been deformed?

2 Explain the different meaning of each of the terms in the pairs listed below.

a Elastic and plastic.
b Stiff and strong.
c Brittle and ductile.
d Elastic limit and yield stress
e Young's modulus and tensile strength

3 Figure 3.16 shows three different stress–strain curves plotted on the same axes. Suggest, with reasons, a material for each of the curves.

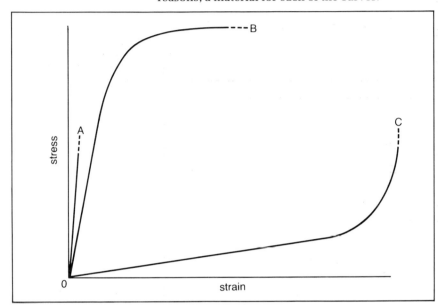

Figure 3.16

Figure 3.17

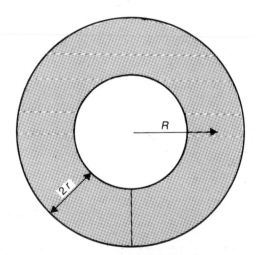

4 The overall shape of an animal is very much dictated by its size. This is especially true of the slenderness of its limbs—look at the photographs below. This question will help you to understand the physics behind this.
A human can hang from one arm without risking a fracture. The stress caused by the person's bodyweight on the bones in the arm must be much less than the tensile strength of bone.

a If the typical arm bone radius and mass of a man are 1 cm and 75 kg respectively, estimate the stress on the bone when he hangs from one arm.

b A man can be approximated as a cylinder of length l and radius r made of material whose density is ρ. Write down an expression for his weight. Hence work out what happens to the weight of a man if all of his dimensions are four times larger than normal.

c Suppose that such a man tried to hang from one arm. Calculate the stress on his arm bone.

d Calculate a value for the radius of his bones which would ensure that they had the same stress as a normal man. Comment on your answer!

5 Although a glass rod cannot be bent very much before it breaks, a thin glass fibre of the same length can be bent into a circle without snapping.
Figure 3.17 shows a cylinder of radius r which has been bent into a circle of radius R. The inner surface of the rod will be compressed and the outer surface will be extended. You can assume that the inner and outer surfaces have equal (but opposite) strains.

a Show that the strain of the outer surface of the cylinder is r/R.

b Glass has a tensile strength of about 9×10^7 Pa and Young's modulus of 8.0×10^{10} Pa. Calculate the maximum tensile strain that glass can have before breaking. What are you assuming about the behaviour of glass?

c Calculate the maximum radius that a glass rod can have if it is to be bent into an arc of a circle of radius 10 cm.

d The wires which carry electric current from the fuse box to the wall sockets in a house contain solid rods of copper. Yet the wires which carry the current from the sockets to appliances are invariably made of copper threads. Why? (Both sets of wires contain the same amount of copper per metre of their length.)

MODELS OF SOLIDS

The last two chapters have, we hope, shown you how solid materials behave when they are subjected to compressive and tensile forces. You have learnt that the relationship between stress and strain for an object depends on the material of which it is made. Thus a wooden table behaves differently from a similar table made from rubber. Each material has a different stress–strain curve associated with a number of intrinsic properties, such as Young's modulus, elastic limit and tensile strength. This chapter will attempt to show how these large-scale (**macroscopic**) properties of a material are related to its small-scale (**microscopic**) structure.

FORCES BETWEEN ATOMS

Chapter 8 will present some evidence that all gases must be made out of large numbers of tiny particles. Since any solid can be converted into a gas by raising its temperature to a high enough value, there is a strong argument for supposing that solids must also be made up of large numbers of tiny particles. Those particles are called **atoms**. However, we are not going to try to convince you that solids are made up of atoms by simply presenting you with evidence for their existence. Instead, we are going to go about convincing you in the way that physicists convince the rest of the scientific community. We will describe a **model** for a solid which is made up of atoms, and show you how that model can predict the known behaviour of solids. As you work your way through this book you will encounter other models which are also based on the existence of atoms.

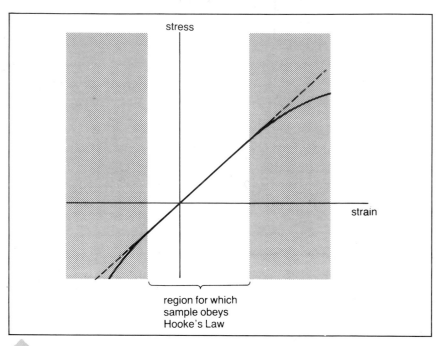

Figure 4.1 Hooke's Law has its limits

Figure 4.2 Modelling a solid with sticky tennis balls

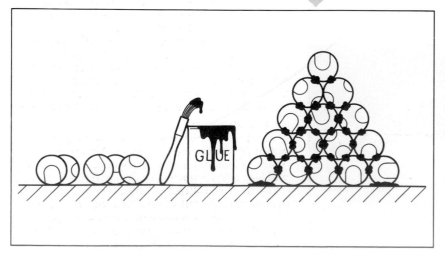

Models

A **model** is something which allows you to describe and explain some phenomenon. Most real phenomena behave in ways that are not easy to describe precisely, and the exact physics which explains that behaviour is often horrendously complicated. So we usually use a simplified description which is roughly equivalent to what actually takes place. We make simplifying assumptions about the system so that the physics becomes possible. It is better to use a simple rough model which can be easily used to make predictions than a complex sophisticated model which is impossible to use! The best model is always the simplest one which successfully accounts for the phenomenon it attempts to describe.

Mathematical models

Hooke's Law is a mathematical model. The formula stress $= E \times$ strain can be used to predict the change of length of a solid when a force is applied to it. Of course, that stress may take the material beyond the linear region of its stress–strain curve (see figure 4.1), so that the actual change in length is not the same as the prediction. Nevertheless, Hooke's Law is a successful model because of its universality and simplicity. These are features which are going to endear any model to a physicist's heart!

Figure 4.3 The force–separation curve for a pair of tennis balls

Figure 4.4 Wet sand can be used to model a solid because its particles attract each other. The individual grains in dry sand do not attract each other, so it cannot be used to model rigid structures

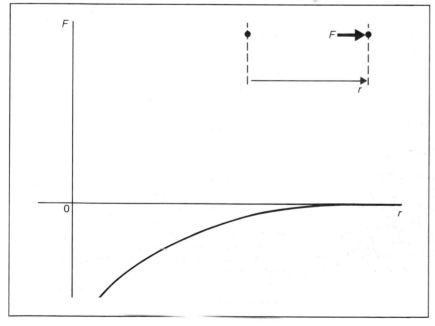

Figure 4.5 The force–separation curve for a pair of very small particles which attract each other

Analogical models

A model is a simplified description of what is going on. Many physics models are mathematical, but less precise models based on analogy are widely used, particularly where the mathematical models are difficult to use. Analogical models use your intuition to help you make predictions. For example, the behaviour of solids can be well described by a model which assumes that matter is made of atoms, small particles with the properties of sticky tennis balls. So by thinking about what a lot of sticky tennis balls would do if you pushed them together (see figure 4.2), you can predict the behaviour of real solids.

The simplest model

The basic properties of solids can be explained by assuming that they are made up of a large number of identical hard spheres. These spheres (which we will call **atoms** for the moment) are very small and are attracted to each other with a force which decreases as they are separated from each other.

Force–separation curves

An important aspect of the model is how the force between two atoms depends on their separation. Correct choice of the force–separation curve is crucial to the success of the model.

The graph of figure 4.3 shows the force–separation curve for a pair of tennis balls. One ball is fixed with its centre at $r = 0$ and the other ball is brought towards it. The force is zero as the second ball approaches (r decreases) and climbs rapidly when they touch. (The repulsive force is positive because it pushes the second ball in the direction of increasing r.) Although atoms with this force–separation curve could be used to explain the incompressible nature of solids, they could not account for their tensile properties. A solid built of this type of atom would simply fall apart into a pile of separate atoms! Figure 4.4 may help you to grasp this point.

A more realistic model of an atom has to incorporate an attractive force to pull the atoms towards each other. Since all solids break if a large enough tensile stress is applied, the attractive force has to decrease with increasing separation of the atoms. Figure 4.5 shows the characteristics of a suitable attractive force. It is always negative, pushing in the direction of decreasing r, becoming zero for large r. If we add the two forces (short-range repulsion and longer-range attraction) together we end up with the force–separation curve drawn in figure 4.6. For $r > d_0$, F is negative, pulling the atoms towards each other. For $r < d_0$, F is positive, pushing the atoms apart from each other. F will only be zero when $r = d_0$ or $r = \infty$. Since r is the separation of the atom centres, d_0 will be the diameter of a single atom, about 1×10^{-10} m.

Regular structure

Predicting the behaviour of two of the atoms postulated by our model is straightforward. Suppose that they are placed near each other. They will be weakly attracted, so they will move towards each other. The attraction will become a repulsion as soon as their centres get closer together than d_0. The only stable arrangement occurs when the attractive and repulsive forces cancel each other out at $r = d_0$.

Figure 4.7 shows a possible stable arrangement of atoms in a solid, each of which is drawn as a hard sphere. It is called a **hexagonal close-packed structure**. The atoms are stacked in **planes**, with each atom touching six other atoms in its own plane. The planes are stacked on top of each other so that the atoms in one plane touch three atoms in the plane above and three in the plane below. So, apart from the atoms near the surface of the solid, each atom is touching twelve other atoms, i.e. has twelve **nearest neighbours**.

An alternative structure, called **face-centred cubic**, is shown in figure 4.8. The atoms in each plane have only four nearest neighbours, but this allows the planes to stack on top of each other with each atom touching four in the next plane. So the atoms in this structure also have twelve nearest neighbours. The **simple cubic structure** shown in figure 4.9a has only six nearest neighbours for each atom. A little thought (or experimenting with small ball bearings on the end of a magnet) should convince you that this is a less stable arrangement than the other two structures. So if our model is a good one, solids should have their atoms arranged in a face-centred cubic or hexagonal close-packed structure; these are both equally stable. The body-centred structure (figure 4.9b) has eight nearest neighbours. So it is more stable than simple cubic, but less stable than hexagonal close-packed.

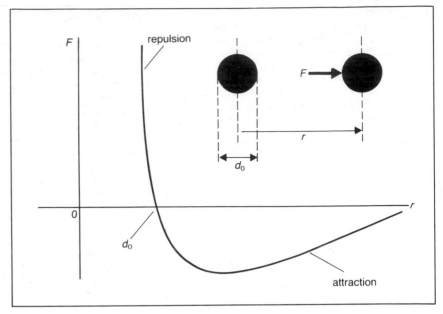

Figure 4.6 The force–separation curve for a pair of ideal atoms

Figure 4.7 How atoms pack together in a hexagonal close-packed structure

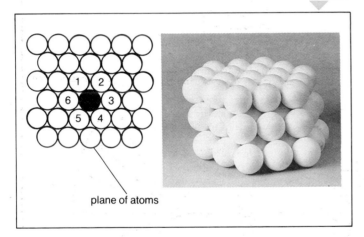

plane of atoms

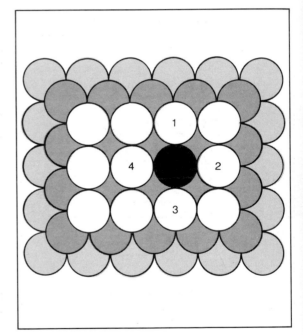

Figure 4.8 A face-centred cubic structure

Figure 4.9 (a) Body-centred cubic and (b) simple cubic structures

Model parameters

A good model makes predictions which agree with experiment. There is a lot of evidence from X-ray diffraction that metals do indeed contain scattering centres in a face-centred cubic or hexagonal close-packed structure, which are separated by about 1×10^{-10} m. So the point at which $F = 0$ in figure 4.11 has to occur when $r \simeq 10^{-10}$ m. This allows us to fix one of the **parameters** of our model, i.e. set $d_0 \simeq 10^{-10}$ m. Another parameter is the slope of the force-separation curve at $r = d_0$: we can relate this to Young's modulus for the material.

Young's modulus

Consider a solid made up of a number of atoms packed in a simple cubic structure, as shown in figure 4.12. The solid has a length l and a cross-sectional area A. No external forces are applied so the atoms will be separated by a distance d_0. Now apply a tensile stress as shown in figure 4.13. The force F makes the solid extend by x, pulling planes of atoms apart by a distance Δr.

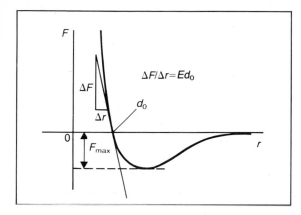

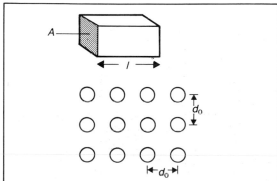

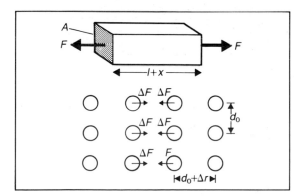

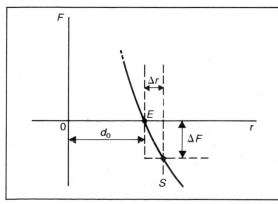

X-ray diffraction is a powerful technique for exploring the structure of solids at an atomic scale. Although we will deal with this topic in detail in a later chapter, it might be useful to see how it is used at this stage. The set up is shown in figure 4.10(b). The specimen to be studied is placed in the path of a beam of X-rays which have a known wavelength λ. As the X-rays pass through the specimen they will be scattered, mostly off the nuclei at the centres of the atoms. The scattered waves will interfere with all the other scattered waves, so that X-rays will emerge from the specimen in the directions which correspond to constructive interference. The specimen therefore acts like a three-dimensional diffraction grating, with X-rays scattered according to the Bragg Law $n\lambda = 2d\sin\theta$. The pattern of the scattered X-rays is recorded on photographic film. An example of an X-ray diffraction pattern for a polycrystalline metal specimen is shown in figure 4.10(a). The pattern of rings can be used to work out both the structure (hexagonal close-packed) of the atoms and their spacing.

Figure 4.10 X-ray diffraction of a powdered sample. (a) The pattern of stripes on the film can be used to infer the arrangement and spacing of the atoms in the crystals. This film was obtained from a metal with a hexagonal close-packed structure. (b) Experimental apparatus

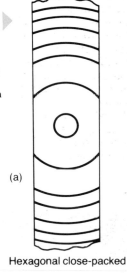

(a)

Hexagonal close-packed

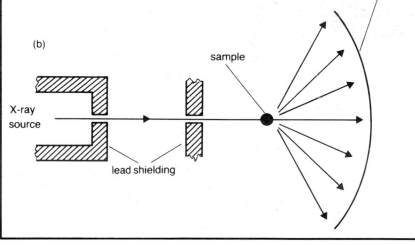

Figure 4.11 Some important parameters of a typical atomic force–separation curve (*top* diagram)

Figure 4.12 Spacing of atoms in an unstressed solid (second diagram)

Figure 4.13 The effects on the atomic spacing of applying a stress (third diagram)

Figure 4.14 The force–separation curve near to the equilibrium position E

Atoms in adjacent planes will be moved from E to S on the force–separation curve shown in figure 4.14. We want to find out how the slope of that curve ($\Delta F/\Delta r$) is related to Young's modulus E for the material.

Each plane will contain n atoms, where n is a very large number. Since the area of the plane is A and the atoms are arranged in a square array separated by a distance d_0, we can get an expression for n:

$$n(d_0{}^2) = A \qquad \therefore n = \frac{A}{d_0{}^2} \qquad (4.1)$$

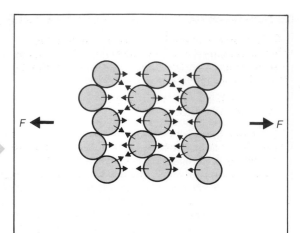

Figure 4.15 Forces on the atoms of a hexagonal close-packed structure as the planes are moved apart by an external stress

Figure 4.16 One plane of atoms in the ball-and-spring model of a solid

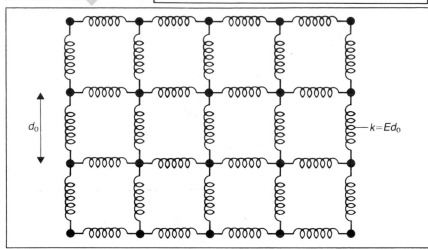

The force F needed to separate two planes of atoms by a distance Δr will be given by

$$F = n\Delta F \qquad \text{(4.2)}$$

where ΔF is the force needed to increase the separation of a pair of atoms by Δr.

Combining equations (4.1) and (4.2), we get an expression for the stress applied to the solid:

$$F = \frac{A\Delta F}{d_0{}^2} \qquad \therefore \ \frac{F}{A} = \frac{\Delta F}{d_0{}^2} \qquad \text{(4.3)}$$

Now consider the extension of the solid. Each of the planes (there are m of them) will move away from its adjacent plane by a distance Δr:

$$x = m\Delta r \qquad \text{(4.4)}$$

Since the planes are nominally separated by a distance d_0, we can get an expression for m in terms of l and d_0.

$$m(d_0) = l \qquad \therefore \ m = \frac{l}{d_0} \qquad \text{(4.5)}$$

Combining equations (4.4) and (4.5) we get an expression for the strain of the solid:

$$x = \frac{l\Delta r}{d_0} \qquad \therefore \ \frac{x}{l} = \frac{\Delta r}{d_0} \qquad \text{(4.6)}$$

Finally, we can put equations (4.3) and (4.6) together into Hooke's Law, i.e. set stress = $E \times$ strain:

$$\frac{F}{A} = \frac{Ex}{l} \quad \therefore \ \frac{\Delta F}{d_0{}^2} = \frac{E\Delta r}{d_0} \quad \therefore \ \frac{\Delta F}{\Delta r} = Ed_0 \quad \text{(4.7)}$$

The quantity $\Delta F/\Delta r$ is known as the **interatomic force constant**. We have managed to show that it should equal Ed_0 for a simple cubic structure of atoms. Using data for iron ($E = 2.1 \times 10^{11}$ Pa, $d_0 = 2.5 \times 10^{-10}$ m) the interatomic force constant is roughly 50 N m^{-1}.

We have used a simple cubic structure rather than the face-centred cubic or hexagonal close-packed structures that our model predicts. Furthermore, we have chosen to apply the external force at right angles to the planes of atoms. This was to keep the algebra simple. In a more realistic structure (figure 4.15), the forces acting on the atoms as the planes were moved apart would have acted in different directions. (When you have learnt how to take components of forces (chapter 6) you can have another go at the calculation!) So our result for the interatomic force constant will only be approximate. This doesn't make the calculation a waste of time. It has told us something that we didn't know before, i.e. that atoms in solids behave as if they are connected to each other by springs whose force constant is approximately 50 N m^{-1}.

The ball-and-spring model

An alternative model for a solid treats it as a collection of infinitely small lumps connected to each other by light springs of length d_0 and force constant k. This is shown in figure 4.16. A simple cubic structure has been assumed to make everything simple. Equation (4.7) can be used to relate Young's modulus for the whole solid to the strength of the individual springs.

> $k = Ed_0$
>
> k is the force constant of the interatomic springs (N m^{-1})
>
> E is Young's modulus for the solid (Pa)
>
> d_0 is the interatomic spacing (m)

This model is particularly useful when you need to consider the behaviour of the energy in a solid as its temperature is raised (chapter 30), when it is irradiated with electromagnetic waves (chapter 26) or when mechanical waves pass through it (chapter 15).

OBJECTIVES

Having studied this section you should be able to do the following.

Explain what a model is to a physicist.

Sketch and explain a typical force–separation curve for two atoms.

Describe different structures for solids.

Quote an approximate figure for the nearest-neighbour distance for an atom in a solid.

Describe the ball-and-spring model of a solid.

Derive the formula $k = Ed_0$.

QUESTIONS

1 Atoms are so small that scientists have devised a special quantity for counting them. One **mole** of atoms is 6.02×10^{23} (Avogadro's number). The **molar mass** of an element is then the mass of one mole of that element. For example, the molar mass of iron is 55.85 g, so 0.05585 kg of iron contains 6.02×10^{23} atoms.

a Consider a material whose density is ρ and molar mass is A. If it is made into a cube with sides of length l, show that it contains $\rho L l^3/A$ atoms, where L is Avogadro's number.

b If the atoms have a simple cubic structure, show that their spacing is given by $d_0 = (A/\rho L)^{\frac{1}{3}}$.

c It is often claimed in text-books that all atoms have roughly the same size. Use the data given in table 4.1 to find out if this is true. What assumptions are you making?

Table 4.1

Element	$\rho/\text{kg m}^{-3}$	$A/\text{kg mol}^{-1}$
lithium	533	0.0069
magnesium	1738	0.0253
aluminium	2698	0.0270
titanium	4508	0.0479
iron	7873	0.0559
copper	8933	0.0635
lead	11343	0.2072
uranium	19050	0.2380

2 The force–separation curve of a material is shown in figure 4.17. The material has its atoms in a simple cubic structure. Use the curve to estimate the following properties of the material.

a The spacing between planes of atoms.
b Young's modulus.

3 Sketch the force–separation curve of figure 4.17. On the same axes, sketch another curve for a material which is stiffer but not as strong.

Figure 4.17

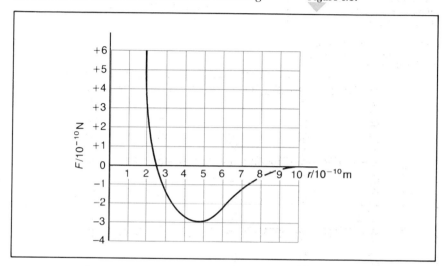

REFINING THE MODEL

If all atoms have force–separation curves of the type shown in figure 4.18, then all solid materials should behave in the same way. In reality, solids have widely different properties. These range from the crystalline hardness of diamond to the amorphous plasticity of plasticene, from the brittle stiffness of concrete to the elastic resilience of rubber. To explain this wide divergence of behaviour, our model has to take account of the different ways in which atoms can pack together to make up solids.

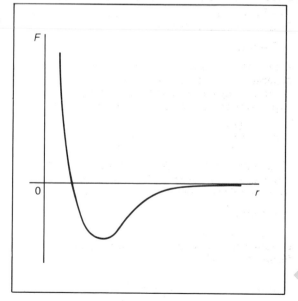

Figure 4.18   A typical force–separation curve for a pair of atoms

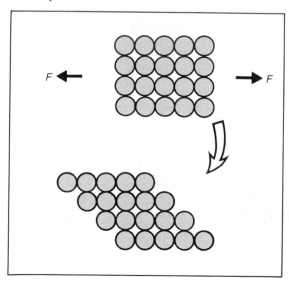

Figure 4.19   Planes of atoms can slip past each other when a large enough stress is applied

Metals

The force which binds metal atoms to each other in a solid is non-directional. This should allow planes of atoms to **slip** when large stresses are applied to a metal sample. This is shown in figure 4.19. The stress is large enough to make each plane of atoms slip past each other. So the plastic deformation of a metal might be similar to the permanent deformation of a pile of sheets of paper when pushed from the side (figure 4.20). However, the regular arrangement of the atoms in figure 4.21

(a **crystalline** structure) suggests that metals should *only* slip if you stress them in certain directions. In practice, metals generally deform the same way in whatever direction the stress is applied. This is because metals are usually **polycrystalline** in nature, i.e. they are made up of small crystals, or **grains**, jumbled up together (figure 4.22). Inside each grain the atoms are arranged in a face-centred cubic or hexagonal close-packed structure, but the atomic planes of one grain are randomly orientated with respect to those of the others around it.

Metallic bonding

When atoms of metallic elements are placed very close to each other they each lose one (sometimes more) electron so that they become singly charged positive ions. Normally those ions would repel each other. However, the negative electrons which are free to roam in the space between the ions provide an attractive force which prevents the ions from drifting apart. Quantum mechanics (chapter 29) says that we must not consider the electrons as particles, at particular places. Instead, a better model is to think of a negatively charged cloud or fluid which fills the spaces between the ions, as shown in figure 4.23. If you think of the electron cloud as a glue which binds the ions together, then the glue can rearrange itself as the ions are displaced and slip over each other. Metallic bonding allows metals to be plastic for large stresses, so that they can be grossly deformed without breaking.

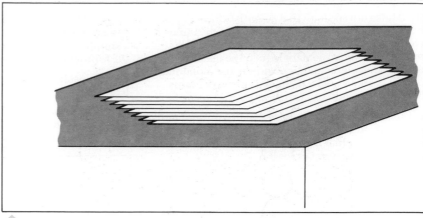

Figure 4.20 Using a pile of sheets of paper to illustrate slip

Figure 4.21 Directions for easy slip in a hexagonal close-packed crystal structure

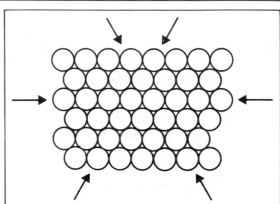

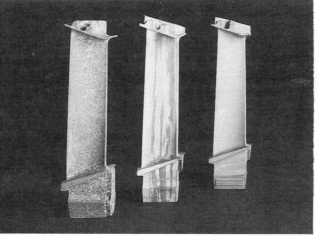

Figure 4.22 These three turbine blades are made from the same metal but have been cast in different ways. Each one has had a surface treatment (acid etching) to make the grains visible. The blade on the left has been cast in the conventional manner and contains many small grains. The blade in the middle has been allowed to solidify along its length, resulting in long crystals. The blade on the right is a single crystal with no grain boundaries at all, giving it greater strength than the other two

Figure 4.23 A representation of metallic bonding

Dislocations

Although the obvious method by which slip can take place is the movement of planes of atoms over each other (figure 4.19), it cannot fully explain the softness of most metals. In a perfect crystal a large stress is needed to pull the planes sufficiently far apart for slip to take place. In reality, metal crystals are never perfect — they contain defects. For example, a whole row of atoms may be missing, giving a **line dislocation** (figure 4.24). Slip can occur very easily in a crystal which contains dislocations. A relatively small force can make the dislocation move rapidly across the crystal, allowing one plane to slip over another in steps rather than all at once. This is shown in the sequence of figure 4.25.

It should be obvious that when a dislocation reaches the edge of a crystal it disappears. However, grain boundaries can be thought of as multiple dislocations, so there is usually no shortage of them. Furthermore, when dislocations cross each other, many new dislocations can be formed. Dislocations can only travel easily through crystals which are otherwise perfect (they rely on the orderly arrangement of atoms). As the dislocation density within a crystal grows, the dislocations are going to find it harder to travel through it — they seem to get tangled up with each other. This leads to the phenomenon of **work-hardening**, illustrated in figure 4.26. After each plastic deformation of the sample, it has a higher yield stress. The process of deformation increases the density of dislocations, making slip more difficult. The large plastic deformation required to draw metals into wires inevitably work-hardens them. This is abundantly clear from the data in table 4.2.

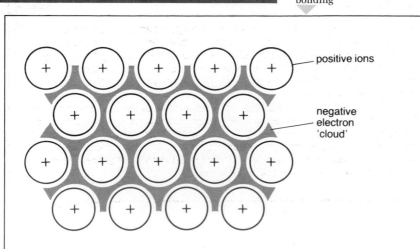

positive ions

negative electron 'cloud'

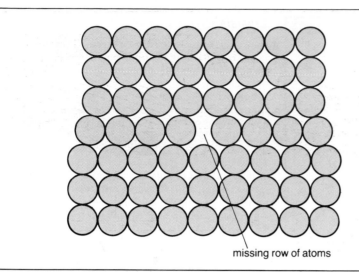

missing row of atoms

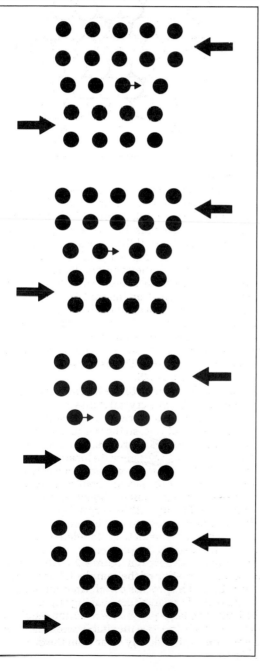

Figure 4.24 A line dislocation in a simple cubic structure. A whole row of atoms at right angles to the plane of the diagram is missing

Figure 4.25 How a dislocation allows slip to occur in a series of small steps. The sequence starts at the top

Figure 4.26 The effects of work-hardening on the stress–strain curve of a metal

Table 4.2

Metal	Tensile strength/Pa	
	Cast	Drawn/Pa
aluminium	9×10^7	4×10^8
copper	1×10^8	4×10^8
steel	4×10^8	1×10^9

Alloys

Any mechanism which will impede the passage of dislocations through a metal will make it stronger, i.e. increase its yield stress. Any break in the orderly arrangement of the atoms will do. Most **alloys** are metals which contain small amounts of impurities. These clump together to form a multitude of small **point defects** in the crystalline structure, defects which will not allow dislocations to pass through them. For example, small amounts of carbon in otherwise pure iron make it considerably tougher, i.e. less likely to break under tensile stress. Table 4.3 shows the tensile strength of some pure metals compared with their alloys.

Table 4.3

Substance	Tensile strength/Pa
iron	2.1×10^8
mild steel (iron + 0.2% carbon)	4.3×10^8
nickel steel (iron + 5% nickel)	8.0×10^8
copper	2.2×10^8
zinc	1.4×10^8
brass (60% copper + 40% zinc)	3.6×10^8

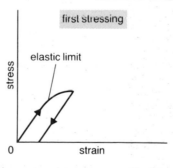

first stressing

elastic limit

stress

0   strain

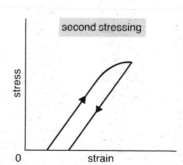

second stressing

stress

0   strain

HEAT TREATMENT ▶▶ 30

At high temperatures there is enough heat energy for an atom to have a significant probability of moving away from its site. If the minimum energy required to change site is ϵ, the probability of an atom obtaining that energy through random thermal exchange with its neighbours is proportional to $\exp[-\epsilon/kT]$, where T is the temperature. This means that dislocations can gradually disappear at high temperatures. So the effects of work-hardening can be removed by heating a metal to a high temperature and letting it cool slowly. This process is called **annealing**. Dislocations cannot cross grain boundaries very easily, so a metal with small grains is going to have a higher tensile strength than one with large grains. Small grains can be achieved by cooling a hot metal very rapidly (**quenching**). For example, the tensile strength of quenched steel can be 50% greater than that of annealed steel.

IONIC BONDING !

The atoms in many crystals are held together by **ionic bonding**. Metal atoms will donate one or more of their electrons to non-metallic atoms they come into contact with. This leaves two types of ion which are strongly attracted to each other because of their opposite charge. In a solid made up of such ions there will be a delicate balance between the attraction of the different types of ion and the repulsion of ions of the same type. Thus sodium chloride (common table salt) has a simple cubic structure as shown in figure 4.27. Because of the long-range nature of the electrical forces between the ions, it is very difficult for planes to slip across each other without completely disrupting the arrangement of ions in adjacent planes. So ionic crystals are not plastic — they fracture well before they reach their elastic limit.

Figure 4.27 The simple cubic structure typical of an ionic solid

COVALENT BONDING !

Covalent bonding occurs between atoms when they share electrons between them. Unlike metallic bonding, where the shared electrons are free to move from ion to ion, the electrons involved in a covalent bond are localised. This means that covalent bonds are strong and directional, able to bind atoms together into **molecules** of definite shape (figure 4.29). There are weak forces between molecules, so they can form crystals at low enough temperatures; molecules of water form ice crystals below 0 °C at atmospheric pressure. The hardest crystals known are **giant molecules**, with every atom locked into position by covalent bonds with its neighbours. Figure 4.30 shows the structure of diamond, which has each carbon atom rigidly held in place by its four nearest neighbours.

Figure 4.29 Models of a number of different molecules (left to right): oxygen, water, ammonia and methane. Each ball represents an atom

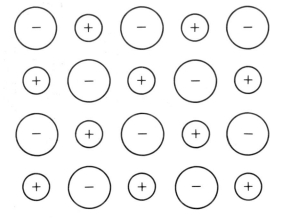

Figure 4.30 The giant molecular structure of diamond

Crystals

As a rule, pure annealed metals are stiff but not very strong. Their strength can be increased in a number of ways (alloying, work-hardening or quenching), but this is always at the expense of toughness. The stronger the metal becomes, the more likely it is to suffer from **brittleness**. This applies to more than just metals; it also applies to crystals.

Cleaving

Some typical crystals are shown in figure 4.28. Their shape, with flat faces and regular angles, implies the orderly stacking of their atoms. Planes of atoms must stretch continuously from one side of the crystal to the other. Any serious attempt to make one of those planes slip will result in complete fracture of the crystal along that plane. This process is known as **cleaving**. A sharp impulse directed at the correct angle will split the crystal with relative ease. Diamonds and other precious gems are cleaved to both improve their shape and create several small gems from one large one.

Glasses

Glasses have the stiffness and brittleness of crystals without their large-scale regularity of structure or planes of weakness. They have an **amorphous** structure, with no regularity in the way that their molecules are locked together in the solid. Glasses are substances which are very viscous just above their melting point, so their molecules are unable to arrange themselves into orderly crystal structures during freezing. Figure 4.31 illustrates the typical disorderly arrangement of silicon and oxygen atoms in window glass. The strong bonds between the atoms in a glass mean that it should be very strong. The lack of crystalline structure makes slip impossible and means that the material will not have planes of weakness along which it can be cleaved. Yet everyone knows that glass shatters easily. It may be stiff, but it certainly isn't strong.

Figure 4.28 Crystals of an ionic material

Cracks

Glasses are brittle because **cracks** can travel through them easily. A relatively small stress can make a microscopic crack on the surface grow uncontrollably through the solid until it snaps in two. This is used to shape sheets of glass, as shown in figure 4.32. Firstly, a small crack is scored on the surface of the glass with a sharp instrument. Then a modest stress is applied to the glass in such a way as to force the crack open. The result is (usually) a clean fracture along the line of weakness defined by the original crack. The initial crack does not have to be very deep, simply sharp.

When a tensile force is applied to a perfect sample, it will be uniformly stressed. If there is a crack in the sample, there will be an increase in the stress around the tip of the crack. The increase in stress depends on the radius of the tip as well as the length of the crack, so that a short, but narrow, crack can result in a large local increase in stress. So the material at the crack tip will reach its tensile stress well before the rest of the material does. The crack will therefore be able to grow even though the *average* stress on the sample is well below the material's tensile strength. Of course, once the crack has started to grow, things go from bad to worse. The crack becomes sharper, the stress increase at the tip becomes larger, etc. The crack tip propagates through the sample at roughly the speed of sound until it reaches the other side!

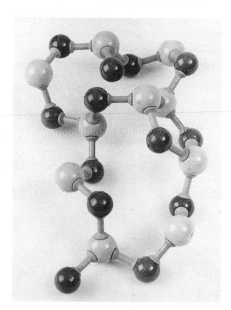

Figure 4.31 The amorphous structure of a typical glass

Figure 4.32 How to snap a sheet of glass by making a small surface crack propagate through it

PHOTOELASTICITY ▶▶ 28

The speed of polarised light through perspex depends on its stress. This can be used to map out the variations of stress within a perspex model of an object. Monochromatic light is shone through a linear polariser (polaroid) onto the model. The light transmitted through the perspex is viewed through a second polariser aligned at right angles to the first one, as shown in figure 4.33. Normally, no light can be transmitted through both polarisers with this arrangement. However, if the model is stressed, the different speeds of the polarisation components parallel and perpendicular to the stress direction allow them to constructively or destructively interfere at the second polariser. Figure 4.33 clearly shows the stress concentration in a sample of perspex. All of the points in a given bright fringe have the same stress as each other, so the arrangement of fringes is effectively a contour map of the stress in the sample.

Figure 4.33 The apparatus needed to study photoelasticity

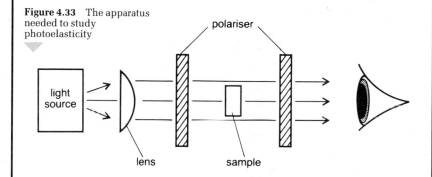

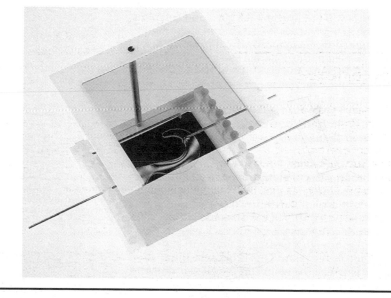

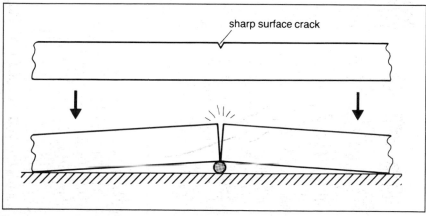

Elastomers

Rubber molecules are long and thin, resembling stiff rods with swivel joints at periodic intervals (figure 4.34). Normally, each rod is randomly oriented with respect to its neighbours, but when a stress is applied the whole molecule can straighten out. In this way, quite modest stresses can achieve strains of up to 5. Once the molecule has been straightened out, then rubber behaves much like any other covalently bonded solid, i.e. it is stiff and strong.

Polythene, a typical man-made polymer, consists of molecules which are much longer than those of rubber. Normally, they are folded as illustrated in figure 4.35, allowing polythene to be elastic like rubber. The bonding between polythene molecules is relatively weak, so they can slip past each other once the stress is sufficiently large to straighten them out. So polythene combines the elasticity of rubber with the plasticity of metals.

Composites

A **composite** material is made by combining two different materials to obtain one which has the best properties of each material without their drawbacks. Most composites try to obtain the strength of one material with the toughness of another.

Reinforced concrete
Concrete is stiff but brittle. Like glass and ceramics, it is weak in tension because it cannot stop small cracks spreading catastrophically through it. Steel rods immersed in the concrete can stop cracks spreading, because steel is stiff and strong. Sometimes the concrete is pre-stressed with bolts or cables running through tubes in it, as shown in figure 4.36. The bolts are stressed, so that the concrete is always in compression, preventing cracks from opening up.

Glass fibre and wood
Glass fibre consists of cloth woven from thin fibres of glass embedded in a matrix of resin. It has the strength of glass and flexibility of glass fibres without the possibility of catastrophic failure. This is explained in figure 4.37. Any crack which propagates through a particular fibre will stop when it meets the resin. This is because the bonding between the resin and the glass is not very strong. Wood is a natural example of the strengthening technique used in glass fibre. It consists of long thin strands of cellulose laid parallel to each other in a matrix of lignin (figure 4.38). If a strand of cellulose is snapped under tensile stress, the lignin prevents that crack from travelling to other strands. Of course, unlike glass fibre which has its strands laid in two directions, wood is relatively weak when stressed at right angles to the grain direction.

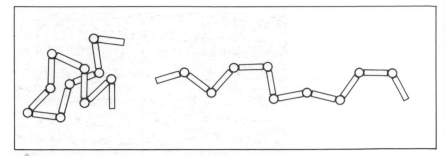

Figure 4.34 A model of a rubber molecule

Figure 4.35 A model of a polythene molecule

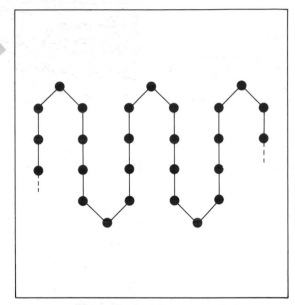

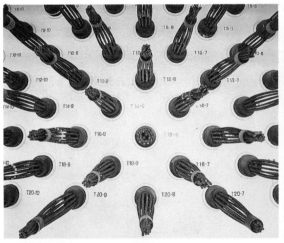

Figure 4.36 Steel reinforcement cables emerging from the concrete pressure vessel of a nuclear reactor

Figure 4.37 A cross-section through a glass-fibre composite

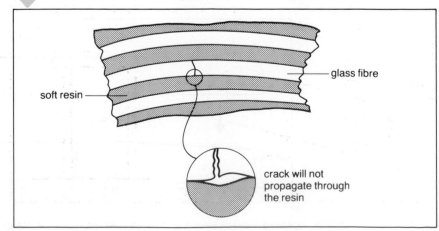

glass fibre

soft resin

crack will not propagate through the resin

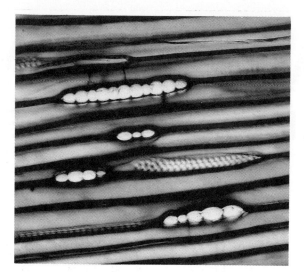

Figure 4.38 The grain structure in wood, a good example of a natural composite material (the pits are cavities which allow exchange of substances between cells)

OBJECTIVES

After studying this section you should be able to do the following.

Describe the arrangement of atoms in a metal.

Understand the meaning of the terms *polycrystalline*, *grain*, *dislocation* and *work-hardening*.

Explain metallic bonding.

Describe the arrangement of atoms in a typical crystal.

Explain the importance of cracks in limiting the strength of materials.

Describe the construction of a composite and explain how it can be both stiff and strong.

QUESTIONS

1 Explain the difference between these pairs of terms;

a amorphous and crystalline,
b point defect and line dislocation,
c slip and fracture,
d annealing and quenching,
e crack and grain boundary,
f alloy and composite.

2 The early civilisations in the Middle East used weapons made of brass. They used to sharpen the blades of their weapons by hammering. The use of a grindstone to sharpen them would have made the edges useless. Can you explain why?

3 The oil in a car's gearbox performs the dual function of lubrication and cooling. Suggest why it might be important to keep the meshing teeth of the gear wheels cool.

Figure 4.39 ▶

Figure 4.40 ▶

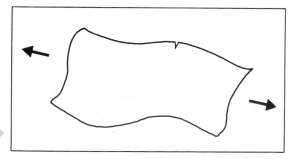

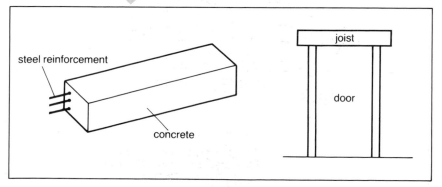

steel reinforcement

concrete

joist

door

4 If you grasp a sheet of polythene and tug on it, it will probably stretch plastically. However, if the sheet has a nick in it (figure 4.39) it will probably tear in two quite easily. Explain why.

5 **Metal fatigue** has been responsible for the failure of many large metal structures such as bridges, ships and aeroplanes. A sample of metal which is subjected to repeated periodic stresses which take it close to its elastic limit will eventually become brittle and prone to crack. You can try this for yourself by repeatedly flexing a steel paperclip.

a Explain why the metal will become brittle when repeatedly flexed.

b Explain why the brittle metal is more likely to crack than the normal plastic metal.

c Suggest why metal fatigue is a particular problem when it occurs at the edges of holes in large structures, e.g. hatchways in ships or windows in aeroplanes.

6 Suppose that you take a steel needle, heat it to red heat and let it cool slowly. You should be able to bend the needle into a right angle without snapping it. On the other hand, if you had held the red hot needle under a stream of cold water, it would have snapped as soon as you tried to bend it. Explain these observations.

7 A rubber molecule can be modelled as being N rods of length l connected with ball-and-socket joints. If the angle between the rods at each joint is totally random, the average length of a rubber molecule should be $N^{\frac{1}{2}}l$. A typical rubber band can be elastically stretched to a maximum of six times its normal length. Calculate a suitable value for N, clearly stating any assumptions that you make.

8 A reinforced concrete girder is shown in figure 4.40. The girder is to be used as a joist above a door, as shown. Draw a diagram to show how the girder should be placed above the door. Explain why it is important that the girder be placed the right way round.

SUMMARY
F O R C E S

The dimensions of an object can be measured with a variety of instruments (ruler, micrometer, radar), each of which has a limited range and precision. Any measurement of length is ultimately a comparison with the distance travelled by light in one second. The length of a second is defined via an atomic (caesium) clock.

Suppose one object has double the volume of the other, but they are otherwise identical. Then one object has double the mass of the other. Mass is proportional to volume: $m = \rho V$. The object's density is the constant of proportionality. It is the slope of an $m-V$ graph; $\rho = \Delta m / \Delta V$.

Weight is also proportional to mass: $W = mg$. The value of g is about 10 N kg^{-1}, varying slightly from one place to another on Earth. It can be measured by measuring the period of oscillation of a point mass suspended on the end of a light cord.

The relative masses of objects can be found by comparing their weights with the help of a forcemeter or lever balance. Absolute mass is found by weight comparison with the standard kilogram. Weight can be measured with a forcemeter calibrated with a number of known identical masses.

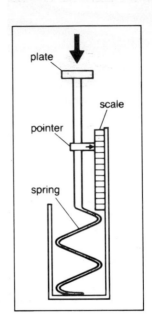

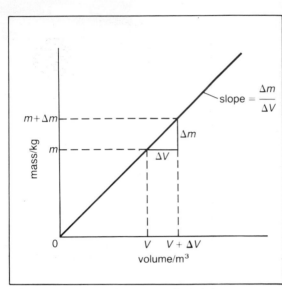

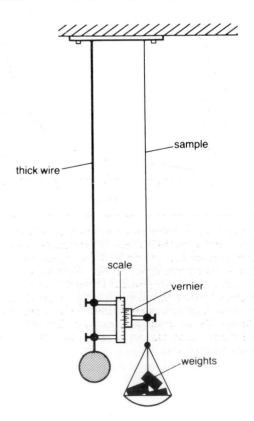

All solid materials obey Hooke's Law: the deformation is proportional to the applied force provided the elastic limit is not reached. $F = kx$ where k is the force constant, an extrinsic property of the object. It has the same value for both compressive and tensile forces.

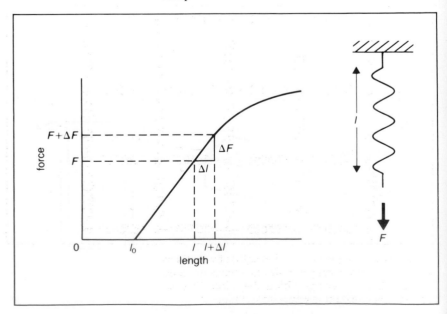

Stress $= F/A$ and strain $= x/l$; stress $= E \times$ strain below the elastic limit. Young's modulus, tensile strength and yield strength are intrinsic properties of a material. The tensile strength is the maximum stress on the material before it breaks. The yield strength is the minimum stress required to plastically deform the material. Materials can be classified as being stiff, strong, elastic, plastic, ductile or brittle. These properties can be inferred from the shape and scale of a stress–strain curve.

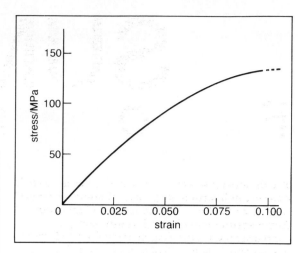

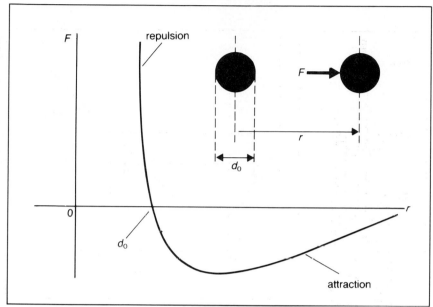

Atoms can be modelled as solid spheres about 0.1 nm across. The forces between atoms are attractive at long range and repulsive at short range. The forces between metal atoms are equally strong in all directions, so they are usually arranged in hexagonal close-packed formation with twelve nearest neighbours. Metals are malleable because dislocations allow planes of atoms to slip over one another for relatively low stresses. Work-hardening increases the dislocation density, making it hard for slip to occur and stiffening the metal. Annealing removes imperfections in a metal's crystal structure, quenching introduces imperfections.

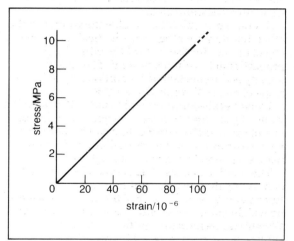

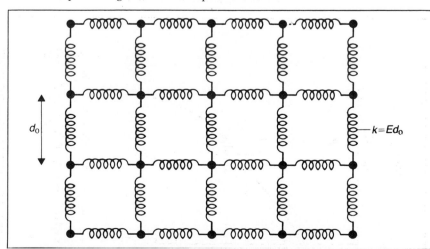

The ball-and-spring model of solids treats them as a simple cubic array of point masses connected to each other by springs which obey Hooke's Law. The spring constant is given by $k = Ed_0$.

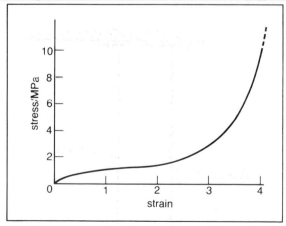

Crystalline materials have strong directional forces between their atoms or molecules. Slip of crystal planes is very difficult, so crystalline materials are strong but brittle. Microscopic cracks can spread catastrophically through brittle materials when they are subjected to tensile stress, so such materials can only be used in compression. Composite materials such as glass fibre and reinforced concrete can be strong in both tension and compression.

MOMENTUM

5

FORCE AND MOMENTUM

There are a small number of **universal laws** which physicists reckon govern the behaviour of everything in our universe. Unlike Hooke's Law, which is just a useful summary of the approximate behaviour of most materials, universal laws are supposed to apply to everything under all circumstances. This chapter will introduce you to one of the members of that select club of universal laws; it is called the Principle of Momentum Conservation. The chapter will also explain Newton's Laws of Motion, an important cluster of laws which are almost universal.

MOMENTUM

The **momentum** of an object is calculated by multiplying its mass by its velocity. This is encapsulated in the following formula.

$$\mathbf{p} = m\mathbf{v}$$

p is the momentum, measured in newton seconds (N s)

m is the mass, measured in kilograms (kg)

v is the velocity, measured in metres per second (m s^{-1}).

The symbols for momentum and velocity are in bold type to show that they are **vectors**, i.e. that they have both a magnitude and a direction. (The obvious unit for momentum is kg m s^{-1}. Later on you will find out why this is the same as N s.) Before we proceed to show why the momentum of an object is worth calculating, you need to know something about the vector nature of velocity.

Velocity

The velocity of an object should tell you two things. First, how fast it is moving, i.e. what its speed is. Secondly, the direction in which it is moving. In order to represent both of these things, a velocity needs to be specified by three numbers instead of just one. Each number will be a **component** of the velocity along one of three coordinate axes at right angles to each other.

Components

Figure 5.1 shows an object in a space. The three coordinate axes (x, y and z) allow us to specify exactly where that object is. Its coordinates are (x,y,z) = (1,2,3). We can define the component of the velocity in the x-direction with the following formula. (Similar formulae can be used to calculate the velocity components in the y- and z-directions.)

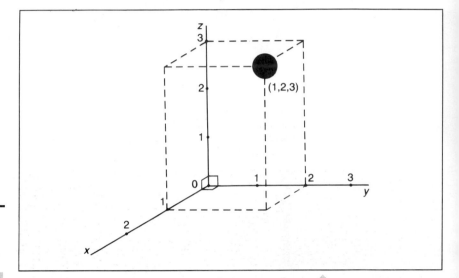

Figure 5.1 The coordinates of an object at one instant

$$v_x = \frac{\Delta x}{\Delta t}$$

v_x is the x-component of the velocity (m s^{-1})

Δx is the change of x-coordinate (m)

Δt is the time taken for the change (s)

Let us suppose that the object travels from (1,2,3) to (5,0,3) in 2 seconds (see figure 5.2). To calculate its velocity, we deal with each component in turn.

Figure 5.2 How the coordinates change in the next 2 s

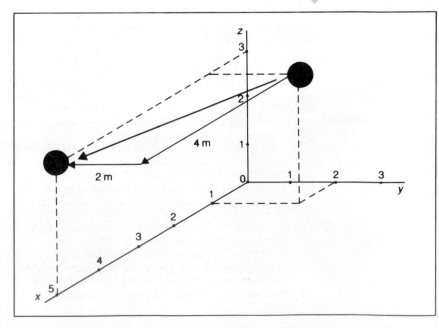

$v_x = ?$

$\Delta x = 5 - 1 = 4$ m

$\Delta t = 2$ s

$v_x = \dfrac{\Delta x}{\Delta t}$

$$\therefore v_x = \frac{4}{2} = +2 \text{ m s}^{-1}$$

$v_y = ?$

$\Delta y = 0 - 2 = -2$ m

$\Delta t = 2$ s

$v_y = \dfrac{\Delta y}{\Delta t}$

$$\therefore v_y = \frac{-2}{2} = +1 \text{ m s}^{-1}$$

$v_z = ?$

$\Delta z = 3 - 3 = 0$ m

$\Delta t = 2$ s

$v_z = \dfrac{\Delta z}{\Delta t}$

$$\therefore v_z = \frac{0}{2} = 0 \text{ m s}^{-1}$$

So our object appears to be moving at 2 m s^{-1} along the x-axis *away* from the origin, at 1 m s^{-1} along the y-axis *towards* the origin and not moving at all along the z-axis.

Figure 5.3 Part of the universe as seen through a telescope

A model universe

The thought experiment which follows should show you why the momentum of an object might be a particularly convenient way of looking at its motion. It should also show how that motion changes during interactions with other objects. The experiment involves trying to measure the velocity of the universe! Although this is obviously too grandiose to be carried out in practice, we can still think about how it might be done.

To measure the velocity of an object, you need two items of data: a displacement (Δx) and how long it takes (Δt). So we need to measure the displacement of the universe during a known time interval. Unfortunately, as figure 5.3 shows, the universe is not a solid object but a widely spread collection of a large number of objects moving in different directions at different speeds. So measuring its displacement is not going to be straightforward. One approach is to decide where the centre of the universe is, and to measure the displacement of that. But how do we find the centre?

Centre of mass

Let us say that the centre of the universe is the average position of all the things in it. The simplest way of finding the average x-coordinate X can be found by adding up the x-coordinates of all pieces of the universe and dividing by the number of pieces n.

$$X = \frac{x_1 + x_2 + x_3 + \ldots + x_n}{n} \quad \text{(5.1a)}$$

However, some of the pieces are bigger than others, so it will be better to use a **weighted average**, with the mass of each object acting as the weighting factor. (After all, the mass of an object is a measure of how much material it contains.) If the total mass of the universe is M, then the x-coordinate of its centre will be given by

$$X = \frac{m_1x_1 + m_2x_2 + m_3x_3 + \ldots + m_nx_n}{m_1 + m_2 + m_3 + \ldots + m_n} \quad \text{(5.1b)}$$

We can simplify equation (5.1b) as M is the total mass of the universe.

$$X = \frac{\Sigma mx}{M} \quad \text{(5.1c)}$$

Note that the summation has to be taken over all of the pieces in the universe. Similar expressions can be written down for the y- and z-coordinates of the centre of the universe.

Now that we have found the centre of the universe, let's think about how its displacement can be measured. Of course, any measurement of displacement requires some sort of ruler which is separate from the object being displaced. Unfortunately, any ruler which is used to measure the displacement of the universe is itself going to be part of that universe. This is similar to attempting to measure the speed of a car without involving anything outside it. For example, the speedometer relies on friction between the tyres and the road to keep the wheels turning. If you raise the wheels off the ground, the speedometer reading is meaningless. All you can do is measure the speed of the car *relative* to the road or some other object outside the car. (Einstein made this idea one of the cornerstones of his famous theory of relativity — see chapter 26.)

In other words, it should not be possible to measure the displacement of the whole universe, without the use of something outside it. Since everything *is* part of the universe it should not be possible to detect its displacement at all! So X is constant, i.e. ΔX should be zero. However, most of the pieces in our universe are moving with respect to each other.

$$\Delta X = \frac{m_1\Delta x_1 + m_2\Delta x_2 + m_3\Delta x_3 + \ldots + m_n\Delta x_n}{M}$$

$$\therefore \Delta X = \frac{\Sigma m\Delta x}{M} \quad \text{(5.2)}$$

Of course, Δx will be different for each object, depending on how fast it is moving. Nevertheless, the weighted mean of those displacements must be zero.

$$\Delta X = \frac{\Sigma m\Delta x}{M} = 0 \qquad \therefore \Sigma m\Delta x = 0 \quad \text{(5.3a)}$$

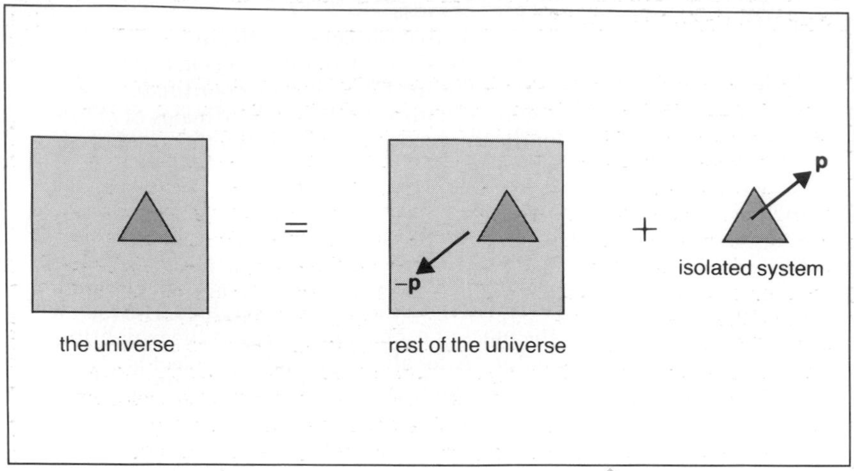

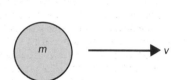

Figure 5.4 An isolated system in the rest of the universe

Figure 5.5 A small isolated system

Figure 5.6 An air track

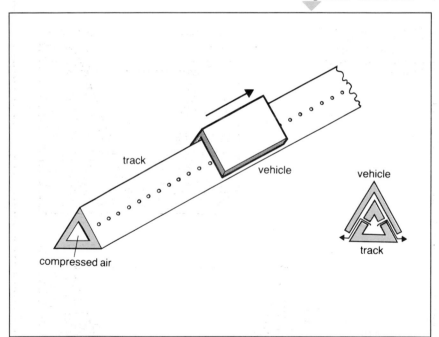

The next step is to divide equation (5.3a) by Δt.

$$\frac{\Sigma m \Delta x}{\Delta t} = 0 \qquad \therefore \Sigma m v_x = 0 \qquad \therefore \Sigma p_x = 0 \qquad \textbf{(5.3b)}$$

Equation (5.3b) says that the sum of the x-components of the momentum (p_x) of the objects in the universe should add up to zero. The same should be true of the y- and z-components of the momentum. So we end up with this dramatic statement about the total momentum of the universe.

$$\Sigma \mathbf{p} = 0 \qquad \textbf{(5.4)}$$

The total momentum of the universe is zero.

Isolated systems

It is a fundamental rule in physics that you should not take too seriously things that you cannot test by experiment. So perhaps we ought to stop thinking about the whole universe and just consider that small part of it which is under our control in the laboratory. Suppose that we arrange a small number of objects in our laboratory and ensure that they cannot interact with the rest of the universe, just with each other. This is shown in figure 5.4.

If the total momentum of this **isolated system** is **p**, then the momentum of the rest of the universe must be $-\mathbf{p}$, so that they both add up to zero, as required by equation (5.4). But if there is no way in which the isolated system can interact with the rest of the universe, its momentum should stay constant at $-\mathbf{p}$. Similarly, the momentum of the system should stay at **p** for as long as it remains isolated. In other words, whatever happens to the objects inside the isolated system, they will always have the same total momentum. They can tug on each other, coalesce into a single lump or explode into a million fragments — provided that they cannot affect the rest of the universe, their total momentum will not change!

Momentum conservation

Momentum is useful because, under the right circumstances, it is conserved. That is, regardless of the nature of the interactions between the parts of a system, its overall momentum does not change. This is an extremely important fact, and is called the **Principle of Momentum Conservation.**

The total momentum of an isolated system remains constant.

Exactly what is meant by the word *isolation* will become clear as we look at some of the experimental evidence supporting the principle.

Newton's First Law of Motion

Figure 5.5 shows a small isolated system, containing a single object. It has a mass m and a velocity **v** at a particular instant, giving it a momentum $\mathbf{p} = m\mathbf{v}$. The Principle of Momentum Conservation states that, provided the object remains isolated, its momentum cannot change. So provided that its mass does not change, its velocity cannot change. It will travel at a constant speed in a straight line.

THE NATURE OF PROOF   **!**

We have *not* rigorously proved that the total momentum of an isolated system remains constant. Our derivation contains a large number of (we hope) reasonable assumptions, some of which may not bear looking at too closely. For example, we have glibly assumed that the correct way of establishing the centre of the universe involves using the mass of an object to provide the weighting. We could have defined the centre another way. Similarly, just because we cannot think of a way of measuring the velocity of the universe as a whole, that does not mean that it is impossible. It may just mean that we are not clever enough to think of a way to do it! However, our thought experiment has been quite successful in one respect. It has shown that the total momentum of a group of objects might be constant if they cannot interact with anything else. However, this is something which has to be confirmed by experiment.

Figure 5.7 Galileo's pin
and pendulum experiment

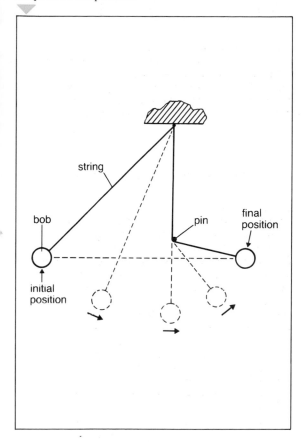

In the Middle Ages it was a popular misconception that an object would only travel at a constant speed if it was pushed by a steady force. Galileo was the first scientist to unravel the effects of friction on moving objects, almost a hundred years before Newton. One of the experiments that he performed is illustrated in figure 5.7. A mass on a string (a pendulum bob) is pulled to one side and released from rest. At the bottom of the swing the string hits a pin, so that the length of the pendulum is effectively shortened. Galileo observed that the bob always rose to almost the same height at the end of its swing as it had at the beginning. Experiments with bobs of the same size but different densities showed that heavy bobs rose higher than light ones. He reasoned that interaction of the bob with the air it was passing through (what we call **friction**) was responsible for the bob failing to get up to exactly the same height as it started. He correctly guessed that if he could do the experiment in a vacuum, the bob would always rise up to its initial height at the end of its swing.

Galileo realised that the exact trajectory followed by the bob was not important. After all, it didn't matter where the pin was placed. So a ball released at the top of a curved track (figure 5.8(a)) should roll back up to the same height on the other side, regardless of the shape of the curve. Galileo argued that if the ball rolled down a track onto a flat section, it would continue along the flat at a constant speed until it got to the rising section at the end and came to a halt at its initial height (figure 5.8(b)). However long the flat section was, the ball would have to keep going (figure 5.8(c)). In practice, of course, the ball does slow down, but its deceleration can be reduced by careful choice of the material used for making the track and the ball. Galileo felt that since reducing friction made the ball roll further, the total absence of friction should make it roll on for ever.

Figure 5.8 (a–c) Stages in Galileo's thought experiment to deduce Newton's First Law of Motion

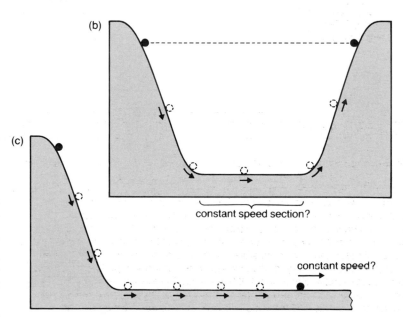

Of course, gravity ensures that it is impossible to completely isolate an object in an Earth-based laboratory. Complete isolation requires that there is no way in which the outside world can influence the object. However, it is possible to observe objects which travel at a constant speed in a straight line by using an **air track**, as shown in figure 5.6. Air is blown down the empty middle of the track and emerges from small holes in the top. Objects (usually called vehicles) placed on the top of the track are supported by these currents of air, and can move along the track without touching it. If the track is made horizontal with the help of a spirit level, then a vehicle will appear to travel at an almost constant speed along the length of the track.

The air cushion below the vehicle reduces the **friction** between it and the track. Friction is the name we give to the force which always seems to act when two surfaces rub against each other. Experience tells us that friction always seems to oppose the motion which causes it in the first place. So it would seem reasonable that the vehicle can have a constant horizontal component of velocity because there is no horizontal force acting on it. Although Isaac Newton did not have access to an air track, in 1686 he encapsulated these ideas in his **First Law of Motion**.

> Provided that no external forces act, an object will travel in a straight line at a constant speed.

Balanced forces

An air track can reduce the friction acting on a vehicle, but it cannot change the vertical force of gravity on the vehicle. The air cushion isolates the vehicle in the horizontal direction, so that its horizontal momentum remains constant. Yet the vertical component of the momentum also remains constant, i.e. zero. If Newton's First Law applies to motion in all directions, then the air cushion must be able to cancel out the effects of gravity, effectively isolating the vehicle from vertical influences as well as horizontal ones. This suggests that an upwards force from the air cushion combined with the downward tug of gravity can give no force at all. This is shown in figure 5.9. So the word 'isolated' in the statement of the Principle of Momentum Conservation simply means that external forces acting on the system must balance each other out.

Sticky collisions

Figure 5.10 shows how an air track can be used to study a collision between a pair of vehicles. Each of them has a vertical plate so that its speed can be monitored by a pair of photodiodes placed at either end of the track. The photodiodes are connected to a computer. A light bulb illuminates the photodiode from the other side of the track. Each time a vehicle passes a light bulb, the plate cuts off the light from the photodiode, sending a signal to the computer. The computer can therefore record the time taken for the vehicle to pass in front of the bulb.

Figure 5.9 The upwards thrust from the air track jets cancels out the downwards tug of gravity on the vehicle

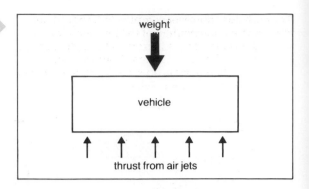

Figure 5.10 Apparatus for investigating the motions of objects in an almost friction-free environment

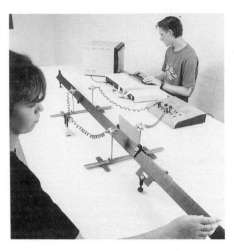

Figure 5.11 A sticky collision

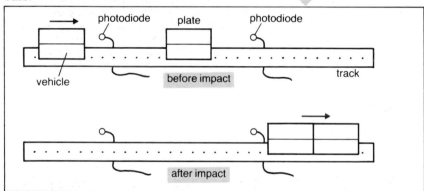

Figure 5.12 A bouncy collision

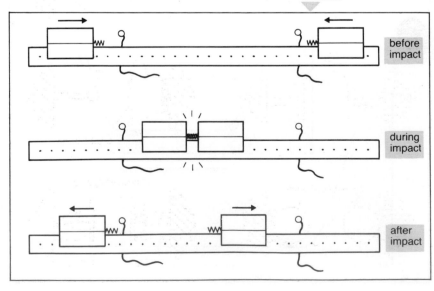

We are going to look at two experiments which could be performed with this system to test momentum conservation. The first one is the simplest, involving the sticky collision of a moving vehicle with an identical stationary one. This is illustrated in figure 5.11. One vehicle is sent towards the other which is initially stationary at the centre of the track. When the two meet they stick together and move on down the air track. Suppose that the computer records that it takes 0.568 s for the vehicle to pass in front of the left-hand photodiode. We can use momentum conservation to predict how long the vehicles should take to pass in front of the right-hand photodiode. All we need to know is the mass of the two trolleys (0.832 kg) and their length (0.100 m).

Start off by calculating the initial momentum of the system. The initial velocity of the moving vehicle has to be calculated first.

$$v = ? \qquad\qquad v = \frac{\Delta x}{\Delta t}$$
$$\Delta x = 0.100 \text{ m}$$
$$\Delta t = 0.568 \text{ s}$$

$$\therefore v = \frac{0.100}{0.568} = 0.176 \text{ m s}^{-1}$$

The momentum of the stationary vehicle is zero, so the total initial momentum will be the initial momentum of the moving vehicle.

$$p = ? \qquad\qquad p = mv$$
$$m = 0.832 \text{ kg}$$
$$v = 0.176 \text{ m s}^{-1}$$

$$\therefore p = 0.832 \times 0.176$$
$$\therefore p = 0.146 \text{ N s}$$

The collision, however complicated, should not alter the total momentum of the two vehicles. So when the vehicles pass in front of the right-hand photodiode, their momentum should still be 0.146 N s. Their mass is now $2 \times 0.832 = 1.664$ kg, so we can calculate their velocity.

$$p = 0.146 \text{ N s} \qquad p = mv$$
$$m = 1.664 \text{ kg}$$
$$v = ?$$
$$\therefore 0.146 = 1.664 \times v$$
$$\therefore v = \frac{0.146}{1.664} = 0.0877 \text{ m s}^{-1}$$

Finally, we can calculate how long the new, double-length vehicle will take to pass in front of the right-hand photodiode.

$$v = 0.0877 \text{ m s}^{-1} \qquad v = \frac{\Delta x}{\Delta t}$$
$$\Delta x = 0.200 \text{ m}$$
$$\Delta t = ?$$
$$\therefore 0.0877 = \frac{0.200}{\Delta t}$$
$$\therefore \Delta t = \frac{0.200}{0.0877} = 2.281 \text{ s}$$

Bouncy collisions

Table 5.1 shows some data gleaned from the experiment illustrated in figure 5.12. The two vehicles are sent towards each other so that they collide and bounce apart in the space between the photodiodes. Both vehicles have the same mass (0.832 kg) and length (0.100 m). Do the data confirm that the total momentum of the two vehicles is unchanged by the collision?

Table 5.1

| | Photodiode reading | |
	Left	Right
initial reading/s	0.332	0.102
final reading/s	0.133	1.376

The first step is to calculate the speed of the vehicles before and after the collision, using the known length of the vehicles and the data from table 5.1. The results are shown in table 5.2. You can check them for yourself.

Table 5.2

| | Vehicle speed | |
	Left	Right
initial speed/m s^{-1}	0.301	0.980
final speed/m s^{-1}	0.752	0.073

Let us choose the x-axis of our coordinate system to run from left to right along the air track (figure 5.13). Now we can calculate the initial momentum of each vehicle before and after the collision (see table 5.3).

Table 5.3

| | Vehicle momentum | |
	Left	Right
initial momentum/N s	+0.250	−0.815
final momentum/N s	−0.626	+0.061

The total initial momentum of the two vehicles is $0.250 - 0.815 = -0.565$ N s. Although the collision changes the momentum of both vehicles, the total momentum ($0.061 - 0.626 = -0.565$ N s) doesn't change.

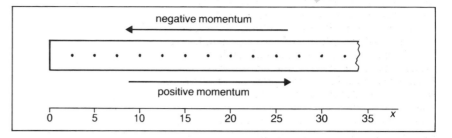

Figure 5.13 The sign convention: vehicles moving to the right have positive momentum as their x-coordinate increases with time

A UNIVERSAL LAW

You will have noticed that in the last example we completely ignored the mechanism by which the two vehicles were able to exchange momentum during the collision. Figure 5.14 shows a number of different arrangements which will allow the vehicles to bounce off each other when they meet in the middle of the air track. Some of them (springs and magnets) will allow the collision to be elastic with no loss of kinetic energy. Others (hard buffers and elastic bands) may mean that some kinetic energy is lost. One (the spring-loaded buffers) will even allow an increase of kinetic energy for the system! If you want to predict the final momentum of *both* vehicles after the collision, then you do need to know something about the collision interaction. The Principle of Momentum Conservation, however, allows you to accurately predict the final momentum of one vehicle once you know the final momentum of the other. Momentum conservation in collisions appears to apply to events on the smallest scale as well as the largest — it governs the interactions of subatomic particles and galaxies. It also appears to apply to high speed (relativistic) collisions as well as the slower ones we can observe on the laboratory bench. This universality of application makes the Principle of Momentum Conservation a very special physical law. It is universally exact, provided that it is applied to an isolated system.

Figure 5.14 Different collision mechanisms for the air track vehicles

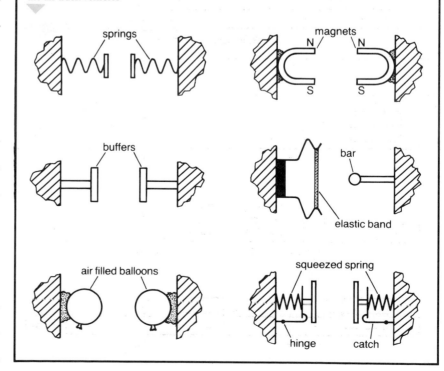

OBJECTIVES

After studying this section you should be able to do
the following.

State and use the formula $\mathbf{p} = m\mathbf{v}$.	State Newton's First Law of Motion.
Calculate the three components of an object's velocity from its coordinates at two different times.	Understand the meaning of the term *isolated system*.
Know that the centre of mass of a system is the weighted average of the positions of its constituent masses.	Describe how an air track can be used to verify momentum conservation.
State and use the Principle of Momentum Conservation.	Apply momentum conservation to calculate velocity changes in one-dimensional bouncy and sticky collisions.

QUESTIONS

1 An astronaut with a jet backpack (figure 5.15) can be considered to be an isolated system when floating outside the spaceship. The jets on the backpack can release a stream of gas at a rate of 0.10 kg s^{-1}. The gas comes out of the jets with a speed of 2000 m s^{-1}. The total mass of the astronaut and backpack is 125 kg.

a Suppose that the astronaut is moving forwards at a steady speed of 4.0 m s^{-1}. What is the momentum of the system?

b The jets now release gas for 5.0 s to slow down the astronaut. Calculate the momentum of the gas.

c What is the momentum of the astronaut after the release of gas?

d A different jet is now used to speed up the astronaut. How long does it have to release gas in order to accelerate the astronaut to a velocity of 20 m s^{-1} forwards?

2 A 20 kg meteorite moving at 500 km s^{-1} collides head-on with a 500 kg satellite moving at 30 km s^{-1}. If the meteorite gets stuck in the satellite, what is their final velocity?

3 Consider the system shown in figure 5.11. Suppose that the left-hand vehicle has momentum p_i when it passes the first photodiode.

a If the length and mass of the vehicle are l and m respectively, show that it takes time $t_i = ml/p_i$ to pass the first photodiode.

b Show that the velocity of the two vehicles after the collision is given by $v_f = p_i/2m$.

c Hence show that the time taken for the vehicles to pass the second photodiode is always $4t_i$.

4 Explain how you would attempt to verify Newton's First Law of Motion with the help of an air track and photodiodes.

5 Figure 5.16(a) shows two children (Rajiv and Sue) on skateboards facing each other, on level ground. We are going to assume that they are an isolated system, i.e. they have perfect, frictionless wheels. Each has a mass M and starts off not moving. Rajiv is holding a ball of mass m. He throws it to Sue with a velocity $+v$.

a What is Rajiv's momentum just after he has thrown the ball?

Figure 5.15

Figure 5.16

b Sue catches the ball. What does her momentum become?

c Sue now throws the ball back to Rajiv. What is her momentum now?

d Show that when the ball is caught by Rajiv his velocity becomes $-2mv/M$.

e By estimating values for M, m and v, calculate the rate at which Rajiv and Sue would be moving apart after they had exchanged the ball five times.

f Suppose that Rajiv and Sue had been standing on the same skateboard (figure 5.16(b)). What would you observe as they threw the ball back and forth between them?

[6] A student sets up a pair of trolleys as shown in figure 5.17. Both trolleys have the same mass and start off in the middle of the room. One trolley has a heavy compressed spring connected to one end so that it can push against the other trolley when the student lets go of them. The friction between the trolley wheels and the floor is *not* negligible. Which of the following statements are true if the student lets go of the trolleys simultaneously?

a Both trolleys have the same momentum as each other before release.

b Both trolleys have the same momentum as each other after release.

c The trolleys move across the floor with a constant momentum.

d The trolley with the spring reaches the wall first.

e Both trolleys arrive at the wall at the same time.

f The trolley without the spring arrives at the wall first.

[7] Alison thinks that the wording of the Principle of Momentum Conservation is very clever. 'It's like Hooke's Law. If you stretch something and find that its stress is *not* proportional to its strain, then Hooke's Law will say that you stretched it too far. Similarly, if you find that the total momentum of a system of objects is *not* constant, then the Principle will tell you that the system wasn't isolated. There is no way that you can show that the Principle of Momentum Conservation is wrong. Either you find that momentum is conserved or that your system was not isolated!' Is Alison right?

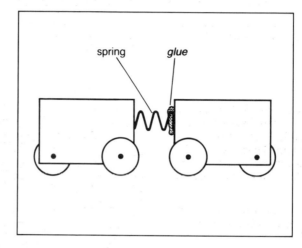

spring   *glue*

Figure 5.17

FORCE

The Principle of Momentum Conservation states that any change of momentum of part of an isolated system causes an equal and opposite change of momentum in the rest of the system. However, everyday experience suggests that to change the velocity of an object you have to push on it in some way, i.e. any momentum change involves a force. This section will show you the link between force and momentum, and how that link leads to Newton's Second and Third Laws of Motion.

Impulse

Suppose that two objects, which are otherwise isolated, interact with each other as shown in figure 5.18. Their total momentum must remain constant. This can be expressed as follows:

$$\mathbf{p_L} + \mathbf{p_R} = \mathbf{p} \qquad (5.5)$$

The interaction will change the momentum of each object without changing their total momentum.

$$(\mathbf{p_L} + \Delta \mathbf{p_L}) + (\mathbf{p_R} + \Delta \mathbf{p_R}) = \mathbf{p} \qquad (5.6)$$

It is a simple matter to combine equations (5.5) and (5.6) to obtain an expression relating the changes in momentum of each object.

$$\mathbf{p_L} + \Delta \mathbf{p_L} + \mathbf{p_R} + \Delta \mathbf{p_R} = \mathbf{p_L} + \mathbf{p_R}$$
$$\therefore \Delta \mathbf{p_L} + \Delta \mathbf{p_R} = 0$$
$$\therefore \Delta \mathbf{p_L} = -\Delta \mathbf{p_R} \qquad (5.7)$$

If we define the **impulse** as being the change of momentum of an object, then equation (5.7) states that when two objects interact their impulses are equal and opposite.

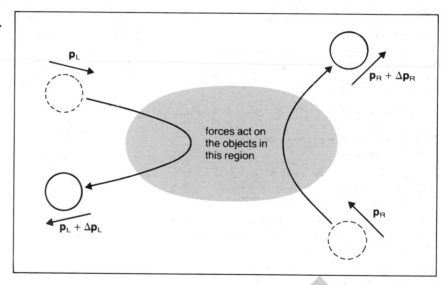

$\mathbf{p_L}$

forces act on the objects in this region

$\mathbf{p_R} + \Delta \mathbf{p_R}$

$\mathbf{p_L} + \Delta \mathbf{p_L}$

$\mathbf{p_R}$

Figure 5.18   Two objects interacting with each other and changing their momenta

In many familiar situations, one half of the interacting system is so massive that its change of momentum is imperceptible. Consider accelerating a car down the road. It is one half of an isolated system, with the Earth acting as the other half. A simple calculation shows that the impulse gained by a car accelerating from rest to 70 m.p.h is about 3×10^4 N s. So the Earth loses an identical impulse, i.e. the road starts moving backwards. However, the large mass of the Earth (6×10^{24} kg) means that the change of its motion (5×10^{-21} m s^{-1}) is negligible. We therefore naturally consider the Earth to be steady throughout and only concern ourselves with the half of the system which actually appears to gain an impulse. The concept of force allows us to do just that.

Newton's Second Law

Let's go back to looking at a two-body interaction, as shown in figure 5.18. Two objects come together, interact and move apart again. We can split the system into two and think about just one of the objects (figure 5.19). Because its momentum changes as time goes on, we say that a **force** is acting on it. But how is the force related to the momentum? Newton correctly guessed that the force is equal to the rate at which the momentum is changing.

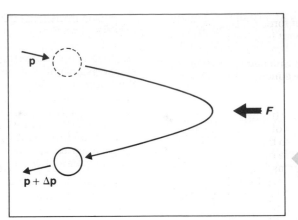

Figure 5.19 A force acting on an object changes its momentum

$$\mathbf{F} = \frac{\Delta \mathbf{p}}{\Delta t}$$

F is the net force acting on the object (N)

$\Delta \mathbf{p}$ is the impulse gained by the object (N s)

Δt is the time during which the impulse is gained (s)

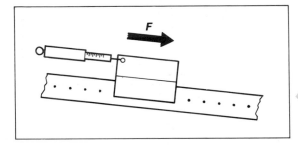

The concept of momentum was unfamiliar in Newton's time, so he had to state his **Second Law of Motion** in terms of mass and velocity instead.

$$\mathbf{F} = \frac{m\Delta \mathbf{v}}{\Delta t}$$

F is the net force acting on the object (N)

m is the mass of the object (kg)

$\Delta \mathbf{v}$ is the change of velocity of the object (m s^{-1})

Δt is the time during which the velocity changes (s)

Figure 5.20   Using an air track to verify Newton's Second Law of Motion

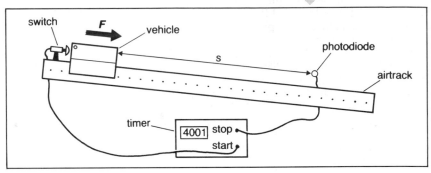

Figure 5.21   Using a forcemeter to measure the force which accelerates the vehicle down the air track

Figure 5.23   Using a graph to combine the results of all the experiments

Figure 5.22   Processing the data to obtain an acceleration for one particular gradient of the air track

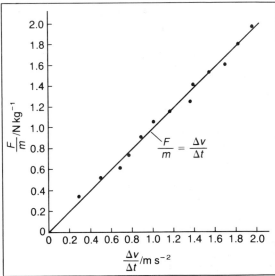

$$\frac{F}{m} = \frac{\Delta v}{\Delta t}$$

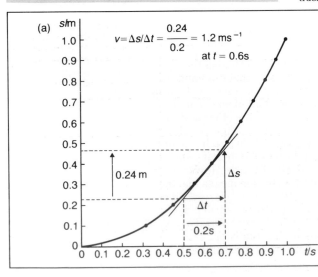

(a) $v = \Delta s / \Delta t = \dfrac{0.24}{0.2} = 1.2 \text{ ms}^{-1}$ at $t = 0.6\text{s}$

0.24 m

Δs

Δt

0.2s

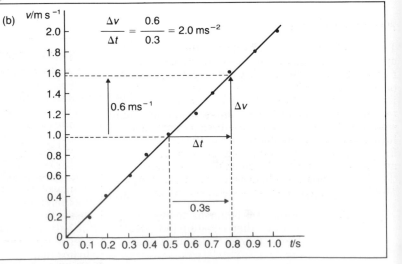

(b) $\dfrac{\Delta v}{\Delta t} = \dfrac{0.6}{0.3} = 2.0 \text{ ms}^{-2}$

0.6 ms^{-1}

Δv

Δt

0.3s

Of course, this definition of force is, to some extent, arbitrary. Only an experiment is going to tell you if the force mentioned in Newton's Second Law is exactly the same as the force discussed earlier in this book, i.e. related to the concept of weight!

Experimental verification

Figure 5.20 shows how an air track could be used to verify Newton's Second Law of Motion. The track has been deliberately tilted so that gravity can pull the vehicle forwards. The size of that force can be measured with a forcemeter, as shown in figure 5.21. The cushion of air reduces friction to a minimum, so gravity will be the only force acting on the vehicle in the track direction. An electronic timer (which could be a computer) starts counting when the vehicle is released at the top of the track and stops when it reaches the photodiode some distance down the track.

Start off with the vehicle touching the start switch at the top of the track. The distance between the front of the vehicle and the photodiode is s. The time taken for the vehicle to cover that distance when released is t. If the photodiode is moved up and down the track, a displacement–time graph for the vehicle can be drawn. It should look like the one shown in figure 5.22(a). The velocity v of the vehicle at various times t can be calculated by measuring the slope $\Delta s/\Delta t$ of the graph. Then you can draw a velocity–time graph for the vehicle (figure 5.22(b)) and draw the best straight line through the points.

Newton's Second Law predicts that if F and m remain constant, then $\Delta v/\Delta t$ should also be constant. In other words, the velocity–time graph should be a straight line with a slope of F/m. In any experiment there are, of course, many sources of error and uncertainty. So the experiment should be repeated many times with totally different values for each variable. The value of F could be altered by changing the slope of the track, and different values of m could be obtained by adding material onto the vehicle. For each combination of F and m you will obtain a value for $\Delta v/\Delta t$. A convenient way of analysing all this data, in order to check the truth of Newton's Second Law, is shown in figure 5.23. Since Newton predicted that F/m should equal $\Delta v/\Delta t$, the points should lie on a line through the origin with a slope of 1.

Newton's Third Law

Two objects approach each other, collide and move apart again. As you can see from figure 5.25, the rate at which the impulse is gained by the left-hand object during the interaction is far from constant — it grows from zero to a negative maximum and then returns to zero. So the force changes with time. The **source** of the force is, of course, the other object involved in the interaction, the right-hand one. As figure 5.26 shows, that object suffers a change of momentum as well. So between the times t and $t + \Delta t$, its momentum changes from $\mathbf{p}_R$ to $\mathbf{p}_R + \Delta\mathbf{p}_R$. The force acting on it must therefore be given by

$$\mathbf{F}_R = \frac{\Delta\mathbf{p}_R}{\Delta t} \qquad (5.8)$$

DEFINING THE NEWTON

At this point, we have to be honest and point out that the unit of force (the newton) has been *deliberately* chosen so that $F/m = \Delta v/\Delta t$. The instrument used to measure the net force acting on the vehicle is simply a spring whose force constant has been previously measured by hanging known masses from its end and noting the extension (figure 5.24). The force exerted by each mass is its weight which has, of course, to be calculated with the formula $W = mg$. But how do you set about finding the value of g? Well, any measurement of g relies on Newton's Second Law. For example, the formula $T = 2\pi(l/g)^{\frac{1}{2}}$ for the period of oscillation of a pendulum relies on the Second Law (see chapter 15). So, strictly speaking, the experiment we have just described indicates that F/m is proportional to $\Delta v/\Delta t$. Then an appropriate choice of the value of g allows us to convert proportionality into equality.

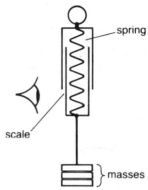

Figure 5.24 Calibrating a forcemeter by hanging a number of known masses from it

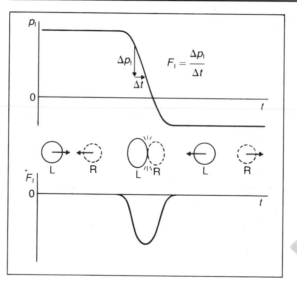

Figure 5.25 How the force and momentum of the object on the left changes during a collision

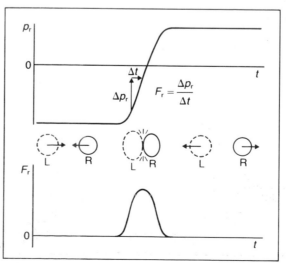

Figure 5.26 The same collision as figure 5.25, seen from the point of view of the right hand object

However, equation (5.7) says that the impulses gained by both objects in that time interval Δt are related.

$$\mathbf{F}_R = -\frac{\Delta \mathbf{p}_L}{\Delta t} = -\mathbf{F}_L \qquad (5.9)$$

So whenever the left-hand object appears to exert a force $\mathbf{F}_R$ on the right-hand one, the right-hand object exerts an equal and opposite force $\mathbf{F}_L$ on the left-hand one (figure 5.27).

Isaac Newton recognised this property of forces (that they always occur in pairs), and formally stated it in his **Third Law of Motion**.

> Whenever two objects interact with each other, the force exerted by the first one on the second is equal and opposite to the force exerted by the second one on the first.

This is often abbreviated to 'action and reaction are equal and opposite'. It is a simple matter to test the Third Law with a couple of forcemeters, as shown in figure 5.28. One forcemeter measures the force exerted by the boy on the table, and the other measures the force exerted by the table on the boy. Both forcemeters always give the same reading.

USEFULNESS OF FORCE

Force is a useful concept because it allows us to temporarily forget that any change of momentum of an object inevitably involves a change of momentum of some other object. Things which are responsible for changing the momentum of other objects are often firmly connected to the Earth, rendering the momentum change of the pusher imperceptible. For example, consider a billiard ball on a snooker table. It can be given an impulse by subjecting it to a short-lived force with a cue. The cue is firmly connected to the player and the Earth beneath him by friction, so the ball can seemingly acquire momentum without anything else acquiring the same momentum in the opposite direction. Similarly, when the ball bounces off the cushion at the end of the table, friction between the table legs and the ground means that the ball is really colliding with the rest of the Earth. So it makes more sense to talk about the forces acting on the ball during its changes of momentum rather than the impulses gained and lost by the ball and the Earth.

Force, however, ceases to become a useful concept on a very small scale. Momentum and energy turn out to be a much more useful way of specifying the behaviour of matter on an atomic and subatomic scale, so Newton's Laws of Motion cannot be considered as truly universal. They are, however, an extremely useful formulation of the Principle of Momentum Conservation for large-scale interactions between matter.

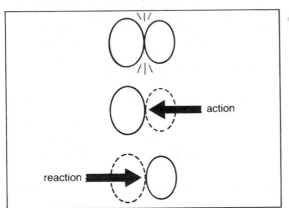

(a)

Figure 5.27 Action and reaction are equal and opposite

Figure 5.28 A simple test of Newton's Third Law of Motion

Figure 5.29 Using a hammer to exert a large force on a nail

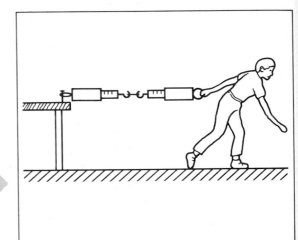

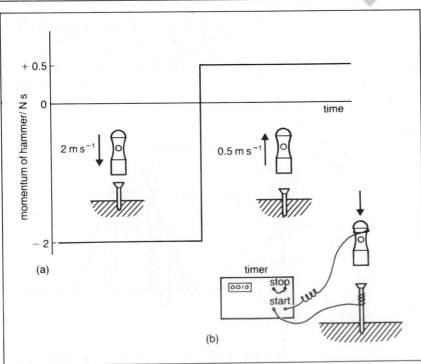

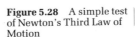

(b)

Impulsive forces

If two objects are in contact with each other, then the net force exerted on one of them is equal to the rate at which the momentum of the other one changes. Here are some examples of this piece of physics in action.

Hammering nails

There are many examples of everyday situations where a rapid change of momentum is used to exert a large force on an object. Figure 5.29(a) shows a hammer being used to push a nail through a piece of wood. Each time that the hammer bounces off the nail, the hammer rapidly gains an impulse and therefore exerts a force on the nail. We can estimate the size of that force as follows, adopting the convention that upwards momentum is positive.

The downwards velocity of the hammer will be about 2 m s^{-1}. If its mass is about 1 kg, the downwards momentum just before contact with the nail must be -2 N s. If the hammer bounces back off the nail with an upwards velocity of 0.5 m s^{-1}, the hammer's momentum after contact will be $+0.5$ N s. The impulse gained by the hammer during contact must therefore be $+2.5$ N s, its *change* of momentum.

ROCKET ENGINES

Rocket engines can generate thrusts in excess of a million newtons by rapidly ejecting a stream of gas through a nozzle. The rate at which the gas is given backwards momentum equals the forward thrust on the rocket. An example is illustrated in figure 5.30. Liquid oxygen and a liquid fuel are burnt at a rate of 500 kg s^{-1} in the combustion chamber. The exhaust gases emerge from the nozzle with an average velocity of -2000 m s^{-1}. So the momentum gained by the exhaust gases per second is $500 \times -2000 = -1.0 \times 10^6$ N s. Therefore the force acting on the rocket is $+1.0 \times 10^6$ N.

Jet engines work on the same principle, except that they take in oxygen from the air to burn the fuel. Look at figure 5.31. Impeller fans at the front of the engine suck in air, giving it an impulse of $-\Delta p_{IN}$ in each second. That air is used to burn the fuel in the combustion chamber, generating a high temperature gas. The exhaust nozzle is shaped so that all of the gas molecules emerge from the back of the engine travelling in roughly the same direction. This process gives the fuel and air a second impulse of $-\Delta p_{OUT}$ in each second. The net forwards thrust on the engine must therefore be $\Delta p_{IN} + \Delta p_{OUT}$.

Figure 5.30   A rocket engine

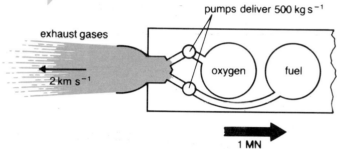

pumps deliver 500 kg s^{-1}

exhaust gases

oxygen   fuel

2 km s^{-1}

1 MN

Figure 5.31   A jet engine

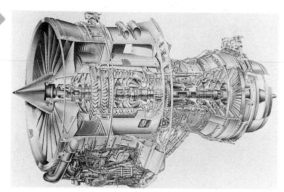

Estimating the time of contact between hammer and nail is not easy. It can be measured by making the hammer and the nail part of an electronic counter circuit (see figure 5.29(b)). The time of contact is about 0.01 s, depending on the material which the nail is being pushed through. We can now calculate the average force exerted on the hammer during this time interval.

$$F = ? \qquad F = \frac{\Delta p}{\Delta t} \qquad \therefore F = \frac{2.5}{0.01} = 250 \text{ N}$$
$$\Delta p = 2.5 \text{ N s}$$
$$\Delta t = 0.01 \text{ s}$$

Newton's Third Law allows us to state that the force exerted on the nail by the hammer during this interaction must be -250 N. Note that the force exerted on the nail is much larger than the weight of the hammer itself. If you consider the tip of the nail as being a circle of diameter 1 mm, it is easily shown that the stress on the wood will be 3×10^8 Pa, much larger than its tensile strength!

Car crashes

Figure 5.32 is a force–time graph for a person strapped into a car which crashes into a solid wall. The force grows to a maximum and then dies away to zero as the car is brought to a halt. This type of graph is a useful way of exploring the various factors which decide the size of the force.

If we split the time axis into a series of short equal time intervals Δt, we can use the graph to work out how the momentum of the person changes during each time interval.

$$F = \frac{\Delta p}{\Delta t} \qquad \therefore F\Delta t = \Delta p \qquad (5.9)$$

Now look at figure 5.33. The graph has been split up into a number of rectangles of height F and width Δt. The area of each rectangle is $F\Delta t$, so we can say that

$$\text{area under curve} \simeq \Sigma F\Delta t \qquad (5.10)$$

where the summation is taken over all of the rectangles. But equation (5.9) says that $F\Delta t$ is equal to the momentum change of the person during the time interval Δt. Furthermore, the sum of the momentum changes must equal the total initial momentum p_i of the person. So we can say that

Figure 5.32   The force–time graph for a person in a car crash

Figure 5.33   The momentum change is equal to the area under the curve of a force–time graph

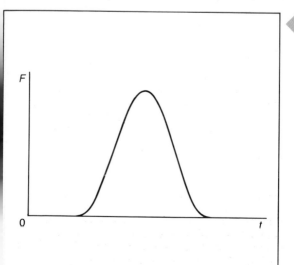

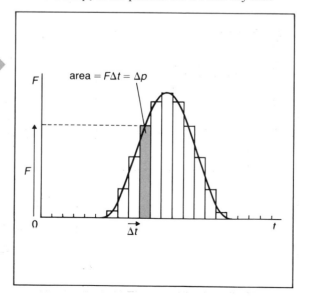

area $= F\Delta t = \Delta p$

area under curve $\simeq \Sigma\Delta p \simeq p_i$ **(5.11)**

We can choose the size of the time interval Δt to be as small as we like. If Δt is large, then equation (5.11) will only be approximately correct. A little thought should convince you that as Δt is made smaller, equation (5.11) becomes a better and better approximation. Ultimately, when Δt is infinitely small, equation (5.11) becomes exactly correct.

area under curve $= \Sigma\Delta p = p_i$ $(\Delta t \to 0)$ **(5.12)**

Of course, when Δt is very small, the summation will be over a large number of terms. We can use an alternative notation to represent this process, with an **integral** sign replacing the summation sign and dp replacing Δp. (Consult Appendix B if you are unsure about integration.)

area under curve $= \int dp = p_i$ **(5.13)**

The area under the curve of a force–time graph is equal to the momentum change of the object being considered. Figure 5.34 shows two such curves for a person sitting in each of two cars which have a head-on collision with a wall at 10 m s^{-1}. The total momentum change must be the same in both cases ($\simeq 700$ Ns), so both curves must have the same area under them. One car (A) is fairly strong, so it stops quite quickly: the impulse is delivered rapidly, requiring a large force to act on the person. The other car (B) is somewhat softer and crumples up on impact, allowing the impulse to be delivered more slowly. Car B will therefore exert a smaller peak force on the person sitting in it.

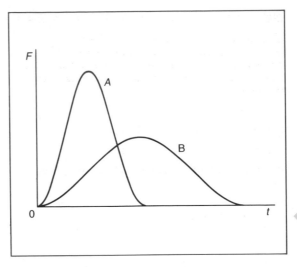

Figure 5.34   The total change in momentum is the same in both cases, so the curves A and B have to enclose the same area

OBJECTIVES

After studying this section you should be able to do the following.

Understand the meaning of the term *impulse*.

State Newton's Second Law of Motion in terms of both momentum and velocity changes.

Describe an experiment to verify Newton's Second Law of Motion.

State Newton's Third Law of Motion.

State and use the formula $F = \Delta p / \Delta t$.

Explain how rocket engines generate thrust.

CRUMPLE ZONES

The ability of a car to crumple during a collision is an important safety feature. A well-designed car will incorporate regions known as **crumple zones** which allow it to change shape in a collision (figure 5.35). The more it crumples, the longer the time during which the momentum of its occupant has to change and the smaller the restraining force has to be. Let us estimate how big that force will be for a head-on collision at 30 m.p.h.

Figure 5.35   A crumple zone in action.

The first step is to calculate the initial momentum of the driver. 30 m.p.h is 14 m s^{-1}, so a 70 kg driver will have an initial momentum of $70 \times 14 = 980$ N s. During the collision the speed will drop rapidly from 14 m s^{-1} to zero, so we can take the average speed as being 7 m s^{-1}. The crumple zone in a modern car might be about 0.5 m, so we can estimate the time during which the driver has to change her momentum.

$v = 7 \text{ m s}^{-1}$
$\Delta x = 0.5 \text{ m}$
$\Delta t = ?$

$v = \dfrac{\Delta x}{\Delta t}$

$\therefore 7 = \dfrac{0.5}{\Delta t}$

$\therefore \Delta t = \dfrac{0.5}{7} = 0.07 \text{ s}$

If we suppose, for simplicity, that the force is constant during the collision, we can easily calculate the size of the restraining force:

$F = ?$
$\Delta p = 980 \text{ N s}$
$\Delta t = 0.07 \text{ s}$

$F = \dfrac{\Delta p}{\Delta t}$

$\therefore F = \dfrac{980}{0.07}$

$\therefore F = 14\,000 \text{ N}$

To put this force into perspective, it is twenty times the passenger's normal weight!

QUESTIONS

1 A tennis ball has a mass of 0.07 kg. It approaches a racket with a speed of 5 m s⁻¹, bounces off it and returns the way it came with a speed of 4 m s⁻¹. The ball is in contact with the racket for 0.2 s. Calculate

a the initial momentum of the ball,

b the final momentum of the ball,

c the impulse given to the ball,

d the average force exerted on the ball by the racket.

2 A particular machine gun can fire bullets continuously at a rate of five per second. Each bullet has a mass of 10 g and leaves the gun at 800 m s⁻¹.

a If the machine gun is held securely, estimate the average force needed to restrain it while it is firing.

b Sketch a realistic force–time graph for the restrainer.

3 A typical 1000 kg car can accelerate from rest to 60 m.p.h. in 10 seconds (10 km is almost exactly 6 miles).

a Calculate the impulse given to the car in this process.

b What is the average force needed on the car?

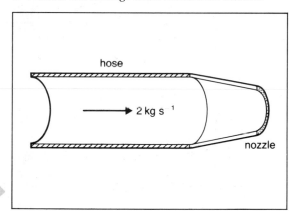

Figure 5.36

Figure 5.37

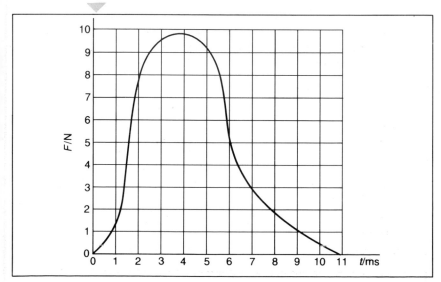

4 Figure 5.36 is a cross-section through the end of a typical fire hose. Water passes along the hose (diameter 2.5 cm) and out through the nozzle (diameter 1.0 cm) at a rate of 2.0 kg s⁻¹. Water has a density of 1000 kg m⁻³.

a What is the volume of 2.0 kg of water?

b If 2.0 kg of water has to pass out of the nozzle per second, how fast must it be moving? (*Hint*: Think of squeezing toothpaste out of a tube.)

c How fast is the water moving as it passes down the hose?

d What is the change of momentum of 0.5 kg of water as it goes through the nozzle?

e How big a force has to be exerted on the nozzle to restrain it?

5 A helicopter is able to hover above the ground by directing a downwards stream of air below it. The density of air is 1.2 kg m⁻³. The rotor blades of a 3000 kg helicopter are 10 m long.

a If the blades give the air a downwards velocity v, what mass of air has to be pushed down per second?

b What is the volume of that air?

If that air has a cylindrical shape with a cross-sectional area equal to that spanned by the rotor blades, the height of the column must equal the velocity of the air.

c Calculate a value for the velocity of the air.

6 Assume that a car can crumple by an amount d in a head-on collision. If the driver of mass m is firmly strapped into the car when it crashes into a solid wall with a velocity v, write down expressions for

a the average velocity of the driver during the collision,

b the time taken for the collision,

c the average force on the driver during the collision.

d Sketch a graph to show how the average restraining force depends on the speed with which the car approaches the wall.

7 The force–time curve for a cue in contact with a billiard ball is shown in figure 5.37. (It can be obtained by placing a piezoelectric crystal at the tip of the cue and recording the voltage across it during the impact.) Suppose that the mass of a billiard ball is 200 g.

a What impulse is delivered to the ball?

b If the ball is initially at rest, how fast does it move away from the cue?

8 Explain why it is good practice to move your hands back when catching a ball rather than keeping your hands still.

9 If momentum is conserved, how come you can change your momentum by walking away from where you are?

FORCED MOTION

If the mass of an object remains constant, then any net force acting on it will change its velocity. Furthermore, if the force remains constant, the rate of change of velocity remains constant. There are many everyday situations which can be approximately modelled as a steady force acting on a constant mass. The concept of acceleration is especially useful for considering the motion of such objects.

Acceleration

The **acceleration** of an object is defined as the rate at which its velocity is changing.

$$a = \frac{\Delta v}{\Delta t}$$

a is the acceleration of the object (m s^{-2})

Δ**v** is the change in velocity of the object (m s^{-1})

Δt is the time taken for the change (s)

Since velocity is a vector quantity, acceleration is also a vector. However, in many applications we are only concerned with motion along a particular direction. For such one-dimensional situations, it helps to use a different formula.

$$a = \frac{v - u}{t}$$

a is the acceleration of the object (m s^{-2})

v is the final velocity of the object (m s^{-1})

u is the initial velocity of the object (m s^{-1})

t is the time taken for the change of velocity (s)

This formula can be used to calculate the velocity of an object of known mass when a constant net force acts on it. You first use Newton's Second Law ($F = ma$) to find the acceleration. Then you plug this into the formula with the time and the initial velocity to find the final velocity.

Displacement
If an object has a constant velocity, then it is not difficult to work out how far it travels in a particular time interval.

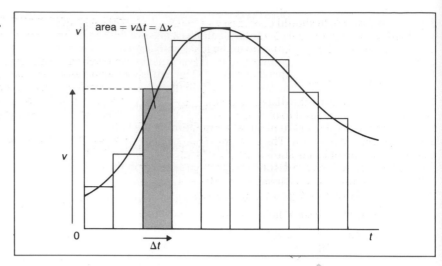

$$v = \frac{\Delta x}{\Delta t} \quad \therefore \Delta x = v\Delta t \qquad (5.14)$$

But what do you do if the velocity is not constant? Look at figure 5.38, the velocity–time graph of an object whose velocity changes with time. We can split up the time into short intervals of length Δt and use equation (5.14) to estimate the distance moved Δx during each time interval. The total **displacement** s of the object should then be the sum of all those small distances.

$$s = \Sigma\Delta x = \Sigma v\Delta t \qquad (5.15)$$

▲ **Figure 5.38** Velocity –time graph of an object which accelerates and then decelerates

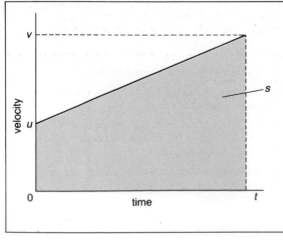

▲ **Figure 5.39** The area under the curve of a velocity–time graph is equal to the displacement

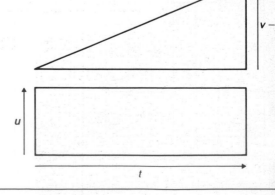

◀ **Figure 5.40** Velocity –time graph for an object with a constant acceleration

A glance at figure 5.38 should convince you that, provided Δt is small enough, $\Sigma v\Delta t$ is just the area under the curve of the graph (figure 5.39). In other words

area under the curve $= s$ **(5.16)**

This way of calculating the distance travelled by a moving object can be used to obtain a useful formula for the displacement of an object which has a constant acceleration. The velocity–time graph for such an object is shown in figure 5.40(a): the shaded area will be the displacement. Figure 5.40(b) shows how that area can be considered as a right-angled triangle sitting on top of a rectangle.

area of rectangle $=$ base $\times$ height $= tu$ **(5.17)**

$$\text{area of triangle} = \tfrac{1}{2} \times \text{base} \times \text{height}$$
$$= \tfrac{1}{2}t(v-u) \qquad \textbf{(5.18)}$$

$$a = \frac{v-u}{t} \qquad \therefore v - u = at \qquad \textbf{(5.19)}$$

Combining equations (5.17), (5.18) and (5.19) we get the following convenient expression for the displacement s:

$$s = ut + \tfrac{1}{2}t(v-u) \qquad \therefore s = ut + \tfrac{1}{2}t(at)$$
$$\therefore s = ut + \tfrac{1}{2}at^2 \qquad \textbf{(5.20)}$$

If we combine equations (5.19) and (5.20) to eliminate t, we end up with another useful equation:

$$v^2 = u^2 + 2as \qquad \textbf{(5.21)}$$

Equations (5.19), (5.20) and (5.21) are the three **VUSAT formulae**. You will be using them a lot in calculations involving motion which has a constant acceleration.

$v = u + at$

$s = ut + \tfrac{1}{2}at^2$

$v^2 = u^2 + 2as$

v is the final velocity (m s^{-1})

u is the initial velocity (m s^{-1})

s is the distance travelled (m)

a is the constant acceleration (m s^{-2})

t is the elapsed time (s)

STOPPING CARS

The Highway Code reckons that a car travelling at 30 m.p.h ($\approx 14 \text{ m s}^{-1}$) can be brought to rest in a minimum distance of 25 m (the stopping distance). This assumes that it takes 0.7 s for the driver to react and put the brakes on. How long will it take to stop a car going at 70 m.p.h ($\approx 32 \text{ m s}^{-1}$) if its acceleration is independent of its speed?

Figure 5.41 Stopping a car in a hurry

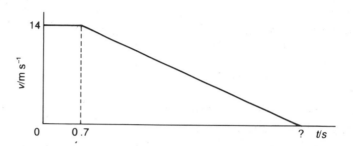

A velocity–time graph for the car stopping at 14 m s^{-1} is shown in figure 5.41. The first step is to use the data to find the acceleration of the car when its brakes are on. During the first 0.7 s the car will have an acceleration of zero.

$u = 14 \text{ m s}^{-1}$ $s = ut + \tfrac{1}{2}at^2$ $\therefore s = (14 \times 0.7) + 0$

$s = ?$ $\therefore s = 9.8 \text{ m}$

$a = 0 \text{ m s}^{-2}$

$t = 0.7 \text{ s}$

Now we can find the acceleration.

$v = 0 \text{ m s}^{-1}$ $v^2 = u^2 + 2as$ $\therefore 0 = 14^2 + (2 \times a \times 15.2)$

$u = 14 \text{ m s}^{-1}$ $\therefore -196 = a \times 30.4$

$s = 25 - 9.8 = 15.2 \text{ m}$ $\therefore \dfrac{-196}{30.4} = a = -6.4 \text{ m s}^{-2}$

$a = ?$

At last, we can think about stopping the car at 32 m s^{-1}. Start off by calculating the time needed to reduce the speed from 32 m s^{-1} to zero.

$v = 0 \text{ m s}^{-1}$ $v = u + at$ $\therefore 0 = 32 - (6.4 \times t)$

$u = 32 \text{ m s}^{-1}$

$a = -6.4 \text{ m s}^{-2}$ $\therefore \dfrac{-32}{6.4} = t = 5.0 \text{ s}$

$t = ?$

Therefore it takes $5.0 + 0.7 = 5.7$ s to stop the car at 70 m.p.h.

You should notice a couple of things about the example we have just worked through. First, the formulae can only be applied to situations where the acceleration is constant. This is why we needed to do separate calculations for the thinking and braking times. Secondly, it helps to list all of the variables whose values you know or need to find *before* you attempt to select an appropriate formula!

Figure 5.42 The leaning tower of Pisa

Free fall

Legend has it that almost 300 years ago Galileo simultaneously dropped two stones of very different weight from the top of the leaning Tower of Pisa (figure 5.42). Contrary to the laws of physics which were then being taught at the university of Pisa, the stones were observed to hit the ground at almost exactly the same time. This simple and dramatic experiment convinced Galileo that, apart from the effects of friction, the motion of an object in free fall is independent of its mass. Furthermore, by studying the motion of balls rolling down ramps (a sort of slowed-down free fall), Galileo concluded that the velocity of falling objects increased steadily with time, i.e. they had a constant acceleration.

Studying free fall

A powerful technique for studying the motion of a freely falling object is illustrated in figure 5.43. It is known as **multiflash photography**. The object is dropped from rest in a dark room which is illuminated with a pulsed light source (a **stroboscope**). The shutter of a camera is held open during the fall, giving a photograph like the one pictured in figure 5.44. If the time interval between the flashes is known, then measurements made on the photograph can be used to plot a displacement−time graph (figure 5.45). In its turn, the slope of that graph at various times can be used to draw a velocity−time graph. Regardless of the mass of the object, the graph is a straight line with a slope of just under 10 m s^{-2}.

Weight and mass

If all objects fall with the same acceleration, then their weight must be proportional to their mass. Consider the situation shown in figure 5.46. Both objects are falling freely with the same acceleration g. We can apply Newton's Second Law to the left-hand object:

$$F = ma \qquad \therefore W_L = m_L g$$

$$\therefore g = \frac{W_L}{m_L} \qquad\qquad (5.22)$$

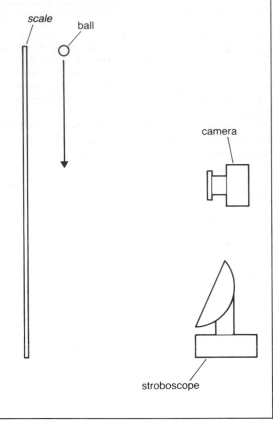

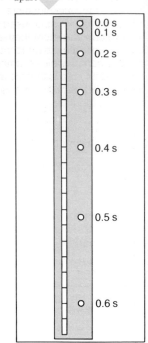

Figure 5.43 Layout of apparatus for multiflash photography

Figure 5.44 Drawing of a multiflash photograph: the scale markings are 10 cm apart

Now do the same thing for the right-hand object:

$$W_R = m_R g \qquad \therefore g = \frac{W_R}{m_R} \qquad (5.23)$$

Combining equations (5.22) and (5.23) to eliminate g we get

$$\frac{W_L}{m_L} = \frac{W_R}{m_R} = g \qquad \text{or} \qquad \frac{W}{m} = g \qquad (5.24)$$

Equation (5.24) is, of course, our old friend W = mg. In other words, the two objects have the same acceleration as each other because their weight is proportional to their mass.

Figure 5.45 Graphical analysis of a multiflash photograph

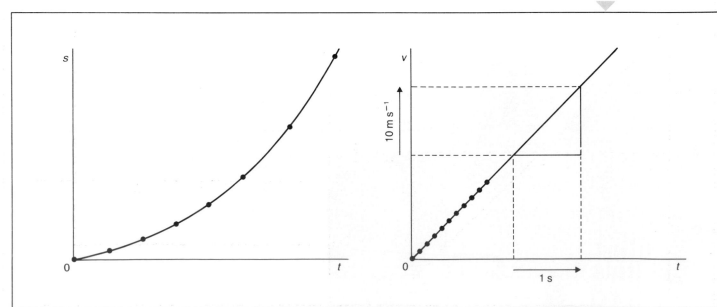

GRAVITY DISTORTION !

The notion that all objects must have the same acceleration whilst falling freely in a friction-free environment can be deduced by making reasonable assumptions about the force of gravity. Consider the situation shown in figure 5.47. Two identical objects are released from the same height at the same time. They will have the same acceleration until they hit the ground. If you assume that the presence of one object does not affect the weight of the other, then joining the two objects before they are released should make no difference to their acceleration. So doubling the mass of the object does not affect its acceleration. You can turn this argument on its head and use the proportionality of mass and weight to prove that the strength of a gravitational field is not changed by any masses placed in that field.

Figure 5.47 Stages in a thought experiment to argue that weight is proportional to mass

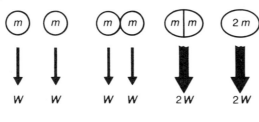

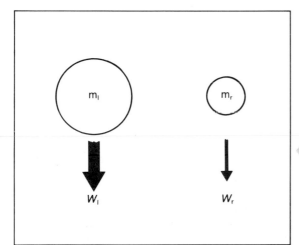

Figure 5.46 If the acceleration of free fall is independent of the mass of an object, then weight must be proportional to mass

Figure 5.48 The velocity and acceleration changes of a ball after being launched vertically upwards

Falling vertically

Any object in free fall will have a constant acceleration of about 10 m s^{-2} if friction is negligible. So the VUSAT formulae can be used to predict the behaviour of such objects. For example, suppose that you throw a ball vertically upwards with a velocity of 20 m s^{-1}. How high will it go? How long will you have to wait before it gets back down to you?

At the top of its trajectory, the ball will momentarily come to a halt before it starts moving downwards. If we take the initial velocity (upwards) of the ball to be $+20 \text{ m s}^{-1}$, then its acceleration (downwards) will be -10 m s^{-2}.

$$v = 0 \text{ m s}^{-1} \qquad\qquad v^2 = u^2 + 2as$$
$$u = 20 \text{ m s}^{-1}$$
$$s = ?$$
$$a = -10 \text{ m s}^{-2}$$
$$\therefore 0 = 400 - (20 \times s)$$
$$\therefore s = \frac{400}{20} = 20 \text{ m}$$

So the ball rises to a height of 20 m before it starts to come down again. To calculate how long it takes to return to the point of launch, we set its displacement to 0 m.

$$u = 20 \text{ m s}^{-1} \qquad\qquad s = ut + \tfrac{1}{2}at^2$$
$$s = 0 \text{ m}$$
$$a = -10 \text{ m s}^{-2}$$
$$t = ?$$
$$\therefore 0 = (20 \times t) - (\tfrac{1}{2} \times 10 \times t^2)$$
$$\therefore 20 \times t = 5 \times t^2$$
$$\therefore 20 = 5 \times t$$
$$\therefore t = 4 \text{ s}$$

During those four seconds of flight, the velocity of the ball has changed steadily from $+20 \text{ m s}^{-1}$ to -20 m s^{-1}. This is shown in the velocity–time graph drawn in figure 5.48. Convince yourself that the acceleration–time graph next to it has the correct shape!

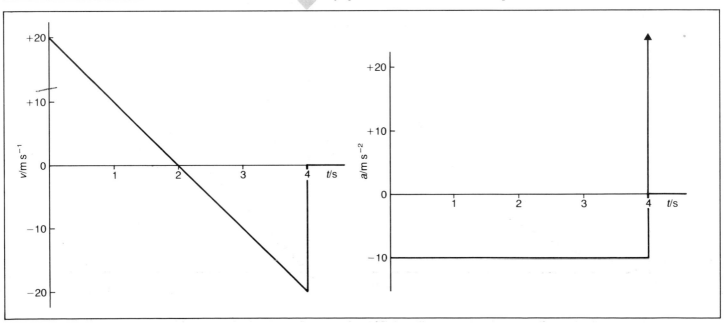

Horizontal and vertical motion

Gravity acts downwards, so it can only alter the vertical component of an object's velocity. It cannot change the horizontal component. The following example should clarify this. A golf ball is launched from ground level with a speed of 50 m s^{-1} at an angle of 30° to the horizontal. How far away will it land, assuming that the ground is flat and level?

The first step is to calculate the horizontal and vertical components of the initial velocity. As figure 5.49 shows, *in the absence of gravity*, the ball would move 50 m in the first second of flight. It would move 50 sin30° = 25 m vertically and 50 cos30° = 43.3 m horizontally in that one second. The vertical and horizontal components of the initial velocity must therefore be 25 m s^{-1} and 43.3 m s^{-1}, respectively.

If we consider only the vertical component of the ball's motion, we can calculate how long it will stay in the air, assuming that g = 10 m s^{-2}.

$u = 25$ m s^{-1} $\qquad s = ut + \frac{1}{2}at^2$

$s = 0$ m

$a = -10$ m s^{-2}

$t = ?$

$$\therefore 0 = (25 \times t) - (5 \times t^2)$$
$$\therefore 25 \times t = 5 \times t^2$$
$$\therefore t = \frac{25}{5} = 5 \text{ s}$$

Now we can apply this flight time to the horizontal motion. In the absence of friction, there are no horizontal forces on the ball to accelerate it.

$u = 43.3$ m s^{-1} $\qquad s = ut + \frac{1}{2}at^2$

$s = ?$

$a = 0$ m s^{-2}

$t = 5$ s

$$\therefore s = (43.3 \times 5) + 0$$
$$\therefore s = 217 \text{ m}$$

The ball travels 217 m down the fairway before it touches the ground. The trajectory (which has a parabolic shape) is shown in figure 5.50.

Air resistance

If you simultaneously release a ping-pong ball and a steel ball bearing they will not reach the ground together! A multiflash photograph of such an experiment is pictured in figure 5.51. It shows that although the ball bearing behaves as expected (i.e. its velocity increases steadily), the ping-pong ball stops accelerating and drifts down at a constant velocity. The behaviour of the ping-pong ball cannot be explained by assuming that a single force acts on it — we need to call upon the force called **friction**.

Friction

As the ball moves down, it has to push aside the air in its path. For simplicity, we are going to assume that the movement of the air is as shown in figure 5.52. From the point of view of the ball falling with a speed v, the air directly below appears to have an upwards velocity v, but the air directly above has an average velocity of zero. In

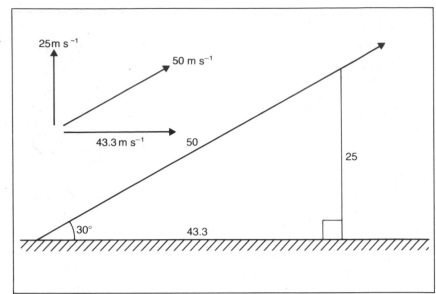

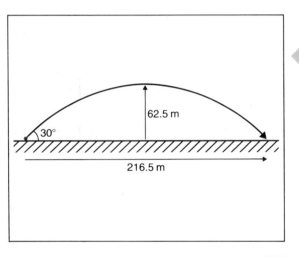

Figure 5.49 The golf ball trajectory in the absence of gravity

Figure 5.50 The golf ball trajectory

Figure 5.51 Drawing of a multiflash photograph for a ping-pong ball and a steel ball-bearing. The scale markings are at 10 cm intervals

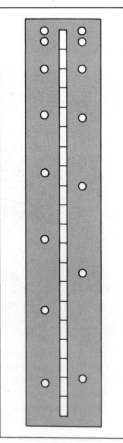

other words, the ball changes the vertical momentum of the air. The rate of change of that momentum will equal the friction between the ball and the air.

We can estimate that friction as follows. The ball has a radius r so it collides with a column of air which has a volume of $\pi r^2 v$. That air will have a mass of $\rho \pi r^2 v$, where ρ is its density. So the momentum of the air pushed aside by the ball per second is $\rho \pi r^2 v \times v = \rho \pi r^2 v^2$. Thus the friction on the ball is approximately given by the formula

$$F \simeq \rho A v^2$$

ρ is the density of the air (kg m^{-3})

A is the cross-sectional area of the object (m^2)

v is the velocity of the object (m s^{-1})

Although this formula is only approximate because of the assumptions made above, it is better than nothing at all. As long as you bear in mind that it is not likely to be a very exact model, the formula can be used to determine the conditions under which gravity is not the only force which has to be considered.

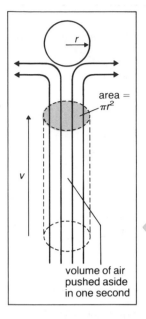

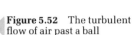

Figure 5.52 The turbulent flow of air past a ball

Figure 5.54 How the weight, friction and resultant force on an object in free fall depend on its velocity

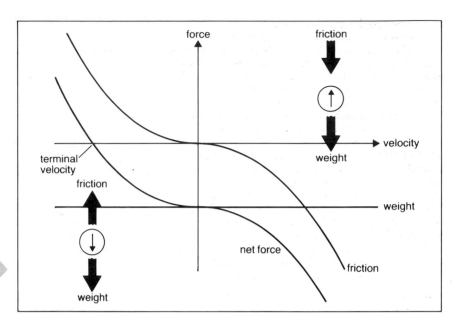

SHAPE FACTORS

Just about the only object whose wind resistance is going to be accurately given by the formula ρAv^2 is a fast-moving flat plate. This is because the path followed by the air as it moves aside from the object falling through it depends on the shape of the object. Things which are streamlined (see figure 5.53) aim not to change the apparent momentum of the air more than necessary, resulting in a low wind resistance. However, **dimensional analysis** (see Appendix C) can be easily used to show that the wind resistance should always be *proportional* to ρAv^2.

$$F = fA\rho v^2$$

Figure 5.53 Using smoke streamers to show the passage of air around a car in a wind tunnel: notice the lack of turbulence

The constant of proportionality f is called the **shape factor**. Its value ranges from 1.0 for a plate to 0.1 for a needle. Shape factors are very difficult to calculate accurately from basic principles, but this does not mean that the formula for fluid friction is useless. On the contrary, it can be used to accurately predict how the friction on a particular object will change as its velocity, size or the fluid it is moving through are changed.

Terminal velocity

The graph of figure 5.54 shows how we expect the forces on an object in free fall to depend on its velocity. We have assumed, as usual, that the positive direction is upwards.

The weight, of course, is independent of the velocity. The friction, however, is proportional to the square of the velocity and acts in the opposite direction to the velocity. So the net force is only the same as the weight for small velocities and can eventually become zero for objects moving downwards. Of course, once the net force becomes zero, there is no further acceleration of the object, i.e. its velocity will stop increasing. Therefore real objects in free fall will reach a **terminal velocity**. We can estimate the terminal velocity of an object with the help of our fluid friction formula:

$$mg = \rho Av^2 \qquad \therefore v = \left(\frac{mg}{\rho A}\right)^{\frac{1}{2}} \qquad \textbf{(5.25)}$$

For a ping-pong ball it is roughly 4 m s^{-1}, so it will reach its terminal velocity after approximately 0.5 s of free fall. A steel ball bearing of the same dimensions would be able to fall for about 5 s before reaching its terminal velocity of 40 m s^{-1}.

OBJECTIVES

After studying this section you should be able to do the following.

Define the acceleration of an object.

State and use the three VUSAT formulae for one dimensional motion with constant acceleration.

Know that the area under a velocity–time graph is equal to the displacement.

Explain why g is constant if weight is proportional to mass.

Use the VUSAT formulae in two-dimensional problems.

Estimate the wind resistance on a moving object.

Explain why falling objects have a terminal velocity.

QUESTIONS

1 A vehicle is set moving on a level air track. If it bounces elastically off the buffers at each end of the track, sketch graphs to show how the displacement, velocity and acceleration of the vehicle changes with time.

2 An 800 kg car can get to 10 m s^{-1} from rest in 3.0 s.

a What is the initial acceleration of the car?

b How big is the initial force between the road and the wheels?

c If the acceleration remains constant, how far does the car travel if it accelerates from rest to 25 m s^{-1}?

3 A driver has a thinking time of 0.5 s. He is travelling at 30 m s^{-1} when he spots a road block 50 m ahead. If it takes him 4.0 s to stop the car at that speed, does he hit the road block?

4 An alien performs some experiments to find the value of g on its planet. With the help of a stopwatch and a tape measure, it measures the time taken for a weight to drop a known distance from rest. The results are shown in table 5.4.

Table 5.4

Distance fallen/m	Time taken/s
1.0	0.5
2.0	0.8
4.0	1.1
8.0	1.5
16.0	2.1

a Use the data to draw a displacement—time graph for the weight.

b Draw a velocity—time graph for the weight. Estimate the value of g on the alien's planet.

5 Figure 5.55 shows a simple experiment which can be used to measure a person's reaction time. Someone else holds the 0 cm mark of a ruler between the subject's thumb and forefinger. The subject has to catch the ruler as soon as she notices that the ruler has been released.

a If the subject is able to catch the ruler after it has fallen 30 cm, how long is her reaction time?

b If the subject's reaction time is 0.20 s, how far does the ruler drop before she catches it?

6 A gun fires shells from ground level with a speed of 300 m s^{-1} at angles of 30°, 45° and 60° with the horizontal. For each angle, neglecting any effects of friction,

a calculate the range of the shell, i.e. how far it goes before it hits the ground,

b calculate the maximum height reached by the shell during its flight,

c sketch a scale diagram of the trajectory.

7 You are going to estimate how high you could jump on the surface of the Moon where g is 1.6 m s^{-2}.

a Start off by estimating how high you can lift your feet off the ground by jumping straight up into the air on Earth. Use this to calculate the velocity of your feet at the instant they leave the ground.

b How big an impulse can your feet give your body?

c Calculate how high off the ground this impulse will lift you on the surface of the Moon.

8 Estimate the terminal velocity of a human being falling freely through the air without a parachute. You can model the human being as being a sphere of radius 0.30 m and density 1000 kg m^{-3}. Air has a density of 1.2 kg m^{-3}. Do a similar calculation for a mouse and an elephant.

9 A man of mass 70 kg hangs underneath a parachute of effective radius r (treat it as a flat disc). If the parachute has to give the man a terminal velocity of 5 m s^{-1} when he drops through air of density 1.2 kg m^{-3}, show that

a about 140 kg of air must hit the parachute per second,

b the radius of the parachute is about 3 m.

10 A car is approximately 1 m high and 2 m wide and has a mass of 1000 kg. Travelling on level ground, it has a top speed of 50 m s^{-1} through air of density 1.2 kg m^{-3}.

a Use this data to estimate the maximum force the car can exert on the road.

b Estimate the time taken for the car to accelerate from rest to 14 m s^{-1}.

11 A ball is released from rest 1.00 m above a hard horizontal surface. The velocity immediately after a bounce is 70.7% of the size of the velocity just before the bounce.

a What is the velocity of the ball just before its first bounce?

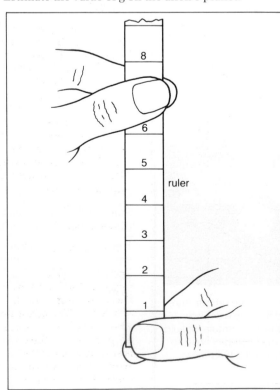

Figure 5.55

b What is its velocity just after it has bounced for the nth time?

c What is the maximum height reached by the ball after the nth bounce?

d What is the time interval between the nth bounce and the next bounce?

e Draw acceleration−time, velocity−time and displacement−time graphs for the ball showing three bounces.

12 The rocket engines of the space shuttle can exert a force of 28.6 MN at lift off when the total mass is 2.0×10^6 kg.

a Calculate the acceleration of the space shuttle on lift off.

b If the average shuttle astronaut has a mass of 65 kg, how big is the net force on her during lift off?

c Imagine that the astronaut is standing on some scales. What do they read just before lift off?

d What do the scales read during lift off? (*Hint:* The scales have to provide the accelerating force for the astronaut.)

e By how much does the astronaut's weight appear to increase on lift off?

f Explain why the acceleration of the space shuttle increases steadily during the first 50 km of flight, although the thrust delivered by the rocket engines hardly changes.

13 It is a well known fact that a cylindrical bottle on the floor of a car rolls backwards when the car is accelerated and rolls forwards when the brakes are put on. How are these observations explained by Newton's Laws of Motion? (Do not use the word *inertia*.) How would an observer *outside* the car describe the motion of the bottle?

Figure 5.56 How v, v_x and v_y are related to each other

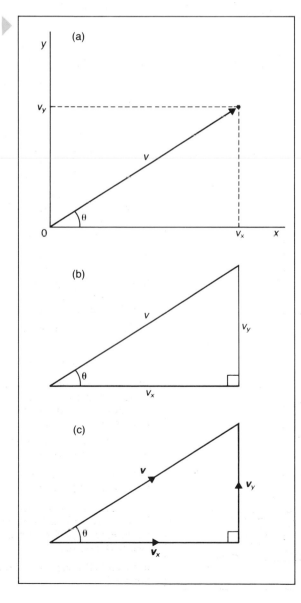

MOMENTUM VECTORS

The momentum of an object is a vector quantity. This means that it has to be specified by three numbers (one for each component) rather than just one. This can make the modelling of interactions between objects fairly complicated, especially when the forces do not act in the same direction as the momentum. The graphical treatment of momentum vectors outlined in this section considerably simplifies the treatment of such situations.

Vectors

Consider an isolated object of mass m and velocity **v** moving in the x-y plane. If it starts off at the origin (0, 0), it will have coordinates (v_x, v_y) after one second of motion, where v_x and v_y are the x- and y-components of the velocity. This is shown in figure 5.56(a). The object has covered a distance v at an angle θ (theta) to the x-axis. In the process it has moved a distance v_x along the x-axis. It has also moved a distance v_y along the y-axis. If you study the right-angled triangle drawn in figure 5.56(b), the following relationships should be obvious. (Consult Appendix B for the properties of right-angled triangles.)

$$v_x = v\cos\theta \tag{5.26}$$

$$v_y = v\sin\theta \tag{5.27}$$

$$v^2 = v_x{}^2 + v_y{}^2 \tag{5.28}$$

Vector triangles

Figure 5.56(c) is an example of a **vector triangle**. Each side represents the magnitude and direction of a vector. The arrow on each line gives the direction of the vector, and the length of the line is proportional to the size of the vector. Figure 5.56(c) is simply a relabelled version of figure 5.56(b) with arrows drawn on the sides. It is useful because it shows how the velocity **v** can be considered as being built out of two component velocities $\mathbf{v}_x$ and $\mathbf{v}_y$ which are at right angles to each other. In other words, the two component vectors add together to make the vector $\mathbf{v}$.

$$\mathbf{v}_x + \mathbf{v}_y = \mathbf{v} \qquad (5.29)$$

Of course, the vector addition referred to in equation (5.29) is governed by the rules in equations (5.26), (5.27) and (5.28). You certainly cannot say that $v_x + v_y = v$!

Momentum

The momentum $\mathbf{p}$ of an object of mass m and velocity $\mathbf{v}$ is given by

$$\mathbf{p} = m\mathbf{v} \qquad (5.30)$$

If you multiply all of the equations which deal with velocity components by the mass m, you get the following useful relationships between the components of the momentum:

$$\mathbf{p}_x + \mathbf{p}_y = \mathbf{p} \qquad (5.31)$$
$$p_x = p\cos\theta \qquad (5.32)$$
$$p_y = p\sin\theta \qquad (5.33)$$
$$p^2 = p_x{}^2 + p_y{}^2 \qquad (5.34)$$

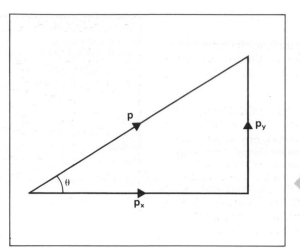

Figure 5.57 A vector triangle showing how p is the sum of p_x and p_y

Figure 5.58 An isolated system which contains two interacting objects

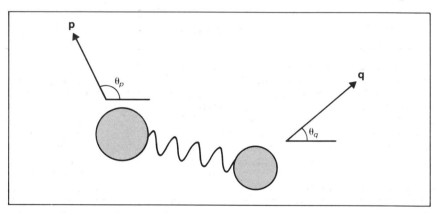

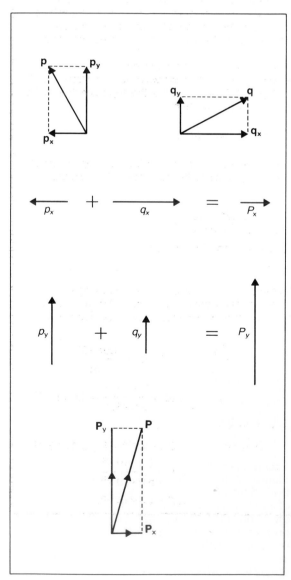

Figure 5.59 Stages in finding the total momentum of a system

Figure 5.60 Adding $\mathbf{p}$ and $\mathbf{q}$ together with a vector triangle

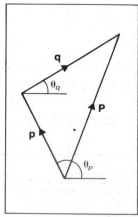

These rules are incorporated in the vector diagram of figure 5.57.

Vector triangles come into their own when you need to find the total momentum of two or more objects. Consider the isolated system shown in figure 5.58. Although the objects interact with each other, changing each other's momentum, their total momentum $\mathbf{P}$ does not change. You can work out the total momentum by considering the momenta $\mathbf{p}$ and $\mathbf{q}$ at a particular instant. There are two ways of doing it. The first method is explained in figure 5.59. It starts off by working out the x-components of the individual momenta.

$$p_x = p\cos\theta_p \qquad q_x = q\cos\theta_q \qquad (5.35)$$

Since these both describe momenta in the same direction, they can be added together to give the x-component of the total momentum.

$$P_x = p_x + q_x \quad \therefore P_x = p\cos\theta_p + q\cos\theta_q \qquad (5.36)$$

A similar procedure can be used to find the y-component of the total momentum. The two components can then be used to find the size and direction of the total momentum.

$$P_x = P\cos\theta \qquad (5.37)$$
$$P_y = P\sin\theta \qquad (5.38)$$
$$P^2 = P_x{}^2 + P_y{}^2 \qquad (5.38)$$

The second (easier) method is represented in figure 5.60. The two individual momenta $\mathbf{p}$ and $\mathbf{q}$ are added together in a triangle to give the total momentum $\mathbf{P}$. A scale drawing of the triangle could be used to determine the magnitude and direction of $\mathbf{P}$.

Sideways impulses

An example of the use of momentum vector triangles to solve a problem should convince you of their usefulness.

Spacecraft control

A spacecraft is drifting at high speed through space. The Earth-based control team want to alter its direction of flight by a certain amount. In this example we show how to calculate for how long the direction-control rockets need to be fired.

The spacecraft has a mass of 2.0 tonnes and a velocity of 15 km s^{-1}. The direction-control rockets can exert a thrust of 2.5 kN. The flight direction has to be changed by 0.017 radians (1°). The first step is to calculate the size of the spacecraft's initial momentum $\mathbf{p_i}$.

$$p = ? \qquad p = mv \qquad \therefore p = 2000 \times 15\,000$$
$$m = 2000 \text{ kg} \qquad \qquad \therefore p = 3.0 \times 10^7 \text{ N s}$$
$$v = 15\,000 \text{ m s}^{-1}$$

Then we draw a triangle showing how this initial momentum equals the vector sum of the spacecraft's final momentum $\mathbf{p_f}$ and the momentum $\mathbf{\Delta p}$ acquired by the rocket gases. This is shown in figure 5.61. The angle between $\mathbf{p_i}$ and $\mathbf{p_f}$, ϕ (phi), is 1.7×10^{-2} radians. Since the rocket gases are ejected at right angles to the direction of motion of the spacecraft, they cannot change the magnitude of its forwards velocity. So we have drawn the triangle with $p_f = p_i = p$.

The next step is to use the triangle to find Δp. As figure 5.61 shows, Δp can be found from the length p of the two long sides and the angle ϕ between them.

$$\frac{\Delta p}{2} = p \sin (\phi/2)$$

$$\therefore \Delta p = 2p \sin (\phi/2) \simeq p\phi$$

$$\therefore \Delta p = 3.0 \times 10^7 \times 1.7 \times 10^{-2} = 5.1 \times 10^5 \text{ N s}$$

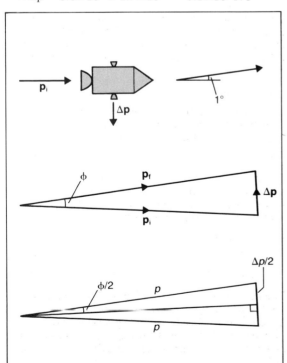

Figure 5.61 Finding the impulse needed to change the direction of flight of a spacecraft

▶▶19

DEFLECTING ELECTRONS

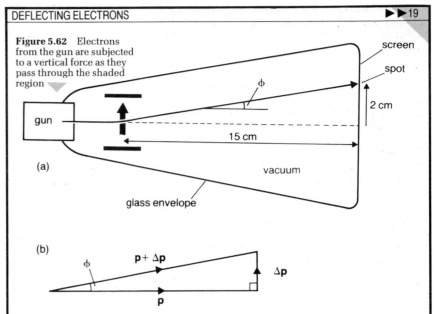

Figure 5.62 Electrons from the gun are subjected to a vertical force as they pass through the shaded region ▽

Figure 5.62(a) shows a cross-section through a device called an oscilloscope. Electrons (mass 9.1×10^{-31} kg) start off from the gun at the left-hand side and travel at 2.0×10^7 m s^{-1} through a vacuum until they meet the screen at the right-hand side. A spot of light appears on the screen where the electrons hit it. Between the gun and the screen the electrons pass through a short region where they can be subjected to a vertical force F: that force is electrical, so it can be switched on and off.

Suppose that when the force is switched on, the spot moves 2.0 cm up the screen. If the force is applied over a region of 1.0 cm which is 15 cm from the screen, how big is that force? Figure 5.62(a) shows that the angle ϕ between the initial and final momentum of an electron is given by

$$\tan\phi = \frac{2}{15} \quad \therefore \phi = \tan^{-1} 0.133 = 0.133 \text{ radians}$$

We can now draw the vector triangle shown in figure 5.62(b). The impulse given to the electron is $\mathbf{\Delta p}$, acting vertically, and $\mathbf{p}$ is the momentum of the electron before it enters the force region.

$$\tan \phi = \frac{\Delta p}{p} \quad \therefore 0.133 = \frac{\Delta p}{9.1 \times 10^{-31} \times 2.0 \times 10^7}$$

$$\therefore \Delta p = 0.133 \times 9.1 \times 10^{-31} \times 2.0 \times 10^7$$

$$\therefore \Delta p = 2.4 \times 10^{-24} \text{ N s}$$

Next, to find the force from this impulse we need to calculate how long the electron spends in the force region. Its horizontal component of momentum is unchanged by the force, so we can assume a constant horizontal velocity of 2.0×10^7 m s^{-1}.

$$v = 2.0 \times 10^7 \text{ m s}^{-1} \qquad \qquad v = \frac{\Delta x}{\Delta t} \quad \therefore 2.0 \times 10^7 = \frac{1.0 \times 10^{-2}}{\Delta t}$$
$$\Delta x = 1.0 \times 10^{-2} \text{ m}$$
$$\Delta t = ? \qquad \qquad \qquad \qquad \therefore \Delta t = \frac{1.0 \times 10^{-2}}{2.0 \times 10^7} = 5.0 \times 10^{-10} \text{ s}$$

Finally, we can find the force on the electron.

$$\Delta p = 2.4 \times 10^{-24} \text{ N s} \qquad \Delta p = F\Delta t \qquad \therefore 2.4 \times 10^{-24} = F \times 5.0 \times 10^{-10}$$
$$F = ?$$
$$\Delta t = 5.0 \times 10^{-10} \text{ s} \qquad \qquad \qquad \therefore F = \frac{2.4 \times 10^{-24}}{5.0 \times 10^{-10}}$$

$$\therefore F = 4.8 \times 10^{-15} \text{ N}$$

(We have used the useful approximation that $\sin\theta \simeq \theta$ if θ is less than 0.5 radians — see Appendix B.) Finally, we can consider the impulse given to the exhaust gas during the firing of the rockets.

$\Delta p = 5.1\times10^5\,\mathrm{N\,s}$
$F = 2.5\times10^3\,\mathrm{N}$ $\qquad \Delta p = F\Delta t$
$\Delta t = ?$

$$\therefore 5.1\times10^5 = 2.5\times10^3 \times\Delta t$$

$$\therefore \Delta t = \frac{5.1\times10^5}{2.5\times10^3} = 2.0\times10^2\,\mathrm{s}$$

So the rockets have to be fired for 200 s to obtain the course correction required.

Motion in a circle

You have probably realised that the example above (deflecting spacecraft) could have been successfully solved without any mention of vector triangles at all! Newton's Second Law and the VUSAT formulae could have been used instead. However, the use of vector triangles makes such problems easier to handle, mainly because they provide a pictorial model of what is going on. This section uses vector triangles to prove an important relationship for objects moving at a constant speed in a circular trajectory (figure 5.63).

$$F = \frac{mv^2}{r}$$

F is the centripetal force on the object (N)

m is the mass of the object (kg)

v is the speed of the object (m s^{-1})

r is the radius of the circle in which the object moves (m)

Figure 5.63 Motion in a circle

Figure 5.64 Centripetal force acts at right angles to the momentum

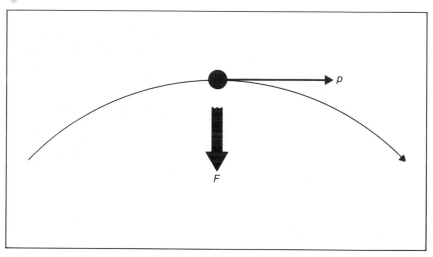

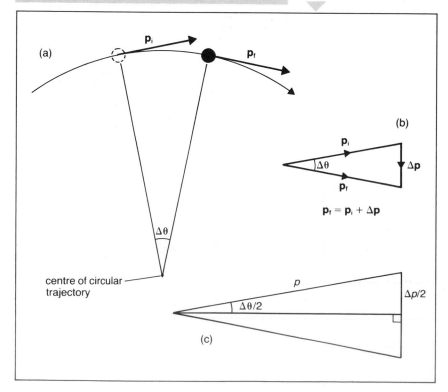

Figure 5.65 Change of momentum when the radius sweeps out $\Delta\theta$; note that Δp points downwards whereas p, the average momentum, is horizontal

Centripetal force

As figure 5.64 shows, the centripetal force **F** has to act towards the centre of the circle, at right angles to the instantaneous momentum **p** of the object. Since the speed of the object is required to remain constant, there can be no force acting in the direction of **p**: any force has to be at right angles.

Consider a small interval of time Δt. In that time a line connecting the centre of the circle to the object sweeps out an angle $\Delta\theta$ (see figure 5.65(a)). The initial and final momenta (**p**$_i$ and **p**$_f$) have the same magnitude p but differ in direction by $\Delta\theta$. If Δ**p** is the impulse given to the object, we can draw a vector triangle for the situation, as shown in figure 5.65(b). The triangle has two equal sides. So we can easily work out the size of Δ**p**.

$$\frac{\Delta p}{2} = p \sin(\Delta\theta/2)$$

$$\therefore \Delta p = 2p \sin(\Delta\theta/2) \simeq p\Delta\theta \qquad (5.40)$$

We can now relate the impulse Δp to the centripetal force F. The vector triangle of figure 5.65(b) should convince you that Δ**p** is at right angles to **p** if $\Delta\theta$ is small enough. So Δ**p** (and hence **F**) will point to the centre of the circle in the limit of small time intervals.

$$\Delta p = F\Delta t \qquad \therefore p\Delta\theta = F\Delta t$$

$$\therefore F = \frac{p\Delta\theta}{\Delta t} \qquad (5.41)$$

CENTRIFUGES

Figure 5.66 shows a small centrifuge, of the type you are likely to find in a laboratory. It is used to separate out the solids suspended in a liquid by spinning the mixture round at a high speed. The centripetal force needed to keep the mixture going in a circle effectively increases its weight, encouraging the solids to settle faster than they would normally. Suppose that a tube of the mixture is forced to travel 50 times a second along the perimeter of a circle of radius 15 cm. By how much does this appear to increase the weight of the mixture? Let the mass of the mixture be m. The centripetal force on it must be given by

$$F = \frac{mv^2}{r} \qquad \therefore \; F = \frac{m(50 \times 2\pi r)^2}{r} \simeq mr \times 10^5$$

$$\therefore \; F = m \times 1.5 \times 10^4$$

Figure 5.66   A centrifuge

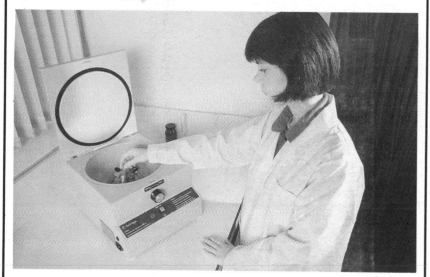

The centripetal force comes, of course, from the tube that the mixture is sitting in. Now, the apparent weight of anything is equal to the restraining force on it. Normally, that restraining force is $m \times 9.81$ and acts upwards on the mixture (figure 5.67). In the spinning centrifuge the effect of Earth's gravity becomes negligible and the restraining force of $m \times 15000$ acts towards the centre of the circle. The centrifuge appears to increase the weight of what it spins by about 1500!

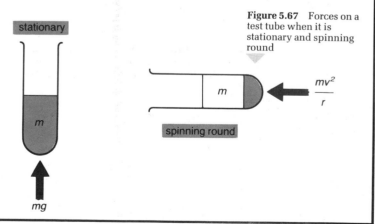

Figure 5.67   Forces on a test tube when it is stationary and spinning round

The quantity $\Delta\theta/\Delta t$ is called the **angular velocity** of the object, represented by the Greek symbol ω (omega). It is the angle (in radians) swept out in one second by a line joining the object to the centre of the circle.

$$\omega = \frac{\Delta\theta}{\Delta t}$$

ω is the angular velocity of the object (rad s^{-1})

$\Delta\theta$ is the angle swept out by the radius (rad)

Δt is the time taken (s)

If we incorporate ω into equation (5.41) we get a particularly simple formula for the centripetal force.

$$F = p\omega \qquad \qquad \textbf{(5.42)}$$

It is more conventional to express the force in terms of the mass, speed and radius. So we need to find an expression for ω in terms of v and r. In time Δt the object travels a distance $v\Delta t$ along the perimeter of the circle. One complete revolution sweeps out an angle of 2π radians, so the angle $\Delta\theta$ is given by

$$\Delta\theta = 2\pi \times \frac{v\Delta t}{2\pi r} \qquad \therefore \; \frac{\Delta\theta}{\Delta t} = \frac{v}{r} \qquad \textbf{(5.43)}$$

If we put equations (5.42) and (5.43) together we obtain the conventional expression for the centripetal force.

$$F = p\omega \quad \therefore \; F = (mv) \times \frac{v}{r} \quad \therefore \; F = \frac{mv^2}{r} \quad \textbf{(5.44)}$$

OBJECTIVES

After studying this section you should be able to do the following.

Use vector triangles to add momenta together.

Know how to calculate the components of a momentum vector.

Use vector triangles to calculate the deflection of moving objects subjected to impulses.

Derive the formula $F = mv^2/r$ for circular motion.

Understand the meaning of the terms *centripetal force* and *angular velocity*.

QUESTIONS

1 A 500 kg communications satellite in geosynchronous orbit around the Earth has a speed of 3.07 km s^{-1}. The satellite is hit by a 5.0 kg meteorite travelling at 20 km s^{-1}. If the meteorite and satellite were moving at right angles before the impact and they stay stuck together after impact,

a calculate the initial momenta of both objects,

b use a vector triangle to find their total momentum,

c calculate the deflection of the satellite,

d calculate the final speed of the satellite.

2 Figure 5.68 shows a 0.50 kg billiard ball bouncing off the cushion of a billiard table at an angle of 60°. If the speed of the ball before and after impact is 0.75 m s^{-1}, use a vector triangle to find the size and direction of the impulse delivered to the ball during the bounce.

3 A bullet of mass 25 g is fired horizontally at 500 m s^{-1} from a gun which is 2.0 m above the ground. Assume that friction is negligible and g is 10 N kg^{-1}.

a Calculate the downward impulse given to the bullet during the first 0.3 s of flight.

b By how much does the direction of flight change during the first 0.3 s of flight.

c If the bullet had been fired upwards at 20° to the horizontal, for how long would it have to fly before it was travelling parallel to the ground?

4 The limiting factor in stopping a car is the friction between the wheels and the ground. Typically, a 1000 kg car going at 14 m s^{-1} can stop in 15 m once the brakes are on. The same limiting factor decides the maximum speed at which a car can go round a corner without skidding.

a Find the maximum frictional force between the wheels and the ground.

b A roundabout has a diameter of 12 m. How fast can a car go round it without skidding?

c The maximum speed limit for motorways in this country is 32 m s^{-1}. What is the minimum radius of curvature a level motorway can have at a bend?

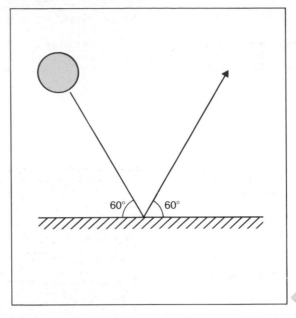

Figure 5.68

5 A communications satellite has to be in an equatorial orbit of radius 42 000 km for it to remain above the same part of the Earth all of the time.

a Calculate the speed of such a satellite, assuming a circular orbit.

b What is the value of g at this distance from Earth if the weight of the satellite is able to keep it in orbit?

c The Moon goes round the Earth once a month at an average distance of 3.8×10^5 km. What is the value of g at this distance from the Earth?

6 Suppose that you are standing at the Equator. You are travelling in a circle of radius 6 400 km, going round once in 24 hours.

a Calculate the centripetal force required for this motion?

b Where does that force come from?

c Explain why the weight of an object increases when you carry it from the Equator to one of the poles.

6
FORCES IN EQUILIBRIUM

Structural engineering is mostly concerned with ensuring that objects stay where they are. For example, bridges and buildings have to be built so that each of their parts do not move out of position, i.e. they are in **static equilibrium**. Of course, if an object is static then its momentum does not change and its net force must be zero. This chapter will show you how to add together all of the forces on an object, how the contact forces (**reaction** and **friction**) between surfaces can help to maintain static equilibrium, and how these principles can be applied to the design of structures from motorways to mosques (figure 6.1).

CANCELLING FORCES

In general, any object whose position does not change with time will have a number of forces acting on it. If the position remains constant, so does the momentum — it remains zero. Since the net force acting on an object is equal to its rate of change of momentum (Newton's Second Law of Motion), the net force on a stationary object must be zero. In other words, if you want an object to stay where it is, you have to arrange for all of the forces acting on it to cancel each other out.

Figure 6.1 A good example of the principles of static equilibrium in action. Each block of stone is firmly held in place by the weight of the blocks above it

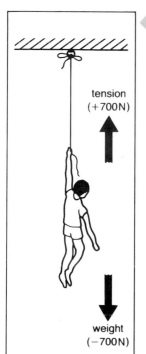

Figure 6.2 Forces on a man hanging from a rope

Figure 6.3 Forces on (a) the girl and (b) the stool

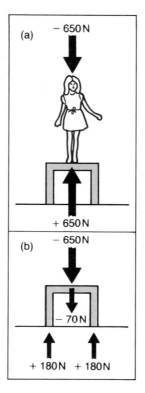

Resultant force

For an Earth-bound object, like yourself, the minimum number of forces for static equilibrium is two. For example, consider the system shown in figure 6.2. The two forces acting on the man are his weight (−700N) and the tension (+700 N) in the rope he is clinging to. Both forces have to add up to exactly zero for the man's momentum to remain constant. Should the tension be less than +700 N, there will be a net negative force, resulting in a change of the man's momentum ($\Delta p = F\Delta t$). The momentum acquired will be negative, with the man moving downwards and making the rope longer. As the rope extends, its tension will increase, taking it nearer to +700 N. Should the tension ever become greater than +700 N, the momentum acquired by the man will be positive, resulting in an upwards acceleration which shortens the rope and decreases its tension. Clearly, the only situation which results in no acceleration of the man is when the tension exactly cancels out his weight.

Reaction forces
Now consider the situation shown in figure 6.3(a). The girl is in static equilibrium, standing on a stool. Her weight (−650 N) tugs her downwards, so there must be an upwards force of +650 N from the stool to make the net force zero. The source of this **normal reaction** is the compression of the stool. As she steps on the stool, her weight stresses the stool, making it shorter. The only situation in which the rate of change of momentum of the girl equals zero is when the upwards force from the stool is exactly the same size as her weight.

Figure 6.3(b) shows the situation from the point of view of the stool. This is somewhat more complicated because it is acted on by six forces. There is its own weight (−70 N), the weight of the girl standing on it (−650 N) and the four reaction forces (+180 N). The four reaction forces are, of course, due to the compression of the floor beneath the legs. The floor has moved downwards just the right amount to provide an upwards force of 180 N on each leg. All six forces add up to zero (check this for yourself) so that the momentum of the stool can remain zero.

Force vectors

So far, our examples have considered situations in which all of the forces act vertically. Upwards forces were assumed to be positive and downwards ones to be negative, taking account of their vector nature. The next example involves horizontal as well as vertical forces. The situation is pictured in figure 6.4. A boy on a skateboard (total weight 600 N) is held at the top of an inclined plane by a piece of string attached to his waist. If the string will snap when its tension exceeds 200 N, what is the maximum value of the angle ϕ for which the string will hold the boy?

The first step is to consider what forces act on the boy. The total weight **W** will act downwards. The tension **T** in the string will act along its length, parallel to the plane. Since **T** is not vertical it cannot cancel out **W**, so we need a third force to act on the boy. If we assume that there is no friction between the skateboard and the surface of the plane, then there is only one possibility for that third force. There has to be a reaction **R** perpendicular to the surface of the plane.

For static equilibrium, the three forces shown in figure 6.4 must add up to zero.

$$\mathbf{W} + \mathbf{T} + \mathbf{R} = 0 \qquad (6.1)$$

Now, if you recall Newton's Second Law, force is a vector because momentum is a vector.

$$\mathbf{F} = \frac{\Delta \mathbf{p}}{\Delta t} \qquad (6.2)$$

Putting equations (6.1) and (6.2) together, we end up with an expression linking the impulses given to the boy by the three forces acting on him for 1 s.

$$\frac{\Delta \mathbf{p}_W}{\Delta t} + \frac{\Delta \mathbf{p}_T}{\Delta t} + \frac{\Delta \mathbf{p}_R}{\Delta t} = 0$$

$$\therefore \Delta \mathbf{p}_W + \Delta \mathbf{p}_T + \Delta \mathbf{p}_R = 0 \qquad (6.3)$$

The vector triangle of figure 6.4 shows the three impulses adding up to zero. A little thought should convince you that the same triangle could be used for adding the forces together, since the impulses will be proportional to the forces. So we can use the vector triangle of figure 6.5 to work out the angle ϕ which will make $T = 200$ N. (The symbol T is not in bold type here because we are only referring to its magnitude.) Notice the order in which the vectors are placed end-to-end to form the triangle. Having chosen the first vector, the second one is found by sweeping round in a clockwise direction.

$$\frac{T}{W} = \sin\phi \qquad \therefore \frac{200}{600} = \sin\phi$$

$$\therefore \phi = \sin^{-1} 0.333 = 19.5°$$

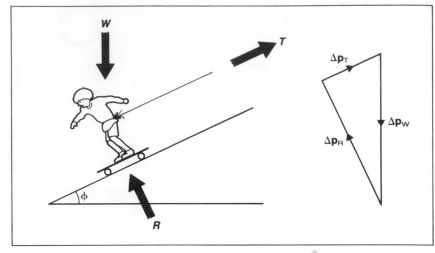

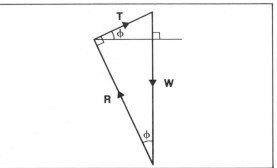

Figure 6.4 Each force acting on the boy delivers momentum to him. If the total rate of change of momentum is zero, the boy will be in static equilibrium

Figure 6.5 A vector triangle for the three forces on the boy

The size of R can also be worked out with the help of the vector triangle of figure 6.5.

$$R^2 + T^2 = W^2 \quad \therefore R^2 + 4.0 \times 10^4 = 3.6 \times 10^5$$

$$\therefore R^2 = 3.2 \times 10^5$$

$$\therefore R = 5.7 \times 10^2 \, \text{N}$$

Resolving forces

Consider the object shown in figure 6.6. A number of forces act on it. For it to be in static equilibrium, all of those forces must add up to zero. This addition can be done diagramatically, with the help of the polygon shown in figure 6.6. However, unlike the right-angled triangle of figure 6.5, a polygon is not always very easy to use to calculate the size and direction of one force required to balance out all the rest. For problems which involve more than three forces, the technique of **resolving** forces into **components** can be more helpful.

Figure 6.6 Four forces acting on an object in static equilibrium

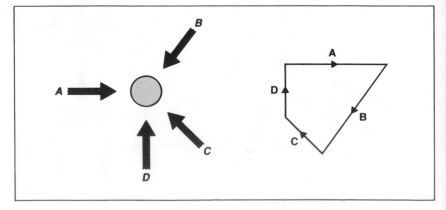

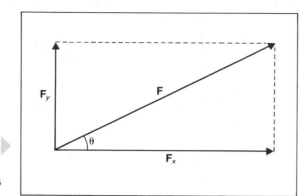

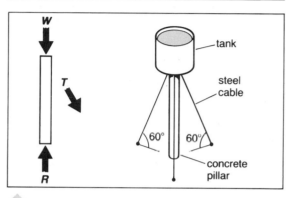

Figure 6.7 Resolving a force into two components

Figure 6.8 An alternative vector polygon for figure 6.6

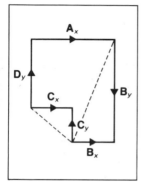

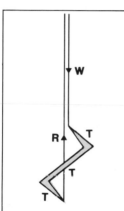

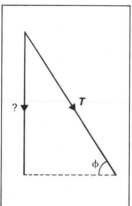

Figure 6.9 Some of the forces acting on the pillar which supports the water tank

Figure 6.10 A three-dimensional force polygon for the pillar

Figure 6.11 Calculating the vertical component of the tension in one of the cables

Figure 6.12 Forces acting on a block in static equilibrium on a rough plane

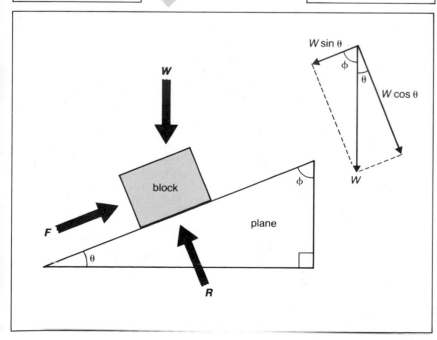

Any force **F** can be considered to be the sum of two other forces F_x and F_y which act at right angles to each other. This is shown in figure 6.7. The vector triangle of figure 6.7 can be used to find the values of F_x and F_y from F and the angle θ.

$$F_x = F \cos\theta \qquad (6.4)$$

$$F_y = F \sin\theta \qquad (6.5)$$

Thus each force in figure 6.6 can be resolved into a pair of **component** forces: one vertical, one horizontal. This changes the force polygon of figure 6.6 into the polygon of figure 6.8. All of the forces are now horizontal or vertical, allowing the condition for static equilibrium to be reduced to two equations.

$$\Sigma F_x = 0 \qquad (6.6)$$

$$\Sigma F_y = 0 \qquad (6.7)$$

Components

For example, consider the situation shown in figure 6.9. A large water tank (weight 100 kN when full) is held 15 m above the ground by a thin concrete pillar. Three steel cables prevent the whole thing from falling over. If the tension in each cable is 10 kN, what is the reaction force **R** on the concrete pillar?

Five forces act on the pillar in three dimensions. Figure 6.10 is an attempt at drawing the force polygon for the pillar — it is clearly too complicated for calculating the size of **R**. However, since **R** acts vertically upwards, we need only consider the vertical components of the five forces. Figure 6.11 shows that the vertical component of the tension in each cable is $T\sin\phi$. So we can say that

$$R - W - 3T\sin\phi = 0 \qquad (6.8)$$

Inserting $W = 100$ kN, $T = 10$ kN and $\phi = 60°$, we can get a value for R:

$$R - 100 - 30\sin 60° = 0$$

$$\therefore R = 100 + (30 \times 0.87) = 126 \text{ kN}$$

Friction

Whenever two objects touch each other, they exert equal and opposite forces on each other. The force which acts at right angles to the surface of the contact region is called the **reaction**, and the force acting parallel to the surface is called the **friction**. For example, if you look at figure 6.12, **R** and **F** are the reaction and friction acting on the block from its contact with the plane. The source of the reaction is obvious. It arises from the compression of the plane by the component of the block's weight acting at right angles to the plane.

$$R = W\cos\theta \qquad (6.9)$$

The reaction will always act away from the plane at right angles to it. The direction of the friction, however, will depend on the direction of the other forces parallel to the plane. For example, suppose that the block shown in figure 6.12 is in static equilibrium. Then the friction **F** acts as shown, against the component of the block's weight parallel to the plane:

$$F = W\sin\theta \qquad (6.10)$$

But suppose that an extra force **P** acts on the block as shown in figure 6.13. For the block to remain in static equilibrium, the friction may have to act down the plane rather than up it.

$$P = W\sin\theta + F \qquad (6.11)$$

Friction rules

Despite the complexities of its origins, friction obeys a number of simple, approximate rules. These can be determined with the apparatus shown in figure 6.14. The forcemeter measures the force applied to the block parallel to the surface it is sitting on. That force can be steadily increased up to a certain value (the **limiting friction**) before the block starts moving. The friction once the block is moving is known as the **sliding friction**. Once the block is moving, the external force needed to keep it moving at a steady speed is a bit less than the limiting friction, and increases slowly with the speed. (This is shown in the graph of figure 6.15.) But most surprisingly of all, the values of both the limiting and the sliding friction are proportional to the weight of the block.

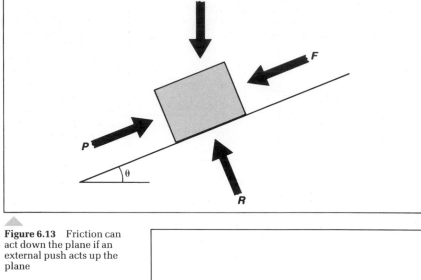

Figure 6.13 Friction can act down the plane if an external push acts up the plane

Figure 6.14 Apparatus for exploring the properties of friction

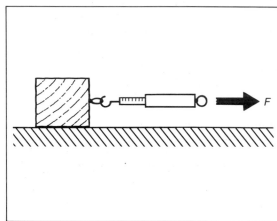

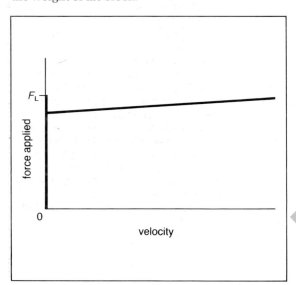

Figure 6.15 Variation of applied force with velocity

Figure 6.16 Forces on a block travelling at constant velocity on the level and up a slope

Coefficients of friction

The sliding friction between two surfaces moving relative to each other always acts in the direction which will slow down that relative movement. If the surfaces are not moving relative to each other, then friction will act so as to prevent them moving. There is an upper limit to the size of this **static friction**. The value of that upper limit (F_L) is proportional to the reaction between the surfaces.

$F_L = \mu R$

F_L is the limiting friction on the surfaces (N)

μ is the coefficient of static friction

R is the reaction between the surfaces (N)

The actual value of μ (mew) depends on the nature of the two surfaces in contact with each other. It can range from almost zero (for oiled surfaces) to almost infinity (for glued surfaces). A similar expression can be written down for the sliding friction.

Consider the situation shown in figure 6.16. If a force of 80 N is needed to make the box move at a constant speed on level ground, what is the value of P, the force needed to keep it moving up a 30° slope? The first step is to calculate the coefficient of sliding friction between the box and the level surface.

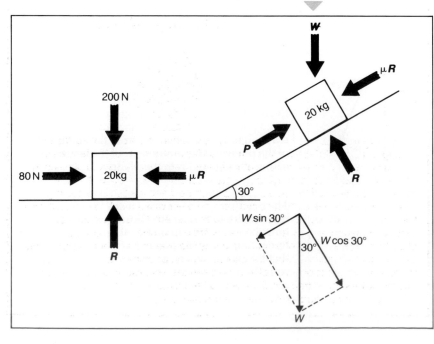

$$F_S = 80\,\text{N} \qquad F_S = \mu R \qquad \therefore 80 = \mu \times 200$$

$$\mu = ? \qquad\qquad\qquad\qquad\qquad \therefore \mu = \frac{80}{200} = 0.40$$

$$R = 200\,\text{N}$$

The next step is to find the value of the reaction R when the box is on the sloping surface. If we consider only the force components acting perpendicularly to the surface of the slope, we can obtain an expression linking R and the weight W of the box.

$$R = W\cos30° \qquad \therefore R = 200 \times 0.87 = 173 \text{ N}$$

Finally, consider the components of the forces parallel to the surface.

$$P = W\sin30° + \mu R$$

$$\therefore P = (200 \times 0.50) + (0.40 \times 173)$$
$$\therefore P = 169 \text{ N}$$

Friction is useful

Friction is often regarded as a nuisance by physics students. This is probably because it is responsible for making their intuitive laws of motion disagree with those of Newton. Friction ensures that any real object will slow down and stop when no external force is applied. It also means that a constant force applied to an object will, after a time, make it have a constant velocity. These observations are, of course, compatible with Newton's Laws, provided that you accept the existence of friction in the first place. This realisation was perhaps Galileo's greatest contribution to the advancement of science. However, friction is indispensable in everyday life. You rely on it to transmit momentum to the Earth each time that you change your velocity. Without friction, the only way you could move forwards would be by throwing your clothes backwards! Friction keeps corks secure in the necks of wine bottles and ensures that nails or screws can hold pieces of wood together. Without friction, plates and cups would slide off tables and food would refuse to stay perched on a fork on its way to your mouth!

OBJECTIVES

After studying this section you should be able to do the following.

Explain the meaning of the term *reaction*.

Know that for static equilibrium the sum of all the forces must be zero.

Resolve a force into two components at right angles to each other.

State the approximate rules governing the behaviour of friction.

Calculate the force required to keep an object on an inclined surface (with friction) in static equilibrium.

THE SOURCE OF FRICTION

The properties of the friction force can be understood by taking a close look at the contact between two surfaces. Suppose that a cube of weight W is gently laid onto a flat plane of the same material, as shown in figure 6.17. Although both the cube and the plane may have surfaces which are apparently smooth and flat, this will certainly not be the case at the microscopic level. As the cube approaches the plane, it will only have atom-to-atom contact in a few sites, giving a true area of contact a which is very small. The stress on these sites (W/a) will be very large, far greater than the yield stress of the material. So the cube and plane will be plastically deformed at the sites of atom-to-atom contact, increasing the value of a until the stress at those sites is just under the yield stress. In other words, the actual area of intimate contact between the block and plane is given by

$a = W/$yield stress

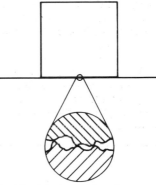

Figure 6.17 The junction between two surfaces is always very rough at a microscopic level

At the sites of atom-to-atom contact the block and the plane are effectively one solid: they are welded to each other. Any force parallel to the surface of the plane which tries to move the block sideways is going to have to make the atoms at those sites slip past each other. Clearly, that force needs to have a certain size before that happens, and it seems reasonable to suppose that it will be proportional to the number of atoms involved which, in turn, is proportional to a, which is proportional to W. So we expect that the limiting friction should indeed be proportional to the force at right angles to the surfaces. A little thought should convince you that once the block has started to move across the plane, the average area of contact will be somewhat less than it was before the movement started. At any given moment, some of the atom-to-atom contact sites will be breaking apart. So the sliding friction should be less than the limiting friction, but still proportional to the reaction between the surfaces.

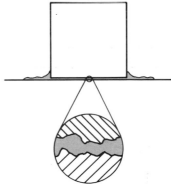

Figure 6.18 A liquid between two surfaces can reduce friction by preventing close contact

It is common practice to reduce the limiting friction between two surfaces by putting a liquid interface between them. Unlike atoms in solids, molecules in liquids are able to slip past each other easily. Thus it is very easy to plastically deform a liquid. Indeed, most liquids are plastically deformed by their own weight. Provided that the chosen liquid stays between the two surfaces (figure 6.18), it will allow one surface to slip past the other with much less friction than if they had been allowed to have atom-to-atom contact. Friction can also be reduced considerably by appropriate choice of solid materials. Graphite, a form of carbon whose planes of atoms can easily slip over one another, is commonly used to coat surfaces to reduce friction. It is good practice in engineering to make rotating shafts out of steel and the bearings which support them out of phosphor-bronze. In general, the use of different metals for the surfaces reduces the force needed to make one slip over the other.

QUESTIONS

1 Figure 6.19 shows a man attempting to pull a stake out of the ground. A rope has been connected between the stake and a tree which is 10 m away. The man tugs on the midpoint of the rope with a force of 300 N, pulling the rope 0.5 m to one side.

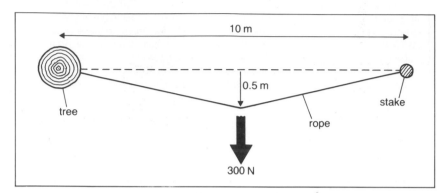

Figure 6.19

a Draw a vector triangle for the three forces acting on the midpoint of the rope. Ignore the weight of the rope.

b Use the triangle to calculate the tension in the rope.

c Suppose that the rope had been tied with less slack, so that the midpoint only moved 0.05 m when the 300 N force was applied. Calculate what the tension in the rope would have been.

2 A classic piece of apparatus to measure the coefficient of static friction is shown in figure 6.20. The value of θ is slowly increased by raising the labjack until the block starts to move down the plane.

Figure 6.20

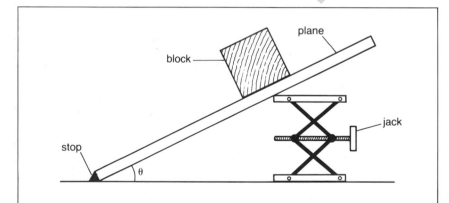

a Suppose that the weight of the block is W and that it is static on the plane. Draw a vector triangle for the three forces acting on it, explaining what the other two forces are.

b Obtain expressions for the reaction force and friction on the block in terms of W and θ.

c The block has a weight of 9.8 N and starts to move down the plane when θ is 30°. Calculate the coefficient of static friction between the block and the plane.

d The experiment is repeated with a 25 N weight resting on top of the block. Calculate the value of θ at which the block will start to move down the plane.

3 The Highway Code assumes that all road vehicles going at 14 m s⁻¹ are able to stop in a distance of 15 m when their brakes are applied. The brakes must not be applied too hard or else the wheels will lock and the vehicles will skid much more than 15 m.

a Consider a typical car with four wheels and a mass of 1000 kg. What do the above data suggest as a value for the limiting friction between each tyre and the ground?

b Suggest reasons why the friction between the car and the ground is much less once the wheels have locked.

c Why should the stopping distance of a car be independent of its mass?

d Why is the stopping distance greater for a wet road surface?

e Racing cars sometimes have aerofoils above the back wheels (figure 6.21). These can generate a downwards thrust on the car when it moves forwards through the air. How can these aerofoils improve the performance of a racing car?

4 A group of teenagers on an Outward Bound course are attempting to transport a heavy load across a stream. Figure 6.22 shows what they decide to do. A rope is slung over the branch of a tree and attached to the 1000 N load. A second rope attached to the load is thrown across the stream to some people on the other side. The figure shows the situation when the load is halfway across the stream.

a By considering the vertical forces on the load, calculate the tension in the right-hand rope.

b Calculate the tension in the left-hand rope.

c What will the two tensions be when the load has reached the left bank but not been let down.?

d If a typical teenager in the group has a weight of 500 N and can exert a maximum horizontal force of 250 N, what is the minimum number of teenagers needed to move the load across the stream this way?

Figure 6.21

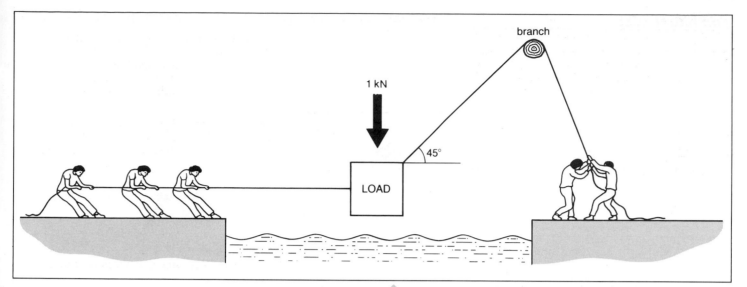

branch

1 kN

45°

LOAD

5 A technique for measuring small forces uses the sideways deflection of a light pendulum, like the one shown in figure 6.23. A magnet exerts a sideways force F on the iron pendulum bob which has a weight W. Static equilibrium is achieved when the string is at an angle ϕ to the vertical.

a Show that $F = W\tan\phi$.

b The iron bob has a mass of 20 g, and is suspended from a support by a cord which is 50 cm long. If the magnet deflects the bob sideways by 3.0 cm, what is the size of the magnetic force on the bob?

6 A pendulum can be used to make an **accelerometer**, an instrument for measuring accelerations. As you can see from figure 6.24, it consists of a mass m suspended a distance l below a pivot, with a scale to measure the angle ϕ of the supporting cord to the vertical.

a Suppose that the accelerometer is accelerated forwards with an acceleration a. By considering the horizontal and vertical forces acting on the mass, show that $a = g\tan\phi$.

b The accelerometer is placed in a car. It accelerates uniformly from rest to 25 m s^{-1} in 10 s. It maintains a constant speed for the next 15 s before braking to a halt in 5 s. Draw a graph to show how ϕ changes with time during the journey.

Figure 6.22

Figure 6.23 ▶

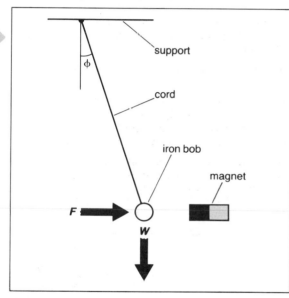

support

ϕ

cord

iron bob

magnet

F

W

Figure 6.24 ▶

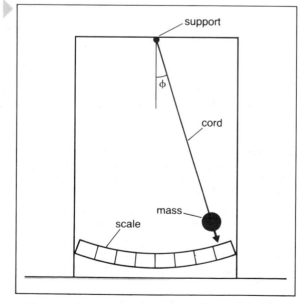

support

ϕ

cord

mass

scale

TWISTING FORCES

Consider the object shown in figure 6.25. It is a bar acted on by three forces. Despite the fact that those forces appear to cancel each other out (look at the vector triangle), your intuition should convince you that the bar is *not* in static equilibrium. On the contrary. the three forces should make the bar twist round. So for an object to be in static equilibrium, the requirement that its forces add up to zero is not enough. This section will show you how the concept of a **couple** and the **Principle of Moments** can be used to work out the other requirements.

Couples

Suppose that you wanted to set a circular object spinning about its axis without altering its position. The application of only a single force to the rim of the object may set it spinning, but will also make it move in the direction of the force. (Imagine trying to twist a rubber ring floating on water.) Two forces, however, of *equal size* and *opposite direction* applied to the rim (as shown in figure 6.26) can set the object spinning without moving it. Those two forces make a **couple** Γ (gamma).

$$\Gamma = Fd$$

Γ is the couple applied to the object (N m)

F is one of the two forces applied (N)

d is the distance between the lines of action of the forces (m)

The only way in which a couple can be zero is if both forces act through the same point ($d = 0$) or both forces are zero. So it is reasonable to state that the object will not be set spinning if the couple acting on it is zero. If the couple is not zero, then the object will spin faster and faster, i.e. it will have an **angular acceleration**.

Figure 6.28 Three formulae for the moment of inertia

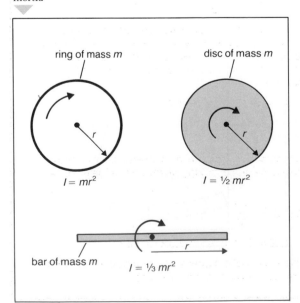

ring of mass m disc of mass m

$I = mr^2$ $I = \frac{1}{2}mr^2$

bar of mass m $I = \frac{1}{3}mr^2$

Figure 6.25 A bar which is *not* in static equilibrium

Figure 6.26 A couple acting on an object can set it spinning

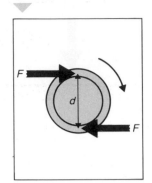

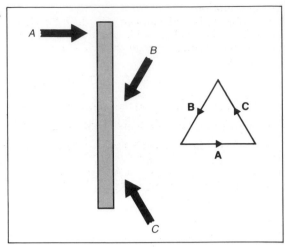

PROVING $\Gamma = I\alpha$!

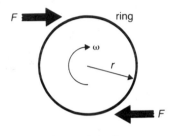
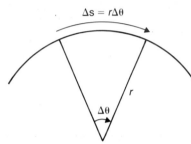

Figure 6.27 The angular motion of a ring when a couple is applied

For simplicity, let the object be a ring of mass m and radius r. The two forces have magnitude F and act as shown in figure 6.27. Provided that the forces remain at right angles to the ring's radius as it moves round, we can apply Newton's Second Law.

$$F = ma \qquad \therefore 2F = \frac{m\Delta v}{\Delta t} \qquad (1)$$

Multiply both sides of (1) by r and use $\Gamma = Fd$.

$$2Fr = \frac{m\Delta vr}{\Delta t} \qquad \therefore \Gamma = \frac{mr\Delta v}{\Delta t} \qquad (2)$$

For objects which rotate, the angular velocity ω is more useful than the linear velocity v. If you refer to figure 6.27, the following link between v and ω should be clear. It may help to remember that $\Delta\theta$ is measured in radians.

$$\Delta s = r\Delta\theta \qquad \therefore \frac{\Delta s}{\Delta t} = \frac{r\Delta\theta}{\Delta t} \qquad \therefore v = r\omega \qquad (3)$$

So if r remains constant, we can use equation (3) to build an expression for the acceleration of the ring ($\Delta v/\Delta t$) in terms of its **angular acceleration** α (alpha):

$$\Delta v = r\Delta\omega \qquad \therefore \frac{\Delta v}{\Delta t} = \frac{r\Delta\omega}{\Delta t} \qquad \therefore \frac{\Delta v}{\Delta t} = r\alpha \qquad (4)$$

Finally, by inserting equation (4) into equation (2) we obtain a useful expression linking the couple with the angular acceleration:

$$\Gamma = mr^2\alpha \qquad \therefore \Gamma = I\alpha \qquad (I = mr^2) \qquad (5)$$

In general the moment of inertia of an object depends not only on its shape, size and mass, but on the axis about which it is being rotated. The moment of inertia is defined by the following formula, with the summation taken over all parts of the object.

$$I = \Sigma mr^2 \qquad (6)$$

m is the mass of a part and r is its distance from the axis of rotation.

Circular motion

For an object pivoted about an axis, the following formula can be used to find its angular acceleration, i.e. the rate at which its angular velocity ω is increasing.

$\Gamma = I\alpha$

Γ is the couple applied to the object (N m)

I is the moment of inertia of the object (kg m^2)

α is the angular acceleration of the object (rad s^{-2})

The moment of inertia depends on the shape and size of the object. A number of formulae for them are given in figure 6.28.

Angular momentum

The formula $\Gamma = I\alpha$ is a version of Newton's Second Law ($F = ma$) tailored for objects which can rotate about an axis. The couple Γ is equivalent to the force F, the moment of inertia I is equivalent to the mass m and the angular acceleration α is equivalent to the linear acceleration a. You will recall that the resultant force on an object is equal to its rate of change of momentum ($F = \Delta p/\Delta t$), so it seems logical to say that the resultant couple on an object is equal to its rate of change of **angular momentum**.

$\Gamma = \dfrac{\Delta L}{\Delta t}$

Γ is the couple acting on the object (N m)

ΔL is the change of angular momentum of the object (N m s)

Δt is the elapsed time (s)

Since the linear momentum of an object is the product of its mass with its velocity, its angular momentum is the product of its moment of inertia with its angular velocity.

$L = I\omega$

L is the angular momentum of an object (N m s)

I is the moment of inertia of the object (kg m^2)

ω is the angular velocity of the object (rad s^{-1})

Angular momentum is an important concept because, like linear momentum, it is a conserved quantity. This means that the total angular momentum of an isolated system cannot change. The following thought experiment will help you to appreciate this. Look at figure 6.29. It shows a heavy disc pivoted at its centre on a turntable which is free to rotate. Suppose that the disc is set spinning when the turntable is stationary. The disc will exert a couple on the turntable via friction at the pivot. So the angular momentum of the turntable will increase with time. However, Newton's Third Law of Motion requires that the turntable applies an equal and opposite couple on the disc. So the angular momentum of the disc will decrease with time. In fact, the *total* angular momentum of the system remains constant if it is isolated.

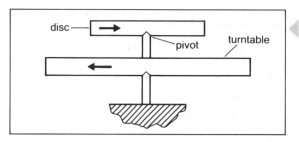

Figure 6.29 A more or less isolated system consisting of two discs on a common pivot

SATELLITE ORIENTATION

It is important that a satellite always has its aerials pointing towards the right area on Earth, otherwise it will be unable to pick up the signals it is supposed to be relaying. The orientation of the satellite is controlled by three discs which rotate about axes which are at right angles to each other. By spinning these discs, the angular velocity of the satellite about any of those axes can be accurately controlled, allowing its orientation to be precisely controlled. The following example will help you to see how it works.

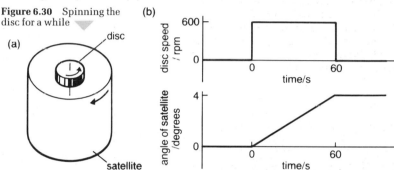

Figure 6.30 Spinning the disc for a while

A simple model of a satellite is shown in figure 6.30(a) — we are only going to consider rotation about the axis shown. Only one of the discs is shown — it has a radius of 5.0 cm and a mass of 1.0 kg. The satellite itself has a mass of 500 kg and a radius of 50 cm. The angular velocity of the satellite is initially zero. If the disc is spun at an average speed of 600 r.p.m. for one minute and then stopped, through what angle does the satellite rotate?

Start off by calculating the angular momentum of the disc during the 60 s. (Its moment of inertia can be calculated with the appropriate formula from figure 6.28.)

$I = \tfrac{1}{2}mr^2 \quad \therefore I = 0.5 \times 1.0 \times (5.0 \times 10^{-2})^2 = 1.25 \times 10^{-3}$ kg m^2

$L = I\omega \quad \therefore L = 1.25 \times 10^{-3} \times 2\pi \times \dfrac{600}{60} = 7.85 \times 10^{-2}$ N m s

Since the total angular momentum of the system must be constant at all times, the angular momentum of the rest of the satellite must be -7.85×10^{-2} N m s during the 60 s. We can calculate its angular velocity once we have found its moment of inertia. (The satellite behaves like a disc if its mass is evenly distributed through its volume.)

$I = \tfrac{1}{2}mr^2 \quad \therefore I = 0.5 \times 500 \times (0.50)^2 = 62.5$ kg m^2

$L = I\omega \quad \therefore -7.85 \times 10^{-2} = 62.5 \times \omega$

$\therefore \omega = -1.26 \times 10^{-3}$ rad s^{-1}

The minus sign means that the satellite spins in the opposite direction to the disc. Finally, we can calculate the angle through which the satellite is rotated during the 60 s.

$\omega = \dfrac{\Delta\theta}{\Delta t} \quad \therefore -1.26 \times 10^{-3} = \dfrac{\Delta\theta}{60}$

$\therefore \Delta\theta = -1.26 \times 10^{-3} \times 60 = -7.5 \times 10^{-2}$ rad

This corresponds to an angle of about 4 degrees. The graphs of figure 6.30(b) show how the orientation of the satellite changes with time.

Conditions for equilibrium

Suppose that more than one couple acts on an object, as shown in figure 6.31. It can be shown that you have to use the sum of the couples to find the angular acceleration

$$\Sigma\Gamma = I\alpha \qquad (6.12)$$

where positive couples are ones which would make the object spin round clockwise.

> An object which is subject to several forces will not start to rotate if the sum of all the couples acting on it add up to zero

For example, consider the object shown in figure 6.31. How large does F have to be for the object to be in static equilibrium? There are three couples acting on it, all trying to twist it about the same axis of rotation. The couples which we can calculate are both positive, so we can work out the total positive couple.

$$\Gamma = Fd$$

$$\therefore 10\times(2\times0.5) + 6\times(2\times0.2) = +12.4\ \text{N m}$$

The unknown couple must therefore be $-12.4\ \text{N m}$, if the total couple has to be zero.

$$\Gamma = 12.4\ \text{N m} \qquad\qquad \Gamma = Fd$$

$$F = ?$$

$$d = 2\times0.4 = 0.8\ \text{m}$$

$$\therefore 12.4 = F \times 0.8$$

$$\therefore F = \frac{12.4}{0.8} = 15.5\ \text{N}$$

Moments

Only rarely are you faced with a real situation where the forces applied to an object can be combined together to make couples. For example, look at figure 6.32. A number of forces act on the beam at different places along it. How do we know if that beam will twist or not? (It doesn't, as it happens.)

Forming couples

Suppose that a number of forces F_n act on a beam at positions x_n, as shown in figure 6.33. For simplicity, we are going to assume that the forces act in only the y-direction. The beam is to rotate around X, the axis of rotation. The first condition for equilibrium is that all of the forces must add up to zero. This prevents any linear acceleration of the beam.

$$\Sigma F_n = 0 \qquad (6.13)$$

The second condition is that all of the couples add up to zero. As the situation stands, there do not appear to be any couples acting on the beam. However, if we add pairs of equal and opposite forces to the system in exactly the right places, we can identify couples and add them together. (Look at figure 6.34. The force F acting at a distance r from the pivot is equivalent to a couple $2Fr$ and a force F acting the other side of the pivot.) Considering the force acting at x_n, we can work out the couple Γ_n it provides (figure 6.33):

$$\Gamma_n = 2F_n(x_n - X) \qquad \therefore \Gamma_n = 2F_nx_n - 2F_nX \qquad (6.14)$$

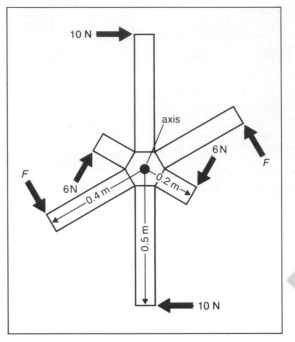

Figure 6.31 What value of F will allow this object to be in static equilibrium?

Figure 6.32 A bar in static equilibrium

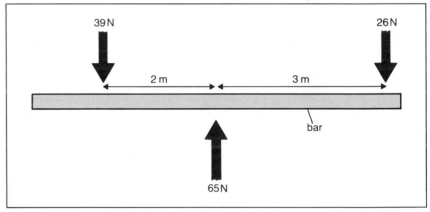

Adding all of these couples together and using equation (6.13), we obtain an expression for the total couple Γ acting on the beam:

$$\Gamma = \Sigma\Gamma_n \qquad \therefore \Gamma = 2\Sigma F_nx_n - 2X\Sigma F_n$$

$$\therefore \Gamma = 2\Sigma F_nx_n \qquad (6.15)$$

At equilibrium, Γ must be zero. So for no rotational acceleration of the beam

$$\Sigma F_nx_n = 0 \qquad (6.16)$$

Figure 6.33 A number of forces acting on a bar

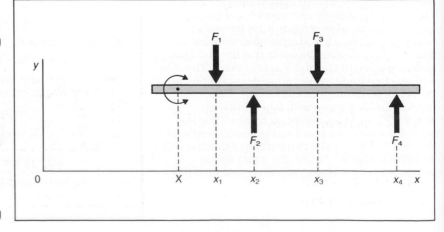

This expression is so useful that the quantity $F_n x_n$ is given a special name and symbol.

> $M = Fd$
>
> M is the moment of the force about a point (N m)
>
> F is the force applied (N)
>
> d is the distance of its line of action from the point (m)

The condition for rotational equilibrium (equation (6.16) can then be stated as the **Principle of Moments**.

> The sum of the moments about any point must be zero for a body to be in static equilibrium

Using moments

The power of the Principle of Moments will become apparent after you have studied a couple of examples of it in action. The first example is shown in figure 6.35. How far can the boy walk along the plank before it tips over and drops him in the water?

The secret of solving this type of problem economically is in choosing the right point to take moments about. We are going to choose point P, the pivot about which the plank will rotate when it tips the boy in the water. The sum of the moments about that point will be zero.

$$M = Fd$$

$$\therefore (750 \times x) - (2000 \times 1.5) + (Q \times 1.0) = 0$$

(Notice how we can ignore the reaction at the pivot because it is the point about which moments are being taken.) At the instant that the plank starts to rotate it will cease to touch the back support and reaction Q will be zero.

$$(750 \times x) - (2000 \times 1.5) = 0$$

$$\therefore 750 \times x = 2000 \times 1.5$$

$$\therefore x = \frac{3000}{750} = 4.0 \text{ m}$$

So the boy can venture as far as 4.0 m away from the pivot P without being in danger of falling into the water.

Supporting loaded beams

Our second example is illustrated in figure 6.36(a). The beam is connected to the wall by a hinge at one end and a cord at the other end. A 2000 N load is supported midway along the beam, 2.0 m away from the hinge. The cord is attached to the wall 1.6 m above the hinge. We want to find the tension T in the cord, and the direction θ of the force F exerted by the hinge. Taking moments about the hinge, we have two moments which have to add up to zero. They are shown in figure 6.36(b).

$$M = Fd \qquad \therefore (2000 \times 2.0) - (T \times x) = 0$$

Before we find T we need to find the distance x of its line of action from the hinge.

$$\tan\phi = \frac{4.0}{1.6} = 2.5$$

$$\therefore \phi = \tan^{-1} 2.5 = 68.2°$$

$$\therefore x = 1.6 \sin\phi = 1.49 \text{ m}$$

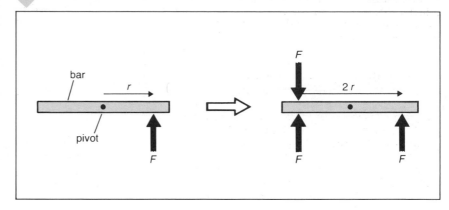

Figure 6.34 A single force can be treated as a couple and a force acting elsewhere

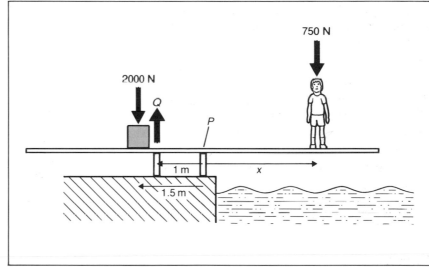

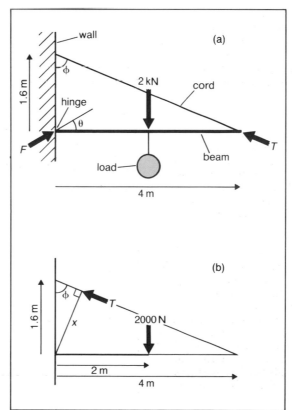

Figure 6.35 How big can you let x get before the boy falls in the water?

Figure 6.36 Three forces acting on the beam

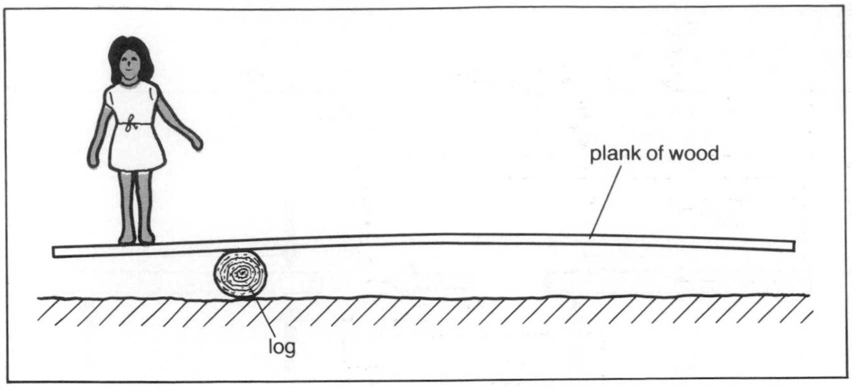

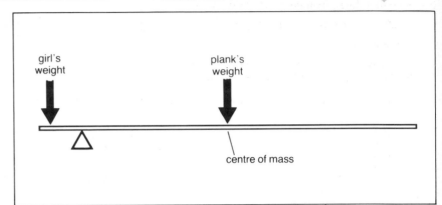

plank of wood

log

Figure 6.37 An apparently unstable situation

Figure 6.38 The weight of the plank acts through its centre of mass

Now we can find T.

$$2000 \times 2.0 = T \times 1.49$$

$$\therefore T = \frac{2000 \times 2.0}{1.49} = 2.69 \times 10^3 \text{ N}$$

With this type of problem it is usually easiest to separately calculate the vertical and horizontal components of F. Consider the horizontal components of the forces acting on the beam first.

$$F\cos\theta = T\sin\phi$$

$$\therefore F\cos\theta = 2.69 \times 10^3 \times \sin 68.2° = 2.50 \times 10^3$$

Now for the vertical forces:

$$F\sin\theta + T\cos\phi = 2000$$

$$\therefore F\sin\theta = 2000 - 999 = 1.00 \times 10^3$$

We are not interested in the value of F, so we can eliminate it from the last two equations to obtain an expression for θ.

$$F = \frac{2.5 \times 10^3}{\cos\theta} = \frac{1.0 \times 10^3}{\sin\theta}$$

$$\therefore \frac{\sin\theta}{\cos\theta} = \tan\theta = \frac{1.00 \times 10^3}{2.5 \times 10^3} = 0.40$$

$$\therefore \theta = \tan^{-1} 0.40 = 22°$$

Centre of mass

At first glance the situation shown in figure 6.37 looks hopelessly unstable. The weight of the girl can be balanced by the reaction at the pivot, but there appears to be no way in which the sum of the moments can be zero. In practice, the weight of the beam itself can keep the system in static equilibrium. The centre of the beam is not on top of the pivot, so the weight of the beam can provide a positive moment to cancel out the girl's negative moment. However, before you can prove this, you need to know something about the **centre of mass** of the beam. This is the point at which all of the beam's weight appears to act — it will be at the centre of the beam if it is uniform (figure 6.38).

Supporting bridges

A simple bridge is illustrated in figure 6.40(a). It has a total weight of 10 kN, a length of 20 m and is supported at either end by pillars. What is the reaction force from each pillar when the back of a 5.0 kN lorry of length 12 m is above a pillar? Assume the lorry is evenly loaded.

girl's weight

plank's weight

centre of mass

MOMENTS OF LARGE OBJECTS

A large bar is shown in figure 6.39. It does not have to be uniform, but, for simplicity, has to have an axis of symmetry along its length. We are going to show how the bar's centre of mass can be used to calculate the moment caused by its weight. The bar has been divided into segments of length Δx. Each segment will have a mass m_n and is at position x_n. (The x-axis is horizontal, along the length of the bar.) The total moment M of the bar's weight will be the sum of the moments of the segments.

Figure 6.39 Dividing an object into a number of segments to find the total moment due to its weight

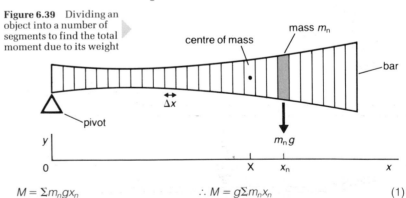

centre of mass

mass m_n

bar

pivot

Δx

$m_n g$

$$M = \Sigma m_n g x_n \qquad\qquad \therefore M = g\Sigma m_n x_n \qquad (1)$$

You will recall from chapter 5 that the centre of mass X of an object is the average position of all the material in it.

$$X = \frac{\Sigma m_n x_n}{\Sigma m_n} \qquad\qquad \therefore \Sigma m_n x_n = mX \qquad (2)$$

Combining equations (1) and (2), we get a simple rule for calculating the moment M of a bar whose total weight is mg.

$$M = mgX \qquad (3)$$

Of course, this is only useful if you know where X is (sometimes called the position of the **centre of gravity**). For a uniform object with a regular shape, such as a box or a plank, the centre of mass is always at its geometric centre.

The first step is to produce a simplified diagram, showing the positions of the four forces acting on the bridge. This is shown in figure 6.40(b). The weight of the bridge can be considered as acting at its centre, 10 m from either pillar, and the total weight of the lorry acts 6 m from the end of the bridge.

We have to find the values of P and Q. The sensible point for taking moments is therefore one of the places where the bridge meets a pillar. Start off with the left-hand pillar.

$$(5.0 \times 6.0) + (10 \times 10) - (Q \times 20) = 0$$

$$\therefore Q = 6.5 \text{ kN}$$

Repeat using the right-hand pillar as the pivot.

$$(P \times 20) - (5.0 \times 14) - (10 \times 10) = 0$$

$$\therefore P = 8.5 \text{ kN}$$

As a check on our answers, note that $P + Q = 15$ kN, the total weight of both lorry and bridge.

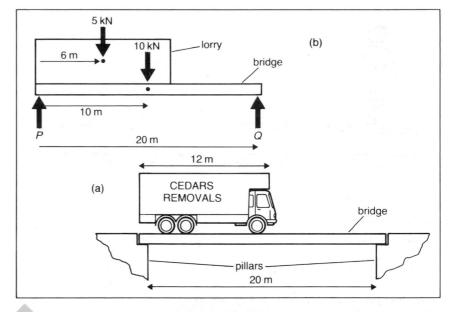

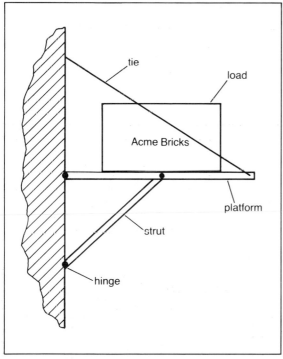

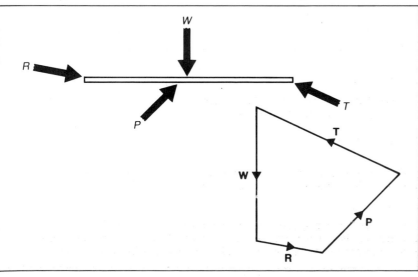

Figure 6.40 Forces on a bridge when a lorry is crossing it

Figure 6.41 A platform held in place by a strut and a tie

Figure 6.42 The forces acting on the platform

Structures

The structures which we live in, walk through and drive on, are generally built out of the minimum amount of material possible to meet safety requirements. Structures such as bridges and buildings have to be strong and light, so that they can support more than just themselves. The materials commonly used for large structures fall into two classes. The first class contains concrete and brick, very good at supporting loads under compression, but disastrously weak under tension. The second class contains wood and steel, strong under both tension and compression. It is clearly important to be able to predict in advance which parts of a structure are going to be in tension so that they can be built from a suitable material.

Platforms

Figure 6.41 shows a platform which is held in place by a **tie** and a **strut**. The tie is in tension and the strut in compression when a load is placed on the platform. Typically, a tie is a cable which can only exert a force along its length. Ideally, the strut should only be compressed. If the force on the strut is not along its length, the bending effect may put part of it in tension and encourage surface cracks to propagate catastrophically through it. This is the reason why the strut is linked to the platform and wall, rather than solidly anchored to them. The links cannot twist the strut, only squeeze or stretch it along its length.

When the platform is loaded, four forces act on it. As figure 6.42 shows, these have to add up to zero for the system not to collapse. The Principle of Moments can, of course, be used to calculate the forces in both the tie and strut as well as the reaction force where the wall touches the platform.

ROOFS

A roof is a heavy structure which has to be supported above an empty space. The fact that roofs can usually only be supported at their edges and have to be angled to shed the rain has consequences for the way in which they are built.

A simple angled roof supported by vertical walls is shown in figure 6.43. The apex of the roof can be considered as a link joint between two flat plates, so the system is unstable — the weight of the roof will flatten it out, pushing the walls outwards. There are two classes of solution to this problem. A **tie beam** (figure 6.44) can be used to prevent any flattening of the roof, allowing the walls to take only a vertical, compressive loading. The tie beam will be in tension, so it can be made from steel or wood. An example of the use of tie beams to stabilise a large roof is shown in figure 6.45.

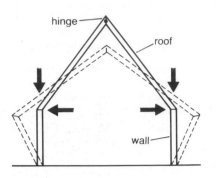

Figure 6.43 The roof pushes the walls outwards

Figure 6.44 A tie beam allows the roof to exert only vertical forces on the supporting walls

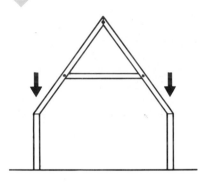

Figure 6.45 Tie beams in action

Figure 6.46 Cathedral buttresses

Figure 6.47 Arches and domes

Alternatively, a series of **buttresses** (figure 6.46) can prevent the walls from moving sideways. Buttresses were widely used by the builders of mediaeval cathedrals because they had to use stone, a material which is only safe if used in compression. An arch can be considered as a pair of buttresses placed side by side. If you have to use stone or brick, then an arch is clearly a good way of supporting a hole (such as a door or a window) in a large heavy structure. An examples of arches and domes in large structures is shown in figure 6.47.

BRIDGES

Figure 6.48 A simple bridge

Figure 6.49 An arched bridge

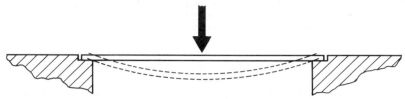

A simple bridge is shown in figure 6.48. It is just a load-bearing structure supported at its edges. The load on the flat beam is going to bend it as shown, putting the bottom surface into tension. Of course, making the beam into an arch (figure 6.49) will ensure that the beam is always in compression when loaded, but this may not be an acceptable solution for a road or railway bridge, unless the arch can be fitted under the road or over it.

An alternative method of stiffening the beam is shown in figure 6.50. The extra struts and ties are linked to the beam and each other, making the structure much stiffer than it was previously without making it much heavier. The structure consists of three triangles linked together. The pattern can be extended sideways to produce longer structures which are stiff and light: an application of this is shown in figure 6.51.

Figure 6.51 Stiffened beams in action

Figure 6.50 Stiffening a beam with struts and ties

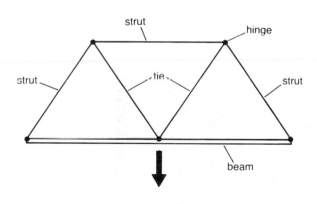

OBJECTIVES

After studying this section you should be able to do the following.

Calculate the couple acting on an object.

State and use the formulae $\Gamma = I\alpha$ and $L = I\omega$.

Know that angular momentum is conserved.

Calculate the total moment acting on an object.

State the Principle of Moments.

Know that the weight of a large object acts through its centre of mass as far as moments problems are concerned.

Use the Principle of Moments to calculate forces on structures.

Explain the difference between a beam, a tie and a strut.

State whether members of a structure are in tension or compression.

QUESTIONS

1 A student has to demonstrate that a bar is in static equilibrium if the total couple acting on it is zero. Her apparatus is shown in figure 6.52. The bar is pivoted about its centre, and the forcemeters can be moved up and down the bar. Write out a set of instructions for her, including details of how she should analyse her data (a graphical presentation would be ideal).

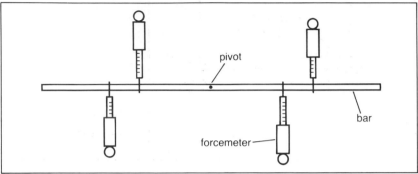

Figure 6.52

Figure 6.53

Figure 6.54

Figure 6.55

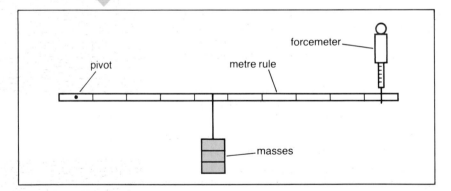

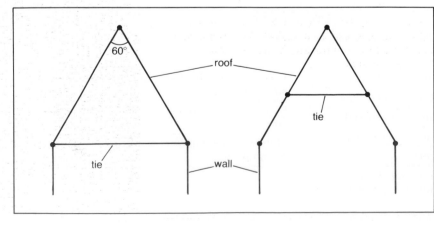

2 Figure 6.53 shows a 2 kN container being supported by a shelf and strut. The container is evenly loaded and centrally placed on the shelf.

a Name the three forces acting on the shelf.

b Calculate the thrust from the strut — you may assume this acts along its length.

c Calculate the size and direction of the force on the shelf where it touches the wall.

3 The apparatus shown in figure 6.54 was used by a student to obtain some data to support the Principle of Moments. The ruler was pivoted at the 5 cm mark. Masses were hung from various places on the ruler, which was kept horizontal at all times. For each placing, the reading of the forcemeter at the 95 cm mark was noted. His data are shown in table 6.1.

Table 6.1

Suspended mass/g	Position/cm	Forcemeter reading/N
0	—	0.5
100	75	1.3
200	50	1.5
300	25	1.7

a Calculate the mass of the ruler.

b The student made a mistake in recording one of the forcemeter readings. Which one? What should the reading have been.

4 Figure 6.55 shows two different tie beams supporting the same roof.

a If the roof weighs 50 kN, calculate the tension in each tie beam.

b If the roof had been less steep, would the tensions in the tie-beams be greater, less or the same as before?

5 Copy the structures drawn in figure 6.56. Decide which of their members will be in tension (T) or compression (C) and mark them accordingly.

6 A simplified drawing of a suspension bridge is shown in figure 6.57. The bridge itself has a weight W and is supported at its edges and by cables a distance d from the edges. The length of the bridge is $3d$.

a If the reaction at the supports at either end of the bridge is $\frac{1}{4}W$, show that the tension in the cables is given by $T = \frac{1}{2}W$.

b The net force on a pillar from the cable and tie attached to its upper end must act vertically downwards. Suggest why.

c Show that the tension in the ties should be $0.87W$.

d In what ways does a real suspension bridge differ from the one drawn in figure 6.57. Explain why.

7 A small electric motor and battery is placed at the centre of a record turntable. A disc of radius 3 cm and mass 100 g is attached to the shaft of the motor. The turntable has a radius of 15 cm and a mass of 2 kg. Assume that the turntable has friction-free bearings.

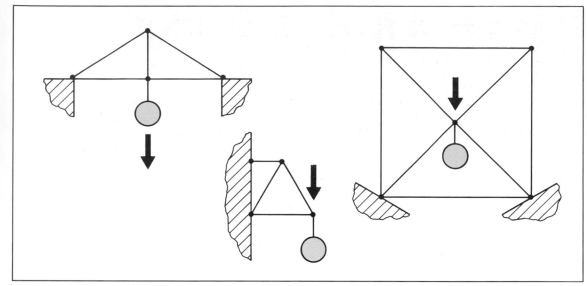

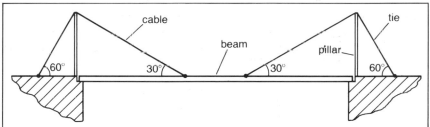

Figure 6.56

Figure 6.57

a Use the formula $I = \frac{1}{2}mr^2$ to calculate the moments of inertia of the turntable and the disc.

b The turntable is stationary when the motor is switched on, rotating the disc clockwise at a speed of 1200 r.p.m. Which way will the turntable start to rotate? How fast will it rotate?

8 Figure 6.58 illustrates a piece of apparatus (called a roundabout) which can be used to demonstrate the conservation of angular momentum. Explain the following observations.

a If a girl jumps on the rotating roundabout, its angular velocity drops.

b If the girl crawls from the rim of the roundabout to its centre its angular velocity increases.

c If the girl crawls around the rim of the roundabout in the direction of its rotation, its angular velocity drops.

9 Ice skaters know a thing or two about angular momentum (figure 6.59)! If they launch themselves into a spin with their arms outspread, they can increase their angular velocity by a considerable amount by pulling their arms into their sides. Explain this.

10 There is widespread belief that bath water always rotates round clockwise when it goes through the plughole, providing you are in the Northern Hemisphere. (It goes anti-clockwise in Australia!) This question will help you to see why this should be so. (The Earth has a radius of 6.4×10^6 m.)

a Consider a 5 kg parcel of water moving round with the Earth at the equator. Calculate its angular velocity and hence find its angular momentum. (Use $I = mr^2$ to find the moment of inertia of the water.)

b Now let that water flow halfway to the North Pole without losing any angular momentum. Calculate its new angular velocity.

c Calculate its velocity relative to the surface of the Earth. Will it be moving east or west?

d Get an atlas and find out how sea water circulates on the Earth's surface. Comment on what you find out.

e Figure 6.60 shows a weather map for the UK. A low pressure area is at the left. Sketch the map and use arrows to indicate the approximate direction of the winds.

Figure 6.58

Figure 6.59

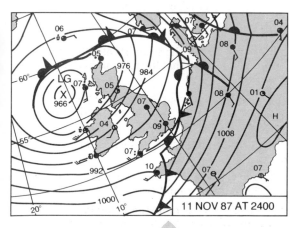

Figure 6.60

SUMMARY
MOMENTUM

The velocity of an object is the rate of change of its displacement: $v = \Delta x/\Delta t$. The total velocity is the vector sum of its three component velocities v_x, v_y and v_z. The momentum of an object is the product of its mass and velocity: $p = mv$. The total momentum of an isolated system remains constant — an isolated system has no resultant external force acting on it. Vector triangles can be used to compute total momentum. The impulse acting on an object is the change of its momentum Δp; a resultant force must act to provide an impulse.

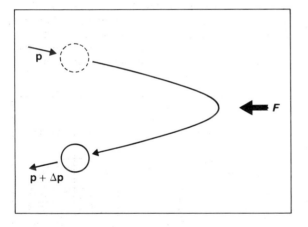

If the resultant force on an object is zero then its momentum will not change (Newton's First Law). The rate of change of momentum of an object is equal to the resultant force on it (Newton's Second Law): $F = \Delta p/\Delta t$. When objects interact with each other the forces they exert have the same size but opposite direction (Newton's Third Law).

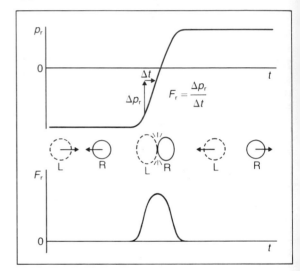

Acceleration is the rate of change of velocity: $a = \Delta v/\Delta t$. The displacement of an object moving in one dimension is the area under its $v-t$ graph. The VUSAT formulae can be used if the acceleration is constant: $v = u + at$, $s = ut + \frac{1}{2}at^2$, $v^2 = u^2 + 2as$.

Wind resistance is approximately modelled with the formula $F \simeq fA\rho v^2$. Objects falling freely have an initial downwards acceleration of g, but eventually reach a constant terminal velocity when the wind resistance is equal to their weight.

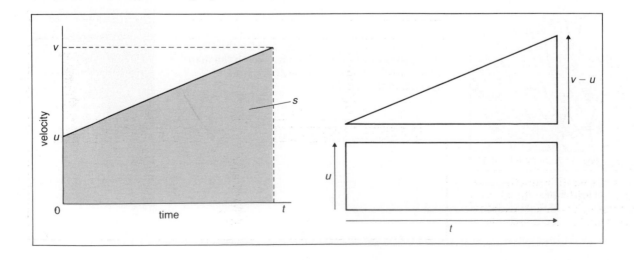

Any force can be resolved into two component forces at right angles to each other: $F_x = F\cos\theta$, $F_y = F\sin\theta$, $F^2 = F_x^2 + F_y^2$. The vector sum of all the forces on an object is zero for it to be in static equilibrium. The limiting and sliding friction is proportional to the normal reaction force between the object and the surface it is in contact with: $F = \mu R$.

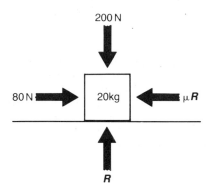

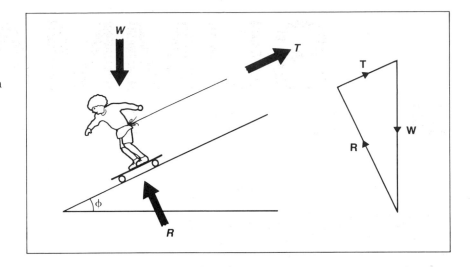

The angular velocity of an object in circular motion is the rate at which its radius sweeps out an angle: $\omega = \Delta\theta/\Delta t$. The centripetal force required to keep an object in circular motion points towards the centre of the circle: $F = mv^2/r$.

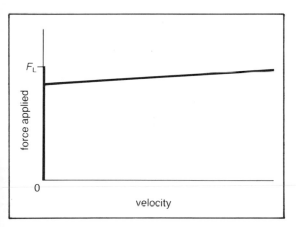

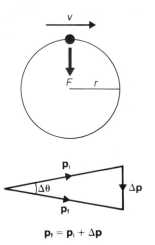

$$p_f = p_i + \Delta p$$

For an object to be in static equilibrium the total moment has to be zero: $M = Fd$. The centre of mass of an object is the point through which its weight appears to act as far as calculating its moment is concerned.

A couple acting on an object will change its angular velocity: $\Gamma = Fd$, $\Gamma = I\alpha$, $\alpha = \Delta\omega/\Delta t$. The resultant couple is equal to the rate of change of angular momentum; $L = I\omega$. The moment of inertia I is the sum of Δmr^2 over the whole object. The angular momentum of an isolated system remains constant: the system is isolated if the resultant external couple is zero.

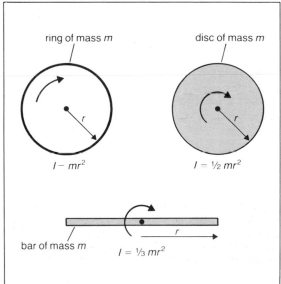

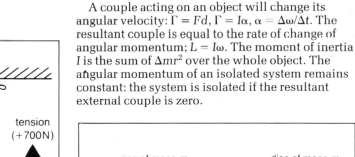

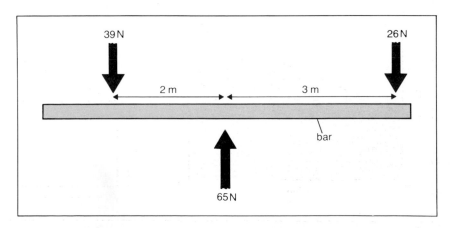

ENERGY

WORK AND ENERGY

7

For most non-scientists, energy is all about fuels. Fuels, of course, are substances like petrol, chocolate, coal or uranium which help to keep us alive, keep us warm, keep us mobile and help us make the things we need. To the non-expert, energy is also considered to be something needed to generate electricity: it can be thermal, solar, wind, wave or nuclear, but it is still energy. Energy appears to be necessary for us to be able to do things — all of our fundamental needs (food, clean water and warmth) require some energy to be made available to us.

However, the true story about energy goes much deeper than this. As this chapter will reveal, energy is one of those rare quantities which is universally conserved. An isolated system cannot lose or gain energy. Energy and momentum share the privilege of being conserved quantities on both the smallest and largest scales that we can find in our universe. In a sense, the concepts of energy and momentum are the twin pillars which support the structure of physics itself.

ENERGY

Energy, despite its mundane importance in everyday life, is an abstract concept. Before you can start to use energy as a useful physical concept, you need to have some way of measuring it. You need some way of quantifying it, of working out how much energy something has. As it happens, Einstein was able to show that the energy of anything is proportional to its mass. This is encapsulated in what is probably the most famous formula in physics, the one that *everyone* knows!

$E = mc^2$

E is the total energy of an object (J)

m is the mass of the object (kg)

c is the velocity of light in a vacuum (m s^{-1})

Work

Defining the energy of something in terms of its mass probably seems very far removed from what you intuitively understand by energy. After all, the mass of an object tells you how hard you have to push on it to change its motion, whereas its energy tells you about its ability to do things. So we will start our unveiling of the true nature of energy by appealing to your intuition with a thought experiment.

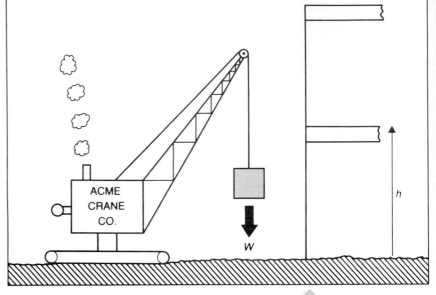

Figure 7.1 A crane doing work on a building site

Lifting objects

Suppose that you have a crane which can lift concrete blocks on a building site (figure 7.1). The crane will, of course, need an engine. Let's choose an engine which uses a liquid fuel so that we can monitor how much it uses up when lifting the blocks up the building. Finally, let us state that the engine runs at a constant speed when it is lifting blocks — it has a regulator which continually adjusts the fuel flow to keep the engine speed constant.

Figure 7.2 Two cranes doing work side-by-side

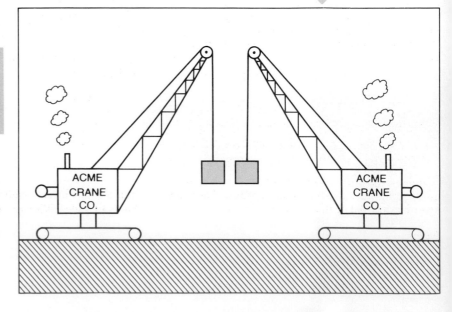

Now for the experiment. The crane is used to lift one block (weight W) up one floor (height h) of the building. In doing so, the crane's engine uses up a volume V of fuel in a time t. How much fuel will the crane use to lift one block up n floors? Well, the crane's engine will need to operate for a time nt, so the volume of fuel consumed will be nV. So the amount of fuel used (nV) is clearly proportional to the height (nh) that the block is raised.

The other variable which will affect the rate of fuel consumption is going to be the weight of the block being raised. In other words, how much fuel will be used up if m blocks are raised up one floor? Well, we could have m identical cranes working side-by-side, each lifting a single block up one floor (figure 7.2). The total volume of fuel used up will be mV, as the performance of each engine cannot possibly be affected by the other engines nearby. So the fuel used (mV) will also be proportional to the weight (mW) of the block being raised.

A little thought should convince you that to lift m blocks up n floors will require a volume nmV of fuel. So the following formula could be used to calculate the amount of fuel V required to raise any weight W up any height h:

$$V = CWh \qquad \text{(7.1)}$$

C is just a constant of proportionality.

Doing work

Figure 7.3 shows the same crane doing a different task, dragging blocks along the ground. The pulley converts the vertical force in the cable into a horizontal one. As far as the engine inside the crane is concerned, this task is no different from the one pictured in figure 7.1. It still has to exert a force F on the cable and move the cable a distance d. Of course, the force exerted by the crane is now the same size as the sliding friction between the block and the ground rather than the weight, but is nevertheless a force. So equation (7.1) is just a special case of a general formula for the fuel used V by the engine when it pulls something a distance d with a force F.

$$V = CFd \qquad \text{(7.2)}$$

The value of C depends on the type of fuel or engine used in the crane. The important thing to note about equation (7.2) is the quantity Fd: it is a measure of the **energy** extracted from the fuel by the engine. Fd is known as the **work** done by the engine.

$E = Fd$

E is the work done by a device (J)

F is the force exerted by the device (N)

d is the distance moved in the direction of the force (m)

Although the unit of work should strictly speaking be N m, it is such a useful quantity that it has been awarded its own unit, the joule.

Power

An important property of any engine is the rate at which it can do work. The **power** of any device is the amount of work it can do in one second. Like work, power has its own special unit, the watt.

$P = \dfrac{E}{t}$

P is the power of the device (W)

E is the work done by the object (J)

t is the time taken to do the work (s)

For example, suppose that you wish to use an electric motor to lift bricks on a building site. The maximum power of a motor plugged into the domestic electricity supply is about 3 kW and a single brick has a mass of 3 kg. If the bricks need to be raised up to the top of a 6 m high building, how many bricks could you raise in a minute?

Start off by calculating how much work the motor can do in a minute.

$P = 3000$ W
$E = \;?$
$t = 60$ s

$P = \dfrac{E}{t} \qquad \therefore 3000 = \dfrac{E}{60}$

$\therefore E = 3000 \times 60$
$\quad = 1.8 \times 10^5$ J

Figure 7.3   Doing work with a horizontal force

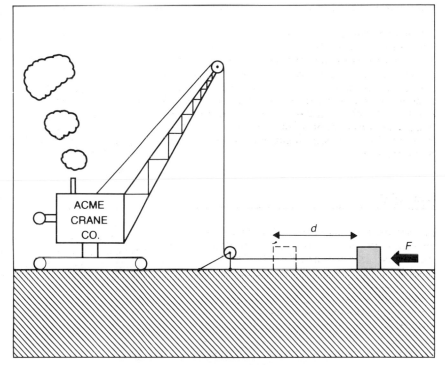

Now we can find the weight which can be raised 6 m by this work.

$E = 1.8 \times 10^5$ J
$F = \;?$
$d = 6$ m

$E = Fd$
$\therefore 1.8 \times 10^5 = F \times 6$

$\therefore F = \dfrac{1.8 \times 10^5}{6}$

$\quad = 3.0 \times 10^4$ N

Since a single brick weighs 30 N, the motor should be able to raise 30000/30 = 1000 bricks per minute!

HUMAN LABOUR

The typical steady power output of a human labourer's legs is about 100 W. Given that the weight of a labourer might be about 750 N, it can be easily calculated that the maximum speed with which he or she can continuously climb a ladder carrying ten bricks will be about 0.1 m s^{-1}. So the maximum theoretical number of bricks a single labourer can deliver to the top of a 6 m building per minute will be only 10, about a hundred times less than the electric motor discussed in the example above. Furthermore, the labourer will cost at least £5 an hour to hire, whereas the electric motor might only cost 20p! Clearly, on economic grounds alone, the use of human labour for doing work is a bad thing. Of course, there are many places on Earth, particularly in developing countries where human beings and animals are the only sources of work which can be reliably maintained.

Measuring energy

Our thought experiment has shown that the work done by a machine is proportional to the amount of fuel it uses up. The fuel does not have to be petrol. It could be a variety of things, depending on the construction of the machine. So we could use batteries, lumps of coal, bottles of gas or even slaves as the source of the fuel used up when work is done (figure 7.4). Clearly, it is only the **energy** contained in the fuel which is important, not the details of the fuel itself. As the machine uses up fuel it loses energy and does work. So we can define the energy lost by the machine as being equal to the work it does.

$$\Delta E = -Fd$$

ΔE is the energy change of the fuel (J)

F is the force applied by the machine (N)

d is the distance moved in the direction of the force (m)

This formula is now going to be used to work out the energy change of objects which are raised up, moved, spun round or squeezed. Each time, we will have to treat the object as the 'fuel' for a machine. (As far as we are concerned, a machine is just something which uses the energy of a fuel to do work!) Although we will have to invent some mechanism for finding the force exerted and the distance moved, the aim each time is to get an expression for the work done by the machine only in terms of the fuel's properties.

Figure 7.4 Each of these machines uses a different fuel

Gravitational energy

We want to find the energy lost by a mass m when it is lowered a vertical distance h near the surface of the Earth. Figure 7.5 illustrates our machine. The balls in the top tray are the fuel which allows the machine to do work by dragging a cloth along a level surface against friction.

Assume that the ball in the pocket keeps the axle turning at a constant speed. (Of course, this is only a thought experiment so we can assume frictionless bearings for the axle.) The belt has only two pockets, so it only holds one ball at a time. The mass of a ball is m, so it exerts a downwards force mg on the belt. The windlass rotates at a constant speed, so the tension in the cord which is wound onto the axle will also be mg. As each ball drops a height h, the cloth will be dragged to the left a distance h by a force mg.

$$E = Fd \qquad \therefore E = mg \times h \qquad \textbf{(7.3)}$$

The energy lost by each ball as it makes its way from the top tray to the bottom tray must therefore be given by

$$\Delta E = -Fd = -mgh \qquad \textbf{(7.4)}$$

Thus any object raised above the surface of the ground is capable of allowing a machine to do some work. This type of energy is called **gravitational energy**. If we assume, somewhat arbitrarily (see page 109) that an object lying on the ground has no gravitational energy, we can use equation (7.4) to write down a formula for its gravitational energy at any height above the ground.

> $E_g = mgh$
>
> E_g is the gravitational energy of the object (J)
>
> m is the mass of the object (kg)
>
> g is the acceleration of free fall (m s^{-2})
>
> h is the height of the object above the ground (m)

Kinetic energy

The machine shown in figure 7.6 is very simple. The polishing cloth is attached to a very light block of wood which has a sticky plate poking out of it. The fuel is the **kinetic energy** of heavy balls of mass m which are thrown horizontally at the block with a velocity v. As soon as each ball hits the wood it will stick to it and set it moving with a velocity v. The collision will conserve momentum, but as the cloth slides across the table friction will steadily transfer the momentum to the table. The cloth will exert a force F on the table and travel a distance d before it stops moving. We can use Newton's Second Law and a VUSAT formula to work out an expression for d.

$$F = ma \qquad \therefore a = -\frac{F}{m}$$

$$v^2 = u^2 + 2as \qquad \therefore 0 = v^2 + 2\left(-\frac{F}{m}\right)d$$

$$\therefore d = \frac{mv^2}{2F}$$

$$\textbf{(7.5)}$$

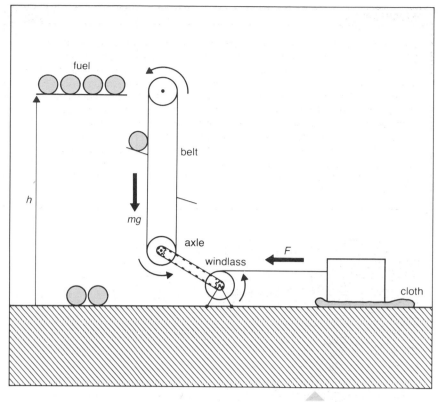

Now we can get an expression for the work done by the machine for one ball.

$$E = Fd \qquad \therefore E = \frac{Fmv^2}{2F} = \frac{mv^2}{2} \qquad \textbf{(7.6)}$$

This must equal the kinetic energy of the ball before it hit the block, assuming that the ball has no kinetic energy once it has stopped moving.

> $E_k = \tfrac{1}{2}mv^2$
>
> E_k is the kinetic energy of the object (J)
>
> m is the mass of the object (kg)
>
> v is the velocity of the object (m s^{-1})

Figure 7.5 A machine which runs off gravitational energy

Figure 7.6 Using kinetic energy to do work

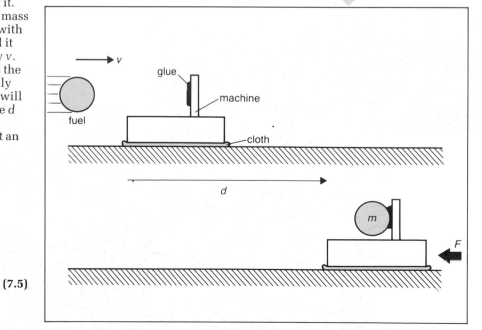

Strain energy

The next machine we are going to consider is shown in figure 7.7: it runs on compressed springs which have **strain energy**. The springs are placed on the holder one at a time. Each spring will make the light piston do some work on the fluid in the cylinder when the restraining cord is cut. However, the force exerted by the spring is going to change as it expands. So we shall assume that it obeys Hooke's Law, with a force constant k, so that the force F depends on compression as shown in figure 7.8.

Consider the work done ΔE by the machine as the spring compression changes from x to $x - \Delta x$.

$$E = Fd \qquad \therefore \Delta E = F\Delta x \qquad (7.7)$$

If we let the spring expand in steps of size Δx, the total work done should be given by

$$E = \Sigma F\Delta x \qquad (7.8)$$

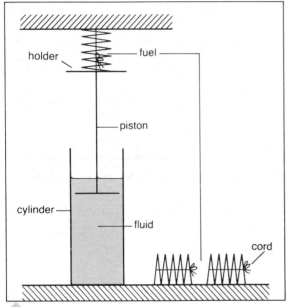

Figure 7.7 A machine which uses strain energy as its fuel

Figure 7.8 Letting the spring expand by Δx

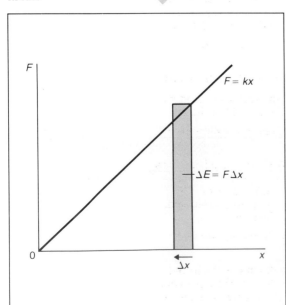

ROTATIONAL ENERGY

The final machine we are going to consider is shown in figure 7.10. It uses the **rotational energy** of a spinning disc to make two small friction pads go round on a flat surface. The disc, which has a moment of inertia I, radius r and angular velocity ω is simply placed on the surface by lowering the axle. (The axle, of course, has frictionless bearings.) As the pads move round, the friction F between them and the surface exerts a couple Γ on the disc. If the disc rotates through a total angle θ as it slows down, the work done by the pads can be calculated.

$$E = Fd \qquad\qquad \therefore E = 2(F \times r\theta) \qquad (1)$$

If the disc starts off with an angular velocity ω and stops spinning in a time t, then the total angle θ turned through is going to be the area under the graph of figure 7.11. (If $\omega = \Delta\theta/\Delta t$, then $\omega\Delta t = \Delta\theta$ and $\Sigma\omega\Delta t = \theta$.)

Figure 7.10 Using rotational energy to do work

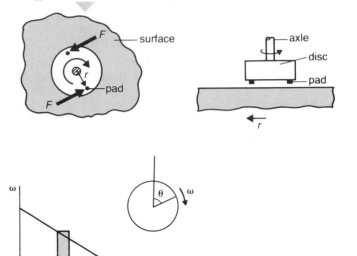

Figure 7.11 How the angular velocity changes with time

$$E = 2Fr \times (\tfrac{1}{2} \times t \times \omega) \qquad\qquad \therefore E = Frt\omega \qquad (2)$$

The friction F exerts a couple on the disc.

$$\Gamma = Fd \qquad\qquad \therefore \Gamma = F \times 2r \qquad (3)$$

The couple will make the disc stop spinning in time t.

$$\Gamma = I\alpha \qquad \therefore \Gamma = I \times \frac{\Delta\omega}{\Delta t} = \frac{I\omega}{t} \qquad (4)$$

Eliminating Γ from equations (3) and (4) we get an expression for F which we can insert into equation (2).

$$\Gamma = 2Fr = \frac{I\omega}{t} \qquad \therefore F = \frac{I\omega}{2rt}$$

$$E = Frt\omega \qquad \therefore E = \left(\frac{I\omega}{2rt}\right) \times rt\omega \quad \therefore E = \frac{I\omega^2}{2} \qquad (5)$$

At last, we obtain an expression for the **rotational energy** lost by the disc as it is made to do some work.

$E_r = \tfrac{1}{2}I\omega^2$

E_r is the rotational energy of an object (J)

I is the moment of inertia of the object (kg m^2)

ω is the angular velocity of the object (rad s^{-1})

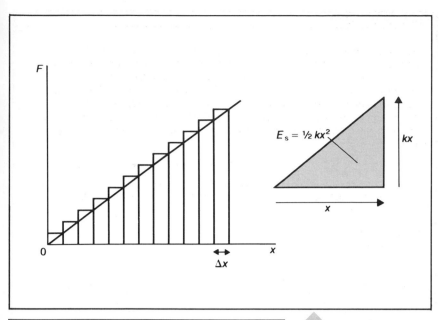

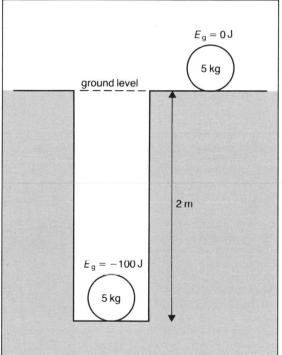

Figure 7.9 The area under the force–extension curve is equal to the strain energy stored in the spring

Figure 7.12 Why negative values for gravitational energy are possible

Zero energy

As figure 7.12 shows, it is quite possible for things to have negative values of E_g. We had to choose a convenient zero for E_g because equation (7.4) only allowed us to calculate the energy *change* of an object when its height is changed. We also had to make arbitrary, but sensible, decisions about the zero of the other three energies we considered. So bear in mind that just because something might have 0 J of energy, it does not mean that it is incapable of doing some work. For example, a large rock sitting on the ground can be made to do some work by making it fall into a hole which has been dug beside it! The four formulae for different types of energy can only be used to work out the energy loss or gain of an object as one or more of its properties (v, ω, x or h) are changed.

OBJECTIVES

After studying this section you should be able to do the following.

State and use the formulae $E = Fd$ and $P = E/t$.

Know that the energy loss of an object is equal to the work that it does.

Calculate the change of gravitational energy of an object when it is raised or lowered.

State and use the formula $E_k = \frac{1}{2}mv^2$.

Derive an expression for the strain energy of a bar.

Be able to calculate the rotational energy of an object.

Understand why the choice of zero for any type of energy is arbitrary.

A glance at figure 7.9 should convince you that, provided Δx is small enough, $\Sigma F \Delta x$ is equal to the area under the curve of the graph. The area has a triangular shape, with a height kx and a base x, so we can easily work out its area.

E = area under curve

$\qquad = \frac{1}{2} \times \text{base} \times \text{height} = \frac{1}{2}kx^2$ **(7.9)**

Equation (7.9) tells how much energy the spring loses as its strain is reduced to zero.

$E_s = \frac{1}{2}kx^2$

E_s is the strain energy of the object (J)

k is the force constant of the object (N m^{-1})

x is the change of length of the object (m)

QUESTIONS

1 A block of ice sits at the top of a smooth inclined surface as shown in figure 7.13. The mass of the ice is 5 kg, and there is no friction between the block and the surface. The block is released from rest and slides 2 m down the slope. Calculate

a the gravitational energy of the block at the moment of release,

b the component of the force parallel to the slope,

c the acceleration of the block, and hence find its velocity when it gets to the bottom of the slope,

d the kinetic energy of the block at the bottom of the slope.

2 A ball bearing of mass 50 g is squeezed against a light spring as shown in figure 7.14. The spring, which has a force constant of 5.0×10^3 N m^{-1}, is shortened by 2.0 cm. When the spring is released, the ball bearing shoots off to the right.

a Calculate the strain energy in the squeezed spring.

b When the spring is released, what is the initial horizontal force on the ball? What is the force when the ball just ceases to touch the spring? What is the average force on the ball as the spring expands?

c Calculate the average acceleration of the ball as the spring expands and hence find its kinetic energy when it leaves the spring.

3 Questions 1 and 2 have asked you to perform similar tasks on different systems. You have been calculating the loss of one type of energy and the gain of another type of energy. Do you notice anything about the answers?

4 Calculate values for the following energies — state clearly any estimates of quantities which you need to use.

a The gravitational energy of a tree.

b The kinetic energy of a sprinting athlete.

c The strain energy of a fully stretched rubber band.

d The rotational energy of one wheel of a bicycle at top speed.

5 Jason is having some trouble understanding about work. This is what he says. 'Suppose I lift a heavy book above my head and hold it there with my arms. I do work on the book as I lift it up, but I also keep on doing work when I hold it up. I must be, because after a while my arms get tired and I have to put the book down again. Now, if lifting up the book gives it gravitational energy, what sort of energy am I giving it when I just hold it up?' Tell Jason where he is going wrong.

6 A lump of mass m is initially a height h_i above the floor. Suppose that you slowly raise it to a new height h_f.

a What is the force you need to apply to it? How far do you move the force along its line of action?

b How does the work done on the lump compare with its increase of gravitational energy?

7 An object of mass m has an initial velocity u. A steady force acts on it for a time t, increasing its velocity to v. Work out expressions for

a the impulse given to the object,
b the force applied to the object,
c the average velocity of the object,
d the distance moved while the force was applied,
e the work done by the force.

8 Look at the answers for questions 6 and 7, then comment on the statement 'the work done on an object is *always* equal to the change of energy of the object'.

9 Estimate the power of a typical motor car by considering its maximum acceleration.

10 A shop escalator is angled at 45° to the horizontal. The steps move at 0.50 m s^{-1} between two floors of a building which are 8.0 m apart.

a Given that the average mass of a human being is 80 kg, calculate how much kinetic energy and gravitational energy the escalator has to give each of its passengers.

b Each step is 20 cm high and two people can stand on each step. Calculate the maximum power required for the escalator motor, given that a power of 1.2 kW is necessary to run the escalator when there are no people on it.

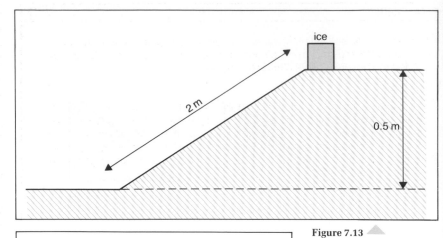

Figure 7.13

Figure 7.14

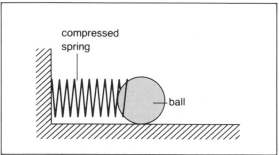

ENERGY CONSERVATION

Some of the problems you worked through at the end of the last section should make you suspect that whenever one object does work on another, one loses some energy and the other gains it. The energy gained or lost by something seems to be exactly equal to the work done. So if a number of objects can only interact with each other, the total amount of energy they share between them cannot change. It can only be shared among them in different ways as they do work on each other. This is called the **Principle of Energy Conservation**. Of course, you have only studied a limited number of types of energy and looked at their changes under ideal conditions. The time has come to look at energy changes on a more general basis so that you can be convinced that energy conservation *always* works. We shall start by looking at what happens to energy at a microscopic level.

Figure 7.15 Allowing a particle to move a distance Δx in a force field

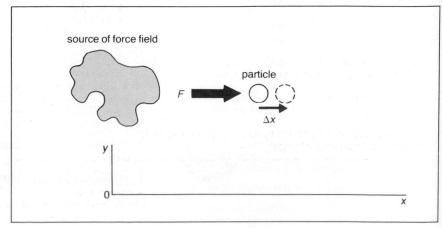

TOTAL ENERGY !

The particle can only have two types of energy. It has potential energy because it is in the field and kinetic energy because it can move about. Its **total energy** is defined as the sum of all its different energies.

$$E_t = E_k + E_p \qquad (1)$$

Now suppose that the external restraint on the particle is removed. Would you expect the total energy to vary with time if the particle was left alone in the field? After all, there is only a single force acting on it, so it cannot be in static equilibrium. The speed with which E_t changes with time is given by $\Delta E_t / \Delta t$, the gradient of the graph in figure 7.17. We can build an expression for this quantity with the help of equation (1).

Figure 7.17 Possible variation of energy with time?

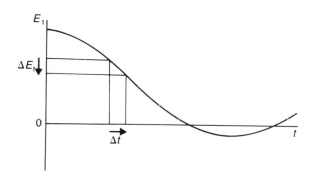

$$\Delta E_t = \Delta E_k + \Delta E_p \qquad \therefore \frac{\Delta E_t}{\Delta t} = \frac{\Delta E_k}{\Delta t} + \frac{\Delta E_p}{\Delta t} \qquad (2)$$

The rate of change of potential energy can be worked out with the help of equation (7.11) and Newton's Second Law.

$$\frac{\Delta E_p}{\Delta t} = - \frac{F\Delta x}{\Delta t} \qquad \therefore \frac{\Delta E_p}{\Delta t} = - \frac{m\Delta v}{\Delta t} \times \frac{\Delta x}{\Delta t}$$

$$\therefore \frac{\Delta E_p}{\Delta t} = - mv \frac{\Delta v}{\Delta t} \qquad (3)$$

Similarly, we can work out an expression for the rate of change of kinetic energy with the help of an identity explained in Appendix B.

If $y = Cx^n$ then $\dfrac{\Delta y}{y} = \dfrac{n\Delta x}{x}$ for small enough Δx and Δy.

$$E_k = \tfrac{1}{2}mv^2 \qquad \therefore \frac{\Delta E_k}{E_k} = \frac{2\Delta v}{v}$$

$$\therefore \frac{\Delta E_k}{\Delta t} = 2E_k \frac{\Delta v}{v\Delta t} = \frac{2}{v} \times \tfrac{1}{2}mv^2 \times \frac{\Delta v}{\Delta t}$$

$$\therefore \frac{\Delta E_k}{\Delta t} = +mv \frac{\Delta v}{\Delta t} \qquad (4)$$

Substituting equations (4) and (3) back into equation (2) we get a surprising result for the rate of change of total energy:

$$\frac{\Delta E_t}{\Delta t} = \frac{\Delta E_k}{\Delta t} + \frac{\Delta E_p}{\Delta t} \qquad \therefore \frac{\Delta E_t}{\Delta t} = mv \frac{\Delta v}{\Delta t} - mv \frac{\Delta v}{\Delta t} = 0 \qquad (5)$$

The total energy of the particle never changes from one small instant of time to the next, so it will never change!

Figure 7.16 The relationship between the potential energy of a particle and the force acting on it

Potential energy

Figure 7.15 shows a small **elementary particle** (such as an electron or a neutron) sitting in a **force field**. The **source** of that field is the large amorphous lump at the left hand edge of the picture. We are not going to be concerned with the exact nature of the force exerted on the particle – it could be electrical, magnetic or gravitational. An external agency (e.g. a human hand) stops the particle from moving. We want to find out what happens to the energy of the particle as it is moved around in the force field. This type of energy, which it has by virtue of its position in the field, is called **potential energy**.

Potential gradient and force
For simplicity, let the force on the particle F act along the x-axis. If the particle starts off at a particular place x in the field and is allowed to move to another position $x + \Delta x$ close by, it will be able to do some work on whatever is holding it in place.

$$E = Fd \qquad \therefore E = F\Delta x \qquad \textbf{(7.10)}$$

(Δx is small, so F is not going to change as the particle moves.) If the particle does work, it must be losing some energy. The change in potential energy is therefore given by

$$\Delta E_p = -F\Delta x \qquad (\Delta x \to 0) \qquad \textbf{(7.11)}$$

Now if you look at the graphs of figure 7.16, you should be able to see how a knowledge of the variation of F with x allows you to work out what E_p is at all points in the force field. The area under the $F-x$ graph for a particular x is equal to $-E_p$. Conversely, the gradient of the E_p-x graph is equal to $-F$.

$$\Delta E_p = -F\Delta x$$

E_p is the potential energy of the particle (J)

F is the force on the particle in the x-direction (N)

x is the position of the particle along the x-axis (m)

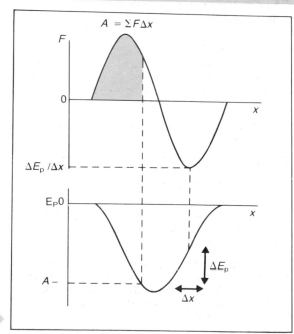

Conserving total energy

To be honest, all we have done so far is to play with algebra, constructing a quantity (the total energy) which, according to Newton's Laws of Motion, should not change with time. Can we predict that the total energy will also remain constant for objects made of billions of particles rather than just one?

Well, the algebra is much more complicated if you have many particles, rather than just one. Each particle will have its own kinetic energy and its potential energy will be the sum of the potential energies due to all of the other particles around it. Furthermore, to do it properly, the sums must include all three dimensions (not just one, like we have been using). Nevertheless, it turns out that if you have any number of particles which can only interact with each other, then Newton's Laws of Motion predict that the total energy does indeed remain constant. So it looks as if we have good theoretical grounds for believing the **Principle of Energy Conservation**.

> The total energy of an isolated system remains constant.

Galileo's experiment

Of course, however persuasive the algebra is, the real test of our model of energy has to be how it compares with the results of some experiments. Some simple apparatus which tests the Principle of Energy Conservation is shown in figure 7.18. Galileo used similar apparatus to study motion. It consists of a large heavy ball which is free to move on a curved track — the ability to change the shape of the track is useful.

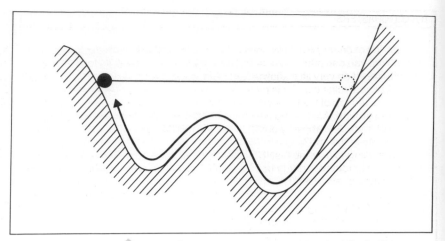

Figure 7.18 A simple experiment to test energy conservation

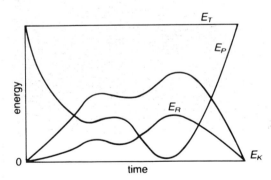

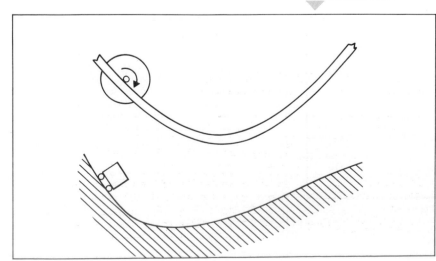

Figure 7.19 How the various forms of energy change when the ball of figure 7.18 is released

Figure 7.20 The ball always rises up to its initial height before stopping

Figure 7.21 Two variations of the apparatus drawn in figure 7.18

The experiment is very simple. The ball is released from rest at a particular point on the track and allowed to roll down it until it comes to rest again somewhere else on the track. As it rolls down, it will gain kinetic and rotational energy and lose gravitational energy. Conversely, as the track forces it to rise up, the ball gains gravitational energy and loses kinetic and rotational energy. However, the sum of all three energies should be constant throughout, as shown in figure 7.19. So wherever the ball stops moving on the track, it must have the same amount of gravitational energy as when it was first released. Regardless of the shape of the track or where the ball was released it should always rise to its initial height above the ground (figure 7.20).

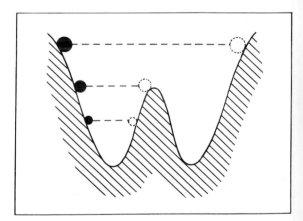

Of course, for the experiment to be a good test of the theory, we need to ensure that the ball is isolated, i.e. cannot do any work on its surroundings. Friction needs to be minimised by careful choice of material for the track, and air resistance can be kept relatively small by using a large ball made of a dense material. In practice, it is possible, with careful attention to friction, to persuade the ball to rise to just under its initial height.

Figure 7.21 shows two variations of the experiment. One uses a wheel and axle to spectacular effect. As the axle rolls down the track, most of the lost gravitational energy is converted to rotational energy. Nevertheless, the axle will only come to rest when it has reached its initial height above the ground. The other variation uses a trolley with wheels, testing the interconversion of gravitational and kinetic energy.

ROLLER COASTERS

The real joy of energy conservation is its universality. Because it applies to everything, you can often make far-reaching predictions about the behaviour of objects based on very little knowledge. The following example should make this clear. A typical roller coaster is pictured in figure 7.22. Suppose that the car starts off at the top of the track with an initial velocity of 2 m s^{-1} at a height of 9 m above the ground. After going over the humps it emerges onto the final straight section of track, 2 m above ground level. If the car has a mass of 1000 kg, what is its velocity at the end?

We are going to assume that the car is an isolated system. This means that it cannot give or receive energy from its surroundings. So there must be no friction between the car and the track which can do work on it as the car moves along. Given these assumptions, we can state that the total energy of the car will be the same all the way through the ride. At the start, the car will have two sorts of energy, both of which we can calculate.

$E_k = \frac{1}{2}mv^2$ $\therefore E_k = 0.5 \times 1000 \times 2^2 = 2000$ J or 2 kJ

$E_g = mgh$ $\therefore E_g = 1000 \times 10 \times 9 = 90\,000$ J or 90 kJ

The total energy will be the sum of the kinetic and gravitational energies.

$E_t = E_k + E_g$ $\therefore E_t = 90 + 2 = 92$ kJ

When the car emerges at the bottom of the hump section, although its total energy will still be 92 kJ, its gravitational energy will be somewhat less than it was.

Figure 7.22 A roller coaster

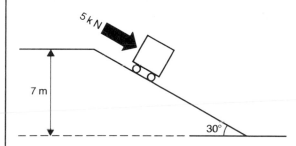

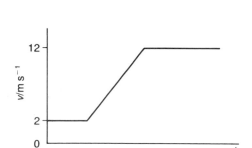

Figure 7.23 A simple situation where kinetic energy increase can be predicted without invoking the Principle of Energy Conservation

$E_g = mgh$ $\therefore E_g = 1000 \times 10 \times 2 = 20\,000$ J or 20 kJ

So we can work out how much kinetic energy it has.

$E_t = E_k + E_g$ $\therefore 92 = E_k + 20$

                 $\therefore E_k = 92 - 20 = 72$ kJ

Finally, we can work out what its final velocity is.

$E_k = \frac{1}{2}mv^2$ $\therefore 72\,000 = 0.5 \times 1000 \times v^2$

$$\therefore v = \left(\frac{72\,000}{0.5 \times 1000}\right)^{\frac{1}{2}} = 12 \text{ m s}^{-1}$$

So, regardless of how complicated the humps of the roller coaster are, the fact that it has changed height by 7 m between start and finish means that it emerges with a speed of 12 m s^{-1}. Without the principle of energy conservation, you would have been unable to make this prediction unless a very simple configuration (such as the ramp shown in figure 7.23) had been used.

Collisions

So far we have been looking at what energy conservation implies for the behaviour of large isolated objects interacting with gravity force fields. What happens if two objects interact with each other instead?

Elastic collisions

Figure 7.24 shows two similar vehicles colliding on a flat, level frictionless surface (e.g. an air track). If their buffers are springs, how will they be moving after the collision? The lack of friction means that the two vehicles form an isolated system. Before and after the collision, they have kinetic energy only. During the collision there will be strain energy in the springs. However, provided that the springs do not pass their elastic limits, any energy given to the springs at the start of the collision will be returned to the vehicles at the end. In fact, we do not need to consider the collision mechanism at all, just to concentrate on the conservation of momentum and energy.

$$p = mv \qquad \therefore mu = mv + MV \qquad \textbf{(7.12)}$$

$$E_k = \tfrac{1}{2}mv^2 \qquad \therefore \tfrac{1}{2}mu^2 = \tfrac{1}{2}mv^2 + \tfrac{1}{2}MV^2 \qquad \textbf{(7.13)}$$

Our goal is to arrive at expressions for v and V in terms of u, m and M. Equations (7.12) and (7.13) will be a lot easier to handle if we introduce a new variable μ, the ratio m/M.

$$mu = mv + MV \qquad \therefore V = \mu(u - v) \qquad \textbf{(7.14)}$$

$$\tfrac{1}{2}mu^2 = \tfrac{1}{2}mv^2 + \tfrac{1}{2}MV^2$$

$$\therefore V^2 = \mu(u^2 - v^2)$$

$$\therefore V^2 = \mu(u - v)(u + v) \qquad \textbf{(7.15)}$$

Combining equations (7.14) and (7.15) to eliminate V:

$$V^2 = \mu^2(u - v)^2 = \mu(u - v)(u + v)$$

$$\therefore \mu(u - v) = (u + v)$$

$$\therefore \mu u - \mu v = u + v$$

$$\therefore v(\mu + 1) = u(\mu - 1)$$

$$\therefore v = u \times \frac{\mu - 1}{\mu + 1} \qquad \textbf{(7.16)}$$

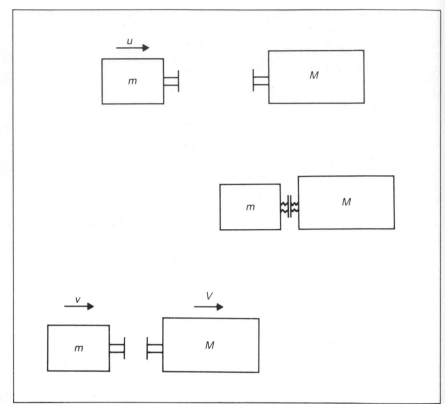

Figure 7.24   An elastic collision

Check for yourself that when equation (7.16) is substituted into equation (7.14) you get the following expression for V:

$$V = u \times \frac{2\mu}{\mu + 1} \qquad \textbf{(7.17)}$$

Table 7.1 shows the values of V and v predicted by equations (7.16) and (7.17) for three different values of μ. Check that they are correct! If you study figures 7.25, 7.26 and 7.27 you will see what the values mean in practice.

Table 7.1

μ	0	1	∞
v	$-u$	0	u
V	0	u	$2u$

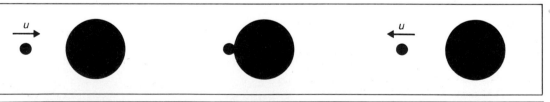

Figure 7.25   A small object collides elastically with a large one

Figure 7.26   An elastic collision between identical objects

Figure 7.27   A massive object colliding elastically with a light one

The case where $\mu = 1$ (i.e. both vehicles have the same mass) is the easiest one to check with simple apparatus, such as an air track. When a moving vehicle hits a stationary one, all of the energy and momentum are transferred from one to the other. The executive toy known as a Newton's cradle shown in figure 7.28 exploits this to startling effect.

You can check the case where $\mu = 0$ by dropping a ball onto a smooth hard surface on the ground. The initially stationary half of the system is the Earth, so M is certainly much larger than m. The speed of the ball is predicted to be unchanged by the collision with the surface, so, in the absence of wind resistance, the ball should rise to its initial height after bouncing off the ground.

Figure 7.28　A Newton's cradle

Figure 7.29　The first of three classic cloud chamber photographs taken in the 1920s by Patrick Blackett. Each line is a trail of tiny bubbles which have condensed on the ions left in the wake of a fast moving charged particle. Most of the lines are due to alpha particles ($m = 4$). You can see that one of the alpha particles has hit a nucleus of the hydrogen gas ($m = 1$) which fills the chamber

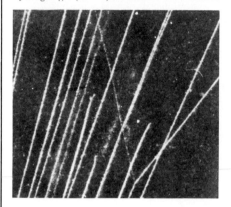

Figure 7.30　The chamber is filled with helium gas ($m = 4$). Notice the approximate right angle between the directions of the scattered alpha particle ($m = 4$) and the helium nucleus it collided with. It is not exactly a right angle because the particles are not quite moving in the plane of the photograph

Figure 7.31　An example of a collision between an alpha particle ($m = 4$) and a nitrogen nucleus ($m = 14$). The nitrogen nucleus track can be recognised from its density and short range

A lot of knowledge about the elementary particles which make up our universe can be gleaned by studying collisions in cloud chambers. Charged particles, such as alpha particles, protons and electrons leave photographable tracks behind them as they pass through these chambers. Figures 7.29, 7.30 and 7.31 show a number of such photographs which show collisions between particles fired into the chamber and nuclei which are initially stationary. The angle between the tracks of the particles which emerge from the collision is a measure of their relative mass.

To see why this should be the case, look at figure 7.32. Both the target and the projectile have the same mass. If they do not hit head on, they will travel in different directions after the collision which must, of course, conserve energy and momentum. If we assume that the particles will only have kinetic energy before and after the collision, we can calculate the angle between their final momenta. The kinetic energy of a particle with momentum p and mass m is $p^2/2m$: $(mv)^2/2m = \frac{1}{2}mv^2$. So we can write down the following pair of equations to represent conservation of momentum and kinetic energy respectively:

momentum:　　$\mathbf{p}_i = \mathbf{p}_f + \mathbf{P}$
energy:　　　　$p_i^2 = p_f^2 + P^2$

The vector triangle of figure 7.32 shows the momentum being conserved. If you consider the conditions imposed by the conservation of energy, it should be clear that they require the triangle to be right angled.

So if you fire alpha particles into a cloud chamber full of helium, some of the collisions show tracks emerging at right angles to each other. This is because helium nuclei have the same mass as alpha particles. However, if the chamber is filled with hydrogen, the tracks are angled at much less than 90° because hydrogen nuclei are protons, four times lighter than alpha particles.

Figure 7.32　An elastic collision between particles of equal mass

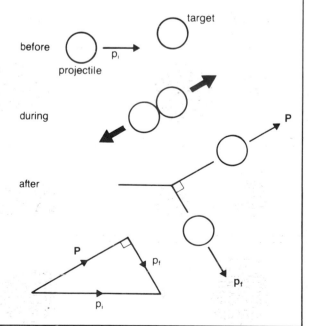

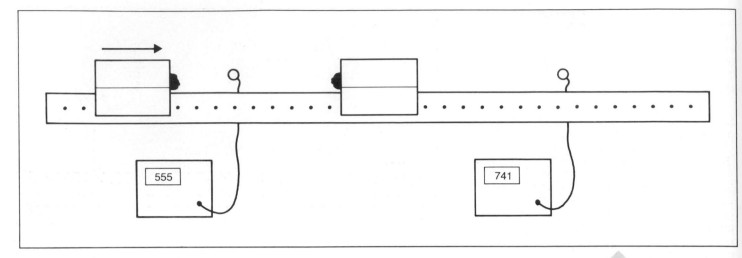

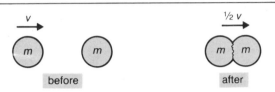

Internal energy

If you drop a rubber ball onto a hard surface it should rise back up to its initial height. In practice it doesn't quite manage it. The ball appears to lose some energy in the bounce. Similarly, a swinging pendulum eventually loses its energy and comes to a halt. Does this mean that the Principle of Energy Conservation is not universal, that it applies to some situations but not to others? Or perhaps neither of these systems are truly isolated, and they are leaking energy into their surroundings? Or even that there is another type of energy which we haven't yet considered? Let's take a look at the evidence.

Inelastic collisions

You could easily do this experiment in a school laboratory with the apparatus shown in figure 7.33. Two identical vehicles sit on a level air track, with the usual array of photodiodes and counters to monitor their speeds before and after they collide with each other. A lump of plasticene is placed at the end of each vehicle so that they will stick to each other when they collide.

The experiment is very simple. One vehicle is launched towards the other, which is initially stationary somewhere between the photodiodes. They collide, stick together and move off with a new constant velocity, as shown in figure 7.34. Momentum is conserved because it is observed that the final velocity of the joined vehicles is half that of the launched vehicle. So is energy conserved as well?

$$\text{initial energy} = \tfrac{1}{2}mv^2$$
$$\text{final energy} = 2 \times \tfrac{1}{2}m\left(\frac{v}{2}\right)^2 = \tfrac{1}{4}mv^2$$

The kinetic energy of the system has been halved in the collision!

The secret behind this energy loss must lie in the plasticene, as its replacement by springs would have resulted in a collision which conserved both kinetic energy and momentum. (Frictional forces would have been the same in both cases, so they cannot be held responsible for the different outcomes either.) Unlike a spring, the plasticene is inelastic, i.e. it is permanently deformed when the two vehicles smack into each other. So the plasticene might be given some **internal energy**

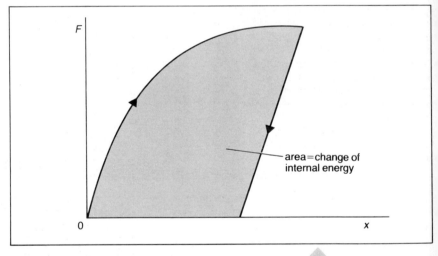

Figure 7.33 Apparatus for showing that kinetic energy does not have to be conserved in a collision

Figure 7.34 An inelastic collision

Figure 7.35 A force—extension curve for the plasticene during the inelastic collision

when it is distorted. Any stress on an object which results in a permanent strain is going to do work, delivering energy to it. If figure 7.35 is the force—extension curve followed during the deformation, then the area enclosed by the curve will equal the energy gained. But does the internal energy simply get absorbed by the deformed object or is there another way, apart from calculation, of verifying that it is there?

Heat energy

Although it is difficult to measure accurately, the plastic deformation of an object raises its temperature. Furthermore, painstaking experiments by many workers over the past two centuries have demonstrated that the temperature rise of a given object is always the same for a given amount of work done on it, regardless of the way in which the work was done. So internal energy can raise the temperature of things — it is therefore referred to as **heat energy**. Heat energy is also generated by friction. You can prove this instantly by rubbing your hands together briskly and sensing their rise in temperature.

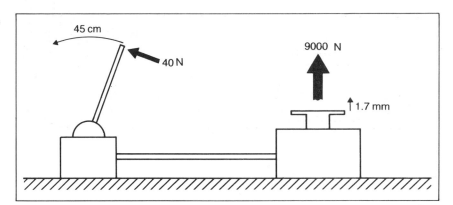

Figure 7.36 A hydraulic jack

Experiments involving precise measurements of heat energy are very difficult to make, mainly because it is impossible to completely isolate an object as far as heat energy is concerned. As soon as the temperature of an object is different from its surroundings, heat energy flows out of it or into it. So a great deal of research had to be done in the nineteenth century before physicists were convinced that the same amount of work done against friction *always* resulted in the same amount of heat energy being generated. (The measurement of heat energy is the subject of the next main section of this chapter.) For now, you will have to accept that whenever kinetic, gravitational, elastic or rotational energy appears to disappear from an isolated object, we have excellent reasons for supposing that it has become heat energy.

Efficiency

Any piece of machinery which contains moving parts will inevitably generate some heat energy through friction. At any place where one surface moves past another, work will be done converting the kinetic energy of the surfaces into heat energy. The reduction of friction in bearings to a minimum is an economic necessity in our society. Too much friction between metallic moving parts will cause them to melt and stick to each other, with disastrous results.

For any piece of machinery, its **efficiency** is a measure of how much energy gets converted to heat energy in its interior.

$$\text{efficiency} = \frac{\text{work output}}{\text{energy input}} \times 100$$

For example, consider the hydraulic jack shown in figure 7.36. When the lever is moved back and forth, oil is pumped into a cylinder, moving up a piston and raising the car. Each complete stroke (45 cm) of the lever raises a 9000 N car by 1.7 mm and a force of 40 N is needed to move the lever. What is the efficiency of the system? Start off by calculating the work done by the machine for each stroke of the input lever.

$$E = Fd \qquad \therefore E = 9000 \times 1.7 \times 10^{-3} = 15.3 \text{ J}$$

Then find the energy input to the system. This will be equal to the work done in moving the lever.

$$E = Fd \qquad \therefore E = 40 \times 0.45 = 18 \text{ J}$$

$$\text{efficiency} = \frac{\text{work output}}{\text{energy input}} \times 100$$

$$\therefore \text{efficiency} = \frac{15.3 \times 100}{18}$$

$$\therefore \text{efficiency} = 85\%$$

Only 85% of the energy put into the jack gets delivered to the car as gravitational energy. The other 15% ultimately becomes heat energy in the moving parts of the machine, including the oil which has been squeezed into the cylinder.

BEARINGS

The reduction of friction to a minimum in machinery is an economic necessity. Not only does excessive friction divert energy from fuels into heat energy, it causes wear which shortens the lifetime of a machine. In fact, friction is so important that there is a whole branch of science (tribology) dedicated to its study. In many of our machines, the principal sources of friction are the places where rotating shafts are supported by **bearings** (figure 7.37). Sleeve bearings, where there is sliding contact between shaft and bearing can have low values of μ with a suitable choice of material. For example, although μ is 0.4 for steel sliding on steel, it is only 0.05 for steel sliding on PTFE–impregnated bronze. The use of lubricants, such as oil, can reduce μ further to 0.01. Roller bearings (figure 7.38) can have a very low effective value of μ (≈ 0.001) because there is only a rolling contact between the cylinders and the races.

Figure 7.37 A sleeve bearing

Figure 7.38 A roller bearing

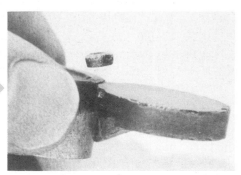

Figure 7.39 A superconductor held above a magnet. Provided that the superconductor is kept at liquid nitrogen temperature and the magnetic field is not too intense, the only friction on the magnet is wind resistance.

The widespread use of superconducting materials to support shafts by magnetic bearings inside large machines may become feasible before the end of the century. Figure 7.39 shows a superconductor suspended above a magnet. Until very recently, all known superconducting materials could only behave this way at liquid helium temperatures ($-269°C$), but the recent discovery of substances which are superconducting at liquid nitrogen temperatures ($-196°C$) has launched an intense research effort into the possibility of room temperature superconductors.

OBJECTIVES

After studying this section you should be able to do
the following.

State the Principle of Energy Conservation.	Know that if kinetic energy has been lost in a collision, total energy has still been conserved.
Apply energy conservation to objects moving in gravitational fields.	Calculate the efficiency of a machine.
Use energy and momentum conservation to predict the behaviour of objects in elastic and inelastic collisions.	

QUESTIONS

1 If you drop a ping-pong ball from rest onto a hard horizontal surface, you will find that it usually returns to 75% of its original height after bouncing.

a Show that the velocity of the ball after it has dropped a height h is given by $v^2 = 2gh$. (Neglect air resistance.)

b What percentage of the energy of the ping-pong ball is lost on each bounce? What happens to that energy?

c In reality, if the initial height is greater than about 0.8 m, the ball bounces back to less than 75% of its initial height. Suggest why.

2 The graph of figure 7.40 shows how the extension of a rubber band changes when it is stretched and released. How much heat energy is generated each time that the band is stretched and released?

3 Two identical balls with mass m approach each other with the same speed u along the x-axis. They have an elastic head-on collision.

a Write down equations relating the initial and final momenta of the balls.

b Write down equations relating the initial and final energies of the balls.

c Show that the balls move apart with the same speed u.

d The experiment is repeated with two balls which stick to each other. How much heat energy is generated in the collision?

4 The device shown in figure 7.41 is sometimes called a Newton's cradle. The two balls are suspended a distance l below a rigid support. One ball is moved a distance d to one side and released from rest. It collides with the other ball which is flung a distance d' to the other side before it starts to swing back.

a Describe and explain what will happen if the two balls have the same mass.

b With the help of the triangle drawn in figure 7.41, show that the vertical displacement h of a ball displaced sideways by a distance d is given by $h = d^2/2l$ if h is small enough.

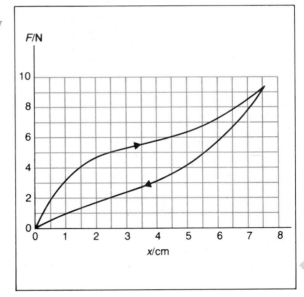

Figure 7.40

Figure 7.41

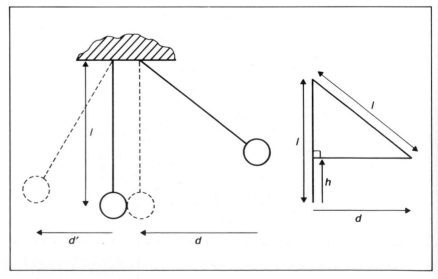

c How are d and d' related if the target ball is much heavier than the other ball?

d What if the target ball is much lighter than the other ball?

5 A yo-yo is illustrated in figure 7.42. Delphine thinks that yo-yos defy the Principle of Energy Conservation. 'When I let go of the yo-yo it takes two seconds to get almost back up to where it started from, so I believe that, apart from some heat energy, it ends up with the same amount of gravitational energy. However, it falls down half a metre, then comes back up again, so its average speed must be 0.5 m s^{-1}. Of course, it is accelerating, so its speed at the bottom must be twice this, 1 m s^{-1}. But $v^2 = 2gh$ says that its speed at the bottom should be at least three times this. My yo-yo loses total energy on the way down and regains it on the way up again!'

Explain to Delphine where she has gone wrong.

Figure 7.42

Figure 7.43

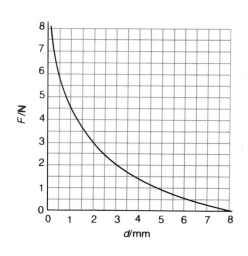

6 The dominant frictional force on a fast-moving vehicle is wind resistance which will be proportional to the velocity squared multiplied by the cross-sectional area. A car engine has a maximum power which can be made roughly independent of its speed with a gearbox.

a Explain why a car going up a hill has a lower top speed than a car going on the flat.

b Explain why a lorry can have the same top speed as a car on a level road, but has a much smaller top speed going up a hill. (Assume that a lorry is simply a larger version of a car, with the same density.)

7 A small rubber ball is placed on a much larger one. The combination is dropped from rest 0.5 m above a hard smooth surface. The small ball is observed to rise up to 4.5 m after the bounce. Does this mean that energy is *not* conserved? Suggest reasons why the small ball ends up with more energy than it started with.

8 Petrol has an energy content of about 5.0×10^7 J kg^{-1} and a density of 700 kg m^{-3}. That energy is converted to heat energy when the petrol is burnt. A typical domestic car going at 30 m s^{-1} has a force of 1.1 kN acting against it from wind resistance and uses up petrol at a rate of 9.0×10^{-4} m^3 for every 5.0 km travelled.

a Calculate the work done by the engine for the car to travel 1.0 km.

b Calculate the energy input to the engine during that time.

c Calculate the efficiency of the car engine.

d Explain why it is true that *all* of the heat energy generated when the petrol is burnt in the engine eventually ends up as heat energy somewhere else.

9 The graph of figure 7.43 shows how the force between two magnets depends on their separation.

a Assuming that the **magnetic potential energy** is zero when the two magnets are far apart, work out the energy when the two magnets are 2.0 mm apart.

b By working out the energy at a number of separations, draw a graph to show how the magnetic energy depends on separation.

10 Gamma rays can convert some of their energy into matter by a process called **pair production**. In a collision with a nucleus, there is a possibility that a gamma ray may disappear and be replaced by a pair of particles: an electron and a positron. These have the same mass (9.1×10^{-31} kg) but opposite charge (the positron is positive). Gamma rays from zinc-65 have energies of 1.12 MeV, where 1 eV = 1.6×10^{-19} J. If the energy needed to make a mass m is mc^2, work out how much kinetic energy each particle has after the gamma ray disappears. Estimate the velocity of the particles. ($c = 3.0 \times 10^8$ m s^{-1}.)

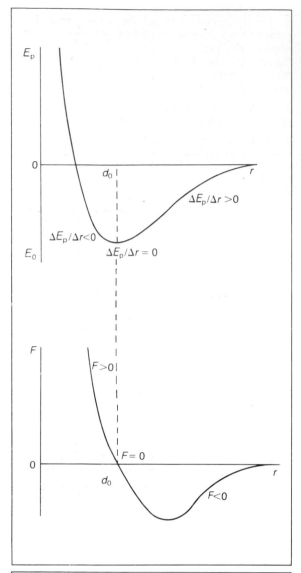

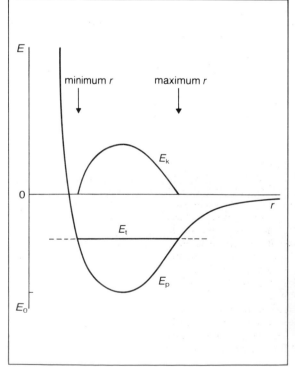

HEAT ENERGY

At first glance, heat energy seems to be just a book-keeping exercise to make sure that total energy is always conserved. If an isolated object appears to lose energy, then some change in heat energy is inferred to keep the total energy constant. In fact, having the right amount of heat energy is crucial to your personal comfort, so it is very real. If you have too little or too much, you die. Your most pressing need in everyday life is to ensure that your heat energy fluctuates by less than 1%. Clothes, food and iced drinks are all involved in keeping your body temperature just right for the chemical processes which keep you alive.

Heat energy in solids

The heat energy of a solid is the kinetic and potential energy of its atoms. This is why it is often called **internal energy**. Since the motion and position of individual atoms cannot be monitored directly in a solid, heat energy has to be measured in terms of macroscopic properties such as size.

Figure 7.44 How the force and potential energy of an atom depend on its separation from another atom

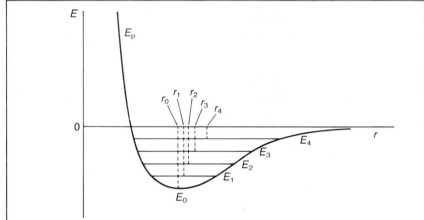

Energy and single atoms

Figure 7.44 is the typical force–separation graph for an atom placed near to another atom. We can use it to build a graph which shows how the potential energy of the atom depends on its position (figure 7.44) with the help of the formula $\Delta E_p = -F\Delta r$, assuming that E_p is zero when r is infinite. Don't worry about the energy being negative, it simply indicates an attractive force.

The minimum potential energy is $-E_0$ and it occurs when $r = d_0$, the equilibrium separation of the atoms. If the total energy of the atom is $-E_0$, then the kinetic energy must be zero and the atom must stay at d_0. However, if the total energy is greater than $-E_0$ (as shown in figure 7.45) then the atom has a range of values of r for which it has kinetic energy. The atom can move to any value of r for which E_k is not zero. It is therefore able to move freely about in the region of the graph for which E_p is less than E_t i.e. E_k is positive. (Kinetic energy cannot be negative; think about it.)

If you study figure 7.46 it should be obvious that the average position of the atom moves to the right as its total energy is increased. A greater total energy means a greater range of movement for the atom, but the asymmetry of the graph also means a greater range above d_0 than below it.

Figure 7.46 The mean separation of the atoms increases as their energy is increased

Figure 7.45 The atom's separation is limited to the region where the kinetic energy is not negative

Thermal expansion

A solid, of course, contains many atoms which interact with each other. If the solid has heat energy, then we would expect each of those atoms to be moving, i.e. to have kinetic energy. The potential energy of each atom in the solid is going to depend on its distance from its neighbours. This distance will be changing all the time, so we cannot think about each atom sitting in a fixed **potential well** like the one shown in figure 7.47. (That would predict *no* expansion on increasing heat energy!) Instead, it is more profitable to turn to a ball-and-spring model of the whole solid and think of all the atoms at once.

Figure 7.44 should remind you that the attractive force between atoms gets weaker as they move apart. So we must remember that the springs connecting the balls of our model get weaker as they are stretched and stronger as they are compressed. A little thought should convince you that such a ball-and-spring structure must get larger as the average kinetic energy of the balls is increased. The graph of figure 7.48 shows the percentage change of length of some metals at various temperatures below their melting points. Note that the curves are not linear, do not have the same shape as each other and that the total expansion before melting is only a few per cent.

Expansivity

It is common practice to quote the **linear expansivity** of a substance as a measure of how much the length of a bar changes for a given change of temperature. As the graph of figure 7.48 shows, the value of the expansivity (the slope of the curve) will be a function of temperature, generally getting larger as the temperature rises.

$$\frac{\Delta l}{l} = \alpha \Delta T$$

$\Delta l/l$ is the fractional change of length of the bar

α is the expansivity of the bar (K^{-1})

ΔT is the temperature change of the bar (K)

Of course, when the temperature of an object increases, every dimension is going to expand, increasing its volume. So the volume expansivity is often a more useful quantity to know about, especially if you are dealing with a liquid or a gas. The volume expansivity is three times the linear expansivity. To see why, consider the object featured in figure 7.49. When its temperature is increased by ΔT, each of its dimensions will get larger (see Appendix B about the expansion for $\Delta V/V$).

$$V = w \times d \times h$$

$$\therefore \quad \frac{\Delta V}{V} = \frac{\Delta w}{w} + \frac{\Delta d}{d} + \frac{\Delta h}{h}$$

$$\therefore \quad \frac{\Delta V}{V} = \alpha \Delta T + \alpha \Delta T + \alpha \Delta T = 3\alpha \Delta T$$

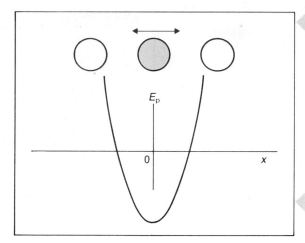

Figure 7.47 Potential well for an atom sitting between two other atoms

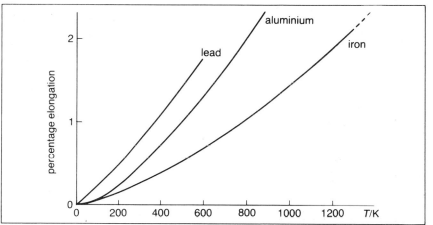

Figure 7.48 The percentage elongation of some metals as a function of temperature

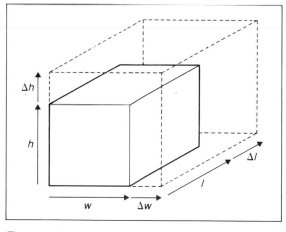

Figure 7.49 Thermal expansion of an object

Temperature

For most people, temperature is what a thermometer measures. A thermometer is just an instrument which can quantify our sensations of hot, warm and cold. So any device which has a property which changes in a measurable way as it is moved from a hot environment to a cold one is, in principle, a thermometer. It will come as no surprise to you that for temperature to be a useful quantity in physics it has to be very carefully defined. Unfortunately, the most useful definition is a very abstract one, so we will approach temperature from a historical point of view. The journey will be worth it, because an understanding of temperature is the key to measuring heat energy and understanding why it flows from one object to another.

Fixed points

In 1742, Anders Celsius proposed a scale of temperature based on the melting and boiling points of water. It was eventually decided quite arbitrarily but conveniently, that water melted at 0°C and boiled at 100°C. These are the **fixed points** of the scale. (Of course, very strict conditions as to the purity of the water and its pressure were specified so that the fixed points were reproducible all over the world.) Celsius also had to specify the procedure by which a thermometer was to be calibrated with the fixed points.

Suppose that you have an uncalibrated mercury-in-glass thermometer. It effectively measures the volume of a blob of mercury to a high precision by making it expand up a very narrow glass tube. The calibration procedure is illustrated in figure 7.50. The thermometer is placed in melting ice until the mercury stops shrinking — the position of the end of the mercury in the tube is marked as 0°C. The thermometer is then transferred to boiling water and the 100°C mark made opposite the end of the mercury column when it has stopped expanding. The region along the tube between the marks is then divided into a hundred equal intervals, each of which corresponds to a temperature change of 1°C. Finally, the region above and below the marks can be engraved with degree markings. The procedure effectively assumes that the expansion of mercury is proportional to its temperature increase.

Unfortunately, although the procedure guarantees that all mercury-in-glass thermometers agree with each other, it cannot guarantee that mercury-in-glass thermometers agree with other types of thermometer. *Any* property of an object which appears to change with temperature can be used to make a thermometer. For example, the changing radius of curvature of a bimetallic strip is the basis of a common domestic thermometer (figure 7.51). The two types of thermometer will only agree exactly at the two fixed points, as there is no reason why mercury should expand in the same way as iron or brass.

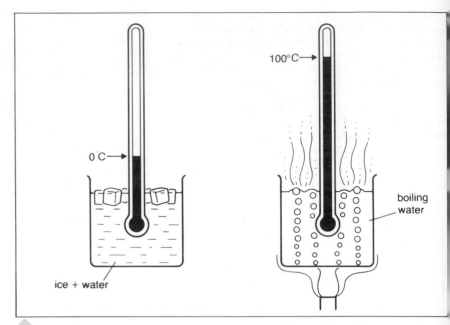

Figure 7.50 The calibration procedure for a thermometer according to the Celsius temperature scale

Figure 7.51 A bimetallic strip thermometer: the spiral loosens or tightens as its temperature is changed

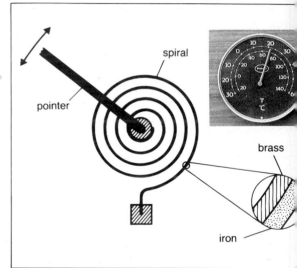

Figure 7.52 Basic features of a constant volume gas thermometer

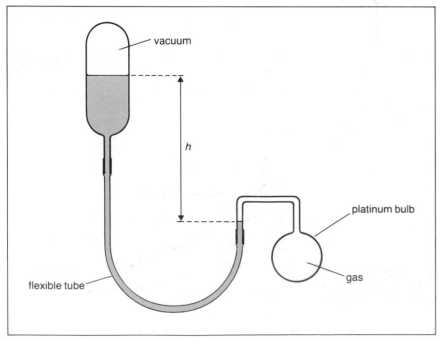

Gas thermometers

The messy procedure outlined above for specifying a quantity is called an **operational definition**. Ultimately, it means that temperature is simply what a particular make of thermometer measures. This severely limits its usefulness in theoretical physics! In an attempt to put temperature on a more sound physical basis Lord Kelvin proposed (in 1854) a different temperature scale based on a single, arbitrarily chosen fixed point and the use of a **constant volume gas thermometer**. Although it fell on deaf ears at the time, his proposal was eventually adopted by international agreement in 1954.

A gas thermometer is shown in figure 7.52. The pressure of some helium gas in the platinum bulb is used to balance a column of mercury. The bulb is immersed in the liquid whose temperature is to be measured. After the helium has stopped changing volume, the mercury reservoir is adjusted up and down until the helium has a standard volume. The pressure of the gas can be calculated from the hydrostatic pressure formula $P = \rho g h$, where h is the vertical distance between the two mercury surfaces.

The Kelvin scale effectively assumes that the pressure P is proportional to the temperature T measured in kelvins (figure 7.53). The thermometer is calibrated by immersing the bulb in water which is in equilibrium with its own solid and gas — this can only happen at one temperature. The temperature of this **triple point** has been conveniently set at 273.16 K. This guarantees that a temperature interval of 1°C is exactly the same as an interval of 1 K, and that 0°C is 273.15 K.

$$P = CT \quad \therefore \quad \frac{P_T}{T} = C = \frac{P_{tp}}{273.16}$$

$$\therefore T = 273.16 \times \frac{P_T}{P_{tp}}$$

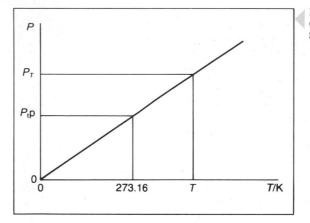

Figure 7.53 Calibration curve for a constant volume gas thermometer

A PRACTICAL TEMPERATURE SCALE

Although a gas thermometer is essentially very simple in construction, it needs a lot of painstaking attention to detail to make accurate measurements with it. Corrections have to be made for the thermal expansion of the bulb, the gas in the thin tube between the mercury and the bulb, the variation of density of mercury with temperature, etc. Gas thermometers are therefore only used in standards laboratories to measure the melting and boiling points of pure substances. These can then be used as secondary standards to calibrate different types of mechanical or electrical thermometers which are more convenient for everyday use. Some of these standard temperatures are shown in table 1.

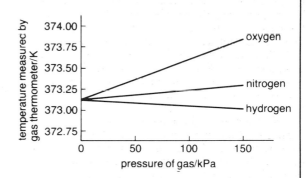

Figure 7.54 All gas thermometers agree on the temperature of condensing steam provided that their gas pressure is low enough

Table 1

Substance	Temperature/K
triple point of hydrogen	13.81
triple point of oxygen	54.36
triple point of water	273.16
freezing point of tin	505.12
freezing point of zinc	692.73
freezing point of silver	1235.08
freezing point of gold	1337.58

An **operational definition** of temperature specifies the use of a particular type of thermometer. Gas thermometers are chosen for defining temperature because they offer a scale which is *not* operationally defined. Although the temperature measured by a gas thermometer does depend on the type of gas used and its pressure, all gas thermometers are found to agree with each other in the limit of zero gas pressure. The graph of figure 7.54 shows this quite clearly.

THERMODYNAMIC TEMPERATURE ▶▶ 30

The temperature of an object is a measure of how its internal energy is shared among its atoms. In chapter 30 you will find out how energy is exchanged between atoms on a random basis, leading to the famous Boltzmann formula.

> $n(E) = A \exp[-E/kT]$
>
> $n(E)$ is the average number of atoms having energy E
>
> A is a constant
>
> E is the energy of the atom (J)
>
> k is Boltzmann's constant (1.38 10^{-23} J K^{-1})
>
> T is the temperature of the object (K)

Figure 7.55 shows the distribution of energy among atoms in solids at low, medium and high temperatures. Although the most likely value of the energy per atom is going to be zero regardless of the temperature, the average energy of the atoms is proportional to the temperature.

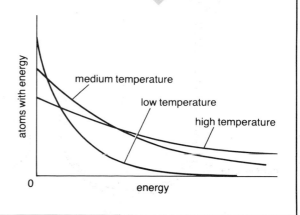

Figure 7.55 The distribution of energy among the atoms of an object at three temperatures

Specific heat capacity

Work done on an object can raise its temperature. (This can be used to light fires by rubbing sticks together (figure 7.56).) This section will explain the experimental approach to linking heat energy with temperature change.

Early experiments

In 1798 Count Rumford performed the first conclusive experiment which demonstrated that heat energy appeared when work was done on an object. He was Bavaria's Minister of War at the time. One of his tasks was to supervise the manufacture of ammunition and cannon. The latter were made by boring large holes into cast brass, using horses as the energy source to drive the boring tool (figure 7.57). Rumford observed that copious quantities of heat energy were produced in the process. For example, he surrounded one cannon with water and found that a single horse turning a blunt boring tool could do enough work to raise 12 kg of water from 0°C to 100°C in $2\frac{1}{2}$ hours, without apparently changing the brass. He concluded from his experiments that the amount of heat energy produced was proportional to the work done by the horse.

Figure 7.56 Using friction to generate fire

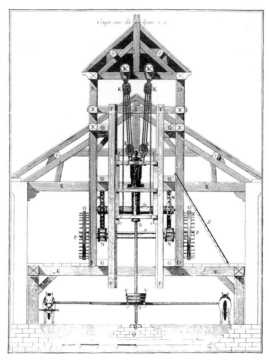

Figure 7.57 A horse-driven cannon borer

Figure 7.58 As the weights fall, work is done on the water by the paddles churning it up

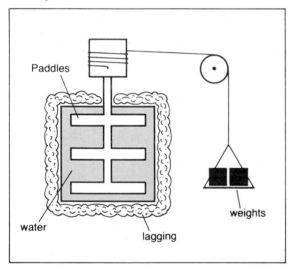

Between 1843 and 1850 James Joule performed a number of experiments to find out how much work had to be done on a fixed mass of water to raise its temperature by 1°C. Figure 7.58 illustrates one of his pieces of apparatus — the work done by the falling weights was converted to heat energy in the water by churning it with paddles. He found that about 4200 J of work, regardless of how it was done, was sufficient to raise the temperature of 1 kg of water by 1 °C.

From the earliest experiments it was obvious that the heat energy ΔQ generated by the work was linked to the temperature change ΔT by an equation of this form.

$\Delta Q = mc\Delta T$

ΔQ is the heat energy given to an object (J)

m is the mass of the object (kg)

c is the specific heat capacity of the object ($J\ kg^{-1}\ K^{-1}$)

ΔT is the temperature rise of the object (K)

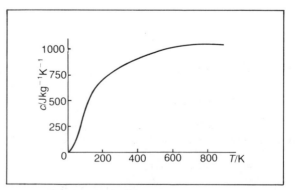

Figure 7.59 Variation of specific heat capacity with temperature for aluminium

The temperature rise of an object was found to be more or less proportional to the heat energy delivered to it. The value of the **specific heat capacity** c varies from one substance to another. It is the heat energy needed to raise the temperature of 1 kg of the substance by 1 K. However, the value of c is not independent of temperature, as figure 7.59 shows. Nevertheless, the variation of c with T is sufficiently gentle for $\Delta Q = mc\Delta T$ to be precise enough for most applications.

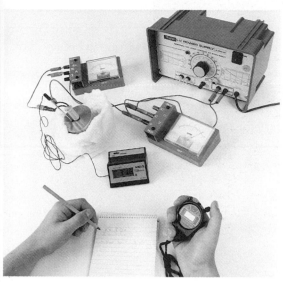

Figure 7.60 Apparatus for measuring the specific heat capacity of aluminium: the lagging around the aluminium block has been partially removed so that you can see the heating element and temperature probe

MASS DEPENDENCE !

The link between heat energy, mass and temperature rise can be deduced by considering a thought experiment. Imagine giving two identical objects of mass m and initial temperature T the same amount of heat energy ΔQ. Both objects will have the same temperature rise ΔT. They are then gently coalesced to form a single object of mass $2m$ and temperature $T + \Delta T$. So an otherwise identical object of mass $2m$ needs an energy of $2\Delta Q$ to raise its temperature by ΔT; ΔQ is proportional to m for a given substance and temperature rise.

ELECTRICAL WORK ▶▶ 24

The use of electricity to deliver known amounts of energy is no happy accident of nature. The size of the volt has been set by international agreement so that $P = VI$ is exactly true. The amplitude of the voltage generated by the apparatus shown in figure 7.61 can then be accurately predicted from the known geometry, the angular velocity of the coil ω, and the current I flowing in the solenoid which surrounds it:

Figure 7.61 Generating a precisely known voltage from a known current in a solenoid

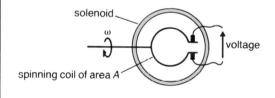

$V = V_0 \times \cos\omega t$

where $V_0 = AB\omega$ and $B = 4\pi \times 10^{-7} \times NI$.

This signal can be used to calibrate a secondary standard voltmeter. Of course, this method of fixing the size of a volt without recourse to a method involving mechanical work relies heavily on a firm understanding of electromagnetism, something which did not exist in Joule's time!

Modern methods

In order to make an accurate measurement of the specific heat capacity of an object, a number of quantities have to be known. A known amount of heat energy has to be generated, the consequent temperature rise has to be measured and the mass of the object must be found.

The most convenient way of delivering a known amount of heat energy is to use an electrical heater. The power of an electrical heater is given by the formula $P = VI$, where V and I are measured with a voltmeter and an ammeter as shown in figure 7.60. The initial temperature T of the object is measured with a thermometer: electronic ones combine precision with convenience. Then the heater is switched on for a time t. After the heater has been switched off, the final temperature $T + \Delta T$ is noted.

Table 7.2 contains some data from a real experiment to find the value of c for aluminium at room temperature.

Table 7.2

mass of aluminium cylinder	m	1.023 kg
initial temperature	T	19.3°C
final temperature	$T + \Delta T$	27.2°C
heater voltage	V	12.0 V
heater current	I	4.05 A
heating time	t	180 s

The first step is to calculate the heat energy delivered to the block.

$E = ?$

$P = VI = 12.0 \times 4.05 = 48.6$ W

$t = 180$ s

$P = \dfrac{E}{t}$

$\therefore 48.6 = \dfrac{E}{180}$

$\therefore E = 180 \times 48.6$

$\therefore E = 8748$ J

Then a value for the specific heat capacity can be calculated.

$\Delta Q = 8748$ J

$m = 1.023$ kg

$c = ?$

$\Delta T = 27.2 - 19.3 = 7.9$ K

$\Delta Q = mc\Delta T$

$\therefore 8748 = 1.023 \times c \times 7.9$

$\therefore c = \dfrac{8748}{1.023 \times 7.9}$

$\therefore c = 1.08 \times 10^3$ J kg^{-1} K^{-1}

Heat energy loss

Our result for the specific heat capacity of aluminium is only approximate. As soon as the temperature of an object is raised above that of its surroundings, heat energy leaks out of it. So we must expect that some of the heat energy given to the block escaped to its surroundings, reducing the final temperature.

Of course, it makes sense to **thermally isolate** the block to reduce this heat energy loss to a minimum. Contact between the block and its surroundings can be minimised by supporting it on points (reducing conduction) and wrapping it round with a light fluffy material (reducing convection). Nevertheless, as the graph of figure 7.62 shows, the temperature of the block will still drop when the heater is switched off, showing that heat energy is escaping. By measuring the temperature drop δT in time t halfway down the cooling curve, we can estimate the total heat energy lost from the block during heating. Reading off the cooling curve of figure 7.62, δT is 1.1°C.

$\Delta Q = ?$

$m = 1.023$ kg

$c = 1.08 \times 10^3$ J kg^{-1} K^{-1}

$\Delta T = 1.1$ K

$\Delta Q = mc\Delta T \quad \therefore \Delta Q = 1.023 \times 1.08 \times 10^3 \times 1.1$

$\therefore \Delta Q = 1.22 \times 10^3$ J

So the actual heat energy delivered to the block was therefore $8748 - 1220 \approx 7530$ J. This can be used to calculate a better value for c.

$\Delta Q = 7530$ J

$m = 1.023$ kg

$c = ?$

$\Delta T = 7.9$ K

$\Delta Q = mc\Delta T$

$\therefore 7530 = 1.023 \times c \times 7.9$

$\therefore c = \dfrac{7530}{1.023 \times 7.9}$

$\therefore c = 932$ J kg^{-1} K^{-1}

Heat capacity

There is one final major source of error in our experiment to measure c for aluminium. Some of the heat energy generated by the heater has to go into the heater and thermometer to keep them at the same temperature as the block. The **heat capacity** (joules per kelvin) of these two items will clearly depend on their mass, so it pays to keep them as small as possible compared with the rest of the block. The effect of the heater and thermometer can be modelled by including an extra term in the heat energy formula.

$$\Delta Q = H\Delta T + mc\Delta T \qquad \textbf{(7.18)}$$

ΔQ is the heat energy generated (corrected for heat energy loss) and $H\Delta T$ is the heat energy given to the thermometer and heater. The effect of this second term can be eliminated by repeating the experiment with a block of different mass m'.

$$\Delta Q' = H\Delta T + m'c\Delta T \qquad \textbf{(7.19)}$$

The heat energy delivered $\Delta Q'$ has to be enough to give the same temperature rise as before. The unknown heat capacity can therefore be eliminated from equations (7.18) and (7.19).

$$H\Delta T = \Delta Q - mc\Delta T = \Delta Q' - m'c\Delta T$$

$$\therefore \Delta Q - \Delta Q' = (m - m')c\Delta T \qquad \textbf{(7.20)}$$

You may be unhappy that the heat loss was calculated with the help of the original, faulty value for c. Of course, you can go back and make a better estimate of the heat loss by using the new value of c; it turns out to be 1049 J. This can then, in turn, be used to calculate a new value for c. You can easily check for yourself that it gives 953 J kg^{-1} K^{-1}, a change of only 2%. This has to be compared with the precision with which δT can be measured ($\approx$10%) to decide if the bother of making the correction is worthwhile.

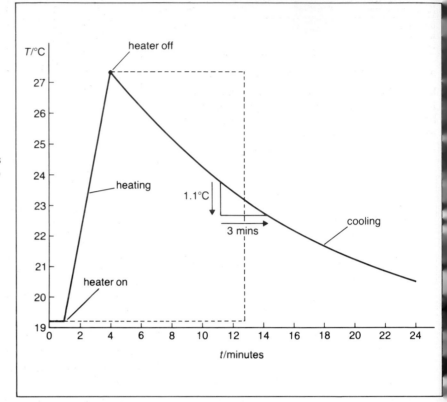

Figure 7.62 Cooling curve for the aluminium block

This technique is very widely used in physics experiments. You do the same experiment with different values of the variables which you *can* measure in order to eliminate the effect of the variables which you *cannot* measure.

OBJECTIVES

After studying this section you should be able to do the following.

Explain why a solid expands when it is given heat energy.

Quote and use the formula $\Delta l/l = \alpha\Delta T$.

Describe how to calibrate a thermometer on the Celsius temperature scale.

Explain the disadvantages of an operational definition of temperature.

Describe the use of a gas thermometer to define the Kelvin temperature scale.

Quote and use the formula $\Delta Q = mc\Delta T$.

Describe a method of measuring the specific heat capacity of a solid.

Explain how to take account of heat energy loss in heat measurements.

QUESTIONS

1 Figure 7.63 shows a simple **thermocouple**. The junction of the two different metals (copper and constantan) generates a voltage which depends on the difference in temperature between the junction and the voltmeter. The voltmeter reading for different junction conditions is shown in table 7.3; the meter is kept at 20°C throughout.

Table 7.3

Junction condition	Voltage/mV
melting ice	−0.80
human armpit	+0.64
boiling water	+3.20

a Calculate the temperature of the human armpit.

b Calculate the reading of the voltmeter when the junction is placed in melting tin (+232°C) and boiling nitrogen (−210°C). What are you assuming to work out the answers?

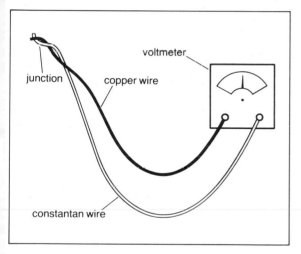

c State at least three advantages that a thermocouple has over a mercury-in-glass thermometer.

2 The platinum resistance thermometer is widely used as a secondary standard thermometer between 14 K and 630 K. Its resistance can, as a first approximation, be assumed to be proportional to its temperature in kelvins over this range. Table 7.4 gives data for the resistance of a copper wire at various temperatures measured by a platinum resistance thermometer.

Table 7.4

Temperature/K	Resistance/Ω
40	0.1
80	2.9
160	7.7
273	15.5
373	23.8

a Plot a graph to show how the resistance of copper varies with temperature.

b A pupil erroneously assumes that the resistance of copper is proportional to its temperature in kelvins. He observes that a copper wire has a resistance of 15.5 Ω in melting ice (273 K). Use the graph you have drawn to measure the temperature that his thermometer will give for boiling water.

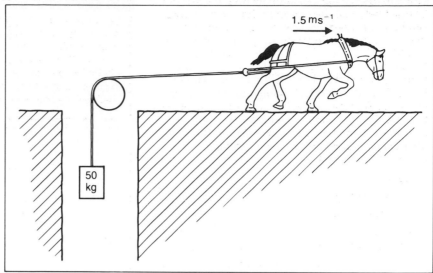

Figure 7.64

Figure 7.63

c Why is the temperature measured by the platinum resistance thermometer considered to be more correct than that measured by the copper resistance thermometer?

3 You are going to estimate a value for the specific heat capacity of water which Count Rumford could have obtained. James Watt estimated the power output of a horse by making one raise a 50 kg load up a well as shown in figure 7.64. He observed that the horse was able to move at a steady speed of 1.5 m s⁻¹.

a Show that the power of an object moving against a force with a steady speed = force×velocity.

b Estimate how much heat energy was generated in the 2½ hours of Rumford's experiment.

c What would Rumford have calculated for the specific heat capacity of water?

d Show that his answer would have to be too high.

4 Legend has it that James Joule measured the temperature difference between water at the top of a waterfall and water at the bottom whilst on honeymoon in Switzerland.

a If the specific heat capacity of water is 4200 J kg⁻¹ K⁻¹, estimate the vertical drop of the waterfall required for a temperature difference of 0.1 K between the top and bottom.

b Rubber has a specific heat capacity of 1380 J kg⁻¹ K⁻¹ and density of 1150 kg m⁻³. A solid rubber ball of radius 2.5 cm is thrown to the ground with an initial speed of 15 m s⁻¹. Estimate how much its temperature will have changed after it has stopped bouncing? What assumptions are you making?

5 A shower water heater contains an electric heating element which raises the temperature of the shower water from 10°C to 40°C as it passes through the heater. c = 4 200 J kg⁻¹ K⁻¹.

a If the maximum power of a domestic electric heater is 3.0 kW, calculate the maximum rate at which the shower heater can deliver hot water; quote your answer in kg s⁻¹.

b The density of water is 1000 kg m^{-3}. If a bath needs 0.25 m^3 of water, calculate how long it would take for the shower heater to run a bath; quote your answer in hours.

c Normally it takes less than five minutes to run a bath. How is this arranged if the water heater cannot have a power of more than 3.0 kW?

6 Newton discovered that the rate at which an object loses heat energy to its surroundings is roughly proportional to the difference of its temperature from that of its surroundings. Furthermore, the rate of loss of heat energy is proportional to the surface area of the object. These facts can be used to explain why mice may die of exposure on a frosty night but elephants will not. Model a lightly clothed human being as a sphere of radius 0.25 m, density 1.0×10^3 kg m^{-3}, temperature 36°C and specific heat capacity 4.0×10^3 J kg^{-1} K^{-1} which loses heat energy at a rate of 7.0 MJ per 24 hours in surroundings at 18°C.

a Calculate the rate at which she loses heat energy through her surface. Give your answer in W.

b Suppose that she stopped generating heat energy on a frosty night when the surroundings were at 0°C. How long would it be before her temperature dropped to 33°C?

c An elephant is made of the same material as a human being, but is about four times larger. Calculate the rate at which an elephant will lose heat energy through its surface on a frosty night.

d If an elephant stops generating heat energy on a frosty night, how long does it take for its temperature to drop to 33°C?

e Repeat part (d) for a mouse.

7 Figure 7.65 shows a piece of apparatus widely used in schools to obtain a value of c for copper without using electricity. It is notoriously inaccurate! Work is done on the drum by turning the handle at a constant rate so that the weight W is supported by friction between the cord and the copper drum. Data gleaned from an experiment with this apparatus is shown in table 7.5.

Table 7.5

mass of copper drum	0.284 kg
radius of copper drum	15.5 mm
suspended weight	49.1 N
number of rotations of handle	100
time taken for handle rotating	120 s
initial temperature of copper	20.20 °C
final temperature of copper	24.25 °C

a Calculate a first estimate for the specific heat capacity of copper. It may help to think of the friction between cord and drum as acting at a single point rather than distributed around the drum.

b The graph shown in figure 7.66 shows how the temperature of the block changed with time after the handle had been rotated. Use it to incorporate a cooling correction into your estimate of the specific heat capacity.

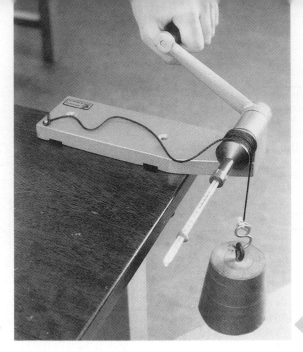

Figure 7.65

Figure 7.66

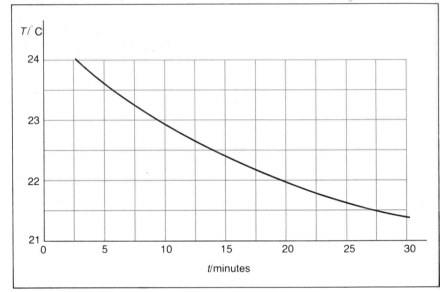

c Explain how you would go about running the experiment to eliminate the effect of the heat capacity of the items (such as the cord and the thermometer) in contact with the copper drum.

8 In 1899 Callendar and Barnes made a very precise measurement of c for water. They used a continuous flow technique to avoid errors due to heat energy loss and the heat capacity of the apparatus. Look at figure 7.67. Water from a constant-pressure tank flows through a glass tube past an electrical heater. The water temperature before and after heating is measured by a pair of thermometers.

a Why is the heating tube surrounded by a vacuum jacket?

b Explain how the flow rate (in kg s^{-1}) of the water going through the tube could be accurately measured.

c Table 7.6 contains data from a couple of experiments performed with the apparatus.

Table 7.6

First experiment

voltmeter reading	12.0 V
ammeter reading	4.2 A
water flow rate	2.10×10^{-3} kg s^{-1}
initial temperature	10.5°C
final temperature	15.9°C

Second experiment

voltmeter reading	8.0 V
ammeter reading	2.8 A
water flow rate	0.86×10^{-3} kg s^{-1}
initial temperature	10.5°C
final temperature	15.9°C

Explain why you would expect both experiments to suffer from the same rate of heat energy loss.

d Use the data to calculate a value of c for water — don't forget to take account of the rate of heat energy loss.

e Callendar and Barnes took no account of the heat capacity of the apparatus in their calculations. Explain why they could safely ignore it.

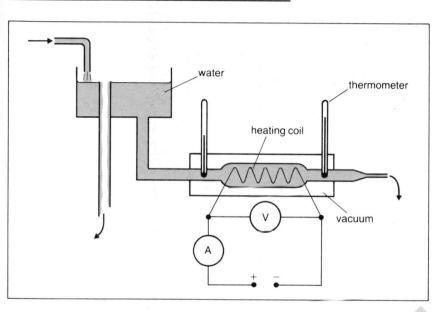

Figure 7.67

G A S E S

8

The concept of an atom is useful because it can explain so much about the behaviour of a solid material. You are about to take the atom concept into new areas, to find out what it can predict for a gas. This chapter relates one of the great success stories of classical physics, the derivation of the Kinetic Theory of Gases.

THE IDEAL GAS EQUATION

In this section we are going to postulate a model for a gas. We are then going to use the principles of momentum and energy conservation to predict how a gas should behave. By the end of the chapter you will see not only how well the model explains the behaviour of real gases, but also how the model can be amended to explain the differences between real gases and ideal ones. Although the Kinetic Theory of Gases is one of the main achievements of nineteenth century physics, it also relies on a twentieth century understanding of temperature and quantum mechanics.

Pressure from collisions

All gases have a number of macroscopic properties which are related to each other. For example, their temperature and pressure are related to their volume. Anyone who has pumped up a bicycle will know that the pressure of a gas increases as its volume is decreased, and hot-air balloons are tangible evidence that gases expand when their temperature is raised. What we want to do is build an expression relating the pressure, volume and temperature of a gas by considering the motion of its atoms. In order to do this we need to make a number of assumptions about the behaviour of the atoms.

- The gas consists of N atoms in a cubical box of side l.
- The atoms will all have the same mass m, but they can have a variety of speeds v.
- The atoms are too small to collide with each other, but they do collide elastically with the walls of the container.
- The atoms have to be moving at right angles to one of the walls.
- The average kinetic energy of the atoms is proportional to the temperature of the gas, i.e. $E_k = 3kT/2$ where k is a constant.

(You may think that some of these assumptions are unrealistic. However, they have been chosen to simplify the algebra. Some of the assumptions will be relaxed later.)

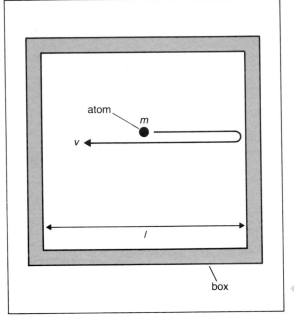

Figure 8.1 A single atom in a box moving back and forth between two walls

Pressure
The pressure on a surface is the force acting at right angles to it per unit area. We want to predict what this will be for a gas.

$$P = \frac{F}{A}$$

P is the pressure on the surface (Pa)

F is the force applied at right angles to the surface (N)

A is the area of the surface (m^2)

Start off by considering a single atom moving at right angles to a pair of walls, as shown in figure 8.1. Each time the atom bounces off the right-hand wall, its momentum will change but its kinetic energy will not. So the momentum changes from $+mv$ to $-mv$ on each bounce, delivering an impulse of $+2mv$ to the wall. The average force on the ball due to these collisions can be worked out with the help of Newton's Second Law, bearing in mind that the atom travels a distance $2l$ between collisions with the right-hand wall.

$$F = \frac{\Delta p}{\Delta t}, \qquad \Delta p = 2mv,$$

$$\Delta t = \frac{2l}{v} \qquad \therefore \ F = \frac{mv^2}{l} \qquad\qquad \text{(8.1)}$$

Of course, there will be a large number of atoms bouncing between the same pair of walls. So the total force on one of the walls will be given by the sum of all the individual forces on it.

$$F = \Sigma \ \frac{mv^2}{l} \qquad \therefore \ F = \frac{m}{l}\Sigma v^2 \qquad \textbf{(8.2)}$$

Because the atoms will be moving at different speeds, v^2 will be different for each one. It will help if we can define an average value for v^2, the **mean square velocity**. We introduce a new term, $<c^2>$.

$$<c^2> = \frac{\text{sum of } v^2 \text{ over all atoms}}{\text{number of atoms}}$$

One third of all the atoms in the box will be moving between a particular pair of walls which face each other.

$$\therefore <c^2> = \frac{\Sigma v^2}{N/3} \quad \therefore \ \Sigma v^2 = \frac{N<c^2>}{3} \qquad \textbf{(8.3)}$$

The pressure on one wall can now be worked out.

$$P = \frac{F}{A} \qquad \therefore \ P = \frac{m}{l}\Sigma v^2 \times \frac{1}{l^2}$$

$$\therefore \ P = \frac{Nm<c^2>}{3l^3} \qquad \textbf{(8.4)}$$

Bearing in mind that l^3 is the volume V of the box, we end up with a very interesting prediction.

$$P = \frac{Nm<c^2>}{3V} \quad \therefore \ PV = \frac{Nm<c^2>}{3} \qquad \textbf{(8.5)}$$

Boyle's Law
In 1660 Robert Boyle published an account of experiments he had performed on air. His apparatus was similar to that shown in figure 8.2. The pressure on the gas trapped in the tube can be altered by moving the mercury reservoir up and down. The length of tube occupied by the gas gives its volume, and the difference in height between the mercury surfaces gives the excess pressure above atmospheric pressure. He had discovered that the product PV remained constant for a fixed mass of gas, provided that its temperature was not allowed to change. This is precisely what equation (8.5) predicts, because $<c^2>$ can only change if the internal energy of the gas is allowed to change. Despite the unrealistic assumptions about the behaviour of atoms in a gas, we appear to have got the right answer!

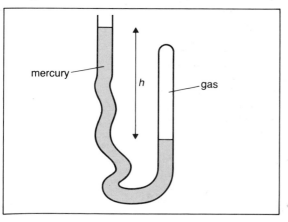

Figure 8.2 Apparatus for verifying Boyle's Law

mercury — h — gas

RELAXING SOME ASSUMPTIONS

Let us relax one assumption and say that each atom can move in any direction in the box. Consider its movement in the x-direction between the two walls in the $y-z$ plane (figure 8.3). On its way between those walls it may bounce off the other walls, but if momentum and kinetic energy are conserved in those collisions, the x-component of its velocity (v_x) will not be changed. So we can insert v_x in place of v in equation (8.2) to find the force on a wall.

Figure 8.3 Each time a particle bounces off a wall, its component of momentum parallel to the wall remains unchanged

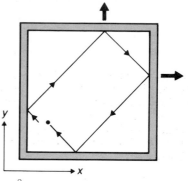

$$F = \frac{m}{l} \Sigma \ v_x^{\ 2} \qquad \therefore \ P = m\Sigma \ \frac{v_x^{\ 2}}{l^3} \qquad (1)$$

The magnitude of the velocity v of an atom will be related to its components v_x, v_y and v_z as follows:

$$v^2 = v_x^{\ 2} + v_y^{\ 2} + v_z^{\ 2} \qquad (2)$$

The motion of the atoms, on average, will be the same in all directions. The next step is to find the mean-square velocity $<c^2>$.

$$<c^2> = <v_x^{\ 2} + v_y^{\ 2} + v_z^{\ 2}>$$

$$\therefore <c^2> = <v_x^{\ 2}> + <v_y^{\ 2}> + <v_z^{\ 2}>$$

$$\therefore <c^2> = 3<v_x^{\ 2}> \quad \therefore <v_x^{\ 2}> = \frac{<c^2>}{3} \qquad (3)$$

If you insert equation (3) into equation (1), you end up with equation (8.5) again.

$$P = m\Sigma \ \frac{v_x^{\ 2}}{l^3} \qquad \therefore \ PV = \frac{mN<c^2>}{3}$$

Figure 8.4 Momentum is always conserved when two particles interact

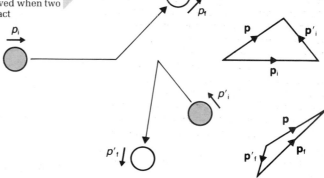

The other unrealistic assumption of our model is that atoms are too small to collide with each other. Clearly then, if Boyle's Law actually works, this cannot be a fundamental requirement of the model. In any collision between two atoms (see figure 8.4), both momentum and kinetic energy are going to be conserved. The short-range forces between the atoms will change their velocities in a complicated fashion during the collision. However, the total momentum in any direction will remain unchanged throughout. If the value of v_x of one atom decreases, that of the other will increase by the same amount. So although the x-component of momentum does not remain with a single atom, it still oscillates back and forth between the walls as if it did so.

You may be experiencing some difficulty in relating the atomic picture of a gas with reality. In everyday life we experience gases as fluids which exert a steady push on surfaces. Daniel Bernoulli was the first person to suggest that the outwards pressure of a gas was due to collisions of particles with the walls. His suggestion came in 1738, well before Newton's Laws of Motion had been formulated, and the atom concept was very revolutionary. It was not until 1850 that James Joule and others persuaded a sceptical scientific community that the Kinetic Theory could convincingly explain the properties of gases.

Root-mean-square velocity
Let's see what our theory predicts for $<c^2>^{\frac{1}{2}}$, the **root-mean-square velocity** of a typical air molecule at room temperature and pressure.

$$PV = \frac{Nm<c^2>}{3} \qquad \therefore \ <c^2> = \frac{3PV}{Nm} \qquad \textbf{(8.6)}$$

The density of the gas will be its total mass divided by its total volume.

$$m = \rho V \qquad \therefore \rho = \frac{Nm}{V} \qquad \textbf{(8.7)}$$

Combining equations (8.6) and (8.7) we get a useful expression for the pressure of the gas in terms of its density.

$$P = \frac{\rho<c^2>}{3}$$

P is the pressure of the gas (Pa)

ρ is the density of the gas (kg m^{-3})

$<c^2>$ is the mean square speed of the atoms (m^2 s^{-2})

Let's calculate the value of $<c^2>^{\frac{1}{2}}$ for the air around you.

$$P = \frac{\rho<c^2>}{3} \qquad \therefore \ <c^2>^{\frac{1}{2}} = \left(\frac{3P}{\rho} \right)^{\frac{1}{2}} \qquad \textbf{(8.8)}$$

The density of air at atmospheric pressure (1.0×10^5 Pa) is about 1.2 kg m^{-3}. Inserting these values into equation (8.8) we find that $<c^2>^{\frac{1}{2}}$ is about 500 m s^{-1}.

This does *not* mean that the average speed of the air molecules around you is 500 m s^{-1}. The average of the velocity squared will be 500^2 or 2.5×10^5 m^2 s^{-2} and the average velocity will be 0 m s^{-1}. Nevertheless, it is useful, if not entirely correct, to think of $<c^2>^{\frac{1}{2}}$ as representing the speed of a typical atom in a gas.

Internal energy

The Kelvin temperature scale is defined by assuming that the pressure of a fixed mass of any gas at constant volume is proportional to its temperature. This can be incorporated into equation (8.5) as follows:

$$PV = \frac{Nm <c^2>}{3} \qquad \therefore \ P = \frac{N}{V} \times \frac{m<c^2>}{3} \qquad \textbf{(8.9)}$$

Let the average kinetic energy of an atom be proportional to the temperature of the gas. (This is our last assumption of the model.)

$$\frac{m<c^2>}{2} = \frac{3kT}{2} \qquad \textbf{(8.10)}$$

The quantity k is called **Boltzmann's constant** (the factor of 3/2 makes the algebra easier later on). The next step is to combine equations (8.9) and (8.10) to eliminate $m<c^2>$.

$$P = \frac{N}{V} \times \frac{m<c^2>}{3} \qquad \therefore \ P = \frac{N}{V} \times \frac{3kT}{3}$$

$$\therefore \ P = \frac{NkT}{V} \qquad \textbf{(8.11)}$$

The kelvin temperature scale assumes that the pressure of a fixed quantity of any gas at constant volume is proportional to its temperature in Kelvins. As you can see from equation (8.11), this is precisely what we predict if we assume that the temperature of a gas is a measure of the average energy of one of its atoms.

Ideal Gas Equation
Equation (8.11) is a remarkably simple statement. It is usually quoted in the form known as the **Ideal Gas Equation**.

$$PV = NkT$$

P is the pressure of the gas on the walls of its container (Pa)

V is the volume of the container (m^3)

N is the number of atoms in the gas

k is Boltzmann's constant ($1.38 \ 10^{-23}$ J K^{-1})

T is the temperature of the gas (K)

Notice that the Ideal Gas Equation requires no details about the type of atom in the gas — the mass of individual atoms does not appear in the equation. So it ought to apply to gases made up of molecules (atoms bound together). This means that a given volume of gas at a set temperature and pressure is predicted to always contain the same number of particles, be they atoms or molecules. The fundamental number commonly used when counting atoms or molecules is the **mole**: 1 mole = 6.02×10^{23}, Avogadro's number L. Let's use this to calculate the **molar volume** of an ideal gas at room temperature and pressure (15°C, 100 kPa).

$P = 100$ kPa $\qquad\qquad PV = NkT$

$V = ?$

$N = 6.02 \times 10^{23}$

$T = 273 + 15 = 288$ K

$\therefore 1.00 \times 10^5 \times V = 6.02 \times 10^{23} \times 1.38 \times 10^{-23} \times 288$

$\therefore V = 0.0239$ m^3

So one mole of *any* gas at 15°C and 100 kPa should have a volume of 0.0239 m^3. Furthermore, it should not matter if the gas is a mixture of different atoms or molecules: it will contain 6.02×10^{23} particles, regardless of their nature. The idea that equal volumes of all gases at a given temperature and pressure contain the same number of particles is known as **Avogadro's hypothesis**: it is much used in chemistry. (You can check for yourself that the molar volume is 0.0224 m^3 at **standard** temperature and pressure (0°C, 101 kPa).)

In practice, atoms are counted by finding their mass and dividing it by their molar mass to find the number of moles. So it is often useful to consider the number of moles n rather than the number of atoms N.

$$N = nL \qquad \therefore PV = nLkT$$
$$\therefore PV = nRT \quad \text{where } R = Lk \quad \textbf{(8.12)}$$

R is called the **universal gas constant** and has the value $8.31 \text{ J mol}^{-1} \text{ K}^{-1}$. L, of course, is Avogadro's number, 6.02×10^{23}.

Real gases

Although the Ideal Gas Equation is a very good description of a gas, it is important that you are able to predict the conditions under which it is likely to fail. Remember, we have chosen the simplest model for atoms which gives the right results. That model will need modifying to allow accurate predictions to be made in extreme conditions.

All gases turn into liquids if their temperature goes low enough. Figure 8.5 shows how the volume of nitrogen at atmospheric pressure changes with temperature. A number of different curves are drawn, each for a different mass of gas. Although their slopes are different, they all have the same intercept i.e. 0 K. However, all of the lines drop to nearly zero at 77 K, the boiling point of nitrogen. Different gases have different boiling points at atmospheric pressure, as shown in figure 8.6.

When a gas gets close to liquefying, the attractive forces between its atoms can no longer be neglected. So we should only expect ideal behaviour from a gas whose temperature is well above its boiling point. This becomes clear from figure 8.7 where PV has been plotted against P for a fixed mass of nitrogen at different temperatures. According to Boyle's Law, the graph should be a horizontal line. However, this only happens at high temperatures.

Figure 8.7 also shows how well a real gas obeys the ideal gas equation when its temperature is fixed. For low pressures, PV remains constant as predicted by Boyle's Law, but deviates from this at high pressures. We can estimate the pressure at which this happens by considering the size of each atom d_0. Once Nd_0^3 is not negligible compared with V, you must assume that Boyle's Law is no longer going to be a good description of the gas.

THERMODYNAMIC TEMPERATURE ▶▶ 30

Although the Kelvin temperature scale is defined by means of a constant volume gas thermometer, it is not inevitable that all gases should obey the Ideal Gas Equation. In practice, they only obey it precisely at low pressures and high temperatures. The real reason for stipulating that the mean kinetic energy of a gas particle is $3kT/2$ comes from thermodynamics and quantum mechanics.

Thermodynamics states that the probability $p(E)$ that a particle has energy E in an environment whose temperature is T is given by the Boltzmann equation:

$$p(E) = \frac{\exp(-E/kT)}{\Sigma \exp(-E/kT)} \qquad (1)$$

The summation is taken over all the possible values for the energy. Quantum mechanics states that a particle in a cubical box with sides of length l can only have certain energies, given by this equation:

$$E = \frac{h^2}{8ml^2}(n_x^2 + n_y^2 + n_z^2) \qquad (2)$$

The quantum numbers n_x, n_y and n_z can be any integer except 0. Equations (1) and (2) can be combined to calculate the average energy $<E>$ of a single gas particle.

$$<E> = \Sigma E p(E)$$

It can be shown that:

$$<E> = \frac{3kT}{2} \text{ if } kT \gg \frac{h^2}{8ml^2} \qquad (3)$$

So the ideal gas equation really contains a temperature which is not defined by a gas thermometer.

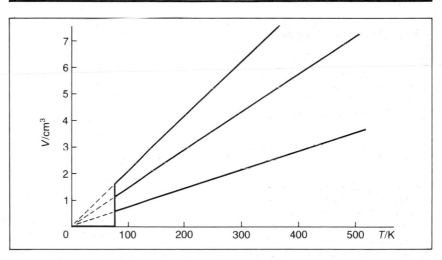

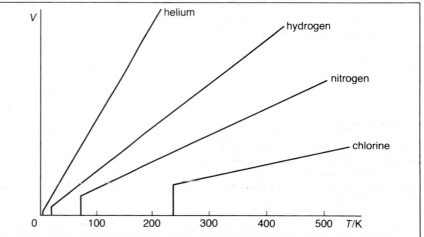

Figure 8.5 The variation of volume with temperature for various amounts of nitrogen at standard atmospheric pressure

Figure 8.6 The variation of volume with temperature for different gases at standard atmospheric pressure

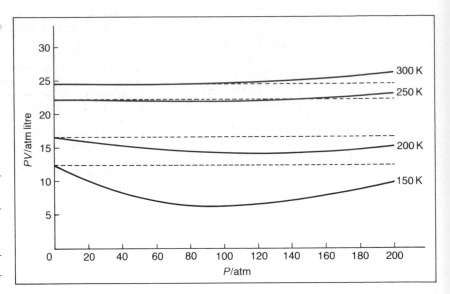

Figure 8.7 *PV* as a function of *P* for one mole of nitrogen at various temperatures. It should be clear that Boyle's Law is a good description of the gas at low pressure and high temperature

OBJECTIVES

After studying this section you should be able to do the following.

State the assumptions used to derive the Ideal Gas Equation.

Show that the pressure of a gas is given by $P = \rho<c^2>/3$ by considering individual atoms in a box.

Explain what $<c^2>^{\frac{1}{2}}$ represents.

State and use the Ideal Gas Equation.

Understand the meaning of the term *mole*.

State and explain how the behaviour of real gases is different from an ideal gas.

QUESTIONS

1 One of the earliest pieces of evidence for the motion of molecules in a gas was the observation of Brownian motion. Smoke particles suspended in air appear to move randomly when viewed with a powerful microscope. The explanation is that the particles have the same temperature as the molecules, so they have the same average kinetic energy as each other.

a Suppose that a smoke particle is about 1 μm across, with a density of about 2×10^3 kg m^{-3}. Calculate its root-mean-square velocity in air at room temperature.

b Explain why the smoke particle will not be seen to move with the velocity calculated in part (a).

c Use the Kinetic Theory of Gases to explain what will happen to the motion of the particle if the air temperature drops.

d If a smoke particle surrounded by a gas displays Brownian motion, why don't you?

2 There is a popular conception that every lungful of air you take contains one molecule of Caesar's dying breath! The data in table 8.1 will allow you to check this for yourself.

Table 8.1

atmospheric pressure/kPa	1.0×10^5
density of air at Earth's surface/kg m^{-3}	1.2
molar mass of air/kg mol^{-1}	0.029
radius of the Earth/km	6400
volume of a typical breath/cm^3	500

a Assuming that the Earth's atmosphere has a constant density, its effective height above the Earth's surface is 9.0 km. Estimate the number of air molecules in the atmosphere.

b Calculate the number of molecules in Caesar's dying breath.

c If those molecules are spread evenly throughout the atmosphere, how many are there in each breath you take?

d 21% of the atmosphere is oxygen. Does this invalidate your calculations?

3 A typical cylinder used for transporting gases in laboratories and hospitals has a length of 140 cm, an internal diameter of 20 cm and is delivered with gas at a pressure of 175 atmospheres and a temperature 20°C. (1 atmosphere = 0.10 MPa.)

a When no more gas will come out of the cylinder, it is said to be empty. Is this true? Estimate how many molecules it contains when it is 'empty'.

b Suppose that the cylinder contains helium at room temperature (20°C). It is used to fill spherical balloons which have a diameter of 40 cm when fully inflated with gas at a pressure of 1.01 atmospheres. How many balloons will the cylinder fill?

c Each cylinder is stamped with the maximum safe pressure. If a cylinder is stamped with 310 atmospheres and contains gas at 145 atmospheres at 20°C, calculate the maximum safe temperature for that cylinder.

4 A typical hot-air balloon has a diameter of 15 m and is approximately spherical. The weight of the fabric, fuel and basket is 1.5 kN, and each passenger weighs 750 N. A hot-air balloon will rise when its average density is less than that of the surrounding air.

a If the density of the air outside the balloon is 1.2 kg m^{-3}, what is the average density of the air inside the balloon when it hovers above the ground with two passengers?

b Explain why the pressure of the hot air inside the balloon is almost the same as the pressure of the air outside.

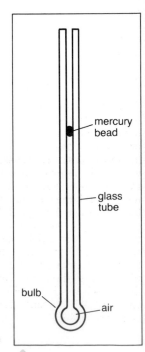

Figure 8.8

c Use the Ideal Gas Equation to show that the density of a gas at constant pressure is inversely proportional to its temperature. If the outside air has a temperature of 10°C, what is the average temperature of the air inside the balloon of part (a).

5 Alexis has built the constant pressure gas thermometer shown in figure 8.8. The air is trapped by a small bead of mercury in a capillary tube of diameter 2.0 mm and length 130 mm; the bulb at its end has an internal radius of 5.0 mm. When she immerses the bulb in melting ice, the top of the bead is 93 mm from the top of the tube. If she can measure the position of the bead with a precision of 1 mm, calculate the precision with which her thermometer will measure temperature. What are the maximum and minimum temperatures that her thermometer will measure? (Ignore the expansivity of glass.) Discuss the main source of error of Alexis' thermometer.

6 Explain carefully how the air in a tyre manages to support the car by colliding with the tyre walls.

7 Figure 8.9 shows a graph of P as a function of V for a fixed mass of gas at constant temperature. Copy the graph and draw curves for

a the same mass of gas at double the (kelvin) temperature,

b half the mass of gas at the same temperature.

8 Michael argues that the weight change of a flask when it is connected to a vacuum pump is *not* the weight of the air which was in the flask. 'When the flask was full of air, only a few of the molecules would have been touching the bottom at any instant. Most of them were flying around in the middle of the flask, not supported by anything. So the real weight of the air in the flask is much greater than its change of weight when the air is pumped out.' Convince Michael that he is wrong by considering a single molecule moving up and down between the bottom and top of a square box, colliding elastically with the walls.

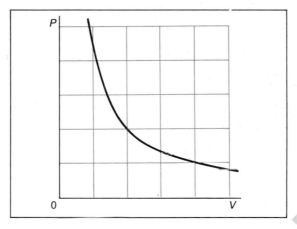

Figure 8.9

DIFFUSION OF GASES

One of the reasons why the Kinetic Theory of Gases had a difficult time being accepted by scientists was the high speed it predicted for gas molecules — about 500 m s⁻¹ at room temperature. After all, it is common knowledge that gases diffuse among each other quite slowly; think how long it takes for perfume from an open bottle to fill the room. Accurate measurements of the speed of gas molecules have only become technically feasible in the last fifty years.

Gas molecule speed

An elegant apparatus for measuring the speed of caesium atoms in a gas is shown in figure 8.10. The experiment was first performed in 1947. Solid caesium in the oven at the left is heated to form caesium gas at a known temperature. Atoms in the gas which 'hit' the hole in the oven pass out of it into the beam chamber. This is kept empty of other molecules by vacuum pumps so that the atoms travel through the rest of the apparatus undisturbed except by gravity and the two screens. Atoms which pass through the horizontal slits in the screens and hit the hot tungsten wire are ionised (lose an electron) and collected by the charged plate behind the wire. The passage of ions between the hot wire and the collector plate is actually a small electric current which, after amplification, can be recorded.

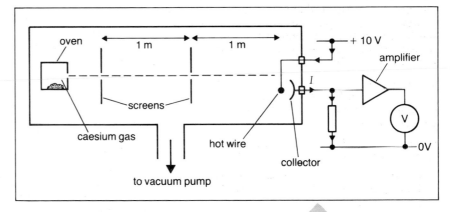

Figure 8.10 Apparatus for measuring the speed of atoms in a gas

Figure 8.11 shows the paths of a number of atoms emerging from the first slit with the same velocity v. Gravity tugs them downwards, so they all have parabolic trajectories. They can only arrive at the hot wire if it is placed a distance s below the slits.

$$s = \frac{gd^2}{v^2} \qquad (8.13)$$

Figure 8.11 Trajectories of some of the atoms through the apparatus

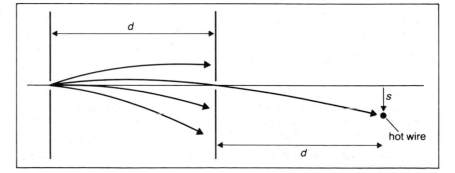

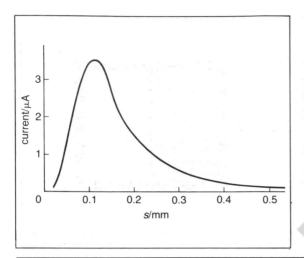

▶▶30

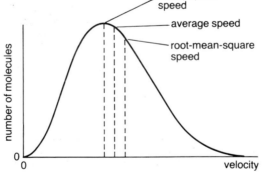

Figure 8.12 Typical results for a gas of caesium atoms

THE VELOCITY DISTRIBUTION

The Boltzmann equation can be used to find the probability that a particular molecule in a gas at temperature T will have an energy E.

$$p(E) = \frac{\exp[-E/kT]}{\Sigma \exp[-E/kT]} \qquad (1)$$

A gas molecule can only have kinetic energy, $E = \frac{1}{2}mv^2$. Taking into account the three-dimensional nature of a gas, it can be shown that the probability that a molecule has a velocity between v and $v + \Delta v$ is given by

$$p(v) = Cv^2 \Delta v \exp[-mv^2/2kT] \qquad (2)$$

where C is a constant. This function is plotted in the graph of figure 8.13. It can be used to find the following quantities.

- The most probable speed $= (2kT/m)^{\frac{1}{2}}$.
- The average speed $= (8kT/\pi m)^{\frac{1}{2}}$.
- The root-mean-square speed $<c^2>^{\frac{1}{2}} = (3kT/m)^{\frac{1}{2}}$.

Figure 8.13 Distribution of particle velocities in an ideal gas

(Question 1 at the end of this section asks you to prove this for yourself.) Furthermore, only atoms with velocities which fit equation (8.13) will be able to get to the hot wire at s. So by changing the value of s we can find out the relative numbers of atoms emerging from the oven at different velocities.

Typical results of this experiment are shown in figure 8.12. Note that there is a distribution of velocities, i.e. the atoms emerge from the oven with a wide range of speeds. Using equation (8.13), you can show that the maximum and minimum speeds recorded are about 500 m s^{-1} and 140 m s^{-1}, with the most likely speed being 320 m s^{-1}.

Diffusion

Consider the thought experiment illustrated in figure 8.14(a). One half of the box contains a gas and the other half contains nothing (a vacuum). What happens when the plug is removed? The answer is obvious. Any atoms which would have collided with the bung carry on moving until they hit the left-hand wall. Thereafter they bounce around the left-hand half of the box until, eventually, they 'hit' the gap and move back to the right-hand half of the box. So although there is an initial flow of atoms from right to left, a **dynamic equilibrium** is swiftly established with atoms going both ways through the gap in equal quantities. This happens when the number density (atoms per cubic metre) is the same in both containers. Since the atoms are moving very fast, this equilibrium is established in a very short time. The graph of figure 8.14(b) shows how the pressure is expected to change with time.

Now suppose that both halves initially contained equal pressures of different gases. What happens when the bung is removed? Well, there is no bulk transfer of gas between the two halves of the box as there is no pressure difference. Nevertheless, the random motion of the molecules in one half of the box guarantees that eventually they will be equally distributed among both halves (figure 8.15). You can see this for yourself if one of the gases is coloured: bromine is a favourite, despite its toxicity.

Figure 8.14 Gases rapidly expand to fill the available volume

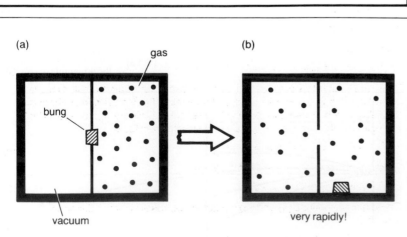

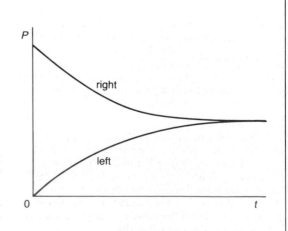

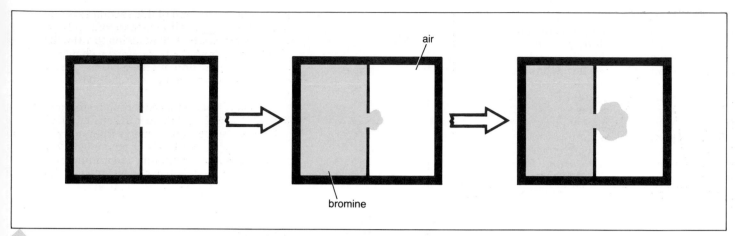

Figure 8.15 Brown bromine gas diffuses very slowly into air

Figure 8.16 A typical random walk of a molecule in a gas

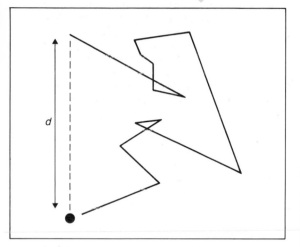

Trajectories

How rapidly will this **diffusion** take place? A single molecule in a gas is not going to travel very far before it collides with another molecule. Each collision is going to change the direction of motion of the molecule in a random fashion, as well as altering its energy. So the trajectory of a molecule through a gas consists of a number of straight line segments of varying lengths and directions, somewhat as shown in figure 8.16. The distance travelled by the molecule depends on the number of collisions it makes and on the average distance it travels between collisions (the **mean free path**).

$d = (n)^{\frac{1}{2}}\lambda$

d is the distance travelled by the molecule (m)

n is the number of collisions with other molecules

λ is the mean free path (m)

Mean free path

The value of the mean free path will depend on three factors: the total number of molecules N, the volume of their container V and the diameter of the molecules d_0. A low density gas will have a large value of λ because the chances of one molecule hitting another will be small. On the other hand, λ is going to be small if the density is high, jamming all of the molecules close together.

RANDOM WALKS

Suppose that a molecule starts off at the origin and makes a random walk of n steps in the x–y plane, as shown in figure 8.17. The final coordinates (x,y) will be given by

$$x = \Sigma\Delta x, \quad y = \Sigma\Delta y \tag{1}$$

Figure 18.17

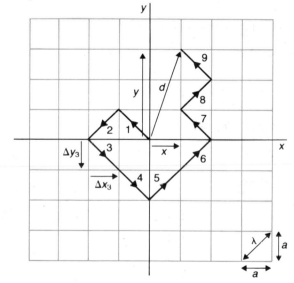

For simplicity, we are going to assume that Δx_n, the displacement in the x-direction during the nth step, was either $+a$ or $-a$, at random. Similarly, Δy_n was $+a$ or $-a$. If the distance travelled after n steps is d, then

$$d^2 = x^2 + y^2 \tag{2}$$

Now, consider x^2.

$$x^2 = (\Sigma\Delta x)^2$$
$$x^2 = (\Delta x_1 + \Delta x_2 + \ldots + \Delta x_n) \times (\Delta x_1 + \Delta x_2 + \ldots + \Delta x_n) \tag{3}$$

When the brackets are multiplied together, two types of term result. Ones like $\Delta x_5 \times \Delta x_5$ will always be $+a^2$, contributing a total of na^2 to the sum. Others like $\Delta x_3 \times \Delta x_6$ which are equally likely to be $+a^2$ or $-a^2$, will add up to zero. (Think about it.) So, if n is large, we get a simple expression for x^2.

$$x^2 = na^2 \quad \therefore d^2 = x^2 + y^2 = 2na^2 \tag{4}$$

However, the mean free path λ is given by

$$\lambda^2 = \Delta x^2 + \Delta y^2 \quad \therefore \lambda^2 = 2a^2 \tag{5}$$

Combining equations (4) and (5) we get an expression for the distance travelled.

$$d^2 = n\lambda^2 \quad \therefore d = (n)^{\frac{1}{2}}\lambda \tag{6}$$

We can obtain an approximate expression for λ as follows. Suppose that we scatter all of the molecules at random throughout the container, but not let them have any kinetic energy. Then take one molecule and let it move through the gas: the result is a bit like a three-dimensional pinball machine. Consider figure 8.18. The molecule is travelling from left to right through the gas. It will collide with any other molecule if their centres get closer than d_0 apart, on the assumption that each molecule behaves like a hard sphere. Let us define the mean free path λ as the distance the molecule has to travel for it to definitely collide with one of the stationary molecules. This means that the gas must have, on average, one molecule in the volume $\pi d_0{}^2\lambda$ (figure 8.19). So the total volume of the gas must be N times $\pi d_0{}^2\lambda$.

$$V = N\pi d_0{}^2\lambda \qquad \therefore \lambda = \frac{V}{N\pi d_0{}^2} \qquad \textbf{(8.14)}$$

$$\lambda = \frac{V}{N\pi d_0{}^2}$$

λ is the mean free path of a single particle (m)

V is the volume of the gas (m^3)

N is the number of particles in the gas

d_0 is the diameter of a single particle (m)

Diffusion rates

So how far will a single molecule travel in a gas? Let's estimate how far an air molecule in the room will travel in five minutes. The first step is to estimate a value for the mean free path. Table 8.2 contains some data we will need.

Table 8.2

diameter of an air molecule	$\approx 4\times10^{-10}$ m
mass of an air molecule	$\approx 5\times10^{-26}$ kg
density of air	≈ 1 kg m^{-3}

$$m = \rho V \quad \therefore \rho = \frac{Nm}{V} \quad \therefore \quad \frac{N}{V} = \frac{\rho}{m} = 2\times10^{25} \text{ m}^{-3}$$

$$\lambda = \frac{V}{N\pi d_0{}^2}$$

$$\therefore \lambda = \frac{1}{2\times10^{25} \times \pi \times 16\times10^{-20}}$$

$$= 1.0\times10^{-7} \text{ m}$$

If we assume, for simplicity, that the molecule's speed is equal to the root-mean-square velocity $<c^2>^{\frac{1}{2}}$, we can work out how many collisions (n) the molecule has in five minutes (300 s). We can assume that $<c^2>^{\frac{1}{2}} = 500$ m s^{-1}, as worked out earlier.

$$n = \frac{<c^2>^{\frac{1}{2}} \times 300}{\lambda} = \frac{500 \times 300}{1.0\times10^{-7}} = 1.5\times10^{12}$$

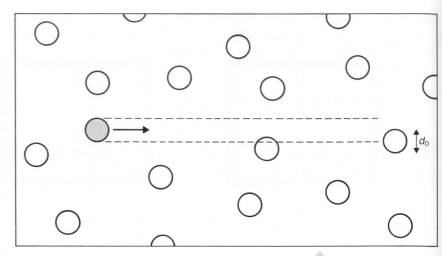

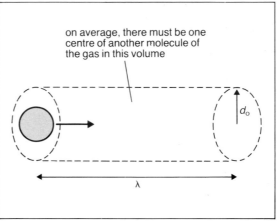

on average, there must be one centre of another molecule of the gas in this volume

Figure 8.18 A single molecule moving through a gas will collide with any other molecule whose centre is less than d_0 from its own

Figure 8.19 The volume swept out by one molecule when it moves through a distance λ

Finally, we can calculate how far, on average, the molecule will have strayed from its starting point.

$$d = (n)^{\frac{1}{2}}\lambda$$

$$\therefore d = (1.5\ 10^{12})^{\frac{1}{2}} \times 1.0\times10^{-7} \simeq 0.1 \text{ m}$$

You can check this prediction for yourself by placing a drop of perfume on the table and screening it from draughts. Your nose should be able to inform you roughly how far the perfume molecules travel in five minutes!

OBJECTIVES

After studying this section you should be able to do the following.

Describe an experiment to measure the distribution of molecular velocities in a gas.

Quote and use the formula $d = (n)^{\frac{1}{2}}\lambda$ for diffusion.

Estimate the mean free path of a gas molecule.

QUESTIONS

1 Figure 8.20 shows the trajectory of an atom through the apparatus of figure 8.10. It has a speed v and emerges from the first slit at an angle θ to the horizontal.

a Obtain an expression for v in terms of θ for the atom to pass through the second slit. Hence show that $s = gd^2/v^2$.

b If $d = 100$ cm, calculate the value for s if v is 300 m s^{-1}. Hence estimate the width of the hot wire if v is to be measured with a precision of $\pm\, 50$ m s^{-1}.

c The pressure of a typical laboratory high vacuum is 1×10^{-4} Pa. How many air molecules per cubic centimeter would you need at room temperature to have this pressure?

d The experiment relies on the mean free path of the atoms being much greater than d. If the residual molecules in the vacuum have a diameter of about 5×10^{-10} m, estimate the maximum tolerable gas pressure in the apparatus. (The molar mass of air is about 0.03 kg mol^{-1}.)

2 A classic experiment to estimate the diameter of an air molecule is illustrated in figure 8.21. The bottom gas jar is filled with brown bromine vapour, the top with transparent air, both at room temperature and pressure. The glass plate between the two gas jars is carefully removed and the time taken for the brown colour to travel a certain distance up into the top jar is measured.

In one attempt at this experiment, the top of the brown region travelled upwards by 10 cm in 7 minutes. Use the data provided in table 8.3 to estimate the diameter of a molecule.

Table 8.3

molar mass of bromine/kg mol^{-1}	0.08
room temperature/°C	12
room pressure/kPa	102

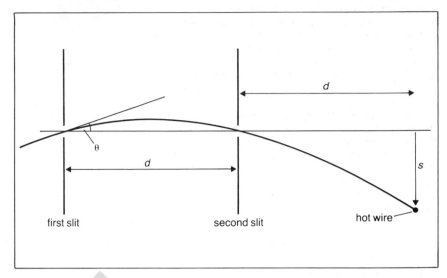

Figure 8.20

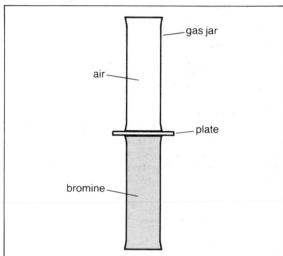

Figure 8.21

Figure 8.22

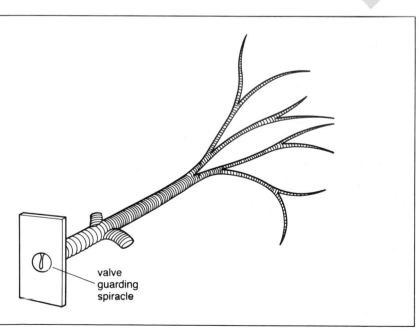

valve
guarding
spiracle

3 Insects breathe through tubes down the side of their bodies (figure 8.22). Apart from forced convection of the air in these tubes due to movement of the insect, diffusion is the means by which oxygen and carbon dioxide are exchanged with the atmosphere. For this question, you can assume that the tubes are not narrow enough to impede the normal diffusion of gases.

a Show that the time taken t for a gas molecule to diffuse a distance d is given by $d \simeq (ct\lambda)^{\frac{1}{2}}$, where c and λ are the root-mean-square velocity and mean free path, respectively.

b Estimate the time taken for a typical air molecule to diffuse 0.5 mm, 5 mm, 50 mm and 500 mm. Assume $\lambda = 0.1$ μm and $<c^2>^{\frac{1}{2}} = 500$ m s^{-1}.

c Why do your answers to part (b) suggest that insects have to be smaller than 1 cm across.

d Insects have to get rid of carbon dioxide (molar mass 0.044 kg mol^{-1}) and absorb oxygen (molar mass 0.032 kg mol^{-1}). Which of these two will diffuse faster through the insect's breathing tubes if a carbon dioxide molecule is 1.5 times larger than an oxygen molecule?

9

L I Q U I D S

It is often taken for granted that if you give enough
heat energy to a solid it turns into a liquid.
However, there are few examples of this in
everyday life. Most of the objects around you will
burst into flames if you give them a lot of heat
energy. Many man-made and natural materials,
such as plastics, wood and cloth, combine
violently with atmospheric oxygen if their
temperature gets high enough. Bricks and concrete
just glow red hot. Only a few things, such as ice,
waxes and metals, will soften and melt when given
heat energy. However, the fact that heat energy can
convert *some* solids into liquids is sufficient
evidence for us to expect that *all* liquids (like all
solids) are made out of atoms. In practice,
modelling the behaviour of a liquid by considering
the behaviour of its individual atoms is not usually
very useful. The first section of this chapter will
deal with liquids at an atomic level to account for
what happens when solids turn into liquids. The
second section will ignore atoms altogether and
discuss how liquids can be put to work in
hydraulic machinery and aerofoils: it will model
liquids as continuous incompressible fluids.

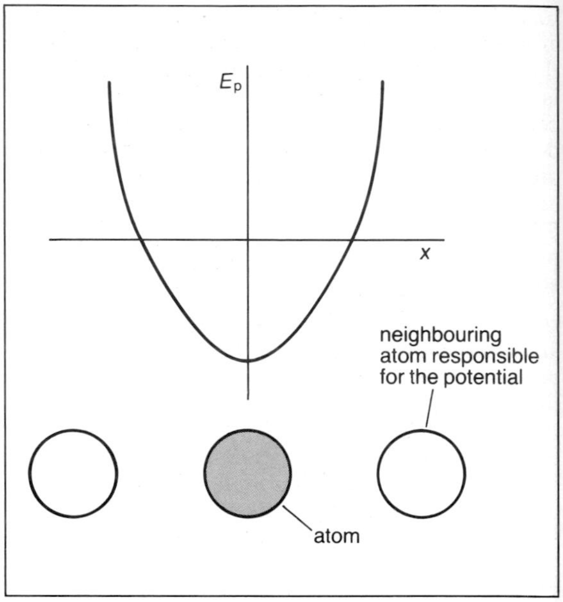

Figure 9.1 Potential well
for an atom in a solid

Figure 9.2 The shape of
the potential well changes
as the neighbouring atoms
move about

ATOMS IN LIQUIDS

Liquids conserve volume but not shape. In other
words, it is difficult to change their volume by
squeezing or stretching them — like solids they are
incompressible, but unlike solids they flow easily.
Our model of atoms assumes that they only repel
each other at close range, so an incompressible
liquid must contain atoms in close proximity with
each other. However, the requirement that liquids
flow (i.e. plastically deform under their own
weight) means that the atoms must also be able to
move past each other freely.

Melting

Figure 9.1 shows the **potential well** for a single
atom in a cold solid. Each atom in the solid has, on
average, a small total energy, so it cannot stray far
from its equilibrium position. (The atom can only
move to places in the well where the kinetic energy
is positive.) The shape of the well is, of course,
dictated by the positions of the atoms around the
one we are considering. So the graph of figure 9.1 is
only a snapshot, i.e. it is only true for an instant. As
the neighbouring atoms move about in their own
potential wells, the potential well of the atom we
are considering will wobble about. The disturbance
will increase as the energy of the atoms is
increased, due to their larger amplitude of
oscillation. This is illustrated in the sequence of
figure 9.2.

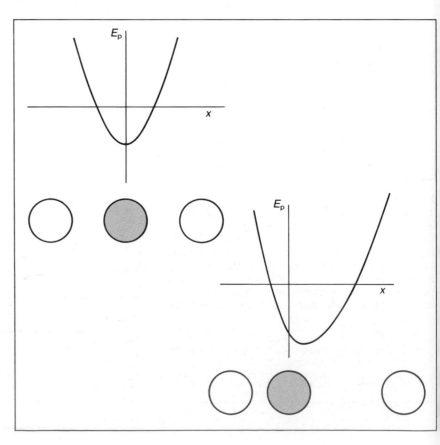

So, not only does an atom move around in its own potential well, it also constantly modifies the potential wells of the atoms around it. One result is thermal expansion: increasing the amount of heat energy in a solid causes its atoms to move apart from each other (figure 9.3). The other result is **melting**. When the temperature reaches the **melting point** of the solid, the disturbance of the potential wells is enough to allow atoms to leave their own well and move into that of a neighbour. (Remember that a solid is three dimensional.) In other words, the movement of each atom affects its neighbours so much that none of them can be locked between the others and the orderly structure of a solid is lost. Figure 9.4 contrasts the typical arrangement of atoms just above and below the melting point. Note that the average separation of the atoms in a liquid is not much greater than in a solid. There is certainly not room for one atom to move freely between all the others. Each atom can only move around because all of the others are moving!

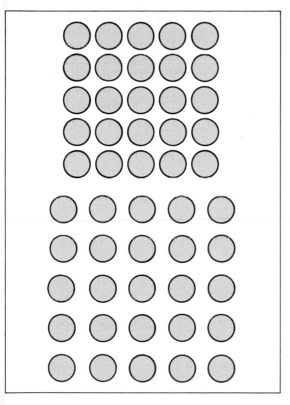

Latent heat

The melting point of a substance is the temperature at which its solid and liquid forms can be in thermal equilibrium with each other. The liquid form has more internal energy than the solid form because the atoms have to be, on average, slightly further apart from each other in order to be able to move around. This difference in energy per kilogram is called the **specific latent heat of fusion**.

$\Delta E = mL_f$

ΔE is the energy needed to melt the object at its melting point (J)

m is the mass of the object (kg)

L_f is the specific latent heat of fusion of the object (J kg^{-1})

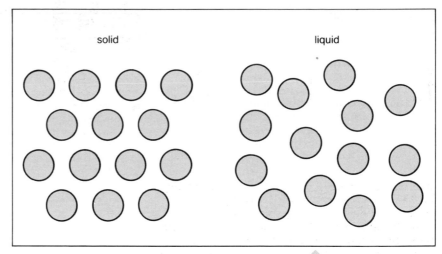

Values of L_f for a number of metals are shown in table 9.1. Although at first sight there seems to be no connection between the melting point and the energy needed to melt one kilogram, the melting point is roughly proportional to the energy needed to melt one mole, i.e. 6.02×10^{23} atoms. (You will be invited to check this for yourself when you get to the questions.)

If you have to give energy to a solid to melt it, then that energy must come out of the liquid when it is converted back into a solid. This is illustrated in the graph of figure 9.5. As heat energy escapes from the surface of the liquid, its temperature drops. However, when the melting point is reached, the temperature remains steady for a while — the liquid can only change to a solid as fast as heat energy loss allows it to lose energy. Once the liquid has been converted to a solid, then any further heat energy loss will result in a drop in temperature.

Figure 9.4 Contrasting the typical arrangement of atoms in a solid and liquid at the melting point

Figure 9.3 The average separation of the atoms in a solid increases as energy is given to it

Figure 9.5 Temperature–time curve for a liquid freezing as it cools

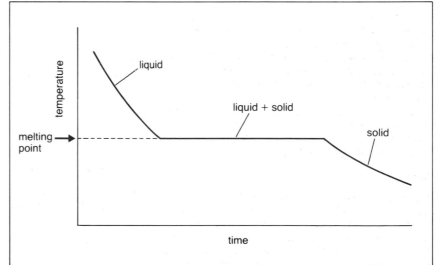

Table 9.1

Substance	Melting point/K	L_f/kJ kg^{-1}	Molar mass/kg
mercury	234	12	0.200
sodium	371	113	0.023
lead	601	25	0.207
aluminium	932	412	0.027
copper	1356	205	0.064
nickel	1728	305	0.059
tungsten	3650	184	0.184

Expansion and viscosity

What other properties of a liquid can the atom model predict, apart from the obvious one of lack of rigidity? Most liquids have a lower density than their solids — water is one of the few exceptions. This is what you might expect if the atoms in a liquid have to be slightly further apart than in a solid. Figure 9.6 shows how this effect is used to control the thermostat in the cooling systems of cars. Since the atoms are further apart in a liquid than in a solid, we would also expect that a given change of temperature should make a liquid expand more than its solid. In general, the volume expansivity of a liquid is larger than that of a solid.

Most liquids flow better at high temperatures than low ones. As their atoms move further apart, they find it easier to move past one another. The **viscosity** of a liquid is a measure of its internal friction as it flows. Treacle is a good example of a liquid with a high value for viscosity. Its atoms cannot move past each other easily, so it does not change its shape easily. Table 9.2 shows how the viscosity of some liquids changes with temperature: notice that they fall with rising temperature. Road tar is another good example of a liquid whose viscosity falls rapidly with temperature: it flows easily when hot, but is virtually solid when cold.

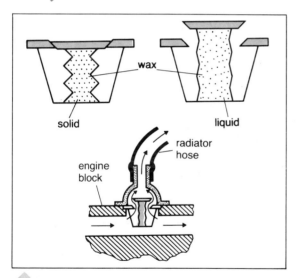

Figure 9.6 The thermostat allows engine-cooling water through to the radiator when its temperature exceeds the melting point of the wax.

Figure 9.7 Apparatus for measuring the viscosity of a liquid

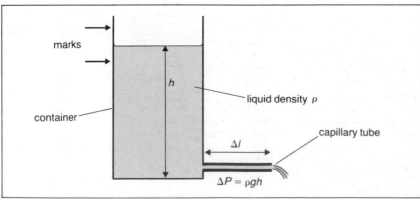

INTERNAL ENERGY

Strictly speaking, heat energy is always associated with changes of temperature. Thus if you do work on an object and its temperature rises, then you can say that it has been given heat energy. However, if you do work on an object at its melting point, then the energy you give it will not raise its temperature, but will convert some solid to liquid. In these circumstances, some would maintain that it is preferable to talk about internal energy rather than heat energy. When the internal energy of an object is changed, the arrangement, separation and motion of its individual atoms can be altered. The distinction between internal energy and heat energy is not significant, provided that you understand that both types of energy are really the kinetic and potential energies of the atoms in the solid.

FREEZING MIXTURES

Before the invention of refrigerators, the forced melting of ice was commonly used to obtain temperatures below 0°C. The melting point of water is lowered by any impurities dissolved in it. For example, a 50:50 mixture of ethylene glycol (antifreeze) and water has a melting point of −36.5°C. A teaspoon of table salt dissolved in a glass of water can easily lower its melting point to −10°C. If some ice at 0°C is placed in some water whose melting point has been lowered in this way, then the temperature of the whole system can drop below 0°C.

Consider this example. An ice cube is dropped into a small glass of salty water at room temperature. Roughly how much ice at 0°C do you need to get the temperature down to −10°C, given that $L_f = 3.3 \times 10^5$ J kg^{-1} and $c = 4.2 \times 10^3$ J kg^{-1} K^{-1}? The glass will hold about 100 cm^3 of water, i.e. 0.1 kg. If its initial temperature is +15°C we can calculate how much heat energy it is going to have to lose.

$$\Delta Q = ? \qquad \Delta Q = mc\Delta T \qquad \therefore \Delta Q = 0.1 \times 4.2 \times 10^3 \times 25 = 10.5 \text{ kJ}$$
$$m = 0.1 \text{ kg}$$
$$c = 4.2 \times 10^3 \text{ J kg}^{-1} \text{ K}^{-1}$$
$$\Delta T = 25 \text{ K}$$

We can now work out how much ice has to melt at 0°C to take this amount of heat energy from the water.

$$\Delta E = 1.05 \times 10^4 \text{ J} \qquad \Delta E = mL_f \qquad \therefore 1.05 \times 10^4 = m \times 3.3 \times 10^5$$
$$m = ?$$
$$L_f = 3.3 \times 10^5 \text{ J kg}^{-1} \qquad \qquad \therefore m = \frac{1.05 \times 10^4}{3.3 \times 10^5} = 0.032 \text{ kg}$$

A 32 g ice cube will have sides of only 32 mm! We have, of course, failed to take account of heat energy loss from the glass and the heat energy lost by the ice cube itself as it drops from 0°C to −10°C. You can check for yourself that the latter only raises the mass of ice required to 36 g.

Table 9.2

Liquid	viscosity/N s m^{-2} × 10^{-3}		
	0°C	50°C	100°C
water	1.79	0.55	0.28
petrol	0.71	0.39	0.26
mercury	1.68	1.41	1.23

The apparatus shown in figure 9.7 can be used to measure the relative viscosity of a liquid. It is poured into the top of the cylinder and allowed to pour out of the narrow tube at the bottom. The time taken for a fixed volume of the liquid to flow out of the apparatus can be measured by timing how long it takes for the top of the liquid to get between the marks on the cylinder. Provided that the flow through the narrow tube is slow, that time will be proportional to the viscosity.

OBJECTIVES

After studying this section you should be able to do
the following.

Describe the difference in atomic structure between solids and liquids.	Explain why, in general, liquids have lower densities than solids.
Explain why latent heat has to be provided to convert a solid into a liquid.	Describe and explain how the viscosity of a liquid changes with temperature.

QUESTIONS

1 You are going to use the data of table 9.1 to find out how the melting point of a metal affects the energy needed to melt one mole of it.

a Use the data to plot a graph of melting point against the molar latent heat of fusion. Can you draw a straight line through the points?

b Use the atom concept to explain why the latent heat of fusion increases with melting point.

c Platinum melts at 2043 K. Estimate the value of its molar latent heat of fusion.

d A newly discovered metal has a melting point of 594 K and a specific latent heat of fusion of 5.4×10^4 J kg^{-1}. Estimate a likely value for its molar mass.

2 The graph in figure 9.8 shows how the temperature of a container of wax changed with time as it cooled down when it was removed from boiling water. The specific heat capacity of the solid wax is 2900 J kg^{-1} K^{-1} and its mass was 0.20 kg.

a Use the graph to calculate the rate at which the container was losing heat while the wax was freezing.

b What is the value of the specific latent heat of fusion of wax? State any assumptions you have made.

3 This question will help you to estimate the rate at which liquids diffuse into each other. It draws on your understanding of diffusion in gases.

a Explain why the mean free path of a single atom in a liquid is approximately its own diameter.

b If the speed of a liquid molecule is roughly the same as that of a gas molecule at the same temperature, estimate how many collisions a water molecule will make per second.

c Calculate how far a single water molecule should diffuse in
(i) one second,
(ii) one minute,
(iii) one hour.

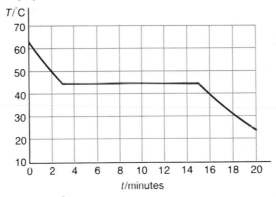

Figure 9.8

BEHAVIOUR OF FLUIDS

Although it should be possible to deduce all of the properties of liquids by considering the behaviour of its atoms, in practice it is very difficult to do. Consequently, it pays to use a much simpler model for many applications. The **fluid model** which will be used in this section completely ignores the microscopic structure of liquids and gases. The basic properties of liquids and gases are taken for granted and idealised, so that we can concentrate on the energy and pressure changes of the whole fluid.

Upthrusts

One of the more unexpected properties of liquids in gravity fields is the anti-gravity forces they exert on objects immersed in them. Those forces, known as **upthrusts**, are responsible for keeping your head above water in the swimming baths.

Archimedes' Principle

Suppose that you take a glass of water with a little salt dissolved in it and very carefully place a blob of ink at its centre with a dropper (figure 9.9). If the salt solution has the same density as the blob then it will not move — it will be in static equilibrium (diffusion rates in liquids are very small). Of course, this does not mean that no forces act on the blob, just that all of the forces cancel each other out. So the weight W of the blob must be balanced by an equal and opposite force U from the water around it. Now, if the blob were replaced with something else which had exactly the same shape and size, the upthrust U would be unchanged. So we expect that any object immersed in a liquid experiences an upwards force. The size of that upthrust is given by **Archimedes' Principle**.

The upthrust on an object immersed in a liquid is equal to the weight of liquid displaced by the object.

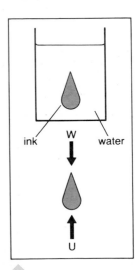

Figure 9.9 The forces on objects immersed in a liquid

The relative importance of this upthrust is dictated by the densities of the solid and the liquid. Suppose that you place a solid block in a liquid, as shown in figure 9.10. The net downwards force on it will be $W - U$. We can write down an expression for W in terms of the volume V and the density ρ_s of the solid.

$$W = mg, \quad m = \rho_s V \quad \therefore W = (\rho_s V) \times g \qquad \textbf{(9.1)}$$

The solid displaces a volume V of the liquid, whose density is ρ_l, so the upthrust U can be worked out.

$$U = \rho_l V g \qquad \textbf{(9.2)}$$

We can combine equations (9.1) and (9.2) to find the net force on the object.

$$F = W - U \quad \therefore F = (\rho_s - \rho_l)Vg \qquad \textbf{(9.3)}$$

It should be obvious from equation (9.3) that the upthrust is greater than the weight if the solid is less dense than the liquid. Since liquids expand as their temperature rises (remember the last section?), we can predict that the warmer portions of a liquid are going to be pushed up on top of the colder portions. So if a heater is immersed in a liquid near the bottom of its container, **convection currents** will carry the hot liquid upwards, replacing it with cold liquid. Many domestic hot water systems rely on convection currents to carry hot water from the heater to the storage tank.

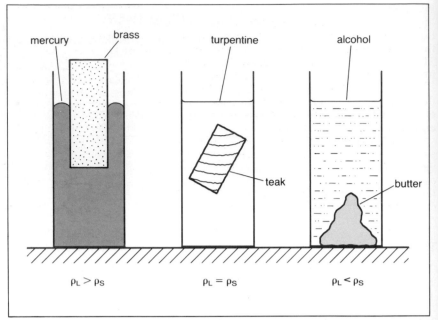

mercury   brass   turpentine   alcohol

teak   butter

$\rho_L > \rho_S$ $\rho_L = \rho_S$ $\rho_L < \rho_S$

Figure 9.10   A solid will float on a liquid if its density is small enough

---

FLOATING

Archimedes' Principle can be used to work out the conditions for objects to float on the surface of a liquid. The following example should help you understand how it works. A punt of the type shown in figure 9.11 is used to ferry people over a river. The punt itself has a mass of 150 kg, and the boatman and passengers have masses of about 80 kg each. How many passengers can the punt transport if its edge has to be at least 10 cm above the water surface?

Figure 9.11   A punt

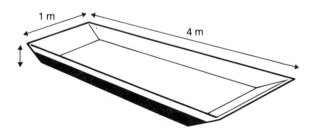

1 m

4 m

For simplicity, we shall assume that the punt has a rectangular shape. Referring to figure 9.11, the volume of water it will displace when fully loaded will be $1.0 \times 0.15 \times 4.0 = 0.6 \text{ m}^3$. This can be used to calculate the weight of water displaced — water has a density of 1000 kg m^{-3}.

$$W = mg, \quad m = \rho V, \quad \therefore W = \rho V g$$
$$\therefore W = 1000 \times 0.60 \times 10 = 6.0 \text{ kN}$$

If the punt contains n passengers, then the total weight of punt and people has to equal the 6 kN upthrust.

$$W = mg \quad \therefore 6000 = (150 + 80 + (n \times 80)) \times 10$$
$$\therefore 6000 = 2300 + (n \times 800)$$
$$\therefore n = \frac{6000 - 2300}{800} = 4.6$$

Of course, to be safe, we have to round n down to 4.

Convection currents in gases

Archimedes' Principle applies to *any* fluid, be it liquid or gas. Gases expand a lot on heating, with a volume expansivity of $3 \times 10^{-3} \text{ K}^{-1}$ at room temperature, about twenty times that of water. So the warmer portions of a gas are going to be pushed upwards quite strongly by the colder portions. Coupled with the fact that gases flow much easier than liquids do (the viscosity of air at room temperature and pressure is about a hundred times smaller than water), convection currents in gases are going to be much more violent than in liquids.

Large-scale convection currents in the Earth's atmosphere are responsible for our weather. What the public would call a breeze, a wind, a gale or a hurricane is, to a physicist, just a convection current driven by the different temperatures at various places on the Earth's surface. On a smaller scale, convection currents are responsible for most of the heat loss from the surface of our unclothed bodies. Clothes, as well as preserving modesty and satisfying the dictates of fashion, perform the useful function of trapping warm air close to our skins and preventing it from floating up and away.

Hydrostatic pressure

Liquids in gravity fields exert pressures on the walls of their containers and any objects placed in them. Although it is obvious that the source of that pressure is the weight of the liquid, it is not so obvious how the pressure is related to the shape of the container.

Pressure

Figure 9.12 shows a liquid touching a surface. If the liquid exerts a force which is not perpendicular to the surface, then it cannot be in static equilibrium. This is because liquids cannot exert static friction forces like solids can: their lack of internal structure means that the slightest force will make them plastically deform. So if the liquid is in static equilibrium, it can only exert a pressure at right angles to the surface it is touching.

Figure 9.13 shows a liquid of density ρ sitting in a container of cross-sectional area A. If the depth of the liquid is h, we can easily work out an expression for the pressure exerted by the liquid on the base of the can. We start off by writing down an expression for the weight of the liquid.

$$W = mg, \quad m = \rho V, \quad V = h \times A \quad \therefore W = \rho hAg \quad \textbf{(9.4)}$$

Then we can find the pressure on the base.

$$P = \frac{F}{A} \quad \therefore P = \frac{\rho hAg}{A} \quad \therefore P = \rho gh \quad \textbf{(9.5)}$$

This pressure acts downwards on the base of the can. But how big is the outwards pressure on the walls of the can? Although it is not intuitively obvious, that pressure is also given by $P = \rho gh$. In other words, the pressure on an object which is a distance h below the surface of the liquid is *always* given by ρgh, regardless of its shape. This is illustrated in figure 9.14.

> $P = \rho gh$
>
> P is the pressure exerted by the liquid on its walls (Pa)
>
> ρ is the density of the liquid (kg m^{-3})
>
> g is the gravitational field strength (N kg^{-1})
>
> h is the vertical distance below the liquid surface (m)

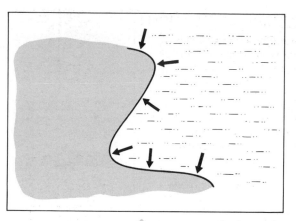

Figure 9.12 Fluids in static equilibrium can only exert forces at right angles to surfaces in contact with them

Figure 9.13 Finding the pressure due to a column of liquid

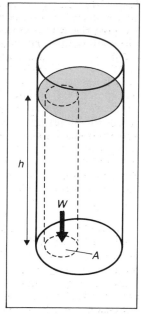

Working on liquids

Figure 9.15(a) illustrates a thought experiment which should convince you that the pressure exerted by a column of liquid depends on its *vertical* height. We are going to assume that an ideal liquid (frictionless and incompressible) is flowing through the pipe at a slow, steady rate. Consider the shaded portion of liquid. Two forces act on it in its direction of motion. These are due to the pressure of the liquid at either end of it. The force at the bottom will be $(P + \Delta P)A$, in the direction of the flow. The force at the top will be PA, against the direction of flow. So if the shaded portion is moved a distance x (figure 9.15(b)) by these forces, some work will be done on it by the pressure at the bottom of the pipe.

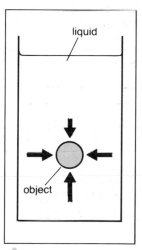

Figure 9.14 The liquid under the ball provides an *upwards* force on the object, despite the fact that the liquid's pressure is due to the *downwards* weight of the liquid

Figure 9.15 Doing work on a liquid pushing it uphill

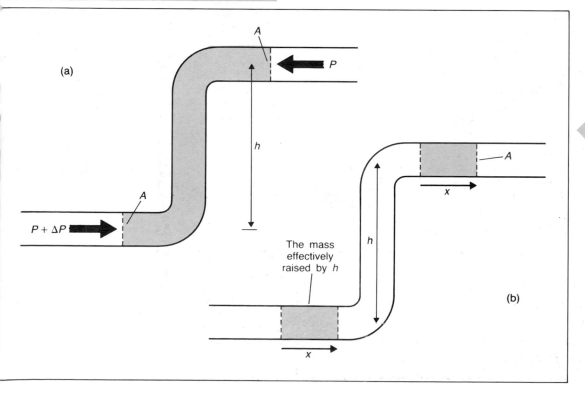

(a)

(b)

$P + \Delta P$

P

h

h

A

A

A

x

x

The mass effectively raised by h

$$E = Fd \qquad \therefore E_{in} = (P + \Delta P)Ax \qquad (9.6)$$

At the same time, the shaded portion of fluid will do work against the pressure at the top of the pipe.

$$E = Fd \qquad \therefore E_{out} = PAx \qquad (9.7)$$

The net work done on the liquid is the difference of equations (9.6) and (9.7), i.e. ΔPAx. That work must increase the energy of the liquid. It cannot change its strain energy because it is incompressible, nor can it change its kinetic energy because it is moving at a steady speed. So the work done increases the gravitational energy of the liquid. In moving a distance x, a volume of liquid Ax has effectively been raised through a vertical distance h. So we can use the density ρ of the liquid to work out the gravitational energy gained.

$$E_g = mgh \qquad \therefore E_g = (\rho Ax) \times gh \qquad (9.8)$$

It is now a simple matter to obtain an expression for ΔP.

$$E_g = \rho Axgh = \Delta PAx \qquad \therefore \Delta P = \rho gh \qquad (9.9)$$

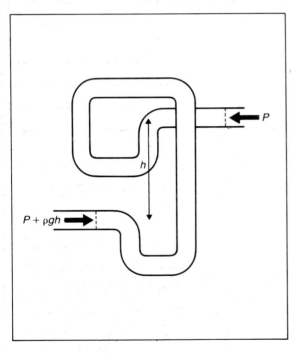

The pressure difference between the two ends of the column of liquid is independent of the amount of liquid. As long as the pipe at the start and end has the same cross-sectional area A, the portion in between can have *any* shape, length or diameter we like. So the systems shown in figures 9.15 and 9.16 have the same pressure difference between their entrance and exit pipes, despite the fact that they contain different weights of liquid.

Moving fluids

Moving fluids are difficult to model precisely. By making certain simplifying assumptions about how the liquid moves from one place to another, it is possible to predict flow rates through pipes and lifts on aerofoils. However, real liquids in the real world rarely flow in this simple fashion, so the results of such calculations can only be used as approximate indicators of what could happen in practice.

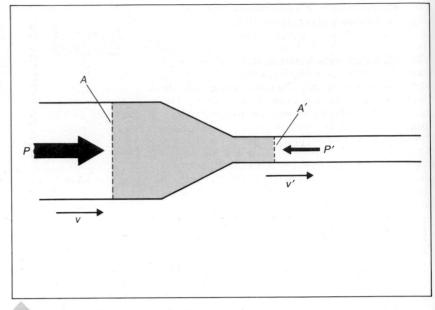

Figure 9.17 Doing work accelerating a frictionless liquid

Figure 9.16 The pressure difference between two points in a static liquid only depends on the vertical separation of the points

Bernoulli's Theorem

The pressure of a liquid depends on its velocity as well as its depth below the surface. Paradoxically, the pressure goes down as the velocity goes up. Once again, a thought experiment will help you see why this arises from energy conservation. The apparatus is shown in figure 9.17. As always, the liquid is assumed to be frictionless so that none of the work done on it can be converted into heat energy. The liquid enters at the left with velocity v at a pressure P and leaves at the right with velocity v' and pressure P'. Between the two regions the cross-sectional area goes from A to A', forcing the liquid to speed up if its volume is to remain constant.

Consider the shaded portion of the liquid in figure 9.17. Let its left-hand end move a distance x to the right; this will require the right-hand end to move a distance x' at the same time (figure 9.18). The work done *on* the liquid at the left-hand end is given by

Figure 9.18 Ax is constant for an incompressible liquid

$$E = Fd \qquad \therefore E = (PA) \times x \qquad (9.10$$

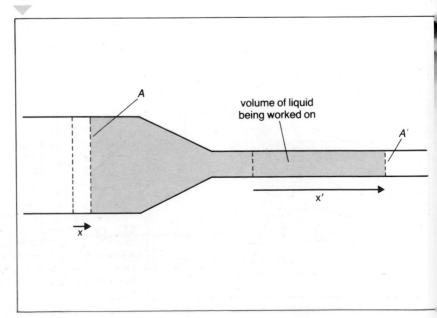

volume of liquid being worked on

Similarly, the work done *by* the liquid at the right-hand end is given by

$$E = Fd \qquad \therefore E = (P'A') \times x' \qquad \textbf{(9.11)}$$

The difference between these two will be the kinetic energy gained by the liquid, provided that there is no turbulence. The volume of liquid which has been accelerated is effectively Ax or $A'x'$, so we can use the density ρ to work out its kinetic energy change ΔE_k.

$$E_k = \tfrac{1}{2}mv^2 \quad \therefore \Delta E_k = \tfrac{1}{2}\rho A'x'v'^2 - \tfrac{1}{2}\rho Axv^2 \qquad \textbf{(9.12)}$$

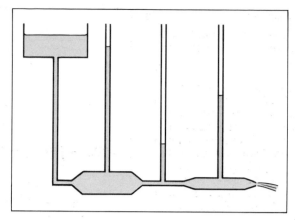

Figure 9.19 A demonstration that the pressure of a liquid decreases as its velocity increases

AEROFOILS

An **aerofoil** is a specially shaped surface which causes fluids to move at different speeds over its two surfaces. Figure 9.20 shows the passage of air over an aerofoil. This sort of motion, with the air following a steady path, is called **streamline flow**. The faster moving air on the top surface of the aerofoil has a lower pressure than the slower moving air underneath, so there is a net upwards force or **lift**. The design of aerofoils is very complicated, and computer modelling is often used to predict their behaviour at different speeds and angles. As well as trying to maximise the lift, the designer has to minimise the **drag** caused by the **turbulent flow** behind the aerofoil where the airstream breaks up into eddies.

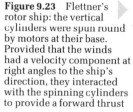

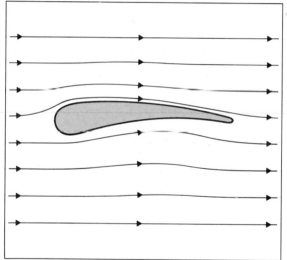

Figure 9.20 Streamline flow of air past an aerofoil

Figure 9.21 The movement of air past an aerofoil generates lift

lift

Figure 9.23 Flettner's rotor ship: the vertical cylinders were spun round by motors at their base. Provided that the winds had a velocity component at right angles to the ship's direction, they interacted with the spinning cylinders to provide a forward thrust

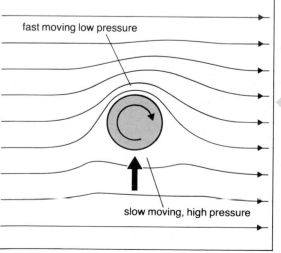

fast moving low pressure

slow moving, high pressure

FLETTNER-ROTOR

Figure 9.22 Flow of air around a spinning cylinder as it moves forwards

An aerofoil works by setting up a circulation of air around it, as shown in figure 9.21. You can think of this as an eddy which moves round close to the aerofoil. As the aerofoil moves forwards, air passing over the top of the aerofoil is speeded up by the circulation and that passing underneath is slowed down. The same effect can be achieved with a rotating cylinder. If you look at figure 9.22, you will see that the pressure on one side of the cylinder will be lower than the other as the cylinder moves through the air, pushing it to one side. In 1925 a ship travelled across the Atlantic using a pair of such cylinders as sails (figure 9.23).

Combining equations (9.10), (9.11) and (9.12) to equate the work done with the energy gained, we obtain **Bernoulli's Theorem**. (Remember that $Ax = A'x'$.)

$$PAx - P'A'x' = \tfrac{1}{2}\rho A'x'v'^2 - \tfrac{1}{2}\rho Axv^2$$

$$\therefore P + \tfrac{1}{2}\rho v^2 = P' + \tfrac{1}{2}\rho v'^2$$

$$\therefore P + \tfrac{1}{2}\rho v^2 = \text{constant} \qquad \textbf{(9.13)}$$

> $P + \tfrac{1}{2}\rho v^2 = $ constant
>
> P is the pressure of the fluid (Pa)
>
> ρ is the density of the fluid (kg m^{-3})
>
> v is the velocity of the fluid (m s^{-1})

Bernoulli's Theorem is essentially a statement of the Principle of Energy Conservation applied to liquids flowing horizontally, without any turbulence to convert kinetic energy to internal energy. If the flow is *not* horizontal, then $P + \tfrac{1}{2}\rho v^2 + \rho gh$ is constant. You can check this for yourself.

Real liquids are not frictionless as assumed by Bernoulli's Theorem. Nevertheless, it *is* found that as liquids speed up their pressure decreases. A simple apparatus for demonstrating this is shown in figure 9.19. The height of each column of water indicates the pressure ($P = \rho gh$) at its base.

Flow along pipes

Real liquids encounter friction forces when they have to flow along pipes. This means that the pressure at the entrance of the pipe has to be greater than at the exit. Consider the pipe shown in figure 9.24. It contains a liquid flowing along horizontally at a constant speed, so the friction forces from the walls must be cancelled out by the forces due to the pressure gradient. The net force on the liquid in Δl must be zero (Newton's First Law). So if the pressure falls from $P + \Delta P$ to P in a distance Δl, then we can write down the following expression for the friction F on the liquid in Δl.

$$(P + \Delta P)\times A - (P\times A) - F = 0$$

$$\therefore \Delta P \times A = F \qquad \textbf{(9.14)}$$

The value of F, the friction, will be proportional to Δl as each bit of the pipe wall will separately exert a force on the liquid as it moves past it. So we can set $F = f\Delta l$, where f is the friction force per metre of pipe.

$$\Delta P \times A = f\Delta l \qquad \therefore \frac{\Delta P}{\Delta l} = \frac{f}{A} \qquad \textbf{(9.15)}$$

Equation (9.15) predicts that the pressure gradient is constant down a pipe of constant radius. This is easily demonstrated as shown in figure 9.25.

Predicting a value for f is not straightforward. It involves assumptions about the movement of the liquid through the pipe. Not all of the liquid will be moving at the same speed because the friction is with the walls. The liquid will move at its fastest down the centre of the pipe and there will be a thin layer next to the walls which does not move at all. Figure 9.26 shows how the velocity is predicted to change with position under conditions of **streamline flow**. Furthermore, the value of f will depend on the viscosity of the liquid, i.e. how easily each layer can move past a slower moving layer.

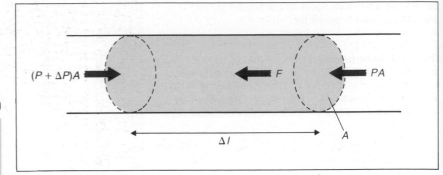

Figure 9.24 Forces on a portion of real liquid flowing down a pipe

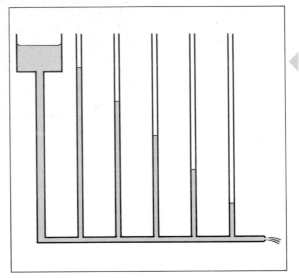

Figure 9.25 A pressure gradient is needed to make a real liquid flow down a pipe

The simplest assumption that gives agreement with the experiment is that f is just proportional to the average velocity v of the liquid. We can use this to find out how the volume flow rate ($\Delta V/\Delta t$) down the pipe depends on the pressure gradient ($\Delta P/\Delta l$) and the radius (r). If you imagine toothpaste coming out of a tube, it should be clear that

$$\Delta V = vA\Delta t \qquad \textbf{(9.16)}$$

We are assuming v is proportional to f. So we can combine equations (9.15) and (9.16) as follows, using $A = \pi r^2$.

$$\frac{\Delta V}{\Delta t} = vA \quad \therefore \frac{\Delta V}{\Delta t} \propto fA \quad \therefore \frac{\Delta V}{\Delta t} \propto \frac{\Delta PA}{\Delta l} \times A$$

$$\therefore \frac{\Delta V}{\Delta t} \propto \frac{\Delta P \times r^4}{\Delta l} \qquad \textbf{(9.17)}$$

Figure 9.26 Relative velocity of portions of liquid in streamline flow down a pipe

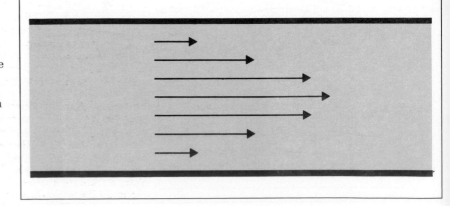

In fact, experiments show that equation (9.17) is correct for many liquids provided that they have streamlined flow down the pipe (figure 9.27). Equation (9.17) is important because it predicts that by doubling the radius of a pipe you can increase the flow rate sixteen-fold! If we set the constant of proportionality to $\pi/8\mu$, where μ is the **viscosity** of the liquid, equation (9.17) becomes **Poiseuille's Formula.**

$$\frac{\Delta V}{\Delta t} = \frac{\pi r^4}{8\mu} \times \frac{\Delta P}{\Delta l}$$

$\Delta V/\Delta t$ is the volume flow rate of the liquid $(m^3\ s^{-1})$

$\Delta P/\Delta l$ is the pressure gradient down the pipe $(Pa\ m^{-1})$

r is the radius of the pipe (m)

μ is the viscosity of the liquid $(N\ s\ m^{-2})$

OBJECTIVES

After studying this section you should be able to do the following.

Explain the reasons for Archimedes' Principle.

Explain why convection currents take place in liquids and gases.

Apply Archimedes' Principle to calculations involving floating objects.

Understand why the pressure in a liquid is at right angles to its surfaces.

Derive and use the hydrostatic pressure formula $P = \rho g h$.

State and derive Bernoulli's Theorem.

Know that there has to be a pressure gradient to drive a real liquid down a pipe.

Know the factors which determine the flow rate of liquids down pipes.

State and use Poiseuille's Formula for streamline flow down pipes.

Figure 9.27 Streamline and turbulent flow of water around an object. Dye injected into the water allows its motion to be tracked. Notice how streamline flow becomes turbulent as the water flows past the end of the wing

QUESTIONS

1 Very precise measurements of mass have to include a **buoyancy correction** if the method involves comparing weights. The upthrust from the air (density $1.2\ kg\ m^{-3}$) has to be taken into account. You are going to see if any measurements you are likely to make in the laboratory need this correction.

a A ping-pong ball has a radius of 2.0 cm. A balance reads 4.14 g when the ball is placed on it. What is the true mass of the ball?

b A balloon has a mass of 5.43 g before it is blown up. It is then blown full of air and placed on a balance. Will the balance reading be greater, smaller or the same as 5.43 g?

c A modern electronic laboratory balance has a precision of ± 0.01 g. Calculate how big the object being weighed has to be before the buoyancy correction becomes important. Quote your answer as a length.

2 Seven shipwrecked mariners on a desert island have constructed a raft from the four palm trees on the island. Each tree trunk is a cylinder of length 5.0 m and diameter 25 cm. When the raft is complete, they float it on the sea (density $1021\ kg\ m^{-3}$) and note that it is half submerged. How many mariners will the raft support if each has a mass of about 80 kg? Will it help if they sit on the raft with their legs in the water?

3 A party is in progress in a small swimming pool. All of the guests have climbed into a large rubber dingy, and are having an argument about Archimedes' Principle. Mark maintains that if all the guests leave the dingy and floated in the pool, the water level will rise. Thalia says that it will fall. Who is right, or are they both wrong? Is the answer different if the guests are replaced with bricks?

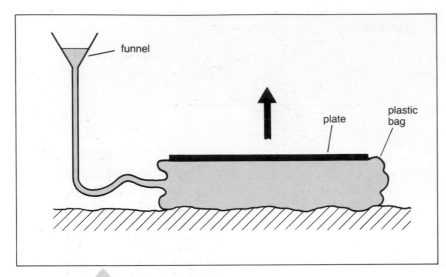

Figure 9.28

Figure 9.29 ▶

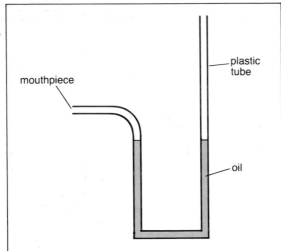

Figure 9.30 ▶

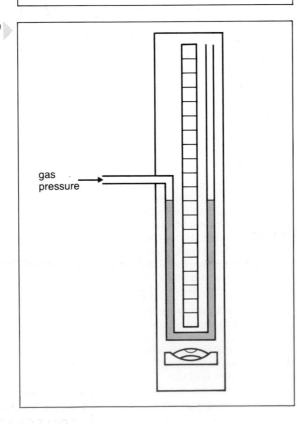

4 Figure 9.28 shows a low-tech hydraulic lift. The circular plate is placed under the back axle of a car (mass 850 kg) and water (density 1000 kg m^{-3}) is poured into the funnel to inflate the plastic bag.

a If the plate has a radius of 20 cm, how high above the plate must the funnel be?

b How much water has to be poured into the funnel to raise the car by 0.30 m? Estimate how long it would take someone to lift the car by this amount if they have an average power of 80 W?

5 A **manometer** is a device for making precise measurements of pressure. It balances the pressure to be measured with a column of liquid whose density is known.

a A student uses the apparatus shown in figure 9.29 to measure the pressure of her lungs. When she blows into the mouthpiece, the surface of the oil in the right-hand plastic tube rises from 0.53 m to 1.72 m above the ground. If the oil has a density of 800 kg m^{-3}, what is the value of her lung pressure?

b A manometer for measuring the pressure of the gas supply is shown in figure 9.30. The difference in level of the water in the two arms can be measured with a ruler of length 20 cm marked at millimetre intervals. Write out a set of simple instructions for the use of the manometer, including details of how to calculate the gas pressure from the readings on the ruler. What is the precision with which measurements can be made? Why does the device have a spirit level?

c A **mercury barometer** is shown in figure 9.31. The height of the mercury column can be used to measure the pressure of the atmosphere to a precision of at least 0.1%, provided that the density of mercury is accurately known. So when the height h is measured, the temperature T is noted so that a correction for the thermal expansion of mercury can be made. Work out a formula for converting h in mm into pressures in kPa. The volume expansivity and density of mercury at 0°C are $1.81 \times 10^{-4} \, \text{K}^{-1}$ and 13 595 kg m^{-3} respectively; the value of g is 9.81 N kg^{-1}.

6 A cross-section through a carburettor is shown in figure 9.32. Petrol in the reservoir is sucked up the jet by the movement of air past the top of it. Estimate the minimum speed with which the air must move to raise the petrol to the top of the jet. Density of air = 1.2 kg m^{-3}, density of petrol = 700 kg m^{-3}.

7 **a** The Victorian industrial landscape featured many tall chimneys. The main energy converter for Victorian industry was the steam engine, and the chimneys carried away the smoke from the burning coal used to generate the steam. Explain why the power of a steam engine increases as the height of its chimney is raised.

b Prairie dogs live undergound in burrows with two entrances, one of which is always raised above the surface of the prairie by a mound of earth. How does this arrangement guarantee adequate ventilation of the burrow? Should the mound be up-wind or down-wind of the other entrance?

8 Two party tricks which use Bernoulli's Theorem to amaze and mystify are shown in figure 9.33.

a Two ping-pong balls are suspended close to each other and air is blown between them with the help of a straw. Why do the balls move towards each other?

b When air is blown down the tube through the top disc, the loose disc under it is pulled upwards. Why? What will happen if the loose disc is pulled up so hard that it touches the top disc?

9 Pearl performs an experiment to find the viscosity of water with the apparatus shown in figure 9.7. The capillary tube has a length of 25 cm and an inner diameter of 1.0 mm.

a If the height h is 6.0 cm, what is the value of the pressure gradient between the ends of the capillary tube?

b 17 cm³ of water flow out of the end of the tube in 5.0 minutes. Use Poiseuille's Formula to calculate the viscosity of water.

c How much liquid will flow out of the end of the tube in five minutes if
  (i) only its radius is halved?
  (ii) only its length is doubled?
  (iii) only the value of h is doubled?
  (iv) the water is replaced with ethanol
    ($\rho = 790$ kg m^{-3}, $\mu = 1.2 \times 10^{-3}$ N s m^{-2})?

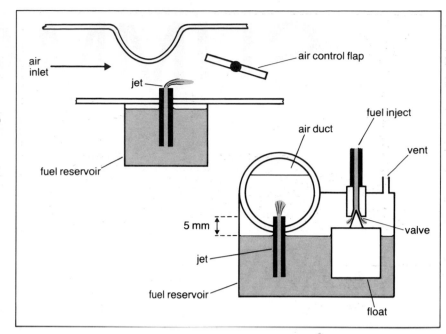

Figure 9.32

Figure 9.33

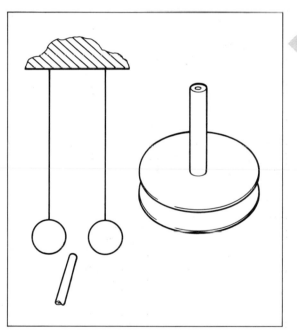

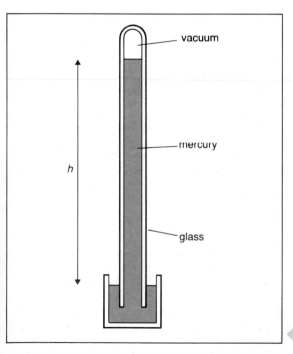

Figure 9.31

SUMMARY
E N E R G Y

The work done on an object is equal to the energy it gains and vice versa: $E = Fd$. Power is the rate of transfer of energy: $P = E/t$. When work is done on an object it may be converted into a number of different types of energy.

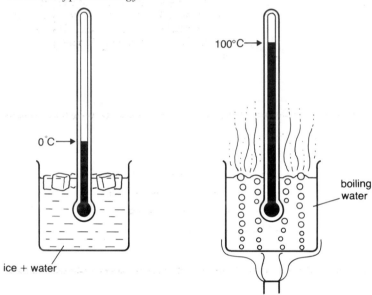

ice + water

boiling water

100°C →

0°C →

kinetic energy: $E_k = \frac{1}{2}mv^2$.
gravitational energy: $E_g = mgh$.
strain energy: $E_s = \frac{1}{2}kx^2$
rotational energy: $E_r = \frac{1}{2}I\omega^2$

The potential energy of a point mass is related to the external forces acting on it: $F = -\Delta E_p/\Delta x$. The total energy of a system of particles is the sum of all

its individual energies. The total energy of an isolated system remains constant; energy is conserved.

An elastic collision conserves kinetic energy; in inelastic collisions some kinetic energy is converted to other forms. The energy transfer in an elastic collision between two particles depends on their relative masses.

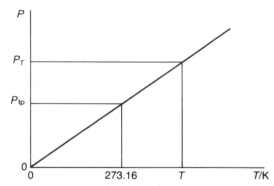

Heat energy is the potential and kinetic energy of individual atoms in a material. The addition of heat energy usually results in expansion which can act as the basis of a thermometer: $\Delta l/l = \alpha\Delta T$, $\Delta V/V = 3\alpha\Delta T$. The Celsius temperature scale fixes the boiling and freezing points of water at 100°C and 0°C respectively. The Kelvin temperature scale defines the triple point of water to be 273.16 K as measured by a constant volume gas thermometer.

The specific heat capacity of an object relates its temperature change to a change of heat energy: $\Delta Q = mc\Delta T$. As soon as the temperature of an object is different from its surroundings, heat energy flows in such a way as to return the temperature back to its previous value. The effects of this heat loss in measurements can be accounted for with the help of cooling curves.

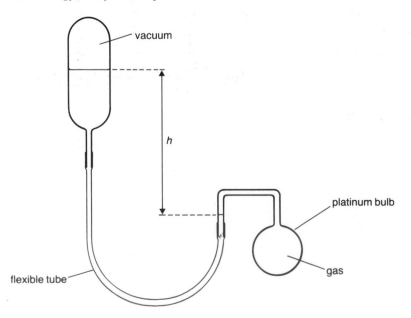

vacuum

h

platinum bulb

gas

flexible tube

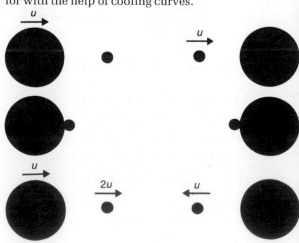

Gases exert pressure on the walls of their containers: $P = F/A$. A gas can be modelled as a collection of point masses with random velocities whose average kinetic energy is $3kT/2$; the pressure arises from the elastic collisions of the particles with the walls. For such an ideal gas $P = \rho<c^2>/3$ and $PV = NkT$. (For n moles of an ideal gas $PV = nRT$; one mole is 6.02×10^{23} particles.)

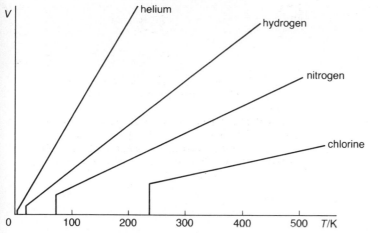

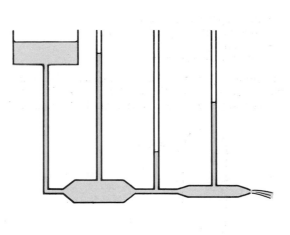

Pressure in a fluid is exerted at right angles to surfaces: $P = \rho gh$. For an ideal frictionless fluid $P + \frac{1}{2}\rho v^2 =$ constant (Bernoulli's Theorem). A real fluid needs a pressure gradient to make it flow along a pipe: $\Delta V/\Delta t = (\pi r^4/8\mu) \times \Delta P/\Delta l$ for streamline flow.

The mean free path of a gas particle is the average distance travelled between collisions: $\lambda = V/N\pi d_0^2$. Each particle in a gas does a random walk as it bounces elastically off the other particles: $d = n^{\frac{1}{2}}\lambda$. The diffusion rate of a gas particle is much smaller than its velocity.

A solid turns into a liquid when its temperature reaches its melting point. Heat energy must be added to the solid to convert it to a liquid: $\Delta E = mL_f$. The atoms in a liquid have too much energy to be confined indefinitely by their nearest neighbours, yet do not have enough energy to escape those forces completely and become a gas.

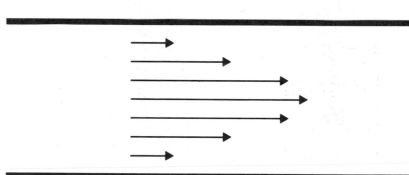

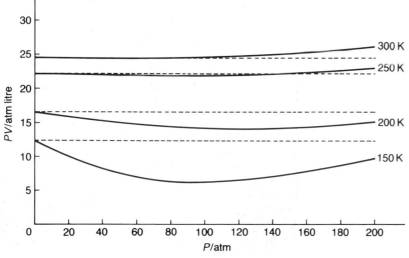

In general, the density of a liquid is less than that of its solid. Liquids have a larger thermal expansivity than their solids. The viscosity of a liquid drops rapidly with temperature as the atoms gain more energy and can move past each other more easily. Liquids are virtually incompressible.

The upthrust on an object immersed in a fluid is equal to the weight of fluid displaced (Archimedes' Principle). Objects can float on a fluid if their density is less than that of the fluid.

ELECTRICITY

Despite its familiarity, electricity can be a very puzzling phenomenon. You use it every day to run the many gadgets on which your comfort and ease depends, to communicate with others and to acquire information. Yet even the most complex electrical device (such as a computer or portable telephone) can be used without needing to have more than an elementary knowledge of electricity. It is a self-effacing technology.

In fact, the whole story of electricity is very complicated. A complete understanding of electricity involves the physics of the very small. You need quantum mechanics to fully predict the behaviour of electrons in metals and semiconductors, using calculations which are fiendishly complex. Fortunately, the story of electricity can be told at various levels. In this chapter, we are going to start off at the simplest level, with a model for the macroscopic behaviour of electricity. Later on we will add to the model, leading you towards an understanding of electricity at a microscopic and atomic level.

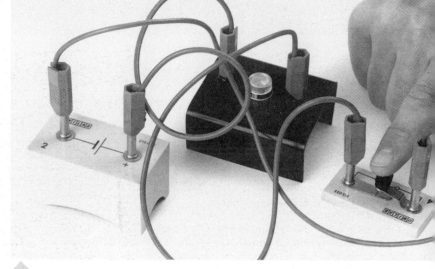

Figure 10.1 A very simple electrical circuit

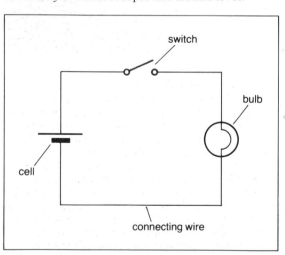

Figure 10.2 The bulb will only glow if the switch is closed

Figure 10.3 The flow of energy in an electrical circuit

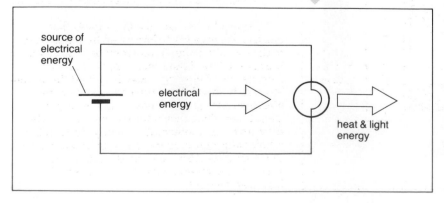

CHARGE

In order to satisfactorily explain electricity you have to assume that some of the fundamental particles out of which our Universe is built have a property called **charge**. Just as the mass of a particle fixes how much gravitational energy it has, the charge fixes its electrical energy. In order to convince you of the reasonableness of this invention, we will start off by reminding you about what electricity can do.

Energy transfer

Figure 10.1 illustrates what was probably the first electrical circuit you built. A light bulb is connected to a cell by a pair of wires. We are going to use your experience of simple circuits of this type to help you towards an understanding of the modern model of electricity.

Elementary facts
The first thing that you learn about electricity is the importance of having two unbroken metallic paths between the bulb and the cell. These metallic paths are called **conductors**, and a break anywhere in either of them is enough to stop the bulb from glowing. In fact, breaks, in the form of **switches**, can be deliberately introduced in the circuit to control the bulb. As you can see from figure 10.2, the bulb will only glow when the switch is **closed**. (Figure 10.2 is a **circuit diagram**, representing the circuit by means of standard **circuit symbols**. These symbols appear in Appendix D.)

Figure 10.4 Some examples of output transducers, devices which convert electrical energy into another sort of energy

Figure 10.5 A number of sources of electrical energy

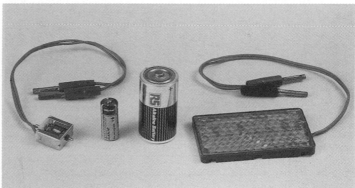

The second thing that you learn is that the bulb will not glow forever. Eventually, the cell becomes exhausted and the bulb goes out. This is what you would expect from the Principle of Energy Conservation. After all, the bulb emits light because it is white hot. That heat energy must have been transferred to the bulb from the cell via the two conductors (figure 10.3). So the rate of generation of heat energy in the bulb must equal the rate at which the cell loses internal energy. Unless there is some external input of energy to the system, the finite available energy in the cell must eventually fall to zero.

The third important fact about electricity is that there exists a wide variety of **output transducers**. A number of them are shown in figure 10.4. Each one produces a different sort of energy when connected into the circuit. The resistor produces heat energy, the motor produces rotational energy and the buzzer produces sound energy. So the **electrical energy** transferred from the cell along the two conductors can be converted into a variety of other energies, depending on the particular output transducer inserted into the circuit.

Fourthly, the chemical cell is not the only possible source of electrical energy. A couple of alternative devices are illustrated in figure 10.5. They require a continuous input of energy (be it light or rotational) in order to feed out electrical energy.

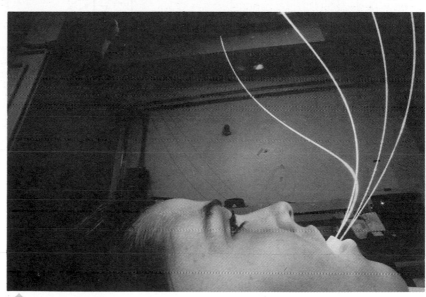

Figure 10.6 Optical fibres carrying red light into a patient's throat to kill a tumour

Figure 10.7 A flow of carriers in a loop can transport energy from left to right

Circulation in conductors

By now it should be obvious that an electrical circuit is simply a way of getting energy from one device to another via a pair of conductors. The puzzling aspect is that the energy transfer *only* takes place when *both* of the conductors are present. So we cannot think of electrical energy as something which can travel from one place to another like light or heat radiation — this would only need a single conductor. For example, a single optical fibre can transfer energy from one place to another. Figure 10.6 shows how the beam from a laser can be piped down an optical fibre to be converted into energy when it emerges from the far end.

The need for two conductors implies that electrical energy has to be carried from the source to the transducer by a circulation of **carriers** inside the conductors. Take a look at figure 10.7. The carriers are all moving clockwise round the system at a steady speed. They leave the source with electrical energy and deposit it in the output transducer. Then they return to the source, where they are given another lot of energy. To keep the whole thing going, energy needs to be fed in from the outside world at one end: the rate at which it enters at the left is equal to the rate at which it leaves at the right.

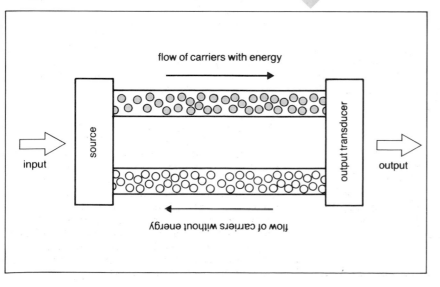

flow of carriers with energy

input

source

output transducer

output

flow of carriers without energy

HYDRAULIC SYSTEMS

In case you are unsure how a circulation of something in a loop can transfer energy one way, consider the hydraulic system shown in figure 10.8. A pump on the left forces oil to flow clockwise round the system through the pipes. On the right the oil flows through a turbine, generating rotational energy. Notice the similarities between the hydraulic and electrical energy transfer systems. Any breaks in either pipe will stop the energy transfer immediately, and the pipes can bend and twist without stopping the energy getting through. If electrical systems behave like hydraulic ones, then perhaps we can calculate the rate of energy transfer (the power) in the same way.

Figure 10.8 Circulating liquids can transport energy

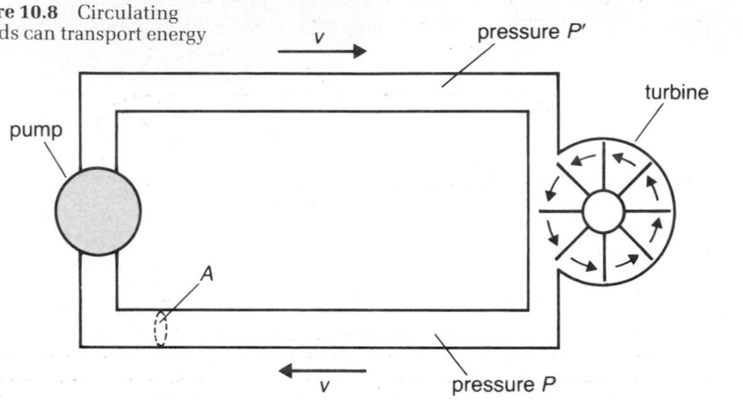

Assume that the oil is ideal, i.e. there is no friction in the flow of oil down the pipes. Suppose that the oil leaves the pump with pressure P' and returns with pressure P, travelling down the pipes (cross-sectional area A) with a constant speed v. Let's find the work done on the turbine in one second. Look at figure 10.8 and consider the oil going through the turbine. In one second, the oil in both pipes will move a distance v. The work done by the oil entering the turbine will be given by

$$E = Fd \qquad \therefore E' = (P'A) \times v \qquad (1)$$

The work done by the turbine on the oil leaving it during the same time will be given by a similar expression.

$$E = Fd \qquad \therefore E = PAv \qquad (2)$$

If we subtract equation (2) from equation (1) we obtain the energy output per second for the turbine, its output power P_{out}.

$$P_{out} = E' - E \qquad \therefore P_{out} = (P' - P) \times Av \qquad (3)$$

Figure 10.9 A modern hydraulic machine

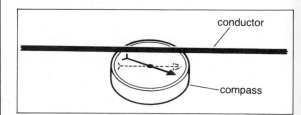

So the output power is the product of two terms. The first is the pressure difference in the two pipes, and the second is the volume flow rate in the pipes. (Notice that the energy delivered to the turbine is *not* the kinetic energy of the oil in the pipes.) The Victorians, who pioneered the application of electricity were familiar with hydraulic machinery (figure 10.9) so were able to spot the similarities between them.

Measuring current

The above examples where a circulation carries energy from one place to another share a general conservation rule.

> Whatever it is that is circulating, the rate at which it passes any point in the loop is the same all the way round the loop.

For example, consider a hydraulic system (figure 10.11). The mass of oil passing any point in one second is the same all the way round, regardless of the cross-sectional area of the pipe, i.e. $\rho v A$ remains constant. Similarly, the mass of belt passing any point per second in a pulley system will also be constant all the way round the belt.

Current

These analogies imply that if electrical energy is transferred by a circulation of carriers within the conductors, then the carrier flow rate will be the same all the way round the circuit. In other words, it seems reasonable to suppose that something called **charge** is circulating within the conductors, and that the rate at which charge flows through a conductor (the **current**) will be the same all the way round the circuit.

$$I = \frac{Q}{t}$$

I is the current in the conductor (A)

Q is the charge flowing past a point (C)

t is the time taken for the charge to flow past the point (s)

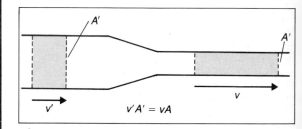

Figure 10.11 The volume flow rate is constant for an incompressible fluid going down a pipe

Figure 10.12 A simple galvanometer

(The standard unit of charge, the coulomb, is the same as an ampere-second, defined via the equation $Q = It$.) Of course, the only way to test the reasonableness of this model is by trying to measure some quantity which is conserved in an electrical circuit. What we need is a charge flowmeter or galvanometer.

Galvanometers

In 1762 Luigi Galvani discovered that the leg of a frog would contract when connected to a chemical cell by a pair of conductors. For many years, investigators of electricity used themselves or frogs' legs as detectors of electricity. Apart from the subjective nature of judging the strength of the shock, the big disadvantage of this method of measuring electricity was the necessity of breaking the circuit to insert the frog's leg. Furthermore, the frog's leg appeared to be acting like an output transducer (an energy converter) rather than a measurer of electric current. It was not until 1820 that Hans Oersted invented a non-invasive method of detecting electricity. His simple **galvanometer** is illustrated in figure 10.12. The conductor has to run over the top of the compass in a North-South direction. Whenever electrical energy passes along the circuit, the compass needle is deflected. Once the needle is in static equilibrium, the compass does not extract any more energy from the circuit, so the angle of deflection can be used as a measure of whatever is going on in the conductor without interfering with it. Furthermore, the deflection of Oersted's galvanometer is independent of the part of the circuit placed over it, supporting the idea that it is measuring the current in the conductors rather than the energy of the charge which is flowing.

Forces between conductors

Shortly after Oersted's discovery, André Ampère found that there are forces between the conductors in an electrical circuit. In particular, there is a weak attractive force between two parallel conductors carrying current in the same direction (figure 10.16). (In chapter 23 you will find out how this interaction can be modelled with the help of something called a **magnetic field**, but you don't need that model in order to use the effect to measure electric current. Provided that the effect is measurable and depends on the current, then it can be used to make a galvanometer.) The magnetic interaction of conductors is the basis of the internationally agreed unit of current, the ampere.

Figure 10.16 The magnetic field created by the current I' interacts with the current I to give the attractive force F

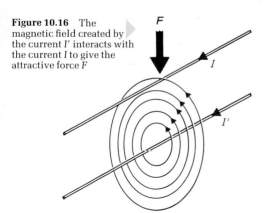

PULLEY SYSTEMS

Another method of transmitting energy by a circulation is illustrated in figure 10.10. The pulley wheel on the left is given rotational energy by the motor — this is transmitted to the windlass on the right by a belt. If the belt moves with a speed v and the tensions before and after the belt moves over the windlass are T' and T, respectively, it can be easily shown that the power transferred from the motor to the windlass is given by

$$P_{out} = (T' - T) \times v$$

This is similar to the same expression for hydraulic systems. The output power depends on both the speed of the circulation and the difference in some property of the circulating medium before and after the output transducer.

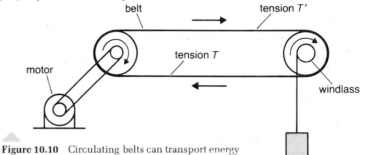

Figure 10.10 Circulating belts can transport energy

AMMETERS ▶▶23

Oersted's galvanometer was not very sensitive. Figure 10.13 shows an early improvement, the **tangent galvanometer**. The conductor which carries the current to be measured is made to loop around the compass several times to make a coil. This increases the deflecting force on the needle, making the instrument more sensitive. An even more sensitive arrangement is illustrated in figure 10.14. It is called a **light-beam galvanometer**. This time the coil which carries the current sits inside a magnetic field which is about 100 times stronger than the Earth's field. The forces on the coil make a couple which causes the coil to twist round. As the coil suspension wires are twisted they exert an opposite couple, so the coil ends up being deflected by an angle proportional to the force. This deflection is measured by bouncing a beam of light off a mirror attached to the coil onto a scale some distance away. The spot of a typical modern light beam galvanometer will deflect 2.5 mm for a current of only 100 nA in the coil. General purpose ammeters have the same basic construction as a light-beam galvanometer, but need a more robust coil mounting to support the pointer (figure 10.15). Nevertheless, a sensitivity of 1 μA is commonplace.

Figure 10.13 A tangent galvanometer. The plane of the coils has to be parallel to the needle when there is no current. The current in the coils is proportional to the tangent of the needle deflection

Figure 10.14 A light beam galvanometer

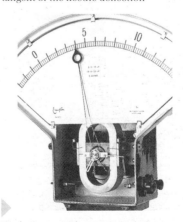

Figure 10.15 The movement of a general purpose ammeter; note the springs which are used to carry current to the coil

A current of 1 A in two straight parallel conductors of infinite length and negligible thickness placed 1 m apart in a vacuum will exert a force of 2×10^{-7} N per metre of conductor.

This definition is exact, but rather cumbersome and difficult to apply directly. In practice, the current balances used by standards laboratories employ coils rather than straight wires (figure 10.17).

Imagine that you want to calibrate an ammeter with the help of the above definition of an ampere. A little thought will convince you that it is not enough to know the force on the conductors for 1 A. You also need to know how the force varies with the current. The following thought experiment should help explain why physicists choose to assume that the force will be proportional to the square of the current.

Figure 10.16 shows a segment of a pair of infinite parallel conductors which carry different currents I and I'. Consider the top conductor. It sits in the **magnetic field** created by the current I' in the bottom conductor and experiences a force F as a consequence. (That field can be detected by its effect on a compass needle. The needle is aligned along the perimeter of a circle centred on the conductor.) Now if that field is not affected by the presence of the top conductor, then the introduction of another identical conductor will not change it. But if the two top conductors are fastened to each other (figure 10.18), this is equivalent to a single conductor carrying a current of $2I$ and experiencing a force of $2F$. In other words, the force on a current-carrying conductor should be proportional to the current in it. This is assumed in the design of modern ammeters.

Now consider the bottom conductor. It carries a current I' and experiences a force F' because it sits in the magnetic field created by the current I in the top conductor. We can use the same arguments as above to suggest that F' must be proportional to I'. Furthermore, Newton's Third Law of Motion tells us that F must be equal and opposite to F'. So F must be proportional to both I and I', i.e. $F \propto I \times I'$. If both conductors carry the *same* current I, then the force between them must be proportional to I^2.

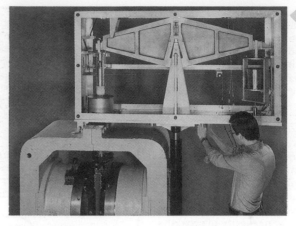

Figure 10.17 A current balance at a standards laboratory

Charge flow

Ammeters can be used to verify that the same current flows in all of the conductors in a simple circuit (figure 10.19). Even though the diameter of the conductors may vary from one place to another as the charge flows round the circuit, the current is found to be the same everywhere. This suggests that the charge in the conductors behaves like the incompressible fluid in a hydraulic system, speeding up where the conductor narrows and slowing down where it widens. So we ought to build a model of electricity which incorporates this property.

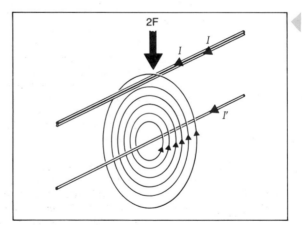

Figure 10.18 F is proportional to I

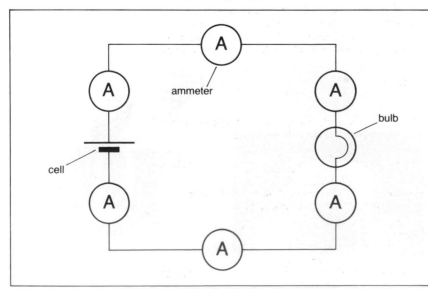

Figure 10.19 How to verify that current in a series circuit is conserved

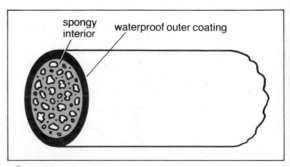

Figure 10.20 A model of a conductor: the gaps in the spongy interior are filled with water

The model

Let's suppose that any conductor contains a number of particles called **charge carriers**. Each cubic metre of conductor contains n carriers, each of which has a charge q. These particles are able to move around inside the conductor, but cannot escape from it. The carrier density n remains constant as the carriers drift along the conductor with a velocity v, because they repel each other. It may help if you consider the following analogy of this model. The conductor behaves like a polythene-coated sponge (figure 10.20). Its interior is therefore riddled with holes which allow water molecules to drift through it. The mass of each water molecule is analogous to the charge of each carrier, and the repulsive forces between the water molecules ensure that the 'charge' density remains almost constant.

Drift velocity

We can use the model to estimate the **drift velocity** of the carriers in a typical metal. Look at figure 10.21. If all of the carriers are moving from left to right with the same velocity v, then each one moves a distance vt in a time t. So all of the carriers in a volume $vt \times A$ will pass a sample point in the conductor in time t. (Think of toothpaste.) Each of the carriers in that volume will have a charge q, so the total charge passing the point per second will be

$$Q = n \times vt A \times q \qquad \textbf{(10.1)}$$

Equation (10.1) can be used to get an expression for the current.

$$I = \frac{Q}{t} \quad \therefore \ I = \frac{nvtAq}{t} \quad \therefore I = nAqv \qquad \textbf{(10.2)}$$

$I = nAqv$

I is the current in a conductor (A)

n is the density of charge carriers (m^{-3})

A is the cross-sectional area of the conductor (m^2)

q is the charge of each carrier (C)

v is the drift velocity of the charge carriers (m s^{-1})

There is evidence that there is at least one carrier with a charge of 1.6×10^{-19} C associated with each atom in a metal. Let's assume this to estimate the drift velocity of the carriers in the wires of a torch. Typically, the wires will be made of copper (8.5×10^{28} atoms per cubic metre) with a diameter of 1.0 mm, carrying a current of 0.10 A.

$I = nAqv$

$\therefore 0.1 = 8.5 \times 10^{28} \times \pi \times (5 \times 10^{-4})^2 \\ \qquad \times 1.6 \times 10^{-19} \times v$

$\therefore v \simeq 1 \times 10^{-5}$ m s^{-1}

You are probably rather surprised at the low value for the drift velocity. A torch might contain about 30 cm of wire altogether: you can check that it will take about 8 hours for the carriers to drift round the whole circuit!

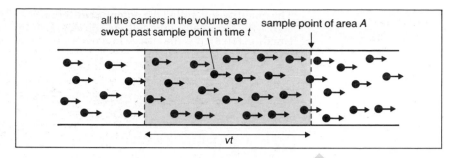

all the carriers in the volume are swept past sample point in time t

sample point of area A

vt

Figure 10.21 Drifting charge carriers

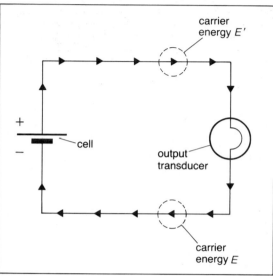

carrier energy E'

cell

output transducer

carrier energy E

Figure 10.22 The charge carriers lose energy as they drift through an output transducer

The average velocity of electrons in a metal is about 1×10^6 m s^{-1}, so they behave like a high temperature gas, moving about freely, reflecting off each other and the edges. The drift velocity is a measure of how fast that electron gas is being moved along inside the metal. The electrical force on the electron gas is associated with the source of electrical energy connected to the ends of the metal.

Potential difference

Consider the carriers moving round the circuit shown in figure 10.22. They leave the plus terminal of the cell with electrical energy E', pass through the output transducer and arrive back at the minus terminal with energy E. They then pass through the cell and emerge once more at the plus terminal with energy E'. Suppose that N carriers go through the output transducer in a time t. The output power will be

$$P = \frac{(E' - E)}{t} \times N \qquad \textbf{(10.3)}$$

If each carrier has a charge q, we can work out the current through the output transducer.

$$I = \frac{Q}{t} \quad \therefore \ I = \frac{Nq}{t} \quad \therefore \ \frac{I}{q} = \frac{N}{t} \qquad \textbf{(10.4)}$$

Now combine equations (10.3) and (10.4) to get a useful expression for the output power.

$$P = \frac{(E' - E)}{q} \times I$$

$$\therefore P = VI \qquad \text{if } V = \frac{(E' - E)}{q} \qquad \textbf{(10.5)}$$

The quantity V is called the **potential difference** across the terminals of the cell. As you can see from equation (10.5), it is the energy loss per unit charge on its way round the circuit.

$$\Delta E = qV$$

ΔE is the energy lost by a carrier (J)

q is the charge of each carrier (C)

V is the potential difference across the conductor (V)

Strictly speaking, the unit of potential difference is joules per coulomb, but it is such a useful concept that it has its own special unit, the volt. Potential difference is something of a mouthful and is often abbreviated to **p.d.** – the alternative word **voltage** is often used.

$$P = VI$$

P is the output power of a device (W)

V is the p.d. across the device (V)

I is the current in the device (A)

The unit for p.d. (the volt) is named after Allessandro Volta who invented the chemical cell in about 1800. The voltaic pile shown in figure 10.23 consists of a number of cells in line with each other to make a battery. Each cell produces a p.d. of about 1.5 V, but the p.d. across the battery of several cells can deliver quite a shock!

Figure 10.24 Measuring the p.d. across the terminals of a battery by measuring the energy delivered to a heating coil

Figure 10.23 An early battery of plates of zinc (Z) and silver (A)

Electrical heating

In principle, the voltage across the terminals of a battery could be measured by finding out how much heat energy was generated in an electrical circuit. The apparatus is shown in figure 10.24(a). An ammeter measures the current in the insulated wire which is wrapped round a thermally isolated lump of copper. The metal is cooled below room temperature before the current is turned on, and its temperature measured at fixed time intervals with a thermocouple. A graph of typical results is shown in figure 10.24(b). The rate of heat energy loss will be zero when the block passes room temperature, so the rate of temperature rise at that point $\Delta T/\Delta t$ can be used in conjunction with the known specific heat capacity of copper to calculate the heating power of the coil. Relevant data are shown in table 10.1.

Table 10.1

temperature gradient at room temperature	4.2 K min^{-1}
mass of copper	250 g
specific heat capacity of copper	381 J kg^{-1}
ammeter reading	0.81 A

Start off by calculating the heat energy given to the block per minute.

$$\Delta Q = mc\Delta T$$

$$\therefore \Delta Q = 0.25 \times 381 \times 4.2 = 400\ \text{J}$$

Then calculate the power output of the heating coil.

$$P = VI \quad \therefore \quad \frac{400}{60} = V \times 0.81$$

$$\therefore V = \frac{400}{60 \times 0.81} = 8.2\ \text{V}$$

So the p.d. across the battery terminals must have been 8.2 V. Of course, we have assumed that no heat energy is lost to the surroundings or is generated in the conductors which carry electrical energy from the battery to the heating coil. It should be obvious that this method of measuring p.d. is totally unsuited for everyday use!

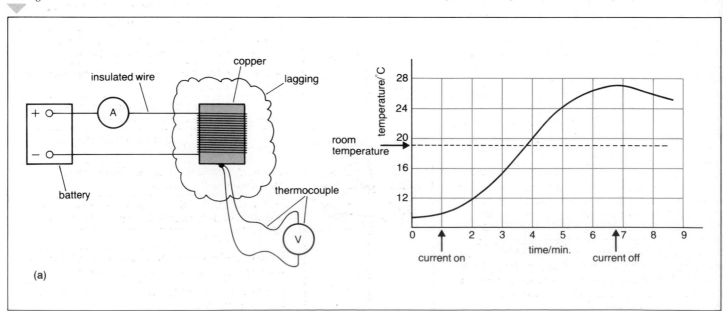

(a)

Electron current

Although ammeters convincingly demonstrate that charge moves in the conductors of an electric circuit, they cannot show the direction in which it is moving. It was agreed a long time ago that charge always flowed in a conductor from the plus terminal of a cell to its minus terminal (figure 10.25). This is known as **conventional current**, and assumes that the carriers have a positive charge. The plus terminal must therefore have a higher potential than the minus terminal, so that the carriers lose electrical energy on their way round the circuit.

Unfortunately, we now believe that the charge carriers in metals are **electrons** which have a negative charge $-e$. In order for them to lose energy on their way round the circuit, electrons have to move from low potential to high potential (figure 10.26).

$$\Delta E = qV \qquad \therefore \Delta E = (-e) \times (-V) = +eV \qquad \textbf{(10.6)}$$

From now on, the word current will exclusively mean conventional current. If we want to talk about the motion of electrons in conductors, the term **electron current** will be used.

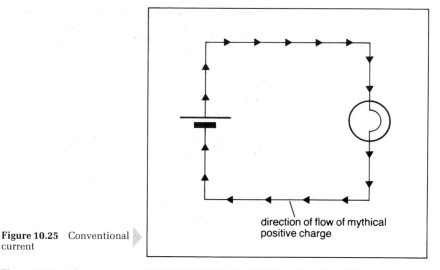

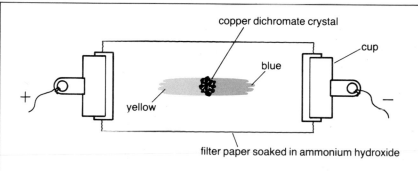

Figure 10.25 Conventional current

Figure 10.26 Electron current

direction of flow of mythical positive charge

direction of flow of real electrons

copper dichromate crystal

cup

blue

yellow

filter paper soaked in ammonium hydroxide

Positive and negative carriers

Non-metallic conductors may have a mixture of positive and negative charge carriers. A dramatic demonstration of this is illustrated in figure 10.27. A length of filter paper soaked in ammonium hydroxide is made part of an electrical circuit and a small brown crystal of copper dichromate is placed at its centre. As the crystal dissolves, it can be seen to separate into two coloured components. A blue component drifts towards the low potential end of the paper and a yellow component drifts towards the high potential end. The blue copper ions are therefore positive and the yellow chromate ions are negative: current flows through solutions by means of both positive and negative charge carriers.

Direct evidence that the charge carriers in metals are negative came from an experiment done by Kettering and Scott in 1944. A coil of wire was suspended as shown in figure 10.28, carefully shielded from magnetic fields and draughts. The direction of the current in the coil was reversed at regular intervals. Each time this happened, the change in momentum of the electrons gave an impulse to the coil, setting it swinging. The current reversals were timed so that they would increase the amplitude of the swing to a level which could be detected by a light beam reflecting off the mirror. They tried several different metals, each of which turned out to have carriers flowing from low potential to high potential.

Figure 10.27 Solutions of ionic solids contain positive and negative charge carriers

Figure 10.28 Apparatus for measuring the sign of charge carriers in a metal coil

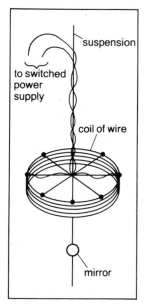

suspension

to switched power supply

coil of wire

mirror

OBJECTIVES

After studying this section you should be able to do the following.

Use the concept of charge to account for the transfer of electrical energy in a circuit.

Know how to recognise and draw a circuit diagram with standard symbols.

Know that an ammeter measures the rate of flow of charge past a point in a conductor.

Use the formula $I = Q/t$ and understand the meaning of *current*.

Use the formula $I = nAqv$ and understand the meaning of *drift velocity*.

Use the formula $\Delta E = qV$ and understand the meaning of *potential difference* and *voltage*.

Use the formula $P = VI$.

Understand how a voltmeter can be calibrated via the heating effect of an electric current.

State the difference between conventional and electron currents.

QUESTIONS

Figure 10.29

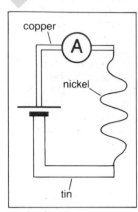

1 The circuit shown in figure 10.29 contains three different wires with the same length. An ammeter has been inserted in the copper wire and reads 0.20 A. Table 10.2 contains some data for the wires.

Table 10.2

	Copper	Nickel	Tin
diameter/mm	0.56	0.15	1.63
density/kg m^{-3}	8940	8900	7310
molar mass/kg mol^{-1}	0.0635	0.0587	0.119

a Calculate the drift velocity of the electrons in each of the wires, assuming that there is one electron for each atom. ($q = -1.6 \times 10^{-19}$ C for electrons).

b Suggest, with reasons, which of the wires is going to generate the most heat energy.

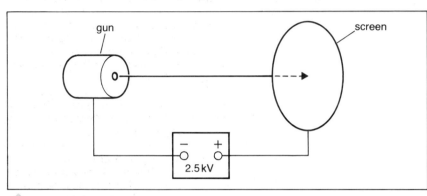

Figure 10.31

2 Savita has done an investigation into how batteries change as they are used up. The graphs in figure 10.30 summarise her results. A fresh battery was connected to a light bulb until it was completely exhausted: a data logger was used to measure the p.d. across the bulb and the current in the wires at intervals.

a Use the graph to estimate how many coulombs of charge flowed through the bulb in the whole experiment. How many electrons does this represent?

b Use the data to draw a graph which shows how the output power changed with time during the experiment. Use your graph to estimate the total available energy in the fresh battery.

3 Sally describes an analogy for electricity to her class. 'It's a bit like how a supermarket gets its cornflakes. Lorries start off at the warehouse full of cornflakes and set off for the supermarket at a steady speed, one after the other and a fixed distance apart. When they get to the supermarket they are unloaded and go back to the warehouse by a different road.'

a What things correspond to conductors, charge carriers, output transducers and cells in this analogy?

b What are Sally's analogies for charge, potential and output power?

c Describe what Sally could use as an analogy for an ammeter.

d When the switch of figure 10.2 is closed, the bulb glows straight away, even though it will take an electron several hours to drift from the cell to the bulb. Use Sally's analogy to explain these facts.

4 Domestic electrical devices in England are designed to operate off an average p.d. of 240 V. They have to be protected with **fuses**. These are thin lengths of wire encased in ceramic which melt when enough current goes through them. The fuses are inserted in the conductors which carry current from the wall socket to the device. Three types of fuse are in common use, rated at 13 A, 5 A and 3 A, respectively. It is good practice to use the fuse with the lowest rating which will not melt when the device operates normally. Choose suitable fuses for each of the following items.

a A 2.5 kW kettle.
b A 50 W word processor.
c A 1 kW drill.

5 In the vacuum of a TV tube, an electron current of 5.0 mA flows from the electron gun to the screen, as shown in figure 10.31. The potential difference between gun and screen is 2.5 kV, and each electron has a charge of -1.6×10^{-19} C.

a If the screen has a potential of 0 V, what is the potential of the electron gun?

b How much electrical energy does each electron lose on its way between gun and screen?

c What is that energy converted to *before* the electrons hit the screen? What about when they hit the screen?

d How many electrons hit the screen per second? At what rate do they deliver energy to it?

e If the mass of an electron is 9.1×10^{-31} kg, how large is the force exerted on the screen by the electrons? Assume they have no kinetic energy after impact.

Figure 10.30

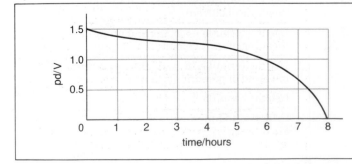

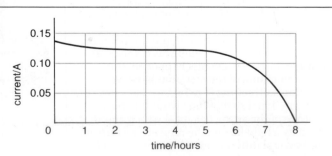

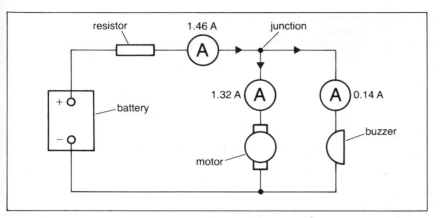

Figure 10.32 Current is conserved at a junction

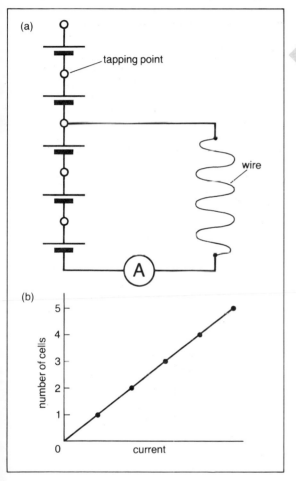

Figure 10.33 Using a battery of cells to show that V is proportional to I for a metal wire

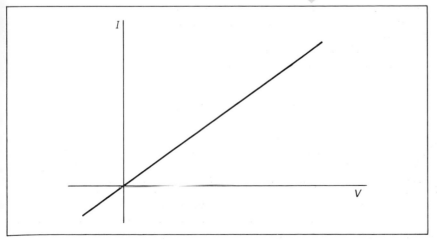

Figure 10.34 The I–V curve of a metal at constant temperature

RESISTANCE

The first section of this chapter showed how you could measure the current in a conductor with a moving-coil ammeter. For example, figure 10.32 shows how three ammeters could be inserted in a circuit to verify that current is conserved at a junction between conductors. However, the measurement of the energy delivered to each part of the circuit is fraught with difficulty. The discovery of a remarkable property of metals by Georg Ohm in 1826 made it possible to adapt an ammeter so that it could accurately measure the p.d. across parts of a circuit. Ohm's Law makes voltmeters a practical possibility.

Ohm's Law

Georg Ohm set out to discover the factors which control the current in a conductor. He reasoned that it must depend on the shape and size of the conductor, its material and the source of electrical energy it is connected to. Among other discoveries, he found a simple and precise relationship between the current in a metal and the p.d. across it. It is called **Ohm's Law**.

> The current in a metal is proportional to the p.d. across it provided that it is kept at a constant temperature and pressure.

Figure 10.33 shows how you could set about verifying Ohm's Law without using a voltmeter. If the cells in the battery are identical, then carriers at their plus terminals have qV more electrical energy than carriers at the minus terminals. So if you **tap** into n cells of the battery, a p.d. of nV is placed across the wire. The graph of figure 10.33(b) shows how the ammeter reading depends on the number of cells in the circuit. Of course, the experiment is more difficult than it looks. All of the electrical energy is going to appear as heat in the wire, so it has to be kept in a constant temperature environment, such as a dish of oil. Then there is the problem of ensuring that all of the cells in the battery are identical. Ohm used thermocouples as his source of electrical energy because the chemical cells available at the time were crude and unreliable. Each cell would have to be tested separately with a standard wire and ammeter to establish that it was the same as all of the others.

Resistance formula

Since the current in all metals is proportional to the p.d. across them, their I–V curve (the graph of figure 10.34) is a straight line through the origin. The **resistance** of a metal (or anything else) is defined as the p.d. divided by the current.

> $$R = \frac{V}{I}$$
> R is the resistance of the object (Ω)
>
> V is the p.d. across the object (V)
>
> I is the current in the object (A)

Resistance is a widely used concept, so it has been blessed with its own unit, the ohm (Ω).

As the p.d. across a metal is proportional to its current, its resistance is going to be independent of the current. In other words, *measurement* of the current in a known resistance allows us to *calculate* the p.d. across it with confidence. A **resistor** is a device designed to have a known constant resistance. For example, suppose that the ammeter in the circuit of figure 10.35 reads 150 μA when the resistor has a value of 10 kΩ.

$$R = 10 \text{ k}\Omega = 1.0 \times 10^4 \,\Omega \qquad R = \frac{V}{I}$$

$$V = ?$$

$$I = 150 \,\mu\text{A} = 1.5 \times 10^{-4} \text{ A}$$

$$\therefore 1.0 \times 10^4 = \frac{V}{1.5 \times 10^{-4}}$$

$$\therefore V = 1.5 \text{ V}$$

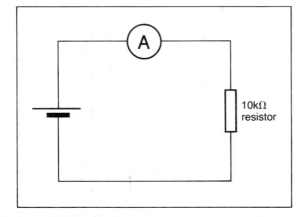

So the p.d. across the resistor must be 1.5 V. If we ignore the p.d. across the ammeter we can assume that the p.d. across the cell terminals is also 1.5 V.

Resistivity

Ohm also established how the resistance of a conductor depends on its shape and size.

$$R = \frac{\rho l}{A}$$

R is the resistance of the conductor (Ω)

ρ is the resistivity of the of the conductor (Ω m)

l is the length of the conductor (m)

A is the cross-sectional area of the conductor (m²)

The **resistivity** is an intrinsic property of the conductor's material: its value is independent of shape or size of the conductor. Table 10.3 shows approximate resistivity values for various materials at room temperature.

Table 10.3

Material	ρ/Ω m
aluminium	3×10^{-8}
copper	2×10^{-8}
iron	9×10^{-8}
carbon	6×10^{-5}
silicon	3×10^{1}
glass	1×10^{6}
rubber	1×10^{11}
polythene	1×10^{14}

The table suggests that there are three classes of material. The **conductors** are the metals with very low values for ρ. **Semiconductors** (e.g. carbon and silicon) have higher resistivity values, around unity. Finally, **insulators** have very high values of resistivity.

Temperature dependence

The graph of figure 10.36 shows how the resistivity of various metals changes with temperature. In general, the resistivity of a metal is roughly proportional to its kelvin temperature. This is the basis of the platinum-resistance thermometer, widely used as a secondary standard between 14 K and 631 K. At very low temperatures, a number of pure metals become **superconductors**: their resistivity drops to zero. Alloys tend to be superconductors up to higher temperatures, and a number of metal oxides have been recently manufactured which are superconducting to at least 100 K. A number of values are given in table 10.4.

Figure 10.35   Measuring the current in a resistor

Figure 10.36   Variation of resistivity with temperature for a number of metals

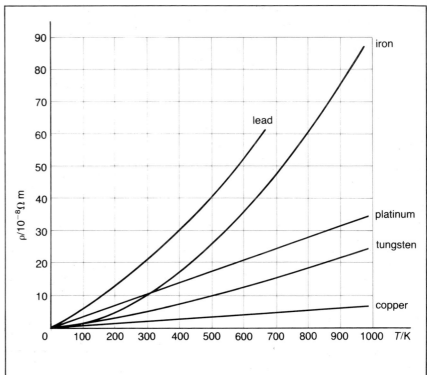

Table 10.4

Metal	Superconducting threshold/K
zinc	0.85
aluminium	1.19
niobium	9.2
niobium–nickel	15.5
niobium–tin	18.4

The resistance of a superconductor is zero, not just very small. This means that charge can flow through a conductor without any p.d. across it — once the charge has been set in motion, it will not stop. The current in a superconductor can be measured by its magnetic effects (like Oersted's galvanometer does), and experiments have shown no detectable decrease in the space of at least a year!

The power output of any conductor of resistance R carrying a current I is given by $P = I^2R$. (You will be asked to prove this for yourself at the end of the chapter.) Normally, some electrical energy is converted to heat in the conductors which link an output transducer to a source of p.d. The existence of superconductors means that, in principle, 100% of the energy which leaves the source of p.d. can be delivered to the output transducer. However, materials which superconduct at room temperature are not yet available, so the phenomenon has only been applied to make scientific toys and large volume electromagnets where the cost of the liquid helium (4 K boiling point) needed to keep the conductors cool can be justified. The newly discovered compounds which are superconducting at liquid nitrogen temperatures (77 K) may have commercial applications as electromagnets in commercial electricity generators and body scanners.

Voltmeters and ammeters

Figure 10.40 shows how a **voltmeter** is used to measure the p.d. across a component in a circuit. The terminals of the voltmeter are connected to either end of the component, in **parallel** with it. Note that the ammeter being used to measure the current in the component is placed in **series** with it.

Multipliers

Moving-coil voltmeters look very similar to ammeters. This is because they actually measure the current in a large resistor, usually known as a **multiplier**. The construction of such a voltmeter is shown in figure 10.41. The galvanometer can be anything which measures current. If a p.d. V is placed across the voltmeter, a small current I_d will be diverted from the source of p.d. into the resistor R_m. That current can be measured by the galvanometer in series with the multiplier. If we know the resistance R_g of the wire in the galvanometer, we can calculate the value of V from the measured value of I_d.

$$R = \frac{V}{I} \quad \therefore R_m + R_g = \frac{V}{I_d}$$

$$\therefore V = I_d(R_m + R_g) \tag{10.7}$$

EFFECT OF SIZE AND SHAPE

The experimentally determined relationship between the resistance of a conductor and its dimensions can be used to test our model of electricity. Look at figure 10.37. The conductor of length l and cross-sectional area A has a current I in it and a p.d. V across it. Suppose that the conductor is split lengthways into two separate conductors, each of cross-sectional area $A/2$ (figure 10.38). It seems reasonable to suppose that the drift velocity of the carriers will be unaffected by this, so each conductor has a current of $I/2$. (Remember, $I = nAqv$.) In other words

$$I \propto A \text{ for constant } V \text{ and } l \tag{1}$$

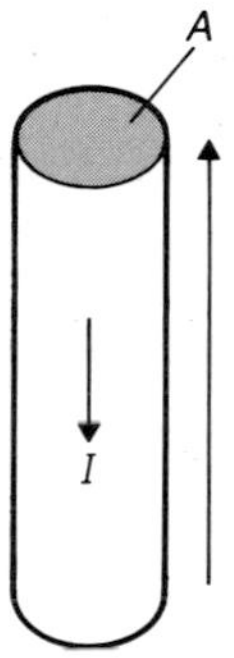

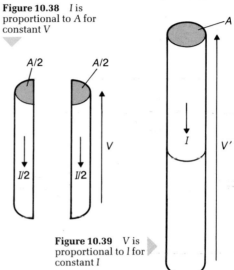

Figure 10.37 A short length of conductor

Figure 10.38 I is proportional to A for constant V

Figure 10.39 V is proportional to l for constant I

Now suppose that we take a second circuit, as shown in figure 10.39. The two conductors in line are equivalent to a single conductor of length $2l$. The p.d. V' across the conductors has been arranged so that the current I in them is the same as in figure 10.37. This means that each conductor in figure 10.39 has the same environment as the conductor in figure 10.37, including the same p.d. across it.

$$V' = 2V \quad \therefore V \propto l \text{ for constant } I \text{ and } A \tag{2}$$

If you study equation (3) carefully you should be able to convince yourself that it is compatible with (1) and (2). In other words, our model agrees with experiment.

$$R = \frac{V}{I}, \quad R = \frac{\rho l}{A} \quad \therefore \frac{V}{I} = \frac{\rho l}{A} \tag{3}$$

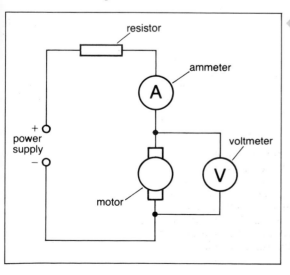

Figure 10.40 Using a voltmeter to measure the p.d. across a motor

Figure 10.41 A voltmeter can be made by putting a resistor in series with a galvanometer

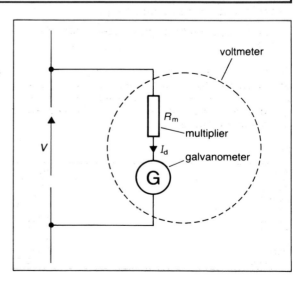

So the galvanometer needle deflection will be proportional to the p.d. across the whole voltmeter.

A popular school galvanometer has a resistance of 1.00 kΩ and a full-scale deflection (**f.s.d.**) of 100 μA. Let's work out the resistance of a multiplier which would convert the galvanometer into a voltmeter with a full-scale deflection of 10.0 V. As figure 10.42 shows, a p.d. of 10.0 V across the multiplier in series with the galvanometer must make the latter read 100 μA. We can therefore calculate the total resistance of the voltmeter.

$$R = ?$$
$$V = 10.0 \text{ V}$$
$$I = 100 \text{ μA} = 1.00 \times 10^{-4} \text{ A}$$
$$R = \frac{V}{I}$$
$$\therefore R = \frac{10.0}{1.00 \times 10^{-4}} = 1.00 \times 10^5 \text{ Ω}$$

1.00×10^5 Ω is 100 kΩ; 1 kΩ of this will be the galvanometer itself, so the multiplier must have a resistance of 99 kΩ.

Shunts

Galvanometers are sensitive instruments, useful for measuring small currents. They can be adapted to make ammeters which can measure large currents by connecting them in parallel with a **shunt**. As figure 10.43 shows, the shunt is a resistor which allows most of the charge flowing in the circuit to bypass the galvanometer.

Suppose that we want to convert a standard school galvanometer (resistance 1.00 kΩ, f.s.d. 100 μA) into an ammeter which can read from 0 to 1.00 A. When there is a current of 1.00 A in the conductors either side of the meter, there must be a current of 100 μA in the galvanometer itself. Since current is conserved at a junction, the current in the shunt must be $1.00 - 0.0001 \simeq 1.00$ A. Furthermore, the p.d. across the shunt must equal the p.d. across the galvanometer—whichever route the charge takes on its way through the ammeter, it must lose the same amount of energy. So we need to calculate the p.d. across the galvanometer first.

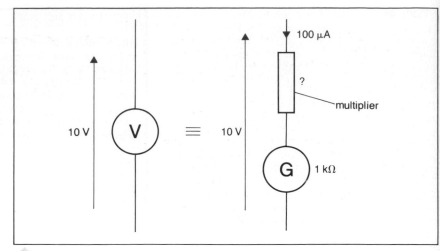

Figure 10.42   Calculating the multiplier resistance

$$R = 1.00 \text{ kΩ} = 1.00 \times 10^3 \text{ Ω}$$
$$V = ?$$
$$I = 100 \text{ μA} = 1.00 \times 10^{-4} \text{ A}$$
$$R = \frac{V}{I}$$
$$\therefore 1.00 \times 10^3 = \frac{V}{1.00 \times 10^{-4}}$$
$$\therefore V = 0.100 \text{ V}$$

Now we can find the resistance of the shunt.

$$R = ?$$
$$V = 0.100 \text{ V}$$
$$I = 1.00 \text{ A}$$
$$R = \frac{V}{I}$$
$$\therefore R = \frac{0.100}{1.00} = 0.100 \text{ Ω}$$

Ideal meters

An ideal ammeter should have an output power of zero, i.e. it does not convert electrical energy into any other sort of energy. This is so that its insertion in a circuit does not alter the current or p.d. in any way. After all, the point of inserting an ammeter is to measure something which you hope is still happening when the ammeter isn't there! So an ideal ammeter should have a resistance of zero. In practice, the resistance of an ammeter depends on its f.s.d. current. Our example above gave an ammeter with a f.s.d. of 1 A which had an effective resistance of 0.1 Ω. It is easily shown that its resistance would have dropped to 0.01 Ω for it to have a f.s.d. current of 10 A.

The ideal voltmeter should also have a power output of zero. Because it is connected in parallel with a component, this means that the ideal voltmeter should have a resistance of infinity. Then connection of the voltmeter will not divert any charge from the component, altering the current in it. In practice, as you saw above, the resistance of a real voltmeter is quite large, but it does depend on the f.s.d voltage. Digital voltmeters have a very high resistance, usually in the region of 10 MΩ, approaching the ideal.

Figure 10.43   Making an ammeter by placing a shunt in parallel with a galvanometer

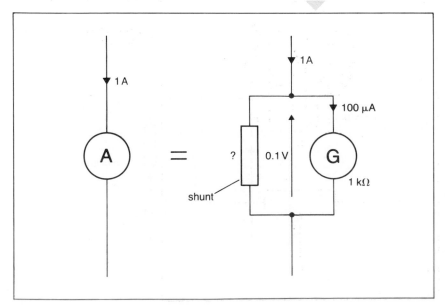

I–V curves

Although everything has a resistance, only some things have a resistance which is independent of current. A metal sample at constant temperature, for example, has an $I-V$ curve which is a straight line, so a single measurement of current and voltage is enough to calculate its resistance. Thereafter, we can invoke Ohm's Law to calculate the current at any other voltage for that sample of metal at that temperature. However, there are many useful electrical devices which do not obey Ohm's Law. Their resistance is a function of current, so their electrical characteristics are best summarised as an $I-V$ curve. Before we introduce you to a number of such non-ohmic conductors, you need some idea about how the curves are obtained.

Obtaining I–V curves

To obtain the $I-V$ curve of a device you need to measure the current in it for different values of p.d. across it. Although modern mains-driven power supplies can provide a continuously variable p.d. at their output terminals, many schools are still equipped with constant voltage power supplies. Figure 10.44 shows how a fixed voltage supply can be used to apply a variable p.d. across a device (the **victim**). The current in the victim can be altered by placing different resistors in the circuit. As the resistor's resistance is reduced from a large value, the current in the victim will increase in steps.

An alternative strategy is to use a variable resistor or **rheostat** to control the current in the victim. In its simplest form, a rheostat is a piece of high resistance wire with a terminal at one end and a sliding contact at the other. This is shown in figure 10.45. The resistance in the circuit will be proportional to the distance between the end terminal and the sliding contact. Modern variable resistors use a circular or helical resistance track, with the sliding contact (or **wiper**) attached to a shaft which can be rotated. One of these is shown in figure 10.46. It is referred to as a **potentiometer**.

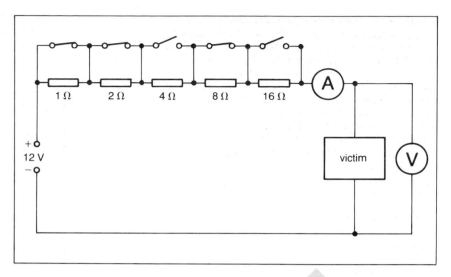

Figure 10.44 Each closed switch allows current to bypass one of the resistors

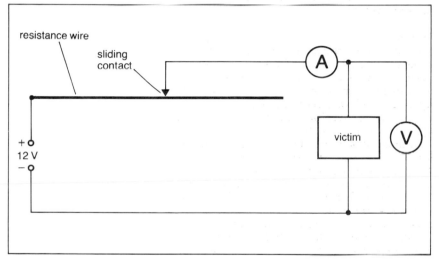

Figure 10.45 The current in the victim can be varied by moving the contact up and down the resistance wire

Figure 10.46 A potentiometer

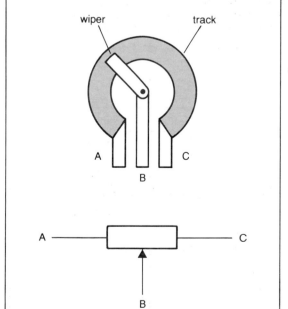

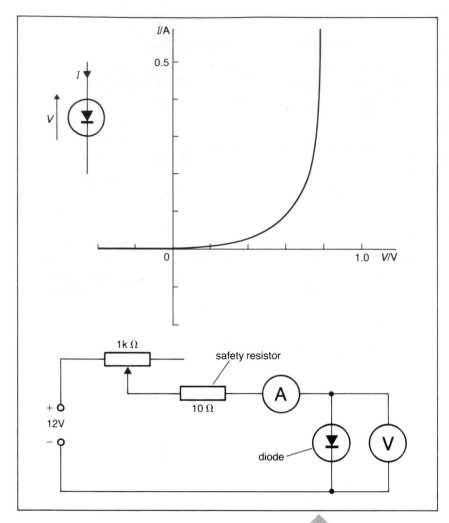

Figure 10.47 Measuring the $I-V$ curve of a silicon diode

Figure 10.48 The $I-V$ curve of an FET current source

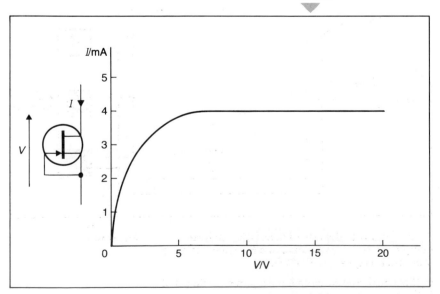

Diodes

A typical $I-V$ curve for a silicon p-n junction **diode** is shown in figure 10.47(a). The circuit used for obtaining data for the positive values of current is also shown in figure 10.47(b); the data for negative values of current are obtained by reversing the diode so that the charge has to flow the other way through it. The curve shows that the current in the diode increases rapidly for positive voltages and is zero for negative voltages. In fact, once the current is above 0.1 A, the voltage hardly changes for any subsequent increase of current. The diode has a p.d. of about 0.7 V across it regardless of the current in it!

Current sources

If the victim is an **FET current source**, the $I-V$ curve looks like the one shown in figure 10.48. Unlike silicon diodes which always have about 0.7 V across them for a finite current, FETs (pronounced 'effeetees') are highly variable. So although their $I-V$ curves have the same shape, each type of FET will have different scales on the axes. We have only drawn the curve for positive currents because this is the only useful region. Note how the FET behaves like a metal at low voltages, with I proportional to V, but has a current which is independent of the voltage above about 5 V.

Filament lamps

A filament lamp (or light bulb) is a small piece of tungsten wire suspended in a mixture of argon and nitrogen gas. As charge flows through the metal wire it gets white hot. Tungsten, like all metals, obeys Ohm's Law, but its resistance increases by a factor of about 10 between room temperature and white heat (3000 K). So its $I-V$ curve will only be a straight line near the origin where the tungsten will be cool. This is shown in figure 10.49. Notice how the curve is symmetrical for both positive and negative currents — this is because the heating effect of a current is independent of its direction in a conductor.

Thermistors

Thermistors are lumps of semiconducting material. The charge carrier density of all semiconductors rises steeply with temperature, so their resistance drops rapidly as their temperature rises. So although thermistors obey Ohm's Law when their temperature is forced to remain constant, they have $I-V$ curves of the type shown in figure 10.50 if they are allowed to heat up. At higher currents enough heat energy is generated in the thermistor to raise it above room temperature and lower its resistance.

OBJECTIVES

After studying this section you should be able to do the following.

State Ohm's Law and explain how it can be verified.

Use the resistance formula.

Use the formula $R = \rho l/A$ and understand the meaning of *resistivity*.

State approximate values for the resistivities of insulators, semiconductors and conductors and how they depend on temperature.

Calculate suitable resistances for shunts and multipliers which convert galvanometers into ammeters and voltmeters with stated f.s.d.'s.

State the properties of ideal ammeters and voltmeters and explain how they are used in circuits.

Know how to use a potentiometer as a rheostat to vary the current in a circuit.

Sketch $I-V$ curves for a wire, a diode, a filament lamp and a thermistor.

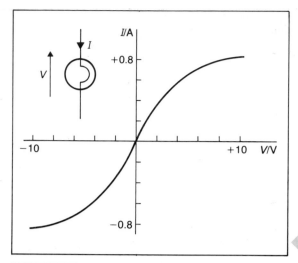

Figure 10.49   The $I-V$ curve of a filament lamp

Figure 10.50   The $I-V$ curve of a thermistor

QUESTIONS

1 You have been given a galvanometer which has a resistance of 100 Ω and a f.s.d. current of 50 μA. Explain how you would adapt it so that it was

a a voltmeter with a f.s.d. of 5.0 V,

b an ammeter with a f.s.d. of 0.50 A.

2 a Show that the rate of generation of heat energy in a wire of resistance R which carries a current I is given by $P = I^2R$.

b A typical domestic mains circuit is designed to carry a maximum current of 30 A between the fuse box and the wall sockets. The arrangement is shown in figure 10.51. Each square loop has an area of 100 m² and is made of copper wire which has a diameter of 1.8 mm. If the resistivity of copper at room temperature is 1.6×10^{-8} Ω m, calculate the resistance of each loop in the ring main.

c Calculate the rate at which heat appears in the ring main when it is run at maximum current; assume that each part of both loops carries a current of 15 A.

d If the ring main delivers a current of 30 A into domestic appliances at an average p.d. of 240 V, what percentage of the energy which passes through the fuse box passes out of the wall sockets?

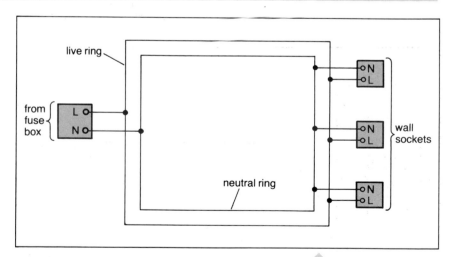

Figure 10.51

3 a Show that the rate of generation of heat energy in a resistor of resistance R which has a p.d. V across it is given by $P = V^2/R$.

b Electrical components have a **power rating**. This is the maximum power output they can tolerate without overheating and being damaged. What is the largest voltage you can safely put across a 100 Ω, 0.5 W resistor?

c A light bulb for use in a car is rated at 12 V, 36 W. What is its resistance in normal use?

4 This question is going to help you to *predict* Ohm's Law from basic principles. It is what is known as a 'fudge' by professional physicists because it applies Newton's Laws of Motion to elementary particles. (Quantum mechanics should really be used to do the job properly.)

Figure 10.52 shows a long, uniform conductor of length l and cross-sectional area A. A p.d. V is placed across it, so there is a current I in it. We want to obtain an expression for the resistivity of the conductor in terms of its microscopic properties, such as the charge carrier density n. Our basic assumption will be that the probability of a single carrier interacting with the conductor in time Δt is $\Delta t / \tau$. This means that the carriers have, on average, $1/\tau$ collisions per second.

a Consider a single charge carrier of mass m and charge q. If it drifts down the conductor at a steady speed $<v>$, show that the change of electrical energy in time τ is given by $\Delta E = -<v>\tau qV/l$.

b τ is the mean time between collisions of the carrier with the rest of the conductor; each collision completely robs the carrier of its kinetic energy. If $<v>$ is the average velocity of the carrier between collisions, show that the kinetic energy gained between collisions is given by $E_k = 2m<v>^2$.

c Use your answers to parts (a) and (b) to show that $<v> = qV\tau/2ml$.

d Now that you have an expression for the drift velocity of the carriers, you can obtain an expression for the current. Rearrange that expression to show that the resistivity of the conductor is given by $\rho = 2m/n\tau q^2$.

e Table 10.5 contains some data for copper. If there is one electron for each atom in the metal, use the data to estimate a value for τ.

Table 10.5

density of copper metal	894 kg m⁻³
molar mass of copper	6.35×10^{-2} kg mol⁻¹
resistivity of copper	1.56×10^{-8} Ω m

f Use the model to explain why conductors generate heat when they have a current in them. Suggest reasons why the resistivity of a conductor increases with increasing temperature.

5 Figure 10.53 shows a number of $I-V$ curves.

a Which curve is for a resistor? What is its resistance?

b One curve is for a cell in series with a resistor. What is the p.d. across the cell and the value of the resistor?

c Use the curve for a diode in series with a resistor to find the value of the resistor.

d Which curve is for a light bulb? Explain why.

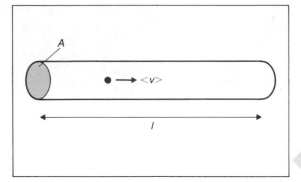

Figure 10.52

Figure 10.53

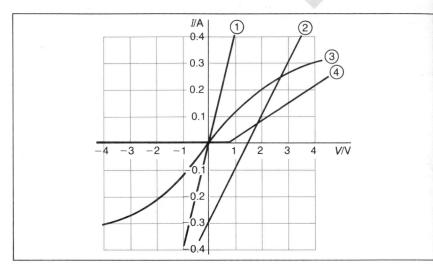

6 A pair of diodes in parallel with a galvanometer can protect it against being overloaded with too much current. The arrangement is shown in figure 10.54(a). The galvanometer has a resistance of 25 Ω and a f.s.d. of 1 mA.

a The $I-V$ graph of figure 10.54(b) is for a single diode. Use it to draw a graph of the resistance of a single diode as a function of the p.d. across it.

b Explain how the diodes in parallel with the galvanometer protect it. Estimate the maximum current and output power of the galvanometer when it is overloaded.

Figure 10.54

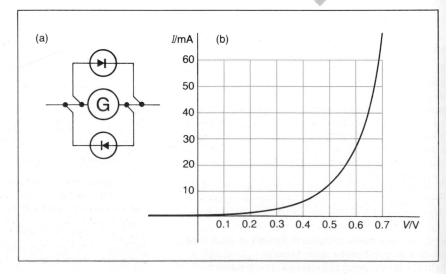

This chapter is going to explain the behaviour of a number of useful circuits. The first group will illustrate how electricity is used to feed output transducers with energy, how several transducers can be run off a single source of p.d., and how to maximise the power drawn from a source of p.d. The second group of circuits use electricity to make precise measurements of quantities such as temperature, pressure and light intensity.

POWER CIRCUITS

To calculate the output power of a transducer you need to know the current in it and the p.d. across it. Current and p.d. are abstract quantities, but they do have the advantage of being easily measured in the laboratory. The electrons which actually carry the energy from one place to another in a circuit are not easily detected, so a macroscopic model of electricity will be used, rather than a microscopic one. Of course, the behaviour of current and voltage can be deduced from our understanding of the properties of electrons in metals. So before we proceed to look at specific circuits, we need to formulate the laws governing the behaviour of current and voltage in a circuit. There are two of them, and they are named after the man who first stated them.

Kirchhoff's Laws

The first law states that electric current is a conserved quantity.

> The sum of the currents approaching a junction in a circuit equals the sum of the currents leaving the junction

Current is conserved because the mobile electrons in a metal behave like an incompressible fluid. Their density (8.47×10^{28} m^{-3} for copper) is independent of their drift velocity. An example of the first law is illustrated in figure 11.1. Each of the bulbs are rated at 6 V, 0.06 A. The four bulbs are in **parallel** with each other and are operating normally. The current in the resistor must therefore be $4 \times 0.06 = 0.24$ A. Furthermore, the ammeter in the circuit must also read 0.24 A: the current in each of the conductors attached to the power supply terminals must be the same as each other.

The second law is arrived at by applying the Principle of Energy Conservation to electrical circuits.

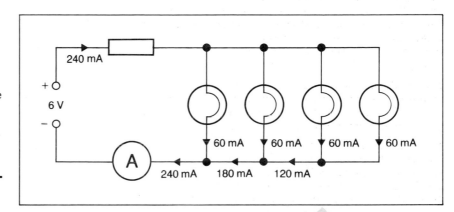

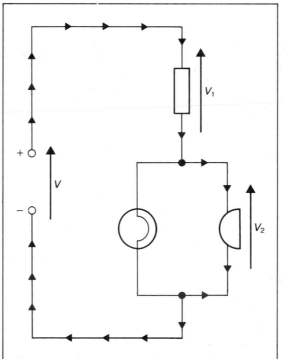

Figure 11.1 Current is conserved

Figure 11.2 $V = V_1 + V_2$

> For any closed loop in an electrical circuit, the sum of the voltages around the loop must add up to zero

Consider a single charge carrier leaving the plus terminal of a battery (figure 11.2). It moves along the conductors through two of the three transducers, losing a certain amount of electrical energy on its way through each. When it arrives back at the minus terminal of the battery, it will have lost a total energy given by

$$\Delta E = qV_1 + qV_2 \tag{11.1}$$

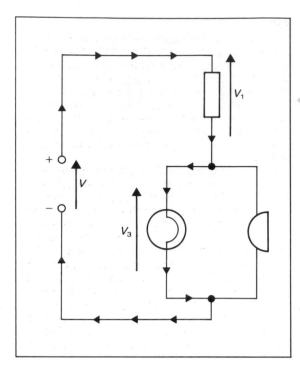

Figure 11.3 $V = V_1 + V_3$

Figure 11.5 The current-limiting resistor protects the filament lamp

Figure 11.4 Connecting a filament lamp directly to a source of p.d.

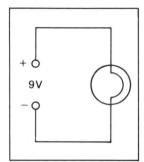

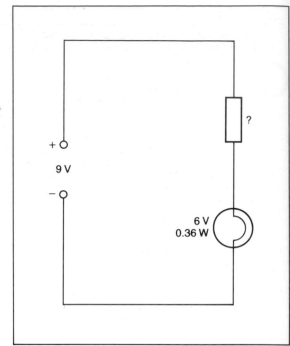

On its way through the battery back to the plus terminal, the charge will be given electrical energy. If the p.d. across the battery terminals is V, then the energy gained must be

$$\Delta E = qV \qquad (11.2)$$

Since energy is conserved, we can set equations (11.1) and (11.2) equal to each other.

$$qV = qV_1 + qV_2 \qquad \therefore V - V_1 - V_2 = 0 \qquad (11.3)$$

So the sum of the p.d.s (taking account of their signs) around the loop of figure 11.2 is zero. Note that by drawing the circuit with the high potential conductors at the top and the low potential ones at the bottom, it is easy to keep track of the p.d. signs as you go round the loop. As the charge moves down the diagram it loses potential (i.e. the p.d. is negative) and as it moves up it gains potential.

Figure 11.3 shows a different loop in the circuit. After all, the charge carrier could just as easily have passed through the bulb on its way round the circuit. Since it is inconceivable that the charge on its way through the resistor will know in advance whether it will go through the bulb or the buzzer, it has to lose the same amount of energy whichever of the two it goes through.

$$V - V_1 - V_3 = 0 \qquad \therefore V_3 = V_2 \qquad (11.4)$$

So components which are in parallel with each other have the same p.d. across them.

Current limiting

A very simple power circuit is shown in figure 11.4. For the circuit to work, the voltage rating of the bulb must be matched to the p.d. of the battery (9 V). If a 6 V bulb is used, there will be too much current in it and the filament will melt. On the other hand, if a 12 V bulb is used, the current will be too small to get the filament up to white heat. In general, a resistor has to be connected in series with an output transducer to limit the current in it to a safe value.

Series resistor

Only a 9 V bulb is going to glow properly when directly connected to a 9 V battery. Batteries which supply a p.d. of 9 V are commonplace, but bulbs rated at 9 V are not. So if you need to run a bulb from a 9 V battery, a resistor must be included in series with the bulb. Suppose that you want to use a bulb rated at 6 V, 0.36 W. What size of resistor do you need to have in series?

The circuit is shown in figure 11.5. (The resistor has been placed before the bulb, although it could just as easily have been put after it.) The first step is to calculate the current in the bulb when it has its rated p.d. (6 V) across it.

$$P = 0.36 \text{ W} \qquad P = VI \qquad \therefore 0.36 = 6.0 \times I$$
$$V = 6.0 \text{ V}$$
$$I = ? \qquad \qquad \therefore I = \frac{0.36}{6.0} = 0.06 \text{ A}$$

The current in the resistor must also be 0.06 A. The p.d. across the resistor must be $9.0 - 6.0 = 3.0$ V, so we have enough information to calculate its resistance.

$$R = ? \qquad R = \frac{V}{I} \qquad \therefore R = \frac{3.0}{0.06} = 50 \text{ }\Omega$$
$$V = 3.0 \text{ V}$$
$$I = 0.06 \text{ A}$$

Of course, the resistor is going to get hot. After all, its purpose in the circuit is to convert some of the electrical energy which would otherwise have been delivered to the bulb. It is important to ensure that the resistor can dissipate that heat energy without being damaged: its **power rating** must be greater than its output power.

$$P = ? \qquad P = VI \qquad \therefore P = 3.0 \times 0.06$$
$$V = 3.0 \text{ V} \qquad \qquad \therefore P = 0.18 \text{ W}$$
$$I = 0.06 \text{ A}$$

Low-power commercial resistors have power ratings of 0.125 W, 0.25 W. 0.5 W or 1 W. Clearly, 0.25 W resistor could be used in the circuit of figure 11.5, but a 0.125 W resistor could not.

LED COLOURS ▶▶29

LEDs are available in three colours: red, yellow and green. The colour is directly related to the minimum p.d. across the LED needed to get it to work. This is shown in table 1.

Table 1

Colour	λ/nm	V/V
red	690 − 635	1.8
yellow	605 − 590	2.0
green	590 − 530	2.1

This relationship is explained if we assume that each electron converts all of the electrical energy it loses into light. A single photon of frequency f is generated by each electron.

$$E = hf \quad \therefore eV = hf \quad \therefore f = eV/h \quad (1)$$

h is Planck's constant, 6.63×10^{-34} J s. The frequency of the photon can be used to calculate the wavelength via the known speed of light, which is 3.0×10^8 m s^{-1}.

$$c = f\lambda \quad \therefore f = c/\lambda = eV/h \quad \therefore V = hc/e\lambda \quad (2)$$

Equation (2) predicts the p.d. needed across the LED for it to emit light which has a wavelength λ. You can check for yourself that the predictions agree quite well with the data in table 1.

You will have noticed that blue LEDs are not available. Nobody has yet managed to engineer an LED with a forward voltage drop of 2.7 V which will generate blue photons ($\lambda \simeq 450$ nm) when electrons go through it. This is not for lack of research effort: as soon as blue LEDs become available, miniature slimline colour TV screens will flood the market place and someone's fortune will be made!

LEDs

Light bulbs are manufactured with a wide range of voltage ratings, from 240 V to 1.25 V. This can be done by appropriate selection of the length and diameter of the tungsten filament, so that its resistance allows just enough current for the filament temperature to get to 1500 K. However, there are some important output transducers whose voltage rating is fixed. They *have* to be matched to the source of p.d. by placing a resistor in series with them.

Consider the **light-emitting diode** shown in figure 11.6. An **LED** (pronounced 'elleedee') is made from the junction of two semiconductors (gallium phosphide and gallium arsenide). Current can only flow one way through such a junction, from the **anode** to the **cathode**, with the charge converting electrical energy to light energy on the way through. The circuit symbol and typical $I-V$ curve for an LED are shown in figure 11.7. As you can see, the current starts to shoot up to infinity once the p.d. exceeds 2.0 V. A series resistor is therefore a must in any circuit which contains an LED. An example is shown in figure 11.8. The 180 Ω resistor limits the current in the LED to a safe value. If we assume the p.d. across the LED to be 2.0 V, that current is easily calculated with the resistance formula.

$$R = 180 \ \Omega$$
$$V = 5.0 - 2.0 = 3.0 \text{ V} \qquad R = \frac{V}{I}$$
$$I = ?$$

$$\therefore 180 = \frac{3.0}{I}$$

$$\therefore I = 1.7 \times 10^{-2} \text{ A}$$

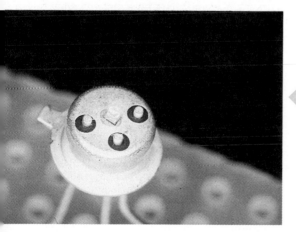

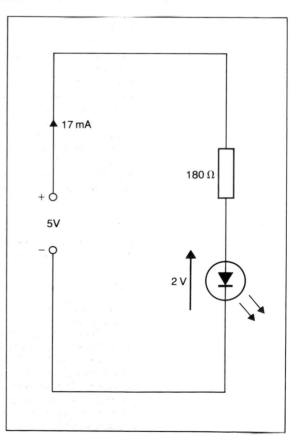

Figure 11.6 A light emitting diode: the small slab of semiconductor converts most of the electrical energy to light

Figure 11.8 An LED should always have a current-limiting resistor in series with the p.d. source

Figure 11.7 The $I-V$ curve of a typical LED

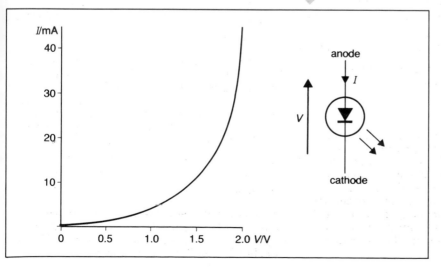

Transducers in parallel

Only rarely do you want to run a single transducer from a single source of p.d. Usually, a single source of p.d. has to run several different output transducers. For example, the battery in a car has to run all the bulbs, the engine ignition, the starter motor and the radio (figure 11.9). The simplest way of doing this is to arrange for all of the output transducers to have the same voltage rating as the source of p.d., and wire them in parallel with each other. Not only does this ensure that each transducer has the correct p.d. across it, it also allows each of them to be switched on and off independently of each other (figure 11.10).

For example, the $I-V$ curves for a buzzer and a bulb are shown in figure 11.11. Both are rated at 12 V, but have different operating currents and output powers. When they are placed in parallel with a 12 V battery (figure 11.12), they each have a p.d. of 12 V across them and their operating current in them. Both bulb and buzzer will work correctly.

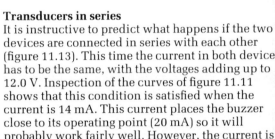

Figure 11.9 All of the output transducers are in parallel with the battery!

Figure 11.10 Each switch can switch a lamp on and off independently of the other lamps

Figure 11.11 The $I-V$ curves of a bulb and a buzzer

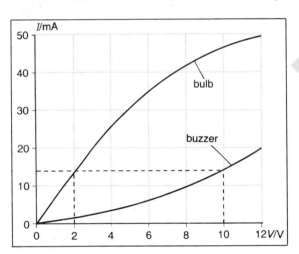

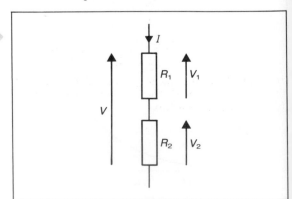

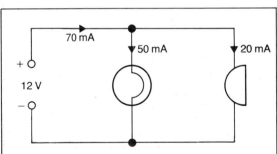

Figure 11.12 The bulb in parallel with the buzzer

Transducers in series

It is instructive to predict what happens if the two devices are connected in series with each other (figure 11.13). This time the current in both devices has to be the same, with the voltages adding up to 12.0 V. Inspection of the curves of figure 11.11 shows that this condition is satisfied when the current is 14 mA. This current places the buzzer close to its operating point (20 mA) so it will probably work fairly well. However, the current is far less than the 50 mA required to get the bulb fully bright, so it will hardly glow.

Resistor networks

The electricity and telecommunications industries are in the business of delivering electrical energy from one place to another via a large network of conductors (figure 11.16). Each conductor will have its own resistance. This has to be taken into account when calculating how much energy has to be pumped into one end of the network for the customer to get a certain amount of energy out of the other end. Engineers who have to cope with such calculations make use of the rules for resistors in series and parallel which we are about to derive.

Figure 11.13 The bulb in series with the buzzer

Figure 11.14 Two resistors in series

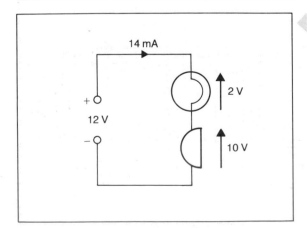

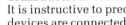

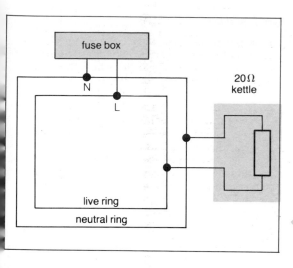

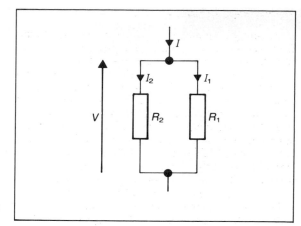

Figure 11.15 Two resistors in parallel

Figure 11.16 A ring circuit taking electrical energy from a fuse box to the heating element of a kettle

Resistors in series

Suppose that you have two resistors R_1 and R_2 in series with each other, as shown in figure 11.14. What is the value R of the single resistor which would have the same current I for the same p.d. V?

The resistance formula can be used to find the p.d. across each of the resistors in turn.

$$R = \frac{V}{I} \quad \therefore V = IR, \quad V_1 = IR_1, \quad V_2 = IR_2 \quad \textbf{(11.5)}$$

The voltages across each of the resistors in series must add up to the voltage across the single resistor.

$$V = V_1 + V_2 \quad \therefore IR = IR_1 + IR_2 \quad \textbf{(11.6)}$$

$$\therefore R = R_1 + R_2$$

So we end up with the obvious rule that the total resistance is the sum of the individual resistors.

Resistors in parallel

Figure 11.15 shows two resistors R_1 and R_2 in parallel. The current in the conductor leading to them is I when the p.d. across them is V. Their total resistance R is therefore given by

$$R = \frac{V}{I} \quad \therefore I = \frac{V}{R} \quad \textbf{(11.7)}$$

The resistance formula can be used to work out the current in each of the two resistors. The sum of those currents must, of course, be I.

$$I_1 = \frac{V_1}{R_1}, \quad I_2 = \frac{V}{R_2} \quad \therefore I = I_1 + I_2$$

$$\therefore \frac{V}{R} = \frac{V}{R_1} + \frac{V}{R_2}$$

$$\therefore \frac{1}{R} = \frac{1}{R_1} + \frac{1}{R_2} \quad \textbf{(11.8)}$$

This time, the rule is not so obvious. The reciprocal of the total resistance is the sum of the reciprocals of the individual resistors.

RING CIRCUITS

An example of a power supply network is shown in figure 11.16. An electric kettle of resistance 20 Ω is plugged into a ring main circuit which has a p.d. of 240 V across it. Each loop in the ring has a total resistance of 8.0 Ω, and the kettle is connected one quarter of the way round the ring. We want to calculate the power output of the kettle.

The first step is to draw an equivalent network for the circuit, replacing each part with a resistor. This is shown in figure 11.17. Each loop of the ring main is represented by a 2.0 Ω resistor in parallel with a 6.0 Ω resistor. The total resistance of each loop is therefore given by

$$\frac{1}{R} = \frac{1}{R_1} + \frac{1}{R_2} \quad \therefore \frac{1}{R} = \frac{1}{2} + \frac{1}{6} = 0.67 \quad \therefore R = 1.5 \, \Omega$$

If we replace each pair of resistors in parallel with a single 1.5 Ω resistor, we end up with the circuit shown in figure 11.18. It has three resistors in series, giving a total resistance of 23 Ω. So we can use the resistance formula to calculate the current in those resistors.

$$R = \frac{V}{I} \quad \therefore 23 = \frac{240}{I} \quad \therefore I = \frac{240}{23} = 10.4 \, \text{A}$$

Finally, we can calculate the power output of the kettle.

$$P = I^2 R \quad \therefore P = (10.4)^2 \times 20 = 2.2 \, \text{kW}$$

It is interesting to compare this with the power which the kettle has when it is connected directly to the 240 V source. You can check for yourself that it is 2.9 kW.

Figure 11.17 Replacing each part of the circuit with its equivalent resistor

Figure 11.18 Condensing the circuit

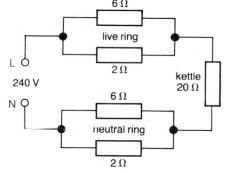

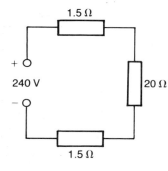

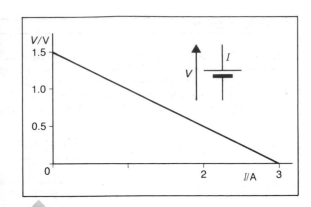

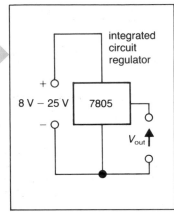

Figure 11.19 The $V-I$ curve of a typical dry cell

Figure 11.20 An integrated circuit regulator. This three-terminal device feeds out a constant 5.0 V when a p.d. between 8 V and 25 V is fed into it, provided that the output current does not exceed 1 A

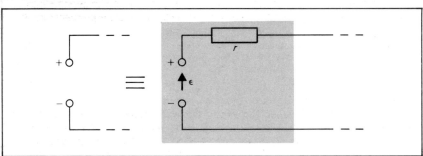

Figure 11.21 Modelling a real p.d. source with an ideal p.d. source in series with a resistor

Figure 11.22 Measuring the p.d. across the terminals of a cell

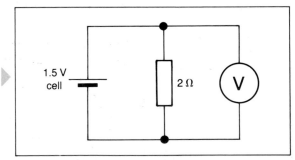

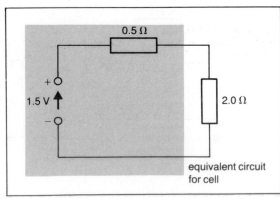

Figure 11.23 Modelling the circuit of figure 11.22

e.m.f. and i.r.

All output transducers have $I-V$ curves which encapsulate their electrical behaviour. Sources of p.d. have similar curves to show how they behave. The $V-I$ curve for a typical dry cell is shown in figure 11.19. The p.d. across the terminals drops steadily as the current in the cell increases. Not all sources of p.d. behave this way. Electronically regulated power supplies can provide a constant p.d. regardless of current up to a certain limit (figure 11.20). However, many common sources of p.d. (such as cells, dynamos and thermocouples) can be accurately modelled with the help of two new concepts, known as electromotive force and internal resistance.

Model of a p.d. source

Many sources of p.d. can be modelled as shown in figure 11.21. The real p.d. source is considered to be an ideal p.d. source in series with a resistor r, the **internal resistance** (i.r.). The ideal p.d. source has a voltage ϵ (epsilon) regardless of the current drawn from it. ϵ is called the **electromotive force** of the p.d. source, and is usually abbreviated to e.m.f. (Electromotive force is a term left over from the earliest days of electrical science, despite the fact that it is a measure of energy rather than force.)

The e.m.f. and i.r. of a typical U2 dry cell are 1.50 V and 0.50 Ω respectively. We will use these values to estimate the reading of the voltmeter in the circuit of figure 11.22. The first step is to draw an equivalent circuit, replacing the cell with an ideal p.d. source and a resistor. This is shown in figure 11.23. (Note how the voltmeter has been ignored because it represents a very large resistance (typically $\geqslant 10\,k\Omega$) in parallel with the 2.0 Ω resistor.) The total resistance in the circuit will be $2.0 + 0.5 = 2.5\,\Omega$, so we can use the resistance formula to calculate the current in it.

$$R = \frac{V}{I} \quad \therefore \quad 2.5 = \frac{1.5}{I} \quad \therefore \quad I = \frac{1.5}{2.5} = 0.60\,\text{A}$$

The voltmeter is measuring the p.d. across the 2.0 Ω resistor. This can now be calculated by applying the resistance formula to the 2.0 Ω resistor.

$$R = \frac{V}{I} \quad \therefore \quad 2.0 = \frac{V}{0.6}$$

$$\therefore V = 2.0 \times 0.60 = 1.2\,\text{V}$$

Notice that the voltmeter reading is $1.5 - 1.2 = 0.3$ V lower than you would expect it to be. This **lost volts** is the potential difference across the internal resistance in the cell.

Measuring e.m.f. and i.r.

The circuit shown in figure 11.24 can be used to measure the e.m.f. and i.r. of a p.d. source. The voltmeter measures the p.d. across the cell terminals and the ammeter measures the current in the variable resistor. The graph in figure 11.24 shows how the voltmeter and ammeter readings (V and I) are related. This will become clear if you study the equivalent circuit of figure 11.25. Applying Kirchhoff's Second Law to the circuit, we get the following expression.

$$\epsilon = Ir + V \qquad \text{(11.9}$$

This can be shuffled to show how V depends on I.

$$V = \epsilon - Ir \qquad \textbf{(11.10)}$$

Equation (11.10) makes it clear that the e.m.f. ϵ is the p.d. across the source terminals when the current I is zero. Furthermore, the internal resistance r is given by the slope of the line.

$$V = \epsilon - Ir \quad \therefore \Delta V = -\Delta Ir \quad \therefore \frac{\Delta V}{\Delta I} = -r \qquad \textbf{(11.11)}$$

Figure 11.24   Measuring the $V-I$ curve of a cell

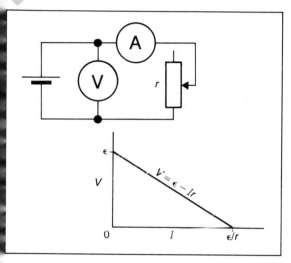

Figure 11.25   The equivalent circuit of that drawn in figure 11.24

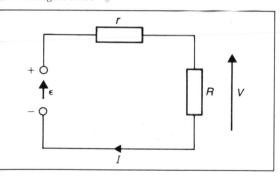

OBJECTIVES

After studying this section you should be able to do the following.

State and use Kirchhoff's Laws.

Select a suitable current-limiting resistor for an output transducer.

Sketch the $I-V$ curve of a typical LED.

Explain why transducers are usually connected in parallel to a common power supply.

State the rules for combining resistors in series and parallel.

Model a real power supply in terms of its e.m.f. and i.r.

Know the condition for maximum power transfer from a power supply to an output transducer.

EXTRACTING POWER

The internal resistance of a p.d. source is an important factor when you want to consider the efficiency with which energy is transferred from the source to the output transducer. The equivalent circuit is shown in figure 11.26. With a transducer of resistance R there will be a current I in the internal resistance r, so some energy from the source will be converted to heat by the internal resistance.

$$P_r = I^2 r, \qquad P_R = I^2 R, \qquad \text{efficiency} = \frac{\text{output power}}{\text{input power}} \times 100$$

$$\therefore \text{efficiency} = \frac{P_R \times 100}{P_R + P_r}$$

$$\therefore \text{efficiency} = \frac{I^2 R \times 100}{I^2 R + I^2 r}$$

$$\therefore \text{efficiency} = \frac{R \times 100}{R + r} \qquad (1)$$

Figure 11.26   A p.d. source feeding energy into an output transducer

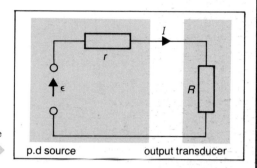

p.d source   output transducer

Equation (1) is plotted in figure 11.27. Notice how the efficiency approaches 100% when R is much larger than r, i.e. the resistance of the transducer is much larger than the internal resistance of the energy source.

However, efficient transfer of energy does not mean maximum transfer of energy from source to transducer! Let's get an expression for the power delivered to the output transducer when it has a resistance R. The current I can be worked out by applying the resistance formula to the whole equivalent circuit.

$$R = \frac{V}{I} \quad \therefore R + r = \frac{\epsilon}{I} \quad \therefore I = \frac{\epsilon}{R + r} \qquad (2)$$

$$P_R = I^2 R \quad \therefore P_R = \frac{\epsilon^2 R}{(R + r)^2} \qquad (3)$$

Equation (3) is plotted in figure 11.28. Note how it peaks for $R = r$, tailing off to zero for very large and small values of R. If you compare the graphs of figures 11.28 and 11.27 you will see that the maximum transfer of energy from source to transducer happens at 50% efficiency, i.e. half of the electrical energy from the source gets wasted as heat energy inside the source itself.

Figure 11.27   The variation of efficiency with load resistance

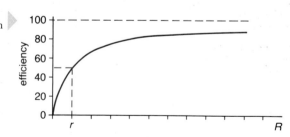

Figure 11.28   The power delivered to the load is a maximum when $R = r$

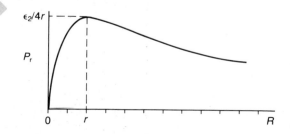

QUESTIONS

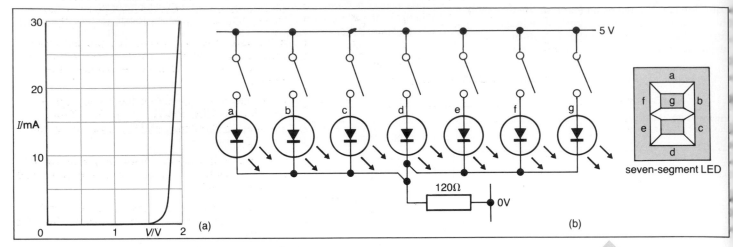

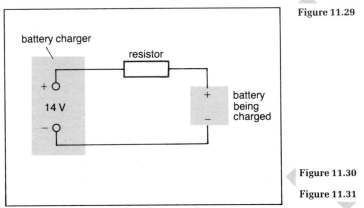

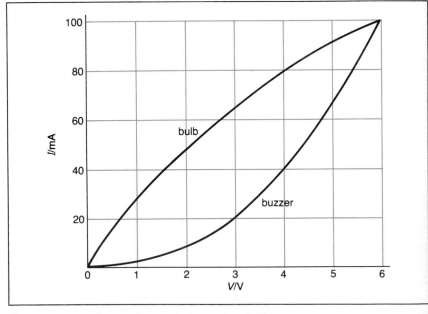

Figure 11.29

Figure 11.30

Figure 11.31

1 The graph of figure 11.29(a) is the $I-V$ curve of a red LED. The maximum current which the LED can safely take is 25 mA. Assume that all of the LEDs in this question have these characteristics.

a A resistor is placed in series with the LED so that it can operate off a 12.0 V supply. If the current in the LED is to be 15 mA, calculate a suitable resistance for the resistor.

b A seven segment LED is an array of seven LEDs arranged to form a figure eight. All of the numbers between 0 and 9 can be displayed by lighting up the appropriate LEDs in the array. It is common practice to use a single current-limiting 120 Ω resistor with a 5 V supply, as shown in figure 11.29(b). Estimate the current in each lit LED when the array displays the numbers 1 and 8. Compare the brightness of the LEDs for these extreme cases.

2 Figure 11.30 is the circuit diagram of a battery charging system. The mains-driven charger supplies a fixed p.d. of 14 V to the battery via a resistor. The battery has a negligible internal resistance.

a When a completely flat battery is connected to the charger, the current in it must not exceed 5 A. Calculate the resistance of the resistor and suggest a suitable power rating for it.

b A fully charged battery has a p.d. of 13 V across its terminals. What is the current in the resistor when the battery has been charged?

c You have to adapt the charging circuit so that it can safely charge a motor-bike battery. This will have a p.d. of 6.5 V across its terminals when fully charged, and can survive a continuous current of 0.25 A once charged. Select a suitable resistor.

3 You may have seen a classic demonstration which involves connecting a 12 V car bulb in series with a domestic light bulb to the mains 240 V power supply. Although most people expect the car bulb to be dramatically destroyed, both bulbs light up normally. If the domestic bulb is rated at 100 W, work out a suitable rating for the car bulb in this demonstration.

4 Figure 11.31 shows the $I-V$ curves for a bulb and a buzzer, both rated at 6 V. Use the curves to say as much as you can about the behaviour of the two devices when they are connected

a in series,
b in parallel with a 6 V supply.

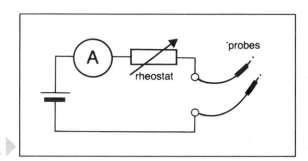

Figure 11.32

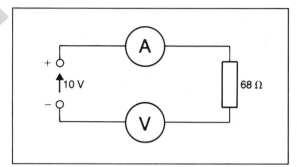

Figure 11.33

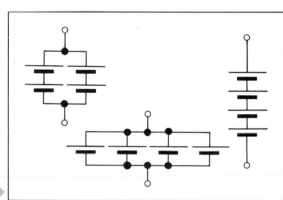

Figure 11.34

Figure 11.35

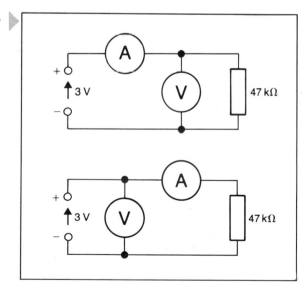

5 A student needs to measure the resistance of some items, so she sets up the circuit shown in figure 11.32. The ammeter has a full-scale deflection of 100 mA and a negligible resistance. The cell has an e.m.f. of 1.50 V and a negligible i.r.

a To start with, she joins the two probes to each other and adjusts the rheostat until the ammeter reads 100 mA. Calculate the resistance of the rheostat.

b Leaving the rheostat fixed, she now clips an unknown resistor between the probes. If the ammeter reads 40 mA, find the resistance of the resistor.

c Draw a calibration graph for the system so that the meter reading in mA can be directly converted into resistance in Ω.

d If the meter scale has marks which are 1 mA apart, estimate the maximum resistance which the system can reliably measure.

6 In an absent-minded moment a student wires up the circuit shown in figure 11.33. (He is attempting to measure the $I-V$ curve of the 68 Ω resistor.) The characteristics of the two meters are shown in table 11.1.

Table 11.1

ammeter	f.s.d.	100 μA
	resistance	1 kΩ
voltmeter	f.s.d.	10 V
	resistance	100 kΩ

a What will the meters read?

b He now wires up the circuit correctly and switches on the power supply, destroying the ammeter! What was the current in the ammeter? Suggest a better choice of ammeter for the circuit!

7 You are supplied with four dry cells, each of which has an e.m.f. of 1.5 V and an i.r. of 0.8 Ω. If you assemble them to form the batteries shown in figure 11.34, what will the e.m.f. and i.r. of each battery be? Which battery can supply the greatest current? Which battery can supply the greatest power?

8 This question highlights the problems of simultaneously measuring the p.d. and current of large resistors. The two circuits shown in figure 11.35 could be used to make measurements of current and voltage for a 47 kΩ resistor connected to a 3.0 V supply with a negligible i.r. The meters in each circuit both have the characteristics shown in table 11.1. For each circuit, calculate the readings you would expect to obtain from the ammeter and voltmeter. Which arrangement gives you the best estimate for the resistance of the 47 kΩ resistor?

SENSOR CIRCUITS

Electricity supplies energy to the world. It also acts as its eyes and its ears. Electrical circuits can be used to detect a long list of things, including temperature, sound, light, pressure and a vast range of electromagnetic radiations. This section will introduce you to the art of using electricity to sense things.

Potential dividers

The simplest form of temperature sensor is shown in figure 11.36. The thermistor is in series with an ammeter and a cell. The resistance of a thermistor depends on its temperature (see figure 11.37), typically dropping by 4% K^{-1}. So the current in the circuit can be interpreted as a temperature with the help of the $R-T$ curve of figure 11.37 and the resistance formula $R = V/I$. This type of thermometer (figure 11.38) has a number of advantages. The thermistor can be a long way from the cell and ammeter, allowing the remote sensing of temperature in hostile or inaccessible locations. Furthermore, the thermistor can be small; its low heat capacity is not going to unduly affect the object whose temperature it is sensing.

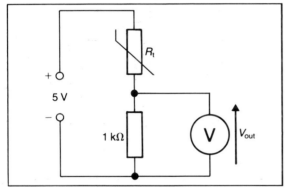

Voltage output

An alternative temperature sensing circuit which also employs a thermistor is shown in figure 11.39. The arrangement of two resistors in series with a p.d. source is called a **potential divider**. The reason for this name is obvious: the two resistors divide the p.d. of the source between them, with the larger resistor taking the lion's share. The output of this circuit V_{out} is the voltage across the 1 kΩ fixed resistor. So when the temperature is low, R_t will have a high resistance and V_{out} will be near 0 V. On the other hand, when the temperature is high, R_t will have a low resistance and V_{out} will be close to 5 V. The graph of figure 11.40 shows how the value of V_{out} will depend on the temperature T of the thermistor.

Potential divider formula

You already know how to calculate the output voltage of a potential divider from the known values of its resistors and the p.d. across them both. (Find the total resistance, calculate the current and then use the resistance formula to find V_{out}.) However, direct calculation hides an important property of the potential divider, so it is worthwhile building a formula which describes its behaviour.

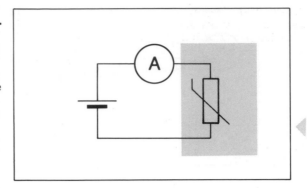

Figure 11.36   A simple temperature sensor

Figure 11.37   Typical variation of resistance with temperature for a thermistor

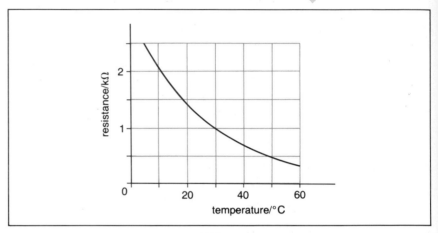

Figure 11.39   A temperature sensor circuit whose output is a voltage

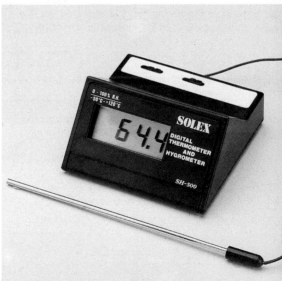

Figure 11.38   An electronic thermometer

Figure 11.40   The value of V_{out} increases as the temperature increases

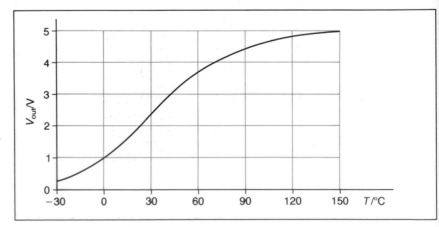

The circuit is shown in figure 11.41. The p.d. across both resistors is V_{in} and the p.d. across the bottom resistor R_b is V_{out}. The first step is to find the current in the resistors.

$$R = \frac{V}{I} \quad \therefore \; R_t + R_b = \frac{V_{in}}{I}$$

$$\therefore I = \frac{V_{in}}{R_t + R_b} \qquad\qquad \textbf{(11.12)}$$

Now we can use the resistance formula (again) to find the p.d. across the bottom resistor.

$$R = \frac{V}{I} \quad \therefore \; R_b = \frac{V_{out}}{I} \quad \therefore \; V_{out} = I \times R_b \quad \textbf{(11.13)}$$

Finally, combine equations (11.12) and (11.13) to obtain the **potential divider formula**.

$$V_{out} = I \times R_b \quad \therefore \; V_{out} = \frac{V_{in} \times R_b}{R_t + R_b} \qquad \textbf{(11.14)}$$

> $$V_{out} = \frac{V_{in} \times R_b}{R_t + R_b}$$
>
> V_{out} is the output voltage (V)
>
> V_{in} is the input voltage (V)
>
> R_b is the resistance of the bottom resistor (Ω)
>
> R_t is the resistance of the top resistor (Ω)

Notice that the output voltage depends on the *ratio* of the resistors in the network, not on their absolute values. So the value of V_{out} is a measure of the relative resistance of the two resistors.

Loading effects

In deriving the voltage divider formula we assumed that the current was the same in both resistors. In other words, there was no current in the device used to measure the output p.d. Unfortunately, voltmeters always draw a small current from the circuit to which they are connected. So if you use a voltmeter, as shown in figure 11.42, the formula is not going to be able to make an accurate prediction of its reading. These **loading effects** are important, because they can give you very misleading data.

Figure 11.41 A potential divider

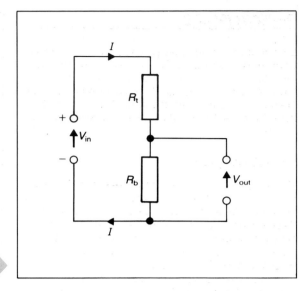

Figure 11.42 Loading a potential divider with a voltmeter

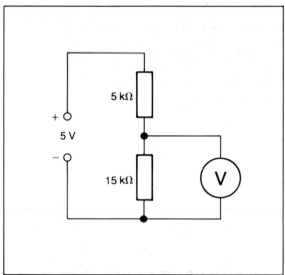

Consider the potential divider shown in figure 11.42. We can use the formula to calculate the reading of an ideal voltmeter, i.e. one which draws no current at all.

$$V_{out} = \frac{V_{in} \times R_b}{R_t + R_b} \quad \therefore \; V_{out} = \frac{5.0 \times 15}{5 + 15} = 3.75 \text{ V}$$

A good quality voltmeter with a f.s.d. of 5 V will probably have a resistance of 50 kΩ. So the potential divider really has a bottom resistor which is 15 kΩ in parallel with 50 kΩ (figure 11.43).

$$\frac{1}{R} = \frac{1}{R_1} + \frac{1}{R_2} \quad \therefore \; \frac{1}{R} = \frac{1}{15} + \frac{1}{50} = 0.087$$

$$\therefore R = 11.5 \text{ k}\Omega$$

When the voltmeter is connected to the circuit, R_b will be 11.5 kΩ instead of 15 kΩ.

$$V_{out} = \frac{V_{in} \times R_b}{R_t + R_b}$$

$$\therefore \; V_{out} = \frac{5.0 \times 11.5}{5 + 11.5} = 3.48 \text{ V}$$

The value of V_{out} has been depressed by about 7% by connecting the voltmeter to the circuit!

Figure 11.43 The equivalent circuit of figure 11.42

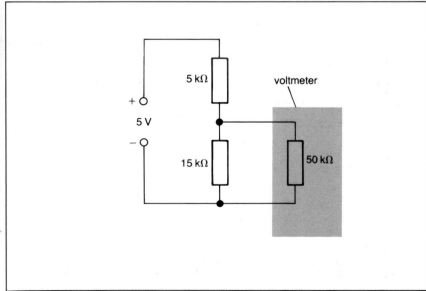

Potentiometers

A potential divider which contains variable resistors can be used to make continuously variable voltage sources. For example, look at the circuit shown in figure 11.46. The value of V_{out} can be varied from 0.0 V to 4.1 V by adjusting the rheostat. The resistance of the rheostat will be proportional to the angle through which its shaft has been rotated (figure 11.47), varying smoothly from 0 Ω to 220 Ω. The graph of figure 11.46(b) shows how the output voltage depends on the setting of the rheostat knob: note that it is not a straight line.

Variable voltage sources

An alternative way of making a variable voltage source is shown in figure 11.48. This arrangement has the advantage that the output voltage is proportional to the angle through which the potentiometer knob has been rotated. The terminals at either end of the potentiometer track have been connected to the p.d. source V_{in} and the wiper provides the variable p.d. V_{out}. The potentiometer track is simply a length of uniform conductor (perhaps resistance wire) of length l_0 and resistance R_p. The wiper is a sliding contact which is free to move along the whole length of the track. So the potentiometer looks like a potential divider with $R_t + R_b = R_p$ and $R_b = R_p \times (l/l_0)$ where l is the distance of the wiper from the bottom of the track (figure 11.49).

$$V_{out} = \frac{V_{in} \times R_b}{Rt + R_b}$$

$$\therefore V_{out} = \frac{V_{in} \times R_p \times (l/l_o)}{R_p}$$

$$\therefore V_{out} = V_{in} \times \frac{l}{l_o} \qquad \textbf{(11.15)}$$

Most modern potentiometers have a circular or helical track, so the distance between the wiper and the end of the track can be measured by the angle through which the central shaft has been rotated. For precision work, the track is made from resistance wire wound on a former. An alloy of copper, manganese and nickel (manganin) is often used for the resistance wire as it has a relatively high resistivity ($\approx 5 \times 10^{-7}$ Ω m) allied with a small temperature coefficient ($\approx 4 \times 10^{-5}$ K^{-1}).

AVOIDANCE OF LOADING EFFECTS

Loading effects can be avoided by arranging for the current in the voltmeter to be much smaller than the current in the resistor network. (In the example of figure 11.42 the current in the voltmeter (≈ 70 μA) was not much smaller than the current in the two resistors (≈ 250 μA).) You can either increase the current in the resistors or decrease the current in the voltmeter.

The first approach is illustrated in figure 11.44. The ratio of the resistors is the same as before, but the current in them is ten times larger (≈ 2500 μA). The same voltmeter is used, so its current will be unchanged (≈ 70 μA). You can check for yourself that the reading of the voltmeter will now be within 1% of the value predicted by the potential divider formula.

The second approach is to increase the resistance of the voltmeter. This is difficult to do with a moving coil instrument without sacrificing sensitivity. So although you could reduce the loading effects in the circuit of figure 11.42 by using a voltmeter with a resistance of 500 kΩ, its f.s.d. of 50 V would make accurate measurement of 3.75 V difficult! Digital voltmeters have a resistance of about 10 MΩ: this draws a current of only 375 nA from the potential divider of figure 11.42. Furthermore, the digital display (typically four digits) allows measurement to be made with a higher precision than is usually possible with a pointer and scale. (However, bear in mind that high precision does *not* automatically guarantee high accuracy!) The addition of an **operational amplifier follower** to a moving coil voltmeter (figure 11.45) can reduce the current drawn from the circuit to below 0.1 nA, approximately 100 000 times smaller than it would have been otherwise. You will find out more about these electronic devices in chapter 14.

Figure 11.44 Increasing the current in the resistors reduces the loading effect of the voltmeter

Figure 11.45 Using an operational amplifier follower to measure the output of a potential divider

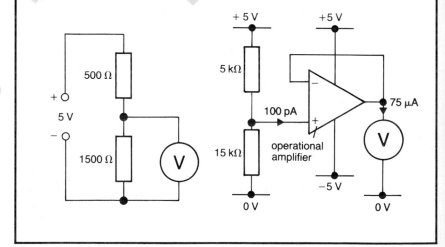

Figure 11.46 A variable voltage source using a rheostat

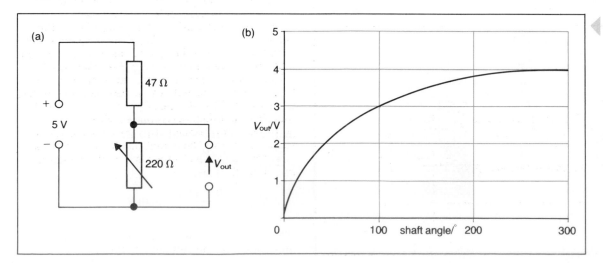

Comparing e.m.f.

Potentiometers can be used to measure the p.d. across a component in a circuit without drawing any current from that circuit. Although the technique has been superseded by the invention of operational amplifiers and the other precision electronic devices which make digital voltmeters possible, a discussion of it makes a good introduction to **bridge circuits** which are really useful!

The basic circuit is shown in figure 11.50. A stable source of p.d. maintains a steady current in a precision potentiometer. A centre-zero galvanometer with a series resistor is connected to the wiper so that the direction of the current in it can be monitored. Some means of reading off the resistance between the wiper and the bottom of the track must be provided, e.g. a dial on the potentiometer knob.

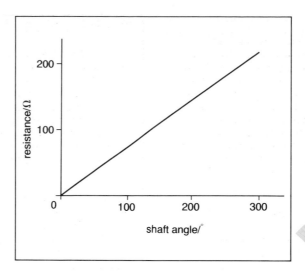

Figure 11.47 The resistance of a rheostat is proportional to the angle through which its shaft has been rotated

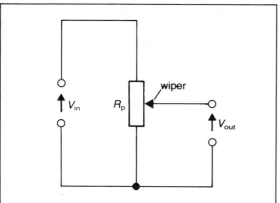

Figure 11.48 A potentiometer as a variable voltage source

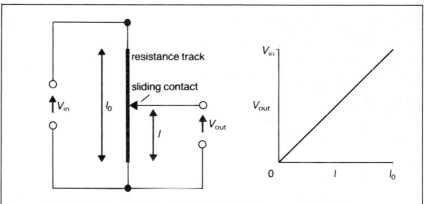

Figure 11.49 V_{out} is proportional to I

Figure 11.50 Using a potentiometer to measure the voltage across a p.d. source

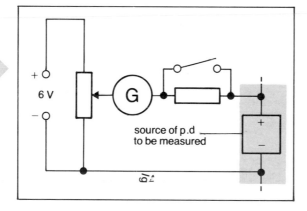

Figure 11.51 Calibrating a potentiometer with a standard p.d. source

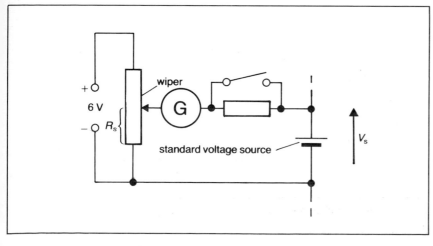

The system has to be calibrated by connecting a standard source of p.d. across the outputs of the device; this is shown in figure 11.51. The time-honoured secondary standard of p.d. is the **Weston cell** (1.0186 V at 20 °C); its e.m.f. has a temperature coefficient of about 6.6×10^{-5} K^{-1}. However, a number of three-terminal sources of e.m.f. (**bandgap voltage references**) are now cheaply available which have accuracies of 0.01% and temperature coefficients of 3×10^{-6} K^{-1}. They can be connected to a wide range of voltages and they feed out a steady, accurately known p.d.

The wiper in figure 11.51 is adjusted until the galvanometer reads zero. This **balance point** can be found accurately if the series resistor is shorted out when the galvanometer reading becomes small. (The resistor is there to protect the galvanometer from too much current.) Once the balance point has been found, the resistance R_s between wiper and track bottom is noted. Of course, when the galvanometer reads zero, there is no p.d. across it, so the p.d. across the potentiometer outputs must be exactly balanced by the e.m.f. of the standard p.d. source.

The p.d. to be measured is then connected to the potentiometer in place of the standard source. This is shown in figure 11.52. The position of the wiper is adjusted until the galvanometer reads zero again, i.e. the p.d. across the potentiometer outputs is exactly the same as the p.d. being measured. The resistance R between wiper and track bottom at this balance point can be used to work out the p.d. V being measured.

$$V = V_s \times \frac{R}{R_s} \tag{11.16}$$

Note that when the balance point is reached, the potentiometer doesn't draw any current from the circuit to which it is connected. So the potentiometer can be used to measure the p.d. of a voltage source without disturbing it, i.e. it acts like an ideal voltmeter.

Wheatstone's bridge

The resistance of a wire is sensitive to both its temperature and its length. So, in principle, changes in the resistance of a conductor attached to an article could be used to measure changes in its temperature or length.

Direct measurement
The obvious way of detecting a change of resistance is illustrated in figure 11.53. A potential divider contains a fixed resistor R_s in series with the one being monitored, R. The reading of the voltmeter (assumed ideal) is given by the potential divider formula.

$$V_{out} = \frac{V_{in} \times R_b}{R_t + R_b} \quad \therefore V = \frac{V_o \times R_s}{R + R_s} \tag{11.17}$$

Provided that the p.d. source has a steady output of V_0, any variation of R will result in a change of V. We can write down an expression for that change, making use of a standard identity from Appendix B.

If $y = Cx^n$ then $\dfrac{\Delta y}{y} = \dfrac{n\Delta x}{x}$

$V = V_0 R_s (R + R_s)^{-1}$

$$\therefore \frac{\Delta V}{V} = \frac{-\Delta R}{R + R_s} \tag{11.18}$$

Let's assume that $R \simeq R_s$, so that $V \simeq V_0/2$.

$$\frac{\Delta V}{V} = -\frac{\Delta R}{2R} \tag{11.19}$$

Now, it is not easy to measure changes in the reading of a voltmeter to better than 0.5%. So a realistic minimum value of $\Delta V/V$ is about 5×10^{-3}. Equation (11.19) suggests that the minimum fractional change of resistance $\Delta R/R$ which can be detected by the circuit is going to be 1×10^{-2}, or 1%. Of course, this does assume that V_0 does not change. Convince yourself that a 1% change of V_0 also results in a 1% change of V.

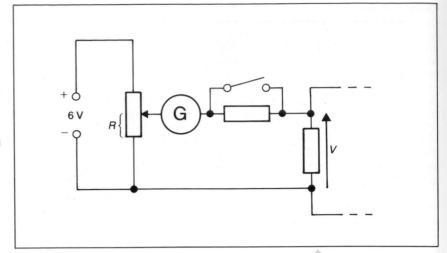

Figure 11.52 Using a potentiometer to measure the p.d. across a resistor without any loading effects

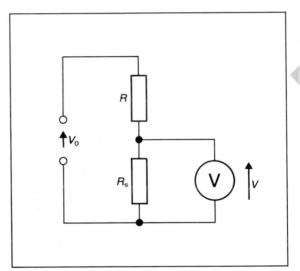

Figure 11.53 Any change in R will make V change

STRAIN CHANGE

Suppose that a conductor of length l and cross-sectional area A is subjected to a stress which increases its length by Δl. What will this do to its resistance?

$$R = \frac{\rho l}{A} \quad \therefore \frac{\Delta R}{R} = \frac{\Delta l}{l} - \frac{\Delta A}{A} \tag{1}$$

When a solid is elongated, its cross-sectional area decreases. The extent of this lateral contraction varies from metal to metal. Let's make the over-simplistic assumption that the volume of the wire remains constant as it is stretched.

$$V = lA \quad \therefore \frac{\Delta V}{V} = \frac{\Delta l}{l} + \frac{\Delta A}{A} = 0 \therefore \frac{\Delta A}{A} = -\frac{\Delta l}{l} \tag{2}$$

Combining equations (1) and (2) we can get an expression for the fractional change in resistance as a function of the wire's strain.

$$\frac{\Delta R}{R} = \frac{\Delta l}{l} - \frac{\Delta A}{A} \quad \therefore \frac{\Delta R}{R} = \frac{\Delta l}{l} - \frac{(-\Delta l)}{l} = \frac{2\Delta l}{l} \tag{3}$$

So we can expect the fractional change of resistance to be about twice the strain, i.e. well below the 1% level.

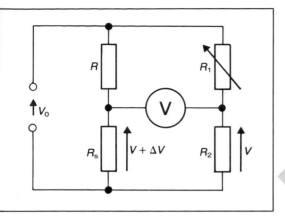

Figure 11.54 A Wheatstone's bridge circuit

Figure 11.55 The standard arrangement of resistors in a Wheatstone's bridge circuit

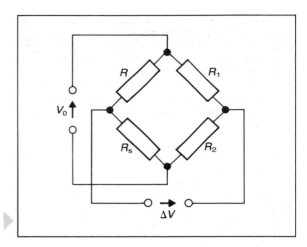

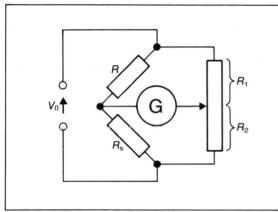

Figure 11.56 A Wheatstone's bridge with a potentiometer in place of two resistors

STRAIN GAUGES

A **strain gauge** is a set of four resistors which can be glued onto an object to measure its strain. The arrangement of resistors is shown in figure 11.57. All four have the same resistance as each other, typically 350 Ω. Two of them are aligned along the direction in which elongation is expected. Any strain in that direction results in an increase in resistance of those resistors, but makes no difference to the other two. Because all four resistors of the bridge are in the same environment, any temperature change alters all four of them in the same way without upsetting the balance of the bridge.

Equations (3) (previous box) and (11.20) can be combined to obtain an estimate for the sensitivity of a strain gauge, bearing in mind that the voltage will change in *both* of its arms.

$$\Delta V = 2 \times \frac{\Delta R}{R} \times \frac{V_0}{4}, \quad \frac{\Delta R}{R} = \frac{2\Delta l}{l} \quad \therefore \quad \Delta V = \frac{\Delta l}{l} \times V_0 \tag{1}$$

So the output voltage should be directly proportional to the strain of the article that the gauge has been glued onto. Although it will be small (≈ 1 mV for a strain of 1×10^{-4} and a 10 V power supply) the output is large enough to be amplified reliably. Strain gauges are extensively used in engineering to measure the strain of large articles when they are stressed.

Figure 11.57 A strain gauge

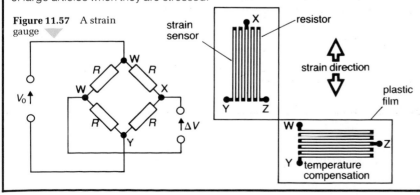

Detecting changes

A circuit which stands a better chance of detecting small changes in resistance is shown in figure 11.54. It is similar to that of figure 11.53, with a second potential divider and the voltmeter measuring the p.d. between their outputs. The rheostat is adjusted until the voltmeter reads zero. Any subsequent change of R will alter the potential at the left-hand end of the voltmeter, placing a p.d. ΔV across it. We can use equation (11.19) to work out what ΔV will be.

$$\frac{\Delta V}{V} = -\frac{\Delta R}{2R}, \quad V \simeq \frac{V_0}{2}$$

$$\therefore \Delta V = -\frac{\Delta R}{R} \times \frac{V_0}{4} \tag{11.20}$$

The resistance of a metal is approximately proportional to its temperature in kelvins, i.e. $R \propto T$. So the fractional change $\Delta R/R$ of resistance for many pure metals at room temperature is about $1/300 = 3.3 \times 10^{-3}$ K^{-1}. So if V_0 is 5.0 V, ΔV will be about 4 mV K^{-1}; this is easily measured with a standard laboratory millivoltmeter.

Not only does this technique of two balanced potential dividers make the system more sensitive to changes in one of the resistors, it also makes it insensitive to changes in the voltage supply. Any change in the value of V_0 will not affect the balance between the potential dividers (think about it). Its only effect will be a change in the sensitivity of the circuit.

The bridge circuit

Figure 11.55 shows the standard arrangement of resistors in a Wheatstone's bridge circuit. It is the circuit of figure 11.54, but drawn differently. When the circuit is balanced, i.e. ΔV is zero, it can be easily shown that

$$\frac{R}{R_s} = \frac{R_1}{R_2} \tag{11.21}$$

The circuit is useful for making precise measurements of resistance in the laboratory. R is the resistor being measured and R_s is a known fixed resistance. If R_1 and R_2 are made from a single precision potentiometer, with the wiper acting as the junction between the resistors (figure 11.56), then the ratio of R_1 to R_2 when the circuit is balanced ($\Delta V = 0$) can be used to determine the resistance of R relative to R_s.

OBJECTIVES

After studying this section you should be able to do the following.

Calculate the output voltage of a potential divider network.

Be aware of loading effects on potential dividers.

Describe how a potentiometer can be used to compare a voltage with a standard e.m.f.

Describe how a Wheatstone's bridge can be used to compare a resistance with a standard resistance.

QUESTIONS

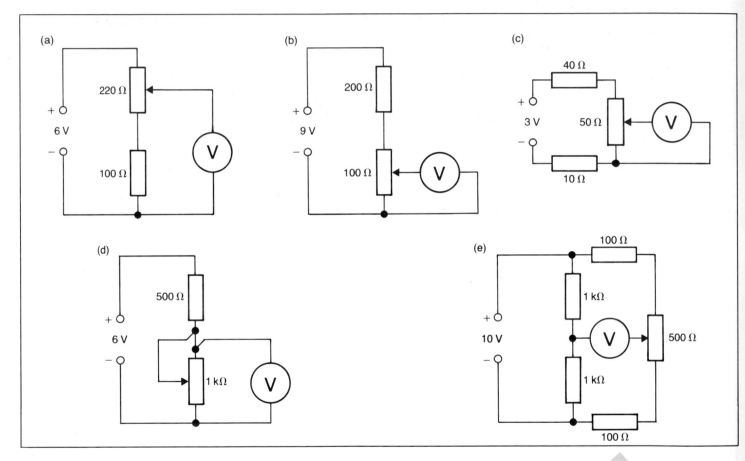

Figure 11.58

1 Figure 11.58 shows a number of circuits, each of which contains an ideal voltmeter. Calculate the maximum and minimum readings of the voltmeter when the potentiometers are adjusted over their full ranges.

2 An LDR is a resistor whose resistance depends on the rate at which light energy is absorbed by its surface. Typical data for the variation of resistance with light intensity are shown in table 11.2.

Table 11.2

Conditions	Resistance/Ω
pitch darkness	1×10^5
dim light	1×10^4
daylight	1×10^3
bright sunlight	1×10^2

Kirsty wants to build a circuit containing a voltmeter whose reading will rise as the circuit is moved into a dark room. She has a choice of two voltmeters: both have a f.s.d. of 10 V, but they have resistances of 1 kΩ and 100 kΩ. Draw a suitable circuit for Kirsty, explaining which voltmeter to use and justifying your choice of resistance for the resistor.

3 Nikos has discovered a good method of measuring large resistances. He connected the resistor in series with a voltmeter to a 6.0 V supply, obtaining a reading of 0.12 V. When he repeated the experiment with a 47 kΩ resistor instead of the unknown one, the same voltmeter read 1.79 V. What is the resistance of the unknown resistor? Does your answer rely on a precise knowledge of the power supply voltage?

4 If the galvanometer in figure 11.59 reads zero, calculate a suitable resistance for the resistor R.

5 This question is about the Wheatstone's bridge shown in figure 11.56. R_1 and R_2 are made from a single 1.00 m length of resistance wire with a sliding contact free to move along its length. The wire is held on top of a metre rule so that the position of the contact from X can be measured.

a Show that $R/R_s = R_1/R_2$ when the bridge is balanced.

b Suppose that R_s is 120 Ω. If the bridge is balanced when the sliding contact is at the 63.0 cm mark, what is the value of R?

c Why is it important that the resistance wire has the same diameter along its length?

6 A Wheatstone's bridge circuit is shown in figure 11.60. R_T is a coil of wire suspended above the laboratory bench: the current in it warms it up well above room temperature. After the bridge has been balanced by adjusting the rheostat R_A, a student blows air across R_T. Explain carefully why this will make a current go through the galvanometer from Y to X. Describe how this circuit can be developed to make a practical wind-speed detector. How would you set about calibrating it? (*Hint*: Can you think of a widely available device which contains a velocity measurer?)

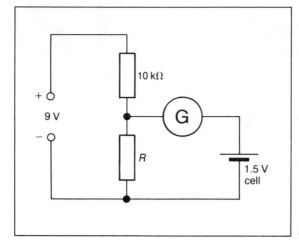

Figure 11.59

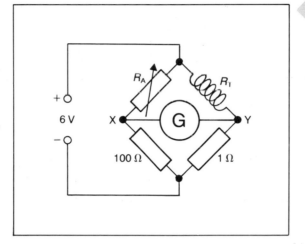

Figure 11.60

12
CAPACITORS

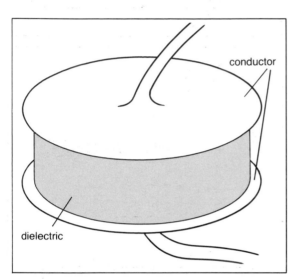

conductor

dielectric

Electronic circuit designers often think of resistors as devices which control how much current there is in a circuit. The larger the resistance, the smaller the current. Similarly, they often insert **capacitors** into circuits to control how quickly the p.d. across a component changes. The larger the capacitor, the longer it takes for the p.d. to change. The existence of capacitors allows us to design electrical circuits whose output changes with time, such as oscillators and timers.

This chapter will explore the electrical properties of capacitors in circuits which contain resistors. Explanations of why a capacitor behaves the way it does, in terms of the electric fields within it, will be left until chapter 19. Applications of capacitors to timing circuits will be dealt with in chapter 13, along with digital electronics.

CHARGE STORAGE

The construction of a capacitor is simplicity itself. It consists of two sheets of conductor separated by a layer of insulator (figure 12.1). The insulator is known as the **dielectric**, and the conducting sheets are known as **plates**. A wide variety of constructions are possible, ranging from metal coatings on thin sheets of mica to aluminium sheets separated by a thin layer of insulating oxide. The construction of a capacitor is not always obvious from its exterior — the flat sheets are usually wrapped up or rolled round before being dipped in plastic or sealed in a can. Capacitors are made in a wide variety of shapes, sizes and colours; some examples are shown in figure 12.2.

The unit of capacitance (the **farad**) is far too big for everyday use. You will probably use capacitors measured in microfarads (μF) in the laboratory; 10 000 μF is a very large capacitor indeed. **Electrolytic capacitors** are greater than 1 μF. They are polarised, i.e. one plate (usually marked +) must *always* be at a higher potential than the other. (To do otherwise risks an explosion.) Capacitors which are less than 1 μF are built in a different way and can safely be used either way round. As figure 12.3 shows, polarised and unpolarised capacitors have different circuit symbols.

Figure 12.1 The construction of a capacitor

Figure 12.2 A variety of capacitors

Current in capacitors

A capacitor is essentially an insulator, so charge cannot flow from one plate to the other. This does not mean, however, that it is impossible to have a current in the conductors connected to the plates! Of course, it is out of the question to expect a steady current, because of the insulator between the plates — but currents which vary with time are possible. The following experiment will show what this means in practice.

Figure 12.3 Circuit symbols for capacitors

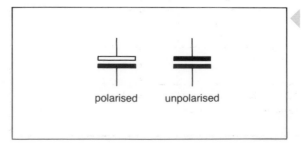

polarised   unpolarised

A simple demonstration

Consider the circuit diagram shown in figure 12.4. The capacitor is connected to the battery via a couple of bulbs and a switch: a third bulb can be connected in parallel with the capacitor by pressing a second switch.

Let us start off by closing the switch marked C. Both of the 6 V bulbs light up briefly, showing that there is a pulse of current in the conductors which connect the plates to the battery. Furthermore, both bulbs light up in exactly the same way at the same time, implying that the current is the same size in both bulbs at any instant. Current seems to be conserved. After that first brief pulse of current, no amount of opening or closing of switch C causes anything to happen. Once the capacitor has been **charged**, it prevents any more current.

If you open the switch marked C and close the switch marked D, the 12 V bulb will briefly glow, but the 6 V bulbs will not. The capacitor appears to behave like a battery which runs out of energy very quickly. Subsequent openings and closing of D have no effect on the 12 V bulb. Once the capacitor is **discharged** it cannot cause any current in the bulb connected across its plates. So closing C for a short while charges the capacitor with a brief burst of current. It stays charged until D is closed, whereupon it can maintain current in the 12 V bulb for a short while. This sequence is illustrated in figure 12.5. The capacitor can be charged and discharged for as long as you care to keep opening and closing the two switches in sequence.

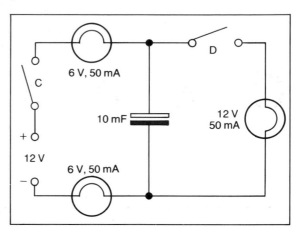

Figure 12.4 A circuit for demonstrating some properties of a capacitor

Figure 12.5 (a) Charging, (b) isolating and (c) discharging a capacitor

Figure 12.6 Charging up a capacitor with a constant current

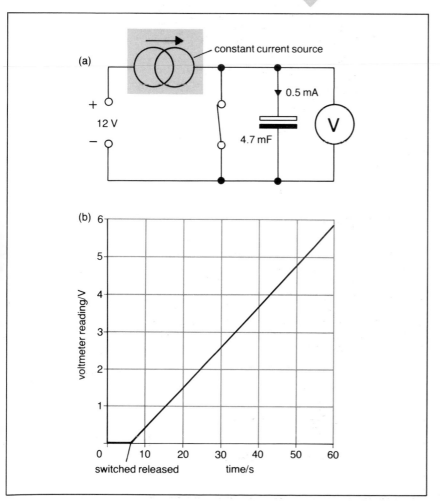

(a)

constant current source

+
12 V
−

0.5 mA

V

4.7 mF

(b)

voltmeter reading/V

0   10   20   30   40   50   60
switched released   time/s

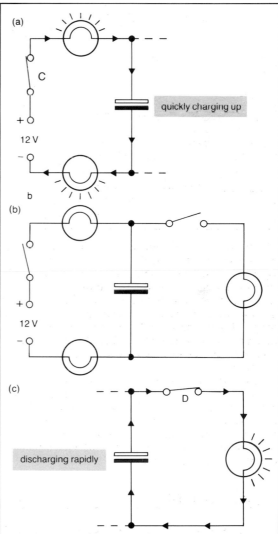

(a)

C

+
12 V
−

quickly charging up

b

(b)

+
12 V
−

(c)

D

discharging rapidly

Charge and voltage

The circuit shown in figure 12.6(a) can be used to explore what happens to the p.d. across a capacitor as it charges. It uses an electronic device known as a **constant current source** to maintain a constant current of about 0.5 mA in the circuit. A high resistance voltmeter measures the p.d. between the two plates; the switch can be used to discharge the capacitor. The graph of figure 12.6(b) shows how the voltmeter reading changes with time when the switch is opened.

Notice how the voltage rises steadily with time. It shows that the p.d. across the plates is proportional to the charge which has flowed onto one of them. To see why this is so, imagine that there is a steady current I in the wire leading to the top plate. After a time t a charge Q will have gone onto it (figure 12.7).

$$I = \frac{Q}{t} \qquad \therefore Q = It \qquad \textbf{(12.1)}$$

Let's suppose that this charge is proportional to the p.d. V across the plates.

$$Q = CV \qquad \textbf{(12.2)}$$

C is a constant, known as the **capacitance** of the capacitor. Combining equations (12.1) and (12.2) we get the result shown in the graph of figure 12.6(b).

$$Q = CV \qquad \therefore It = CV \qquad \therefore V = \frac{I}{C} \times t \qquad \textbf{(12.3)}$$

Equation (12.3) predicts that not only will the voltage rise uniformly with time but that its rate of change will be proportional to the current. This is easily verified by using two current sources in parallel, as shown in figure 12.8. As the graph shows, the rate of change of voltage is indeed doubled.

Capacitance

A capacitor is a device whose p.d. is proportional to the charge which has flowed onto it.

$$C = \frac{Q}{V}$$

C is the capacitance of the capacitor (F)

Q is the charge stored on one of its plates (C)

V is the p.d. across the plates (V)

You will recall that the currents in the conductors connected to both plates are always the same as each other. Therefore, when a capacitor is charged, its top plate has gained a certain amount of charge and its bottom plate has lost exactly the same amount of charge. It is common practice to refer to the charges on the top and bottom plates as $+Q$ and $-Q$ respectively.

Measuring capacitance
One way of calculating the capacitance of a capacitor is to measure the p.d. across it when a known amount of charge has been placed on the top plate. Figure 12.9(a) shows one way of doing it. A known resistor R is placed in series with the capacitor and the p.d. across it V is measured with a voltmeter. When the switch is closed, the reading of the voltmeter is recorded at set time intervals until it becomes zero. Each voltmeter reading can be converted into a value for the current at that instant with the help of the resistance formula.

$$R = \frac{V}{I} \qquad \therefore I = \frac{V}{R} \qquad \textbf{(12.4)}$$

Typical variation of current with time is shown in figure 12.9(b). The area under the curve is equal to

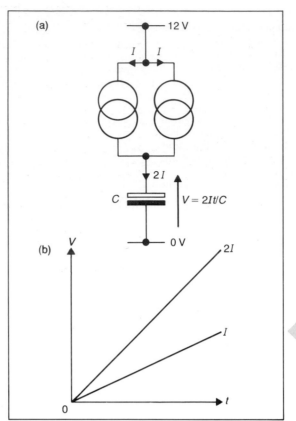

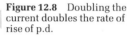

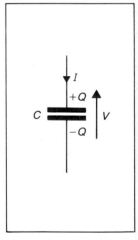

the charge placed on the top plate during the charging process.

$$I = \frac{Q}{t} \qquad \therefore Q = It \qquad \therefore \Delta Q = I\Delta t \qquad \therefore Q = \Sigma I\Delta t \quad \textbf{(12.5)}$$

Taking data from figure 12.9(b), each square has an area of $100 \times 10^{-6} \times 10 = 1.00 \times 10^{-3}$ C. There are about 20 squares under the curve, so $+Q$ is $20 \times 1.00 \times 10^{-3} = 2.0 \times 10^{-2}$ C. The capacitor is being charged up from a 9.0 V supply, so the p.d. across it at the end must also be 9.0 V. (To have no current in the 10 kΩ resistor requires that both of its ends must be at the same potential.)

$$C = \frac{Q}{V}$$

$$\therefore C = \frac{2.0 \times 10^{-2}}{9.0} = 2.2 \times 10^{-3} \text{ F or } 2\,200 \text{ μF}$$

Figure 12.8 Doubling the current doubles the rate of rise of p.d.

Figure 12.7 The charge on the top plate is equal and opposite to the charge on the bottom plate

Figure 12.9 Charging up a capacitor via a resistor

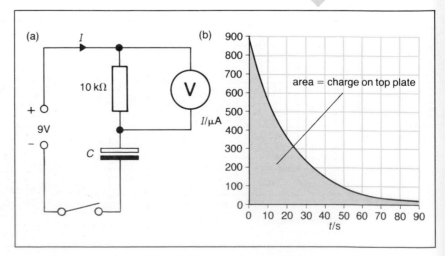

Stored energy

Since a capacitor behaves like a rechargeable battery, it must be able to store electrical energy. We can obtain a formula for that energy by considering a capacitor C being charged from a supply V_0 via a resistor R. The set-up is shown in figure 12.11.

Suppose that the current in the circuit is I at a particular instant. (It will, of course, decrease as the capacitor charges up.) During a sufficiently short interval of time Δt the current will hardly change, so we can write down an expression for the energy which leaves the power source.

$$P = VI \quad \therefore \frac{\Delta E}{\Delta t} = V_0 I \quad \therefore \Delta E = V_0 I \Delta t \quad \textbf{(12.6)}$$

Some of that energy gets converted to heat energy E_h by the resistor.

$$P = VI \quad \therefore \frac{\Delta E_h}{\Delta t} = (V_0 - V)I$$

$$\therefore \Delta E_h = (V_0 - V)I\Delta t \quad \textbf{(12.7)}$$

The rest of the energy from the power supply must be stored in the capacitor. It can be calculated by subtracting equation (12.7) from equation (12.6).

$$\Delta E_c = V_0 I \Delta t - (V_0 - V)I\Delta t \quad \therefore \Delta E_c = VI\Delta t \quad \textbf{(12.8)}$$

However, $I\Delta t$ is the charge placed on the top plate during the interval Δt.

$$I = \frac{Q}{t} \quad \therefore I\Delta t = \Delta Q \quad \textbf{(12.9)}$$

Combining equations (12.9) and (12.8) we get an expression for the energy change of the capacitor when its charge increases by a small amount.

$$\Delta E_c = VI\Delta t \quad \therefore \Delta E_c = V\Delta Q$$

$$\therefore E_c = \Sigma V\Delta Q \quad \textbf{(12.10)}$$

If you look at the graph of figure 12.12, it should be obvious that $\Sigma V\Delta Q$ is the area under the $V-Q$ curve. Furthermore, because $C = Q/V$, that curve has got to be a straight line through the origin. So calculating the area when the final voltage is V_0 is easy.

$$E_c = \tfrac{1}{2} \times V_0 \times CV_0 \quad \therefore E_c = \tfrac{1}{2}CV_0^2 \quad \textbf{(12.11)}$$

By combining equation (12.11) with $C = Q/V$, it is easy to obtain other expressions for the energy stored in the capacitor.

$E = \tfrac{1}{2}CV^2$ or $\tfrac{1}{2}Q^2/C$ or $\tfrac{1}{2}QV$

E is the energy stored in the capacitor (J)

C is the capacitance of the capacitor (F)

V is the p.d. across the plates of the capacitor (V)

Q is the charge placed on the top plate of the capacitor (C)

DATA LOGGERS !

The voltmeter used in the circuit of figure 12.9(a) has to have a resistance which is much larger than 10 kΩ, otherwise the p.d. across it will not be a true measure of the current going towards the top plate of the capacitor. You need to use a large resistor so that you have time to record the voltage across it several times before the capacitor has become fully charged. Now, it should be obvious that small capacitors will charge up more rapidly than large ones (they need less charge to acquire the p.d. of the supply), so it will be difficult to get reliable data for them.

The use of a **data logger** gets round this difficulty: one is shown in figure 12.10. It is a sophisticated voltmeter which can be programmed to read voltages at set time intervals and store them in its memory. After the data have been gathered, the logger can feed them into a computer for display and printing out. Apart from the fact that a logger is capable of reading voltages far faster than human beings (once every 100 μs at least), the computer can be programmed to analyse the data as well as display it. So it can calculate the area under the $I-t$ curve to find the charge given to the capacitor. A data logger is essentially a robot whose function is to make precise measurements at set intervals of time. They are extensively used outside the laboratory to make routine measurements in industry and to monitor the environment.

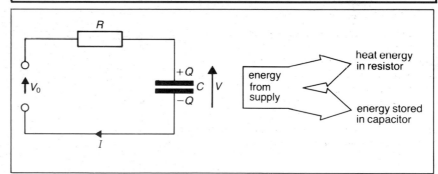

Figure 12.10 Using a data logger and computer to record and display measurements from an experiment ▶

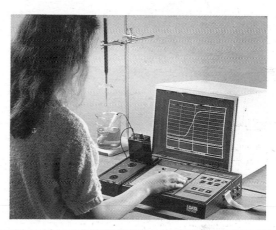

Figure 12.11 Energy flows in a capacitor charging circuit

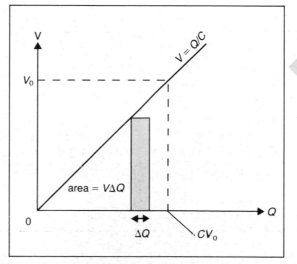

Figure 12.12 $\Sigma V\Delta Q$ is the area under the $V-Q$ curve

Series and parallel

It should be intuitively obvious that two capacitors in parallel behave like a single larger capacitor: after all, two batteries in parallel will last twice as long as one. Look at figure 12.15. The total charge Q transferred to the capacitor top plates from the power supply will be given by

$$Q = Q_1 + Q_2 \qquad \textbf{(12.12)}$$

Both capacitors will have the same p.d. across them. So we can calculate how much charge they each hold.

$$C = \frac{Q}{V} \quad \therefore Q = CV,$$

$$Q_1 = C_1 V_2, \quad Q_2 = C_2 V \qquad \textbf{(12.13)}$$

Combining equations (12.12) and (12.13) we obtain the expected expression for the total capacitance of two capacitors in parallel:

$$Q = Q_1 + Q_2 \quad \therefore CV = C_1 V + C_2 V$$

$$\therefore C = C_1 + C_2 \qquad \textbf{(12.14)}$$

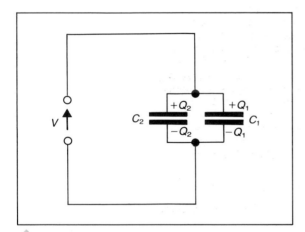

Figure 12.15 Capacitors in parallel

The effect of connecting two capacitors in series is not so obvious. Consider two different capacitors connected in series with a power supply (figure 12.16). When they are fully charged, their voltages must add up to the supply voltage (energy conservation) but they must have the same charge on their top plates (current conservation). (At all times during the charging process, the current must be the same in all of the conductors, including the one joining the two capacitors to each other. Any charge which enters one end of it must leave the other end.)

$$C = \frac{Q}{V} \quad \therefore V = \frac{Q}{C}, \quad V_1 = \frac{Q}{C_1}, \quad V_2 = \frac{Q}{C_2}$$

$$V = V_1 + V_2 \quad \therefore \quad \frac{Q}{C} = \frac{Q}{C_1} + \frac{Q}{C_2}$$

$$\therefore \quad \frac{1}{C} = \frac{1}{C_1} + \frac{1}{C_2} \qquad \textbf{(12.15)}$$

So the reciprocal of the total capacitance is the sum of the reciprocals of the individual capacitors.

INTEGRATION

If you combine equation (12.10) with $C = Q/V$, it is easy to show that

$$E_c = \Sigma CV \Delta V \qquad \qquad \therefore E_c = \int CV \, dV \qquad (1)$$

The integration sign simply means a summation over an infinite number of terms, each of which is infinitely small, i.e. $\Delta V \rightarrow 0$. The art of doing this sort of summation is central to theoretical physics (one of its co-inventors was Isaac Newton: he needed it to test his theory of universal gravitation). If you look in Appendix B you will see a list of **standard integrals**. This is the one which you can use for equation (1).

$$\int t^n dt = \frac{t^{n+1}}{n+1} + c \qquad (2)$$

If you choose E_c to be zero when V is zero, you should be able to use equation (2) to show that $E_c = \frac{1}{2}CV_0^2$.

INSTANT ENERGY

A camera flash is an example of a capacitor in action. A typical circuit, with many of the electronic details omitted, is shown in figure 12.13. It takes about 20 s for the 2 000 µF capacitor to be more or less fully charged from the 50 V supply.

$$E = \frac{CV^2}{2} \quad \therefore E = \frac{2000 \times 10^{-6} \times 50^2}{2} = 2.5 \text{ J}$$

This does not appear to be a great deal of energy. However, when the discharge tube is triggered by a sharp pulse from the control electronics, the capacitor can discharge itself in about a millisecond. So the energy gets converted into light very rapidly, i.e. the power of the flash is large, albeit only for a small time.

$$P = \frac{E}{t} \quad \therefore P = \frac{2.5}{1.0 \times 10^{-3}} = 2.5 \text{ kW}$$

Compare this with the power of a domestic light bulb: it is typically 100 W, only 10% of which is light energy!

So capacitors are very good at supplying electrical energy in a short space of time. They can be charged up slowly by moderate currents, usually limited by the internal resistance of the power supply. When they are discharged, capacitors behave like power supplies which have extremely low internal resistances. So they can, if necessary, maintain huge currents, but only for a short time. The average current through the flash discharge tube can be estimated by considering how much charge was stored on the top plate of the capacitor.

$$I = \frac{Q}{t}, \quad C = \frac{Q}{V} \quad \therefore I = \frac{CV}{t} \quad \therefore I = \frac{2.0 \times 10^{-3} \times 50}{1.0 \times 10^{-3}} = 100 \text{ A}$$

This needs to be compared with the average current from the power supply which delivered energy to the capacitor in the first place. Check for yourself that it was only 5 mA!

Figure 12.13 Using a capacitor to store energy for a camera flash

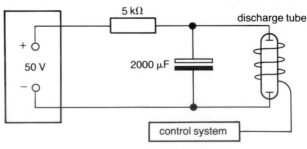

EFFICIENCY

The charging up of a capacitor is only 50% efficient; only half of the energy delivered by the power supply gets stored in the capacitor. This surprising result is easily shown as follows.

Suppose that the power supply has a constant p.d. V. When the capacitor is connected to it, a charge Q is dumped onto its top plate, also giving it a p.d. of V. The energy stored in the capacitor will be $QV/2$. However, the power supply has delivered Q coulombs, each having an energy V, so it has supplied an energy of QV. The missing $QV/2$ of energy must be converted to some other form in the circuit! As figure 12.14 shows, there is usually some resistance in a circuit, even if it is only the internal resistance of the power supply. So it seems likely that the missing energy gets converted into heat energy in any part of the charging circuit which has resistance.

However, it is possible for a capacitor to be charged by a circuit made from superconducting materials. Then there would be no resistance to convert electrical energy into heat energy. In this case, the brief pulse of current which charges the capacitor would generate radio waves of energy $QV/2$!

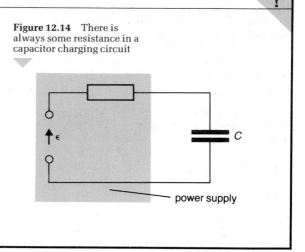

Figure 12.14 There is always some resistance in a capacitor charging circuit

power supply

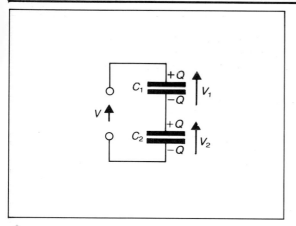

Figure 12.16 Capacitors in series

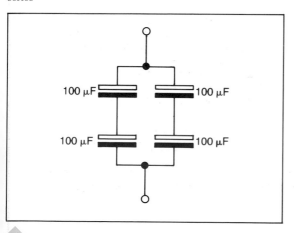

Figure 12.17 Doubling the voltage rating of a capacitor without changing its capacitance

Voltage rating

There is a limit to the voltage you can place across a capacitor without endangering it. Too high a voltage will cause the insulating dielectric to turn into a conductor, converting the energy stored in the capacitor to heat. The result can be a nasty explosion. So capacitors have a **voltage rating**, the maximum safe p.d. which can be placed across them. If you double the p.d. across a capacitor you quadruple the energy stored in it ($E = \frac{1}{2}CV^2$). So there is a big incentive to increase the voltage rating of a bank of capacitors by connecting them in series with each other. For example, figure 12.17 shows how four 100 μF capacitors rated at 63 V can be used to make a single capacitor rated at 126 V. Let us calculate the total capacitance of the circuit. Start off by considering a pair of capacitors in series:

$$C = C_1 + C_2 \qquad \therefore C = 100 + 100 = 200 \ \mu F$$

The circuit is effectively a pair of 200 μF capacitors in parallel.

$$\frac{1}{C} = \frac{1}{C_1} + \frac{1}{C_2} \qquad \therefore \frac{1}{C} = \frac{1}{200} + \frac{1}{200} = \frac{2}{200}$$

$$\therefore C = \frac{200}{2} = 100 \ \mu F$$

So the circuit of figure 12.17 has a capacitance of 100 μF and a voltage rating of 126 V.

POWER SUPPLIES

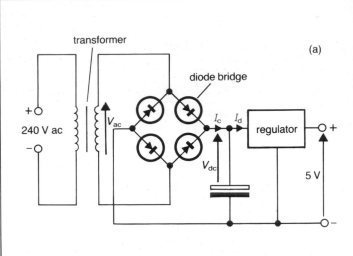

Capacitors are widely used as temporary energy stores in commercial power supplies which run off the mains electricity supply. We are going to use the 5 V power supply for a domestic microcomputer as another example of capacitors in action.

A suitable circuit is shown in figure 12.18(a). We are going to calculate a suitable value for the capacitor. Don't worry about exactly how the system works: the operation of the transformer will be explained in chapter 25. In any case, most of the complex circuitry is hidden from sight in the **regulator**. This is a three-terminal device designed to feed out a steady p.d. of 5.0 V with currents of up to 2.0 A, provided that its input voltage is between 8 V and 23 V. On the left is a **diode bridge**: this clever network of four diodes allows the alternating voltage fed out of the transformer to charge up the capacitor once every 10 ms. The graphs of figure 12.18(b) show how the voltages and currents in various parts of the circuit change with time.

To work out a suitable size for the capacitor we have to assume that the regulator is providing its maximum output power, i.e. 5×2 = 10 W. The diode bridge charges up the capacitor to about 12 V at every peak of the alternating voltage from the transformer. In between those peaks, which are 10 ms apart, the capacitor has to provide the regulator with energy. The charge ΔQ lost by the capacitor in 10 ms is easily calculated.

$$I = \frac{Q}{t} \quad \therefore 2.0 = \frac{\Delta Q}{10 \times 10^{-3}} \quad \therefore \Delta Q = 0.02\,C$$

This charge loss will cause the voltage across the capacitor to drop. Since the regulator has to have at least 8 V going into it, we shall play safe and say that the voltage must not dip below 9 V.

$$C = \frac{Q}{V} \quad \therefore \frac{\Delta V}{V} = \frac{\Delta Q}{Q} \quad \therefore Q = \frac{\Delta Q V}{\Delta V} \qquad (1)$$

Now although equation (1) is only exact for *small* changes of charge and voltage, we can still use it to get an approximate value for the charge Q which the capacitor has to store.

$$Q \approx \frac{\Delta Q V}{\Delta V} \quad \therefore Q = \frac{0.02 \times 12}{12 - 9} = 0.08\,C$$

Now we can estimate a suitable value for the capacitance.

$$C = \frac{Q}{V} \quad \therefore C = \frac{0.08}{12} \approx 7000\ \mu F$$

Power supplies for large computers (see figure 12.19) may have to supply currents of 20 A rather than just 2 A. This would require a capacitor of 70 000 μF!

Figure 12.19 A 5 V power supply for a computer

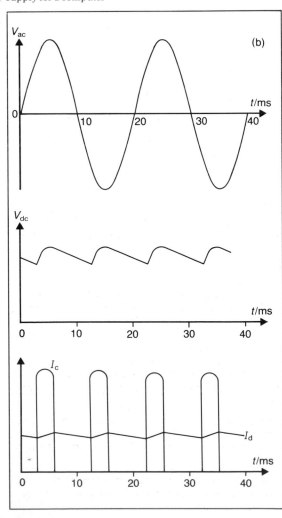

Figure 12.18 Circuit diagram of a 5 V power supply

OBJECTIVES

After studying this section you should be able to do
the following.

Describe the construction of a capacitor.	Describe how the capacitance of a capacitor can be measured.
Describe how a capacitor can be charged and discharged through resistors.	Calculate the electrical energy stored in a capacitor.
Describe the changes of current in the conductors leading to a capacitor which is being charged or discharged.	Calculate the total capacitance of capacitors in series and parallel with each other.
Use the formula $C = Q/V$.	

QUESTIONS

1 A student sets about measuring the size of a capacitor with the apparatus shown in figure 12.20. She presses the switch to charge up the capacitor from the battery. Then she releases it at the same time as starting a stopwatch, allowing the capacitor to discharge itself through the voltmeter. Her results are given in table 12.1.

Table 12.1

Time on stopwatch/s	Voltmeter reading/V
0	1.50
5	1.07
10	0.77
15	0.55
20	0.40
30	0.20
40	0.10
60	0.03

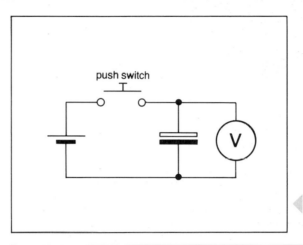

push switch

Figure 12.20

Figure 12.21

a Her voltmeter has a resistance of 20 kΩ. Use the data of table 12.1 to draw an $I-t$ curve for the capacitor as it is discharged.

b Explain why the current gets progressively smaller during the experiment.

c Use your graph to estimate the initial p.d. across the capacitor and the charge stored on its top plate. Hence find a value for the capacitance of the capacitor.

2 A method of measuring the size of small capacitors is illustrated in figure 12.21. The **reed switch** is controlled by the oscillator, in such a way that the capacitor is charged from the supply and discharged through the galvanometer f times per second. The resistor in the discharge circuit is included to protect the galvanometer. You can assume that it allows the capacitor to completely discharge itself before being recharged via the reed switch.

a The galvanometer records the *average* current in the discharge circuit. If it is I, show that the charge stored on the capacitor when it is charged is given by $Q = I/f$.

b Table 12.2 shows some data for a particular capacitor inserted in the circuit. Use it to calculate a value for its capacitance.

Table 12.2

frequency f	50 Hz
supply p.d.	5.8 V
galvanometer reading	7.3 μA

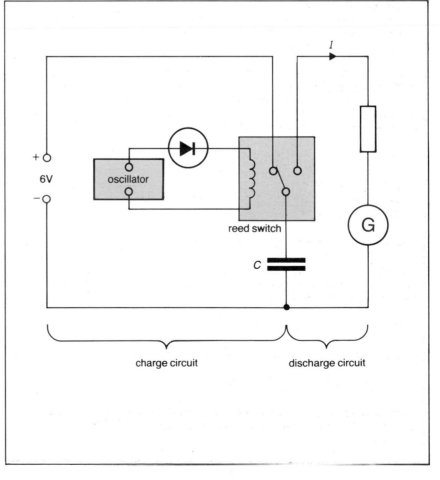

6V

oscillator

reed switch

charge circuit   discharge circuit

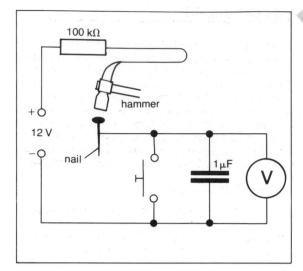

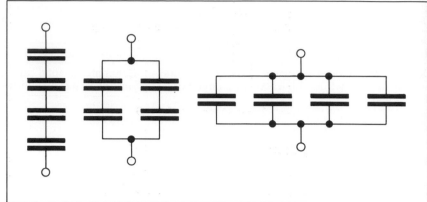

Figure 12.22

Figure 12.23

3 Capacitors can be used to measure small time intervals. For example, the apparatus shown in figure 12.22 can be used to measure the time taken for a hammer to bounce off a nail. A digital voltmeter with a very high resistance is used to measure the p.d. across the 1.0 μF capacitor.

a Assuming that the capacitor p.d. remains much smaller than 12 V, calculate the current in the circuit when the hammer is touching the nail.

b The capacitor is discharged by pressing and releasing the switch. Then the hammer is bounced off the nail, causing the voltmeter reading to rise to 243 mV. For how long were the nail and hammer in contact with each other?

c The voltmeter has a resistance of 10 MΩ. Why would a 100 kΩ moving-coil voltmeter be unsuitable?

4 You are supplied with four 100 μF capacitors which are rated at 10 V. For each of the networks shown in figure 12.23, work out

a the total capacitance,

b the voltage rating,

c the maximum energy it can store.

5 Chris and Pat are having an argument about energy transfer when a capacitor is discharged across a second, initially uncharged, capacitor. Look at figure 12.24. They are discussing what happens to the total stored energy when the switch is closed if the left-hand capacitor has been charged up from a 12 V supply.

Chris argues as follows. 'The charged capacitor acts just like a battery. You know that when you charge a capacitor from a battery, only half the energy from the battery gets to the capacitor. So half the energy gets lost.'

Pat disagrees. 'When the capacitors are connected, the p.d. across one falls and that across the other rises until they are the same. So it's not like a battery charging up a capacitor: no energy is lost at all.'

What is the correct answer? You might care to back up your argument with calculations or some algebra.

6 A circuit which could be used as a capacitance-meter is shown in figure 12.25. It incorporates a high resistance voltmeter and a known 1.0 μF capacitor. The capacitor to be measured is inserted between X and Y. Switch C is briefly pressed to charge it up, and the voltmeter reading V_1 is noted. Then switch D is pressed and the voltmeter reading V_2 is noted.

Show that the value of the unknown capacitor, in μF, is given by $C = V_2/(V_1 - V_2)$.

7 Small capacitors have been recently developed which have capacitances of 3.3 F with dimensions 43 mm × 43 mm × 15 mm. They are used for maintaining current in computer memories when the computer is switched off; this means that the information stored in the memory is not lost.

a Calculate the energy density of the capacitor when it is charged up to 5.0 V. Quote your answer in J cm^{-3}. How does this compare with the energy density of petrol (heat of combustion 4.8×10^7 J kg^{-1}, density 700 kg m^{-3})?

b If a capacitor C supplies a current I for a time t, show that the drop in voltage is given by $\Delta V = It/C$.

c The **leakage current** through the dielectric of the capacitor is 0.4 mA. Estimate how long it will take for the p.d. across the capacitor to drop from 5 V to 3.5 V, the minimum supply voltage for memory integrated circuits.

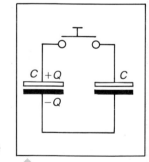

Figure 12.24

Figure 12.25

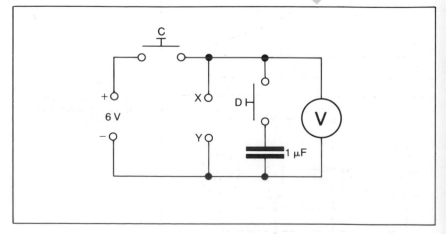

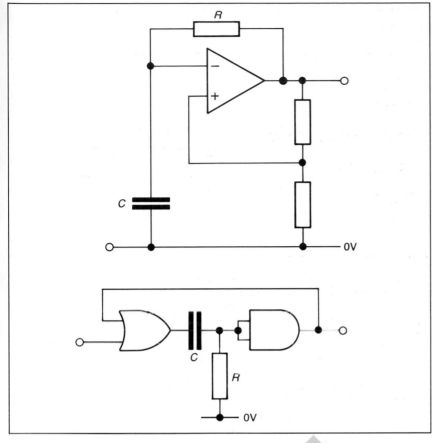

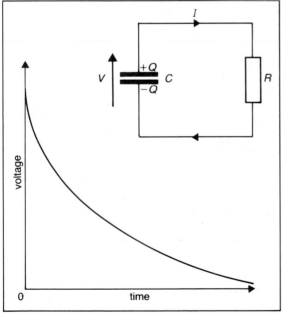

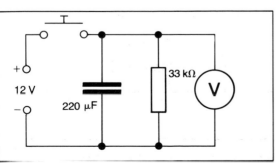

Figure 12.26 Two useful circuits which use RC networks as their timing elements

Figure 12.27 Discharging a capacitor

Figure 12.28 A circuit whose time constant is roughly 10 s

TIME CONSTANTS

There are many useful electronic circuits which contain resistors in series with capacitors. A couple of them are illustrated in figure 12.26. Their output is either a single pulse or a train of pulses, but their duration is fixed by the **time constant** RC. This section is going to show you how to predict the way in which currents and voltages in an RC network change with time. Along the way, you will be introduced to a number of new techniques, such as **dimensional analysis** and **numerical integration**.

Approximate solutions

Figure 12.27 shows how you might expect the p.d. across a capacitor to change with time when you discharge it with a resistor. How long do you have to wait for the voltage to die down to zero?

The battery model
Calculating how long the discharge process lasts is difficult because the current in the resistor is continually changing. As the p.d. across the resistor falls, so does the current in it. However, we can make a stab at the calculation by assuming that the current does *not* change, i.e. remains steady for a time τ (tau) before suddenly dropping to zero. In other words, we are going to model a capacitor with a battery. After all, an approximate solution to a problem is better than no solution at all!

So let's suppose that the capacitor started off with a charge Q on its top plate. If that charge has to go through the resistor in time τ, we can work out the current in it.

$$I = \frac{Q}{\tau} \tag{12.16}$$

The p.d. across the resistor must be the same as the p.d. across the capacitor (they are in parallel).

$$R = \frac{V}{I}, \quad C = \frac{Q}{V} \quad \therefore V = IR = \frac{Q}{C}$$

$$\therefore I = \frac{Q}{RC} \tag{12.17}$$

If we combine equations (12.16) and (12.17) to eliminate the current I, we end up with an expression for τ:

$$I = \frac{Q}{\tau} \quad \therefore \frac{Q}{RC} = \frac{Q}{\tau} \quad \therefore \tau = RC \tag{12.18}$$

Of course, we must not place too much faith in this result. It can only be used to make a rough estimate of the discharge time for the circuit of figure 12.28.

$$\tau = RC \quad \therefore \tau = 33 \times 10^3 \times 220 \times 10^{-6} \simeq 10 \text{ s}$$

However, we can still use it to make two strong predictions. First, equation (12.18) does not contain any reference to the initial charge on the top plate of the capacitor. It therefore predicts that the value of τ is independent of the charge which goes through the resistor. In other words, doubling the voltage of the power supply in figure 12.28 should make no difference to the discharge time. Secondly, the value of τ is proportional to RC. So if we measure τ for one pair of values of R and C, we can predict what it will be for any other pair of values. The quantity RC is called the **time constant**.

Dimensional analysis

We can have some confidence in the truth of equation (12.18) because it is dimensionally correct. That is, both sides of the equation have the same units as each other; an ohm farad is the same thing as a second.

$$\tau = RC \quad \therefore [T] = [R][C] \tag{12.19}$$

The contents of the square brackets show the **dimensions** of the variables in the equation. Thus τ is measured in seconds so it has the dimensions of time, T. In order to demonstrate the truth of equation (12.19), we have to establish the dimensions of resistance and capacitance in terms of the four fundamental units. These are mass M, length L, time T and current A. Let's start with the ohm, tracing it back to fundamental definitions.

$$R = \frac{V}{I}, \quad P = VI \quad \therefore R = \frac{P}{I^2} \tag{12.20}$$

Power can be traced back to force, distance and time.

$$P = \frac{E}{t}, \quad E = Fd \quad \therefore P = \frac{Fd}{t} \tag{12.21}$$

In turn, we can trace force back to the fundamental units of mass, length and time.

$$F = \frac{m\Delta v}{\Delta t}, \quad v = \frac{\Delta x}{\Delta t} \quad \therefore F = \frac{m\Delta x}{\Delta t^2} \tag{12.22}$$

We can use equation (12.22) to write down the dimensions of force, i.e. $[F] = [M\,L\,T^{-2}]$. Equation (12.21) can then be used to find the dimensions of power, i.e. $[P] = [F][L][T^{-1}] = [M\,L^2\,T^{-3}]$. Finally, this can be used in conjunction with equation (12.20) to find the dimensions of resistance.

$$[R] = [P][A^{-2}] = [M\,L^2\,T^{-3}][A^{-2}]$$
$$\therefore [R] = [M\,L^2\,T^{-3}\,A^{-2}]$$

A similar analysis leads to the dimensions of capacitance. Start off with the defining equation in terms of charge and voltage.

$$C = \frac{Q}{V}, \quad I = \frac{Q}{t} \quad \therefore C = \frac{It}{V}$$

$$\therefore [C] = [AT][V^{-1}] \tag{12.23}$$

The dimensions of voltage can be obtained from those of current, power and time.

$$P = VI, \quad P = \frac{E}{t} \quad \therefore V = \frac{E}{It}$$

$$\therefore [V] = [E]\,[A^{-1}][T^{-1}] \tag{12.24}$$

In turn, the dimensions of energy come from those of force and distance.

$$E = Fd \quad \therefore [E] = [F][L]$$
$$\therefore [E] = [M\,L\,T^{-2}][L] = [M\,L^2\,T^{-2}] \tag{12.25}$$

By combining equations (12.25), (12.24) and (12.23) we arrive at the dimensions of capacitance.

$$[C] = [A\,T][V^{-1}]$$
$$\therefore [C] = [A\,T][E^{-1}][A][T] = [A^2\,T^2][E^{-1}]$$
$$\therefore [C] = [A^2\,T^2][M^{-1}\,L^{-2}\,T^2]$$
$$\therefore [C] = [M^{-1}\,L^{-2}\,T^4\,A^2] \tag{12.26}$$

Now we can find out if RC has the dimensions of time.

$$[R][C] = [M\,L^2\,T^{-3}\,A^{-2}][M^{-1}\,L^{-2}\,T^4\,A^2] = [T]$$

If both sides of $\tau = RC$ have the same dimensions, then there may be some truth in the equation. However, we can multiply either side by a number without affecting its dimensions, because numbers are dimensionless. So our dimensional analysis indicates that $\tau = nRC$, where n is a number.

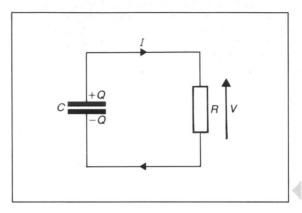

Figure 12.29 The current I depletes the charge $+Q$ on the top plate

Exact solutions

Most problems in physics cannot be solved exactly. Either the situation being modelled is too complicated or the algebra becomes impossible. This is particularly true when quantum mechanics, the physics of fundamental particles, is involved. So physicists often have to make do with approximate solutions. Fortunately for you, the discharge of a capacitor can be solved exactly: that makes it an exception to the general rule.

Differential equations

Consider the situation shown in figure 12.29. It shows an instant during the discharge process. The current I in the resistor is a consequence of the p.d. V across it. During a short interval of time Δt the p.d. is going to drop by ΔV because some charge will have left the top plate.

$$C = \frac{Q}{V} \quad \therefore \Delta V = \frac{\Delta Q}{C} \tag{12.27}$$

The charge which leaves the top plate can be calculated from the current and the time.

$$I = \frac{Q}{t} \quad \therefore \Delta Q = -I\Delta t \tag{12.28}$$

The minus sign is included because the charge has to decrease as time progresses. The drop in p.d. will make the current also drop by a small amount.

$$R = \frac{V}{I} \quad \therefore \Delta V = R\Delta I \tag{12.29}$$

If we combine equations (12.27), (12.28) and (12.29) we obtain a useful expression for the fractional change of current.

$$\Delta V = \frac{\Delta Q}{C} \quad \therefore R\Delta I = -\frac{I\Delta t}{C}$$

$$\therefore \frac{\Delta I}{I} = -\frac{\Delta t}{RC} \tag{12.30}$$

Equation (12.30) is an example of a **differential equation**. It states how the current changes during a small interval of time. We now have to use that equation to tell us the value of the current at *any* time. There are two ways of doing this. You will be shown **numerical integration** first.

Numerical integration
Providing that you have access to a large enough computer and you are willing to wait as long as necessary for the answer, a differential equation can always be solved by numerical integration. So although what follows is specific to equation (12.30) as applied to the circuit of figure 12.28, the recipe is universal.

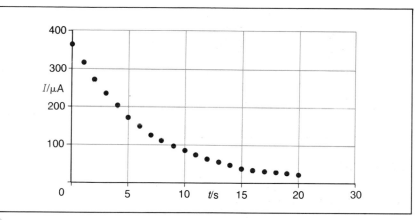

Figure 12.30 Results of the numerical integration

Start off by choosing an initial value for *I*. A glance at figure 12.28 should convince you that when the discharge process starts *I* will be $12.0 \div 33 \times 10^3 = 3.63 \times 10^{-4}$ A or 363 µA. This is the value of *I* for $t = 0$. The value a short while later can be obtained with the help of a variant of equation (12.30).

$$\Delta I = -I \times \frac{\Delta t}{RC} \qquad \textbf{(12.31)}$$

The time constant *RC* is $33 \times 10^3 \times 220 \times 10^{-6} = 7.26$ s. Equation (12.31) can be used to calculate the drop in current, in microamps, during the first second if we set $\Delta t = 1.0$.

$$\Delta I = -I \times \frac{\Delta t}{RC}$$

$$\therefore \Delta I = -\frac{363 \times 1.0}{7.26} = -50 \ \mu\text{A}$$

So the current at $t = 1.0$ s should be $363 - 50 = 313$ µA. This value can now be inserted into equation (12.31) to find the change in current during the next second. It turns out to be -43 µA, giving a current of $313 - 43 = 270$ µA for $t = 2.0$ s.

The process can be repeated time after time, using the latest value for the current to calculate the next one. This sort of calculation is tedious to do by hand, so it is advisable to do it by computer. Table 12.3 shows data obtained from the following program written in BASIC. Figure 12.30 shows the same data in graphical form.

```
10 LET I = 363
20 FOR T = 0 TO 20 STEP 1
30 LET D = -I/7.26
40 PRINT T,I,D
50 LET I = I + D
60 NEXT T
70 END
```

Table 12.3

t/s	I/µA	ΔI/µA
0.0	363	−50
1.0	313	−43
2.0	270	−37
3.0	233	−32
4.0	201	−28
5.0	173	−24
6.0	149	−20
7.0	129	−18
8.0	111	−15
9.0	96	−14
10.0	82	−11
11.0	71	−10
12.0	61	−8
13.0	53	−7
14.0	46	−7
15.0	39	−5
16.0	34	−5
17.0	29	−4
18.0	25	−3
19.0	22	−3
20.0	19	−3

The computer effectively works out the change in current during successive time intervals of one second. Since that change is fairly large ($\approx 14\%$) the numbers listed in table 12.3 are not going to be exactly correct. This is because the differential equation is only true if the time interval Δt is sufficiently short. The smaller the value of Δt we choose for the calculation, the more accurate will be the calculated values of *I*. Of course, small values of Δt mean that there are more steps to be calculated to cover the same timespan of 20 s! Table 12.4 shows some values for *I* calculated with four different values of Δt (figure 12.31).

Figure 12.31 The effect of the value of Δt on the results of the numerical integration

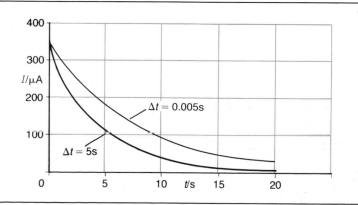

Table 12.4

t/s	I/µA			
	$\Delta t{=}5.0$s	$\Delta t{=}0.5$s	$\Delta t{=}0.05$s	$\Delta t{=}0.005$s
0.0	363.0	363.0	363.0	363.0
5.0	113.0	177.8	181.9	182.3
10.0	35.2	87.1	91.1	91.5
15.0	11.0	42.7	45.7	45.9
20.0	3.4	20.9	22.9	23.1

Using calculus

Numerical integration has one major flaw as a technique for solving differential equations in physics. Each problem has to be solved separately from all the others. This is because the technique has to represent all of the variables (such as R, C, I and Δt) as numbers, and each problem will have its own set of numbers. A more general solution, which leaves the variables in algebraic form, is more useful in the long run. As you are about to find out, consulting tables of standard integrals can sometimes yield an algebraic solution to a differential equation.

The first step is to write down the differential equation with a re-defined τ.

$$\frac{\Delta I}{I} = -\frac{\Delta t}{\tau} \quad \text{where } \tau = RC \qquad (12.32)$$

Then sum both sides of the equation and let Δt become infinitely small. This gives an **integral equation**.

$$\frac{\Sigma \Delta I}{I} = -\frac{1}{\tau} \Sigma \Delta t$$

$$\therefore \int \frac{dI}{I} = -\frac{1}{\tau} \int dt \qquad (12.33)$$

If you consult the list of integrals in Appendix B, you will find the following:

$$\int \frac{dt}{t} = \ln t + c, \qquad \int t^n dt = \frac{t^{n+1}}{n+1} + c$$

Plugging these integrals into equation (12.33), we obtain an expression for the current as a function of time; c is a constant.

$$\ln I = -\frac{t}{\tau} + c \qquad (12.34)$$

Using a couple of identities from Appendix B, we can shuffle this into a more friendly format.

If $\ln x = y$, then $x = \exp[y]$

$$\exp[a + b] = \exp[a] \times \exp[b]$$

$$\therefore I = \exp[-\frac{t}{\tau} + c]$$

$$\therefore I = \exp[-\frac{t}{\tau}] \times \exp[c] \qquad (12.35)$$

The final step is to find the value of the constant $\exp[c]$. When you solve differential equations this way, you always end up with one or more constants which have to be fixed by considering what happens at $t = 0$.

$$I = \exp[-\frac{t}{\tau}] \times \exp[c]$$

$$\therefore I = \exp[0] \times \exp[c] \text{ for } t = 0$$

$$\therefore I = \exp[c] \qquad (12.36)$$

(We have used the fact that $\exp[0] = 1$: check this with your calculator.) So $\exp[c]$ is just the initial current I_0 in the resistor.

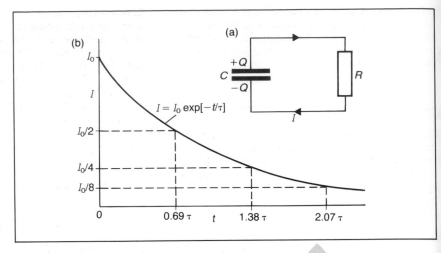

Figure 12.32 $I = I_0 \exp[-t/\tau]$

$$I = I_0 \times \exp[-\frac{t}{\tau}]$$

$$t = \tau \times \ln[\frac{I_0}{I}]$$

I is the current in the resistor (A)

I_0 is the initial current in the resistor (A)

t is the time (s)

τ is the time constant of the RC network (s)

Halving-time

Our solution $I = I_0 \times \exp[-t/\tau]$ is plotted in figure 12.32. Notice that the current never dies down to zero, i.e. the time taken for the discharge is always infinity! However, we can predict how long it will take for the current to drop to half of its initial value. Let that time be $t_{\frac{1}{2}}$.

$$t = \tau \times \ln[\frac{I_0}{I}]$$

$$\therefore t_{\frac{1}{2}} = \tau \times \ln[\frac{I_0}{\frac{1}{2}I_0}]$$

$$\therefore t_{\frac{1}{2}} = \tau \times \ln[2]$$

$$\therefore t_{\frac{1}{2}} = 0.69\tau \qquad (12.37)$$

Figure 12.33 Charging up a capacitor via a resistor

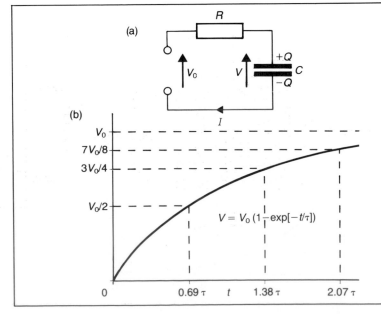

So the time taken for the current in the resistor to halve is *only* dictated by the value of the time constant. Regardless of the value of the current at a particular instant, it will be halved in the next 0.69 RC seconds.

Charging capacitors

The time has come to work out how the current changes when a capacitor is charged up from a constant voltage supply. The arrangement is shown in figure 12.33(a). Our target is to find a differential equation linking the current with the time and then to solve it.

The equation

Suppose that the p.d. across the capacitor at a particular instant is V. We can use the resistance formula to find the current in the resistor.

$$R = \frac{V}{I} \quad \therefore \ R = \frac{V_0 - V}{I} \quad \therefore \ I = \frac{V_0 - V}{R} \quad \textbf{(12.38)}$$

If the current remains steady for a short time Δt, then the p.d. across the capacitor will rise.

$$C = \frac{Q}{V}, \qquad I = \frac{Q}{t}$$

$$\therefore \ \Delta V = \frac{\Delta Q}{C} \quad \therefore \ \Delta V = \frac{I\Delta t}{C} \quad \textbf{(12.39)}$$

We can use equations (12.38) and (12.39) to work out the fractional change of current in a small interval of time.

$$I = \frac{V_0 - V}{R} \quad \therefore \ \Delta I = -\frac{\Delta V}{R}$$

$$\therefore \ \Delta I = -\frac{I\Delta t}{RC} \quad \therefore \ \frac{\Delta I}{I} = -\frac{\Delta t}{\tau} \quad \textbf{(12.40)}$$

The solution

You may have noticed that the charging process obeys the same differential equation as the discharging process. So they both have the same variation of current with time, i.e. $I = I_0 \times \exp[-t/\tau]$. However, this does *not* mean that the p.d. across the capacitor behaves the same way in both circuits! Let's use equation (12.38) to find out how V varies with time.

$$I = \frac{V_0 - V}{R} \quad \therefore \ I_0 \times \exp\left[-\frac{t}{\tau}\right] = \frac{V_0 - V}{R}$$

$$\therefore \ V = V_0 - I_0 R \times \exp\left[-\frac{t}{\tau}\right]$$

$$\therefore \ V = V_0\left(1 - \exp\left[-\frac{t}{\tau}\right]\right) \qquad \textbf{(12.41)}$$

Equation (12.41) is shown in graphical form in figure 12.33(b). Notice how the capacitor is never fully charged, but gains half of its charge in the first 0.69 RC seconds.

Capacitors in action

This section has been difficult! Now that we have obtained a formula for the current in an RC network, we can apply it to a useful device. The example we are going to look at involves a **transistorised relay**.

Relays

A transistorised **relay** is a switch controlled by an electromagnet. There is a diagram of one in figure 12.34. It is a five-terminal device. Two of the terminals are for connection to a power supply. Another two go to the switch. This is open when there is no current in the input terminal. To close the switch, there must be a current of at least 120 μA in the input terminal. Once the switch has closed, the current can drop to 60 μA before it opens again. The input terminal behaves like a 50 kΩ resistor.

Figure 12.34 A transistorised relay

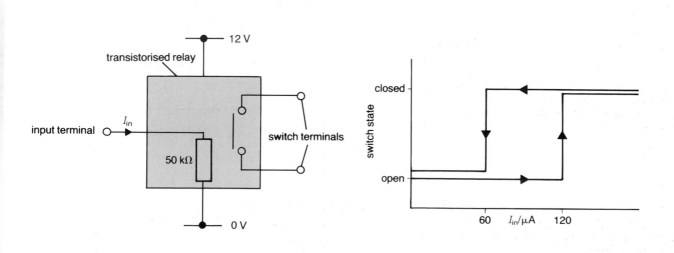

Look at the circuit of figure 12.35(a). When the switch S is pressed the capacitor is instantly charged up from the 12 V supply and the relay switches on the bulb. As soon as the switch S is released, the capacitor starts to discharge through the input terminal. For how long does the bulb glow after the switch is released? Start off by calculating the time constant.

$$\tau = RC \qquad \therefore \tau = 50\times10^3 \times 1\,000\times10^{-6} = 50\ \text{s}$$

The final current I is 60 μA. The initial current can be calculated with the help of the resistance formula.

$$R = \frac{V}{I} \qquad \therefore 50 \times 10^3 = \frac{12}{I_0} \qquad \therefore I_0 = 240\ \mu\text{A}$$

Now we can find out how long it takes for the current to drop from 240 μA to 60 μA:

$$t = \tau \times \ln[I_0/I] \qquad \therefore t = 50\times\ln[240/60] = 69\ \text{s}$$

So when the switch is released, there is a time delay of 69 s before the bulb stops glowing. This is shown in the graph of figure 12.35(b).

Figure 12.35 A circuit with a time delay

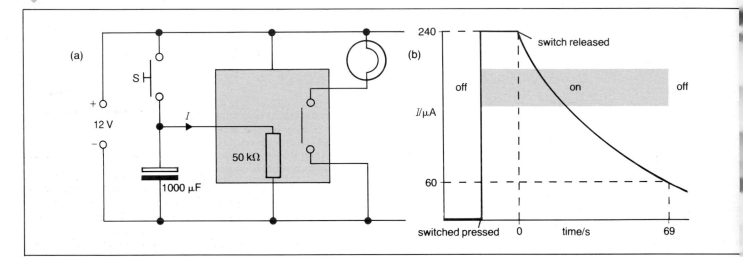

QUESTIONS

1 You are going to find an approximate expression for the discharge time of a capacitor by assuming that its voltage drops steadily to zero in a time τ.

a If the initial voltage across the capacitor is V_0, sketch a graph to show how the current I in the discharging resistor R varies with time.

b Use the sketch to show that the initial charge on the capacitor is given by $Q = V_0\tau/2R$. Hence show that $\tau = 2RC$.

c Suppose that $t_{\frac{1}{2}}$ is defined as the time taken for a capacitor to lose half of its charge when a resistor is connected in parallel with it. Assuming that the voltage drops steadily with time, show that $t_{\frac{1}{2}} = 2RC/3$. How does this compare with the actual value of $t_{\frac{1}{2}}$?

2 a Find the dimensions of the following quantities: velocity, acceleration, force, pressure and density.

b Use dimensions to show that fluid friction could be equal to ρAv^2.

3 This question is about the acceleration of rockets. This is awkward to calculate because the mass of the rocket decreases as its fuel gets ejected. So you will use numerical integration to keep track of the rocket's velocity as it uses up its fuel.

The rocket has a mass M and velocity v. It is going upwards in an environment whose gravitational field strength is g. The rocket motors provide a constant upwards thrust T, ejecting fuel at the rate of m kg s^{-1}.

a Show that in a short interval of time Δt, the changes of velocity and mass of the rocket are given by

$$\Delta v = (\frac{T}{M} - g)\Delta t, \quad \Delta M = -\,m\Delta t$$

b The total mass of the space shuttle on the launch pad is 2.0×10^6 kg. The thrust of the first stage rocket engines is a constant 2.9×10^7 N, consuming fuel at a rate of 1.1×10^4 kg s^{-1}. Use the answer to part (a) to estimate the velocity and mass of the shuttle 10 s after ignition of the rocket engines.

c Use numerical integration to find the mass and velocity of the shuttle during the first minute of its flight, using $\Delta t = 5$ s. Use your results to plot a graph of the velocity as a function of time. Use it to estimate how far the shuttle travels during that first minute.

4 Instruments which run off batteries often switch themselves off after a few minutes to conserve power. The circuit diagram of an electronic thermometer which keeps itself on for 2 minutes when the switch S is pressed and released is shown in figure 12.36. There has to be a p.d. of at least 2.5 V across the relay input terminals for the thermometer to switch on; the relay input has a resistance of 100 kΩ.

a What is the current in the relay input when switch S is closed?

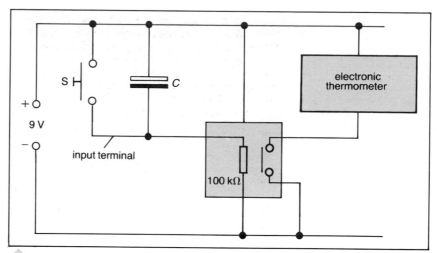

Figure 12.36

◀ **Figure 12.38**

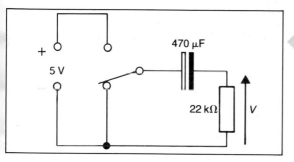

b Sketch a graph to show how the current in the relay input changes with time when switch S is released.

c Calculate a suitable value for C if the thermometer is to function for 120 s after the switch S is released.

5 The graph in figure 12.37 shows how the p.d. across the capacitor changes with time when the switch is pressed and released. Copy the graph and sketch on it the curves you would expect if

a only the voltage of the power supply was doubled,

b only the capacitor was replaced with two similar ones in series,

c only the resistance of the resistor was doubled.

6 This question is about the circuit shown in figure 12.38. It starts off with the switch as drawn, with $V = 0$.

a What is the value of V immediately after the switch setting is changed?

b Sketch a graph to show how the current in the resistor subsequently changes with time.

c Calculate how long it takes for the value of V to subsequently drop to 1.7 V.

d What is the value of V 10 s after the switch setting is changed?

e When V has returned to 0 V, the switch is returned to its *original* setting. What is the direction of the current in the resistor? Sketch a graph to show how V subsequently changes with time.

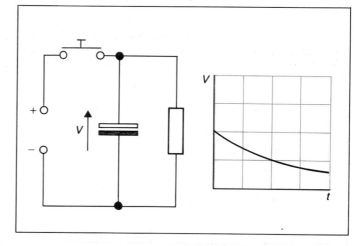

Figure 12.37 ▶

7 A popular integrated circuit timer called the NE555 uses an RC network to time the length of its pulses. The arrangement for producing single pulses is shown in figure 12.39. The box marked NE555 is the integrated circuit. Normally it keeps the capacitor fully discharged, so that V_{in} is 0.0 V. However, when the switch marked T is pressed, the integrated circuit allows the capacitor to charge up through the resistor R and V_{out} rises immediately from 0.0 V to 4.0 V. As soon as V_{in} reaches 3.3 V, V_{out} is lowered back to 0.0 V and the capacitor is rapidly discharged.

a Suppose that $C = 470$ μF and $R = 33$ kΩ. What is the current in R for V_{in} to be 3.3 V? For how long will V_{out} be 4.0 V when the switch is pressed?

b Show that the length of the pulse fed out by the NE555 is 1.1 RC.

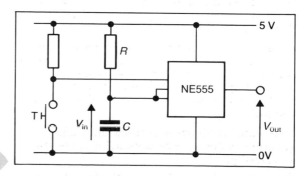

Figure 12.39 ▶

SUMMARY
ELECTRICITY

Electrical energy is transported from a source of p.d. to an output transducer by a circulation of charged particles through a pair of conductors. Conductors contain particles which can be positively or negatively charged. The total number of these charge carriers in a conductor remains constant.

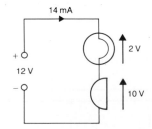

Current, the rate at which charge moves past a point in a conductor, is measured by inserting an ammeter into the circuit: $I = Q/t$, $I = nAqv$. The potential difference across a component is the energy loss per coulomb which drifts through it: $\Delta E = qV$, $P = VI$. P.d. is measured by connecting a voltmeter in parallel with the component.

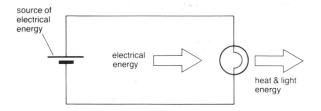

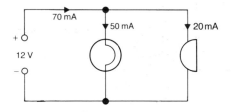

Conventional current assumes positive charge carriers which drift from high to low potential. Metals have negative charge carriers called electrons. The current in metals is proportional to the p.d. across them for constant temperature (Ohm's Law): $R = V/I$. Metals have a resistance which is independent of current. Metals, semiconductors and insulators can be classified according to the value of their resistivity: $R = \rho l/A$.

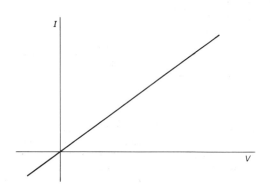

Shunts and multipliers are used to convert galvanometers into ammeters and voltmeters with useful ranges. Ideal ammeters have no resistance; ideal voltmeters have infinite resistance.

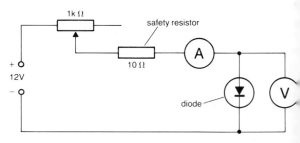

The shape of a component's I–V curve is, in general, different for each type of component. Resistors in series with a component limit the current in it; rheostats (potentiometers) can vary the current.

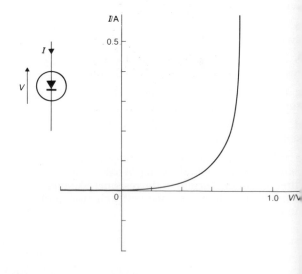

Two or more output transducers can be run off a single source of p.d. if they are connected in parallel. They can be controlled independently if a switch is connected in series with each one.

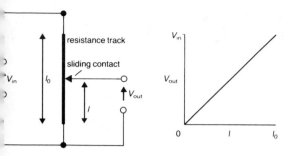

Current is conserved at every junction in a circuit. The sum of the voltages around any loop in a circuit must add up to zero. For resistors in series $R = R_1 + R_2$; for resistors in parallel $1/R = 1/R_1 + 1/R_2$. Two resistors in series with a p.d. source make a potential divider; $V_{out} = V_{in} \times R_b/(R_t + R_b)$ provided that the current drawn from the circuit is much smaller than the current in it.

Most p.d. sources can be well modelled by specifying values for their e.m.f. and i.r. The maximum power is extracted from a p.d. source by an output transducer whose resistance equals the i.r.

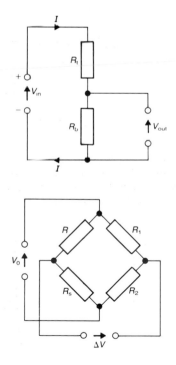

Potentiometers provide a variable p.d. from a fixed p.d. source; they can be used to compare the e.m.f. of p.d. sources with the help of a galvanometer. A pair of potential dividers in a Wheatstone's bridge can be used to compare resistors: $R/R_S = R_1/R_2$.

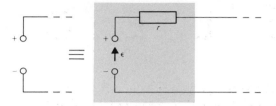

No charge can flow through a capacitor, the charge on the plates is always equal in magnitude and opposite in sign: $C = Q/V$. The area under the $I-t$ curve for the current in a capacitor terminal is equal to the charge dumped on that plate.

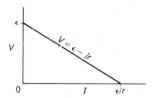

Capacitors store electrical energy: $E = \frac{1}{2} QV$ or $\frac{1}{2}Q^2/C$ or $\frac{1}{2}CV^2$. The current a series RC network connected to a constant p.d. source is given by $I = I_0 \exp[-t/\tau]$: $\tau = RC$, the time constant.

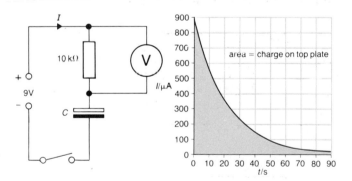

ELECTRONICS

13
DIGITAL
ELECTRONICS

Not only can electronic devices make reliable measurements for us, but they can also control variables in experiments. Electronic feedback systems are extensively used to keep variables, such as temperature, constant. Furthermore, the large output of data from electronic measuring instruments can be fed straight into computers for analysis, storage and display. So a study of some electronics is vital to your physics education; modern science depends on it.

ELECTRONIC SYSTEMS

Modern electronics is firmly based on the use of **integrated circuits**. One of these is shown in figure 13.2. It comes in a rectangular plastic package (usually black) with a number of silvery pins coming out of the side which can be used for electrical connections to the integrated circuit. If you want to find out how integrated circuits actually work, you are going to have to search elsewhere – the detailed physics of transistors and their construction is beyond the scope of this book. Instead, you are going to learn how to use integrated circuits. After all, you can learn how to use a calculator without knowing anything about how it reads numbers from the keypad, does the sums and presents the results on the display. We are not saying that the insides of integrated circuits are not interesting, just that knowledge of them is not necessary to put them to use.

Electronics is a technology, not a science. It uses a physicist's understanding of electricity and semiconductor materials to design and produce devices which suit our needs. Although a study of electronics may advance your own intellectual capabilities, it is not going to deepen your understanding of the natural world. So why include electronics as part of a physics course at all?

Electronics provides many of the basic tools for today's scientists. Electronic sensors can measure an enormously wide range of quantities, and they can be incorporated into precision instruments. Some of these are shown in figure 13.1. So a physicist uses electronics to gather data faster and more reliably than she could do with her unaided five senses. Electronic devices have become our eyes and ears, allowing us to look at and listen to information from the natural world which we might otherwise not notice, either because it is too weak or outside the range of our senses.

Figure 13.1 Electronic tape measure and spirit level

Figure 13.2 An integrated circuit package: the circuit itself is etched on the silicon slab at the centre underneath the glass window

A Ratemeter

The circuit diagram of a useful electronic system is shown in figure 13.3. It is a simple **ratemeter**, designed to count and display the number of pulses coming out of an alpha particle detector per second. Each of the blocks represents a separate integrated circuit.

A circuit diagram shows *all* of the conductors connecting the various components to each other and to the power supply. As you can appreciate by looking at figure 13.3, it can be bewilderingly complicated. So circuit diagrams are only used when you actually have to wire up a circuit from its individual components. Simpler diagrams are used to show what a circuit does.

Supply connections

The first thing to notice about figure 13.3 is that all of the components are connected in parallel to a single 5 V power supply. Each block has one connection to the **top supply rail** and one to the **bottom supply rail**. These deliver electrical energy to each component, most of which ends up as heat energy. Secondly, each component is connected to the other by a series of wires, allowing electrical energy to be fed from one component to another. This flow of energy is from left to right in the diagram, and it carries information through the system. It is these **signals** which are the important things in an electronic circuit, so the power supply connections are usually omitted for clarity.

An electronic version of figure 13.3 is shown in figure 13.4. Only the wires which carry signals have been drawn. Each component now looks like a device with a number of **inputs** and **outputs**. The secret of 'electronics without tears' is to focus on how the output voltages and currents depend on the input voltages and currents. There is no need to worry about why they have to behave in this way.

Block diagrams

A **block diagram** for the ratemeter is shown in figure 13.5. It shows how the **information** flows through the circuit. Each block represents a specific part of the circuit, and the arrows on the lines show which way signals flow between them. The name inside each block describes its function, i.e. what it does to the signals fed into it. (At this stage, most of the names will not make much sense to you, but don't worry about that. All will become clear later on.) It is important that you don't confuse a block diagram with a circuit diagram: the former is a flowchart, whereas the latter is a construction blueprint. Block diagrams are useful for analysing complicated electronic systems. By considering what each block does to the signals which are fed into it, you can work out what the whole thing does. You will be introduced to each block as you work your way through this chapter, but it will help if you can see that they each have useful functions. So we are now going to use the block diagram of the ratemeter to explain what it does.

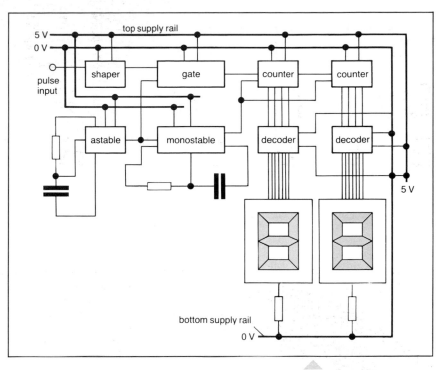

Figure 13.3 The circuit diagram of a ratemeter

Figure 13.4 Omitting the power supply rails and some minor components

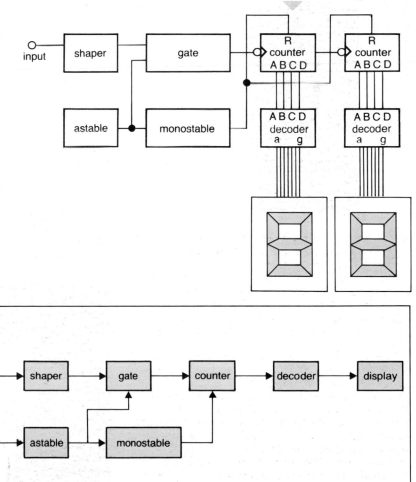

Figure 13.5 A block diagram of the ratemeter

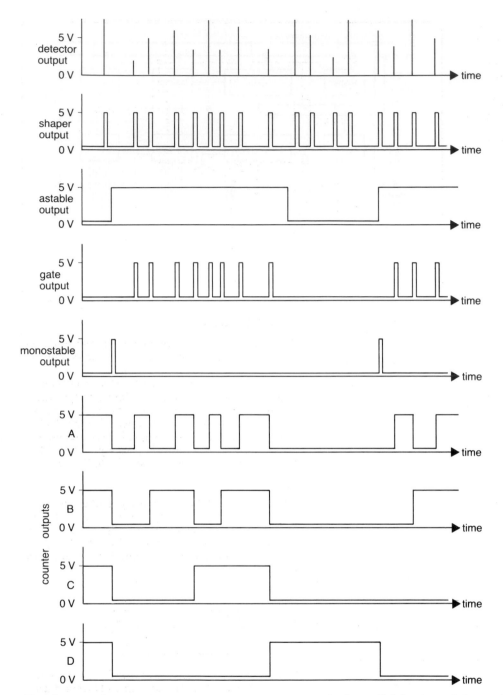

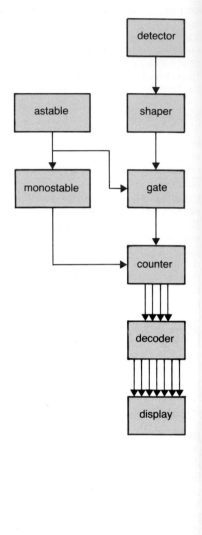

Signal processing

Figure 13.6 illustrates what happens to the signals from the detector as they pass through the system. It will help if you look at it from time to time as you read this section.

The detector produces brief voltage pulses each time an alpha particle is absorbed by it. Those pulses have erratic shapes and heights, so they are standardised by a **pulse shaper** before being fed into the **counter** via a **gate**. The gate only lets the pulses through to the counter when the output of the **astable** is at 5 V. This only lasts for one second and during that time the pattern of the four output signals from the counter (labelled A, B, C and D) change each time a pulse is recorded. The four signals from the counter go into the **decoder** which, in turn, produces the seven voltages needed to make the **seven segment LED** display the pulse count.

At the end of the second the astable output goes to 0 V, closing the gate so that no more pulses enter the counter. One second later the astable output rises back up to 5 V, opening up the gate to let pulses through once more. At the same instant a **monostable** fires a brief pulse into the counter to reset it to zero.

Coding signals

You will have noticed that when information is fed from one block to another it is generally in the form of high and low voltages. The conductors feeding signals between the blocks are mostly either at 5 V or 0 V, with the output of the detector being the only exception. This **coding** makes the information precise, allowing it to be processed by the counter and decoder without any errors being introduced.

Figure 13.6 What happens to the signals as they pass through the ratemeter

The information enters the system coded as a train of pulses. It is standard practice to refer to a 5 V signal as **1** (**one**) and to a 0 V signal as **0** (**nought**), so the arrival of each alpha particle is represented by a brief 1 coming out of the pulse shaper.

The counter codes the number of pulses which enter it as a set of four parallel signals on the wires labelled D, C, B and A. Table 13.1 shows the standard coding, called **binary coded decimal**.

Table 13.1

Number	D	C	B	A
0	0	0	0	0
1	0	0	0	1
2	0	0	1	0
3	0	0	1	1
4	0	1	0	0
5	0	1	0	1
6	0	1	1	0
7	0	1	1	1
8	1	0	0	0
9	1	0	0	1

Circuits which have been designed to process signals which are 1 or 0 are called **digital systems**. Systems which process signals which can have any voltage rather than just two are called **analogue systems**: they are the subject of chapter 14.

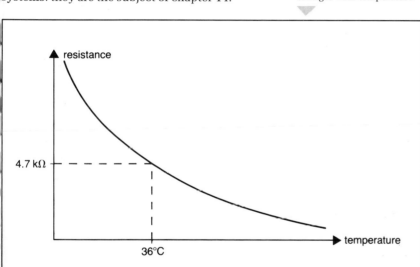

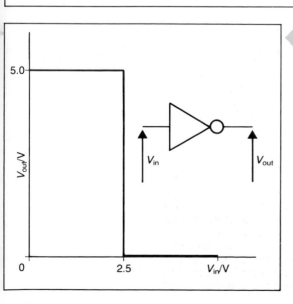

Figure 13.9 The $V_{in}-V_{out}$ curve of an ideal driver

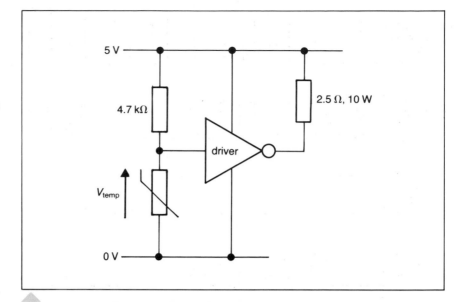

Figure 13.7 A simple thermostat circuit

Figure 13.8 How the thermistor resistance changes with temperature

Control systems

Any useful electronic system must have inputs and outputs. These are the places where the system has to exchange information with the rest of the universe, so they are a good place for you to start your electronics education. A simple, but useful, system which illustrates all the important factors about outputs and inputs is shown in figure 13.7. It is a thermostat, i.e. it is designed to keep something at a constant temperature. For example, it could keep a small insect cage at a steady 36°C.

The input
The input end of the circuit is a potential divider. The value of V_{temp} will depend on the temperature of the thermistor. As the graph of figure 13.8 shows, the thermistor resistance goes below 4.7 kΩ at a temperature of 36°C, so V_{temp} will behave as shown in table 13.2.

Table 13.2

Temperature/°C	V_{temp}/V
<36	>2.5
>36	<2.5

Of course, the temperature at which V_{temp} crosses over the threshold between high and low voltage (2.5 V) is set by the value of the fixed resistor. Convince yourself that a value smaller than 4.7 kΩ would have raised the temperature at which V_{temp} is 2.5 V.

The driver
The triangle in the centre of figure 13.7 represents the **driver**. Its task is to sense the value of V_{temp} and control the current in the heater accordingly. The graph of figure 13.9 shows how the voltage of the output terminal depends on the voltage of the input terminal. Its behaviour is summarised in Table 13.3.

Table 13.3

Input voltage/V	Output voltage/V
<2.5	5
>2.5	0

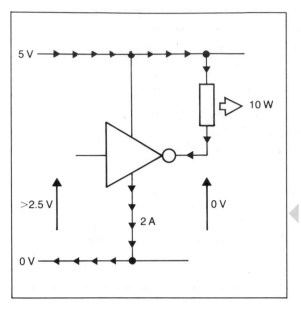

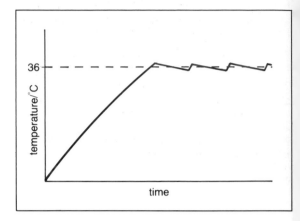

The input terminal of a driver is designed to divert the minimum amount of current from the potential divider which feeds it a signal. On the other hand, the output is designed to handle large currents so that it can control relatively large amounts of electrical energy. So when the output is at 0 V (figure 13.10) it can maintain a current of 2 A in the heater, giving an output power of 10 W. On the other hand, when the output is at 5 V there will be no current in the heater. The driver controls the energy delivered to the heater from the 5 V power supply. The energy that the driver absorbs from the potential divider is comparatively negligible.

Figure 13.10 A driver can handle large currents at its output without having a large current in its input

Figure 13.11 The variation of temperature with time when the thermostat circuit is switched on

REAL DRIVERS

There are many ways in which drivers can be constructed. Some of them are shown in figure 13.12. Although they all have the same function, they have different characteristics. Some can handle larger output currents than others, some take less current in at their inputs than others, etc. Integrated circuit drivers generally give the best performance from the input's point of view, but relays can handle the largest output currents. It is common practice to get the best of both worlds and make an integrated circuit driver control a relay as shown in figure 13.13.

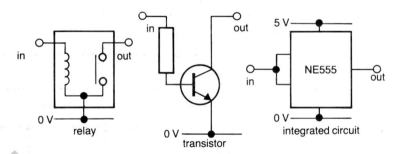

Figure 13.12 Three ways in which drivers can be constructed

Figure 13.13 Boosting the output current of a semiconductor driver with a relay

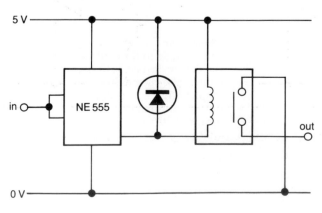

Feedback
You are now in a position to understand the overall behaviour of the circuit drawn in figure 13.7 when it is placed in a small box. If we combine tables 13.2 and 13.3, we can make a new table to work out what the heater does at various temperatures (table 13.4).

Table 13.4

Temperature/°C	Heater power/W
<36	10
>36	0

So if the system starts off at room temperature, the heater will come on. As soon as the thermistor temperature goes above 36°C, the heater will be switched off by the driver. The box will lose heat energy to its surroundings, so after a while the thermistor temperature will drop below 36°C and the driver will switch on the heater once more. And so on. The expected variation of temperature with time is shown in figure 13.11.

OBJECTIVES

After studying this section you should be able to do the following.

State the differences between block diagrams and circuit diagrams.

Recognise that digital systems can encode information using signals called 1 and 0.

Understand that a useful electronic system has inputs and outputs.

Describe the electrical behaviour of a typical driver.

QUESTIONS

The driver mentioned in these questions has all of the characteristics of the driver in figure 13.14.

1 A **light dependent resistor** is a piece of semiconductor whose resistance depends on the light intensity. The characteristics of a popular **LDR** are shown in the graph of figure 13.15(a). The LDR is incorporated into the circuit of figure 13.15(b).

a Use figure 13.15(a) to estimate the minimum light intensity on the LDR required to make the bulb light up.

b Suppose that the bulb is placed close to the LDR and that the system is initially in the dark. What happens when a torch is briefly shone on the LDR?

c Draw a circuit which will make a bulb come on automatically when it gets dark.

2 A number of circuits involving drivers are shown in figure 13.16. For each one, describe how the behaviour of its output transducer (motor, bulb or heater) depends on the state of its input transducer (switch, thermistor or LDR). Suggest a practical application for each circuit.

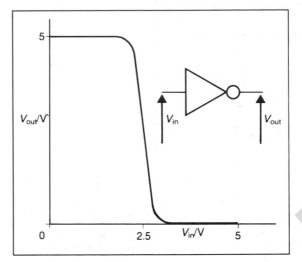

Figure 13.14 Driver characteristics

Figure 13.15

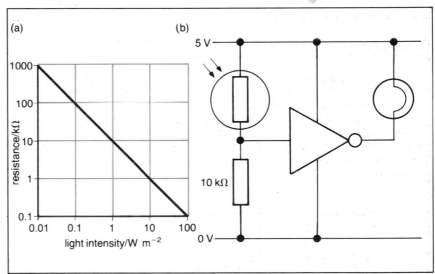

Figure 13.16

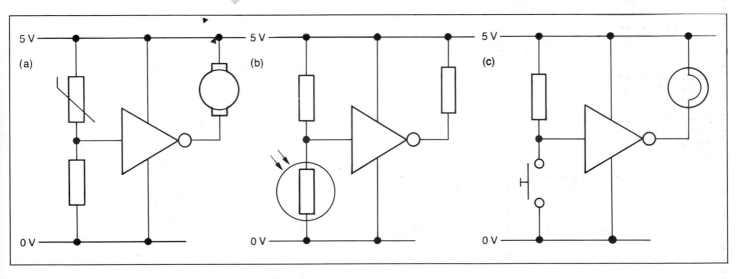

LOGIC GATES

A **logic gate** is a component which has been designed to process signals which are either 1 or 0. They can be assembled in many different ways, using relays or transistors, but their function is independent of their construction. We are going to assume the use of integrated circuit logic gates, and show how they can be connected together to make some useful digital systems.

Basic gates

Any digital system can be constructed by interconnecting different types of logic gate. For example, if you look at figure 13.17 you will see the circuit diagram for a **latch**. Don't worry about what it does (it can store a single bit of information), just notice that it only contains three types of component. This section is going to show you how those components behave and explain how you can work out what the whole system does.

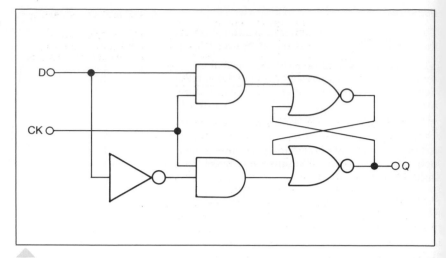

Figure 13.17 An example of a useful circuit made from a number of interconnected logic gates

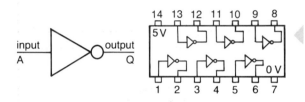

NOT gates

The simplest logic gate is shown in figure 13.18. It is a **NOT gate** or **inverter**. Its function is to invert the signal fed into it. In general, you have to buy six NOT gates at a time: they are internally connected in parallel with two power supply connections to the integrated circuit package.

Figure 13.19 shows how you might set about investigating the behaviour of a NOT gate. The wiper of the potentiometer can be set at any voltage between the two supply rails by rotating its knob. The two voltmeters can be used to measure the values of V_{in} and V_{out}. The results of an experiment on a typical **CMOS** (pronounced 'sea moss') NOT gate are shown in the graph of figure 13.20. Table 13.5 summarises its behaviour.

Table 13.5

Input voltage/V	Output voltage/V
<2.0	5.0
>3.0	0.0

If we define any signal below 2.0 V as being a 0 and any signal above 3.0 V as being a 1, we can represent the behaviour of a NOT gate with the help of a **truth table**.

A	Q
0	1
1	0

The signal going into the gate is labelled A, and the output is labelled Q (figure 13.18). Each row of the table shows the value of Q for a particular value of A.

Figure 13.18 A NOT gate. Six of them are available in a single integrated circuit package

Figure 13.19 A circuit for exploring the behaviour of a NOT gate — the two supply connections for the NOT gate have been omitted

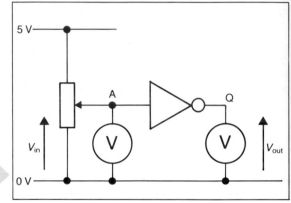

AND gates

As you can see from figure 13.21, an AND gate has two inputs (A and B) and one output Q. You get four of them in a standard integrated circuit package. AND gates are designed to only feed out a 1 when both of their inputs are also 1. This is shown in the truth table below.

B	A	Q
0	0	0
0	1	0
1	0	0
1	1	1

Figure 13.20 Typical behaviour of a CMOS NOT gate

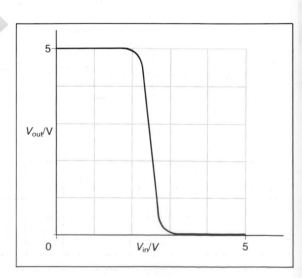

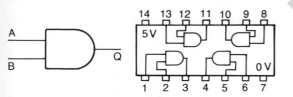

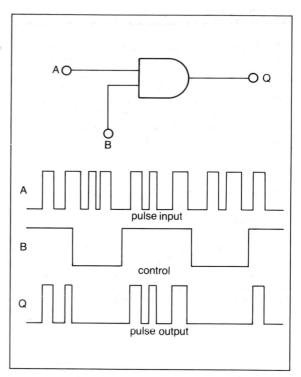

Figure 13.21 An AND gate

Figure 13.22 Using an AND gate to control the flow of pulses from A to Q

An AND gate in action is shown in figure 13.22. A train of pulses are fed into A from some device not shown; it could be an alpha particle detector. Provided that B is a 1, then those pulses will be fed out of the gate's output. (If you look at the last two rows of the truth table you will see that Q = A.) However, if B is a 0, then none of the pulses will get through as Q is forced to be a 0. The behaviour of the AND gate in this application is summarised in the **timing diagrams** of figure 13.22: this is a stylised representation of graphs showing how the voltages at A, B and Q change with time.

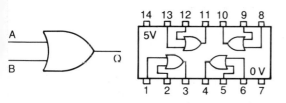

Figure 13.23 An OR gate

OR gates
The circuit symbol for an OR gate is shown in figure 13.23. It can only feed out a 0 when both of its inputs are a 0. For it to feed out a 1, either or both of its inputs have to be a 1. Here is its truth table:

B	A	Q
0	0	0
0	1	1
1	0	1
1	1	1

OR gates can be used to merge trains of pulses from different sources, as shown in figure 13.24. The pulse trains are fed into A and B: each time a pulse enters either input it is fed out of the output.

Figure 13.24 Using an OR gate to combine two streams of pulses

Figure 13.25 A multiplexer

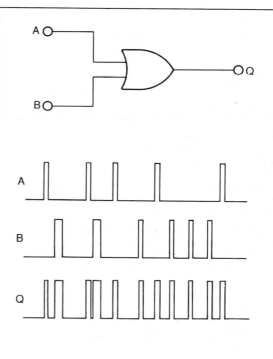

Combining logic gates
We are now going to show you a number of useful digital systems which have been made by connecting NOT, AND and OR gates together. We will not expect you to be able to design such systems for yourself. Instead, you will simply see how to work out what they do.

A multiplexer
The circuit drawn in figure 13.25 is known as a **multiplexer**. Before we explain what it does, we are going to show you how to build a truth table for the whole system.

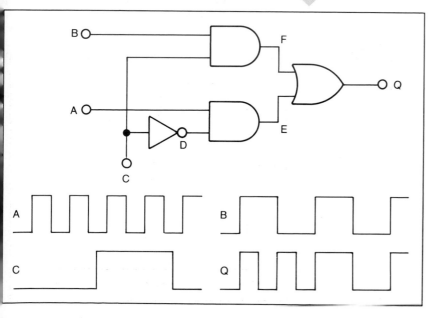

The first step is to write out a blank truth table. The system has three inputs (A, B and C) and one output (Q) so the table will need four columns and eight rows to cover all possible combinations of input signals.

C	B	A	Q
0	0	0	
0	0	1	
0	1	0	
0	1	1	
1	0	0	
1	0	1	
1	1	0	
1	1	1	

Next we go through the circuit labelling the outputs of each gate with an arbitrary letter of the alphabet. This has been done in figure 13.25. Each label needs its own column in the truth table.

C	B	A	D	E	F	Q
0	0	0				
0	0	1				
0	1	0				
0	1	1				
1	0	0				
1	0	1				
1	1	0				
1	1	1				

Now fill in the columns one by one. D is the output of a NOT gate whose input is C, so each time C is 0 D is 1 and vice versa.

C	B	A	D	E	F	Q
0	0	0	1			
0	0	1	1			
0	1	0	1			
0	1	1	1			
1	0	0	0			
1	0	1	0			
1	1	0	0			
1	1	1	0			

Figure 13.26 A keyboard encoder

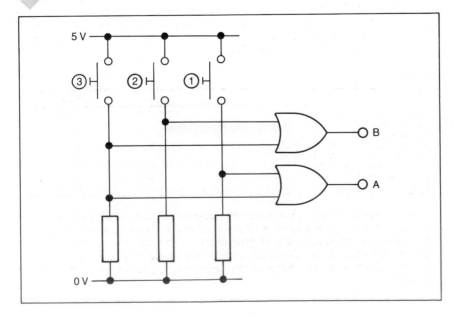

E is the output of an AND gate whose inputs are A and D. So E has to be 1 each time both A and D are 1; otherwise it has to be 0. Similarly, F can only be 1 when both B and C are 1.

C	B	A	D	E	F	Q
0	0	0	1	0	0	
0	0	1	1	1	0	
0	1	0	1	0	0	
0	1	1	1	1	0	
1	0	0	0	0	0	
1	0	1	0	0	0	
1	1	0	0	0	1	
1	1	1	0	0	1	

Finally, because Q is the output of an OR gate it can only be 0 when both E and F are 0. This allows us to fill in the final column of the truth table.

C	B	A	D	E	F	Q
0	0	0	1	0	0	0
0	0	1	1	1	0	1
0	1	0	1	0	0	0
0	1	1	1	1	0	1
1	0	0	0	0	0	0
1	0	1	0	0	0	0
1	1	0	0	0	1	1
1	1	1	0	0	1	1

Now, although we have managed to build the truth table for the whole circuit, it still may not be immediately obvious what it does! So look carefully at the first four rows of the table — can you see that Q = A? Similarly, in the last four rows of the table you should be able to spot that Q = B. So if trains of pulses are fed into A and B, one of them will emerge at Q depending on the signal fed into C. The timing diagram in figure 13.25 should make this clear. The circuit could, for example, be used to select which of two alpha particle detectors fed its pulses into a counter.

A keyboard encoder

The circuit shown in figure 13.26 reads information from a set of three switches (labelled 1, 2, 3) and feeds out a **binary word** which represents the label on the switch being pressed. It performs a function similar to that of the keyboard you might find on a calculator or a telephone.

The three resistors ensure that the gate inputs are held at 0 V when the switches are open. For this reason, they are known as **pull-down** resistors. When a switch is pressed it raises an input terminal from 0 to 1; the resistor in series with the switch pulls the input back down to 0 when the switch is released. The truth table below shows what B and A are when each switch is pressed; it is assumed that only one switch will be pressed at any time. Convince yourself that it is correct.

3	2	1	B	A
1	0	0	1	1
0	1	0	1	0
0	0	1	0	1
0	0	0	0	0

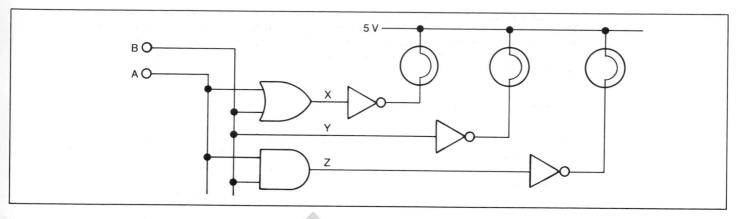

Figure 13.27 Using drivers to increase the output current of logic gates

A display driver

Logic gates can only handle currents of a few milliamps at their outputs, just about enough to make an LED glow faintly. The output of a digital system generally needs a driver to boost the current handling capacity. An example of this is shown in figure 13.27. Each bulb is controlled by a driver: a bulb glows when the input of its driver is a 1. The circuit is designed to read in a binary word BA and light up a number of bulbs according to the truth table shown below.

B	A	X	Y	Z
0	0	0	0	0
0	1	1	0	0
1	0	1	1	0
1	1	1	1	1

Using only NAND gates

Although NOT, AND and OR gates are widely used in real electronic systems, it is possible to assemble *any* digital system out of one type of gate only. Furthermore, that gate can be either a NAND gate or a NOR gate: the former is the preferred device for electronics professionals.

NAND and NOR gates

The circuit symbol of a NAND gate is shown in figure 13.28. It behaves like an AND gate followed by a NOT gate, with this truth table:

B	A	Q
0	0	1
0	1	1
1	0	1
1	1	0

Similarly, a NOR gate (figure 13.29) behaves like an OR gate followed by a NOT gate.

B	A	Q
0	0	1
0	1	0
1	0	0
1	1	0

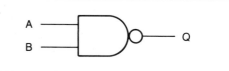

Figure 13.28 A NAND gate

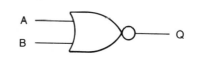

Figure 13.29 A NOR gate

TTL versus CMOS

Two types of integrated circuit logic gate are widely available, based on different technologies. Neither is perfect, and their strengths complement their weaknesses.

The number stamped on a TTL (transistor–transistor logic) integrated circuit package begins with the digits 74. The last two or three numbers denote the function of the gate, e.g. 00 means NAND gates, 04 means inverters, etc. A CMOS (complementary metal oxide semiconductor) integrated circuit package will look the same as a TTL one, except that the number stamped on it begins with 40. The same range of functions are available from both families at roughly the same price. Some of the differences between the two families are listed in table 1. There is quite a lot of variation between integrated circuits of the same family, so the values given in the table are only approximate.

TTL is useful because it is a thousand times faster than CMOS: its outputs change from 1 to 0 in a few nanoseconds rather than microseconds. So TTL is used extensively in computers and other devices where speed is important. On the other hand, CMOS is useful because of its elastic power supply requirements and because it needs far less energy than TTL. Hybrid families of logic gates have been introduced recently which attempt to combine the speed of TTL with the energy efficiency of CMOS.

Table 1

	TTL	CMOS
power supply voltage V_s/V	4.3 − 5.7	3 − 18
output voltage (1)/V	4	V_s
output voltage (0)/V	0	0
maximum output current (1)/mA	0.4	2
maximum output current (0)/mA	16	3
1/0 input threshold voltage /V	1.4	$\frac{1}{2}V_s$
input current (1)/mA	0.04	0
input current (0)/mA	1.6	0

An interesting feature of TTL is that an unconnected input will automatically drift up to 1.4 V, i.e. the gate will treat that input as a 1. This is not the case with CMOS: any unconnected input will float up and down erratically, sometimes giving a 0, sometimes a 1. So CMOS circuits often incorporate pull-down or pull-up resistors to ensure that an otherwise unconnected input is definitely a 0 or a 1.

NAND only

When you get to the questions at the end of this section you will be invited to prove that each of the NAND gate assemblies shown in figure 13.30 behaves like the basic logic gate drawn next to it. In other words, the AND, OR and NOT functions can be obtained from NAND gates only, making it possible to assemble any digital system using only NAND gates. This makes for economy of integrated circuit packages and often simplifies the wiring between them.

An example should make this clear. The circuit shown in figure 13.31 has the truth table of an **Exclusive OR (EOR)** gate. It contains one OR gate, three AND gates and a NOT gate, so it needs three integrated circuit packages, only using five out of the fourteen gates in them.

B	A	Q
0	0	0
0	1	1
1	0	1
1	1	0

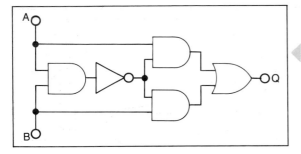

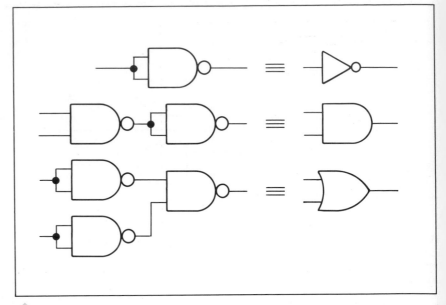

Figure 13.30 Making basic logic gates from NAND gates

Figure 13.31 A circuit which has the truth table of an EOR gate

We can make a more efficient circuit by replacing each of the gates in figure 13.31 with its equivalent made from NAND gates. This is shown in figure 13.32. If you study that circuit you will see that it contains three pairs of NOT gates in series with each other. A little thought should convince you that each of those pairs can be replaced by a wire, so that we end up with the circuit of figure 13.33. This still has the same truth table, but only uses four gates, i.e. one integrated circuit package. Using only NAND gates is clearly more economical and makes circuits easier to construct.

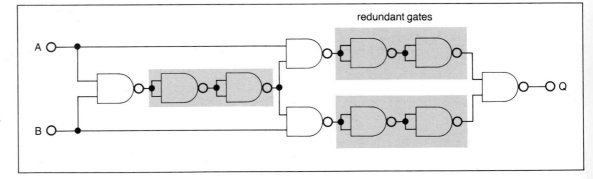

Figure 13.32 Replacing each gate of figure 13.31 with its NAND gate equivalent

Figure 13.33 A NAND gate circuit for an EOR gate

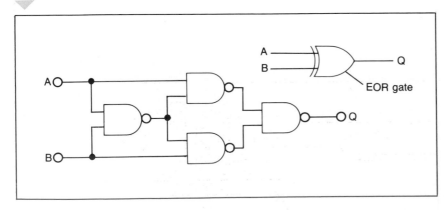

OBJECTIVES

After studying this section you should be able to do the following.

State the range of voltages represented by 1 and 0 for CMOS logic gates.

Write out the truth tables for NOT, AND, OR, NAND, NOR and EOR gates.

Work out the truth table of an assembly of logic gates from their individual truth tables.

Understand that combinations of logic gates can be used to process information in a number of different ways.

Be able to draw a circuit containing only NAND gates which has the same function as a circuit made up from a mixture of other logic gates.

QUESTIONS

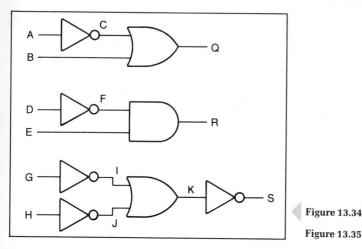

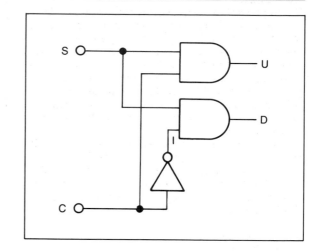

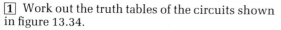

Figure 13.34

Figure 13.35

1 Work out the truth tables of the circuits shown in figure 13.34.

2 The circuit shown in figure 13.35 is a demultiplexer. Draw up a truth table for it. Describe what the circuit does and suggest a use for it.

3 The LED and buzzer shown in figure 13.36 are low current devices which can be operated by the outputs of logic gates.

a Draw up a truth table for the circuit.

b What do you have to do to the switches to make the buzzer emit sound without making the LED glow?

c What happens to the LED and the buzzer if all three switches are pressed?

4 The digital system shown in figure 13.37 displays a number on the seven segment LED. Work out what number it displays for each combination of switches being pressed. Refer to figure 11.29 if you are unsure about the arrangement of LEDs in the seven segment display.

Figure 13.36

Figure 13.37

5 A number of circuits assembled from only NAND gates are shown in figure 13.38. For each circuit, work out its truth table and state which type of logic gate it behaves like.

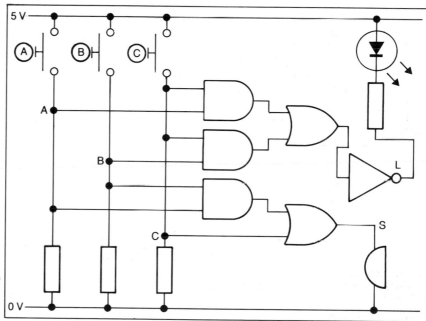

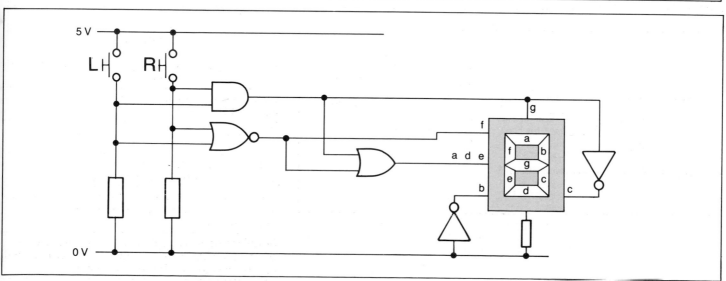

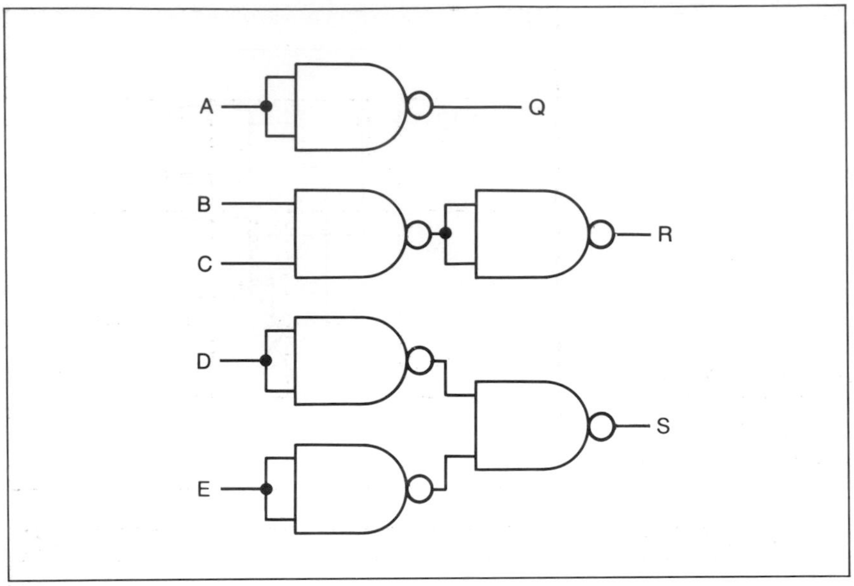

Figure 13.38

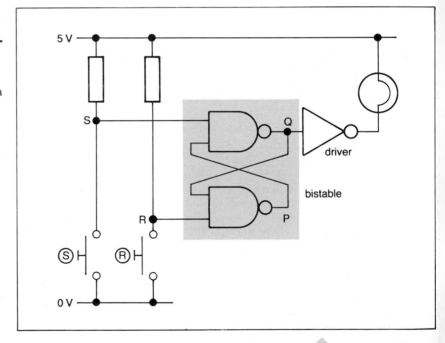

LATCHES, COUNTERS AND TIMERS

Thanks to modern electronics, time is the easiest of quantities to measure precisely. Cheap digital watches routinely keep time to within one minute a year (i.e. better than one part in five million). School laboratory timers can measure intervals up to 999 s with millisecond precision (one part in a million) and quartz laboratory timers can be accurate to better than one part in a hundred million! This section is going to describe all of the components needed for a useful laboratory timing system. Once they have been introduced, you will be shown how they interact with each other and the outside world.

Bistables

The systems described below are all based on the **NAND gate bistable**. This simple circuit, made from a pair of NAND gates, can do something which most other digital systems find impossible. Its output can be 1 or 0 when both its inputs are 1. When the bistable is embedded in more logic gates, you end up with systems which can remember information and count pulses.

NAND gates

The bistable circuit shown in figure 13.39 has two inputs (S and R) and a single output Q. A pair of push switches and a bulb have been included so that signals can be fed in and out of the system. The driver makes the bulb glow when its input is a 1. Bistables are puzzling devices to understand at first. So we will take you through a series of input signals and try to explain why the output behaves the way it does. The sequence is shown in figure 13.40 – consult it from time to time as you read the following description. It will help if you remember that the output of a NAND gate has to be a 1 if either, or both, of its inputs are a 0.

Figure 13.39   A circuit containing a bistable

- Start off with S held at 0. This forces Q to be 1, turning on the bulb. The bottom gate now has a 1 at both of its inputs (R and Q), so P is a 0.
- S is then allowed to rise up to a 1. Q still has to be a 1 because the other input (P) of the top gate is a 0. Furthermore, if neither Q nor R have changed, there is no reason for P to change. So the bulb remains on.
- As soon as R is lowered to a 0, P *has* to become a 1. In turn, this forces Q to be a 0 since both inputs to the top gate are now 1. So the bulb goes off immediately.
- There is no change in the bulb when R is allowed to rise back up to 1. The 0 at Q holds the output of the bottom gate at 1. In its turn, P being a 1 ensures that Q is going to be a 0, provided that S is also a 1.

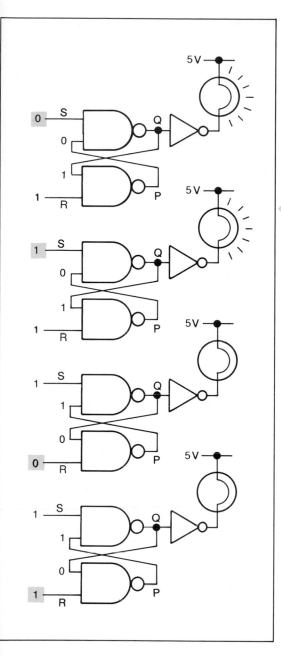

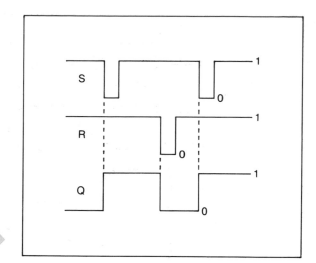

Figure 13.40 Setting and resetting a bistable

Figure 13.41 Timing diagram for a NAND gate bistable

REMEMBERING WORDS

Suppose that we want an electronic system to store some information about four students called Dave, Carl, Beatrice and Anna. We want to record if they are present or absent on a particular day. Four bistables will be needed, one for each student. If the bistable outputs are labelled D, C, B and A, then the **binary word** DCBA will hold the information. A circuit which could be used to obtain and store this word is shown in figure 13.42. A single switch is pressed to reset all four bistables at the start of the school day. As each student arrives they press their switch to set a bistable. So if DCBA = 1110, then Dave, Carl and Beatrice are present but Anna is absent.

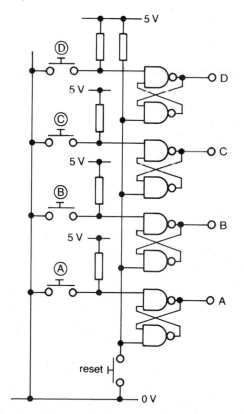

Figure 13.42 A registration circuit

Two stable states

The interesting feature of a NAND gate bistable is contained in the second and fourth diagrams in the sequence of figure 13.40. Both of them have the same input signals (S and R are both 1), but they have different output signals (Q is 1 or 0). Furthermore, the output can be pushed from one state to the other by briefly feeding a 0 into one or other of the inputs. This is shown in the timing diagram of figure 13.41.

S	R	Q
1	1	1/0
0	1	1
1	0	0

The NAND gate bistable is able to remember which of its inputs was last a 0. As soon as S becomes a 0 the bistable is **set** and Q is a 1. The bistable will remain set until R becomes a 0, whereupon it is **reset** and Q becomes a 0.

This system has one great drawback because each bit can be set at any time. So it cannot distinguish between a student who arrived at school on time and one who was late: both will be able to press their switches to set their bistables when they arrive. An improved system would only allow its stored word to be changed at a particular time. This requires the use of a **clocked bistable** or **latch**.

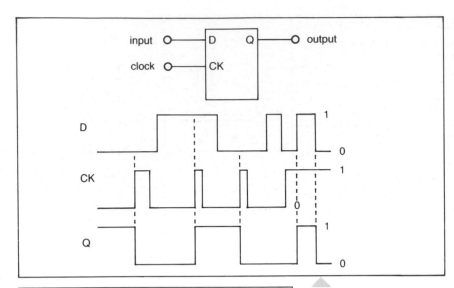

Figure 13.43 Timing diagram for a latch

Figure 13.44 A better registration circuit

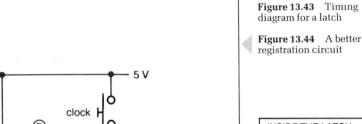

Latches

A simple clocked bistable known as a **latch** is shown in figure 13.43. Although its interior is fairly complicated (see figure 13.45), it is quite easy to use. If you study the timing diagram of figure 13.43, you should see that Q stores whatever was at D when CK was last lowered to 0. In other words, when CK is a 1, Q is the same as D; but once CK is a 0, Q is frozen.

For example, suppose that you want to make Q a 1. First you hold D at 1. This will have no effect on Q if CK is 0. Then you pull CK up to 1, allowing Q to become the same as D. Finally, you let CK go low again so that Q cannot change.

Timed data capture

A registration system which uses latches instead of bistables is shown in figure 13.44. Imagine that it is being used to register the presence or absence of the four students Dave, Carl, Beatrice and Anna. Each student that is present presses their switch and keeps it pressed. At 9 o'clock exactly the teacher briefly presses the clock switch. The four outputs D, C, B and A now hold information about the presence of the four students at 9 o'clock. So if DCBA = 0111, Dave was absent (or late) but the other three were there.

INSIDE THE LATCH   !

Figure 13.45 shows how a bistable can be converted into a latch with the help of three more NAND gates. The truth table for those three gates is shown below. You can check it for yourself.

CK	D	S	R
0	0	1	1
0	1	1	1
1	0	1	0
1	1	0	1

The first two rows of the table show quite clearly that the state of D can have no effect on Q while CK is a 0. (In order to set or reset the bistable, one of its inputs (R or S) has to be a 0.) On the other hand, the last two rows show that when CK is a 1, Q is always the same as D.

Figure 13.45 A latch made from NAND gates

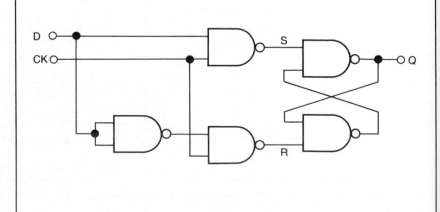

Counters

The binary word stored by the four-bit latch of figure 13.46 can represent anything, depending on how it is coded. If it represents a number, then you have to wait for the next clock pulse to arrive before that number can be changed. When each clock pulse arrives, DCBA becomes the same as dcba, a binary word fed in from some other circuit. However, the addition of some more logic gates, as shown in figure 13.47, allows the latch to generate its own input dcba. Every time that a clock pulse arrives, the number represented by DCBA increases by one. The system is a **pulse counter**, recording the number of pulses in binary.

Flip-flops

A **flip-flop** is a basic component which can be used to construct counters. Its circuit symbol is shown in figure 13.48. Flip-flop behaviour is summarised in the timing diagram: each time that its input falls from 1 to 0, its output changes state. (The name flip-flop reflects this behaviour — each falling edge fed into the device *flips* its output into the other state.) In terms of electronics jargon, flip-flops are **falling-edge triggered**: this is shown by the circle and triangle at their inputs.

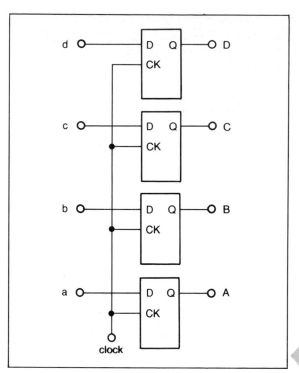

Figure 13.46 A four-bit latch

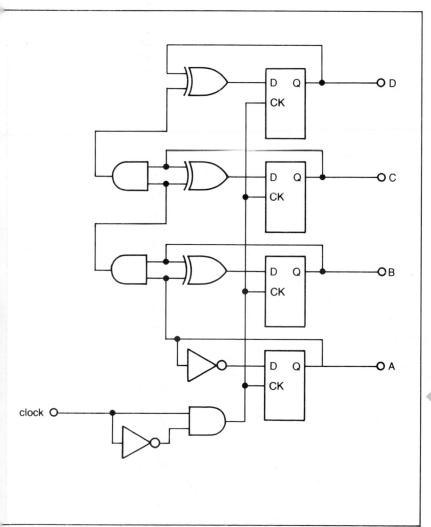

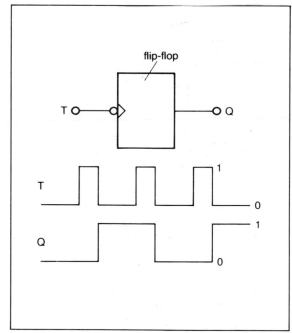

Figure 13.48 Timing diagram for a flip-flop

Figure 13.47 A pulse counter

Figure 13.49 shows what happens when you put three flip-flops in series with each other. The output of one flip-flop provides the input to another. Each time the output of one falls, the output of the flip-flop to its right changes. This is exactly the behaviour required if CBA is to count up in binary. (Think of A as being worth 1, B being worth 2 and C being worth 4. Study the truth table below and convince yourself.) The whole system is called a **three-bit counter**. It can count up to seven events before starting again at zero.

pulse number	C	B	A
0	0	0	0
1	0	0	1
2	0	1	0
3	0	1	1
4	1	0	0
5	1	0	1
6	1	1	0
7	1	1	1
8	0	0	0

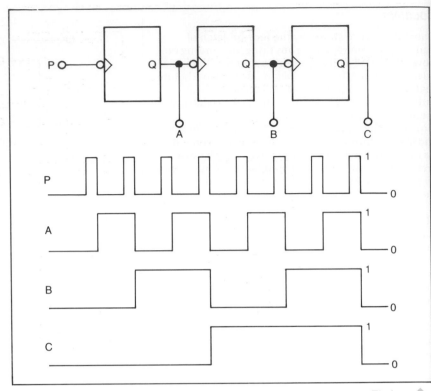

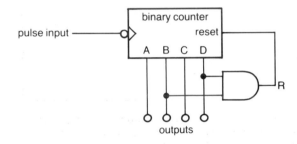

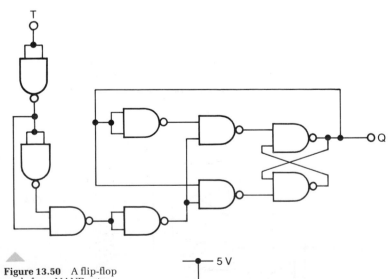

Figure 13.52   A decimal counter

Figure 13.49   Timing diagram of a three-bit counter

Decimal counters

Although electronic systems naturally count in binary, human beings are accustomed to counting numbers in decimal. The numbers between 0 and 9 are normally represented by a four-bit binary word DCBA, with D representing 2^3, C representing 2^2, B representing 2^1 and A representing 2^0. A group of four flip-flops (a **four-bit counter**) can be used to count in decimal if matters can be arranged so that DCBA is reset to 0000 on every tenth pulse which enters the system. Figure 13.52 shows how this can be accomplished with an AND gate. Integrated circuit four-bit counters often incorporate a separate logic gate for this purpose. Each time that DCBA is 1010 the AND gate resets all of the flip-flops, immediately forcing DCBA back to 0. This is shown in the truth table below:

pulse number	D	C	B	A	R
0	0	0	0	0	0
1	0	0	0	1	0
2	0	0	1	0	0
3	0	0	1	1	0
4	0	1	0	0	0
5	0	1	0	1	0
6	0	1	1	0	0
7	0	1	1	1	0
8	1	0	0	0	0
9	1	0	0	1	0
10	1→0	0→0	1→0	0→0	1→0
11	0	0	0	1	0

REAL FLIP-FLOPS

A NAND gate circuit which behaves like a flip-flop is shown in figure 13.50. Don't try to puzzle out how it works! In practice, you could use something called a J−K flip-flop with both of its inputs held at 1. This is shown in figure 13.51. J−K flip-flops are versatile devices with a number of different applications. You get two in a single integrated circuit package.

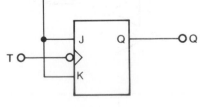

Figure 13.50   A flip-flop made from NAND gates

Figure 13.51   A one-bit counter from a J−K flip-flop

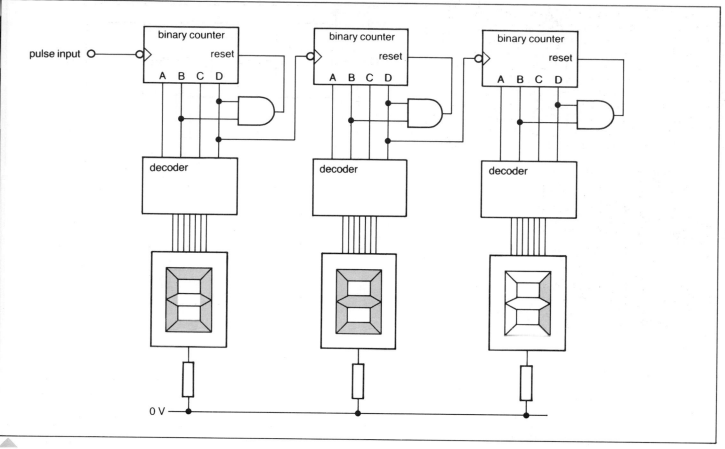

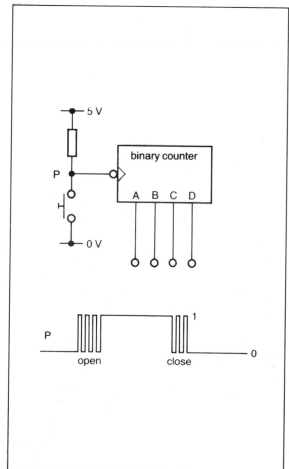

Decimal counters can be connected in series to count higher powers of ten. For example, the circuit shown in figure 13.53 can count and display up to 999 pulses. Since flip-flops are triggered by falling edges, the D output of each counter is used to provide the clock pulses for the counter on its right. (If you study the truth table above, you will see that D only falls from 1 to 0 once for every ten pulses fed into a decimal counter.)

Switch bounce

What events can an electronic counter count? The answer is 'almost anything', provided that you can invent a suitable interface to convert each event into a falling edge. For example, you might attempt to use a push switch as shown in figure 13.54. Each time the switch is pressed P should drop from 1 to 0 and be noticed by the counter. Unfortunately, electronic counters respond very rapidly. The counter will count *all* of the falling edges fed out by the switch when it is closed. Since a switch is just two bits of metal being pushed together, it is inevitable that they will bounce apart at least once before they settle down in contact with each other. So the signal fed out from the switch will be as shown in figure 13.54, with several falling edges spread over a few milliseconds.

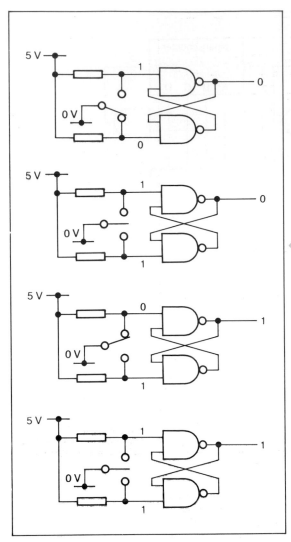

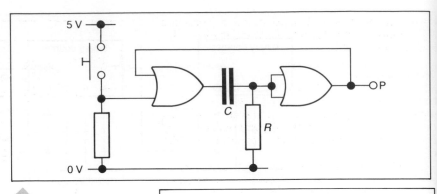

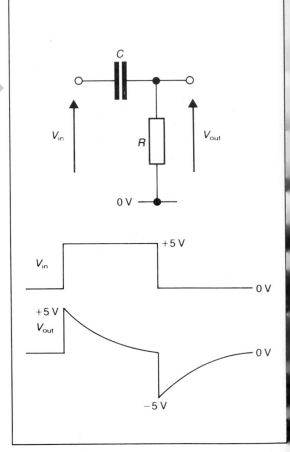

Figure 13.56 A monostable

Figure 13.55 Using a NAND gate bistable to debounce a switch

Figure 13.57 Feeding rising and falling edges into an RC network

One technique for avoiding this bounce problem is illustrated in figure 13.55. A switch is used to connect one of the inputs of the bistable to 0 V. The sequence in figure 13.55 shows why a single rising or falling edge is fed out of the bistable each time the setting of the switch is changed. Another technique employs a **monostable**, as shown in figure 13.56. This emits a single pulse each time the switch is pressed and released. Provided that the switch has been released before the pulse is over, the counter should only detect a single falling edge.

Monostables and astables

RC networks can be inserted into digital systems to allow signals to change with time. **Monostables** emit single pulses and **astables** emit continuous trains of pulses. We are going to show you how each of them can be built from CMOS logic gates and RC networks; our circuits are not the only way in which monostables and astables can be assembled.

Generating spikes
Both monostables and astables contain the RC network shown in figure 13.57. The graphs show what happens to the output voltage V_{out} when the input voltage V_{in} is suddenly changed from 0 to 1 and back to 0.

Why does the network behave this way? Initially when V_{in} is 0 V, the capacitor is completely discharged. When V_{in} rises to 5 V the capacitor will start to charge up through the resistor. The current in it will be given by

$$I = I_0 \times \exp[-t/RC] \qquad \text{(13.1}$$

V_{out} is the p.d. across the resistor, so we can use the resistance formula to obtain an expression for its change with time.

$$R = \frac{V}{I} \qquad \therefore V_{out} = I_0 R \times \exp[-t/RC]$$

$$\therefore V_{out} = 5 \times \exp[-t/RC] \qquad \text{(13.2}$$

As the capacitor charges up, the current in the resistor will gradually fall. So V_{out} shoots rapidly up to 5 V before slowly dropping back to 0 V. It will get halfway there in $t_{\frac{1}{2}} = 0.69RC$ seconds. When V_{in} is lowered back down to 0 V, the same thing happens. The charge which flowed off the right hand plate now has to flow back onto it, so the current in the resistor changes direction. Therefore V_{out} shoots rapidly down to −5 V and then slowly rises back up to 0 V.

The monostable

The whole circuit is shown in figure 13.58. Each time that the input T is raised to 1, the output Q goes to 1 for 0.69RC seconds, regardless of the time that T stays at 1. The following paragraph explains how it works; it will help if you consult the graphs of figure 13.58.

Initially the capacitor is completely discharged so B is at 0 V. So Q is a 0. If T is a 0, then A is also a 0. Now T is raised to a 1. Immediately, A becomes a 1 as well. B shoots up to 5 V as the capacitor starts to charge up via the resistor: because B is a 1, Q also has to be a 1. The feedback loop from Q to the left-hand gate ensures that A will now remain a 1, even if T is immediately lowered back to a 0. So B will drop steadily from 5 V towards 0 V: it will reach 2.5 V after 0.69RC seconds. As soon as that happens Q will go back to a 0, allowing A to also go back to 0. B will shoot rapidly down as the capacitor tries to discharge itself via the resistor. When B gets below 0 V the capacitor is rapidly discharged through the inputs of the right-hand gate.

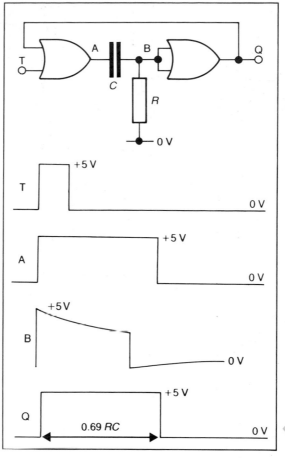

Figure 13.58   The sequence of events when a monostable is triggered

The astable

The astable of figure 13.59 uses two RC networks to fire out a continuous train of pulses. Each pulse lasts for 0.69RC seconds, with a gap of 0.69RC seconds between the pulses. Once the circuit has started to oscillate, it will carry on until its power supply is switched off. The outputs of the NOT gates always have opposite states to each other. Each time that the output of one gate rises from 0 to 1, the input of the other is pushed up to a 1 for 0.69RC seconds before falling back to a 0.

Timing circuits

The block diagram of an event timer is shown in figure 13.60. The whole system is designed to measure the time for which a signal is fed into the input terminal. The gate controls the flow of pulses from the astable to the counter and the value of the count is displayed with some seven-segment LEDs. A reset signal forces the counter output back to zero.

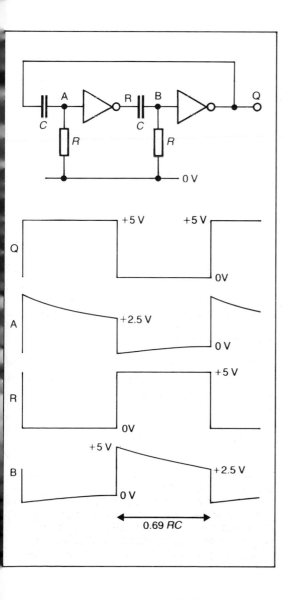

Figure 13.59   An astable

Figure 13.60   Block diagram of an event timer

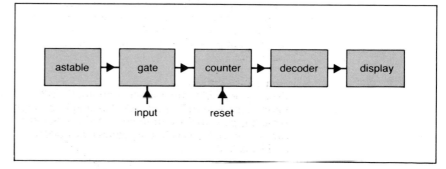

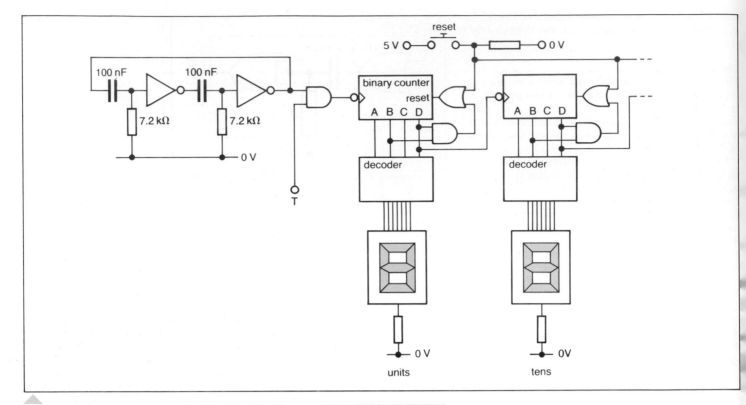

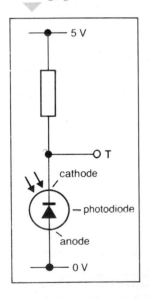

Figure 13.61 Circuit diagram of an event timer

Figure 13.62 Using a photodiode to generate the timing signal

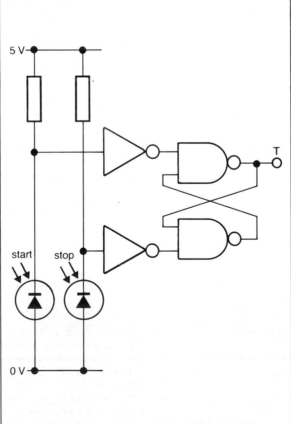

Figure 13.63 One photodiode starts the timer, the other stops it

The timer

Figure 13.61 shows how the system may be implemented with familiar components. In general, each box represents a single integrated circuit package, although the circuit could, if necessary, be fitted onto a single integrated circuit. The astable frequency has been set at 1.00 kHz so that it fires out one pulse every millisecond. Provided that T is a 1, those pulses get through to the counter chain. Each binary counter has been forced to behave as a decimal counter, so the first stage counts units, the second stage counts tens, and so on. The four outputs of each counter are converted into the seven signals needed to drive the seven segment LED displays by the **decoders**: these are, of course, just assemblies of logic gates with a driver for each output. A reset switch is provided to zero the display.

Interfacing

In order to use the circuit of figure 13.61 to time real events, you have to persuade each event to feed a suitable signal into T. **Photodiodes** are widely used to interface electronic timers to the outside world, as shown in figure 13.62. When visible light falls on their surface, charge can flow through them from from cathode to anode; the current is proportional to the light intensity. In the dark, the photodiode behaves like an ordinary diode so there is no current in it, allowing the resistor to 'pull' T up to 1. So if you arrange for a beam of light to shine on the photodiode, the timer can be used to measure the time taken for something to pass through the beam.

It often happens that you want to use one event to start a timer and another event to stop it. The inclusion of a bistable, as shown in figure 13.63, accomplishes this. One light beam has to be cut to make T a 1: only when the other light beam has been cut will T return to being a 0.

OBJECTIVES

After studying this section you should be able to do
the following.

Draw the circuit of a NAND gate bistable and describe its behaviour with a timing diagram and truth table.	Know how to connect flip-flops in series to make four-bit counters.
Describe the behaviour of a latch.	Explain how a binary counter can be converted into a decimal counter.
Know how to connect latches to store binary words.	Be aware of switch bounce and the need to eliminate it.
State the difference between the rising edge and the falling edge of a pulse.	Draw the circuit diagram of a monostable and describe its behaviour with a timing diagram.
Describe the behaviour of a flip-flop with a timing diagram.	Draw the circuit diagram of an astable and describe its behaviour with a timing diagram.

QUESTIONS

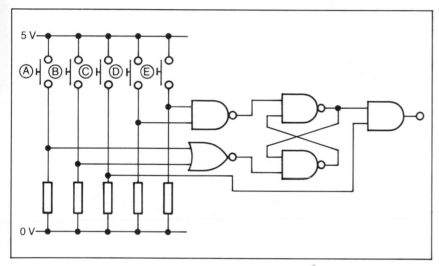

Figure 13.64

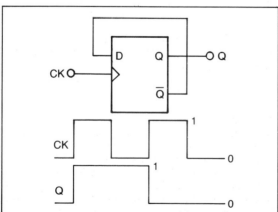

Figure 13.65

Figure 13.66

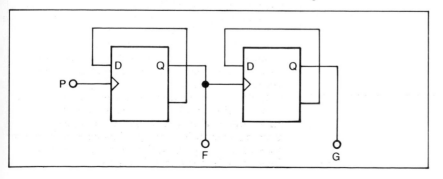

1 The circuit shown in figure 13.64 could be used to control a piece of factory machinery, such as a hydraulic press. Two switches have to be pressed simultaneously to start the machine — these switches are placed so that the operator's hands are in a safe place when the machine is started. Two other switches are provided to stop the machine — pressing either one will bring it to a halt. A fifth switch is closed when a barrier is in position between the machine and the operator: the machine cannot operate when the barrier switch is open. Which of the switches is which?

2 A device known as a D flip-flop is shown in figure 13.65, along with a timing diagram which relates its output Q to its input CK.

a Does Q change on rising or falling edges?

b Two D flip-flops are connected as shown in figure 13.66. With the help of figure 13.65, draw a timing diagram to show how the outputs F and G change when six pulses are fed into P. Assume that F and G both start off at 1.

c Copy and complete this table.

pulse number	G	F
0	1	1
1	?	?
2	?	?
3	?	?
4	?	?
5	?	?
6	?	?

3 Photodiodes which respond to infra-red radiation are often used in burglar alarms. Should the beam of radiation from an infra-red LED be cut off momentarily, the alarm has to sound for a few minutes. Draw a circuit diagram for an alarm system of this type which has three separate photodiode detectors in different places around the house.

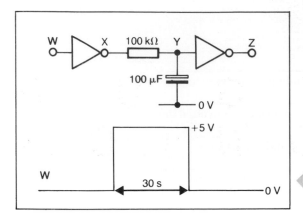

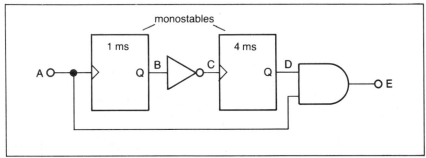

Figure 13.67

Figure 13.68

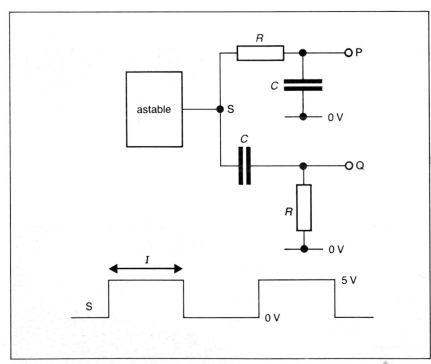

Figure 13.69

Figure 13.70

4 The system shown in figure 13.68 is a **coincidence detector**. It is designed to detect the presence of pairs of short pulses which arrive at its input separated by less than 5 ms and more than 1 ms. With the help of some timing diagrams, explain how the system works.

5 An astable feeds the series of pulses drawn in figure 13.69 into a pair of RC networks. Both the width of the pulses and their spacing is T. A number of possible graphs for the output voltages are shown in figure 13.70. Select, with reasons, the correct ones if

a $T \gg RC$,

b $T \simeq RC$,

c $T \ll RC$.

6 Figure 13.67 shows how an RC network can be used to delay the change of a digital signal. The NOT gates have 1/0 thresholds of 2.5 V. The signal shown in the graph is fed into W.

a Calculate the time constant of the circuit. Estimate how long it takes for Y to reach 2.5 V if X is suddenly raised from 0 V to 5 V.

b Draw a series of graphs — one under the other and to the same scale — to show what happens to the voltages at X, Y and Z over the same time. You can assume that Y starts off at 5 V.

c Select suitable values for R and C to allow the circuit to delay changes of digital signals by 1.0 s.

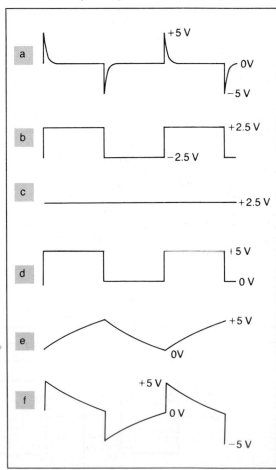

14

ANALOGUE
ELECTRONICS

Nature's messages are analogue rather than digital. Quantities which scientists are interested in measuring appear to have an infinite range of values, not just two. For example, in a digital world, the temperature of an object might have to be either 0.00 K or 273.15 K. Of course, in our analogue world, an object can have any temperature above 0 K.

This property is reflected in the outputs of sensors designed to translate physical quantities into electrical signals. They provide currents or voltages whose values can vary continuously over a wide range. For example, four sensors are illustrated in figure 14.1. The chromel/alumel **thermocouple** provides a tiny voltage of $41.6\ \mu V\ K^{-1}$ at room temperature. The **photodiode** measures light intensity, maintaining a current (about $200\ \mu A$ in daylight) which is proportional to the rate at which it absorbs light energy. The **Hall probe** measures the component of magnetic field at right angles to its surface. The p.d. between two terminals is $1\ mV\ mT^{-1}$: it can be positive or negative because it represents a vector. Finally, the **piezoelectric microphone** detects compression waves. Its output is a small alternating voltage (typically less than a millivolt) fed out through an internal resistance measured in megohms.

The principal aim of this chapter is to show you how these signals can be moulded into a form suitable for conversion to digital signals, which can then be understood by a computer. You will meet two new tools along the way: the operational amplifier and the oscilloscope.

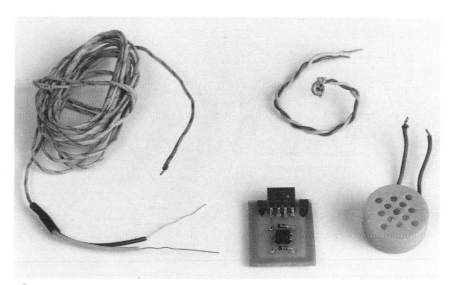

Figure 14.1 (a) Four analogue sensors: a thermocouple, a photodiode, a Hall probe and a microphone

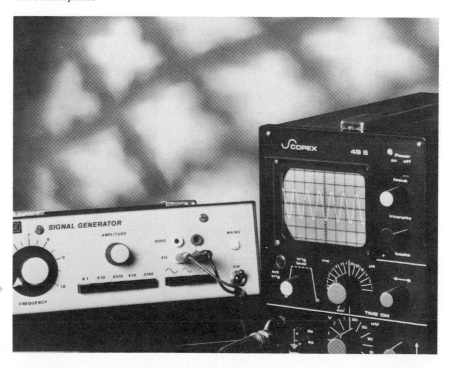

(b) An oscilloscope displaying the signal being fed out of an oscillator. The analogue signal varies rapidly, so it is displayed on the screen as a voltage – time curve. (See page 244.)

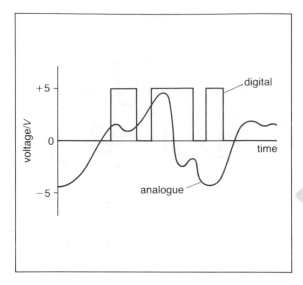

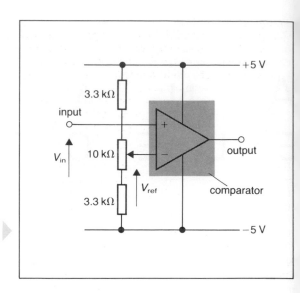

Figure 14.2 Analogue and digital signals

Figure 14.3 A comparator

Figure 14.4 Input and output signals for a comparator

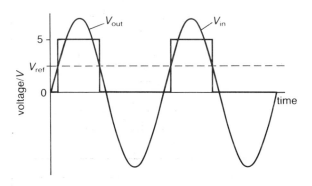

NEGATIVE VOLTAGES

You will recall that the voltage of a conductor is a measure of the electrical energy of its charge carriers. Furthermore, the choice of zero for an energy is usually arbitrary. In electronics it is the accepted convention that any conductor which is in good electrical contact with the Earth is at 0 V. The earth loop of a ring main system therefore provides a convenient zero of electrical energy. So conductors whose charge carriers have *less* electrical energy than those in the earth loop have negative voltages. Figure 14.5 shows how a pair of 9 V batteries can be arranged to establish a pair of supply rails which are at +9 V and −9V. In electronics, it is standard practice to talk about the 'voltage of a terminal', implying that the ground is at zero volts. Purists prefer to talk of 'voltage differences between a terminal and ground', but this can get tiresome after a while!

Figure 14.5 Generating supply rails at +9 V and −9 V with batteries

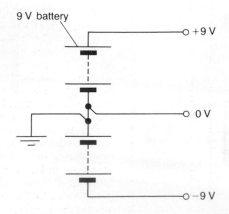

COMPARATORS

The difference between analogue and digital electrical signals is illustrated in figure 14.2. The digital signal is either +5 V or 0 V, jumping straight from one to the other, whereas the analogue signal varies smoothly over the whole range. The signals from electrical sensors are generally analogue, but the storage and processing of the information in those signals is best done by digital systems like computers. **Comparators** are one means by which analogue signals can be converted into digital ones.

Analogue to digital

Look at figure 14.3. The triangle in the middle represents the comparator. It has an analogue input and a digital output, with the characteristics shown in table 14.1. Since it has to be able to process signals which are negative as well as positive, its supply rails are held at +5 V and −5 V by the power supply.

Table 14.1

Input	Output
$V_{in} < V_{ref}$	0
$V_{in} > V_{ref}$	1

The analogue signal is fed into the **non-inverting input**. This is compared with the reference voltage at the **inverting input**. If the signal voltage is greater than the reference voltage then the output is a 1; otherwise it is a 0. The value of the reference voltage can be varied between +3.0 V and −3.0 V by adjusting the potentiometer. The graph of figure 14.4 shows the effect of the value of V_{ref} on the output signal.

Temperature control

Comparators are useful if you need precise control of a variable such as temperature. A circuit which can be used to keep an object below a certain temperature is shown in figure 14.6. A thermistor connected to the object is used to monitor its temperature: the thermistor resistance is converted to a voltage V_{temp} by making it part of a potential divider. The comparator compares this signal with V_{ref}. At high temperatures, V_{temp} will be higher than V_{ref}, so Q will be a 1. The driver will switch on the relay, turning on the fan which will blow cold air over the object, lowering its temperature. As the temperature drops the thermistor resistance rises, making V_{temp} fall. As soon as V_{temp} goes below V_{ref}, the driver turns the relay off and the fan stops turning. So the temperature of the object is kept below a certain value; each time the temperature get too high the fan is switched on to bring it down again. The potentiometer can be used to set the temperature at which the cooling mechanism is switched on. (The diode stops the **back e.m.f.** across the relay coil from destroying the driver each time that it goes from 0 to 1. You will find out more about this in chapter 24.)

Operational amplifiers

The **operational amplifier** does for analogue electronics what the NAND gate does for digital electronics. It is a cheap and easy-to-use basic component which can be used in a wide variety of ways to build systems that process analogue signals. Nearly all of the devices you are going to meet in this chapter will contain an operational amplifier. So before we show you how an **op-amp** can be made to behave like a comparator, you ought to be formally introduced to one. However, be warned! What follows is unlikely to make much sense unless you try to get some practical experience of operational amplifier circuits in action!

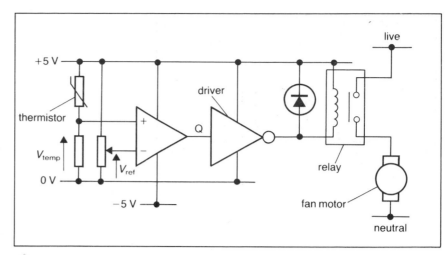

Figure 14.6 A comparator in action

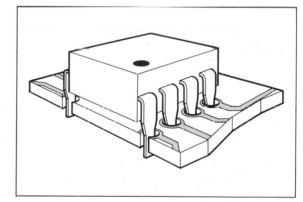

Figure 14.7 A typical op-amp package

Figure 14.8 The circuit diagram for a TL081 op-amp

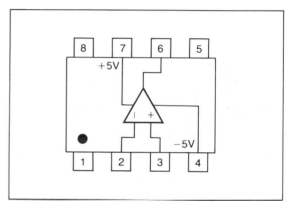

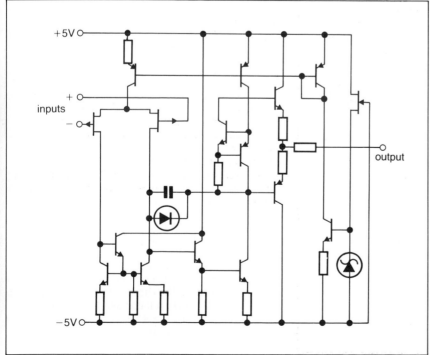

TL081

The TL081 is a cheap, widely available, easy-to-use, high quality integrated circuit operational amplifier with input and output characteristics which are well matched to the requirements of scientific instruments. It is a typical operational amplifier, coming in integrated circuit form, enclosed in a black plastic package which has eight terminals emerging from it. The function of those terminals is shown in figure 14.7.

Two terminals (4 and 7) are needed for the power supply which can range from ± 3 V to ± 18 V. Two more terminals (2 and 3) are needed for the inverting and non-inverting inputs and one (6) for the output. Despite the complexity of its interior (see figure 14.8 for a circuit diagram of the TL081), an op-amp has deceptively simple behaviour which can be modelled with an equation.

ELECTRONICS

$$V_{out} = A(V_+ - V_-)$$

V_{out} is the voltage of the output terminal (V)

A is the open-loop gain of the op-amp

V_+ is the voltage of the non-inverting input (V)

V_- is the voltage of the inverting input (V)

An op-amp is a **differential amplifier**. Look at figure 14.9. The op-amp's function is to measure the p.d. between its input terminals, multiply it by a set scale factor (A) and use the answer to fix the p.d. between the output terminal and ground.

Saturation

Table 14.2 contains data which we will need from time to time in this chapter. Although only some of the information is relevant now, we have included the rest so that you know where to find it. The numbers are quoted for a typical TL081 run off supply rails of ± 5 V. (The mass production process by which integrated circuits are manufactured results in a wide variation in properties from one op-amp to the next. This means that every op-amp has its own unique open-loop gain, etc.)

Table 14.2

maximum output voltage	$+4$ V
minimum output voltage	-4 V
maximum output current	10 mA
typical input current	50 pA
maximum input voltage	$+5$ V
minimum input voltage	-4 V
open-loop gain A	2×10^5
maximum frequency	3 MHz
output slew rate	13 V μs^{-1}

As you can see, the value of A is quite large. You will appreciate this best with the example shown in figure 14.10. The op-amp is attempting to measure the p.d. across a standard thermocouple. One junction is 2.0 K higher than the other, giving a p.d. between them of about 83 μV.

$$V_{out} = A(V_+ - V_-)$$
$$\therefore V_{out} = 2 \times 10^5 \times (-83 \times 10^{-6}) = -17 \text{ V}$$

If you consult table 14.2, you will find that V_{out} cannot get as low as -17 V. So the op-amp is going to do the best it can by pushing V_{out} as low as it can. Its output **saturates** at -4 V. You can check for yourself that the voltages of the input terminals have to be within 20 μV of each other for the op-amp output *not* to saturate. So provided that we don't aim for a precision of more than $\pm$ 20 μV, we can summarise the behaviour of an op-amp with Table 14.3.

Table 14.3

Input	Output
$V_+ < V_-$	-4 V
$V_+ = V_-$	0 V
$V_+ > V_-$	$+4$ V

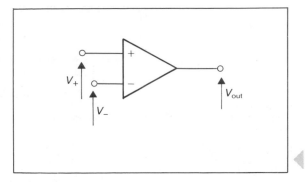

Figure 14.9 An operational amplifier

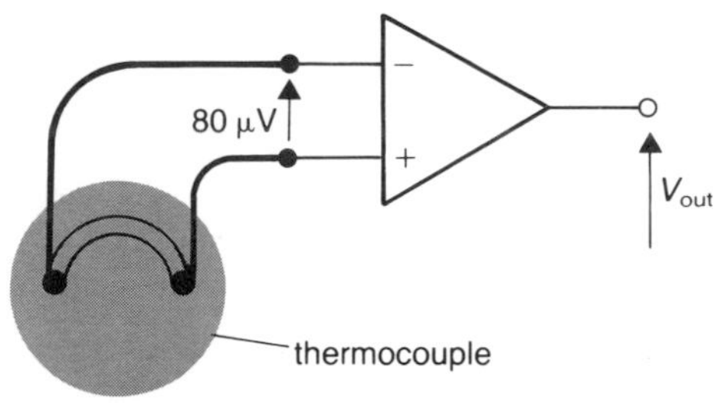

Figure 14.10 Amplifying the signal from a thermocouple

80 μV

thermocouple

V_{out}

OFFSET ADJUSTMENT

Figure 14.11 shows the procedure you need to adopt if you want the middle row of table 14.3 to be true. It is not possible to build op-amps which have perfectly balanced inputs without substantially increasing their cost. So if you connect both inputs of an op-amp to the same voltage source, e.g. the 0 V supply rail, the output will not necessarily sit at 0.0 V. This is not important for many applications of op-amps. However, if it is crucial for an application that $V_{out} = 0.0$ V when $V_+ = V_-$ then you can insert a potentiometer as shown in figure 14.11 and adjust it until the inputs are correctly balanced.

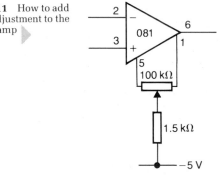

Figure 14.11 How to add an offset adjustment to the TL081 op-amp

081

100 kΩ

1.5 kΩ

-5 V

Digital output

Although an operational amplifier behaves like a comparator at its input end, its output is definitely not digital because it can go negative. (Digital signals tend to be close to either $+5$ V or 0 V.) One way of arranging for the output of an op-amp to be compatible with the inputs of digital systems is shown in figure 14.12. The diode **rectifies** the op-amp output, ensuring that V_d cannot go below 0 V. This is how it works. When V_{out} is $+4$ V, there can be a current in the diode, giving a voltage drop of about 0.7 V across it (see page 170). So the p.d. across the resistor $V_d \simeq 4 - 0.7 = +3.3$ V. However, when V_{out} is -4 V, there can be no current in the diode or the resistor. So $V_d = 0.0$ V.

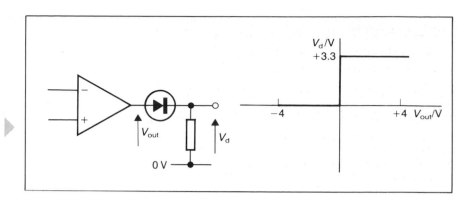

Figure 14.12 Converting an op-amp into a comparator

Figure 14.13 Q is only high if V_{in} lies between V_{upper} and V_{lower}

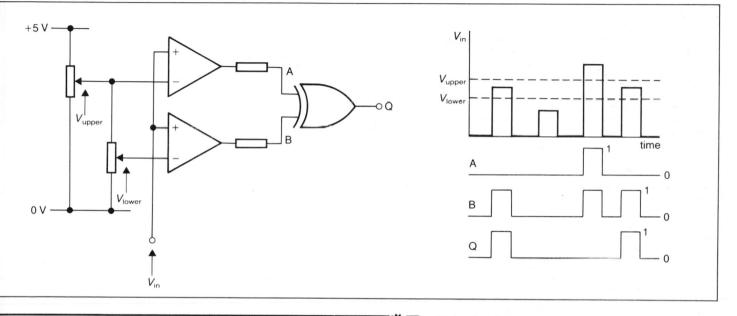

SAFE LIGHT LEVELS

An interesting use of op-amps to indicate that a physical quantity is neither too large nor too small is illustrated in figure 14.14. The circuit could be useful for photography. The LED glows when the ambient lighting is neither too bright nor too dark. The light level is monitored by an LDR in a potential divider whose output is compared with +2.0 V and +3.0 V by a pair of op-amps. In the dark, both T and B are at −4 V so the LED will not glow. Similarly, in bright light both T and B are +4 V. The LED can only glow when the op-amp outputs have different voltages, i.e. when T is at +4 V and B is at −4 V. (The resistor limits the current in the LED to a safe 6 mA.).

Figure 14.14 The LED only glows if the light level is not too high or too low

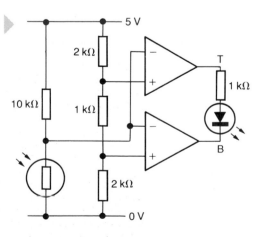

Pulse-height sorter

As an example of op-amp comparators in action in the laboratory, consider the circuit shown in figure 14.13 (the op-amps are drawn upside down for convenience!). Its function is to feed out a digital pulse each time it detects a pulse whose height is between V_{upper} and V_{lower}. The pulses come from a **solid-state radiation detector**. The pulses from alpha, beta and gamma particles absorbed by such detectors have different heights. The circuit can be used to let through the pulses produced by one type of radiation and reject those produced by the other two.

The graphs in figure 14.13 illustrate how the circuit works. One op-amp compares V_{in} with V_{lower}, the other compares it with V_{upper}. The EOR gate processes the outputs of the two op-amps: its output will only be a 1 when its inputs are different.

B	A	Q
0	0	0
0	1	1
1	0	1
1	1	0

The **slew rate** of an op-amp is a measure of how fast its output voltage can change. A TL081 output can swing from −4 V to +4 V in about 0.5 μs, so the circuit of figure 14.13 can reliably sort pulses which only exist for a couple of microseconds.

CHART RECORDERS

Chart recorders are widely used in laboratories, hospitals and industry to record how voltages change with time. The voltage controls the sideways movement of a pen across a sheet of paper which moves forwards at a constant speed. The result is a voltage–time graph, a permanent record of the time variation of the signal.

Figure 14.15 The electronics of a chart recorder

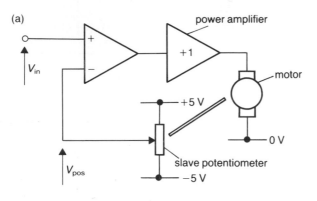

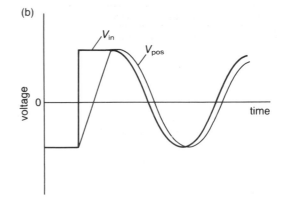

Figure 14.16 Some mechanical aspects of a chart recorder

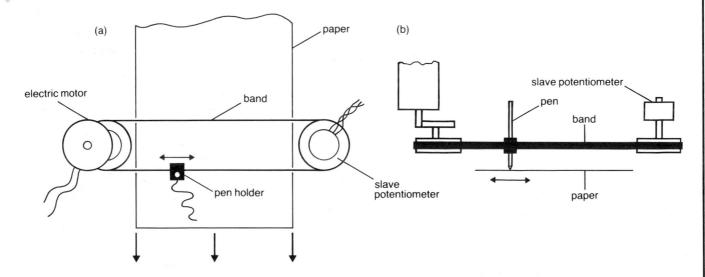

Figure 14.15(a) shows the electronic aspects of a simple chart recorder. The important mechanical aspects are shown in figure 14.16. The position of the pen is controlled by an electric motor and monitored by a potentiometer. The voltage of its wiper is going to be a function of the pen position, so as the pen is moved across the paper, V_{pos} will change accordingly. The op-amp compares V_{in} with V_{pos}. Unless they are the same, the op-amp will feed +4 V or −4V into the **power amplifier**. A **power amplifier** is an analogue version of a driver, designed to control large amounts of current at its output for very little current at its input. So if V_{pos} is less than V_{in}, the power amplifier will feed +4 V into the motor, making it turn clockwise. Similarly, as soon as V_{pos} becomes greater than V_{in}, the driver will feed −4 V into the motor, making it turn anticlockwise and changing the direction of the pen movement.

Provided that the mechanical side of the chart recorder has been arranged so that clockwise rotation of the motor results in an increase of V_{pos}, the whole system will eventually settle down with V_{pos} equal to V_{in}. As the graph of figure 14.15(b) shows, subsequent changes of V_{in} result in proportional changes in the position of the pen, with a time lag due to the finite response time of the mechanical system.

OBJECTIVES

After studying this section you should be able to do the following.

Describe the difference between digital and analogue signals.

Describe the behaviour of an operational amplifier.

Show how an op-amp can be used as a comparator.

Explain how a simple chart recorder works.

Describe the behaviour of a power amplifier.

QUESTIONS

1 The graph of figure 14.17 shows how the resistance of the thermistor in the circuit changes with temperature. The buzzer is a low current device which needs at least 5 V across it before it makes a noise.

a Calculate the voltage at X. Use the graph to estimate the temperature at which Y will be at the same voltage as X.

b Describe and explain what happens to the buzzer as the thermistor is slowly warmed from 0 °C to 100 °C.

2 Figure 14.18 shows a simple bargraph voltmeter. Circuits like this are used in hi-fi amplifiers to monitor the strength of the signal being fed to the loudspeakers.

a Calculate the voltages at W, X, Y and Z.

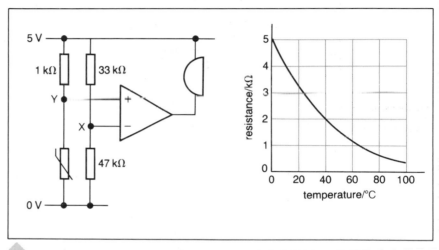

Figure 14.17

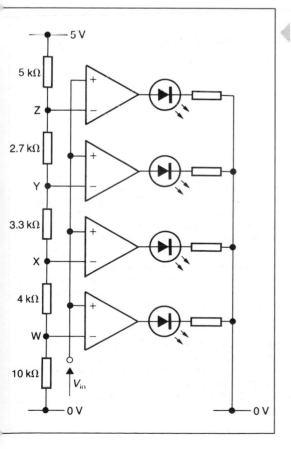

Figure 14.18

Figure 14.19

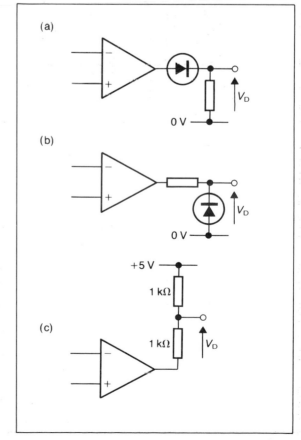

(a)

(b)

(c)

b State what the number of glowing LEDs tells you about the value of V_{in}.

c The power of a signal is proportional to the square of its voltage. How is the number of glowing LEDs related to the power of V_{in}?

d What advantages and disadvantages does the circuit have compared with the use of a moving-coil voltmeter?

3 Three different ways of converting the analogue output of an op-amp into a digital signal V_D are shown in figure 14.19. Assuming that the p.d. across the diode is 0.6 V when there is a current in it, copy and complete table 14.4 for each circuit.

Table 14.4

Op-amp output/V	V_D/V
+4.0	?
−4.0	?

4 One of the problems encountered in the use of comparators is called **chatter**. When the two inputs are at the same voltage, small fluctuations in them cause rapid changes of the comparator output. This can be avoided by incorporating some **positive feedback**, as shown in figure 14.20.

a Suppose that V_{out} is +4 V. What is the value of V_+?

b To what voltage do you have to raise V_- in order to persuade V_{out} to change to −4 V?

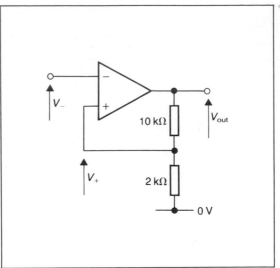

Figure 14.20

Figure 14.21

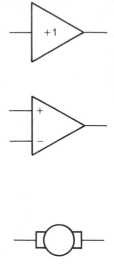

c What does V_+ become when this happens?

d How far do you have to lower V_- in order to persuade V_{out} back up to +4 V?

5 The p.d. across the terminals of a d.c. electric motor is proportional to the speed with which its shaft is spinning. There are many devices which rely on having a constant angular velocity: a record turntable is one example. Use the components drawn in figure 14.21 to draw the circuit diagram of a system which could be used to keep a turntable rotating at a constant speed. Explain how it works.

AMPLIFIERS

This section of the chapter will introduce you to a number of useful circuits based on op-amps. Although each will be accompanied by at least one useful application, you will have to wait for the next section to see them in action together.

Figure 14.22 An amplifier with a gain of +2

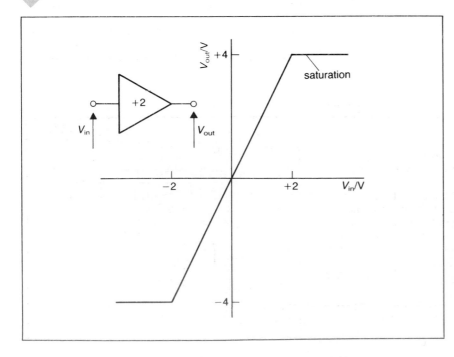

Followers

The output voltage of an ideal amplifier is proportional to its input voltage.

> $V_{out} = GV_{in}$
>
> V_{out} is the signal fed out by the amplifier (V)
>
> G is the voltage gain of the amplifier
>
> V_{in} is the signal fed into the amplifier (V)

For example, the amplifier of figure 14.22 has a gain of +2: V_{in} is half the size of V_{out}. The graph is a straight line through the origin unless V_{out} is sufficiently large to **saturate** the amplifier. An op-amp on its own does not make a very good amplifier, despite the large value of its gain ($\approx 2 \times 10^5$). As you can see from figure 14.23, its V_{out}–V_{in} curve is not a straight line. This means that the output signal will be distorted, i.e. it will not be an exact copy of the input signal. Nevertheless, as you are about to find out, the imposition of **negative feedback** makes an op-amp into a near-ideal amplifier.

Negative feedback
Negative feedback in op-amps consists of taking the output signal and feeding part (or all) of it back into the inverting input. Consider the arrangement shown in figure 14.24. Let's work out the overall gain of the circuit.

$$V_{out} = A(V_+ - V_-), \quad V_+ = V_{in}, \quad V_- = V_{out}$$

$$\therefore V_{out} = A(V_{in} - V_{out}) \qquad (14.1)$$

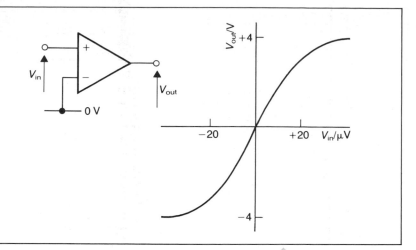

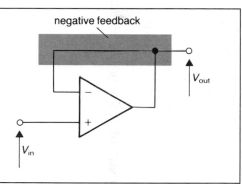

Figure 14.23   The $V_{out} - V_{in}$ curve of a typical op-amp

Figure 14.24   An op-amp follower

Figure 14.25   The voltage gain of a follower is +1

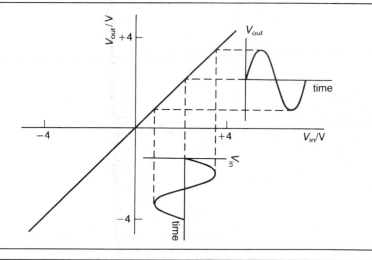

Equation (14.1) can be rearranged to give V_{out} as a function of V_{in}.

$$V_{out}(1 + A) = AV_{in} \qquad \therefore V_{out} = \frac{A \times V_{in}}{1 + A} \quad \textbf{(14.2)}$$

Given the enormous size of A, we can show that the gain is going, for all practical purposes, to be exactly 1.

$$V_{out} = GV_{in}$$

$$G = \frac{A}{1 + A} \qquad \therefore G = \frac{2 \times 10^5}{1 + 2 \times 10^5} = 0.999995$$

So the negative feedback has reduced the overall gain of the op-amp circuit to +1. The system is called a **follower** because the voltage of its output follows that of its input. The $V_{out} - V_{in}$ curve is a straight line with a slope of 1.

Power gain

You may question the value of an op-amp follower. After all, what is the point of making an exact copy of a signal, as shown in figure 14.25? In fact, the circuit provides something vital in dealing with analogue signals from sensors: it provides **power gain**. It can push out a lot more electrical energy than it takes from the source of its input signal.

For example, suppose that V_{in} is +2.0 V. The current in the input terminals is about 50 pA, so the power drawn from the signal source is easily calculated.

$$P = VI$$

$$\therefore P_{in} = 2.0 \times 50 \times 10^{-12} = 1.0 \times 10^{-10} \text{ W}$$

The maximum current available from the output terminal will be 10 mA. Since the output voltage is constrained to be +2.0 V by the negative feedback, the maximum output power can be worked out.

$$P = VI$$

$$\therefore P_{out} = 2.0 \times 10 \times 10^{-3} = 2.0 \times 10^{-2} \text{ W}$$

Although 2.0×10^{-2} W may seem a pathetic power for the op-amp to deliver, it is a phenomenal two hundred million times greater than the power drawn from the signal source! The extra energy has not, of course, been conjured out of thin air: it comes from the power supply connected to the op-amp.

COULOMB METERS

A practical application of an op-amp follower is shown in figure 14.26. It is sometimes called an **electrometer**, but is more usually known as a **coulomb meter** because it can be used to measure charge.

Initially, the switch is briefly pressed to discharge the capacitor, so that $V_{out} = 0$ V. Then the charged object is placed in contact with the input terminal, dumping its charge Q on the top plate of the capacitor; an equivalent amount of charge flows off the bottom plate into the 0 V supply rail. V_{out} will rise to follow the p.d. across the plates of the 1 μF capacitor.

$$C = \frac{Q}{V} \qquad \therefore V_{out} = \frac{Q}{1 \times 10^{-6}} \qquad \therefore V_{out} = Q \times 10^6$$

So the instrument has a sensitivity of one volt per microcoulomb, with the sign of the voltage being the same as the sign of the charge on the object.

Figure 14.26   A coulomb meter

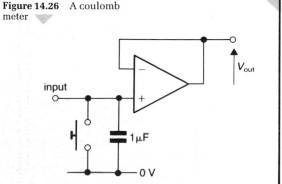

Non-inverting amplifiers

Negative feedback via a potential divider converts an op-amp into an almost perfect amplifier with predictable gain. (A naked op-amp has a gain whose value depends on the size of the signal it is amplifying — look at figure 14.23.) The arrangement is shown in figure 14.27. The potential divider feeds a fixed fraction β (beta) of the output voltage back into the inverting input. That fraction can be worked out with the help of the potential divider formula.

$$V_{out} = \frac{V_{in} \times R_b}{R_t + R_b}$$

$$\therefore V_- = \frac{V_{out} \times R_g}{R_f + R_g}$$

$$\therefore V_- = \beta V_{out}, \quad \text{where } \beta = \frac{R_g}{R_f + R_g} \qquad \textbf{(14.3)}$$

Let's use equation (14.3) to get an expression for the overall gain of the circuit.

$$V_{out} = A(V_+ - V_-) \qquad \therefore V_{out} = A(V_{in} - \beta V_{out})$$

$$\therefore V_{out}(1 + A\beta) = AV_{in}$$

$$\therefore V_{out} = \frac{A}{1 + A\beta} \times V_{in} \qquad \textbf{(14.4)}$$

A, of course, is enormous ($\approx 2 \times 10^5$). Let's assume that Aβ is much larger than 1, i.e. $\beta \gg 1/2 \times 10^5$.

$$V_{out} = GV_{in} \quad \therefore G = \frac{A}{1 + A\beta} \simeq \frac{A}{A\beta} = \frac{1}{\beta} \qquad \textbf{(14.5)}$$

So the gain simply depends on the value of β, provided that the open-loop gain A is large enough. Furthermore, the value of β can be accurately predicted as it only depends on the values of the two resistors.

$$G = \frac{1}{\beta}, \quad \beta = \frac{R_g}{R_f + R_g}$$

$$\therefore G = \frac{R_f + R_g}{R_g} \qquad \textbf{(14.6)}$$

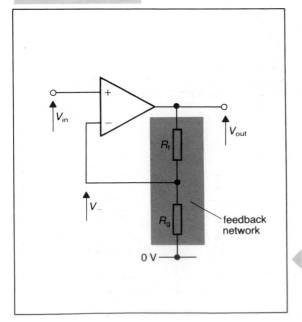

0 V

Figure 14.27 A non-inverting amplifier

Figure 14.28 Amplifying the output from a thermocouple

The op-amp in figure 14.26 is needed to allow measurement of the p.d. across the charged capacitor without discharging it too rapidly. The current in the op-amp input terminal is about 50 pA, many orders of magnitude lower than the current drawn by a voltmeter. We can estimate the discharge rate as follows:

$$C = \frac{Q}{V}, \quad I = \frac{Q}{t} \quad \therefore \Delta V = \frac{\Delta Q}{C} \quad \therefore \frac{\Delta V}{\Delta t} = \frac{1}{C} \times \frac{\Delta Q}{\Delta t}$$

$$\therefore \frac{\Delta V}{\Delta t} = \frac{I}{C} = \frac{50 \times 10^{-12}}{1 \times 10^{-6}} = 50 \ \mu V \ s^{-1}$$

This is three millivolts per minute, not exactly negligible, but slow enough for you to be able to make charge measurements with a precision of at least one nanocoulomb.

The resulting amplifier *has* to be linear because the expression for its gain contains neither A nor V_{in}. Its output signal will be a faithfully magnified copy of the input.

Figure 14.28 shows a non-inverting amplifier converting the output of a thermocouple into a signal which can be detected with a voltmeter. The thermocouple provides 41.6 μV K⁻¹, so the values of the resistors can be used to calculate the output sensitivity.

$$G = \frac{R_f + R_g}{R_g}$$

$$\therefore G = \frac{430 + 1.8}{1.8} = 240$$

$$V_{out} = 240 \times 41.6 \times 10^{-6} = 10.0 \ mV \ K^{-1}$$

The use of a 4.3 MΩ resistor in place of the 430 kΩ resistor would have increased the gain of the amplifier to just over 2000. However, Aβ would only be 100, no longer very much larger than 1, leading to some degradation of performance. As you are about to find out, a large gain leads to major difficulties if the signal changes rapidly with time.

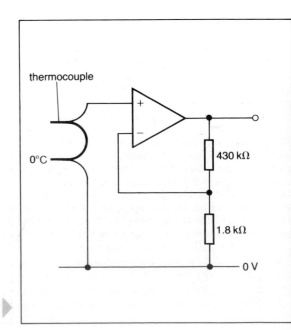

The output of a flip-flop changes state each time that its input falls from high to low. A chain of flip-flops in series can be used to make a binary counter, with the signals at the flip-flop outputs representing the number of falling edges fed into the system: number = 8D + 4C + 2B + A where D, C, B and A are 1 or 0.

A monostable uses an RC network to generate a single pulse of fixed length $0.69RC$ when the circuit is triggered by a rising edge. Astables use two RC networks to produce a continuous train of pulses.

An operational amplifier is a general purpose circuit for processing analogue signals whose voltage can have any value between those of the supply rails (approximately +5 V to −5 V). An op-amp is a high gain differential amplifier whose output voltage is fixed by the voltage difference of its two input terminals: $V_{out} = A(V_+ - V_-)$, $A \simeq 10^5$.

The current in the input terminals of an op-amp is small enough to be negligible. An op-amp can be used to compare the signals from a pair of potential dividers. The output voltage will saturate to a value near to one of the supply voltages depending on which of the two input terminals is being held at the higher voltage.

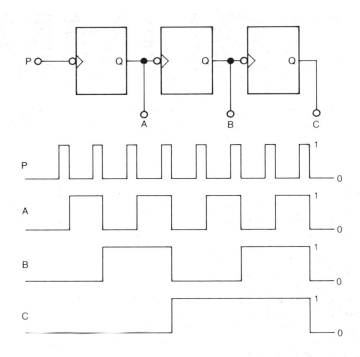

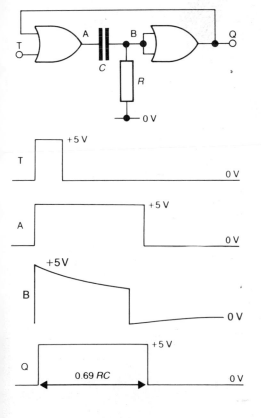

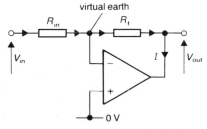

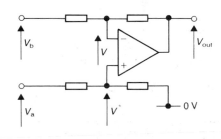

When negative feedback is applied to an op-amp it becomes an amplifier whose gain is fixed by the resistors in the feedback loop. The voltage difference between the two op-amp inputs is effectively zero when negative feedback is applied.

follower: $V_{out} = V_{in}$
non-inverting: $V_{out} = V_{in} \times (R_f + R_g)/R_g$
inverting: $V_{out} = V_{in} \times (-R_f/R_{in})$
difference: $V_{out} = (R_f/R_{in}) \times (V_a - V_b)$
summing: $V_{out} = -R_f \times (V_1/R_1 + V_2/R_2)$

A power amplifier is a circuit which has a voltage gain of 1 but can handle large current at its output terminal without drawing too much current from the device connected to its input terminal.

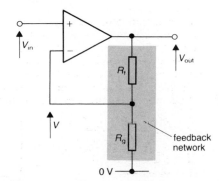

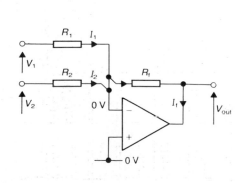

15

OSCILLATIONS

There are oscillations all around us. The motion of a child on a swing, of a floating bottle bobbing up and down in the water, of a ball bouncing on the ground, of a tree swaying in the breeze are all oscillations. Wherever you look, you will find objects which move from side to side in a regular manner. Give them a push away from equilibrium and they swing backwards and forwards, moving less on each swing until they return to rest where they started.

Since oscillation appears to be such a widespread phenomenon, its cause must be embedded deep in the fundamental laws of physics. We can therefore expect that many oscillating systems, regardless of their nature, should oscillate in the same way. The vertical motion of a cruise liner should be similar to the side-to-side motion of an atom trapped in a solid. So an in-depth analysis of one system should give us results which we can easily apply to all.

SIMPLE HARMONIC MOTION

It is intuitively obvious that things only oscillate when they are given some energy. For example, you have to pluck a guitar string to get it oscillating. A pendulum clock eventually stops working if you don't rewind it. A child on a swing needs a push to get it going. So we shall start our analysis of oscillations by looking at what happens to objects in static equilibrium when they are given some energy.

Parabolic wells

The potential energy curve for an object near to a position of static equilibrium is shown in figure 15.1. The curve is called a **potential well**. Its shape is decided by the force which acts on the object. That force F is linked to the potential energy E_p by the following formula from chapter 7:

$$F = -\frac{\Delta E_p}{\Delta x} \tag{15.1}$$

We have chosen to place the origin of the coordinates (energy and position) at the lowest point on the curve. Since the total energy of the object is the sum of its kinetic and potential energies, this choice of coordinates means that it can never have negative values of energy.

Energy conversion

Suppose that we start off by holding the object in the well at the place marked X in figure 15.1. It will have a total energy E_t, with no kinetic energy at all. What happens when we release it?
Suppose that it moves to the right. Let's look at what this does to the kinetic energy of the object.

$$E_t = E_k + E_p \qquad \therefore \Delta E_t = \Delta E_k + \Delta E_p \tag{15.2}$$

The total energy of the object cannot change if we are no longer holding it. It becomes an isolated system, so its energy is conserved.

$$\Delta E_t = 0 \quad \therefore \Delta E_k = -\Delta E_p \tag{15.3}$$

If the object moves to the right, ΔE_p is going to be positive, leading to ΔE_k being negative. Since E_k was zero to start with, this means that the object now has negative kinetic energy. This is impossible as $\frac{1}{2}mv^2$ always has a positive value (for positive mass anyway!).

So the object cannot move to the right. If it moves to the left, its potential energy drops. ΔE_p is negative, allowing ΔE_k to be positive, i.e. the object's velocity increases. It should be obvious that once the object has started moving to the left, it will move faster and faster as its potential energy gets converted into kinetic energy. It accelerates towards the point of minimum potential energy. Figure 15.1 shows what will happen to the kinetic energy as the object moves across the well. As soon as it moves past the origin, ΔE_p is going to be positive. So ΔE_k will be negative, making the object's kinetic energy progressively smaller as it moves further away from the origin. Eventually, the object will come to a halt when its kinetic energy has become zero. Thereafter, it will accelerate back towards the origin, reconverting potential energy into kinetic energy. Clearly, the object is going to

Figure 15.1 Potential well for an object near to equilibrium

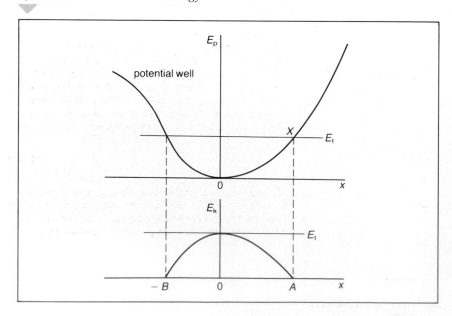

oscillate backwards and forwards about the origin with an **amplitude** fixed by its total energy E_t. The graphs of figure 15.2 show how we expect the kinetic energy and position of the object to change with time. The motion is **cyclic**, endlessly repeating itself once started.

Ball-and-bowl analogy
It may help to understand what is going on in figure 15.1 if you consider the following analogy. The object is a ball-bearing in a bowl (figure 15.3). The potential energy in this case will be gravitational energy, so the shape of the bowl's cross-section will be the same as the potential well. If the ball starts off at the rim of the bowl it rolls from side to side, losing gravitational energy on the way down and regaining it on the way up the other side. Analogies are useful ways of translating theoretical physics into a form which can be easily visualised. However, they must not be taken too seriously, as they may be misleading. For example, if you did some experiments with a ball moving around in a bowl you would not get the results predicted by the theory we are going to develop in this chapter. This is because the analogy is not exact. The theory assumes that the gravitational energy is converted into kinetic energy, whereas the ball-bearing acquires rotational energy as well.

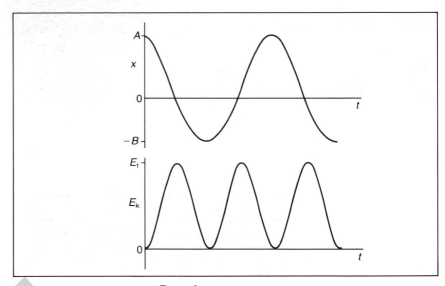

Figure 15.2 The change of position and kinetic energy of an object displaced from equilibrium and released

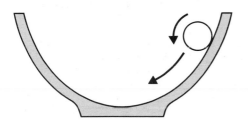

Figure 15.3 The ball-and-bowl analogy

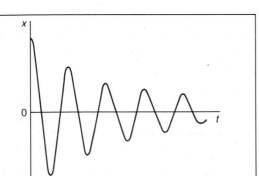

Figure 15.4 Damped oscillations

Figure 15.5 A parabolic potential well

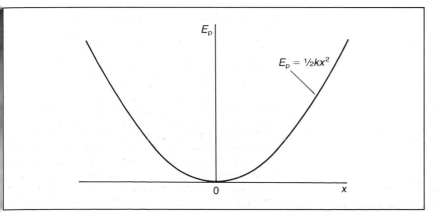

Damping
Figure 15.2 is unrealistic. It ignores friction, that all-pervading converter of kinetic energy to heat energy. We can expect any real object which is moving to lose energy to its surroundings. So as the object moves across the well its total energy E_t will decrease, as shown in the graph of figure 15.4. (Exactly how rapidly it falls depends on the details of the friction mechanism. In many cases the total energy drops exponentially.) The amplitude of each oscillation will be smaller than that of the previous one, so excursions of the object away from the origin will get progressively smaller and smaller. The oscillatory motion of the object is **damped**.

Damping of the oscillation means that the object eventually ends up with a total energy of zero. Of course, as the amplitude decreases, the rate of conversion of kinetic energy to heat energy is also likely to decrease. (The dominant source of friction for many oscillating systems is wind resistance: this is proportional to the velocity for slowly moving objects.) So the amplitude may take a long time to die down to zero. Indeed, it may appear to carry on getting smaller for ever. However, the object eventually ends up at the origin where it started.

Minimum energy
So *any* object which is displaced from its equilibrium position and then released should oscillate with a progressively smaller amplitude until it returns to rest. The equilibrium position is, of course, the point of minimum potential energy. If the minimum value of E_p is zero, then it can be shown that E_p has to be proportional to the square of the displacement near to the origin.

$$E_p = \tfrac{1}{2}kx^2 \tag{15.4}$$

This is shown in figure 15.5. The value of E_p is always positive, regardless of the sign of x, and is zero at $x = 0$. (The value of the force constant k is fixed by the strength of the forces acting on the object when it is displaced from equilibrium.)

PARABOLIC MINIMA !

The potential energy of *any* particle can be represented by this polynomial expansion;

$$E_p = \Sigma c_n x^n \quad \therefore E_p = c_0 + c_1 x + c_2 x^2 + c_3 x^3 + \ldots$$

The values of the coefficients c_n fix the shape of the potential well. Thus $c_0 = 0$ if $E_p = 0$ at $x = 0$. Similarly, $c_1 = 0$ if the slope $dE_p/dx = 0$ at $x = 0$. Therefore any particle which has a minimum energy of zero at $x = 0$ can have its potential energy represented as follows:

$$E_p = c_2 x^2 + c_3 x^3 + c_4 x^4 + \ldots$$

Provided that none of the coefficients are infinite, only the first term in the expansion is important if x is small enough.

$$E_p = c_2 x^2 \quad \text{if} \quad x \ll 1$$

So *all* wells are parabolic for small enough displacements from equilibrium!

SHM

Provided that an object is not displaced too far from its equilibrium position, we expect its potential energy to have the form of equation (15.4). This means that we can predict how the force acting on the object is going to depend on its displacement from equilibrium.

$$F = -\frac{\Delta E_p}{\Delta x}, \quad E_p = \tfrac{1}{2}kx^2$$

$$\therefore \frac{\Delta E_p}{E_p} = \frac{2\Delta x}{x} \quad \therefore \frac{\Delta E_p}{\Delta x} = \frac{2E_p}{x}$$

$$\therefore F = -\frac{2}{x} \times (\tfrac{1}{2}kx^2) \quad \therefore \boxed{F = -kx} \quad \textbf{(15.5)}$$

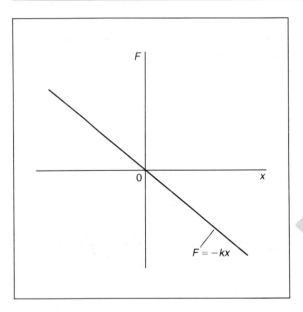

Figure 15.7 How the potential, kinetic and total energies depend on the displacement

Figure 15.6 The restoring force is proportional to the displacement

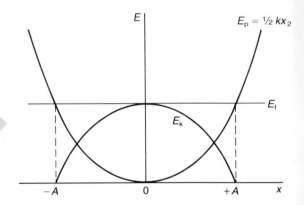

This is particularly simple: the force on the object is proportional to its displacement from equilibrium (figure 15.6). The minus sign shows that the force is always directed in the opposite direction to the displacement. For this reason F is sometimes called the **restoring force**.

Systems which obey equation (15.5) are said to oscillate in **simple harmonic motion**. This is usually abbreviated to **SHM**. Equation (15.5) is important because it leads to some interesting predictions about the motion of the system when it oscillates. For example, it can be used to predict the total energy of the system when it oscillates with an amplitude A. Consider figure 15.7. The furthest distance that the object can get from the origin is A. This happens when the kinetic energy is zero, i.e. the potential energy equals the total energy.

$$E = \tfrac{1}{2}kA^2$$

E is the total energy of the oscillating system (J)

k is the force constant of the system (N m^{-1})

A is the amplitude of the oscillation (m)

HOOKE'S LAW ◀◀2

Figure 15.8 shows how the potential energy of one atom changes when it is moved near to another atom. The exact shape of the curve depends on the mechanism by which the atoms interact, but one thing is certain: there is a point at which the potential energy is a minimum. (If there wasn't, all matter would be in the form of a gas.) Equation (15.5) says that for an atom sufficiently close to that point of minimum energy, the force on it *must* be proportional to its displacement from equilibrium. This is just another way of stating Hooke's Law. In a sense, you can think of Hooke's Law as being inevitable in a universe which has attractive forces between hard atoms which allow them to form solids!

Figure 15.8 Typical energy-separation curve for a pair of atoms ▽

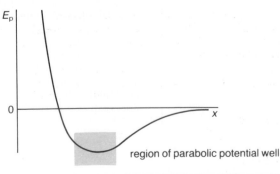

region of parabolic potential well

Mass on a spring

The most obvious system which undergoes SHM is going to be a lump hung from the end of a spring, as shown in figure 15.9. Since springs obey Hooke's Law, the restoring force on the lump is going to be proportional to its displacement from equilibrium. So we expect the motion of a mass on a spring to be typical of the oscillation of all objects when they are slightly displaced from equilibrium. One way of measuring the motion of the lump is shown in figure 15.10(a). A potentiometer is used as a position-to-voltage converter; its output can be fed to a data logger, oscilloscope or chart recorder. A typical curve showing how the displacement changes with time is shown in figure 15.10(b).

Estimating the period

We expect *all* objects displaced slightly from equilibrium to obey $F = -kx$. What does this imply about their motion? Can we use it to work out how the object moves? The force will, of course, accelerate the object. If its mass is m we can apply Newton's Second Law of Motion.

$$F = -kx, \quad F = ma \qquad \therefore ma = -kx$$

$$\therefore a = -\frac{kx}{m} \qquad \textbf{(15.6)}$$

Using equation (15.6) to work out how the displacement changes with time is going to be difficult. The acceleration is not going to be constant, but will vary as the object wobbles back and forth. You cannot use the VUSAT formulae to work out the distance travelled in a certain time because they assume a constant acceleration. The next section of this chapter will show you how numerical integration or calculus can be used to find x as a function of t from equation (15.6). In the meantime, we are going to show you how to find an approximate solution of the problem — this will highlight the important properties of SHM. (It is often the case in physics that an approximate solution of a difficult problem provides excellent insights into a system, without the confusion of a large amount of algebra.)

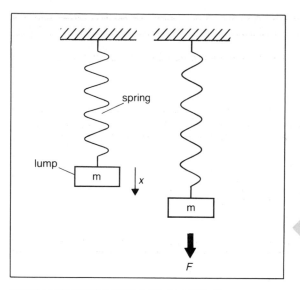

Figure 15.9 Displacing a mass on a spring

Figure 15.10 Measuring the motion of a mass on a spring

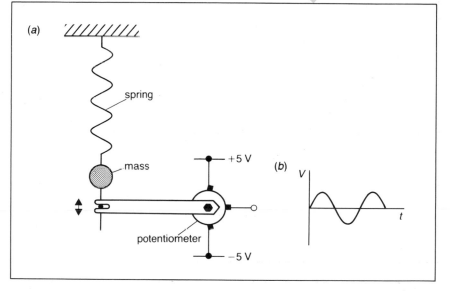

Each cycle of oscillation can be divided into quarters, each of duration $T/4$. Let's make the approximation that the restoring force is constant during each of those quarters, giving a conveniently constant acceleration. In reality the force drops from $-kA$ to 0, giving an average force of $-\frac{1}{2}kA$. Let's assume that this average force $<F>$ acts all the time and work out the consequent average acceleration.

$$<F> = -\tfrac{1}{2}kA, \quad F = ma$$

$$\therefore <a> = -\frac{kA}{2m} \qquad \textbf{(15.7)}$$

Let the object start off at $x = A$ with an initial velocity of zero. (It has no kinetic energy there.) It will reach $x = 0$ after a time $t = T/4$, having travelled a distance A.

$$s = ut + \tfrac{1}{2}at^2 \quad \therefore A = 0 + \tfrac{1}{2} \times \left(\frac{kA}{2m}\right) \times \left(\frac{T}{4}\right)^2$$

$$\therefore T^2 = 64 \times \frac{m}{k}$$

$$\therefore T = 8\sqrt{\frac{m}{k}} \qquad \textbf{(15.8)}$$

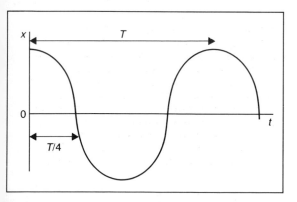

Period

Figure 15.11 shows how we expect the displacement to change with time. The exact shape of the curve is not important at the moment, provided that it has the correct symmetry. The **amplitude** of the oscillation is A and its **period** is T. We want to find out how the value of T depends on the other variables of the system, i.e. A, k and m.

Figure 15.11 Expected variation of displacement with time

Equation (15.8) predicts that the period of oscillation is going to be proportional to $(m/k)^{\frac{1}{2}}$. Furthermore, it predicts that the period is going to be independent of the amplitude (A does not feature in equation (15.8)). Since equation (15.8) is dimensionally correct, these predictions are upheld by the more exact solutions of $a = -(k/m)x$ which you will meet in the next section of this chapter.

$$T = 2\pi \sqrt{\frac{m}{k}}$$

T is the period of oscillation of the system (s)

m is the mass of the system (kg)

k is the force constant of the system (N m^{-1})

It is standard practice to quote the **frequency** of an oscillator rather than its period. This is the number of cycles of oscillation that the oscillator goes through in a second.

$$f = \frac{1}{T}$$

f is the frequency of oscillation (Hz)

T is the period of the oscillator (s)

Pendulums

Simple harmonic motion is historically very important for physics because it made accurate time-keeping possible. Galileo is supposed to have been the first person to notice that the frequency of oscillation of a pendulum is independent of its amplitude. (He used his pulse to time the motion of the lamps hung from the ceiling of Pisa Cathedral.) So we have chosen the simple pendulum as an example of simple harmonic motion in action.

Figure 15.12 Forces on a displaced pendulum

Figure 15.13 $\tan\phi \simeq x/l$

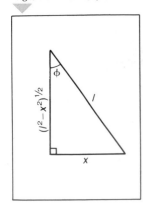

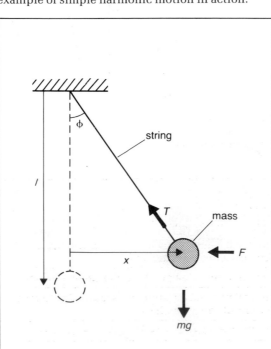

string

T

mass

x

F

mg

The force constant

Figure 15.12 shows a lump of mass m hanging from the end of a string of length l. Minimum gravitational energy is achieved when the lump is directly underneath the place where the string is tethered to its support. The first thing we have to do is find out what the force constant is.

Suppose that the lump is displaced a small distance x from equilibrium. The force F pushing the lump back to its equilibrium position will be the horizontal component of the tension in the string.

$$F = T\sin\phi \qquad (15.9)$$

T can be found by considering the vertical forces on the lump.

$$mg = T\cos\phi \qquad (15.10)$$

Combine equations (15.9) and (15.10) to eliminate the tension T.

$$\frac{F}{\sin\phi} = \frac{mg}{\cos\phi} \quad \therefore F = mg\tan\phi \qquad (15.11)$$

Now consider the right-angled triangle shown in figure 15.13.

$$\tan\phi \simeq \frac{x}{(l^2 - x^2)^{\frac{1}{2}}} \simeq \frac{x}{l} \quad \text{if} \quad l \gg x \qquad (15.12)$$

So, taking into account the opposite directions of F and x, we end up with an expression for the restoring force on the lump.

$$F = mg\tan\phi \therefore F = -\frac{mgx}{l} \quad \therefore k = \frac{mg}{l} \qquad (15.13)$$

(Notice that our value for k is only valid for small values of x.)

Period

Once the expression for k is known (and it will be different for each system you look at), you can immediately predict the period of the oscillation.

$$T = 2\pi \sqrt{\frac{m}{k}}, \qquad k = \frac{mg}{l}$$

$$\therefore T = 2\pi \sqrt{\frac{l}{g}} \qquad (15.14)$$

$$T = 2\pi \sqrt{\frac{l}{g}}$$

T is the period of oscillation (s)

l is the length of the pendulum suspension (m)

g is the acceleration due to gravity (m s^{-2})

Interestingly, the period is not only independent of the amplitude but also of the mass. It only depends on the distance l from the lump's centre of mass to its support and the gravitational field strength g. For example, how long does the string have to be for the pendulum to have a period of 1.00 s?

$$T = 2\pi(l/g)^{\frac{1}{2}} \qquad \therefore l = \frac{T^2 g}{4\pi^2}$$

$$\therefore l = \frac{1.00^2 \times 9.81}{4\pi^2} = 0.248 \, \text{m}$$

EXPONENTIAL DAMPING

Figure 15.14 shows how the oscillation of a pendulum can be investigated in a school laboratory. A weight is suspended below a firm support. The shaft of a low-friction potentiometer is connected to the string as an angle-to-voltage converter. The voltage at the wiper of the potentiometer is fed to a chart recorder. A typical chart is shown in figure 15.15. Note that the period of the oscillations remains constant as their amplitude decreases. Furthermore, the amplitude of the oscillations appears to decrease exponentially with time. This can be modelled with the following piece of algebra.

$$A = A_0 \exp[-t/2\tau] \tag{1}$$

Exponential functions have a very important property: their fractional change is proportional to the time interval over which the change takes place. Appendix B contains the following useful identity.

$$y = A\exp[\alpha t] \qquad \therefore \frac{\Delta y}{y} = \alpha \Delta t \tag{2}$$

Applying equation (1) to equation (2) we obtain an expression which can be used to test for the exponential drop of A with time. It will only be true if the fractional change of A during one cycle is small.

$$\frac{\Delta A}{A} = -\frac{\Delta t}{2\tau} \qquad \therefore \frac{\Delta A}{A} \approx -\frac{T}{2\tau} \tag{3}$$

Table 1 contains data from an $x-t$ graph similar to that of figure 15.15. As you can see, the fractional change of amplitude per cycle is, within limits of the precision, constant.

Table 1

t/s	A/mm	ΔA/mm	$\Delta A/A$
0	100		
2	82	−18	−0.180
4	67	−15	−0.183
6	55	−12	−0.179
8	45	−10	−0.182
10	37	−8	−0.178

We can use the data from table 1 to work out an approximate value for the constant τ.

$$\frac{\Delta A}{A} = -\frac{T}{2\tau} \qquad \therefore -0.18 = -\frac{2.0}{2\tau} \qquad \therefore \tau = 5.6 \text{ s}$$

The value of τ tells you how rapidly the pendulum is losing energy. It is called the **damping time**.

$$E = \tfrac{1}{2}kA^2 \qquad \therefore E = \tfrac{1}{2}k \times (A_0 \times \exp[-t/2\tau])^2$$
$$\therefore E = E_0 \exp[-t/\tau] \tag{4}$$

The energy leaks out of the system just like the current in an RC network changes with time. τ is the equivalent of the time constant RC. So the energy of the pendulum is halved in a time of $0.69 \times 5.6 \approx 4$ s — this is just two periods of oscillation.

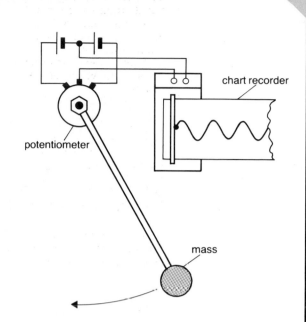

Figure 15.14 Recording the motion of a pendulum

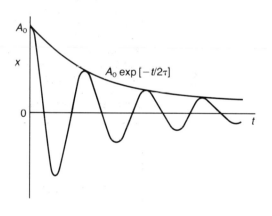

Figure 15.15 Exponential damping

OBJECTIVES

After studying this section you should be able to do the following.

Understand that the potential well near a point of static equilibrium is parabolic, i.e. $E_p = \tfrac{1}{2}kx^2$.

State that $F = -kx$ for an object near a point of static equilibrium.

State the condition necessary for an object to oscillate with SHM.

Use $a = -kx/m$ to obtain an approximate formula for the period of oscillation.

Use the formula $T = 2\pi(m/k)^{\frac{1}{2}}$.

Work out the value of k for a simple pendulum.

Understand that damping progressively reduces the amplitude of oscillation.

Use the formulae $E = \tfrac{1}{2}kA^2$, $E = E_0 \exp[-t/\tau]$.

QUESTIONS

1 A student sets up the apparatus shown in figure 15.16. The mass of the object is 100 g. She finds that 50 vertical oscillations of the object take 25 s.

a Show that $T = 2\pi(m/k)^{\frac{1}{2}}$ is dimensionally correct.

b What is the force constant of the spring she is using?

c Calculate how long 50 oscillations should take if she set up each of the mass-and-spring assemblies shown in figure 15.17. Each spring is identical to the one shown in figure 15.16.

2 A loaded test-tube of mass m floating in a liquid is shown in figure 15.18. It has a cross-sectional area A and the liquid has a density ρ.

a What is the restoring force on the tube when it is pushed down a distance x.

b Show that the frequency of oscillation of the tube is given by $f = (A\rho g/4\pi^2 m)^{\frac{1}{2}}$.

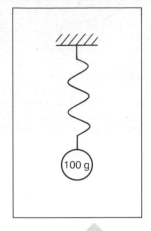

Figure 15.16

Figure 15.17

Figure 15.19

Figure 15.18

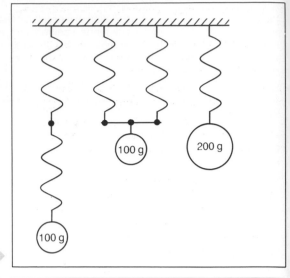

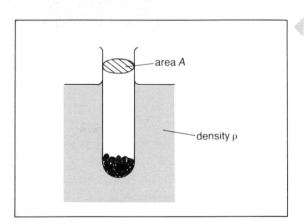

c Comment on the feasibility of using the frequency of oscillation of the tube to measure the density of the liquid.

d Estimate the period of vertical oscillations of a large ocean-going cruise liner. The QE2 displaces about 7×10^7 kg of seawater and has a length of about 300 m.

3 Not everything which oscillates does so with SHM. State and explain which of the following are examples of simple harmonic motion.

a A girl sitting on a trampoline moving up and down.

b A ball bouncing up and down on the floor.

c A vehicle on a horizontal air track moving between two sprung buffers.

d A diving board when a man jumps off it.

4 A teacher sets up the apparatus shown in figure 15.19 to demonstrate SHM to his class. The vehicle has a mass of 1.5 kg and each spring has a force constant of 20 N m^{-1}.

a Do both springs have to be stretched when the vehicle is at rest? Should the teacher arrange for the springs to be unextended before he gives the vehicle a push?

b Calculate the expected period of oscillation of the vehicle.

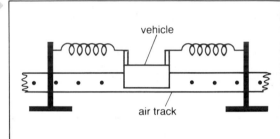

c Suppose that the teacher has not set up the air-track so that it is truly horizontal. State and explain what effect this will have on the period of oscillation.

d The teacher displaces the vehicle 10 cm to the left of its equilibrium position and lets go. How fast will it be moving when it passes the equilibrium position?

e Sketch graphs to show how the displacement, velocity and acceleration of the vehicle change with time when it is released. Label both axes with values: show two complete cycles of oscillation.

5 The U-tube shown in figure 15.20 has a cross-sectional area A. It contains a liquid of mass m and density ρ. Obtain an expression for the frequency of vertical oscillations of the liquid in one arm of the tube.

Figure 15.21

Figure 15.20

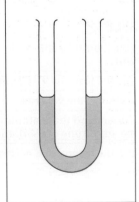

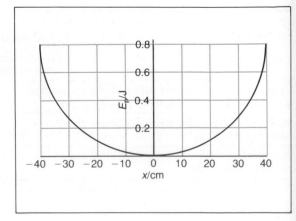

6 The graph in figure 15.21 shows how the gravitational energy of a simple pendulum depends on its horizontal displacement. The potential well is *not* parabolic.

a Use the graph to estimate the length and mass of the pendulum. Hence calculate the period of small oscillations of the pendulum.

b Sketch the graph of figure 15.21. Draw on it the parabolic well assumed by your answer to part (a).

c Does the force constant of a real pendulum increase or decrease with increasing displacement? How does this affect the period of large oscillations?

7 The pendulum of the clock which controls Big Ben is shown in figure 15.22. The clock was built in 1860 and it is reputed to be the most accurate mechanical public clock in the world. The period of oscillation of its pendulum is 4.00 s.

a If g is 9.81 N kg^{-1} at Westminster, calculate the length of a simple pendulum which would have a period of 4.00 s. The actual pendulum is 4.49 m from one end to the other. Why is this different from your answer?

b Table 15.1 shows the properties of some alloys which could be used for building the pendulum. Which is the most suitable? Why?

Table 15.1

Alloy	E/GPa	α/K^{-1}	ρ/kg m^{-3}
stainless steel	220	1.6×10^{-5}	7800
invar	140	1.1×10^{-6}	8000
brass	190	2.0×10^{-5}	8400

c The time kept by the clock in the Big Ben tower is controlled by adjusting the number of pennies placed on the top of the pendulum lump. Sue reckons that the weight of the pennies changes the length of the pendulum, hence altering its period. Is she right? If not, what is the true explanation? Would you expect the number of pennies to steadily increase or decrease over the years? Why?

8 Figure 15.23 shows a simple instrument which is widely used in industry to measure the viscosity of a liquid. A long torsion wire holds up a cylinder — a scale attached to the top of the cylinder allows its angular movement to be measured. The cylinder is immersed in the liquid whose viscosity is to be measured. When the cylinder is rotated and released, it oscillates in simple harmonic motion.

a When the cylinder is rotated through 45° the torsion wire has 10 mJ of strain energy. Draw a graph to show how the strain energy in the wire depends on the angle of rotation of the cylinder from −360° to +360°.

b Initially the cylinder is rotated to −180° and released. The amount of energy transferred to the liquid can be measured by noting the maximum angle of the cylinder when it is released. Suppose that this is +160°: how much energy is transferred to the liquid?

Figure 15.22

c Once the cylinder has been released, you can assume that its energy drops exponentially with time. If the cylinder is released at −180° and temporarily stops at +120°, estimate the values of the angles at the next three temporary stops.

9 Atoms in a solid should oscillate with simple harmonic motion at temperatures sufficiently low for their potential wells to be approximately parabolic. Table 15.2 gives some data for solid aluminium.

Table 15.2

density	2700 kg m^{-3}
separation	0.26 nm
Young's modulus	7.0×10^{10} Pa
molar mass	2.7×10^{-2} kg mol^{-1}

a Use the data to work out the mass of a single aluminium atom and its force constant when bound in a solid.

b Calculate its frequency of small oscillations.

c If the energy in the oscillator is kT where k is Boltzmann's constant, estimate the amplitude of the oscillation at room temperature.

d It has been suggested that a solid melts when the amplitude of oscillation of its atoms becomes 15% of their separation d_0. Show that this implies that the melting point T_m of all solids should be proportional to Ed_0^3. Does the data in table 15.3 support this hypothesis?

Table 15.3

Metal	T_m/K	E/GPa	d_0/nm
aluminium	932	70	0.26
copper	1356	130	0.23
lead	601	16	0.31
iron	1812	211	0.23

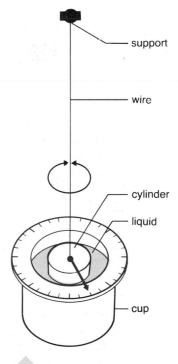

Figure 15.23

DISPLACEMENT–TIME CURVES

The equation $a = -(k/m)x$ is a **mathematical model**. It is a concise statement about the behaviour of any object oscillating about its equilibrium position. Mathematical models are usually rated pretty highly by physicists. They are exact and precise. However, they often suffer from being difficult to use. It is common to find situations in physics that are easy to model with a piece of algebra which is almost impossible to work with; most of quantum mechanics falls into this category.

In the previous section of the chapter you used $a = -(k/m)x$ to find an approximate expression for the period of oscillation. By assuming a constant acceleration during each quarter cycle we were able to show that $T \propto (m/k)^{\frac{1}{2}}$. That assumption leads to the $x-t$ curve shown in figure 15.24. What we want to do now is use the acceleration equation to find out *exactly* how the displacement and velocity of the object change with time. This section is going to show you how it can be done. It will be somewhat mathematical in places, but the experience will be vital when you tackle the work on waves.

Numerical solutions

A computer can always be programmed to apply a mathematical model to any system you like. All you need is the model and some initial values for the variables you are interested in. Unfortunately, the solution produced by the computer is unique to the system you specify with the numbers fed into the program. The computer cannot come up with a general solution, i.e. a formula for the individual variables. Nevertheless, numerical integration is a valuable technique because it always works.

The algorithm

Figure 15.25 shows the system which we are going to try and model. A 0.5 kg mass is suspended from a spring which has a force constant of 20 N m^{-1}. We want to use the SHM model to predict what will happen to the mass if it is displaced 10 cm and released. The first step is to put some numbers into the model.

$$a = -\frac{kx}{m} \quad \therefore a = -\frac{20}{0.5} \times x \quad \therefore a = -40x \quad \textbf{(15.15)}$$

We need an **algorithm** (a sequence of operations) to enable the computer to work out how the variables change in a small time interval Δt. The model tells the computer how to calculate the acceleration from the initial value of the displacement. It can then be used to find the final velocity from the initial velocity.

$$a = -40x$$
$$\Delta v = a\Delta t \qquad \therefore \Delta v = -40x\Delta t$$
$$\therefore v \rightarrow v + \Delta v \qquad \textbf{(15.16)}$$

At the same time, the initial value for the velocity can be used to calculate how the displacement changes in the time interval.

$$\Delta x = v\Delta t \qquad \therefore x \rightarrow x + \Delta x \qquad \textbf{(15.17)}$$

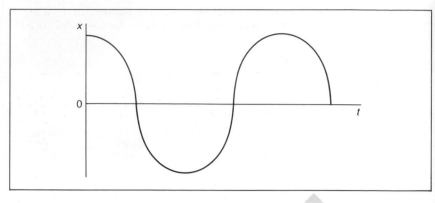

The new values for v and x obtained from equations (15.16) and (15.17) can then be used as starting points for the next time interval. The computer moves steadily forward through time, using the current values of the variables to work out new values.

The choice of time interval Δt is crucial to the success of the algorithm. It must be sufficiently short so that changes of x, v and a are all relatively small. This is where an approximate solution (equation (15.8)) comes in handy.

$$T \simeq 8(m/k)^{\frac{1}{2}} \qquad \therefore T \simeq 8 \times (0.5/20)^{\frac{1}{2}} = 1.3 \text{ s}$$

This guess is the approximate time for one cycle. Clearly, Δt needs to be *much* smaller than this. We shall try $\Delta t = 0.01$ s to start with. The computer will then take about a hundred steps to work out one cycle of oscillation.

The solution

The algorithm we have discussed is built into the following program written in BASIC. Once the initial variables have been fixed ($x = 0.1$ m, $v = 0.0$ m s^{-1}), the program goes from $t = 0.00$ s to $t = 2.00$ s in steps Δt of 0.01 s, printing values for x and t along the way.

```
10 LET X = 0.100
20 LET V = 0.000·
30 FOR T = 0.00 TO 2.00 STEP 0.01
40 PRINT T, X
50 LET DV = − 40*X*0.01
60 LET DX = V*0.01
70 LET V = V + DV
80 LET X = X + DX
90 NEXT T
100 END
```

Figure 15.24 The $x-t$ curve for an object whose restoring force has a constant magnitude

Figure 15.25 Mass on a spring

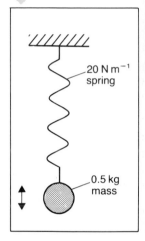

Figure 15.26 The calculated $x-t$ curve for $\Delta t = 0.01$ s

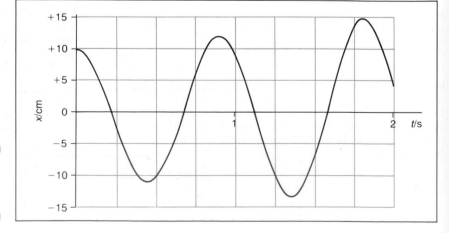

The results of this program are shown in the first two columns of table 15.4 and the graph of figure 15.26.

Table 15.4

t/s	x/m		
	$\Delta t = 0.01$ s	$\Delta t = 0.001$ s	$\Delta t = 0.0001$ s
0.0	+ 0.100	+ 0.100	+ 0.100
0.1	+ 0.079	+ 0.081	+ 0.081
0.2	+ 0.019	+ 0.030	+ 0.030
0.3	− 0.052	− 0.033	− 0.032
0.4	− 0.102	− 0.083	− 0.082
0.5	− 0.105	− 0.101	− 0.100
0.6	− 0.059	− 0.080	− 0.080
0.7	+ 0.018	− 0.029	− 0.028
0.8	+ 0.089	+ 0.035	+ 0.034
0.9	+ 0.120	+ 0.085	+ 0.083
1.0	+ 0.098	+ 0.102	+ 0.100
1.1	+ 0.027	+ 0.080	+ 0.078
1.2	− 0.060	+ 0.027	+ 0.026
1.3	− 0.122	− 0.037	− 0.036
1.4	− 0.129	− 0.087	− 0.084
1.5	− 0.075	− 0.103	0.100
1.6	+ 0.017	− 0.079	− 0.077
1.7	+ 0.106	0.025	− 0.024
1.8	+ 0.148	+ 0.039	+ 0.038
1.9	+ 0.122	+ 0.089	+ 0.086
2.0	+ 0.037	+ 0.104	+ 0.100

The overall pattern is more or less what we would expect, but the steady growth of amplitude (defying energy conservation) shows that the solution is not to be relied upon. It indicates that we did not choose a small enough value for Δt. As you can see from table 15.4, reducing the value of Δt results in a much more believable variation of displacement with time.

The results for $\Delta t = 0.0001$ s are presented in graphical form in figure 15.27. The amplitude remains constant, so the solution obeys energy conservation. The period, measured off the graph, is 1.00 s. We know already that $T \propto (m/k)^{\frac{1}{2}}$ from approximate solutions and dimensional analysis. Our computer solution can fix the constant of proportionality.

$$T = ? \times (m/k)^{\frac{1}{2}} \qquad \therefore 1.00 = ? \times (0.5/20)^{\frac{1}{2}}$$

$$\therefore ? = 6.32$$

$$\therefore T = 6.32(m/k)^{\frac{1}{2}} \qquad \textbf{(15.17)}$$

This is less than 1% different than the true answer of 2π; since our precision has only been 1% anyway, this is the best we could expect.

Algebraic solutions

We want a formula which can be used to calculate the displacement and velocity at any time after the oscillation has been started. The starting point has to be the SHM mathematical model.

$$a = -\frac{kx}{m} \qquad \therefore a = -\omega^2 x, \quad \omega = (k/m)^{\frac{1}{2}} \quad \textbf{(15.18)}$$

The new quantity ω, the **angular frequency**, has been introduced because it will make things easier later on. Our final answers are going to contain ω. They are given here:

$$x = A\cos(\omega t), \qquad v = -A\omega\sin(\omega t) \qquad \textbf{(15.19)}$$

The journey from equation (15.18) to (5.19) involves the use of calculus. Don't worry about it. Although you need advanced mathematics to understand how and why calculus works, anyone who understands algebra can use calculus with the help of the tables of integrals and differentials given in Appendix B!

Setting up the equation
Acceleration is the rate of change of velocity. In its turn, velocity is the rate of change of displacement. So acceleration must be the rate of change of the rate of change of displacement! This statement is a bit cumbersome – algebra is more succinct.

$$a = \frac{\Delta v}{\Delta t}, \quad v = \frac{\Delta x}{\Delta t} \quad \therefore a = \frac{\Delta}{\Delta t}\left(\frac{\Delta x}{\Delta t}\right) \qquad \textbf{(15.20)}$$

In other words, the velocity is the gradient of the x–t curve and the acceleration is the gradient of the v–t curve. This is shown in figure 15.28. To make matters exact, we are going to assume that Δt is extremely small. This is shown in the usual way by replacing Δ with d. In this notation, the gradient of a variable is called its **differential**.

$$a = \frac{\Delta}{\Delta t}\left(\frac{\Delta x}{\Delta t}\right) \qquad \therefore a = \frac{d}{dt}\left(\frac{dx}{dt}\right)$$

$$\therefore a = \frac{d^2 x}{dt^2} \qquad \textbf{(15.21)}$$

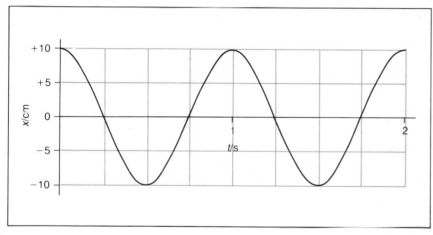

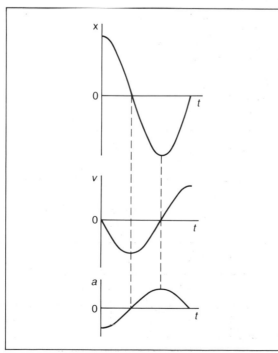

Figure 15.27 The calculated x–t curve for $\Delta t = 0.00001$ s

Figure 15.28 Variation of x, v and a with t for an object in SHM

Equation (15.21) uses the standard calculus notation for the differential of a differential, i.e. the gradient of a gradient. We can now insert equation (15.21) into the SHM model to get a **differential equation**.

$$\frac{d^2x}{dt^2} = -\omega^2 x \qquad (15.22)$$

Solving the equation

All we have to do now is guess a function for x. The table of standard differentials in Appendix B can be used to differentiate the guess twice so that it can be inserted into equation 15.22. If the insertion works, then our guess was correct and we have a formula for x as a function of t. On the other hand, if the insertion does *not* work, then our guess must be wrong and we must try again. This hit-and-miss procedure may seem tedious, but it is the only one which works. Of course, it helps if you have some approximate idea of the behaviour of x to guide your guess. For example, you already know that x = t is not going to work. We are not going to waste time by taking you through lots of wrong guesses — our guess here is going to be right first time! Here it is:

$$x = A\cos(\omega t) \qquad (15.23)$$

A is a constant: it will turn out to be the amplitude of the oscillation. We can differentiate x twice with the help of Appendix B.

$$\frac{dx}{dt} = -\omega A \sin(\omega t)$$

$$\frac{d^2x}{dt^2} = \frac{d}{dt}\frac{dx}{dt}$$

$$\therefore \frac{d^2x}{dt^2} = -\omega A \times \frac{d}{dt}(\sin(\omega t))$$

$$\therefore \frac{d^2x}{dt^2} = -\omega^2 A \cos(\omega t) \qquad (15.24)$$

If you now compare equation (15.24) with equation (15.23) you will see that they agree with equation (15.22). So x = Acos(ωt) is an acceptable solution.

Behaviour of the solution

You can only find the cosine of an angle, so ωt has to be measured in radians. Since t is measured in seconds ω must therefore be measured in radians per second. This is the reason why ω is called the **angular frequency**, despite the fact that it has nothing to do with circular motion! Figure 15.29 shows how the function cosϕ depends on ϕ. Note how cosϕ starts off at +1 and oscillates between +1 and −1, with the cycle repeating itself every time ϕ increases by 2π radians. Our solution, x = Acos(ωt), is plotted in figure 15.30. When t = 0, x = A. It returns to A at t = 2π/ω, 4π/ω, 6π/ω etc., so the period must be 2π/ω.

$$T = \frac{2\pi}{\omega}$$

T is the period of the oscillator (s)

ω is the angular frequency $(k/m)^{\frac{1}{2}}$ of the oscillator (rad s^{-1})

Since f = 1/T, the angular frequency of a system is related to its natural frequency of oscillation.

$$\omega = 2\pi f$$

ω is the angular frequency of the oscillator (rad s^{-1})

f is the natural frequency of the oscillator (Hz)

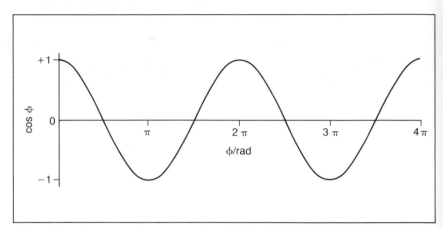

Figure 15.29 cosϕ as a function of ϕ

Figure 15.30 x = Acos(ωt)

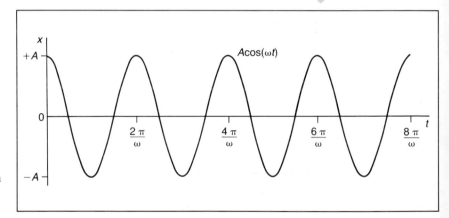

ALTERNATIVE SOLUTIONS !

Just because we have found one solution to the differential equation, it does not preclude the existence of other solutions. If you study the tables of differentials in Appendix B you should be able to convince yourself that x = Asin(ωt) also fits equation (15.22). That function is plotted in figure 15.31. As you can see, it has an amplitude of A and a period of 2π/ω just like the other solution. The only difference is that x = 0 at t = 0. It can therefore be used to describe objects which are set into oscillation by an impulse rather than by a displacement.

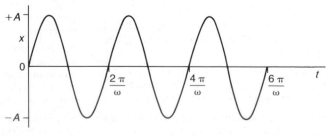

Figure 15.31 x = Asin(ωt)

ENERGY CHANGES

It is instructive to use our solution to predict exactly how the kinetic and potential energy of the system are going to evolve with time. The potential energy is easy.

$$E_p = \tfrac{1}{2}kx^2, \quad x = A\cos(\omega t) \qquad \therefore E_p = \tfrac{1}{2}kA^2\cos^2(\omega t) \tag{1}$$

For the kinetic energy, we need an expression for the velocity.

$$v = \frac{dx}{dt}, \quad x = A\cos(\omega t) \qquad \therefore v = -\omega A\sin(\omega t) \tag{2}$$

$$E_k = \tfrac{1}{2}mv^2 \qquad \therefore E_k = \tfrac{1}{2}m\omega^2 A^2\sin^2(\omega t) \tag{3}$$

These functions are plotted in figure 15.32. Note how the two energy curves are always positive and add up to $\tfrac{1}{2}kA^2$ at all times, just as you would expect (see question 3 at the end of this section).

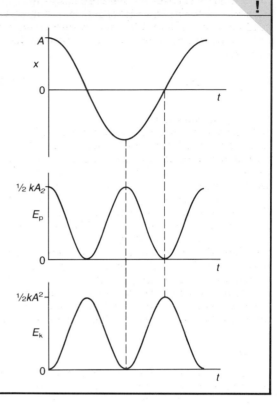

Figure 15.32 Variation of potential and kinetic energy with time

OBJECTIVES

After studying this section you should be able to do the following.

Solve $a = -\omega^2 x$ by numerical integration.

Use the formulae $x = A\cos(\omega t)$, $v = -A\omega\sin(\omega t)$, $\omega = (k/m)^{\frac{1}{2}}$, $T = 2\pi/\omega$, $\omega = 2\pi f$.

Sketch graphs to show how the displacement, velocity and acceleration of an object with SHM varies with time.

Sketch graphs to show how the potential, kinetic and total energy of an object with SHM varies with time.

QUESTIONS

1 You will need access to a computer to solve this problem. It will take you a long time if you attempt it by hand with a calculator!

You are going to calculate how the distance dropped by a free-fall parachutist changes with time. She has a total mass of 80 kg and presents an effective area of 160 cm × 30 cm to the air as she falls. The density of air is 1.2 kg m^{-3} and g is 9.81 N kg^{-1}.

a The dominant source of friction is wind resistance. Show that the downwards acceleration will be given by $a = g - \rho A v^2/m$.

b If the initial values of x and v are both zero, work out what they will be during the first 10 s of free-fall. Use a time interval of 0.5 s for the calculations.

2 A 0.20 kg mass is suspended from a spring whose force constant is 15 N m^{-1}. It is displaced from equilibrium by 50 mm and then released.

a Write down expressions for the displacement, velocity and acceleration of the mass at time t after it is released.

b What is the period of the oscillations going to be?

c Calculate the maximum velocity of the mass.

d Sketch graphs which show how the displacement and velocity change with time for the first two seconds after release. Mark the scales on both axes.

3 Use equations (1) and (3) (Energy Changes 'box') to write down an expression for the total energy of a system in SHM at time t. Use the identity $\cos^2\theta + \sin^2\theta = 1$ to show that the total energy is $\tfrac{1}{2}kA^2$ at all times.

4 Use the table of differentials in Appendix B to find a solution of the differential equation $d^2x/dt^2 = g$, where g is a constant.

5 The apparatus shown in figure 15.33 is widely used to show students that $x = A\cos(\omega t)$ without resorting to calculus. The pendulum is suspended above the centre of the turntable and set swinging with an amplitude equal to the turntable's radius r. The angular velocity of the turntable ω is adjusted until the stick pointing up from its rim appears to track the pendulum bob when the apparatus is viewed from the side at a distance.

Figure 15.33 ▶

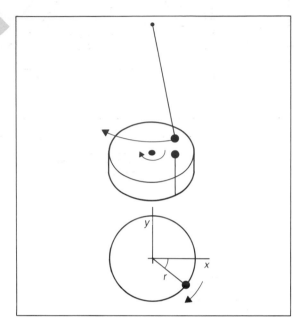

a If the pendulum oscillates along the x-axis as shown in figure 15.33, show that the x-component of the stick's position at time t is given by $x = r\cos(\omega t)$.

b Suppose the pendulum has a length of 0.5 m. At what speed (in revolutions per minute) will the turntable have to rotate?

c For the demonstration to be effective, the damping of the pendulum must be minimised. Gary has a choice of two solid pendulum bobs. Both have the same shape and size, but one is plastic, the other metal. Explain which one he should use, giving reasons for the choice.

6 A 500 g mass is attached to the end of a spring which has a force constant of 100 N m^{-1}. Initially the mass is held so that the spring is unstretched. Then it is released.

a What is the amplitude of the subsequent oscillations?

b Assuming that the mass had zero gravitational energy when it was released, sketch a graph to show how its gravitational energy changes with time.

c In another experiment with the same apparatus, the mass starts off at rest suspended from the stretched spring. It is set oscillating by hitting it with a hammer. If the hammer gives the mass a downwards velocity of 0.50 m s^{-1}, sketch a graph to show how the displacement of the mass changes with time after being struck.

FORCED OSCILLATIONS

A classic example of forced oscillation is shown in figure 15.34. By applying a push to the girl at the apex of each swing, the man can increase the amplitude of her oscillation. He is applying a **periodic force** which is synchronised with the oscillation of the swing. You probably know from your own experience with playground swings that the pushes have to be carefully timed for the energy in the oscillator to increase with time; the frequency of the applied force has to match the frequency of the oscillation. This section is going to take you through the physics of such forced oscillations. You will find out how the amplitude of a forced oscillation is related to its damping time and how to prevent a system from being destroyed by forced oscillations when it goes into resonance.

Exploring resonance

The apparatus shown in figure 15.35 can be used to explore the effects of a periodic force on an oscillator. The magnet of mass m is hung on the end of a spring whose force constant is k. If the system is given some energy and isolated, it will oscillate with its **angular frequency** ω_0.

$$T = \frac{2\pi}{\omega}, \quad T = 2\pi(m/k)^{\frac{1}{2}}$$

$$\therefore \omega_0 = (k/m)^{\frac{1}{2}} \tag{15.25}$$

The coil of wire below the magnet carries an alternating current. The amplitude and frequency f of the current is controlled by the signal generator. The magnetic field around the coil applies a periodic force to the magnet (see chapter 23).

$$F = F_0\cos(\omega t) \quad \text{where } \omega = 2\pi f \tag{15.26}$$

Figure 15.34 An example of forced oscillation

The copper wire suspended in the copper sulphate solution allows the displacement of the magnet to be monitored with an oscilloscope. A small constant current is maintained in the wire so that the p.d. between the wire and the can is proportional to the resistance between them. This will depend on the length of wire immersed in the copper sulphate solution, so the vertical displacement of the oscilloscope spot mirrors the up and down movement of the magnet.

Figure 15.36 shows the results of measuring the amplitude of oscillation at various frequencies near to the natural frequency of the system. The amplitude is a maximum when the frequency of the current in the coil is equal to the natural frequency. The system goes into **resonance**. Furthermore, the magnet always oscillates at the same frequency as the current in the coil.

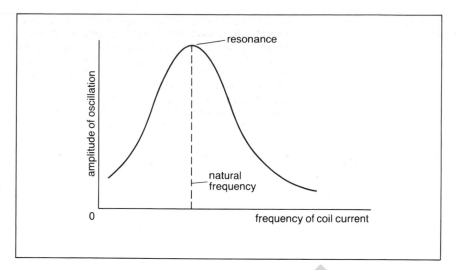

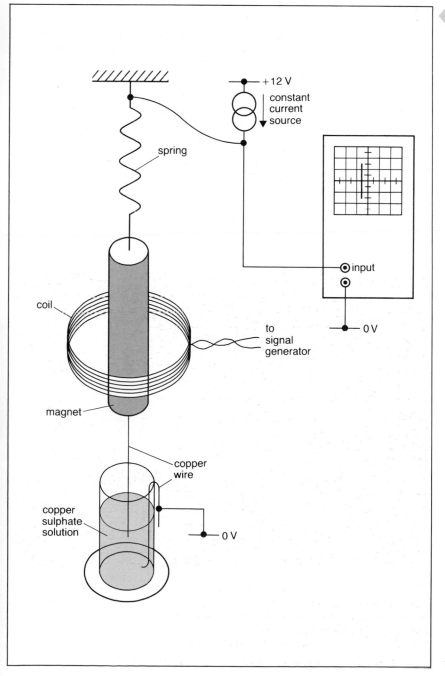

Figure 15.35 Apparatus for investigating the motion of a mass on a spring when subjected to a periodic force

Figure 15.36 Typical variation of oscillator amplitude with driving force frequency

MODELLING RESONANCE

To simplify matters, we shall assume that the oscillating system is undamped, i.e. there is no friction. If the only source of energy for the oscillator is the periodic force from the coil, we can model the system with an equation. When the magnet has a displacement x from equilibrium, the restoring force $-kx$ and the periodic force $F_0\cos(\omega t)$ act on it. Their resultant can be plugged into Newton's Second Law.

$$F = ma \qquad \therefore F_0\cos(\omega t) - kx = ma \qquad (1)$$

Using the calculus notation for a, we obtain a differential equation:

$$a = \frac{F_0\cos(\omega t)}{m} - \frac{kx}{m}$$

$$\therefore \frac{d^2x}{dt^2} = \frac{F_0}{m}\cos(\omega t) - \omega_0^2 x \quad \text{where } \omega_0^2 = \frac{k}{m} \qquad (2)$$

It is easily shown that the solution of this differential equation is

$$x = A\cos(\omega t), \quad A = \frac{F_0}{m(\omega_0^2 - \omega^2)} \qquad (3)$$

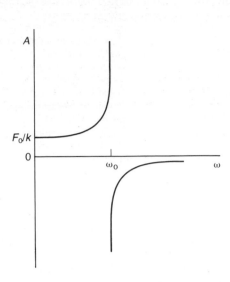

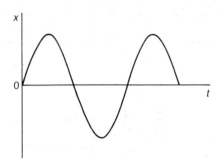

Figure 15.37 Variation of A with ω for an undamped oscillator

So the magnet oscillates at the same frequency as the driving force. The amplitude of the oscillation depends on the frequency of the driving force as shown in figure 15.37. Note how it shoots up to infinity when the driving frequency matches the natural frequency of the oscillator ($1 \div 0 = \infty$) and has different signs for high and low frequencies. The new concept of **phase** will help you understand the significance of the sign of A.

Phase

At very low driving frequencies ($\omega \ll \omega_0$) the amplitude becomes constant and positive.

$$A = \frac{F_0}{m(\omega_0^2 - \omega^2)} \qquad \therefore A \simeq \frac{F_0}{m\omega_0^2} \quad \text{if } \omega \ll \omega_0$$

$$\omega_0^2 = \frac{k}{m} \qquad \qquad \therefore A \simeq \frac{F_0}{k} \qquad (4)$$

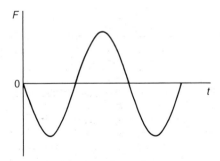

Figure 15.38 Displacement out of phase with applied force

Figure 15.39 Variation of amplitude and phase with driver frequency

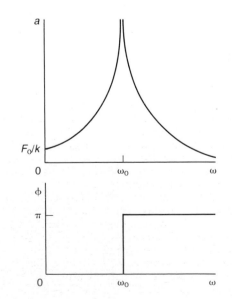

This is exactly what you would expect: the applied force stretches and compresses the spring by the amount calculated from its force constant.
At very high frequencies ($\omega \gg \omega_0$) the amplitude is small and negative.

$$A = \frac{F_0}{m(\omega_0^2 - \omega^2)} \quad \therefore A \simeq -\frac{F_0}{m\omega^2} \quad \text{if } \omega \gg \omega_0 \qquad (5)$$

The negative amplitude means that the oscillator's displacement is **out of phase** with the driving force. This is shown in figure 15.38: the force and displacement always have different signs. This can be easily described with the use of a **phase angle** ϕ.

$$x = A\cos(\omega t) \qquad \therefore x = a\cos(\omega t + \phi) \qquad (6)$$

The graphs of figure 15.39 show how the values of a and ϕ depend on the value of ω. It splits the information contained in figure 15.37 into two parts. The size of the oscillation is given by a and the amount by which the oscillation is out of step with the driving force is given by ϕ.

MODELLING EFFECTS OF DAMPING

The amplitude of oscillation at resonance clearly depends on the damping time τ. If the energy of the isolated oscillator drops exponentially with time, then we can estimate how much it loses in one cycle.

$$E = E_0\exp[-t/\tau] \quad \therefore \frac{\Delta E}{E} = -\frac{\Delta t}{\tau} \quad \therefore \Delta E \simeq -\frac{ET}{\tau} \qquad (1)$$

For the amplitude to remain steady, that energy loss must be replaced by the driving force. If we assume that the driving force is in phase with the displacement, then we can work out the average energy given to the oscillator in one cycle.

$$<Fd> = <F_0\cos(\omega t)\times A\cos(\omega t)> = F_0A\times<\cos^2(\omega t)> \qquad (2)$$

Figure 15.42 shows that $<\cos^2(\omega t)> = \frac{1}{2}$ over one complete cycle.

$$\Delta E = -\frac{ET}{\tau} \quad \therefore \frac{1}{2}F_0A = \frac{\frac{1}{2}kA^2T}{\tau} \quad \therefore A = \frac{F_0\tau}{kT} \qquad (3)$$

We cannot rely on equation (3) too much because of the assumptions behind it. Nevertheless, it implies that the maximum amplitude at resonance should be proportional to the damping time. Systems which are heavily damped (i.e. have short values of τ) will have small amplitudes of oscillation at resonance. The damping of a system is sometimes specified by its Q-factor: a large Q-factor means light damping and large resonant oscillations.

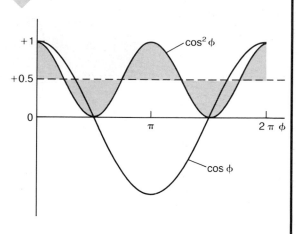

Figure 15.42 The average value of $\cos^2\phi$ over one cycle is 0.50

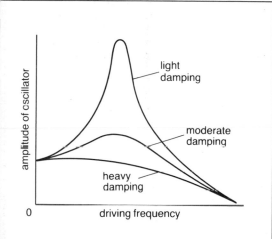

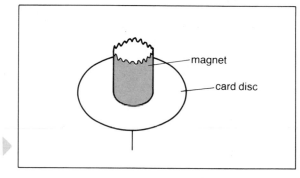

Figure 15.40 Effects of different amounts of damping

Figure 15.41 Adding extra damping to the apparatus of figure 15.35

Damping

No system can have an infinite amplitude of oscillation. As the amplitude increases, so will the velocity. Many friction mechanisms (including wind resistance) increase rapidly with velocity, so at a large enough amplitude friction will remove energy from the oscillator as fast as the driving force injects it. A realistic graph for the amplitude of the oscillator as a function of the driving frequency is shown in figure 15.40.

Figure 15.41 shows how some damping can be incorporated in the apparatus of figure 15.35. The card disc provides air resistance: the amount of friction can be varied by altering the area of the disc. The damping time τ of the system for a particular area of disc can be found by setting the magnet into oscillation and noting how long it takes for the amplitude of the oscillations to die down: 0.69τ is the time taken for the energy in the system to be halved. Figure 15.40 shows how the amount of damping affects the shape of the resonance curve.

EXPLORING PHASE DIFFERENCE

The oscilloscope used in figure 15.35 can also be used to measure the phase difference between the driving force and the displacement of the oscillator. The displacement signal controls the vertical motion of the spot as before. The timebase is switched off and the signal generator voltage is used to control the horizontal motion of the spot. Since the force will be proportional to the current in the coil (chapter 23), the horizontal motion of the spot will be in phase with the driving force. Figure 15.43 shows the paths followed by the spot for various phase differences between the driving force and the oscillator. The spot follows a straight line when the two signals are in phase. When the phase difference is $\pm\pi/2$, the path is an ellipse with the sign fixing whether the spot travels round clockwise or anticlockwise.

Figure 15.43 Typical oscilloscope traces for different phase differences between driver and oscillator

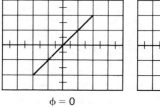

$\phi = 0$ · · · · · $\phi = \pi/2$ · · · · · $\phi = \pi$

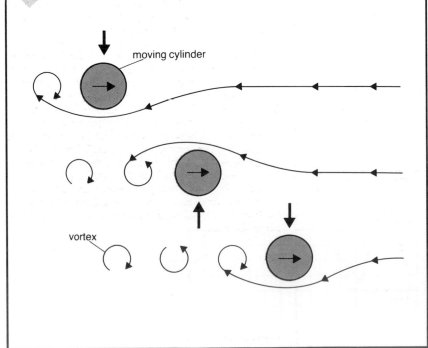

Figure 15.44 The Tacoma Narrows bridge

Avoiding resonance

Resonant oscillations are a bad thing for engineering. The classic example of the destructive power of forced oscillations is the Tacoma Narrows bridge disaster in 1940. The bridge is shown in figure 15.44. The oscillation of its road deck can be clearly seen. When it was built in 1939 it was one of the longest suspension bridges in the world. In order to reduce the forces on the suspension cables and the towers, the road deck was made as light as possible. Unfortunately, this low mass proved to be its undoing. The wind passing over the road deck was able to set it oscillating at its natural frequency as there was insufficient damping. Eventually the bridge collapsed. Since then, all large structures have been designed to prevent destructive resonant oscillations occuring.

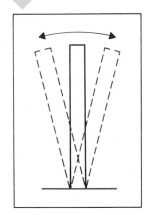

Figure 15.47 Expected oscillation of a chimney due to vortex shedding in the wind

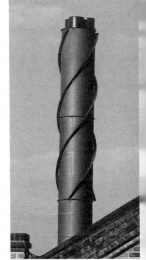

Figure 15.46 The vanes on the side of this chimney prevent it from being set into oscillation by the wind

VORTEX SHEDDING !

The driving force which set the Tacoma Narrows bridge oscillating was due to **vortex shedding** as the wind passed over it. When a fluid passes a cylindrical obstacle, vortices can be set up in its wake. This is shown in figure 15.45. Each vortex is an eddy, a circulation of the fluid. When it has built up to a certain size it breaks away from the cylinder and moves downstream. The vortices are produced one at a time from alternate edges of the cylinder as shown in figure 15.45. Each time a vortex breaks away it changes the force on the cylinder, so the shedding of vortices applies a periodic force at right angles to the direction of fluid flow. The frequency of vortex shedding is given by an approximate rule.

$$f \simeq 0.2 \frac{v}{d}$$

v is the velocity of fluid flow and d is the diameter of the obstacle. Appropriate shaping of the cylinder is often used to prevent the vortices happening. An example of this is shown in figure 15.46.

Figure 15.45 Vortex shedding

moving cylinder

vortex

Chimneys

Tall, thin structures like chimneys have to be designed to avoid self-destructive resonant oscillations caused by wind. A chimney is going to oscillate like an elastic beam, as shown in figure 15.47. Even if the amplitude of the oscillations is not large enough to cause immediate damage, the repeated stressing of the structure is likely to encourage metal fatigue.

The most obvious strategy is to raise the natural frequency well above the frequency of vortex shedding in high speed winds. This entails a stiff construction (large k) coupled with a small mass. The alternative is to ensure that the system is heavily damped. This means that you have to provide mechanisms whereby the energy of the oscillation can be converted to heat energy. Brick and concrete structures are highly damped because of the multitude of cracks in them: movement of the structure generates heat energy in the cracks as the surfaces move past each other. Joints are good places where friction can convert kinetic energy into heat energy. Rubber pads under the bases of tall structures are very good at absorbing energy because of the loops in their stress–strain curves.

Thin cables are very susceptible to forced oscillations from the wind. Dampers are placed on overhead transmission lines to prevent the oscillations building up to a dangerous level. Some are shown in figure 15.48. The weights are connected to the line by a short length of stranded steel cable. As the line starts to oscillate, it feeds energy to the weights via the stranded cable — the damper has the same natural frequency as the line. As the weights in the damper move up and down, the movement of the strands against each other converts the energy to heat energy.

Critical damping

In the absence of damping, an impulse will often set a system oscillating. Sometimes this is a good thing, but often it is not. For example, tapping the side of a bell with a hammer will set it ringing. Bells are made of alloys similar to brass which provide very little internal damping. Similarly, the quartz crystals used for timekeeping have little internal damping because of their regular structure, so they require only a small amount of electrical power to keep them going.

Motor vehicles, on the other hand, must not go into resonant oscillation when they go over bumps in the road. So they are provided with shock absorbers to damp out the oscillations once they have started. As you can see from figure 15.49, any vertical movement of the car wheels moves the piston inside the shock absorber, generating heat energy through friction. Figure 15.50 shows the effect of applying different amounts of damping to an oscillating system. **Critical damping** has been applied when the oscillation dies down in the quickest possible time. As a rule of thumb, it happens when $\tau \simeq T$. Critical damping of car wheels prevents them from bouncing off the road when they go over bumps.

Figure 15.48 Oscillation dampers on overhead transmission lines

Figure 15.49 Car shock absorber

Figure 15.50 Different amounts of damping

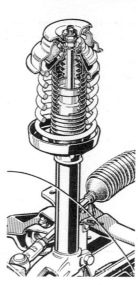

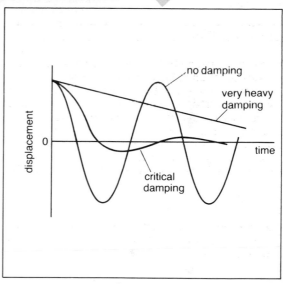

Coupled oscillations

Suppose that you have two identical oscillators which can interact with each other. What happens when you give some energy to one of them? The result is dramatic and unexpected.

For example, you might set up a pair of pendulums as shown in figure 15.51(a). When one of them is set swinging its energy can 'leak' through to the other other one via the string which supports them. The result is shown in the graphs of figure 15.51(b). The energy oscillates between the two systems, rather than just ending up being shared equally between them. The rate at which the energy is transferred from one pendulum to the other depends on the strength of their **coupling**. The stronger the coupling, the more rapid the transfer. So, as the two pendulum supports are moved closer to each other along the string, the period of oscillation of the energy from one to the other decreases.

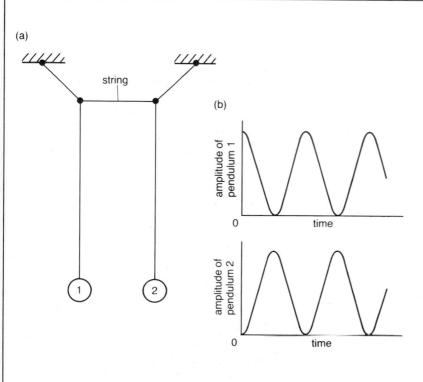

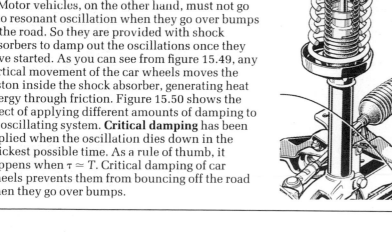

Figure 15.51 Coupled pendulums

Coupled modes

This oscillation of energy can take place in a single oscillator if it has more than one **mode** of oscillation. For example, suppose that a mass on a spring can oscillate both vertically and horizontally. If both modes have the same natural frequency, then oscillation in one mode will alternate with oscillation in the other. So if you set the mass swinging it will start off with all its energy in the horizontal mode. Some time later it will have stopped swinging and all of the energy will be in the vertical mode. Then the energy will be transferred back to the horizontal mode and the whole cycle will start again. The sequence is illustrated in figure 15.52.

Barton's pendulums

An interesting apparatus for demonstrating resonant oscillations is shown in figure 15.53. A number of pendulums, all of different lengths, are suspended from the same length of string. At one end of the string a relatively massive pendulum, the driver, is hung. When the driver is set oscillating, it feeds energy along the string to the other pendulums. Each pendulum, of course, has a different natural frequency. The one whose natural frequency is the same as the frequency of the driver pendulum is the one which ends up with the largest amplitude oscillations, as shown in figure 15.54. (The effects of damping can be investigated by placing paper cones on the pendulums, increasing their wind resistance.) The driver, having a much larger mass, is hardly affected by the oscillations of the other pendulums, so it provides a periodic force of almost constant amplitude. The whole effect is very beautiful: your physics education is incomplete if you have not experienced Barton's pendulums!

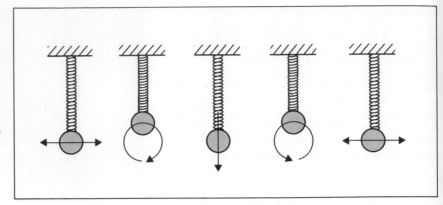

Figure 15.52 A mass on a spring has two modes of oscillation

Figure 15.53 Barton's pendulums

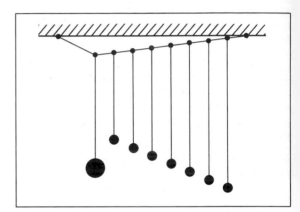

Figure 15.54 The amplitude of oscillation depends on the length of each pendulum

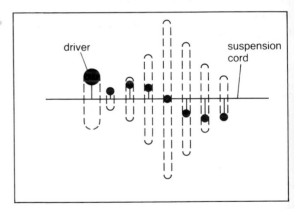

driver

suspension cord

OBJECTIVES

After studying this section you should be able to do the following.

Sketch a graph to show how the amplitude of a driven oscillator depends on the frequency of the driving force.

Understand the meaning of *resonance*.

Describe the effect of changing the damping on the amplitude of a driven oscillator.

Describe the mechanisms by which dangerous resonances in large structures can be avoided.

Describe the behaviour of coupled oscillators.

QUESTIONS

1 Figure 15.55 shows some apparatus which Ian is going to use to study forced oscillations of a hacksaw blade. He is going to set the pendulum swinging so that it applies a periodic force to the hacksaw blade via the elastic band. Masses can be stuck on the end of the blade, and the length of the pendulum can be altered. The amount of damping can be varied by placing different sized pieces of card at the top of the blade.

a Should the mass of the pendulum be large or small? Explain why.

b Ian sticks a 50 g mass on the end of the hacksaw blade and sets it oscillating. It does 10 complete cycles of oscillation in 20 s. What length of pendulum will set the hacksaw blade (with 50 g) into resonance?

The graph of figure 15.56 shows Ian's results, for a 5 cm × 5 cm card stuck on the top of the blade. The amplitude of oscillation of the blade tip is plotted against pendulum length.

c What is the mass Ian used on the end of the hacksaw blade?

d Copy the graph of figure 15.56. Draw on it the curve you would expect to find if Ian had
  (i) only replaced the card with a 5 cm × 10 cm card,
  (ii) only used two elastic bands side by side instead of just one,
(iii) only increased the mass on the end of the blade by 25%.

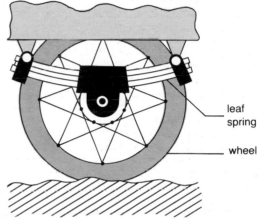

Figure 15.56

Figure 15.57

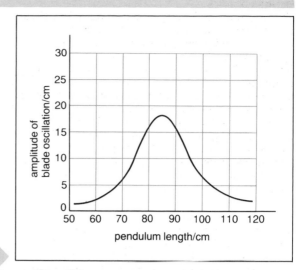

leaf spring

wheel

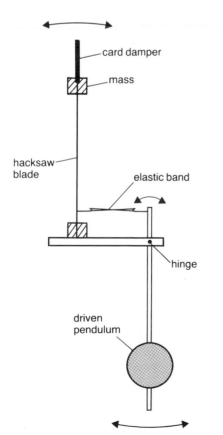

Figure 15.55

card damper

mass

hacksaw blade

elastic band

hinge

driven pendulum

2 A car has a mass of 1 000 kg. Each time a person sits in the car, it is depressed by 15 mm. Assume that each person has a mass of 75 kg.

a Estimate the natural frequency of the car body if the wheels stay firmly on the ground.

b If the car is driven at a steady 20 m s^{-1} over a road with bumps in it, how far apart do the bumps have to be to set the car body oscillating vertically?

c Estimate the natural frequency of the car wheels if the car body remains fixed. How far apart would the bumps in the road have to be to make the wheels oscillate when the car speed is 20 m s^{-1}?

d Leaf springs (figure 15.57) have an advantage over coiled springs for vehicle suspensions. Each leaf can move relative to the leaves clamped on either side of it. Explain why this makes a better suspension system.

e It is possible to tell if a moving lorry is full or empty by studying the way it oscillates when it goes over bumps in the road. Explain how it can be done.

Figure 15.59

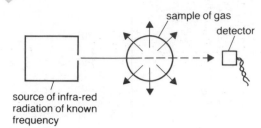

sample of gas

detector

source of infra-red
radiation of known
frequency

infra-red radiation whose frequency is equal to their natural frequency. An arrangement for detecting this is shown in figure 15.59. When the sample of gas is set into oscillation it absorbs the radiation and re-radiates it in all directions so that the amount getting to the detector falls. Table 15.5 gives some data for the resonant absorption of radiation by a number of molecules.

Table 15.5

Molecule	Absorption frequency/Hz
HCl	8.66×10^{13}
HBr	7.68×10^{13}
HI	6.69×10^{13}

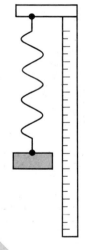

Figure 15.58

Figure 15.60

3 A record stylus behaves like a mass on the end of a beam. As it follows the groove in the disc it is forced to oscillate from side to side (and up and down) with a frequency equal to the note recorded on the disc. The mechanical properties of a record stylus are usually specified by two parameters. The **compliance** is the reciprocal of the beam's force constant, and the **tip mass** is the effective mass on the end of the beam. Sound has frequencies between 16 Hz and 16 kHz.

a Friction between the needle and the record groove leads to wear, damaging the groove. Is a high or a low tip mass desirable? Explain.

b Similarly, is a high or a low compliance desirable?

c If the tip mass is 2 mg, suggest an optimum value for the compliance.

4 Eyeball vibration is a problem in helicopters. The vibration caused by the rotating blades can set the pilot's eyeballs oscillating in their sockets, blurring her vision. Suggest modifications to the pilot's chair which might help combat this problem.

5 Figure 15.58 shows two different masses (M and m) tethered by a spring of force constant k. When they are set vibrating their centre of mass does not move. This means that $mx + MX = 0$ at all times during the vibration, where x and X are the displacements of the two masses from equilibrium. The angular frequency of the oscillation is ω.

a Explain why the centre of mass does not move during the oscillation.

b By applying Newton's Second Law to the small mass, show that $k(X - x) = -m\omega^2 x$.

c Eliminate X to show that $\omega^2 = k/\mu$ where μ is the **reduced mass** given by $\mu = Mm/(M + m)$.

d A diatomic molecule, such as HCl, can be modelled as a pair of tethered masses. They can be set into resonant oscillation by exposing them to

Each of these molecules consists of a hydrogen atom bonded to a halogen atom. It is tempting to suppose that the strength of the bond between them is always the same. Use the data in tables 15.5 and 15.6 to see if this is supported by the experimental data.

Table 15.6

Atom	Molar mass/kg mol^{-1}
H	0.0010
Cl	0.0355
Br	0.0799
I	0.1269

6 Elanit wants to use a mass on a spring to measure the vertical acceleration of skyscraper lifts. The apparatus is shown in figure 15.60: the displacement of the mass can be measured with the ruler. When the lift is moving at a constant velocity, the displacement $x = 0$.

a Show that $x = -ma/k$ when the lift is accelerated upwards; (a is the acceleration, m is the mass and k is the force constant of the spring).

b Suppose that the lift is moving upwards at a steady speed of 2.0 m s^{-1} and then suddenly stops in 0.10 s. Describe the subsequent motion of the mass as precisely as you can ($m = 0.5$ kg and $k = 20$ N m^{-1}).

c When the system is critically damped, the oscillation dies away in about one cycle. Suggest how the mass could be damped, and how Elanit could go about setting up critical damping.

d Elanit chooses to use a mass of 200 g on the end of a 10 N m^{-1} spring. How quickly will she be able to measure accelerations reliably? What is the sensitivity of her equipment if she can read the value of x to within 0.25 cm?

e Describe a similar system which could be used to measure the acceleration of a car when it is going along a level road. Suggest suitable values for force constants and masses of your system.

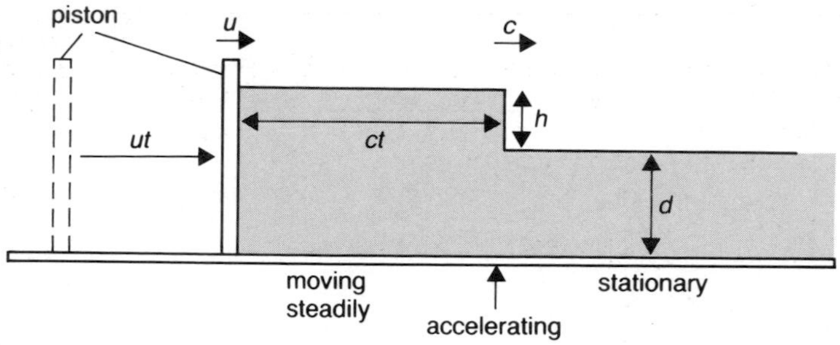

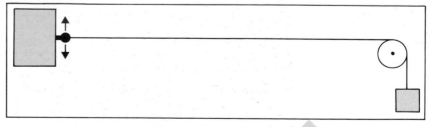

Figure 16.10 A step pulse on the surface of a liquid

SHALLOW WAVES !

Since the speed of shallow water waves is independent of their wavelengths or amplitudes. we can choose any shape of pulse to prove that $c = (gd)^{\frac{1}{2}}$. Figure 16.10 shows a step pulse travelling across a shallow tray of water of width w. It is caused by a piston moving at a steady speed u at one end of the tray, giving momentum to the water. Since the water is incompressible, the water behind the step is raised up a distance h above the water in front of the step.

Suppose that the piston has been moving for a time t, as shown in figure 16.10. Use the pressure difference on the water just in front of the step to calculate the force on it.

$$P = \rho gh, \qquad P = \frac{F}{A} \qquad \therefore \Delta P = \rho gh$$
$$\therefore F = dw \times \rho gh \qquad (1)$$

Next, find the total momentum given to the water in the time t.

$$p = mv, \quad m = \rho V \qquad \therefore p = \rho wdct \times u \qquad (2)$$

Newton's Second Law can now be used to combine equations (1) and (2).

$$\Delta p = F\Delta t \qquad \therefore \rho wdctu = dw\rho gh \times t$$
$$\therefore cu = gh \qquad (3)$$

Since the water is incompressible, the volume of water swept out by the piston is equal to the volume of raised water behind the step (see figure 16.10).

$$ut \times w \times d = ct \times w \times h \qquad \therefore h = \frac{ud}{c} \qquad (4)$$

So we can combine equations (3) and (4) to get what we are after.

$$cu = gh, \quad h = \frac{ud}{c} \qquad \therefore c^2 = gd \qquad (5)$$

OBJECTIVES

After studying this section you should be able to do the following.

Know that the velocity of a transverse wave in a stretched string is independent of its shape.

Know that transverse pulses are damped as they travel through the medium.

Quote the wave formula $y(x,t) = A\cos(\omega t - Kx)$.

Use the formulae $\omega = 2\pi f$ and $K = 2\pi/\lambda$.

Explain the meaning of *amplitude, period, cycle, wavetrain, frequency* and *wavelength*.

Sketch graphs to show the displacement of a medium at various places when a wave passes through it.

Use the formula $c = f\lambda$.

Predict the velocity of transverse waves in stretched strings.

Describe the use of a ripple tank to investigate water waves.

Understand why the amplitude of a water wave decreases as it moves away from its source.

QUESTIONS

1 A 3 Hz oscillator is connected to one end of a stretched string, as shown in figure 16.11. The wave velocity for pulses going down the string is 0.50 m s^{-1}. The oscillator is switched on for 2.0 s and then switched off again.

a Calculate the wavelength of the waves generated in the string.

b Draw a diagram to show what figure 16.11 looks like immediately the oscillator has been switched off.

c Draw another diagram to show what it looks like 1.0 s after the oscillator has been switched off.

2 This question takes you through an alternative way of deriving the formula $c = f\lambda$. An oscillator of frequency f is switched on for a time t, producing waves of wavelength λ.

a How many cycles are there in the wavetrain?

Figure 16.11

b Use part (a) to obtain an expression for the length of the wavetrain. Hence prove that $c = f\lambda$.

c Light waves travel at 3.0×10^8 m s^{-1}. The atoms which emit light in a sodium streetlight lamp only do so for about 1.0×10^{-9} s at a time. If the frequency of sodium light is 5.1×10^{14} Hz, estimate the length of each wavetrain and the number of cycles it contains.

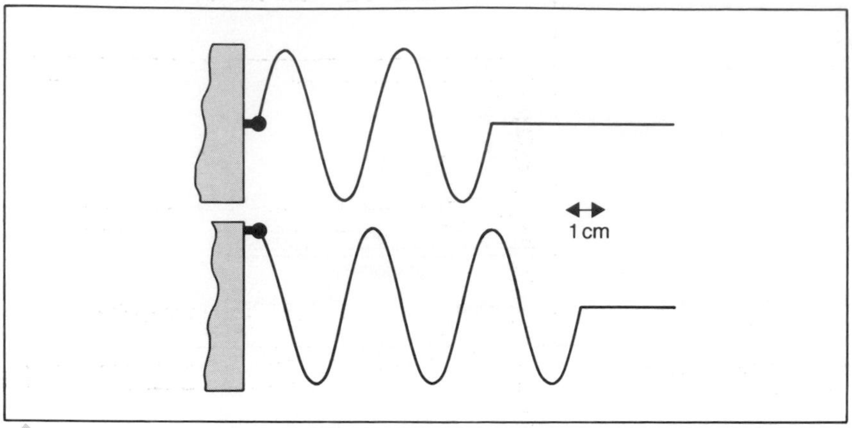

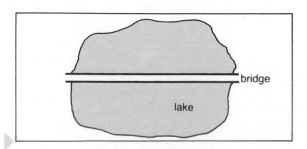

Figure 16.12

3 Figure 16.12 represents two photographs of a wave travelling down a stretched string. The photographs were taken 0.50 s apart.

a Use figure 16.12 to calculate the amplitude, wave velocity, wavelength and frequency of the wave going down the string.

b The tension in the string is doubled, but the oscillator is exactly the same as before. Draw a graph to show how the displacement of the string at a particular place would change with time.

4 If an oscillator is to send a wave down a string, it has to inject energy into it. This question will show you how to calculate the power output of the oscillator.

a Sketch a couple of cycles of a wave of amplitude A and wavelength λ. Mark on it a place where the energy of the wave is exclusively kinetic energy.

b Each portion of the string oscillates in SHM. Show that the kinetic energy of the length Δx you marked is $\frac{1}{2}\mu\Delta x A^2\omega^2$.

c Show that the energy in one cycle of the wave is $\pi\mu c\omega A^2$.

d Use your answer to part (c) to show that the power output of the oscillator is $\frac{1}{2}\mu c\omega^2 A^2$.

5 This question is about the use of the wave formula $y(x,t) = A\cos(\omega t - Kx)$ to describe a wave travelling along the x-axis. The quantity $\omega t - Kx$ is called the phase angle of the wave. Each point on the wave has a unique value for its phase angle.

a A particular point on the wave has a phase angle of 4π. Write down an expression for the position of that point as a function of time.

b Draw an $x-t$ graph for the point on the wave which has a phase angle of 4π. Obtain an expression for the point's velocity in terms of ω and K.

c Write down a wave formula which describes a wave travelling in the direction of decreasing x.

6 The speed of waves on the surface of shallow water is given by $c = (gd)^{\frac{1}{2}}$, where d is the depth of the water.

a A level ripple tank contains water with a uniform depth of 10 mm. A dibber at its centre oscillates at 10 Hz. If the dibber is switched on for 0.50 s, make a scale drawing to show what the ripples will look like 0.25 s after the dibber has been switched off.

b A particular ripple tank is 50 cm × 50 cm, and is arranged so that the depth of water changes uniformly from 2 mm at one end to 22 mm at the other along the x-axis. Draw a graph to show how the wave velocity changes along the x-axis. If a single pulse is generated in the centre of the tank, estimate what it looks like after 0.50 s.

c The disc used to strobe the light through the ripples has four slots in it. If the dibber has a frequency of 6.0 Hz, what is the angular velocity of the disc needed to freeze the pattern of ripples seen on the screen?

d State and explain what happens to the pattern on the screen if the angular velocity of the disc is
   (i) slightly higher,
  (ii) slightly lower,
 (iii) exactly double your answer for part (c).

7 This question is going to introduce you to the Doppler effect. Imagine that there is a bridge going over the centre of a large pond, as shown in figure 16.13. Joe walks across the bridge at a steady speed of 1.0 m s^{-1}, dropping one stone into the water at the end of each second, so that each stone produces a crest. Ripples from the stones travel outwards at a steady speed of 2.0 m s^{-1}.

a If Joe starts to drop stones from the centre of the bridge, draw a scale diagram to show what the ripples look like at the instant Joe drops his fifth stone.

b Carmel is standing on the bridge ahead of Joe. She measures the wavelength, velocity and frequency of the ripples. What answers does she get?

c Kevin is on the bridge behind Joe. What answers does he get for the wavelength, velocity and frequency of the ripples?

d Joe now sits at the centre of the bridge and drops stones into the water at a rate of one per second. Kevin starts off at the far end of the bridge and walks towards Joe at a steady speed of 1.0 m s^{-1}. What will Kevin think the frequency, velocity and wavelength of the ripples are? A scale drawing may help.

e Carmel starts off next to Joe and walks away from him at 1.0 m s^{-1}. What answers does she get for the frequency, velocity and wavelength of the ripples?

Figure 16.13

LONGITUDINAL WAVES

If you pick up one end of a bar, a **transverse pulse** travels down its length imparting upwards momentum to it (figure 16.14). The speed with which the pulse moves down the bar depends on its stiffness and mass per unit length. But what happens if you push one end of the bar, as shown in figure 16.15? A **compression pulse** travels down its length, imparting sideways momentum to it. It turns out that compression pulses can travel through any material, be they solid, liquid or gas. This section is going to explain the properties of compression waves and show how they can be investigated.

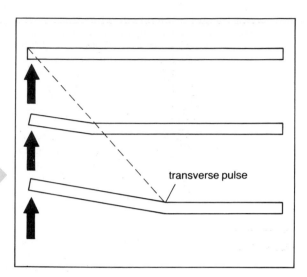

Figure 16.14 A transverse pulse in a bar

Figure 16.16 The pulse has a speed c

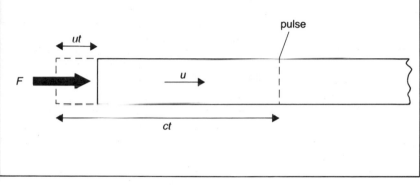

Compressing solids

The speed of compression pulses depends on the bulk properties of the solid. Consider a portion of solid which has a compression pulse moving through it, as shown in figure 16.16. The solid behind the pulse is moving with a constant velocity u, whereas the solid in front of the pulse is not moving. Clearly, forces must be acting on the solid as the pulse passes over it. The solid in front of the pulse is compressed by the solid moving forwards behind the pulse; the stress involved with this strain will depend on Young's modulus E. Furthermore, the acceleration of the solid by this stress will depend on its density ρ. So we expect the pulse velocity c to be a function of E and ρ.

$c = (E/\rho)^{\frac{1}{2}}$

c is the speed of longitudinal waves in a solid (m s^{-1})

E is Young's modulus for the material (Pa)

ρ is the density of the material (kg m^{-3})

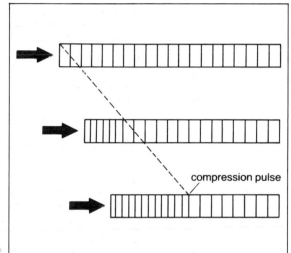

Figure 16.15 A compression pulse in a bar

PREDICTING PULSE VELOCITY !

Suppose that one end of a bar has been pushed with a constant force for a time t. A compression pulse will travel down its length as shown in figure 16.16. As the pulse passes through the material it imparts a forward velocity u to it. The pushed end of the bar has moved forwards a distance ut, so the material behind the pulse has a strain.

$$\text{strain} = \frac{x}{l} \qquad \therefore \ \text{strain} = \frac{ut}{ct} \qquad (1)$$

If the cross-sectional area of the bar is A, the strain can be used to work out the force F needed to push the end of the bar.

$$\text{stress} = E \times \text{strain} \qquad \therefore \ \frac{F}{A} = E \times \frac{u}{c} \qquad \therefore \ F = \frac{EuA}{c} \qquad (2)$$

The momentum transferred to the bar by this force can be worked out by considering the material behind the pulse.

$$p = mv, \quad m = \rho V \qquad \therefore \ p = \rho Act \times u \qquad (3)$$

Newton's Second Law can now be used to combine equations (2) and (3) to obtain the expression we are after.

$$\Delta p = F\Delta t \qquad \therefore \ \rho Actu = \frac{EuA}{c} \times t \qquad \therefore \ c^2 = \frac{E}{\rho} \qquad (4)$$

Of course, you have noticed that none of the parameters of the pulse (i.e. u) are involved in the expression for the pulse velocity c. This means that we can be hopeful that *all* compression pulses in a solid travel at the same speed.

Measuring the pulse velocity in solids

Figure 16.17 shows an arrangement which can be used in a school laboratory to verify that $c = (E/\rho)^{\frac{1}{2}}$. A compression pulse is generated in a long steel bar by tapping it at one end with a hammer. The mass of the hammer needs to be larger than the mass of the rod, so that the rod emerges from the collision with a greater velocity than the hammer (see page 114). The pulse travels down the bar, bounces off the far end, travels back up the bar and imparts its momentum to the hammer. The sequence is shown in figure 16.18. So the hammer is only in contact with the bar while the pulse is travelling down its length. Let's predict how long that will be for a steel bar of length 1.00 m.

$c = ?$ $\qquad\qquad$ $c = (E/\rho)^{\frac{1}{2}}$

$E = 2.1\times10^{11}\,\mathrm{Pa}$

$\rho = 7.7\times10^{3}\,\mathrm{kg\ m^{-3}}$

$$\therefore c = \left(\frac{2.1\times10^{11}}{7.7\times10^{3}}\right)^{\frac{1}{2}}$$

$$\therefore c = 5\,200\ \mathrm{m\ s^{-1}}$$

$$v = \frac{\Delta x}{\Delta t} \quad \therefore\ 5\,200 = \frac{2.0\times1.00}{\Delta t}$$

$$\therefore \Delta t = 3.8\times10^{-4}\ \mathrm{s}$$

A standard school laboratory timer has a precision of ±1 ms, clearly useless for measuring a time interval of only 0.38 ms. An alternative method involving the charging of a capacitor is used in figure 16.17. When the hammer is touching the rod, the 0.10 μF capacitor is charged up from the 0.5 mA current source. An op-amp follower and voltmeter are used to measure the p.d. across the capacitor.

$$C = \frac{Q}{V},\quad Q = It \qquad \therefore V = \frac{It}{C}$$

$$\therefore V = \frac{0.5\times10^{-3}\times3.8\times10^{-4}}{0.1\times10^{-6}} = 1.9\ \mathrm{V} \qquad \textbf{(16.10)}$$

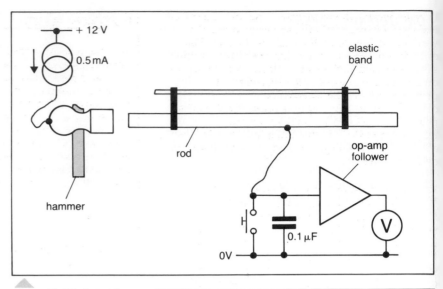

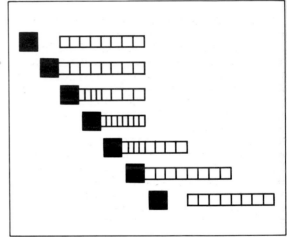

Figure 16.17 Apparatus for measuring the speed of compression pulses in a metal rod

Figure 16.18 Stages in the collision between the hammer and the rod

Longitudinal waves

All compression pulses travel through a solid with the same speed. So a number of pulses injected at one end of a bar, as shown in figure 16.19, will move down the bar as a wavetrain which preserves its shape. In particular, a sinusoidal pressure variation will be able to travel through the solid, similar to the transverse waves which can travel down strings and sheets.

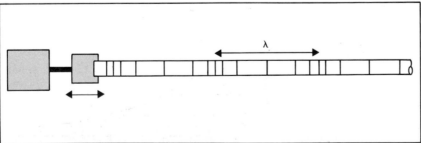

Figure 16.19 A longitudinal wave in a rod: the lines are equally spaced when the vibrator is switched off

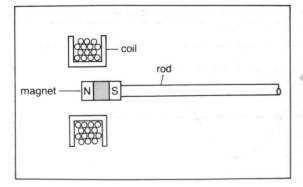

Figure 16.20 Using a coil and a magnet to generate longitudinal waves in a rod

Displacement

Suppose that one end of a bar is moved back and forth by a periodic force. (One arrangement, involving a magnet and a coil connected to a signal generator, is shown in figure 16.20.) The end of the bar ($x = 0$) will move in SHM.

$$\Delta x(0,t) = A\cos(\omega t) \qquad \textbf{(16.11)}$$

$\Delta x(0,t)$ is the displacement in the x-direction of the piece of the bar normally at $x = 0$.

Consider the material in the bar which is a distance x from the end. The waves take a time x/c to get from the end to this bit of the bar. Since the wave travels down the bar without changing shape, we expect the displacement $\Delta x(x,t)$ to be the displacement $\Delta x(0, t - x/c)$.

$$\Delta x(x,t) = A\cos(\omega(t - x/c))$$

$$\therefore \Delta x(x,t) = A\cos(\omega t - Kx),\quad K = \omega/c \qquad \textbf{(16.12)}$$

In other words, the wave travelling through the bar is described by exactly the same algebra as the waves in strings or on the surface of water. The only difference is that the displacement is in the same direction as the wave velocity; in strings and on the surface of water, the displacement is perpendicular to the wave velocity. Waves which cause displacement of the medium in a direction parallel to the flow of energy are called **longitudinal**. Waves which displace the medium in a direction perpendicular to the flow of energy are called **transverse**.

Representing longitudinal waves

When dealing with transverse waves, it is natural to represent them with pictures like the ones shown in figure 16.21. Graphs which show the displacement at one place as a function of time, or the displacement at all places at one time, are convenient for showing what we mean by the concepts of amplitude, period, frequency and wavelength.

Figure 16.22 attempts to show the same features for a longitudinal wave. Each full line represents a site in the medium and the adjacent dotted line shows its equilibrium position. The wavelength is marked: it is the distance between sites which have the same displacement and velocity. Because this type of representation is difficult to draw and even more difficult to use, it is common practice to draw graphs of the displacement Δx as a function of x. As you can see from figure 16.23, these can illustrate all the useful parameters of a wave (A and λ) in a comprehensible fashion. However, you must keep in mind that the displacement of the wave portrayed in these graphs is *not* at right angles to the direction of travel of the wave!

MICROSCOPIC PULSES

The mechanism by which longitudinal waves progress through solids is fairly obvious, particularly if you use a ball-and-spring model (figure 16.24). Pressure applied to the first layer of atoms in the solid causes them to move forward. This squeezes the springs between the first and second layers of atoms, exerting a pressure on the second layer of atoms, causing them to move forward. This squeezes the springs between the second and third layer of atoms, etc.

A longitudinal wave is going to propagate through a perfect solid without any **attenuation**. If the crystalline structure is perfect, there is no mechanism by which the energy of the wave can be converted into heat energy. However, real solids are rarely perfect, so longitudinal waves are damped as they travel through them. We can represent this damping with a modified form of the wave formula.

$$\Delta x(x,t) = A\exp[-x/\delta]\cos(\omega t - Kx) \qquad (1)$$

The quantity δ is the **attenuation distance**. When the wave has travelled a distance 0.69δ, its amplitude will have halved: this is shown in figure 16.25. Attenuation distances for a number of common materials are shown in table 1: they are for waves with frequencies between 2 MHz and 10 MHz. Notice that the attenuation distance is very long for crystalline materials which have very ordered microscopic structures, whereas composites (such as bone) have very short attenuation distances. Of course, the attenuation distance of a particular sample is going to depend on its history. The more microscopic cracks and grain boundaries it has, the shorter its attenuation distance will be.

Table 1

Material	c/m s^{-1}	δ/mm
quartz	5440	78 700
duralumin	5120	810
glass	5342	500
steel	5196	200
nylon	2680	87
bone	4000	2

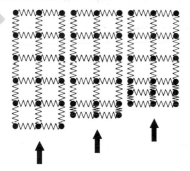

Figure 16.24 A compression wave in the ball-and-spring model

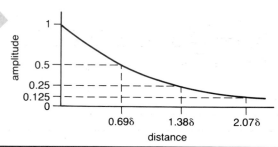

Figure 16.25 Attenuation of waves through a solid

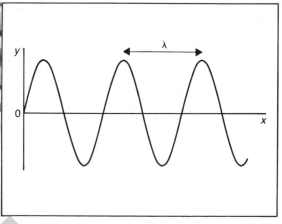

Figure 16.21 Representing a transverse wave

Figure 16.22 Attempting to represent a longitudinal wave

Figure 16.23 A clearer representation of a longitudinal wave

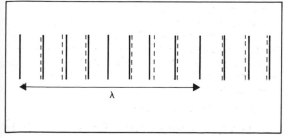

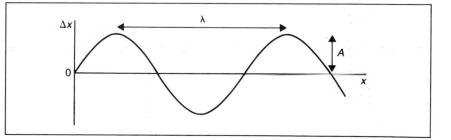

Compressing liquids

If you ignore the microscopic structure of a liquid, then there is no reason why longitudinal waves should not propagate through it. However, the lack of order on a microscopic scale means that the waves are quickly attenuated. Nevertheless, compression waves in liquids have important applications in medicine and industry, mainly because water is the dominant compound in human beings and oceans.

Macroscopic considerations

The thought experiment shown in figure 16.26 can be used to find an expression for the velocity of compression pulses in a liquid. The procedure is similar to that adopted above for solids. A sudden force F is applied to the piston at one end of the cylinder. This imparts momentum to the liquid, giving it a velocity u, etc. Eventually, after applying Newton's Second Law to the system, you end up with the following expression.

$$c = (K/\rho)^{\frac{1}{2}} \tag{16.13}$$

K is the **bulk modulus** of the liquid, the equivalent of Young's modulus for compression.

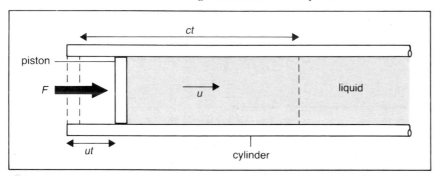

Figure 16.26 Generating a compression pulse in a liquid

Microscopic considerations

Although the molecules in a liquid are able to move around freely, their separation is hardly different from that of solids. (The densities of solids and liquids are comparable.) So we expect the value of the bulk modulus to be slightly less than Young's modulus for the solid. Table 16.1 contains data for the speed of longitudinal waves in a number of liquids at room temperature: they are a bit less than typical values for solids.

Table 16.1

Liquid	$c/\text{m s}^{-1}$	δ/mm
water	1482	40 000
alcohol	1162	19 000
turpentine	1225	7 000
glycerol	1860	500

However, the chaotic behaviour of molecules in a liquid provides mechanisms for converting the energy of the wave into heat energy. In general, the attenuation distance is proportional to f^{-2}: the data in table 16.1 are for frequencies of 1 MHz.

Compressing gases

Longitudinal waves in gases with frequencies between 20 Hz and 20 kHz are called **sound waves**. They are, of course, a vital mechanism for communication between human beings.

Speed of sound

The formulae for the speed of longitudinal waves in liquids and solids are similar.

$$c_{\text{liquid}} = (K/\rho)^{\frac{1}{2}}, \qquad c_{\text{solid}} = (E/\rho)^{\frac{1}{2}} \tag{16.14}$$

Both K and E have the units of pressure. It is therefore very tempting to propose that the speed of sound is given by a similar expression involving the gas pressure P.

$c_{\text{gas}} = (\gamma P/\rho)^{\frac{1}{2}}$

c_{gas} is the speed of sound in a gas (m s^{-1})

P is the pressure of the gas (Pa)

ρ is the density of the gas (kg m^{-3})

γ is the ratio of the molar heat capacities

γ (gamma) is a 'fudge factor' which can absorb any discrepancy between our guess and reality: it has no dimensions. (In fact, it can be shown that γ is the ratio C_p/C_v, where C_p and C_v are the molar heat capacities at constant pressure and constant volume, respectively.) Some experimentally determined values of γ at room temperature are shown in table 16.2. In general, the value of γ depends on the number of atoms in each gas molecule: it is 1.40 for air. At room temperature and pressure, the speed of sound is about 340 m s^{-1}.

Table 16.2

Gas	γ
argon	1.66
neon	1.64
nitrogen	1.40
oxygen	1.40
carbon dioxide	1.30
methane	1.31

Sound waves travel relatively slowly because solids and liquids are much stiffer mediums. The displacement of one of their atoms is quickly communicated to its neighbours, allowing the rapid propagation of compression waves. However, the structure of gases is much looser, with the atoms only interacting with each other during brief collisions.

A useful alternative expression to $(\gamma P/\rho)^{\frac{1}{2}}$ for the speed of sound can be obtained with the help of the Ideal Gas Equation $PV = nRT$. Suppose that you have n moles of a gas whose molar mass is M. Its density can be worked out as follows.

$$m = \rho V \qquad \therefore \rho = nM/V \tag{16.15}$$

The Ideal Gas Equation can be used to obtain an expression for the pressure of the gas.

$$PV = nRT \qquad \therefore P = nRT/V \tag{16.16}$$

If equations (16.15) and (16.16) are inserted into the wave velocity formula, we obtain the expression we are after.

$$c = (\gamma P/\rho)^{\frac{1}{2}} \qquad \therefore c = \left(\frac{\gamma nRT/V}{nM/V}\right)^{\frac{1}{2}}$$

$$\therefore c = (\gamma RT/M)^{\frac{1}{2}} \tag{16.17}$$

The temperature dependence of the speed of longitudinal waves in gases is much stronger than for solids or liquids. $\Delta c/c$ is about $2 \times 10^{-3}\,\text{K}^{-1}$ for gases and $1 \times 10^{-7}\,\text{K}^{-1}$ for solids at room temperature.

Measuring the speed of sound
The apparatus shown in figure 16.27 can be used to measure the speed of sound in a school laboratory. Sinusoidal sound waves of a known frequency are generated by a **loudspeaker** attached to a signal generator. The sound waves are detected by a pair of **microphones** which feed their signals into a **double-beam oscilloscope**. The oscilloscope is able to display both signals at once on its screen; it is triggered by one of the signals.

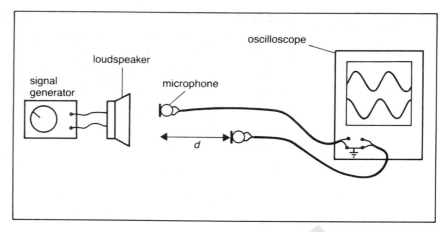

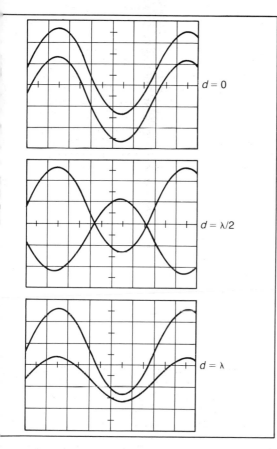

A microphone detects the displacement of the air just in front of it. So the $V-t$ curves drawn in figure 16.28 can be interpreted as $\Delta x-t$ curves. The top drawing of figure 16.28 is the screen trace obtained when the two microphones are the same distance from the loudspeaker. The signals are identical because the sound takes the same time to travel from the loudspeaker to either microphone. The sequence of traces drawn in figure 16.28 shows what happens as one of the microphones is moved away from the loudspeaker, leaving the other one fixed. Eventually, the two waveforms are in phase again, indicating that the microphones are exactly one wavelength apart. The frequency of the sound waves can be determined by measuring the period of the waveform on the screen. Knowledge of both frequency and wavelength allows the velocity to be calculated via the formula $c = f\lambda$. The experiment can be repeated for a number of frequencies to check that c is independent of wavelength.

Microscopic nature of sound
You may be a bit puzzled about the mechanism which allows a pressure wave to travel through a gas. Figure 16.29 may help. It represents a pressure pulse travelling from left to right through a gas. At a microscopic level, the pressure of a gas is a measure of the particle density, i.e. concentration of atoms. So the atoms are closer together behind the pulse.

Suppose, for simplicity, that all of the atoms are moving in random directions with the root-mean-square velocity $>c^2<^{\frac{1}{2}}$. Consider the regions Y and X just before and behind the pulse. In a short interval of time, more atoms are going to move from X to Y than move from Y to X. So the concentration of atoms at Y increases, raising its pressure. (The pressure at X does not fall because the atoms moving from W replace the ones which moved into Y.) Therefore, in a short time Δt the pulse moves a distance $<c^2>^{\frac{1}{2}}\Delta t$ to the right: the time can be sufficiently short for the probability of inter-atomic collisions to be negligible. The pulse velocity appears to be just $<c^2>^{\frac{1}{2}}$.

$$P = \frac{\rho}{3}<c^2> \quad \therefore <c^2>^{\frac{1}{2}} = (3P/\rho)^{\frac{1}{2}} \qquad \textbf{(16.18)}$$

If you compare equations (16.17) and (16.18) you can see that this rough model gives almost the right answer for the speed of sound. In other words, it looks as though ordered variations of pressure are transported through a gas by the random motion of its atoms! This is one of many examples where random motion on a microscopic scale leads to ordered behaviour on a macroscopic scale. It is the subject of chapter 30.

Figure 16.27 Measuring the speed of sound in air

Figure 16.28 The effect on the oscilloscope traces of moving one microphone away from the speaker

Figure 16.29 Representing a compression pulse in a gas

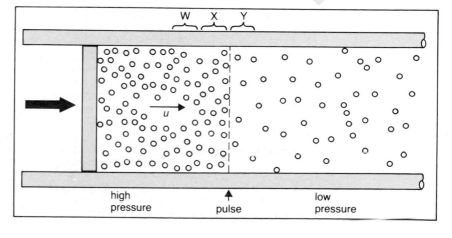

PITCH AND LOUDNESS

The ear–brain system is able to measure the frequency and amplitude of a sound wave. However, it uses a **logarithmic** scale to measure both quantities. The perceived amplitude of a sound wave is called its loudness. The **root-mean-square pressure** of a sound wave p_{rms} is converted to a **sound pressure level (s.p.l.)** on the **decibel (dB) scale** by the following procedure:

s.p.l. in dB $= 20 \times \log_{10}(p_{rms}/p_0)$, where $p_0 = 2 \times 10^{-5}$ Pa

The perceived frequency of a sound wave is known as its **pitch**. The pitch of a note goes up by one octave if its frequency is doubled. To complicate matters further, the efficiency of the human ear is a function of both the amplitude and frequency of the sound wave it is detecting. The graph of figure 16.30 shows how the perceived loudness of a sound depends on its pitch. (The threshold of hearing at 1 kHz is 4 dB and a sound pressure level of 130 dB causes pain. A quiet classroom is about 50 dB.)

Figure 16.30 Variation of amplitude with frequency of sound waves which have the same perceived loudness

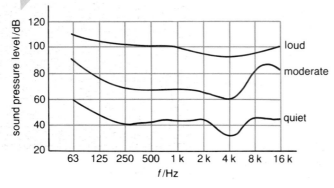

Ultrasonic probing

Ultrasound is the name given to any longitudinal wave whose frequency is too high to be heard, i.e. above 20 kHz. Ultrasonic waves are widely used for non-destructive probing of solids and liquids in industry and medicine.

Figure 16.31 shows how ultrasound can be used to probe the interior of a solid object. A piezoelectric disc inside the transducer acts as both emitter and detector of ultrasonic waves. The transducer injects brief pulses of ultrasound into the object. Subsequent reflections of those pulses are picked up by the transducer and displayed on the oscilloscope screen.

The electronic pulse generator feeds a regular series of sharp pulses into the disc, each one setting it ringing at the resonant frequency of 10 MHz (figure 16.32). The transducer is efficiently coupled to the solid by a thin layer of liquid between the two, so oscillations of the transducer set up longitudinal waves in the object. Those waves take energy from the transducer, damping its oscillations so that they die away in a few cycles. A short wavetrain is therefore injected into one end of the solid and travels down it at a known speed. Any cracks or sudden density changes (including the end of the object) will reflect part or all of the pulse back to the transducer where its energy will be converted back into a brief electrical pulse.

After some amplification, the reflected pulses are fed into the oscilloscope. Each time a fresh pulse is injected into the solid, the spot starts its sweep across the screen. So the trace on the screen contains information about the flight-time of the reflected pulses. For example, suppose that the object is made of steel and the trace looks like the one shown in figure 16.33. The timebase is set at 10 μs cm^{-1}. The first pulse of the trace is the one injected by the transducer: the other two are reflections. The large reflection comes from the end of the bar. The trace shows that its flight-time is $6.8 \times 10 = 68$ μs. A pulse in steel travels at 5.19×10^3 m s^{-1}, so the flight-time can be converted into a distance.

$$v = \frac{\Delta x}{\Delta t} \qquad \therefore \Delta x = v\Delta t$$

$$\therefore \Delta x = 5.19 \times 10^3 \times 68 \times 10^{-6} = 0.35 \text{ m}$$

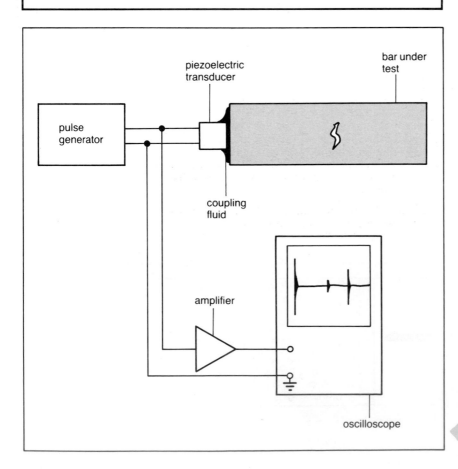

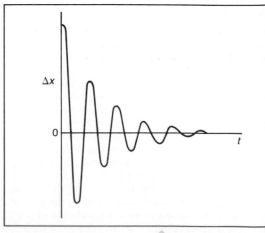

Figure 16.31 Using ultrasound to find flaws in a metal bar

Figure 16.32 The piezoelectric transducer produces a short pulse

Bearing in mind that the pulse has to travel to the end of the bar and back, the length of the bar must be 17.5 cm.

Of course, the length of the bar could have been measured with a lot less fuss by using a ruler. However, the ultrasound has detected a crack deep inside the bar, about 13 cm from one end (check this for yourself). Furthermore, the amplitude of the crack's reflection can be used to estimate its size. The width of the pulses ($\approx$0.5 μs) allows the crack position to be determined with a precision of at least $\pm$ 2 mm. Pulse–echo techniques with ultrasound are widely used for testing important components of engineering structures

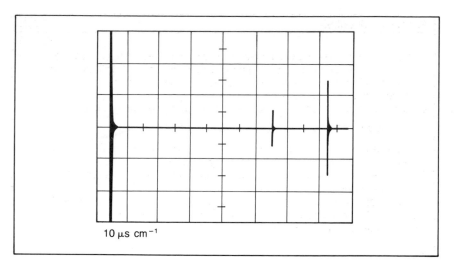

10 μs cm^{-1}

Figure 16.33 Typical screen trace for figure 16.31

USING ULTRASOUND

Ships use ultrasonic pulses to measure the distance between the hull and the seabed. The technique is very similar to that used for finding cracks in solids. A regular series of pulses is fired at the seabed from a transducer attached to the hull, and the time taken for the echo to return is used to compute the distance travelled by the pulse. The echo can even be used to return information about the nature of the sea floor. A sharp, well-defined echo comes from a rocky seabed, whereas a diffuse, spread-out pulse comes from a muddy or sandy seabed.

It is now commonplace for a pregnant woman to have an ultrasonic scan to give information about the size and well-being of the baby she is carrying. The transducer sends harmless pulses into her body, detecting the reflections off boundaries between different types of tissue. The reflections are combined with information about the angle of the transducer by a computer, so that a picture of a cross-section through her womb can be built up and displayed on a screen (figure 16.34).

Figure 16.34 Using ultrasound to check on the development of a child in its mother's womb

OBJECTIVES

After studying this section you should be able to do the following.

State the difference between a longitudinal and a transverse wave.	Understand why longitudinal waves are attenuated.
Predict the speed of longitudinal waves in solids, liquids and gases.	Explain in microscopic terms how compression waves travel through solids and gases.
Describe a method of measuring the speed of sound in solid objects.	Describe a method of measuring the wavelength of a sound wave.
Sketch graphs to show how the displacement of the medium changes with position and time as a longitudinal wave passes through it.	Understand how ultrasound can be used to detect hidden structure in solids and liquids.

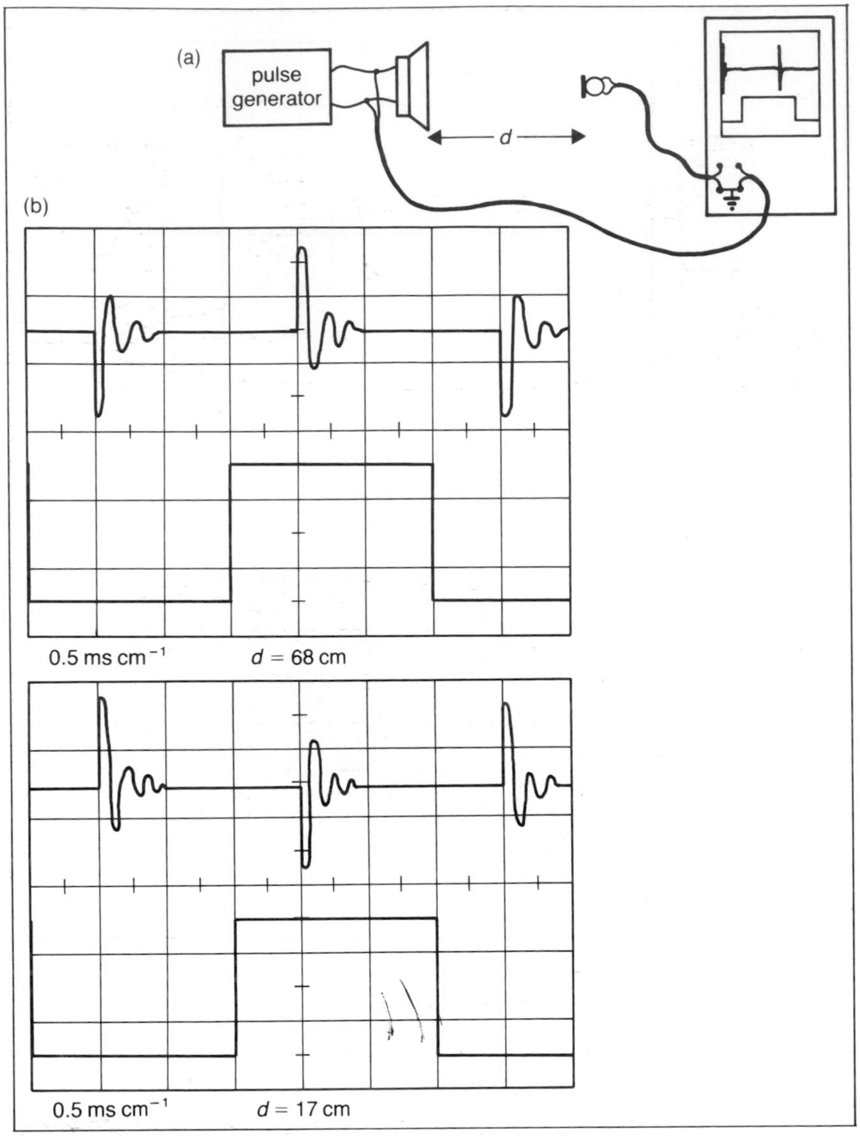

(a)

pulse
generator

d

(b)

0.5 ms cm⁻¹   d = 68 cm

0.5 ms cm⁻¹   d = 17 cm

Figure 16.35

Figure 16.36

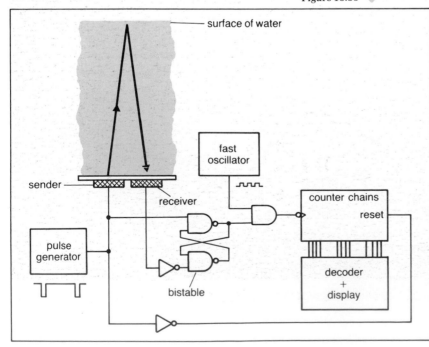

surface of water

sender

receiver

pulse
generator

fast
oscillator

counter chains

reset

decoder
+
display

bistable

QUESTIONS

1 An arrangement for measuring the speed of sound in air by a pulse–echo technique is shown in figure 16.35(a). A square wave from a pulse generator is fed into a loudspeaker: the resulting clicks are picked up by a microphone some distance from the speaker. Both signals are displayed with a double-beam oscilloscope. Typical traces are shown in figure 16.35(b) for different distances between the microphone and the loudspeaker.

a Use the data provided in figure 16.35 to calculate the velocity of sound.

b Explain the shape of the pulses received by the microphone.

c What is the frequency of the square wave used in the experiment? Show what the screen trace would look like if the frequency was changed to 250 Hz and the microphone was placed 68 cm from the loudspeaker.

2 Pulses of ultrasound can be used to measure the amount of water in a cylindrical tank. The set-up is shown in figure 16.36. A transducer at the bottom of the tank emits brief pulses of ultrasound which travel up the tank and are reflected back down to the piezoelectric pickup. The maximum height of water in the tank is 2.00 m.

a If the speed of sound in water is 1500 m s^{-1}, calculate the flight-time of pulses when the tank is full.

b The electronic system is designed to give a direct readout of the water height in centimetres on the display. Each pulse of ultrasound fed into the water sets the bistable, allowing pulses from the fast oscillator to get through to the counter. The reflected pulse resets the bistable, interrupting the flow of fast pulses. What should the frequency of the fast oscillator be?

c The transducer has a resonant frequency of 5 MHz and its oscillations die out completely after ten cycles. Yet the quartz in the transducer will ring for at least a million cycles when set into oscillation in a vacuum. Why is the transducer so heavily damped?

d Estimate the maximum precision with which the water depth could be measured with this transducer.

3 The amplitude of a compression pulse in a solid gets progressively smaller as the pulse travels. This can be represented with the formula $A = A_0\exp[-x/\delta]$, where x and δ are the distance travelled and the attenuation distance respectively. Ultrasound in steel has a velocity of $5.19 \times 10^3 \text{ m s}^{-1}$ and an attenuation distance of 0.20 m.

a How far can a pulse travel in steel before its amplitude is reduced to 1% of its original value?

b For how long does a pulse have to travel through steel before its energy is 0.1% of its original value?

c Ultrasound is commonly used to detect microscopic cracks in lengths of steel. If a reflected pulse is undetectable when its amplitude has fallen below 2% of its original value, estimate the maximum length of steel bar which could be probed with this technique.

4 Figure 16.37(a) shows the apparatus used by Suzanne in an investigation of the speed of sound in metals. Magnets have been stuck to the ends of the rod and placed in coils. The drive coil is fed alternating current from a signal generator. The pick-up coil produces an alternating voltage caused by longitudinal oscillation of the magnet in it. A double-beam oscilloscope is used to display the voltages from the signal generator and the pick-up coil, as shown in figure 16.37(b).

a Use the information given in figure 16.37 to calculate the period and frequency of the longitudinal wave in the rod.

b At very low frequencies, the two waveforms on the screen are in phase. If the length of the rod is 0.50 m, use the information in figure 16.37 to calculate the speed of the waves in the rod.

c The waveforms in figure 16.37 are $\pi/2$ out of phase. What frequency would give a waveform which was 2π out of phase?

d Suzanne hopes to be able to detect changes in the speed of the waves as the bar is heated and cooled. If the coefficient of linear expansion is 3.0×10^{-5} K^{-1}, work out the change in velocity per kelvin you would expect for her bar. (Remember, the volume will increase as the temperature increases.)

5 The amplitude of a sound wave decreases as it travels away from its source because the energy is spreading in three dimensions. This question will show you why the amplitude of a wave is proportional to the reciprocal of its distance from the source.

a A small explosion at ground level suddenly produces a sound pulse which has an energy E. A hemispherical wavefront centred on the explosion carries the energy away. What is the energy per unit area of wavefront when it is r from the source? Hence show that the amplitude $A \propto 1/r$.

b Suppose that the explosion had a sound pressure level of 110 dB when you were 10 m away from it. If the level of background noise is 50 dB, how far away can the explosion be heard? (An increase of 20 dB corresponds to a ten-fold increase in amplitude.)

c The loudest sound which can be produced in air has an amplitude of one atmosphere (10^5 Pa). The eruption of Krakatoa in 1883 probably produced such a wave. If the amplitude of sound waves in a quiet environment are about 10^{-2} Pa, over what sort of distance could such a sound be heard? Could it be heard all round the Earth?

d In reality, sound waves in air are damped. Table 16.3 shows the attenuation α of sound in air at room temperature at three frequencies.

Table 16.3

f/kHz	α/dB km^{-1}
1.0	0.16
5.0	4.00
10.0	16.00

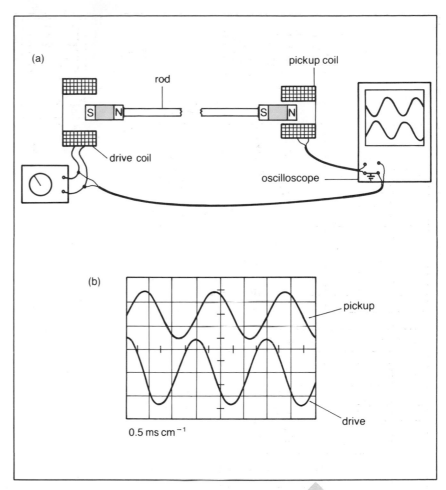

(a)

rod

pickup coil

S N

S N

drive coil

oscilloscope

(b)

pickup

drive

0.5 ms cm^{-1}

The rumble of thunder from a distant flash of lightning sounds different to the sharp crack produced by a nearby flash of lightning. Explain why — there are at least two different mechanisms involved.

Figure 16.37

Figure 16.38

Waves carry energy from one place to another. Interesting things happen to the distribution of energy if two different waves pass through the same medium. The waves can **interfere** with each other so that the energy can only go in certain directions. In particular, if a wave can interfere with itself a very special and important type of oscillation known as a standing wave can occur.

SUPERPOSITION

Figure 17.1 shows what happens when a pair of **wavetrains** in a stretched string meet each other. The waves preserve their identity when they collide, and appear to glide through each other. They emerge with their shape, amplitude and phase unchanged. This is a general property shared by all waves. When they collide, they act as if the other wave was simply not there. So the total displacement of the medium is equal to the sum of the individual displacements. This is known as the **Principle of Superposition**.

Beats

A simple experiment to demonstrate the superposition of sound waves is illustrated in figure 17.2. The frequencies of the sound waves emitted by the two loudspeakers are very slightly different. The waves are picked up by a microphone and displayed on the screen of an oscilloscope.

Constructive interference
Let's consider what happens when the two sound waves arrive at the microphone **in phase** with each other. Figure 17.3 shows how the displacement Δx changes with time for the two waves separately and then together. Each wave apparently has the same amplitude and frequency, so they can be represented as follows if we choose to set the microphone at $x = 0$:

$$\Delta x_1 = A\cos(\omega t), \quad \Delta x_2 = A\cos(\omega t) \qquad (17.1)$$

We can use the Principle of Superposition to find the total displacement when both waves arrive together at the microphone.

$$\Delta x = \Delta x_1 + \Delta x_2, \qquad \therefore \Delta x = 2A\cos(\omega t) \qquad (17.2)$$

The two waves **constructively interfere** to generate a similar wave with twice the amplitude.

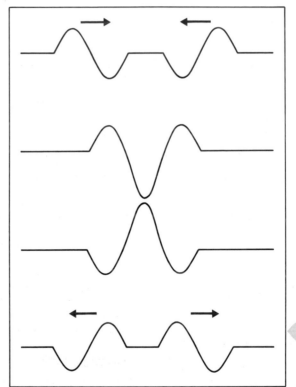

Figure 17.1 Transverse pulses in a string passing through each other

Figure 17.2 Apparatus for demonstrating beats

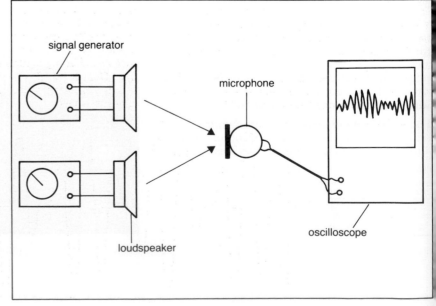

signal generator

microphone

oscilloscope

loudspeaker

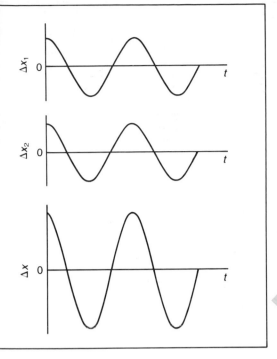

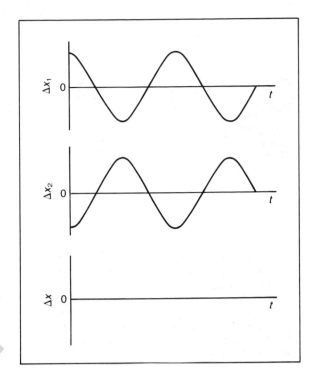

Figure 17.3 Constructive interference

Figure 17.4 Destructive interference

Destructive interference

Of course, the two waves do not have exactly the same frequency. So, after a while, they get out of step with each other. Figure 17.4 shows the situation where one wave source has produced half a cycle more than the other. The two waves are **out of phase**, with equal and opposite displacements at all times.

$$\Delta x_1 = A\cos(\omega t), \quad \Delta x_2 = -A\cos(\omega t)$$

$$\therefore \Delta x = 0 \tag{17.3}$$

The waves **destructively interfere** to give no displacement at all.

Fluctuating amplitude

Figure 17.5 shows how the total displacement changes with time: it is the signal picked up by the microphone in figure 17.2. When the two waves are combined, they alternately reinforce and cancel each other out, giving the effect of a single wave whose amplitude fluctuates regularly with time. The frequency of the amplitude fluctuations (the **beat frequency**) is equal to the difference in the frequencies of the two separate sound waves, i.e. $f_b = f_2 - f_1$.

To understand why this is so, consider the signal detected by the microphone in t seconds. The two waves will have gone through $f_1 t$ and $f_2 t$ cycles

respectively. Each time the waves are out of phase they destructively interfere with each other. This happens $f_2 t - f_1 t$ times during the t seconds, once for each time that one wave gets one more cycle ahead of the other. If we define the beat frequency f_b as the number of times the two waves destructively interfere per second, then

$$f_b = \frac{f_2 t - f_1 t}{t} \qquad \therefore f_b = f_2 - f_1 \tag{17.4}$$

Beats are widely used for tuning musical instruments so that they emit notes of the same frequency. Any difference between the notes can be detected by listening for the beats produced when the instruments are played together.

The Doppler shift

Anyone who lives by a railway line or a busy road will know about the Doppler shift. Things sound different when they move towards you or away from you. If the sound source is moving towards you, its pitch appears to be raised above its normal value. Similarly, if the sound source is moving away from you, its pitch appears to be lowered. This **Doppler shift** in frequency of the sound from a moving object is widely used to detect motion and measure speed.

Figure 17.5 The result of superposing two waves with the same amplitude but different frequency

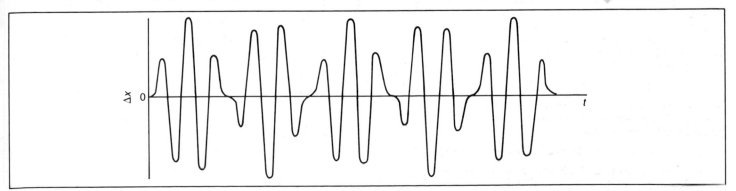

Moving source

Suppose that you stand a fixed distance from a sound source at $x = 0$, shown in figure 17.6. The source makes the air next to it move in SHM and that motion travels through the air towards you with a velocity c, arriving after a time delay of x/c. So the motion of the air around you at time t was the motion of the air near the source at time $t - x/c$. Neglecting any changes in amplitude, we can use this to write down the usual expression for the displacement of the air at position x and time t.

$$\Delta x(0,t) = \cos(\omega t)$$

$$\therefore \Delta x(x,t) = \cos(\omega t - \omega x/c) \qquad \textbf{(17.5)}$$

What happens if the source starts to move towards you with steady speed v at $t = 0$, as shown in figure 17.7? Assume that the speed of the source (v) is much smaller than the speed of the wave (c). Then the portion of the wave which passes you at time t has travelled a distance $x - vt$, giving a time delay of $t - (x - vt)/c$. The displacement at x and t is therefore given by the following expression:

$$\Delta x(x,t) = \cos(\omega(t - (x - vt)/c))$$

$$\therefore \Delta x(x,t) = \cos((\omega + \omega v/c)t - \omega x/c) \qquad \textbf{(17.6)}$$

If you concentrate on the time dependence in equation (17.6), you will see that the motion of the source has increased the angular frequency of the wave. The frequency f has been shifted upwards by Δf.

$$\omega \to \omega + \omega v/c, \quad \omega = 2\pi f \therefore \frac{\Delta f}{f} = +\frac{v}{c} \qquad \textbf{(17.7)}$$

Of course, the wave is still travelling at the same speed c — this can only be changed by altering the medium in some way. So the frequency shift is also accompanied by a wavelength shift.

$$c = f\lambda \quad \therefore 0 = \frac{\Delta f}{f} + \frac{\Delta \lambda}{\lambda} \therefore \frac{\Delta \lambda}{\lambda} = -\frac{v}{c} \qquad \textbf{(17.8)}$$

Equations (17.7) and (17.8) apply to *all* types of wave motion, including light and other electromagnetic waves. (The above argument, however, can only be used for waves whose velocity is much lower than the speed of light. Waves which travel at the speed of light only obey equation (17.7) if $v \ll c$.)

$$\frac{\Delta f}{f} = +\frac{v}{c}$$

Δf is the increase in frequency of the wave (Hz)

f is the frequency of the wave when the source does not move (Hz)

v is the speed of the source towards the observer (m s^{-1})

c is the wave velocity (m s^{-1})

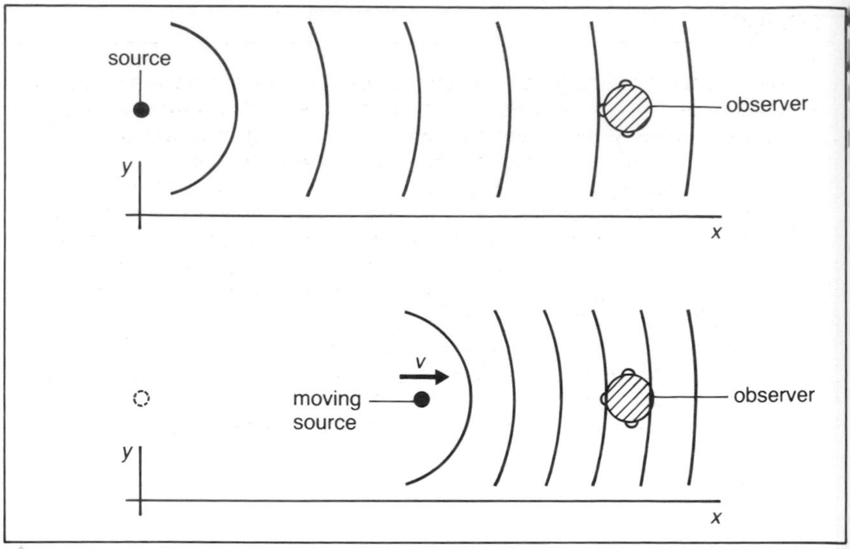

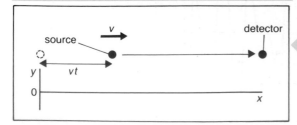

Figure 17.7 Moving source

Figure 17.8 Demonstrating the Doppler shift with the circular motion of a sound source

Figure 17.6 The wavelength decreases when the source moves towards the observer

The plus sign is included in equation (17.7) to show that v is the component of the source's velocity along the line connecting the source to the observer. So if the source is moving away from you, the frequency of the wave is shifted down instead of up.

Demonstrating Doppler shifts

You can demonstrate the existence of the Doppler shift by whirling a sound source around your head on the end of a long piece of string (figure 17.8). Suppose that you used a piezoelectric buzzer which emits a piercing note at 3.5 kHz. If it goes round twice per second on the end of a 1.0 m length of string, it will have a speed of 4π m s^{-1}. The speed of sound in air is about 340 m s^{-1}, so we can calculate the maximum frequency shift heard by the other people in the room.

$$\frac{\Delta f}{f} = \frac{v}{c} \quad \therefore \Delta f = \frac{fv}{c}$$

$$\therefore \Delta f = \frac{3500}{340} \times 4\pi = 130 \text{ Hz}$$

So the sound heard by other people will shift up and down by 130 Hz as the source alternately moves towards them and away from them. However, since the component of velocity in your direction is always zero, you will hear a constant frequency of 3.5 kHz.

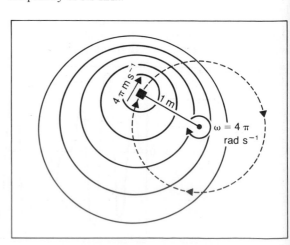

RED SHIFT

The Doppler shift of the light emitted by stars can be used to measure the speed with which they are moving towards or away from the Earth. It turns out that the further they are away, the faster they appear to be moving away from us. Although stars emit a wide range of wavelengths, there are always two wavelengths missing due to absorption by calcium ions in the gases on the star's surface. Have a look at figure 17.9. It shows the spectrum of light emitted by the sun, with wavelength increasing from one end of the photo to the other. The black portions indicate missing wavelengths. The wavelength of these **absorption lines** for a star is usually higher than in an Earth-bound laboratory, moving them nearer to the red end of the spectrum.

For example, the wavelength of one of the calcium absorption lines in the spectrum of Alpha Centauri is 396.820 nm. The same line in the Sun's spectrum has a wavelength of 396.849 nm. This can be used to calculate the speed with which Alpha Centauri is moving away from us, since $c = 3.00 \times 10^8 \text{ m s}^{-1}$.

Figure 17.9 Emission spectrum of the Sun.

$$\frac{\Delta\lambda}{\lambda} = -\frac{v}{c}$$

$$\therefore v = -\frac{c\Delta\lambda}{\lambda}$$

$$\therefore v = -\frac{3.00 \times 10^8 \times (396.849 - 396.820) \times 10^{-9}}{396.8 \times 10^{-9}}$$

$$\therefore v = -21.9 \text{ km s}^{-1}$$

Although this speed may seem alarmingly large, it is not going to make much difference to the distance between Alpha Centauri and Earth in your lifetime. At present, that distance is 4.3 light years, i.e. $4.3 \times 365 \times 24 \times 60 \times 60 \times 3 \times 10^8 = 4.1 \times 10^{16}$ m!

Moving reflector

Waves from a stationary source are Doppler shifted when they are reflected off a moving object. The frequency shift can be used to measure the speed of the object. Suppose that a detector can only receive waves from a source which bounce off a moving reflector, as shown in figure 17.10. The source S and detector D are at $x = 0$, with a barrier between them. If the reflector is at x when $t = 0$, the distance travelled by the waves at time t is $2(x - vt)$. So the time delay between waves being generated at S and arriving at D can be used to calculate the displacement at D.

$$\Delta x(0,t) = \cos(\omega(t - (2x - 2vt)/c))$$

$$\therefore \Delta x(0,t) = \cos((\omega + 2\omega v/c)t - 2\omega x/c) \qquad \textbf{(17.9)}$$

The time dependence of equation (17.9) shows that the angular frequency is shifted up by $2\omega v/c$. This is double the shift from a source moving with the same velocity as the reflector.

$$\frac{\Delta f}{f} = +\frac{2v}{c}$$

Δf is the frequency shift of the waves arriving at the detector (Hz)

f is the frequency of the waves emitted by the source (Hz)

v is the velocity of the reflector towards the detector (m s^{-1})

c is the velocity of the waves (m s^{-1})

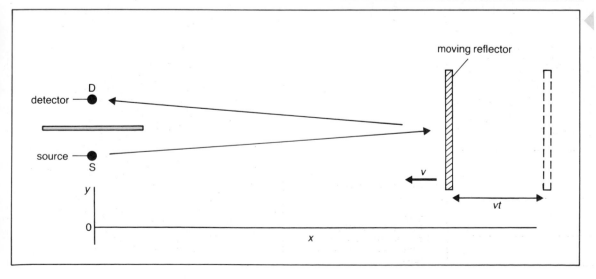

Figure 17.10 Moving reflector

RADAR SPEED MEASUREMENT

The police often use the Doppler shift of **microwaves** reflected off moving vehicles to measure their speed. Microwaves for such radar purposes have a wavelength of 3 cm and travel at the speed of light, 3×10^8 m s^{-1}. They can be produced in several ways. The emitter shown in figure 17.11 uses a Gunn diode to generate the high frequency (10^{10} Hz) alternating current needed to create the microwaves. The frequency is far too high to be measured directly, so a clever beats technique is used to detect the Doppler shift.

The arrangement is shown in figure 17.12. A small reflector in front of the source diverts some of the waves directly into the receiver. The rest of the waves go towards the vehicle. Any waves reflected from the vehicle which enter the receiver are Doppler shifted. The two waves entering the receiver produce beats because they have different frequencies. So the signal being rectified by the diode fluctuates with a frequency equal to the Doppler shift. Those fluctuations can be counted with a suitable electronic system to give the value of the beat frequency.

For example, let's work out the beat frequency for a vehicle velocity of only 10 cm s^{-1}.

$$\frac{\Delta f}{f} = \frac{2v}{c} \qquad \therefore \Delta f = \frac{2fv}{c} \qquad \therefore \Delta f = \frac{2 \times 10^{10} \times 0.1}{3 \times 10^8} \approx 7 \text{ Hz}$$

The technique is clearly quite sensitive (a car at 30 m.p.h. produces a beat frequency of about 1 kHz), but conveys no information about the direction in which the vehicle is moving.

Figure 17.11 Measuring the speed of road vehicles with microwaves

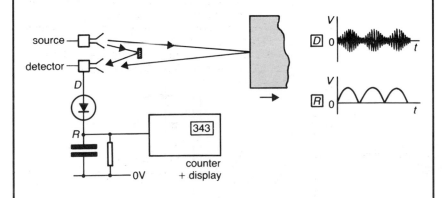

Figure 17.12 Using the Doppler shift to measure the speed of a moving object

Double sources

Interference of waves from two separate sources can be very dramatic if the sources are **coherent**. Coherent sources have a constant phase difference between them. This means that they have to produce waves with identical frequencies, usually in phase with each other. This is illustrated in figure 17.13.

Spatial interference

Coherent sources are easy to make for sound waves. For example, figure 17.14 shows two loudspeakers being driven by the same signal generator, so that they produce identical sound waves. However, the waves are not necessarily identical when they reach the microphone. The two waves have travelled different distances, so they will have different phases. If they arrive in phase, then they will constructively interfere, allowing the microphone to detect a signal. On the other hand, they could just as well arrive out of phase and destructively interfere so that the microphone detects nothing at all.

Figure 17.14 shows the microphone placed so that the waves arrive in phase. The points of maximum amplitude are shown for a particular instant of time. Clearly, one of the waves has travelled a whole wavelength more than the other. In fact, the condition for constructive interference is that the **path difference** for the waves has to be an even number of half-wavelengths. For the waves to arrive out of phase and destructively interfere, the path difference has to be an odd number of half-wavelengths. This is shown in figure 17.15.

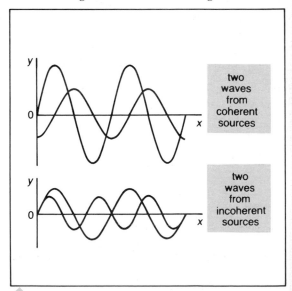

Figure 17.13 Coherence

Refering to figure 17.16 (overleaf), we can state the condition for waves from two coherent sources to constructively interfere with the following piece of algebra.

$\Delta r = n\lambda$

Δr is the path difference for the two waves (m)

n is any whole number

λ is the wavelength of the waves (m)

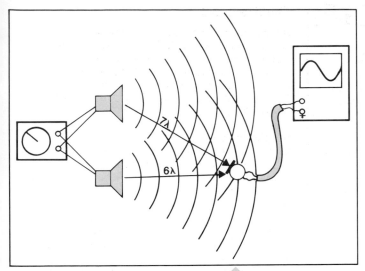

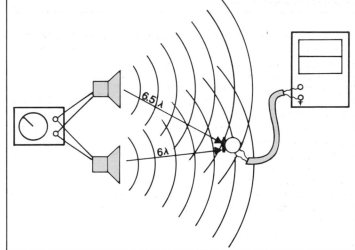

Figure 17.14 Constructive interference

Figure 17.15 Destructive interference

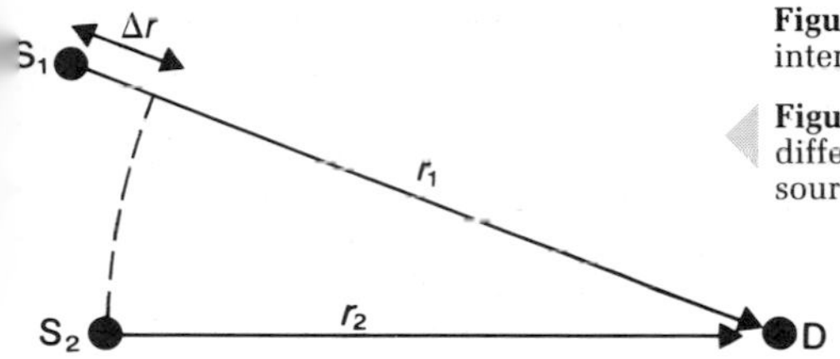

Figure 17.16 The path difference from the two sources is Δr

THE SPATIAL INTERFERENCE FORMULA !

Suppose that the distances of the detector D to the two coherent sources S_1 and S_2 are r_1 and r_2 respectively, as shown in figure 17.16. The following algebra can be used to represent the two waves which arrive at D, neglecting any amplitude differences between them.

$$\Delta x_1 = \cos(\omega t - Kr_1), \quad \Delta x_2 = \cos(\omega t - Kr_2)$$

$$\therefore \Delta x = \cos(\omega t - Kr_1) + \cos(\omega t - Kr_2) \tag{1}$$

With the help of an identity from Appendix B and the use of two new quantities r and Δr, a useful form of equation (1) can be obtained.

$$\cos A + \cos B = 2\cos(\frac{A + B}{2}) \times \cos(\frac{A - B}{2})$$

$$\frac{r_1 + r_2}{2} = r, \quad r_1 - r_2 = \Delta r$$

$$\therefore \Delta x = 2\cos K\Delta r/2 \times \cos(\omega t - Kr) \tag{2}$$

Equation (2) describes a single travelling wave $\cos(\omega t - Kr)$ whose amplitude depends on the value of $\cos K\Delta r/2$.

$$\Delta x = \pm 2\cos(\omega t - Kr) \quad \text{if} \frac{K\Delta r}{2} = \frac{n\pi}{2}, \quad n = 0, 2, 4, \text{etc.} \tag{3}$$

$$\Delta x = 0 \quad \text{if} \frac{K\Delta r}{2} = \frac{n\pi}{2}, \quad n = 1, 3, 5, \text{etc.} \tag{4}$$

Equations (3) and (4) give the conditions for constructive and destructive interference. These can be restated in terms of the wavelength.

$$K = \frac{2\pi}{\lambda}, \quad K\Delta r = n\pi \quad \therefore \frac{2\pi\Delta r}{\lambda} = n\pi$$

$$\therefore \Delta r = \frac{n\lambda}{2} \tag{5}$$

If n is odd, then equation (5) is the condition for destructive interference. On the other hand, it is the condition for constructive interference if n is even.

Energy conservation

The ability to interfere with each other is common to all waves. Interference of water waves in a ripple tank is most students' introduction to the phenomenon. The effect of having two dibbers creating identical waves with circular wavefronts is illustrated in figure 17.17. The energy injected into the water surface by the dibbers can only be extracted from the places where there is constructive interference: there is no oscillation of the surface along the lines of destructive interference.

Of course, the amplitude of the wave from each dibber dies down as it travels across the tank. So convincing destructive interference can only take place when the path difference is not too great. However, suppose that both waves do have the same amplitude A when they meet. Then the amplitude of the resultant wave for constructive and destructive interference will be $2A$ and 0 respectively. The energy of a wave is proportional to the square of its amplitude. So the energy of the resultant wave will be $4A^2$ for constructive interference. Compare this with the energy of the wave from just one of the dibbers, i.e. A^2. For interference to conserve energy, the average energy of the resultant wave must be $2A^2$. So for every portion of the wave whose energy is $4A^2$, there must be another portion whose energy is 0 to keep the average at $2A^2$.

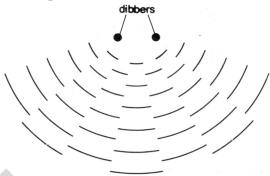

Figure 17.17 Interference pattern of water waves from two point sources

OBJECTIVES

After studying this section you should be able to do the following.

State the Principle of Superposition.

Describe and explain constructive and destructive interference.

Calculate the frequency of beats produced by two interfering waves.

Use the formula $\Delta f/f = v/c$ to calculate the Doppler shift from a moving wave source.

Use the formula $\Delta f/f = 2v/c$ to calculate the Doppler shift from a moving reflector.

Understand the meaning of *coherent sources, in phase, out of phase* and *path difference*.

Quote the conditions on the path difference for waves to constructively or destructively interfere.

Realise that the interference of waves conserves energy.

QUESTIONS

1 Sally is investigating waves travelling in opposite directions along a coiled spring. She gets Nick and Mandy to send pulses down the spring and she videos the waves as they cross in the middle. Figure 17.18 represents two frames of the video taken when the clock reads 10.0 s and 14.0 s. The ruler is 1.0 m long.

a What is the speed of the pulses?

b Sketch what the frames taken at 11 s, 12 s and 13 s should look like.

c Sally is a bit concerned about the 12 s frame. 'The waves seem to have lost all their energy. The fact that the energy reappears in the 13 s frame, implies that waves do not conserve energy.' Convince Sally that the total energy of the waves is the same in all of the frames.

2 Whenever two sinusoidal waves with the same frequency are superposed, the result is a sinusoidal wave with the same frequency. Figure 17.19 shows the displacement of a wave at various times at a fixed place. It can be represented by $y = A\cos(\omega t + \phi)$.

a What are the values of A, ω and ϕ for the wave?

b Two waves with the same amplitude and frequency but different phase arrive at the same place. Draw graphs to show what the resultant waveform looks like when the phase difference is 0, $\pi/2$, π and $3\pi/2$.

c What is the average energy of the waves you have drawn in part (b)? Is it what you would expect?

d Suppose that the waves of part (b) have different amplitudes A and B. What are the maximum and minimum amplitudes of the wave obtained after interference? Is the average amplitude of the wave compatible with energy conservation?

3 Some domestic burglar alarms use the Doppler shift of ultrasound to detect intruders. The space to be protected is flooded with ultrasonic waves of frequency 40 kHz. Waves reflected back to the detector D are combined with some waves direct from the emitter E, as shown in figure 17.20.

a The speed of sound is 340 m s^{-1}. Estimate the frequency shift of waves reflected from a stealthy burglar moving towards the detector.

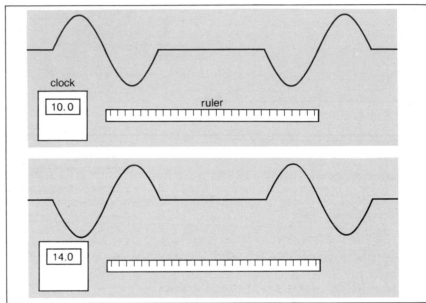

Figure 17.18

Figure 17.19

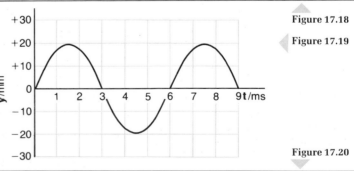

Figure 17.20

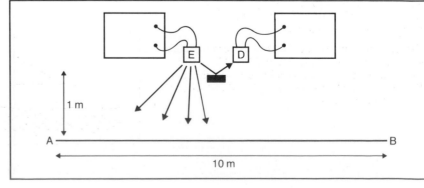

b The electronics which process the signal from the detector will trigger off the alarm if it detects beats between 5 Hz and 250 Hz. How slowly do you have to walk towards the detector for it not to notice you?

c Suppose you walked from A to B (figure 17.20) at a steady speed of 0.5 m s^{-1}. Draw a graph to show how the beat frequency at the detector would change with time. (*Remember*; Frequencies cannot be negative.)

4 Sam is worried that the Doppler shift is going to mess up the radio reception in his car. 'When the car goes towards the transmitter, the radio waves will be shifted up the tuning scale. Every time I turn a corner I'm going to have to adjust the tuning.' Set his mind at rest; Radio 1 broadcasts on the FM band at 104.8 MHz in London.

5 The Mekon is an alien who travels around the galaxy in a space craft which is painted fluorescent green; it emits light of wavelength 560 nm. Table 17.1 gives approximate wavelengths for different colours of light. The velocity of light is 3.0×10^8 m s^{-1}.

Table 17.1

Colour	λ/nm
purple	400 – 420
blue	420 – 480
cyan	480 – 520
green	520 – 580
yellow	580 – 630
red	630 – 680

a If the Mekon's spacecraft appears to be red, what can you say about its velocity? Similarly, what can you say if it appears to be blue?

b If table 17.1 covers all of the visible wavelengths, what is the minimum velocity for the spacecraft to be invisible?

c The Mekon decides to circle the Moon to flash a warning to the Earth. It chooses an orbit of radius 10^7 m, and a velocity such that the colour of the spacecraft alternates from blue to green to red as it passes between Earth and Moon on each orbit. Choose a suitable velocity. How long will the Mekon take to make one orbit? How big will the g forces be inside the spacecraft? What will the colours look like from the surface of the Moon?

6 Figure 17.21 shows an arrangement of two loudspeakers and a signal generator. A microphone can be moved along the line XY. The output of the microphone can be studied with an oscilloscope.

a The maximum amplitude sound wave is detected when the microphone is at A — it is 100 mV. Explain why it has to be at A.

b The microphone is slowly moved from A to C. The minimum amplitude detected is at B — it is 20 mV. Calculate the amplitude you would expect at B if an absorbing surface was placed in front of each loudspeaker in turn.

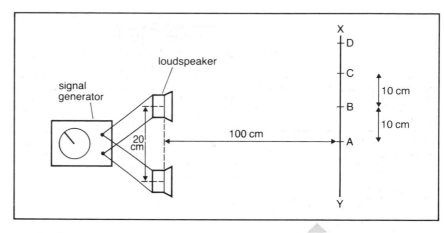

Figure 17.21

c Calculate the path difference for the waves which arrive at B — use Pythagoras' Theorem. Hence calculate the wavelength of the sound waves.

d Predict the amplitude of the signal from the microphone when it is placed at C and D in turn.

7 Figure 17.22 shows the paths followed by radio waves from the transmitter T to a receiver R. The **sky wave** reflects off the ionosphere, a layer of ionised gas high up in the atmosphere. It makes an efficient reflector for radio waves on the Medium Wave band ($\approx$ 1MHz). Furthermore, the ionosphere moves towards the Earth at night when the atmosphere is cooling down. Destructive interference between the sky wave and the **ground wave** can lead to weak signals at the receiver.

a Suppose that the receiver is 180 km from the transmitter and is tuned to 1.0 MHz. The ionosphere is about 90 km above the Earth's surface. If the signal at the receiver is a maximum at a particular instant, how far down must the ionosphere move for the signal to become a minimum?

b If the signal at the receiver fades to almost zero once every 15 minutes during the early evening, how fast is the ionosphere moving down?

c Katrina has found a new way of solving part (b). 'The sky wave is Doppler shifted when it bounces off the ionosphere. The sky wave and ground wave then produce beats at the receiver.' Spiros is sceptical. 'How can you explain one thing in two such different ways?' Which one of them is right? A calculation will seal the argument.

Figure 17.22

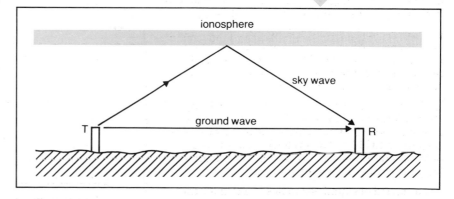

REFLECTING WAVES

Consider a wave travelling through a medium. Any sudden change in the properties of the medium is going to alter the flow of energy through it. The wave will be wholly or partially **reflected**, so that its direction is changed. If the reflected wave travels back through the incident wave, then there is the possibility that a **standing wave** will occur and the whole medium will be set into oscillation.

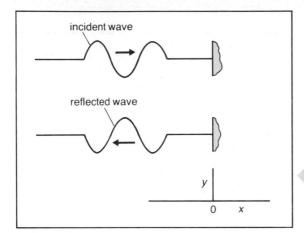

Reflections in one dimension

Waves in strings or rods can only travel in one dimension. So when they reach the end of the medium, any reflection will alter the sign of their velocity. It could also change the other parameters, such as amplitude and frequency. However, it is easily demonstrated with sound waves that reflection does not alter their pitch. (Think about it: if every reflection increased the frequency of a sound wave, what would a concert in a large hall sound like?) Furthermore, if the reflecting surface cannot absorb any wave energy, the amplitude has to remain constant. So the only other parameter that a reflection can change is the phase. The phase change caused by reflection is crucial to the establishment of standing waves, the main theme of this section.

Closed ends

Suppose that a wavetrain reflects off the end of a stretched string as shown in figure 17.23. The incident and reflected waves can be represented by the usual expression for a progressive wave.

$$y_i = I\cos(\omega t - Kx), \quad y_r = R\cos(\omega t + Kx) \quad \textbf{(17.10)}$$

We want to find the relationship between the amplitudes I and R of the incident and reflected waves. If we place the fixed end of the string at $x = 0$, we get a simple expression for the total displacement there.

$$y = y_i + y_r \quad \therefore y = I\cos(\omega t) + R\cos(\omega t) \quad \textbf{(17.11)}$$

Because the string has to be stretched, its end cannot move: its displacement has to be zero at all times. This can only be true if $I = -R$, equivalent to a phase change of π.

$$I\cos(\omega t + \pi) = I\cos(\omega t)\cos\pi - I\sin(\omega t)\sin\pi$$
$$\sin\pi = 0, \quad \cos\pi = -1$$
$$\therefore I\cos(\omega t + \pi) = -I\cos(\omega t) \quad \textbf{(17.12)}$$

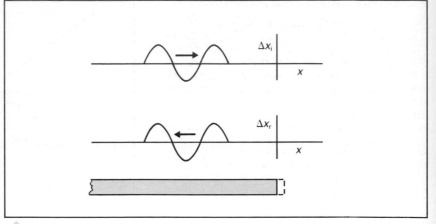

Figure 17.23 The phase change of a transverse wave reflecting from the end of a stretched string

Figure 17.24 There is no phase change when a longitudinal pulse reflects from the unrestrained end of a bar

Figure 17.25 Reflecting a sound wave from the closed end of a tube

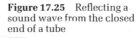

This phase change is easily demonstrated with a long length of stretched rubber tubing. The phase change of π caused by the reflection turns the incident pulse upside down when it reflects.

Open ends

The end of a stretched string has to be fixed, otherwise it is impossible to maintain the tension in it. However, the end of a bar carrying a longitudinal wave can be free to move. This means that the phase change caused by reflection does not have to be π.

Figure 17.24 represents a longitudinal wave in a bar travelling towards the end. If the bar is suspended in a vacuum, then there is no mechanism by which movement of its end can extract energy from the wave. (There is nothing for the bar to push against.) So the amplitude of the reflected and incident waves must be the same as one another.

$$\Delta x_i = I\cos(\omega t - Kx), \Delta x_r = R\cos(\omega t + Kx) \quad \textbf{(17.13)}$$

If we place the end of the bar at $x = 0$, we can show that if there is no phase change on reflection the end moves in SHM.

$$\Delta x = \Delta x_i + \Delta x_r, \quad \therefore \Delta x = I\cos(\omega t) + R\cos(\omega t)$$
$$\therefore \Delta x = 2I\cos(\omega t) \text{ if } I = R \quad \textbf{(17.14)}$$

Of course, the end of a medium carrying a longitudinal wave may not be free to move. For example, the air at the end of the tube in figure 17.25 cannot be displaced in the x-direction. So sound waves which are reflected off the end of the tube suffer a phase change of π.

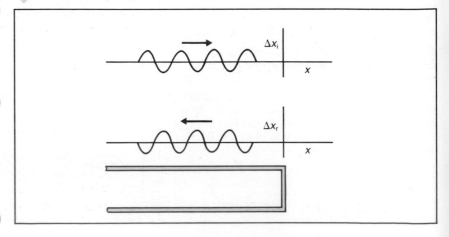

Reflections in two dimensions

Everybody knows that light waves reflect off a shiny surface like a ball bounces off a wall (figure 17.26). Careful experiments with mirrors and strips of light from lamps can show that the angle of incidence *i* always has the same value as the angle of reflection *r*. But do *all* waves obey the same rule?

Direct evidence

Figure 17.27 shows how reflections of sound waves in two dimensions can be studied. The tube in front of the microphone limits the direction of the sound waves which it can detect. The tube is moved around until a maximum amplitude of sound is detected by the microphone — this occurs when the tube is orientated as shown in figure 17.27. Similar experiments can be performed with microwaves, with the same result. This suggests that the velocity of the wave parallel to the reflecting surface remains unchanged by the reflection, but its velocity perpendicular to the surface is reversed. (Think of a ball bouncing off a wall.) It is standard practice to measure the directions of the flow of energy in the incident and reflected waves relative to the **normal**. As you can see from figure 17.26, the normal is a line which is perpendicular to the reflecting surface.

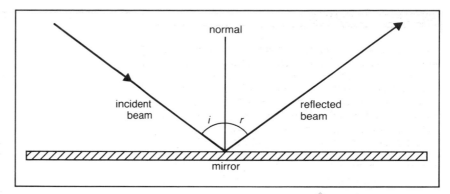

Figure 17.26 Reflecting a light beam from a mirror

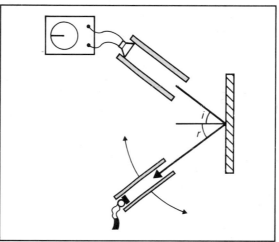

Figure 17.27 Apparatus for demonstrating the reflection of sound waves

Reflecting wavefronts

A ripple tank can be used to study the reflection of single wavefronts from a flat surface. The sequence of figure 17.28 illustrates what happens as a short wavetrain bounces off the reflector. An interesting feature of figure 17.28 is how the wavelength of the wavetrain is preserved during the reflection. This is exactly what you might expect. After all, the frequency of a wave is fixed by its source and its velocity is fixed by the medium, so the reflector cannot change the wavelength. It should be clear from figure 17.29 that the wavelength is not preserved if *i* ≠ *r*.

Standing waves in strings

Standing waves happen when a wave is reflected in such a way that it can constructively interfere with itself. Many useful devices rely on standing waves for their operation: they include guitars, flutes, lasers and digital watches. Standing waves are also a considerable threat to engineering structures.

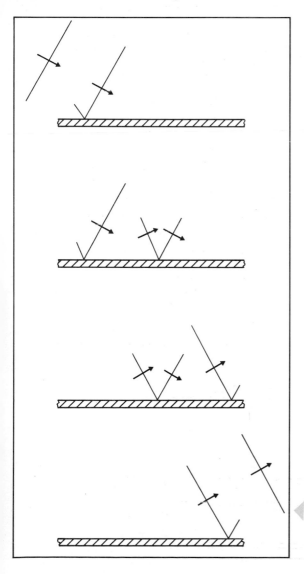

Figure 17.28 The wavelength remains unchanged if *i* = *r*

Figure 17.29 The effect on λ if *i* ≠ *r*

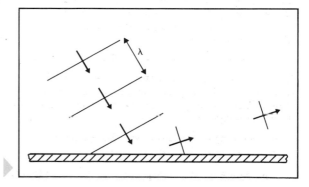

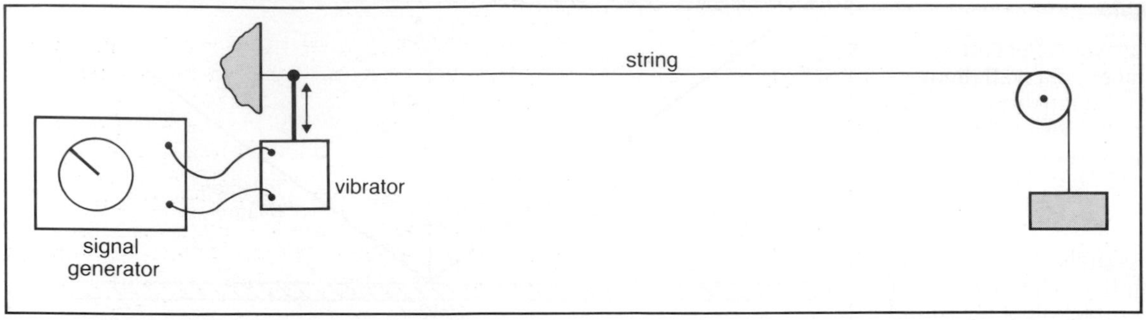

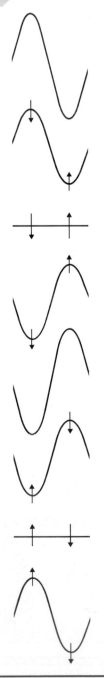

Figure 17.30 Apparatus for exploring standing waves in a stretched string

CONDITIONS FOR STANDING WAVES

The relationship between the frequencies needed to set up standing waves in the string is strikingly simple. We are going to show you how it arises.

Suppose that we have a string stretched from $x = 0$ to $x = l$. Transverse waves of angular frequency ω are injected into the string and travel both ways with a speed c, reflecting off the ends with a phase change of π. The following expression can be used to model the waves in the string:

$$y(x,t) = A\cos(\omega t - Kx) - A\cos(\omega t + Kx) \tag{1}$$

Of course, if equation (1) is a good description of the waves then it has to give zero displacement at both ends of the string. Let's check this at $x = 0$ first:

$$y(0,t) = A\cos(\omega t) - A\cos(\omega t) \qquad \therefore y(0,t) = 0 \tag{2}$$

What about at $x = l$?

$$y(l,t) = A\cos(\omega t - Kl) - A\cos(\omega t + Kl) \tag{3}$$

Equation (3) can be moulded into a more useful shape with the help of a trigonometrical identity from Appendix B.

$$\cos A - \cos B = -2\sin\left(\frac{A + B}{2}\right)\sin\left(\frac{A - B}{2}\right)$$

$$\therefore y(l,t) = -2A\sin(\omega t)\sin(Kl)$$

$$\therefore y(l,t) = 0 \text{ if } \sin(Kl) = 0 \tag{4}$$

So we can only have waves travelling both ways down a string with fixed ends if $\sin(Kl) = 0$.

$$K = 2\pi/\lambda, \quad \sin(n\pi) = 0, \quad \sin(Kl) = 0$$

$$\therefore n\pi = Kl \quad \therefore n\pi = \frac{2\pi l}{\lambda}$$

$$\therefore \frac{n\lambda}{2} = l \tag{5}$$

The rule linking the frequencies of the various harmonics is now obvious.

$$c = f\lambda, \qquad \frac{n\lambda}{2} = l \qquad \therefore \frac{nc}{2f_n} = l \qquad \therefore f_n = \frac{nc}{2l}$$

$$\therefore f_n = nf_1, \quad \text{where } f_1 = c/2l \tag{6}$$

We can also account for the shapes of the different standing waves in strings.

$$y(x,t) = A\cos(\omega t - Kx) - A\cos(\omega t + Kx)$$

$$\cos A - \cos B = -2\sin\left(\frac{A + B}{2}\right)\sin\left(\frac{A - B}{2}\right)$$

$$\therefore y(x,t) = -2A\sin(Kx)\sin(\omega t) \tag{7}$$

Each point on the string moves in SHM (displacement proportional to $\sin(\omega t)$) with an amplitude given by $2A\sin(Kx)$. The displacement at various times for the second harmonic is shown in figure 17.32.

Figure 17.32 Various stages in the displacement of a string which carries a standing wave

Figure 17.31 Different standing waves in the same length of string

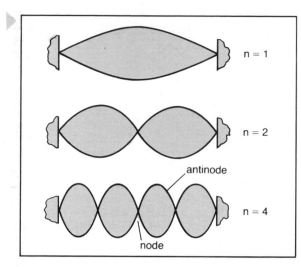

ENERGY IN STANDING WAVES !

The energy stored in the standing wave can be calculated as follows. Consider a portion of length Δx. Its amplitude will be $2A \sin(Kx)$ (see previous box), so its maximum velocity will be $2A \sin(Kx)\omega$ (remember SHM?).

$$E_k = \tfrac{1}{2}mv^2 \qquad \therefore \Delta E = \tfrac{1}{2} \times \mu \Delta x \times (2A\sin(Kx)\omega)^2 \qquad (1)$$

Equation (1) gives us the energy stored in part of the string as a consequence of its SHM. The total energy stored is obtained by summation over its whole length.

$$E = \Sigma \Delta E \qquad \therefore E = 2\mu A^2 \omega^2 \times \Sigma(\sin^2 Kx \Delta x) \qquad (2)$$

The summation in equation (2) is the area under the curves in figure 17.33. It is clearly just $\tfrac{1}{2}l$.

$$E = \mu A^2 \omega^2 l \qquad (3)$$

So the energy stored in a standing wave is proportional to the square of its frequency. The energy, of course, comes from the object which sets up the standing wave, i.e. the vibrator. Each cycle of its motion pumps more energy into the standing wave. However, the damping of the oscillations in the string increases with amplitude, so it will only grow until the rate of damping is equal to the power of the vibrator.

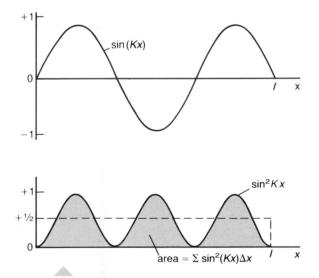

Figure 17.33 The average value of $\sin^2 Kx$ is $\tfrac{1}{2}$

Standing waves

The string in figure 17.30 is stretched between two supports and transverse waves are injected near one end by a vibrator connected to a signal generator. In general, nothing dramatic happens when the signal generator is turned on. The vibrator moves up and down, making part of the string move in SHM, but the amplitude of any transverse waves moving along the string is pretty small. However, if the frequency of the vibrations is altered, you can set up one of the spectacular patterns shown in figure 17.31. At particular frequencies, almost the whole string appears to oscillate in large amplitude SHM, with a few places (the **nodes**) not moving at all. This pattern of oscillation is called a **standing wave** because there is no apparent flow of energy along the string.

The frequency needed to set up the standing wave which has only one point of maximum amplitude oscillation (an **antinode**) is called the **fundamental frequency** or **first harmonic** f_1. The frequencies needed to set up the other standing waves are integral multiples of the fundamental frequency.

$$f_n = nf_1$$

f_n is the frequency of the nth harmonic (Hz)

f_1 is the frequency of the first harmonic (Hz)

You can only have a standing wave in a string if a whole number of half-wavelengths fit into its length. No other wavelengths are possible.

$$\frac{n\lambda}{2} = l$$

n is the number of the harmonic

λ is the wavelength of transverse waves in the string (m)

l is the length of the string (m)

Stringed instruments

A wide range of musical instruments use standing waves in strings to create sounds; they range from the piano to the sitar, from the violin to the double bass. For example, consider the guitar shown in figure 17.34. Each string is set into oscillation by plucking it (pulling it to one side and letting go), feeding energy into waves whose half-wavelengths fit exactly into the length of the string. Therefore, waves with frequencies that are whole-number multiples of the string's fundamental frequency travel up and down it, ultimately generating longitudinal waves in the surrounding air.

Figure 17.34 An acoustic guitar

The **quality** of the note produced by an instrument is dictated by the relative amplitudes of the various harmonics in the string. Figure 17.35 shows the signals picked up by a microphone from a number of musical instruments. The higher frequency harmonics die away rapidly, so that the fundamental frequency is generally the one with the largest amplitude. (The rate at which a string is damped is proportional to the square of its frequency.) However, certain harmonics can be preferentially excited by plucking the string at one of its antinodes.

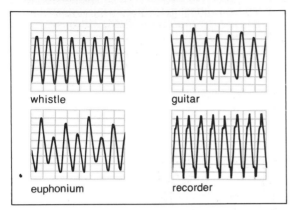

whistle guitar

euphonium recorder

The **pitch** of the note is usually dominated by the fundamental frequency. This is varied for a guitar string by placing a finger on one of the frets: this point acts as one end of the string. The shorter the string, the higher its fundamental frequency will be. Heavy strings are used for the lower notes and lighter strings for the higher notes. In this way, six strings can cover a wide range of octaves. Pianos and harpsichords use a different string for each note. The length and mass of the strings are varied to obtain the different notes required: each string is tuned by adjusting its tension. Like guitars, the strings are given energy in bursts by hitting them with hammers or plucking them with quills. Violins, on the other hand, are continuously fed energy by drawing a bow across the strings. The bow material is rough, so its motion across the string gives it a series of small shocks, setting it into oscillation.

All stringed instruments need some form of **sounding board** to amplify the sound. The vibrating string on its own cannot produce large amplitude sound waves because it is so thin. So its vibrations are coupled to a flat sheet, forcing it to oscillate at the same frequency as the string. The large area of the sheet can set a large body of air moving, increasing the volume of the sound. It is important, of course, that the sounding board does not have lightly damped modes of oscillation which could be set off by the vibrating string.

Standing waves in sheets

Transverse waves can travel across flat sheets, so standing waves can be set up in them when the conditions are right. For example, figure 17.36 shows a standing wave in a strip of steel caused by a vibrator. The ends of the strip are not constrained, so they are antinodes rather than nodes. However, the centre has to be near a node because it is fastened to the vibrator and is therefore constrained to have a near-zero displacement at all times.

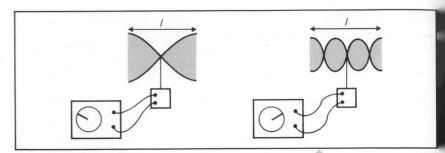

Figure 17.36 Standing waves in a steel strip

Resonance conditions

Since the distance between nodes of a standing wave is $\lambda/2$, the distance from node to antinode must be $\lambda/4$. We can use this to predict the relative frequencies (f_1 and f_3) of the two standing waves shown in figure 17.36.

$$\frac{2\lambda_1}{4} = l, \quad c = f\lambda \qquad \therefore f_1 = \frac{c}{2l}$$

$$\frac{6\lambda_3}{4} = l \qquad\qquad \therefore f_3 = \frac{3c}{2l}$$

$$\therefore f_3 = 3f_1 \qquad\qquad \textbf{(17.15)}$$

Clearly, only the odd numbered harmonics are going to occur. The speed c of the waves in the strip is going to depend on its mass and its stiffness, so the value of the fundamental frequency f_1 will depend on the length, stiffness and mass of the strip.

Tuning forks

Tuning forks are widely used in the music industry as secondary frequency standards. Not only are they robust and portable, they have no batteries to go flat. As you can see from figure 17.37, a tuning fork is basically two steel strips which vibrate in antiphase. Each prong vibrates with a node at its base and an antinode at its free end. When the vibration of the prongs squeezes the air between them, it also stretches the air on the other side of them. So a tuning fork behaves like three sound sources, one of which is out of phase with the other two. (You can check this for yourself by rotating a tuning fork close to your ear — the sound should die away to nothing four times per revolution.) The coupling between the strips and the surrounding air is weak, so a tuning fork is normally lightly damped. If you increase the coupling by holding the base of the fork on a solid surface, the note dies away much more quickly.

Figure 17.35 Microphone signals from a variety of musical instruments: the traces were recorded by a data logger and displayed with a computer

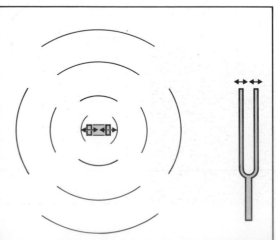
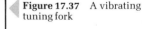

Figure 17.37 A vibrating tuning fork

Resonance in sheets

The oscillation of a strip can be observed by looking at it from the side. This is not feasible for a flat sheet, especially when different parts oscillate out of phase with each other (figure 17.38). The standard laboratory technique for finding the nodes in standing waves on flat sheets is illustrated in figure 17.39. The sheet is horizontal and covered in a thin layer of a fine powder — pollen was frequently used in the past, but any fine powder will do. When standing waves are set up in the sheet, the powder is joggled at random along the surface until it gets to a node. Since there is no displacement at a node, the powder stays there. In figure 17.39 the sheet is being set into oscillation by a vibrator attached to its centre.

Longitudinal standing waves

The existence of longitudinal standing waves is easily demonstrated. Look at figure 17.41. Each time the 1.00 m steel rod is tapped with the hammer it rings, emitting a note whose loudness dies away in a few seconds. (The microphone and oscilloscope can be used to measure the frequency of that note.)

Figure 17.41 shows how the displacement of the rod changes with time after it has been tapped. Remember, the displacement is *along* the length of the rod since we are dealing with longitudinal waves.) The centre of the rod is firmly clamped, so only modes of oscillation which have nodes at that point will be undamped. The ends of the bar have to be antinodes as there is no phase change when the wave is reflected from them. So two quarter-wavelengths fit into the length of the bar when it is set oscillating. We can use this to predict the frequency of the sound wave produced by the oscillating ends of the bar, knowing that $c = 5190$ m s^{-1} for steel.

$$2 \times \frac{\lambda}{4} = 1.00, \quad c = f\lambda \quad \therefore f = \frac{c}{\lambda}$$

$$\therefore f = \frac{5190}{2.00} = 2.60 \text{ kHz}$$

Figure 17.38 A standing wave in a flat sheet!

The shapes taken up by the powder on a vibrating sheet are known as Chladni figures. A number of them are shown in figure 17.40. Each one represents a possible **mode** of oscillation of the sheet. Knowledge of the various modes of oscillation of flat sheets is very important for engineers. Should the sheet be subjected to a vibration whose frequency corresponds to one of the modes, then a standing wave will build up. At best, this will just make a lot of noise. At worst, the structure will vibrate itself to pieces. These resonances can be avoided in two ways. First, by stiffening the sheet with bars so that the standing wave has to have its nodes at those places. Provided that the stiffening is correctly placed on the sheet, it can damp out modes whose frequencies match those of periodic forces which are likely to occur. Secondly, the resonances can be avoided by preventing the generation of periodic forces in the first place. Therefore, wherever shafts and wheels are rotated in machinery, it is important that their centre of mass lies on their axis of rotation. This 'balancing' of spinning parts of machinery is necessary to stop destructive vibration occuring.

Figure 17.40 Chladni figures

Figure 17.39 Apparatus for demonstrating standing waves in sheets

Figure 17.41 Demonstrating standing waves in a rod

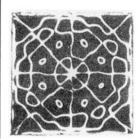

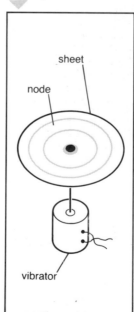

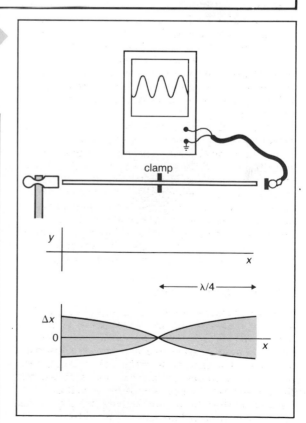

Air columns

Similar standing waves can also be set up in columns of air. Figure 17.42 shows how it can be done. A small loudspeaker at one end of a transparent tube sends longitudinal waves down it. Those waves are partially reflected from the far end of the tube and head back towards the loudspeaker. (The reflection involves no phase change as the air at the open end is unconstrained.) If the waves which reflect off the loudspeaker are in phase with its motion, then a standing wave will build up inside the tube. The volume of the sound coming from the open end of the tube will grow dramatically, and the dust on the bottom of the tube will be joggled around until it settles in piles at the nodes.

Figure 17.42 shows some possible $\Delta x - x$ curves for the standing waves in the tube. In general, the wave has to have an antinode at the open ends of the tube, so an even number of quarter-wavelengths have to fit into the length of the tube. However, as far as the sound waves are concerned, the tube appears to be slightly longer than it really is. This **end correction** is about half the radius of the tube, but decreases as frequency increases. To obtain the best coupling of sound waves into the tube, the loudspeaker of figure 17.42 needs to be placed near an antinode.

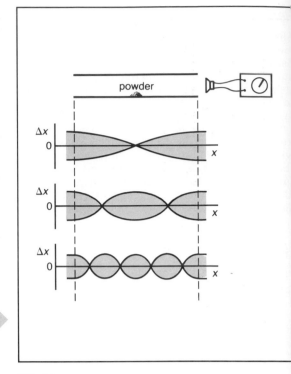

Figure 17.42 Standing waves in the air inside an open-ended tube

Figure 17.43 A wind instrument

Wind instruments

There is a wide variety of wind instruments which use standing waves in tubes to generate musical sounds: one of them is shown in figure 17.43. In general, they have one closed end and one open end, with some arrangement of holes or stops to encourage particular standing waves in the tube. The rapid increase in diameter at the open end of the tube in some instruments improves the coupling with the open air: these instruments (such as trumpets and saxophones) can make a lot of noise, compared with others (such as flutes) which have poor coupling.

The simplest wind instrument, from a physics point of view, is an organ pipe. As you can see from figure 17.44, it is a tube with one open end and one closed end, so that standing waves of the type shown can be set up in it. The gap at the bottom of the tube means that it is effectively open at that end. (Notice the node at the closed end where the reflection involves a phase change of π.) Vortex shedding of air blown through the bottom of the tube past the edge (figure 17.44) sets the air vibrating. Standing waves which can fit an odd number of quarter-wavelengths in the tube can build up, giving rise to a sound wave of large amplitude. If the effective length of the tube is l, then we can predict the mixture of frequencies in the sound.

$$(2n + 1)\frac{\lambda}{4} = l, \quad c = f\lambda, \quad \therefore f = (2n + 1)\frac{c}{4l}$$

$$\therefore f = f_1, 3f_1, 5f_1 ..., \quad f_1 = c/4l \qquad \textbf{(17.16)}$$

An open pipe (figure 17.45) will support a different range of frequencies. You can convince yourself that it will produce all the harmonics, not just the odd ones which the closed pipe produces. It is the mixture of harmonics which tends to make a musical note interesting: organ pipes with open and closed ends sound very different even when they have the same fundamental frequency.

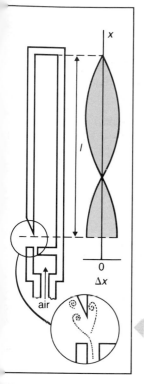

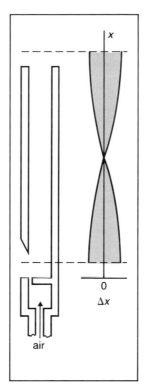

Figure 17.44   A closed organ pipe

Figure 17.45   An open organ pipe

After studying this section you should be able to do the following.

State the phase change suffered by a wave when it is reflected from the end of the medium.

State the law governing the reflection of waves in two dimensions.

Explain why standing waves are only set up in a medium at particular frequencies.

Understand the meaning of *node*, *antinode*, *fundamental* and *harmonic*.

Use the formula $n\lambda/2 = l$ to predict the frequencies of standing waves in strings.

Describe how standing waves in strings are used in certain musical instruments.

Describe a method of detecting standing waves in sheets.

Use the rule that the distance from node to antinode is $\lambda/4$.

Describe how standing waves in air columns are used in certain musical instruments.

QUESTIONS

1 A student uses the apparatus shown in figure 17.46 to measure the wavelength of some microwaves. He moves the detector away from the emitter, moving parallel to the reflector and 12.0 cm from it until he finds a place where there is complete destructive interference. This is 12.0 cm from the emitter.

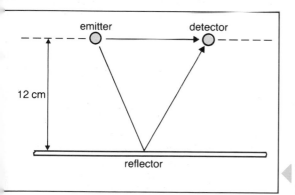

Figure 17.46

Figure 17.47

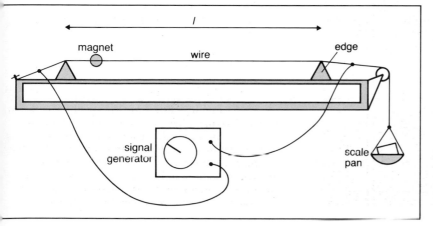

a Calculate the path difference for the two waves which arrive at the detector. Use it to state two possible values for the wavelength of the microwaves. (The reflector changes the phase of the reflected wave by π.)

b He now moves the detector away from the emitter by 6.0 cm so that the signal is a minimum once more, keeping 12.0 cm away from the reflector. Calculate the wavelength of the microwaves.

2 The apparatus shown in figure 17.47 is known as a **sonometer** — your school may have one. A wire is stretched between two edges and kept in tension T by weights placed in the scale pan. An alternating current of frequency f is maintained in the wire by a signal generator — the current interacts with the magnet to give a vertical periodic force on the wire. The length l of the wire between the edges can be varied until standing waves occur.

a Obtain an expression for the frequencies f at which standing waves can occur in terms of c and l. Hence write down an expression for f in terms of T, l and μ.

b Suppose that you arrange for the fundamental standing wave to be set up in the wire. State how you have to adjust the frequency of the signal generator to keep the wire vibrating that way if you
  (i) only halve the length of the wire,
  (ii) only halve the weights in the scale pan,
  (iii) double both the weights in the scale pan and the length of the wire.

c It is a fact that the amplitude of the standing waves in the wire decreases as the number of nodes they have is increased, even though the power injected by the oscillator remains the same. Suggest why this is so.

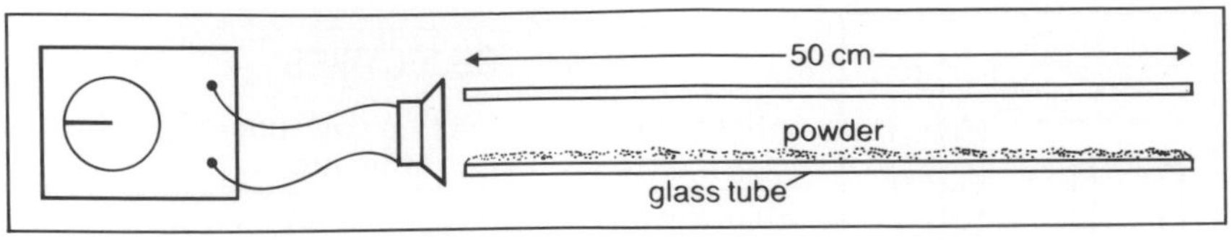

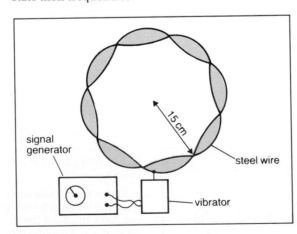

Figure 17.48

3 Table 17.2 gives the frequencies of the white notes of a piano in the octave starting at middle C.

Table 17.2

Note	Frequency/Hz
C	261.6
D	293.7
E	329.6
F	349.2
G	392.0
A	440.0
B	493.9

Suppose that you want to get this full range of notes from one string of a guitar. Estimate the length of the string, its mass and tension so that you can calculate exactly where to place the frets. You may prefer to present your answer in the form of a diagram.

4 Joanne wants to demonstrate standing waves in air to the rest of the class with the apparatus shown in figure 17.48. Suggest three different sound frequencies which will set up visible standing waves in the tube. For each frequency, sketch what you would expect to see.

5 Standing waves in a ring are very spectacular. The apparatus shown in figure 17.49 can be used to demonstrate them (the frequency of the signal generator can be varied).

a The standing wave shown in figure 17.49 occurs when the frequency of the vibrator is 200 Hz. Calculate the speed of transverse waves in the ring.

b Draw the first three harmonics of the ring and state their frequencies.

Figure 17.49

Figure 17.50

c Suppose that the ring is replaced with another made of the same material but with twice the diameter. What effect will this have on the value of the fundamental frequency; would it increase, decrease or stay the same? Explain your answer.

6 Richard is using the apparatus shown in figure 17.50 to explore the standing waves in lengths of rubber. He changes the tension by stretching the rubber over the pulley. For each value of the tension he finds the frequency needed for the vibrator to set the rubber oscillating in its fundamental mode. His results are shown in table 17.3.

Table 17.3

Tension/N	Frequency/Hz
20	61
40	94
60	122
80	150
100	177

a Richard expects the tension to be proportional to the square of the frequency. Why ? Draw a graph of the square of the frequency against the tension to show that his results do not fit this pattern.

b Explain why they do not fit the pattern.

c Suppose that Richard uses a thin rubber tubing which has an unstretched length of 50 cm, a force constant of 250 N m^{-1} and mass of 50 g. Tell him the vibrator frequency required to set up the third harmonic standing wave in a 40 cm length of the tubing when its tension is 50 N.

7 It is well known that deep-sea divers who breathe an oxygen/helium mixture instead of the normal oxygen/nitrogen mixture have squeaky voices. Table 17.4 gives the molar masses of the three gases: both mixtures have about 21% oxygen by volume.

Table 17.4

Gas	Molar mass/kg mol^{-1}	γ
oxygen	0.032	1.4
nitrogen	0.028	1.4
helium	0.004	1.7

a Estimate the speed of sound waves in both mixtures at room temperature and pressure.

b Your ears detect the frequencies present in a sound wave without relying on standing waves in the atmosphere. Your larynx however, produces sounds with particular wavelengths by setting up standing waves in your throat and mouth. Use this information to explain why a helium/oxygen mixture makes your voice sound funny. Estimate the frequency shift caused by breathing such a mixture.

c A classical symphony orchestra is largely made up of wind instruments and stringed instruments. Ideally, these are always adjusted so that they are in tune. In practice, the two classes of instruments drift out of tune as the concert hall warms up. Estimate the shift of concert A (440 Hz) for each 10°C rise in temperature for each class of instrument. Is the shift positive or negative?

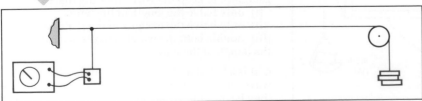

SUMMARY
WAVES AND OSCILLATIONS

If an object is slightly displaced from static equilibrium its potential well is parabolic: $E_p = \frac{1}{2}kx^2$. The restoring force is proportional to the displacement $(F = -kx)$, leading to an acceleration which is proportional to the displacement: $a = -(k/m)x$. In the absence of damping the following equations describe the subsequent motion (SHM) of the object when it is released:

$$x = A\cos\omega t, v = -A\omega\sin\omega t, \omega = (k/m)^{\frac{1}{2}}$$

The period of oscillation of the object is independent of its amplitude. For a mass on a spring $T = 2\pi(m/k)^{\frac{1}{2}}$. For a pendulum $T = 2\pi(l/g)^{\frac{1}{2}}$.

The energy of an oscillating object is given by $E = \frac{1}{2}kA^2$. Friction and radiation of waves can rob the system of energy, usually damping down the oscillations in an exponential manner.

If an oscillator is set into motion by an external periodic force, the amplitude of oscillation is a maximum when the frequency of the applied force matches the object's natural frequency of oscillation. The effect of such resonances depends on the amount of damping present. The amplitude increases until the power of the driving force is equal to the rate of energy loss through damping.

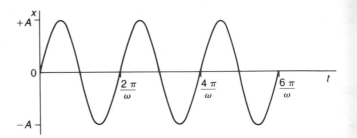

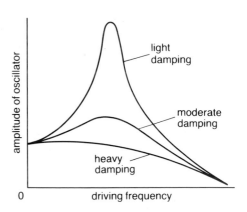

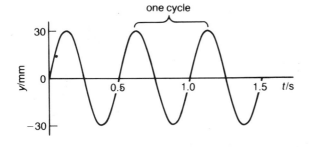

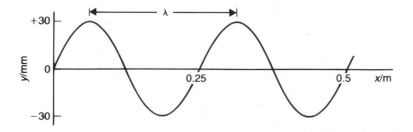

The displacement of a transverse wave travelling along the x-axis can be represented by the equation $y(x,t) = A\cos(\omega t - Kx)$ where $\omega = 2\pi f$ and $K = 2\pi/\lambda$. The amplitude A is the maximum displacement of the medium as the wave passes through it. The frequency f is the rate at which places of maximum displacement on the wave pass a point. The wavelength λ is the distance between adjacent points of maximum displacement. A longitudinal wave is represented by the equation $\Delta x(x,t) = A\cos(\omega t - Kx)$.

The speed of a wave through an ideal medium is independent of its amplitude or wavelength: $c = f\lambda$. For transverse waves in strings $c = (T/\mu)^{\frac{1}{2}}$. For longitudinal waves in solids $c = (E/\rho)^{\frac{1}{2}}$. The speed of sound in a gas is given by $c = (\gamma P/\rho)^{\frac{1}{2}}$.

When waves are superposed, the resultant displacement of the medium at a point is the sum of the displacements of the individual waves at that point. If two identical waves are in phase they can constructively interfere to give a wave with twice the amplitude. Destructive interference occurs when the two waves are out of phase, resulting in complete cancellation.

The energy of a wave is proportional to the square of its amplitude. As a wavefront spreads out from its source, the energy is shared over a progressively increasing area. So, in the absence of damping, the intensity (power per unit area) of a wave is inversely proportional to the square of the distance from the source.

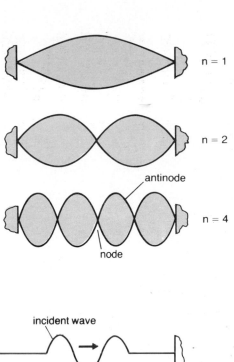

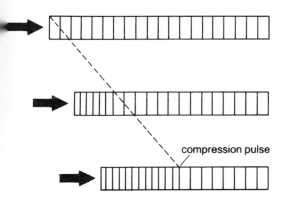

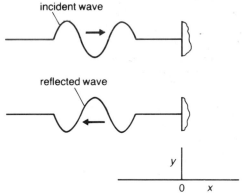

The superposition of two waves with different frequencies results in beats: $f_b = f_1 - f_2$. The motion of a wave source results in a Doppler shift of the wave's frequency: $\Delta f/f = \pm v/c$. For a moving reflector $\Delta f/f = \pm 2v/c$.

For two waves to produce an interference pattern they have to be coherent, i.e. have a constant phase difference. For constructive interference the path difference must be a whole number of wavelengths: $\Delta r = n\lambda$. For destructive interference $\Delta r = (n + \frac{1}{2})\lambda$.

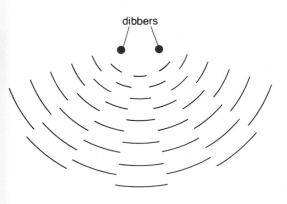

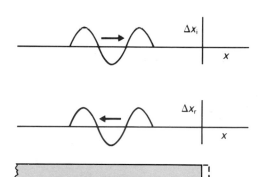

When a wave is reflected from a place where the medium's displacement has to be zero, it has a phase change of π, equivalent to a path difference of $\frac{1}{2}\lambda$. A transverse wave which interferes with its own reflection can set up a standing wave if it has the right wavelength: $n\lambda/2 = l$. Nodes of a standing wave occur where the medium has zero displacement. Longitudinal waves can set up standing waves in tubes: open ends correspond to antinodes of displacement, with the distance between antinode and node being $\lambda/4$.

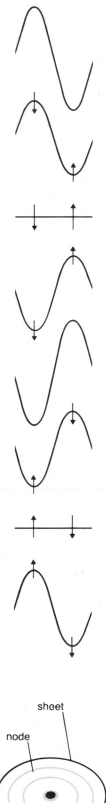

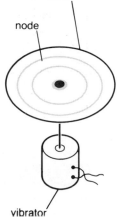

FIELD

AND POTENTIAL

18
E L E C T R I C
F I E L D

There are very few models in physics which work all of the time. The atom model of matter is no exception. This chapter is going to show you how that model can be adapted to explain the electrical behaviour of matter. Not only will you find out more about electrons and ions, but you will also find out how the concepts of electric field and potential can be used to model the interactions between them.

ELECTRIC FORCES

You will recall from chapter 10 that electricity can be explained by supposing that metals contain large numbers of small particles (electrons) which are free to move around within them. Each electron carries a charge of -1.6×10^{-19} C, and its movement through the metal carries energy from one place to another. But why does the electron move in the first place? The answer has to do with **electrostatic forces**.

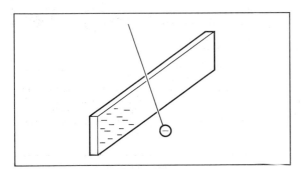

Charge

Everybody knows that static electricity is made by rubbing insulators against each other. For example, a balloon will stick to a wall or a ceiling if it is briskly rubbed against someone's clean hair or pullover. It is *not* obvious that the effects of static electricity and current electricity are caused by the same basic mechanism, i.e. the attraction and repulsion of charged particles. The following experiment clearly demonstrates the link between the two.

Negative charge

The light plastic sphere in figure 18.1 is coated with a thin layer of metal and suspended from a nylon thread. A 5 kV power supply is connected to a pair of small metal balls, some distance apart.

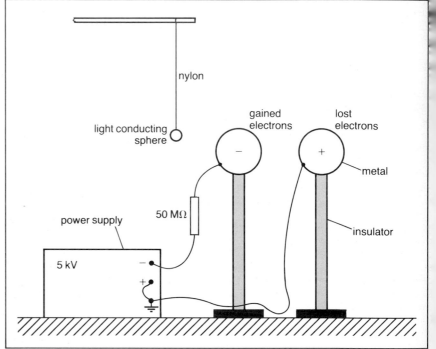

Figure 18.1 Apparatus for demonstrating that charged objects can attract and repel each other

Figure 18.2 Charged insulators can repel the charged sphere

These two conductors are separated by an insulator (the air), so they must behave like a capacitor. As soon as the power pack is switched on there is a brief current in the 50 MΩ safety resistor as electrons flow onto one ball and off the other. (The resistor limits the current in anybody who is rash enough to touch the balls to a safe 100 µA.) The sphere is brought up to the ball at −5000 V and is attracted towards it. However, if the sphere is allowed to touch the ball it is repelled from it quite dramatically. The conclusion is obvious. The sphere has picked up some electrons from the ball, so the experiment shows that electrons repel each other.

Now suppose that the sphere, with its extra electrons, is taken near to a strip of dry polythene which has been briskly rubbed with a cloth (figure 18.2). (You can check that this has given the strip static electricity by seeing if it can pick up small bits of paper.) The sphere is repelled from the polythene. Clearly, rubbing the polythene has given it some extra electrons, just as the metal ball was given extra electrons by the power supply. Somehow, the polythene strip becomes **negatively charged** when rubbed with a duster.

Positive charge

A similar experiment can be performed to demonstrate the existence of positively charged materials. The arrangement is shown in figure 18.3. This time, the minus terminal of the power supply has been earthed so that one of the balls is raised to +5000 V when electrons are pulled off it. The sphere moves away from that ball once they have touched, so two conductors which have lost electrons repel each other. Furthermore, the sphere will now repel a dry strip of perspex which has been briskly rubbed with a cloth. Rubbing the perspex with a cloth must remove electrons from it: objects which have had electrons removed from them are said to be **positively charged**.

It is easily shown that things which are oppositely charged are attracted to each other. For example, a sphere which is negatively charged with the arrangement of figure 18.1 will be attracted to a positively charged perspex strip. So an object with surplus electrons is always attracted to an object which has lost some electrons.

Atomic structure

Every atom of a metallic element has to contain at least one electron. This has to be the case, otherwise metals could not conduct electricity. The fact that electric current is a conserved quantity in a circuit suggests that the free electrons in a metal behave like an incompressible fluid. This would certainly be the case if electrons repelled each other strongly. On the other hand, the free electrons are only free to roam around *inside* the metal, so there must also be a force holding them close to the atoms.

We can account for this with the following model of atomic structure. Each atom is made up of three different particles whose properties are summarised in table 18.1. (Not all of them are relevant to explaining electrostatic forces, but they have been included for completeness. Evidence for the various numbers in the table will be presented in later chapters.)

Table 18.1

Particle	Diameter/m	Mass/kg	Charge/C
electron	$\leqslant 10^{-15}$	9.1×10^{-31}	-1.6×10^{-19}
proton	$\simeq 10^{-15}$	1.7×10^{-27}	$+1.6 \times 10^{-19}$
neutron	$\simeq 10^{-15}$	1.7×10^{-27}	0

►► 29

ELECTRON BEHAVIOUR

You may be somewhat concerned that most of the space in an atom is taken up by a number of particles which appear to have no size at all and virtually no mass. After all, there is a lot of evidence that atoms have diameters of about 10^{-10} m and masses equivalent to a few dozen neutrons and protons. So how can atoms behave like hard spheres when they bump into other atoms if they are mostly empty space? The answer is *not* that the electrons orbit around the nucleus like the planets orbit around the sun.

Particles as small and light as electrons have their own inimitable behaviour which is totally foreign to anything which you have ever experienced. The precision with which you can measure their position or follow their trajectory gets worse as you give them energy. Any electron which moves towards the nucleus under the influence of the electric force is going to gain kinetic energy, making it harder to determine exactly what it is doing. It turns out that electrons which are within 10^{-10} m of a proton can only have their position measured to within 10^{-10} m. The best model you can adopt at this stage is to assume that you are equally likely to find an electron *anywhere* within the atom. You may not like this idea, but it is fairly close to the hugely successful model for atoms offered by quantum mechanics!

We also have to say something about the forces between the particles. Since we have only two charged particles, they can be paired off in three different ways as shown in figure 18.4. The sign of the **electric force** is repulsive if the two particles have the same charge as each other, but is attractive if the particles have different charges. However, the magnitude of the electric force is the same for any pairing of the charged particles, provided they are the same distance apart. The **strong force** causes the neutrons to be attracted to the protons, but to completely ignore the electrons. Since neutrons have zero charge they are not affected by electric forces.

The arrangement of these particles in an atom is illustrated in figure 18.5. The **protons** and **neutrons** are grouped together to form a small **nucleus** at the centre, and the electrons take up the rest of the space. All of the positive charge and nearly all of the mass of the atom is concentrated in its centre, surrounded by the negative charge symmetrically disposed through the rest of the atom. Once the number of electrons matches the number of protons, the whole atom is neutral.

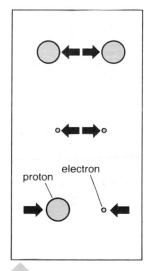

Figure 18.4 Particles with the same charge repel each other; particles with opposite charge attract each other

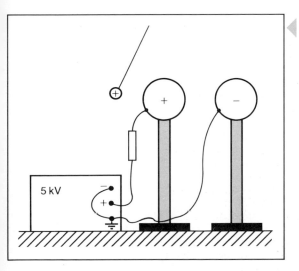

Figure 18.3 Giving the light conducting sphere positive charge

Figure 18.5 A possible arrangement of neutrons, protons and electrons in a single atom of lithium

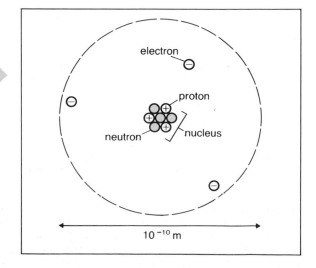

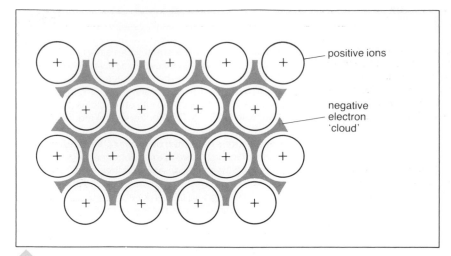

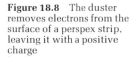

Figure 18.6 A metal can be modelled as a number of positive ions bound together by the mobile electrons which surround them

Figure 18.7 Giving a polythene strip negative charge by letting it pull electrons from the surface of a duster

Figure 18.8 The duster removes electrons from the surface of a perspex strip, leaving it with a positive charge

Figure 18.9 Variation of resistivity with temperature for typical metals and semiconductors

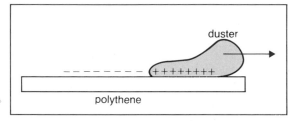

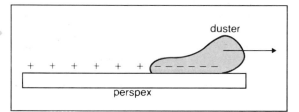

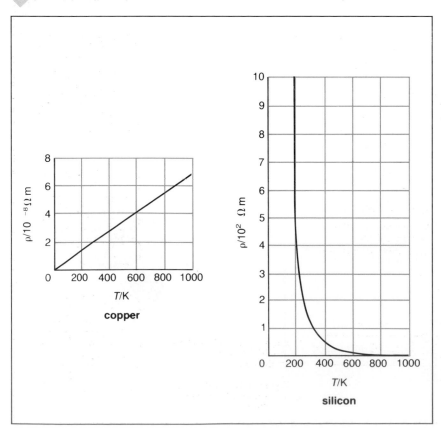

Friction charging

Figure 18.6 reminds you of the structure of metals. Each atom loses an electron to become a **positive ion** — the overall charge of the metal is zero, but the negative charge of the free electrons is able to move around between the ions. Clearly, insulators are made of atoms which do not lose electrons in this fashion when they are bound to each other in a solid. Insulators contain plenty of electrons, but they cannot escape from inside the atoms or move around freely between them.

When a polythene strip is rubbed violently with a woollen cloth, electrons in the cloth can be knocked out of their atoms and carried away on the surface of the polythene (figure 18.7). Since polythene is an insulator, the electrons have no choice but to stay put, giving the strip an overall negative charge. Of course, for every electron left behind on the polythene, there is a positive ion on the cloth — this **friction charging** always generates two objects with equal and opposite charges.

Electrons are obviously more strongly bound to their atoms in polythene than in wool. Since perspex becomes positively charged when rubbed with wool, its electrons are clearly less tightly bound: they get carried away by the cloth, leaving the perspex with a layer of positive ions on its surface (figure 18.8). Provided that there is no moisture on the surface of the perspex which could give a conducting path for electrons to neutralise those positive ions, the perspex should stay positively charged.

Semiconductors

About 70% of the hundred or so known elements are metals. Most of the rest are non-metals, i.e. do not contain free electrons when packed together to make solids. The metals and non-metals are grouped together at opposite ends of the periodic table of elements – a group of about five elements along the boundary are **semiconductors**. They have some free electrons when packed together, but nothing like one per atom which is the norm for metals. Furthermore, the number of free electrons rises dramatically with temperature, lowering the resistivity of the semiconductor. The graphs of figure 18.9 contrast the temperature dependence of resistivity for typical semiconductors and metals.

INTRINSIC CONDUCTION

The behaviour of pure semiconductors can be modelled by assuming that an atom with a free electron in a semiconductor has an energy ϵ more than an atom with a bound electron. The atoms in a solid are continually moving as they exchange heat energy between them: the energy of a particular atom fluctuates from one moment to the next as it gains and loses energy from its neighbours. The number of atoms which have an energy E when the solid has a temperature T can be predicted with the help of the Boltzmann formula.

$$n(E) = A\exp[-E/kT] \qquad (1)$$

Suppose that each atom needs an energy ϵ to shake an electron free. If only a few of the atoms have enough energy to do this, then we can write down an expression for the number of free electrons n as a function of the number of atoms N.

$$n = N\exp[-\epsilon/kT] \qquad (2)$$

(This function is plotted in figure 18.10: notice how rapidly it rises with temperature.) Doubling the number of charge carriers in a resistor halves its resistance. So the resistance of a semiconductor should be proportional to $1/n$, i.e. $\exp[\epsilon/kT]$.

$$R = R_0\exp[\epsilon/kT] \qquad (3)$$

Light-dependent resistors are made from semiconducting material, usually cadmium sulphide. The energy gap ϵ is somewhat larger than in thermistors, so that thermal fluctuations at room temperature produce very few free electrons. However, light energy absorbed by the semiconductor can give the atoms enough energy to free an electron. Of course, once an electron has been freed it will drift around inside the solid, leaving behind a fixed positive ion. Eventually, the electron will encounter another positive ion and will usually combine with it to form a neutral atom once more. So there is a dynamic equilibrium within the semiconductor, with free electrons being continuously liberated and absorbed. The number of free electrons at any one time is roughly proportional to the intensity ($W\,m^{-2}$) of the light on its surface.

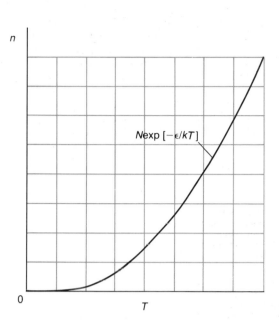

Figure 18.10 How the number of mobile charge carriers in a semiconductor is predicted to rise with temperature

HOLES !

If a p.d. is maintained across a semiconductor, the free electrons will drift from low potential to high potential. This allows them to convert electrical energy into kinetic energy. Of course, for each free electron, there is a fixed positive ion somewhere. Figure 18.11 shows how an electron in a neighbouring atom can move across to the ion, neutralising it. This is likely to happen when the atom and ion hit each other because the electron moves closer to the high potential end of the material. The electron **tunnels** through the potential barrier between the hole and the atom. The net effect is a transfer of positive charge from high potential to low potential. The sites of positive charge in a semiconductor are called **holes**. They behave in many respects like positive electrons, drifting through the material in the direction a positive charge carrier would take (figure 8.12). So the movement of charge through a semiconductor has two components: an electron flow and a hole flow in opposite directions. In general, the hole current is smaller than the electron current — although there is always the same number of holes and electrons, the holes find it more difficult to move. Of course, the two currents do not cancel each other out: even though the charge carriers responsible for them flow in *opposite* directions, the currents are in the *same* direction.

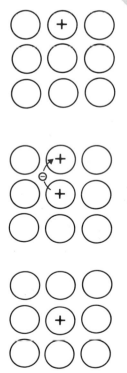

Figure 18.11 How a hole can drift through a semiconductor

Figure 18.12 Holes and electrons drift in opposite directions

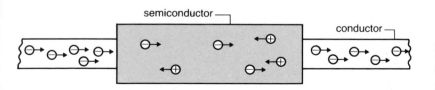

Extrinsic conduction

Semiconductors are rarely used in a pure state because their resistance varies so rapidly with temperature. They are usually **doped** to increase the number of charge carriers and hence reduce the temperature dependence. For example, suppose that a sample of otherwise pure silicon contains a few phosphorous atoms scattered within it, as shown in figure 18.13. Both types of atom have similar sizes, so the phosphorous atoms fit neatly into the crystal lattice. However, very little energy is needed to pull an electron out of the phosphorous when it is in such a lattice, so at room temperature the semiconductor contains one free electron and one fixed hole for every phosphorous atom. The silicon becomes an **n-type semiconductor**, with most of its charge carriers being negative. Figure 18.14 shows how a **p-type semiconductor** can be created by doping silicon with boron atoms. Each boron atom grabs an electron from one of its neighbouring silicon atoms, creating a hole. That hole can then migrate freely throughout the solid via tunnelling of electrons from neighbouring silicon atoms. So p-type semiconductors effectively contain equal numbers of mobile positive charge carriers (holes) and fixed negative charges (boron ions).

Plasmas

Any material can be made to conduct electricity, provided that you can get its temperature up high enough. It is simply a matter of giving it enough heat energy for its atoms to stand a good chance of shaking free an electron. Thus insulators can often be converted into conductors by heating them. For example, the apparatus shown in figure 18.15 can be used to demonstrate that glass can conduct electricity when it gets red hot. The current should be proportional to $\exp[-\epsilon/kT]$, rising strongly as the temperature increases (ϵ is the energy needed to extract an electron from the atoms). The bulb provides the combined function of current indicator and current limiter.

Many insulators become gases before their atoms have enough thermal energy to shake free an electron. A gas which is at a high enough temperature for most of its atoms to be ionised is called a **plasma**. The electric current in a plasma is due to the flow of the positive ions and negative free electrons in opposite directions. Plasmas of inert gases are widely used to obtain the high temperatures needed to weld metals to each other, as shown in figure 18.16.

Figure 18.13 n–type semiconductor

Figure 18.14 p–type semiconductor

OBJECTIVES

After studying this section you should be able to do the following.

State how the direction of the electrical force between charged objects depends on their charge.

Know that charges are either positive or negative.

Describe a model of the atom in terms of protons, neutrons and electrons.

State the relative charges, masses and dimensions of protons, neutrons and electrons.

Explain how objects become charged by friction.

State and explain the temperature variation of resistance of a semiconductor.

Know that the current in a semiconductor is due to a flow of holes and electrons.

Describe a plasma.

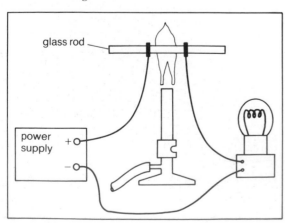

Figure 18.15 Demonstrating that glass is a semiconductor

Figure 18.16 A plasma welding torch. A high temperature argon plasma is produced in the torch and blown onto the metal surfaces to be welded. The inert gas ensures that the metal is not oxidised as it melts, giving a clean weld

QUESTIONS

1 The apparatus shown in figure 18.17 is often used to convince students that static and current electricity are different aspects of the same thing. The galvanometer shows the current in the circuit; the 50 MΩ resistor is included for safety reasons. The ball is a light expanded-polystyrene sphere which is coated with aluminium. It is hung exactly halfway between the plates.

a What are the voltages of the two plates when the power pack is switched on? If they act as a 10 pF capacitor, what is the charge on each plate after switching on?

b Initially, the ball does nothing. The teacher pushes the nylon thread so that the ball touches the negative plate. Immediately, the ball proceeds to move rapidly back and forth between the plates. Explain these observations.

c Sketch a graph to show how you think the displacement of the ball varies with time. Underneath, and to the same time scale, sketch how you think the current at X and Y changes with time.

d The galvanometer shows the average current in the circuit. State and explain what you think will happen to its reading if
(i) only the separation of the plates is doubled,
(ii) only the voltage of the power pack is doubled,
(iii) only the mass of the ball is doubled.

2 Describe how you would set about determining the type of charge which builds up on an LP when it is rubbed with a duster.

3 A thin piece of aluminium foil is glued to a dry glass rod as shown in figure 18.18. When a charged polythene strip is lowered towards the foil on the glass, its ends splay out. There is no direct contact between the strip and the foil.

a Carefully explain why the ends of the foil are repelling each other.

b State and explain what happens when the strip is removed.

c State and explain what happens when a charged perspex strip is lowered towards the foil.

4 Water films are usually blamed as the culprit when static electricity experiments fail to work. This question will help you to see why.

a The resistivity of pure water at room temperature is about 3×10^7 Ω m. Suppose that a polythene rod of length 20 cm and radius 0.5 cm was covered in a film of water a hundred molecules deep, i.e. about 10 nm thick. What is the resistance to a current down the length of the rod?

b The maximum charge which can be placed on one end of the rod by friction is about −4 nC, lowering its potential to about −15 kV. If the other end is earthed, estimate how long it will take for the charge to leak down the rod via the water film.

c In practice, the film is unlikely to be just pure water. If it has been handled by human beings, it is likely that the rod will be covered in a thin layer of sweat which has a resistivity of about 10 Ω m. How long would it take a ten molecule thickness of sweat all over the rod to discharge it?

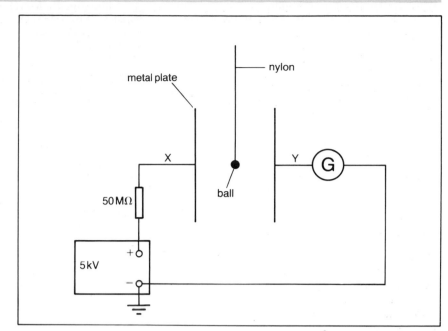

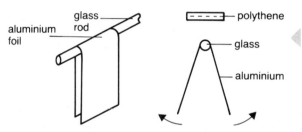

5 Krista scatters some very small pieces of thin aluminium foil over the surface of the bench. When she holds a strip of charged polythene over them, the foil pieces are attracted towards the polythene and stick to it. She reckons that this has something to do with the free electrons in the metal foil, but is puzzled as to why the foil is not repelled from the polythene once they have touched. Explain why you think the foil behaves the way it does.

6 The number of free electrons in an LDR (light-dependent resistor) is supposed to be proportional to the rate at which light energy hits its surface. An LDR is made part of a circuit as shown in figure 18.19 and the current I is measured for several values of r, the distance of the LDR surface from the centre of a filament lamp.

a Explain why you would expect the current to be inversely proportional to the square of the distance between the LDR and the lamp.

Figure 18.17

Figure 18.18

Figure 18.19

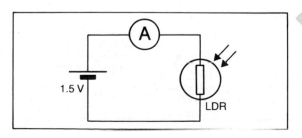

b By drawing a suitable graph, see if the data in table 18.2 agrees with this prediction. Can you explain any discrepancies?

Table 18.2

I/mA	r/cm
145	4.0
68	6.0
40	8.0
28	10.0
21	12.0
15	14.0
14	16.0
11	20.0

7 A **junction diode** is shown in figure 18.20. It consists of two slabs of semiconductor pushed together, one of which is p-type, the other n-type. This question should give you some idea of how such a diode can **rectify** signals.

a State the charge of the principal charge carrier in each half of the diode. Also state the sign of the fixed charges in each half.

b Suppose that the cathode is held at a higher potential than the anode. Explain why the current in the diode is only short-lived.

c Now suppose that the anode is held at a higher potential than the cathode. Explain why there can now be a current in the diode — think carefully about what happens at the metal ends.

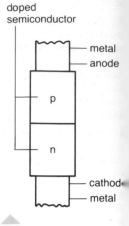

Figure 18.20

FIELDS

The electric force between charged objects is an example of action-at-a-distance. Somehow, the objects are able to sense each other's presence without touching. There are a number of ways of modelling this type of interaction, none of which are entirely satisfactory.

Force fields

Consider the interaction between a small charged sphere and a large charged strip, as shown in figure 18.21(a). Both are positively charged. The sphere experiences a force F which pushes it away from the strip. Each positive ion on the sphere which is missing an electron will have force on it: F will be the sum of those forces. So it seems reasonable to assume that the value of F will be proportional to the charge q on the sphere, provided that any change of q does not alter the distribution of charge on the strip.

$$F \propto q \quad \therefore F = Eq \qquad (18.1)$$

The constant of proportionality E in equation (18.1) is called the **electric field strength**. Its value will be a function of the charge distribution on the strip and how far away it is from the sphere.

Strictly speaking, equation (18.1) is only valid if the presence of q does not alter the distribution of charge which is responsible for the field. In practice, this is usually no problem: real applications often involve small charged particles moving through fields generated by large charged plates or tubes.

> $\mathbf{F} = q\mathbf{E}$
>
> $\mathbf{F}$ is the force on the charged particle (N)
>
> q is the charge of the particle (C)
>
> $\mathbf{E}$ is the electric field strength at the particle (N C^{-1})

Measuring field strength
One method of measuring the field strength near a charged object is shown in figure 18.21. It is not very precise, but useful nevertheless. The light conducting sphere has a mass of 0.10 g and is

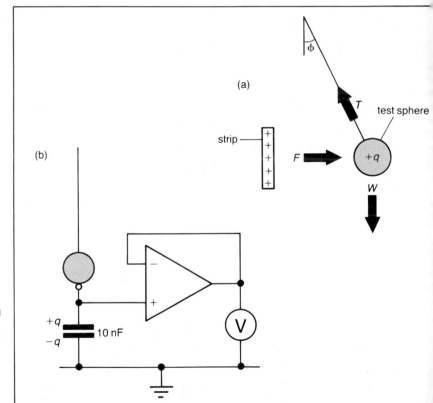

charged up to +5000 V by letting it touch the plus terminal of a power pack, as shown in figure 18.3. It is then brought near to the charged object (figure 18.21(a)). The deflection of the nylon thread ϕ can be used to estimate the horizontal force on the sphere.

$$F = T\sin\phi, \quad W = T\cos\phi, \qquad W = mg$$

$$\therefore F = mg\tan\phi \qquad \therefore F \simeq mg\phi \qquad (18.2)$$

Let's suppose that the deflection is 10°. It has to be converted into radians before it can be plugged into equation (18.2).

$$\phi = 10 \times \frac{2\pi}{360} \simeq 0.17 \text{ rad}$$

$$\therefore F = 10^{-4} \times 9.8 \times 0.17 = 1.7 \times 10^{-4} \text{ N}$$

Figure 18.21 (a) Using a test charge to measure the electric field strength at a point near a charged strip. (b) Measuring the size of the test charge

he charge q on the sphere can be measured with a
oulomb meter as shown in figure 18.21(b). When
1e sphere is discharged onto the top plate of the
.01 μF capacitor, the voltmeter reads 0.4 V.

$$C = \frac{Q}{V} \quad \therefore Q = CV$$

$$\therefore q = 0.01 \times 10^{-6} \times 0.4 = 4 \times 10^{-9} \, C$$

Ve now have all we need to estimate the field
trength near the charged strip.

$$F = qE \qquad \therefore E = \frac{F}{q}$$

$$\therefore E = \frac{1.7 \times 10^{-4}}{4 \times 10^{-9}} \simeq 4 \times 10^4 \, N \, C^{-1}$$

ield lines

lectric fields are **vector fields**. Figure 18.22 shows
he strength and direction of the field around a
harged sphere: at each location we have to specify
oth the size and direction of **E**. This can be very
umbersome, so an alternative, but less precise,
epresentation is useful. Look at figure 18.23. Each
ield line has an arrow on it, showing the direction
f the electric field at all the points the line goes
hrough. The size of the field at a point can be
udged by looking at the spacing of the lines
iearby: the closer the lines are drawn, the stronger
he size of the field. Since the universe appears to
ie neutral, every isolated positive charge has an
ssociated negative charge somewhere, so field
ines start on positive charges and end on negative
:harges.

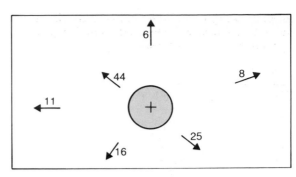

Figure 18.22 A poor
representation of the
electric field around a
charged sphere

Figure 18.23 Using field
lines to represent an electric
field

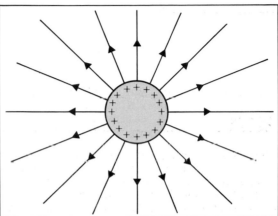

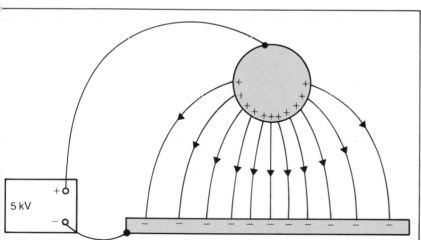

Figure 18.24 The electric
field between a sphere and a
flat plate

Figure 18.25 Motion of
small charged particles in
the field of figure 18.24

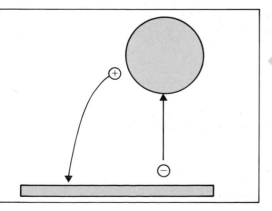

An example of field lines in action is shown in
figure 18.24. A metal sphere and plate are
connected to the terminals of the power supply, so
that the sphere becomes positively charged and the
plate becomes negatively charged. If the sphere
were not there, we would expect the negative
charge on the plate to be spread evenly over both its
surfaces because of the mutual repulsion of
electrons. The positive charge on the sphere will
distort the distribution of electrons on the plate,
pulling them onto the top surface and slightly
increasing the charge density at its centre.
Similarly, the symmetrical distribution of positive
charge on the sphere is distorted by the presence of
the negative charge on the plate.

Having established the charge distribution, we
can draw in the field lines, each one starting on a
positive charge and ending on a negative charge.
Each field line must approach a conducting surface
at right angles to it. Any component of the field
parallel to the surface will exert a force on all the
free electrons in it, redistributing the charge around
that part of the surface. The only stable
arrangement of charge is the one which gives an
electric field perpendicular to the surface.

The field line diagram can be used to work out
the path followed by charged specks which are
placed in the field. Two examples are shown in
figure 18.25. We are assuming the presence of air,
so that the specks are subject to friction. This
means that they reach a slow terminal velocity
when the electric force tugs on them. In each case
the specks drift along the field lines, but in
opposite directions: the arrow on a field line shows
the direction of the force on a positive charge
placed in the field. The force on the specks is
greatest at the sphere surface because the field lines
are closest together there. So the positive speck
drifts quickly to start with, slowing down later on
as it approaches the plate.

Energy fields

Field lines are useful because they allow us to visualise an electric field, but are useless when it comes to numerical work. They only give the direction and approximate relative field strength. It is difficult to work with **E**, the electric field strength, because it is a vector: we have to keep track of all three components. It is also difficult to directly measure the field strength at a point. For numerical work, it is far more convenient to deal with the **electrical potential** V, because it is a **scalar field** and is relatively easy to measure in practice. (Scalar fields can be represented by a single number at each point in space: vector fields have to be represented by three numbers at each point in space.)

Potential

Suppose that a charged particle is placed in an electric field **E**, as shown in figure 18.27. If the particle has a charge q, we can work out **F** as follows.

$$\mathbf{F} = q\mathbf{E} \tag{18.3}$$

As soon as the particle is released, this force will move it in the field direction. The work done by the field on the particle when it moves a distance Δr must equal the kinetic energy E_k it gains.

$$\Delta E_k = Fd \quad \therefore \Delta E_k = qE\Delta r \tag{18.4}$$

However, the total energy of the particle must remain constant after we have released (and isolated) it. So the gain of kinetic energy is matched by a loss of electrical potential energy. You will recall from chapter 10 that if a charge q has a potential V, then its electrical energy is qV.

$$q\Delta V = -\Delta E_k$$
$$\therefore q\Delta V = -qE\Delta r \quad \therefore \Delta V = -E\Delta r \tag{18.5}$$

Equation (18.5) is a very useful general relationship between field strength and potential. It only applies when Δr, the displacement in the field direction, is sufficently small for the field strength not to change. For this reason, we usually rewrite equation (18.5) to express the field strength in terms of the **potential gradient**.

$$E = -\frac{\Delta V}{\Delta r}$$

E is the field strength (N C^{-1} or V m^{-1})

$\Delta V/\Delta r$ is the potential gradient in the field direction (V m^{-1})

Equipotentials

By measuring the potential at various places around a charged object, you can work out the field strength. It is the rate at which the potential changes as you move along a field line. For example, figure 18.28 shows how the potential varies as you move away from a long wire held at a high potential. By measuring the gradient of the graph at various points you can draw another graph which shows how the field strength changes along a field line.

ELECTROSTATIC SPRAYING

Field lines are useful when you want to work out the trajectories of small charged particles in air. Crop spraying is a good example. Figure 18.26 shows the field lines between a spray nozzle which is held at a high potential and the plants beneath it. The nozzle acts as one plate of a capacitor with the ground and plants acting as the other plate. (Provided it is not powder dry, soil is a reasonable conductor.) The power supply gives the nozzle a positive charge, so there is an equal and opposite amount of negative charge distributed over the plants beneath it. Each field line starts from the nozzle and ends somewhere on a plant or the ground. As droplets emerge from the nozzle they acquire a small positive charge and drift along the field lines until they reach a plant or the ground. Not only does the spray coat the whole plant (including under the leaves where many pests reside), but the mutual repulsion of the droplets also ensures an even distribution. The spray is used efficiently, so less is used than with conventional methods, and drifting of the droplets onto other crops is suppressed.

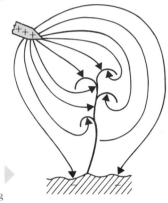

Figure 18.26 Electrostatic crop spraying

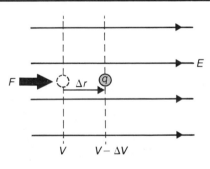

Figure 18.27 Moving a charge in a uniform electric field

Figure 18.28 Variation of electric field and potential around a long charged rod

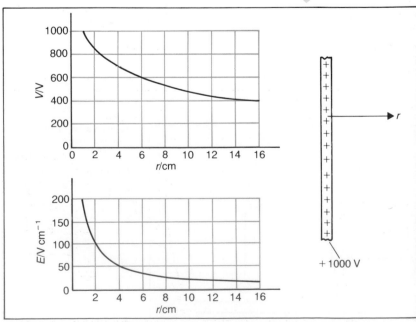

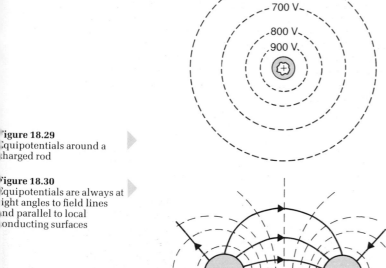

Figure 18.29
Equipotentials around a charged rod

Figure 18.30
Equipotentials are always at right angles to field lines and parallel to local conducting surfaces

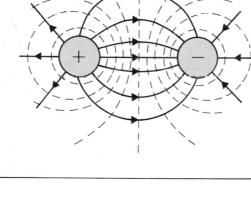

It is helpful to represent the variation of potential around a charged object with a picture. This can be done by drawing contours which join places which are at at the same potential. It is standard practice to draw these **equipotentials** the same number of volts apart, so that the potential gradient can be estimated. Figure 18.29 shows the equipotentials around the wire of figure 18.28 — both diagrams contain the same information. A rather more complex situation is modelled in figure 18.30: notice how the equipotentials are always at right angles to the field lines.

Flame probes

How would you set about obtaining the data of figure 18.28? Of course, to measure potentials you use a voltmeter. However, the voltmeters used for electrical circuits are not much use when it comes to measuring the potentials in insulators, so you need to use special electrostatic voltmeters called **electroscopes**. As you can see from figure 18.31, these rely on the deflection of a thin leaf of metal from a fixed plate. The potential difference between the cap and the case is usually proportional to $\tan\phi$, but direct calibration is usually best. Electroscopes have the advantage over normal voltmeters of not drawing any current, apart from the initial surge needed to charge them up.

Figure 18.32 shows an arrangement of apparatus which could be used to explore the potential around a long rod held at $+1$ kV. The **flame probe** is a hypodermic needle, on an insulating stand, which is connected to the cap of the electroscope by an insulated wire. A jet of natural gas from the needle is ignited so that there is a small flame which is effectively a plasma, i.e. it contains positive and negative ions. Suppose that the needle is placed in a location where the potential is $+500$ V. The needle starts off at 0 V so positive ions in the plasma will move towards it. When they get there, the ions are neutralised by free electrons in the needle. This results in a steady loss of free electrons from the needle and the electroscope it is connected to, making the needle and electroscope positively charged and increasing their potential. Once the needle has reached $+500$ V, there is no further exchange of charge with the plasma. Should the needle get above $+500$ V, negative ions in the plasma will drift towards it, eventually reducing its potential to $+500$ V once more.

Figure 18.31 A gold leaf electroscope. The tangent of the leaf deflection is theoretically proportional to the p.d. between the cap and the conductor inside the case

Figure 18.32 Using a flame probe to measure the potential near a charged rod

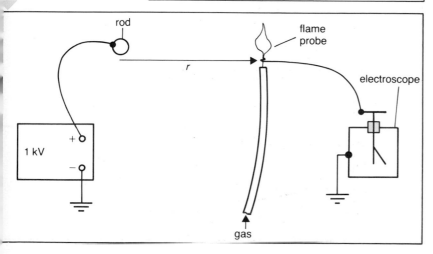

Spark discharges

Sparks between charged conductors are both a boon and a menace. Small sparks between objects which have been friction-charged by airstreams or jets of water have set off disastrous explosions in the fuel tanks of aeroplanes, ships and lorries. Lightning bolts are large scale examples of sparks in our atmosphere: they can be extremely destructive. On the other hand, the physics governing the production of sparks is crucial to the manufacture of spark plugs for petrol engines, for cleaning smoke, for detecting radioactive emissions, for plasma welding, for photocopying, etc.

SMOKE CLEANING

Particles of ash in the smoke from industrial furnaces can be a major pollutant. Electrostatic ash precipitators at the base of chimneys can remove dust particles from smoke with an efficiency approaching 100%. As you can see from figure 18.33, an ash precipitator is basically a long thin wire which is held at a negative voltage inside an earthed tube. As the dirty gases from the furnace pass through the precipitator, the particles of ash pick up electrons and are pulled towards the walls of the tube. They are neutralised when they touch the walls and fall down into the collector under the influence of gravity. Friction reduces the velocity of the furnace gas near the walls so that the ash there is not swept up the chimney.

The electrons which get attached to the ash particles are generated by a **corona discharge** around the central wire (figure 18.34). If the electric field strength around a charged object gets large enough, then the air around it can be ionised and turned into a conductor. For air at atmospheric pressure, this **breakdown field strength** is about 5×10^6 N C^{-1}. It is tempting to suppose that this field is strong enough to tear electrons out of their atoms, but this is usually not the case. In any sample of gas, there will always be a few ions created by random collisions and background radioactivity. Any free electrons will be rapidly accelerated by the electric field. If they acquire enough kinetic energy before they hit an atom, they can ionise it and liberate at least one more electron, each of which is accelerated by the field. The result is an **avalanche breakdown** which creates an enormous number of positive ions and negative electrons in a short space of time.

The positive ions are much more massive than the electrons, so although the forces on both are equal and opposite, only the electrons can obtain enough energy between collisions to cause ionisation. The positive ions drift towards the wire where they are discharged. The electrons outside the avalanche region drift away from the wire, attaching themselves to any specks of dust they hit and tugging them towards the wall.

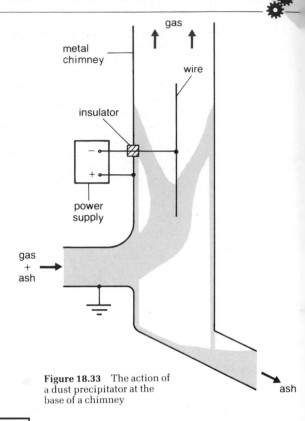

Figure 18.33 The action of a dust precipitator at the base of a chimney

BREAKDOWN FIELD STRENGTH !

The field strength needed to cause avalanche breakdown in a gas can be estimated as follows. Suppose that the energy needed to ionise an air molecule is ϵ and that the mean free path of an electron is λ. If we assume that every time an electron hits an atom it loses all of its kinetic energy, then the kinetic energy gained when the field accelerates it over a distance λ has to be at least ϵ for the avalanche process to start.

$$\Delta E_k = Fd, \quad F = qE \qquad \therefore \epsilon = qE\lambda$$

$$\therefore E = \frac{\epsilon}{q\lambda} \tag{1}$$

We can quote the usual expression for λ from the kinetic theory of gases.

$$\lambda = \frac{V}{N\pi d_0{}^2}, \quad PV = NkT \qquad \therefore \lambda = \frac{kT}{P\pi d_0{}^2} \tag{2}$$

The quantity $\pi d_0{}^2$ is the **collision cross-section** σ (sigma). (We can estimate its value by setting d_0 equal to the radius of an air molecule, about 10^{-10} m.) If we combine equations (1) and (2) we get a useful expression for the breakdown field strength.

$$E = \frac{\epsilon P \sigma}{qkT} \tag{3}$$

So the breakdown field strength is proportional to the pressure of the gas and inversely proportional to its temperature. The ionisation energy for nitrogen and oxygen atoms is about 2×10^{-18} J. If we use this for ϵ, then we can estimate the breakdown field strength for air at room temperature and pressure (300 K, 10^5 Pa).

$$E = \frac{2 \times 10^{-18} \times 10^5 \times \pi \times 10^{-20}}{1.6 \times 10^{-19} \times 1.4 \times 10^{-23} \times 300} \approx 9 \times 10^6 \text{ V m}^{-1}$$

This result is in excellent agreement with the measured value of 5×10^6 V m^{-1} for dry air, considering the approximate nature of the model we have used!

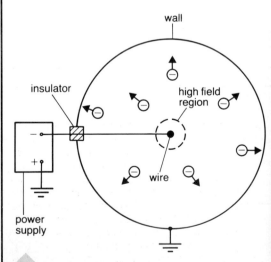

Figure 18.34 Electrons produced near the wire by corona discharge drift outwards to the walls

GEIGER-MÜLLER TUBES

Avalanche discharges are used to amplify the ionisation caused by the emissions of radioactive substances. A single electron−ion pair can trigger the production of at least a hundred million electrons!

The structure of a Geiger-Müller (GM) tube is shown in figure 18.35. The outer tube is earthed and the rod down its axis is held at about +400 V. Argon at a pressure of about 10^4 Pa fills the space between them. A thin film of mica (the window) at one end of the tube allows emissions into the argon. Any ionisation of the gas next to the rod caused by an emission sets off an avalanche breakdown, with electrons accelerating towards the rod and ions drifting towards the walls. When the electrons hit the rod they are absorbed by it, producing a voltage pulse which can be detected by suitable electronics. It takes about 200 μs for the ions to reach the wall — during this **dead time** the tube is unable to respond to any other emissions entering it.

Correct setting of the voltage difference between wall and rod is vital for the GM tube to operate properly (figure 18.36). If it is too low, the avalanche will not start at all, or only be triggered by the more energetic emissions. If the voltage is too high the avalanche will not stop: collisions of the positive ions with the walls will release secondary electrons which will keep the discharge going. (**Quenching agents**, such as bromine, are mixed with the argon to absorb the kinetic energy of the positive ions and stop secondary electrons being emitted.)

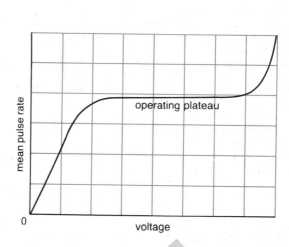

Figure 18.36
Characteristic curve of a GM tube

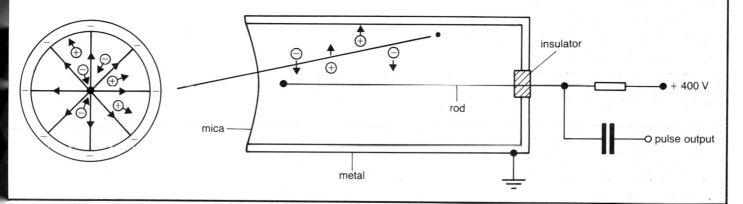

Figure 18.35 Geiger-Müller tube

PHOTOCOPYING

The photocopier shown in figure 18.37 uses three separate corona discharges to copy an image from one piece of paper to another. The process is a continuous one, with a drum rotating round through one complete revolution for each copy of the master which is transferred to the paper.

The first discharge at A sprays positive ions onto the surface of the drum. The drum is coated with a thin layer of selenium, a semiconducting material which is an insulator in the dark. When the charged selenium passes in front of the slit (B) any light reflected off the master is focused onto it with a cylindrical lens. The areas of selenium which are exposed to light become conductive and their charge leaks into the aluminium drum underneath. So by the time the drum has reached D the pattern of positive charge on its surface is a mirror image of the black parts of the master.

The powder poured over the drum at D is a mixture of a black thermosetting plastic (toner) and some glass carrier beads. These have been churned together so that they get charged by friction. The toner is negatively charged, so it sticks to the parts of the drum which are still positively charged: it will get carried away by the carrier beads from the neutral sections. A piece of paper whose surface has been strongly positively charged by a second corona discharge at F is placed in contact with the drum at F. It picks up most of the toner from the drum before passing through the heater at G. This fuses the toner to the paper, giving a permanent image of the master. Finally, the drum is neutralised by passing it close to an alternating voltage corona discharge at H so that any remaining toner can be brushed off.

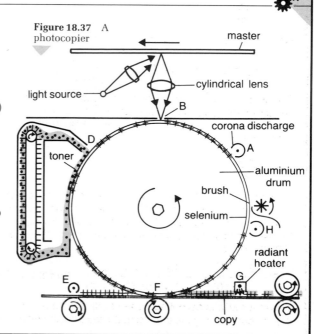

Figure 18.37 A photocopier

OBJECTIVES

After studying this section you should be able to do
the following.

Use the formula $F = qE$.	Describe how a flame probe and electroscope can be used to measure the equipotentials around a charged object.
Use the deflection of a charged pendulum to estimate the strength of an electric field.	
Sketch the field lines around charged objects and conductors.	Know that a corona discharge results if the field strength is too large.
Use the formula $E = -\Delta V/\Delta r$.	Describe and explain the operation of a Geiger–Müller tube.
Sketch equipotentials around charged objects and conductors.	

QUESTIONS

1 Figure 18.38 shows the layout of the conductors in a **triode valve**; the diagram is drawn to scale. The glass tube contains a vacuum. The **cathode** is earthed. It is heated by a current in a separate coil so that free electrons have enough energy to *just* leave its surface by **thermionic emission**. The **anode** and **grid** are held at +30 V and −10 V respectively.

a Copy the diagram and sketch some field lines on it.

b Draw a graph to show how the potential in the tube varies along its axis.

c Estimate the value of the field strength in the region between
  (i) the cathode and the grid,
  (ii) the grid and the anode.

d Draw a graph to show how the energy of an electron changes as it moves along the axis of the tube. Measure the energy in eV (electron–volts): $1\ \text{eV} = 1.6\times10^{-19}\ \text{J}$. Use the graph to explain why there is no current between the the anode and the cathode.

e The grid voltage is now raised to +5 V. State and explain the effect this has on the anode–cathode current.

2 Two light spheres suspended on nylon threads repel each other as shown in figure 18.39. Each has a mass of 0.20 g and has a conducting surface. The sphere on the left has a charge of +0.30 μC.

a Say what you can about the charge on the other sphere.

b Calculate the force on the left-hand sphere and hence work out the field strength at that point. What is the source of the field?

c If both spheres have the same charge as each other, draw a diagram to show the field lines and equipotentials around them.

3 The graph of figure 18.40 shows how the electric field strength changes as you move away radially from a positively charged sphere of radius 10 cm.

a If the potential a long way from the sphere is zero, estimate the potential at the surface of the sphere? (*Hint*: think about $\Delta V = -\ E\Delta r$.)

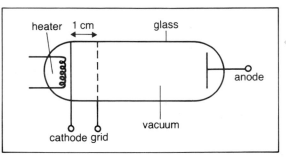

Figure 18.38

Figure 18.39

b How much work would you have to do to place +0.50 μC of charge on the surface of the sphere? Do you have to make any assumptions?

4 Copy the pairs of charged conducting objects shown in figure 18.41. The two items in each pair have equal and opposite charges. Draw the charge distribution, field lines and equipotentials around each object.

5 Two conducting spheres on insulating stands are linked with a wire, as shown in figure 18.42. Both spheres are earthed, then a charged polythene strip is brought up close to one sphere.

a State and explain what happens to the free electrons in the spheres. Draw a diagram to show the distribution of charges on the spheres.

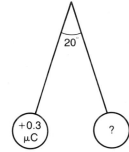

Figure 18.40

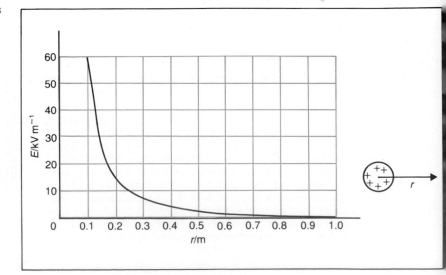

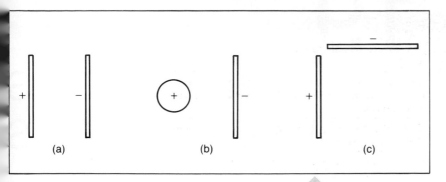

(a)　　　　　　(b)　　　　　　(c)

Figure 18.41

◁ **Figure 18.42**

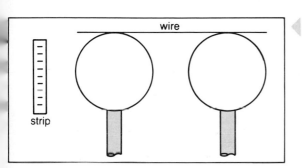

wire

strip

7 Tariq has invented an electric field direction-finder. As you can see from figure 18.44, it consists of a thin piece of metal foil pivoted at its centre so that it can rotate freely. Tariq finds that any electric field around the foil will make it line up along the field direction (unlike figure 18.44), but he can't explain why. Help him out. Will the pointed end of the foil *always* point in the direction of the field?

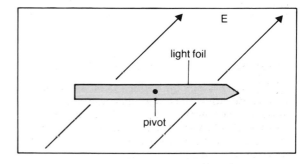

Figure 18.44 ▷

Figure 18.43 ▷

b The wire is knocked off by an insulator, then the polythene strip is removed. Draw a diagram to show the resulting distribution of charge on the spheres, with field lines and equipotentials.

c The system now looks like a charged capacitor, so it must have some electrical energy. Exactly where did that energy come from?

d State and explain what happens to the p.d. between the two spheres if they are moved further apart without discharging them.

6 Figure 18.43 shows a cross-section through an **electrogasdynamic generator** of the type used to generate voltages of 50 kV for powder spray guns. Air containing the powder is blown into the insulator tube, past the needle and towards the collector.

a Draw some of the field lines between the needle and the attractor. Where is avalanche breakdown likely to occur? Which way will the electrons and ions produced by the breakdown move?

b Explain why the collector becomes positively charged.

c Explain why the collector rises to a voltage many times larger than the power supply voltage.

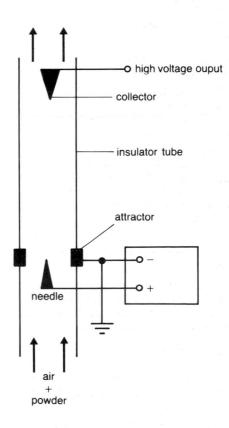

19

CHARGED SHEETS
AND SPHERES

You cannot claim to have any real understanding of electric phenomena unless you know how the field strength around an electron changes as you move towards it. This chapter will lead you to a formula for the field around a charged particle via a consideration of the fields around flat sheets and spheres.

CHARGED SHEETS

Beams of charged particles can be accelerated and deflected by electric fields: some practical applications are described at the end of this section. Fortunately, the field between charged parallel plates can be accurately predicted from their spacing and p.d., so the design of items of technology which employ electric fields does not have to be done by trial and error.

Figure 19.1 A parallel plate capacitor ▶

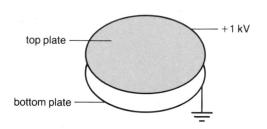
+1 kV

top plate

bottom plate

Figure 19.2 Possible electric fields inside a parallel plate capacitor ▶

Figure 19.3 The results of investigating the potential in and around a parallel plate capacitor with a flame probe ▼

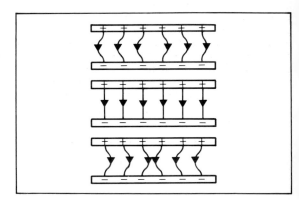

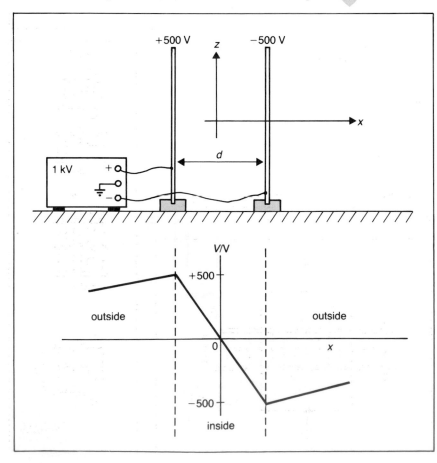

Parallel plate capacitors

An air-filled parallel plate capacitor is shown in figure 19.1: the air between the plates acts as the insulator between the two conducting sheets. We are interested in the electric field around it when it is charged up. Ultimately, of course, we have to let nature tell us via an experiment, but it helps to have an initial guess so that we can design the experiment in the first place. Let's assume that the spacing between the plates is *much* smaller than their width, so that **edge effects** are not important.

Uniform field
The two plates have equal and opposite charge. It is reasonable to suppose that the charges are spread uniformly over the inside surface of each plate because of their mutual repulsion and the attraction of the charges on the other plate. But how do we draw the field lines between the plates? Three possibilities are drawn in figure 19.2. The middle one probably seems the most reasonable. After all, if the charge is evenly smeared over the plates, why should a speck of charged dust between them feel any sideways forces?

A flame probe (chapter 18) can be used to map out the equipotential surfaces around a real parallel plate capacitor. The results (figure 19.3) suggest that there is a uniform potential gradient between the plates provided you keep well away from the edges. Furthermore, the potential gradient in the region outside the plates is much smaller than it is between the plates. This is summarised in the graph of figure 19.4. It shows the potential and electric field strength at various places around an ideal parallel plate capacitor whose plate spacing is *much* smaller than its width. Of course, a uniform potential gradient means a constant electric field strength.

$$E = -\frac{V}{d}$$

E is the field strength between the plates (V m^{-1})

V is the p.d. between the plates (V)

d is the separation of the plates (m)

Permittivity of free space

If the electric field inside a parallel plate capacitor is uniform, we can easily show that its capacitance only depends on the area of its plates and their separation.

Consider the capacitor shown in figure 19.5. Its plate area is *A* and the plate separation is *d*, giving a capacitance *C*. If it is connected in parallel with an identical capacitor (figure 19.6), we end up with a device which has a capacitance of 2*C*, an effective plate area of 2*A* and a plate separation of *d*. So *C* ∝ *A*. Similarly, if you connect two identical capacitors in series (figure 19.7), you end up with a device which has a capacitance of ½*C*, a plate area of *A* and a plate separation of 2*d*. So *C* ∝ 1/*d*.

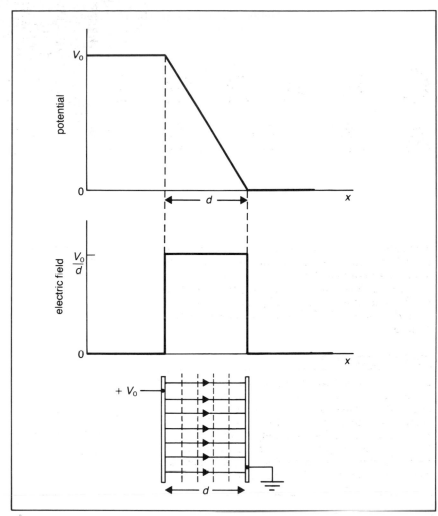

Figure 19.4 shows potential versus *x* (top) with value V_0, and electric field versus *x* (bottom) with value $\frac{V_0}{d}$.

Figure 19.4 Variation of field and potential around an ideal parallel plate capacitor

Figure 19.5 A capacitor

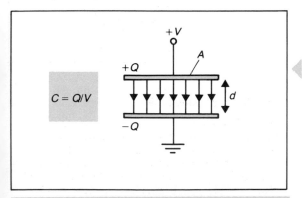

$$C = Q/V$$

Figure 19.6 Two capacitors in parallel look like one

Figure 19.7 Two capacitors in series look like one

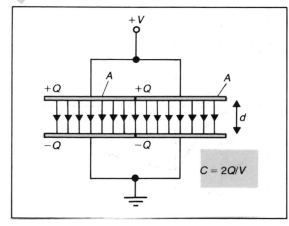

$$C = 2Q/V$$

$$C = \frac{\epsilon_0 A}{d}$$

C is the capacitance of the parallel plates (F)

ϵ_0 is the permittivity of free space (8.89×10^{-12} F m^{-1})

A is the area of the plates (m^2)

d is the separation of the plates (m)

The constant ϵ_0 (the **permittivity of free space**) is usually referred to as 'epsilon-nought'. Later on, we will show you how it can be measured by an experiment, but it may help if you first have some idea of its significance for the strength of fields around charged objects.

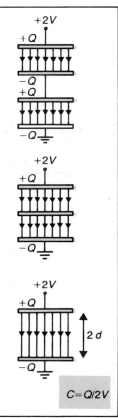

$$C = Q/2V$$

Fields around uniform sheets of charge

Consider a parallel plate capacitor. It has a p.d. V between its plates, each of which holds a charge Q. If we define a new term, the **charge density** σ, we can obtain an interesting expression for the electric field intensity between the plates.

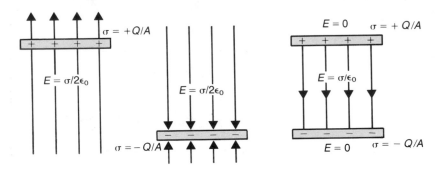

$$C = \frac{\epsilon_0 A}{d}, \qquad C = \frac{Q}{V} \qquad \therefore \frac{V}{d} = \frac{Q}{\epsilon_0 A}$$

$$E = \frac{V}{d}, \qquad \sigma = \frac{Q}{A} \qquad \therefore E = \frac{\sigma}{\epsilon_0} \qquad (19.1)$$

Figure 19.8 Combining the fields around charged sheets to find the field inside a parallel plate capacitor

Of course, this field is due to the charge on both of the plates. Now consider the field around each plate if the other plate was not there at all (figure 19.8). The field will be uniform, acting perpendicularly to the surface of the plate with a strength $\sigma/2\epsilon_0$. When the two plates are placed next to each other, the fields reinforce each other in the space between to give $E = \sigma/\epsilon_0$, and cancel in the space outside to give $E = 0$.

$$E = \frac{\sigma}{2\epsilon_0}$$

E is the field strength of an infinite flat sheet $(V\,m^{-1})$

σ is the charge density on the sheet $(C\,m^{-2})$

ϵ_0 is the permittivity of free space $(F\,m^{-1})$

ϵ_0 is a universal constant whose value fixes the strength of the electric forces between charged particles. It features in any expression for the electric field intensity or the potential around an assembly of protons or electrons. Precise knowledge of its value is therefore very important.

Figure 19.9 Apparatus for measuring ϵ_0

Measuring ϵ_0

You can measure ϵ_0 by building a parallel plate capacitor, with a known plate area and separation, and finding out its capacitance. This is easier said than done, because ϵ_0 is rather small: it is actually $8.85 \times 10^{-12}\,F\,m^{-1}$. To get a large capacitance, you need a large plate area and a small separation — square plates of side 33 cm separated by 1.0 mm are feasible for a school laboratory.

$$C = \frac{\epsilon_0 A}{d}$$

$$\therefore C = \frac{8.85 \times 10^{-12} \times (0.33)^2}{1.0 \times 10^{-3}} = 0.96\ nF$$

One strategy for measuring this capacitance is illustrated in figure 19.9. The two plates are separated by nylon spacers at the edge. The bottom plate is earthed and the top plate charged from the power supply via a 50 MΩ safety resistor and a flying lead. The top plate is then isolated from the power supply and discharged onto the 1.0 μF capacitor of the coulomb meter. The reading of the voltmeter tells you the charge on the top plate. For example, suppose that the voltmeter reads 0.87 V when the parallel plate capacitor is charged up to 1.0 kV: the charge on its top plate was therefore 0.87 μC, giving a capacitance of $8.7 \times 10^{-10}\,F$. Of course, we are assuming that there is no leakage of charge between the top and bottom plate: this can be checked by seeing if a time delay between charging and discharging makes any difference to the coulomb meter reading. Leakage is often due to thin films of water on the surface of the spacers. This can be avoided by using a water-repellant material such as nylon.

Of course, a single measurement is not enough to get a good value for ϵ_0. You need to vary every variable you can to check that the model $(C = \epsilon_0 A/d)$ is an accurate description of the capacitor. So for each area and separation of the plates, Q should be measured for several different values of V: the slope of the best straight line on the Q–V graph gives a value for C. Figure 19.9 shows how the plate area can be altered without cutting up the plates — stacks of nylon spacers can be used to obtain different separations. All of your results can be used to draw a graph of C against A/d. The slope of the best straight line drawn through the origin should give a value for ϵ_0. Of course, if you don't get a straight line through the origin, this is an indication that you have done something wrong and some of your results are suspect!

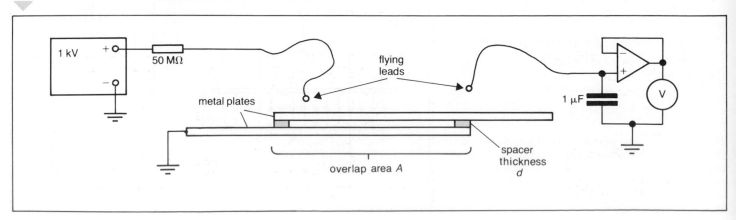

Dielectrics

The charge stored by a capacitor for a given p.d. across it can be increased many times over by the insertion of a suitable material between its plates! Since the obvious way of getting a small separation between the plates of a capacitor is to use a thin layer of insulator as a spacer, this capacitance increase comes as an extra bonus. However, the effect is of more than just technical interest. It is further evidence in favour of our model of atomic structure.

Polarisation

If the gap between the plates of a parallel plate capacitor is filled with an insulator, the capacitance is increased by a factor ϵ, the **relative permittivity** of the material. Some values for ϵ are shown in table 19.1.

Table 19.1

Dielectric	ϵ
glass	7.5
mica	7.0
porcelain	5.5
perspex	3.3
polythene	≈ 2.2
paper	≈ 2.0
oil	2.0
balsa wood	1.2
air	1.0005

Figure 19.10 shows what happens when a dielectric is slipped between the plates of a capacitor connected to a fixed voltage supply. The electric field between the plates **polarises** the material, making equal and opposite charges appear on its surfaces. These **induced charges** allow extra charge to flow from the power supply, so that the total charge near each plate remains constant.

$$Q \to \epsilon Q, \quad V \to V, \quad C = \frac{Q}{V} \quad \therefore C \to \epsilon C \qquad \textbf{(19.2)}$$

Figure 19.10 Stages in the insertion of a dielectric between the plates of a capacitor. Note that the total charge near each plate remains constant

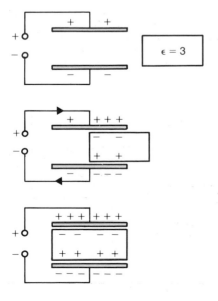

INDUCED CHARGES

The appearance of induced charges on the surface of a dielectric can be explained by considering the effect of an electric field on a single atom. Look at figure 19.11. The external electric field pushes the nucleus to the left and tugs the electrons to the right, distorting the atom so that it no longer has a symmetrical charge distribution. The electric field creates a **dipole** in the atom, making it appear to have equal and opposite charges at either end. Figure 19.12 shows how these charges do not affect the net charge in the body of the dielectric, but make equal and opposite charges appear on the surfaces perpendicular to the field direction. A little thought should convince you that these **induced** charges are independent of the thickness of the material but proportional to the area of its surface. Let us assume that they are also proportional to the field strength.

$$Q_i = \delta AE \qquad (1)$$

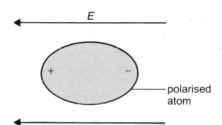

Figure 19.11 A polarised atom

The total charge Q_t near the top plate will be the sum of the induced and free charges (Q_i and Q_f). As far as the power supply is concerned, only the free charges are on the top plate.

$$Q_t = Q_f - Q_i, \qquad C = \frac{Q}{V} \qquad \therefore C = \frac{Q_f}{V}$$

$$\therefore C = \frac{Q_t}{V} + \frac{Q_i}{V} \qquad (2)$$

The total charge density on the capacitor plates fixes the value of the field strength.

$$E = \frac{\sigma}{\epsilon_0}, \qquad \sigma = \frac{Q}{A} \qquad \therefore E = \frac{Q_t}{\epsilon_0 A} \qquad \therefore Q_t = \epsilon_0 AE \qquad (3)$$

By combining equations (1), (2) and (3) we can see where the relative permittivity comes from.

$$C = \frac{\epsilon_0 AE}{V} + \frac{\delta AE}{V} \qquad \therefore C = (\epsilon_0 + \delta) \frac{AE}{V}$$

$$E = \frac{V}{d} \qquad \therefore C = (\epsilon_0 + \delta) \frac{A}{d}$$

$$\therefore C = \frac{\epsilon \epsilon_0 A}{d}, \qquad \epsilon = 1 + \frac{\delta}{\epsilon_0} \qquad (4)$$

Figure 19.12 Induced charges

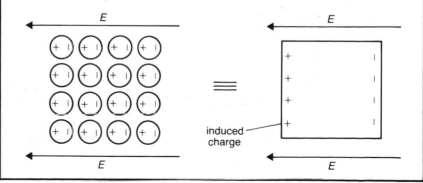

Millikan's oil drop experiment

In 1917 Robert Millikan used the uniform field between two parallel plates to make the first precise measurement of the charge on a single electron. Although the current value of e $(-1.602\ 189 \times 10^{-19} \pm 0.000\ 005 \times 10^{-19}$ C) is obtained indirectly from precise measurements of other quantities, Millikan's elegant technique deserves your appreciation.

Balancing gravity

The essential details of Millikan's apparatus are shown in figure 19.13. Oil is squirted through a nozzle to obtain a fine spray of droplets. Some of these drift through the hole in the top plate. The space between the parallel plates is observed through a microscope. Light from a lamp is reflected off the droplets so that they appear like tiny dots of light on a dark background. A calibrated scale in the microscope eyepiece allows the vertical displacement of the drops to be measured.

As the oil comes out of the nozzle it is charged by friction. So each droplet will contain a number of electrons, giving it a net charge of $-q$. The top plate is positively charged when the power supply is switched on, giving an electric field which points downwards. By varying the voltage of the power supply, the field strength can be adjusted until the droplet in view stops moving. The electric force will then be equal to the weight of the drop.

$$F = qE, \quad W = mg \qquad \therefore qE = mg \qquad \textbf{(19.3)}$$

The electric field, of course, can be calculated from the measured p.d. between the plates and their separation. The mass of the drop, however, is not so easy to find, as it is too small for its diameter to be measured through the microscope.

Terminal velocity

Millikan found the mass of his droplets by switching off the electrical field and measuring their terminal velocity. (He timed how long it took the spot of light to fall between two points on the microscope scale.) The frictional force on a spherical object moving slowly through a fluid is given by **Stoke's Law**.

$F = 6\pi\mu rv$

F is the frictional force acting on the sphere (N)

μ is the viscosity of the fluid (N m^{-2} s)

r is the radius of the sphere (m)

v is the velocity of the sphere (m s^{-1})

(The viscosity of air can be determined by experiments on a larger scale.) At its terminal velocity, the weight of the droplet is exactly equal to the frictional force.

$$mg = 6\pi\mu rv \qquad \textbf{(19.4)}$$

The mass of the spherical drop can be expressed in terms of its known density.

$$m = \rho \times \frac{4}{3}\pi r^3 \qquad \therefore \frac{4}{3}\pi \rho r^3 g = 6\pi\mu rv$$

$$\therefore r = \left(\frac{9\mu v}{2\rho g}\right)^{\frac{1}{2}} \qquad \textbf{(19.5)}$$

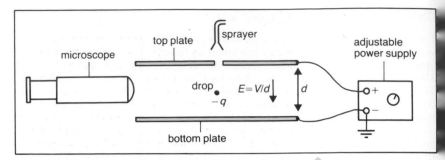

Figure 19.13 Apparatus for measuring the charge of an electron

Equation (19.5) can be used to calculate the radius of the droplet from its measured terminal velocity. It is then a simple matter to use the density to find its mass.

Quantisation

Having found the mass of the droplet, the charge on it can be found from equation (19.3). Finding the mass of the droplet is tedious, so it pays to use the same one time after time. The charge on the droplet can be altered by allowing beta particles from a radioactive source into the space between the plates for a few seconds. This generates ions in the air, some of which will be picked up by the droplet. The new charge on the droplet can be measured by finding the field needed to balance out the force of gravity on it, exactly as before.

Figure 19.14 shows the results of a series of measurements made on a single droplet. They clearly show that the charge on the droplet is **quantised**, i.e. it is an integral multiple of 1.6×10^{-19} C. The number of electrons gained or lost each time the radioactive source floods the air with beta particles is unpredictable, but the change is always a whole number of electrons.

Figure 19.14 The results of a number of measurements of the charge on a single oil drop — the drop was allowed to pick up ions between measurements

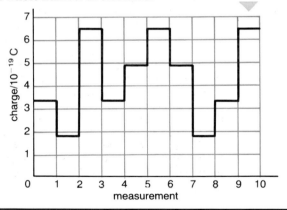

PRECAUTIONS !

Millikan won the Nobel Prize for measuring the charge on the electron. Previous experiments on charged clouds of water droplets had given approximate values for the electronic charge, but Millikan was the first to convincingly demonstrate the existence of the electron itself. This required a very high precision, so that experimental error did not mask the quantisation of the charges on his droplets. Millikan even took the upthrust on his droplets due to the air around them into consideration (a correction of only 0.1%). The whole apparatus was immersed in a bath of oil to keep its temperature stable and the pressure of the air was carefully controlled. These two precautions allowed Millikan to accurately estimate the viscosity of the air, a quantity which changes rapidly with temperature and pressure. Millikan's value for e was within 2% of today's accepted value. Most of this error was his failure to realise that the viscosity of a fluid decreases slightly as the radius of the sphere dropping through it decreases.

Charged beams

Beams of charged particles are routine items of today's technology. Electron beams are used to paint images on the screens of cathode ray oscilloscopes and televisions, to scan the light-sensitive surfaces of TV cameras and to etch printed circuits onto silicon. Beams of ions are used to do intricate chemistry in a vacuum, to carry out precision doping of semiconductors and may turn out to be the only way of building the crystal structure necessary for room-temperature superconductors.

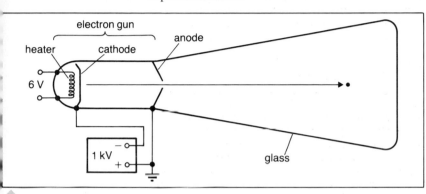

Figure 19.15   An electron gun

Accelerating beams

Figure 19.15 shows the important details of an **electron gun**. (Each colour TV contains three of these.) The gun has to be in a vacuum so that the electrons do not lose energy through collisions with gas molecules. The **cathode** is coated with a material which has a low **work function** so that electrons can escape from its surface at moderate temperatures (≈ 1000 K, red heat) through **thermionic emission**. The cathode is raised to this temperature by radiant heat from a white hot tungsten filament behind it. A separate 6 V supply provides current for this **heater**.

The kinetic energy of the electrons which leave the cathode and enter the vacuum will be a bit less than kT, where k is Boltzmann's constant. (An electron has to lose some energy as it escapes from the attractive forces of the rest of the metal.) It is standard practice to quote the energy of a charged particle in **electron-volts** (eV). One electron-volt is the energy change of an electron when its potential is changed by one volt; 1 eV $= 1.60 \times 10^{-19}$ J.

$$E_k < kT$$

$$\therefore E_k < 1.38 \times 10^{-23} \times 1000 \approx 1.6 \times 10^{-20}\,\text{J}$$
$$\text{or } 0.1\text{ eV}$$

Figure 19.16   Deflecting an electron beam in an oscilloscope

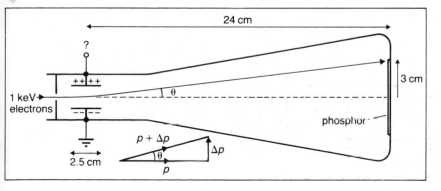

The cathode in figure 19.15 is held at -1.0 kV so the electrons are accelerated towards the **anode** which is **earthed**, i.e. 0 V. We can calculate the velocity of the electrons when they reach the anode, regardless of the route they follow, by considering their loss of electrical energy between cathode and anode. The electrical energy at the cathode is $(-e) \times (-V) = +eV$ and is 0 at the anode.

$$\tfrac{1}{2}mv^2 = eV \qquad \therefore v = \left(\frac{2eV}{m}\right)^{\frac{1}{2}} \qquad \textbf{(19.6)}$$

You can use equation (19.6) to convince yourself that 1 keV electrons have a velocity of 1.87×10^7 m s^{-1}. (This is about 6% of the speed of light, so the mass of the electron will be slightly larger than its rest mass of 9.1×10^{-31} kg. We will return to this in chapter 26.)

Although many of the electrons will be absorbed by the anode, a significant fraction of them will pass through the hole in its centre — they are moving too fast to be deflected when they get close to it. Once on the far side of the anode, the electrons are in a field-free environment where everything appears to be earthed. So they move at a constant velocity, forming a beam which travels in a straight line through the vacuum. Eventually, of course, each electron will hit the glass envelope and lose its kinetic energy, and will be conducted back to the anode by a thin conducting layer on the inner surface of the glass.

Oscilloscopes

An oscilloscope uses two pairs of deflecting plates to control where the electron beam arrives on a screen coated with a **phosphor**. The arrangement is shown in figure 19.16. The phosphor converts the kinetic energy of the electrons in the beam to visible light so that vertical and horizontal movement of the beam can be used to trace out a shape on the screen.

Let us work out the p.d. you need to put across the X-deflection plates to get the beam to the top of the screen, as shown in figure 19.16. The electric field between the plates will not change the horizontal momentum of the beam. The vertical momentum acquired will depend on the electric field strength and the time that each electron spends between the plates.

$$\Delta p = F\Delta t, \quad F = qE \quad \therefore \Delta p = eE\Delta t \qquad \textbf{(19.7)}$$

The velocity of the 1.00 keV electrons in the beam is 1.87×10^7 m s^{-1} so they only take 1.33×10^{-9} s to pass through the 25 mm long deflection region. The vector triangle in figure 19.16 should convince you that $\Delta p/p = 3/24$.

$$p = mv, \quad v = 1.87 \times 10^7 \text{ m s}^{-1}$$
$$m = 9.11 \times 10^{-31} \text{ kg}$$

$$\therefore p = 1.70 \times 10^{-23} \text{ N s}$$

$$\frac{\Delta p}{p} = \frac{3}{24}$$

$$\therefore \Delta p = 1.70 \times 10^{-23} \times \frac{3}{24} = 2.13 \times 10^{-24} \text{ N s}$$

Equation (19.7) can now be used to find the field strength between the deflection plates.

$$\Delta p = eE\Delta t \quad \therefore E = \frac{\Delta p}{e\Delta t}$$

$$\therefore E = \frac{2.13\times10^{-24}}{1.60\times10^{-19} \times 1.33\times10^{-9}}$$

$$= 1.00\times10^{4}\ V\ m^{-1}$$

Since the two plates are 10.0 mm apart, we can work out the p.d. needed across them.

$$E = \frac{V}{d} \quad \therefore V = Ed$$
$$\therefore V = 1.00\times10^{4} \times 10.0\times10^{-3} = 100\ V$$

If the bottom plate is earthed, changing the potential of the top plate from about $+100$ V to -100 V is going to move the spot from the top of the screen to the bottom. Convince yourself that the displacement of the spot from the centre of the screen will be almost exactly proportional to the potential of the top deflecting plate.

OBJECTIVES

After studying this section you should be able to do the following.

Sketch the field lines and equipotentials around and inside a parallel plate capacitor.

Know that the electric field is uniform between the plates of an ideal parallel plate capacitor.

Use the formula $E = \sigma/2\epsilon_0$ for the field near to the surface of a sheet of charge.

Calculate the capacitance of a parallel plate capacitor from its dimensions.

Describe a method by which ϵ_0 can be measured.

Describe the effect of inserting a dielectric between the plates of a capacitor.

Explain the appearance of induced charges in an electric field.

Describe Millikan's oil drop experiment.

Describe how a beam of electrons can be generated and directed at an oscilloscope screen.

Calculate the deflection of a beam of charged particles travelling at right angles to an electric field.

QUESTIONS

1 The electrodes in a spark plug are usually spaced 0.60 mm apart (figure 19.17). The breakdown field strength for air at atmospheric pressure is $5\times10^{6}\ V\ m^{-1}$.

a Estimate the minimum p.d. across the electrodes to get a spark between them at atmospheric pressure.

b The petrol–air mixture in a car engine has its volume reduced by a factor of about 10 before it is ignited by the spark. Estimate the minimum p.d. across the electrodes to get an ignition spark.

c Suggest how you could test the spark voltage at atmospheric pressure to see if it will ignite the compressed petrol–air mixture.

2 **a** The dielectric of an electrolytic capacitor is a layer of aluminium oxide whose thickness is $0.50\ \mu m$. The relative permittivity of aluminium oxide is 8.5. If the rectangular plates have a width of 2.0 cm, what is their length for a 100 μF capacitor? How is the capacitor packed to make it manageable?

b A polystyrene capacitor is made by placing a $15\mu m$-thick sheet of the plastic between two sheets of aluminium. If each sheet is in the form of a disc of radius 10 mm, what is the value of their capacitance? ($\epsilon = 2.6$ for polystyrene.)

3 A parallel plate capacitor of plate area A and separation d is connected to a battery so that it charges up to a voltage V, before being isolated. The plates are then pulled apart, doubling their separation, without discharging them.

a What does this do to the p.d. between the plates?

Figure 19.17

b What does this do to the energy stored in the capacitor? Does the system conserve energy?

c What does this do to the electric field strength between the plates?

d Figure 19.18 shows a flat metal sheet with an insulating handle placed on top of an earthed conducting surface with a 25 μm layer of polythene ($\epsilon = 2.3$) between them. If the top plate of this capacitor is charged up to $+9.0$ V and isolated, estimate its voltage when it has been raised up by 10 mm.

4 A parallel plate capacitor is connected between the terminals of a power supply as shown in figure 19.19. State and explain what happens to the following quantities as the dielectric between the plates is slowly removed:

a the p.d. between the plates,

b the electric field between the plates,

c the charge on the plates,

d the energy stored in the capacitor.

5 A wooden ruler is suspended from its centre so that it can swing freely. A strip of charged polythene and charged perspex is brought close to one end in turn: the ruler is attracted to the strip in each case. Nigel is puzzled. 'There are as many positive as negative charges induced in the ruler by the uniform field from the strip, so all the pushes are cancelled out by the pulls.' Tell him what is actually going on. Would he be better off using charged rods rather than strips?

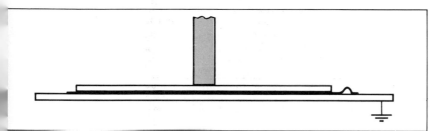

Figure 19.18

Figure 19.19

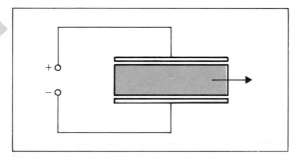

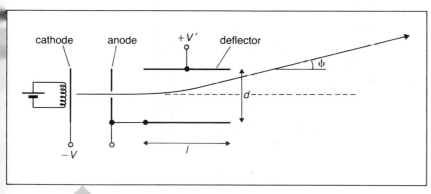

Figure 19.20

Figure 19.21

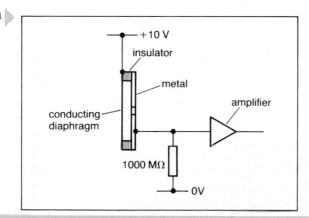

6 Debbie investigates the force between the two plates of a capacitor, using an electronic balance to find the mass of the bottom plate when the top plate is suspended a short distance d above it. Each plate has a radius of 100 mm.

a Explain why the weight of the bottom plate decreases as the capacitor is charged.

b Debbie reckons that the balance reading will be given by $A\epsilon_0(V/d)^2$: she is wrong. Work out what her formula should be.

c Some of her data are shown in table 19.2. By drawing a suitable straight line graph, find out the spacing of Debbie's capacitor plates.

Table 19.2

Voltage of top plate/V	Mass of bottom plate/g
0	50.32
100	50.31
200	50.27
400	50.14
800	49.57
1600	47.40

7 Figure 19.20 shows a simple accelerator and deflector for electrons of charge e and mass m.

a Show that the momentum of the electrons when they enter the deflection region is given by $(2eVm)^{\frac{1}{2}}$.

b Show that the deflection of the electrons caused by their passage between the plates is given by $\phi \simeq V'l/2Vd$.

c Can you use the electrical deflection of electron beams to give you information about their mass or charge?

8 A typical **capacitor microphone** consists of a thin conducting diaphragm supported close to a flat metal sheet as shown in figure 19.21. Variations of air pressure in front of the diaphragm force it to vibrate back and forth, changing the capacitance of the system.

a If the diaphragm has a radius of 10 mm and is held 100 μm from the metal sheet, calculate the capacitance of the system.

b What happens to the capacitance of the system as the diaphragm moves towards the plate. Estimate the change in capacitance for a movement of 1 μm.

c What is the time constant of the circuit?

d Suppose that the diaphragm is forced to vibrate in SHM with an amplitude of 1 μm and a frequency of 1 kHz. Explain why the charge on the plates remains constant, and estimate the amplitude of the sinusoidal voltage at the input of the amplifier.

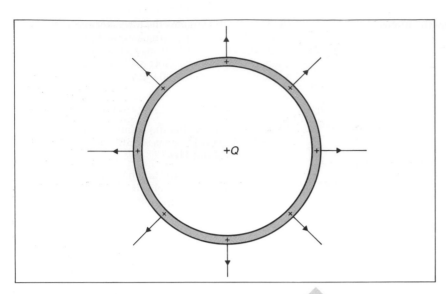

CHARGED SPHERES

The electric field strength close to a large sheet of charge does not depend on how near that sheet is. It only depends on the charge density and the value of ϵ_0. This fact alone is enough for us to deduce how the electric field varies around a single point charge. The first step is to make an educated guess at the algebra which describes the field around a single electron. The next step is to find the field at a point above the flat sheet due to a single electron somewhere on the sheet. The final step is to add together the fields due to all the electrons scattered evenly over the sheet and see if our guess leads to $E = \sigma/2\epsilon_0$. However, that approach relies on an understanding of integration, so we shall adopt a more roundabout route to obtain the same result.

Capacitance of spheres

The thought experiment outlined below uses your understanding of parallel plate capacitors to make some predictions about spherical capacitors which can be tested in the laboratory. The argument appears circular because we have to make some assumptions at the outset which can only be justified at the end!

Figure 19.22 Electric field outside a charged sphere

Figure 19.23 Electric field between concentric charged spheres

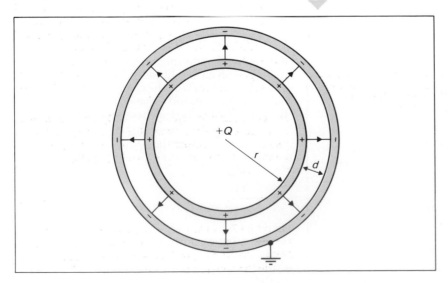

Concentric shells

Figure 19.22 shows the distribution of charge you would expect to find on a charged spherical shell made of a conducting material. The mutual repulsion of the charges forces them to sit as far away from each other as possible, giving a uniform charge density.

$$\sigma = \frac{Q}{A}, \quad A = 4\pi r^2 \quad \therefore \ \sigma = \frac{Q}{4\pi r^2} \quad \text{(19.8}$$

Figure 19.22 also shows the electric field lines around the shell. Notice that there are none *inside* the shell. This is a convenient guess on our part, but we will eventually show that there is never any electric field inside a conducting shell due to the charge on its surface.

The lack of field lines inside a shell allows us to place another, slightly larger, shell around the first one (figure 19.23). It seems reasonable to assume that this affects neither the charge distribution on the inner sphere nor the electric field at its surface. The outer shell has been earthed so that it has a charge equal and opposite to that on the inner shell, making the two-shell system look like a capacitor. If the spacing between the shells d is small compared with their radius r, then the field between them is going to be the same as the field in a parallel plate capacitor.

$$E = \frac{\sigma}{\epsilon_0} \quad \therefore \ E = \frac{Q}{4\pi\epsilon_0 r^2} \quad \text{(19.9}$$

Now suppose that we allow the outer shell to grow. As it gets bigger, the electric field at the surface of the inner shell remains fixed because the distribution of charge on that shell doesn't change. So equation (19.9) is an expression for the field strength at the surface of a sphere in isolation.

$$E = \frac{Q}{4\pi\epsilon_0 r^2}$$

E is the field strength at the surface of the sphere (V m^{-1})

Q is the charge on the surface of the sphere (C)

r is the radius of the sphere (m)

Spherical capacitors

To find the capacitance of a sphere, you need its potential V when it holds a charge Q. Suppose that the sphere starts off being very large, large enough to fill the universe, so that each charged particle on its surface is as far away from all the others as it can get. The sphere now proceeds to shrink until it has a radius r. If we can work out how much energy is needed to cram the charge together this way, then we have the potential of the sphere.

When the sphere shrinks by $-\Delta r$, each charge q on the surface has to be pushed against the electric field E at the surface due to all the other charges. The work done on the charge equals its change of electrical energy.

$$qE\times(-\Delta r) = q\Delta V, \quad E = \frac{Q}{4\pi e_0 r^2}$$

$$\therefore \ \Delta V = -\frac{Q\Delta r}{4\pi e_0 r^2} \quad \text{(19.10)}$$

The potential at the surface of the sphere when it has reached a radius r can be found by integrating equation (19.10) with the help of Appendix B.

$$\int dV = -\frac{Q}{4\pi\epsilon_0}\int\frac{dr}{r^2}$$

$$\therefore V = \frac{Q}{4\pi\epsilon_0 r} + c \qquad (19.11)$$

The constant c can be set to zero if we assume that V is zero when r is infinite.

$$V = \frac{Q}{4\pi\epsilon_0 r}$$

V is the potential at the surface of the sphere (V)

Q is the charge on the sphere (C)

r is the radius of the sphere (m)

A charged sphere is one half of a capacitor, since there must be an equal and opposite amount of charge spread around the rest of the universe. In practice, the equal and opposite charge is on the nearest earthed conductor, as shown in figure 19.24. Provided that the sphere is sufficiently isolated, the capacitance of the whole system can be found from equation (19.11).

$$C = \frac{Q}{V}, \qquad V = \frac{Q}{4\pi\epsilon_0 r} \qquad \therefore C = 4\pi\epsilon_0 r \qquad (19.12)$$

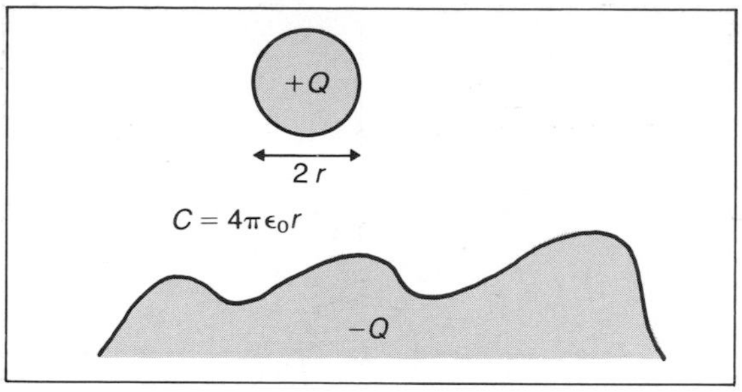

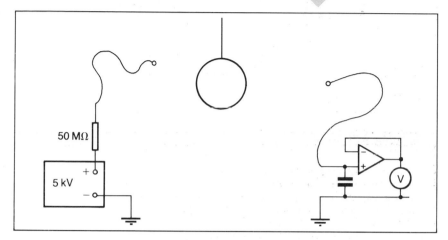

Figure 19.24 An isolated charged object is one plate of a capacitor. The other plate is the nearest earthed surface

Figure 19.25 Apparatus for measuring the capacitance of a sphere

Equation (19.12) is a prediction which can be checked in the laboratory with the apparatus shown in figure 19.25. A number of different sized conducting spheres suspended by nylon threads are charged up from a high voltage supply and then discharged onto the capacitor of a coulomb meter. A sphere of radius 1 cm is predicted to have a capacitance of about 1 pF (convince yourself), so it will hold a charge of 5 nC at a potential of 5 kV, easily measured by a school coulomb meter.

Fields around point charges

A flame probe can be used to investigate the variation in potential as you move away from the surface of a sphere. It should be clear that the rest of the laboratory is going to interfere with the experiment, unless the sphere is suspended well away from other earthed conductors. So we can only expect values of the potential fairly close to the surface of the sphere to be of any significance. Results from such an experiment are presented in the graph of figure 19.26. For small values of r, $V \propto 1/r$.

$$V = \frac{c'}{r} \qquad (19.13)$$

The constant c' in equation (19.13) can be obtained by considering the potential at the surface of the sphere. If you compare equation (19.13) with equation (19.11), it should be obvious that $c' = Q/4\pi\epsilon_0$.

$$V = \frac{Q}{4\pi\epsilon_0 r} \qquad (19.14)$$

Figure 19.27 shows how the potential changes as you move outwards from the centre of the sphere. Notice that the potential is the same everywhere inside the sphere because the electric field is zero.

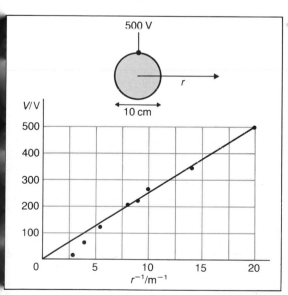

Figure 19.26 Results of a flame probe investigation of the potential around a charged sphere

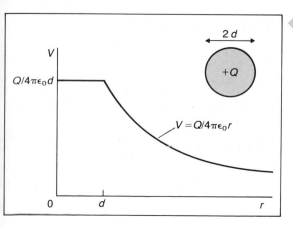

Figure 19.27 Variation of potential around and inside a charged spherical conductor

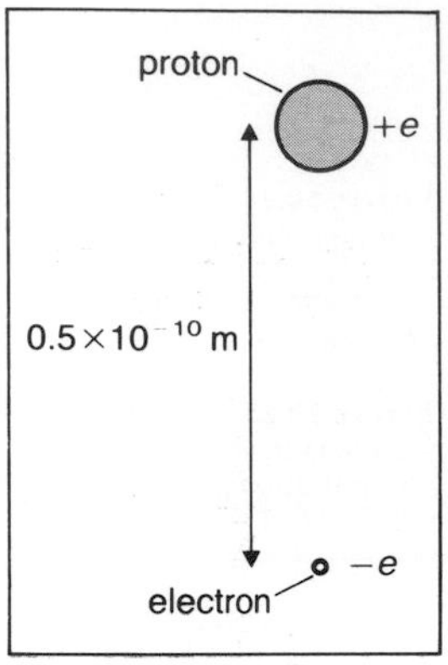

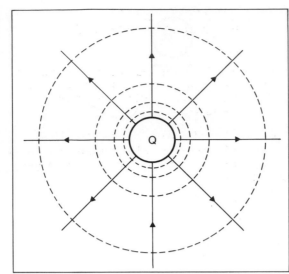

proton

$+e$

0.5×10^{-10} m

electron $\quad \circ \quad -e$

Figure 19.28 Particles in a hydrogen atom

Figure 19.29 The field around a charged sphere

Q

FIELDS INSIDE SPHERES !

Earlier on we assumed that there is no electric field inside a charged conducting sphere. Now that we can describe the field due to a single charge, we can add up the fields inside a sphere due to the charge uniformly spread over its surface. Look at figure 19.30. We want to show that the field at an arbitrary point P is zero. The symmetry of the system means that if there *is* a field at P it has to point towards or away from the centre of the sphere. So we are going to consider the fields due to the areas X and Y at opposite ends of the diameter going through P. (The sizes of X and Y have been exaggerated in the diagram for the sake of clarity.) The field at P due to the small area at X will be given by the following expression. The charge density on the surface of the sphere is σ.

$$E = \frac{q}{4\pi\epsilon_0 r^2} \qquad \therefore E_x = \frac{\sigma A_x}{4\pi\epsilon_0 x^2} \qquad (1)$$

A_x is sufficiently small for it to appear as a point charge at P. A similar expression can be written down for the electric field due to the charge at Y.

$$E_y = \frac{\sigma A_y}{4\pi\epsilon_0 y^2} \qquad (2)$$

These two fields act in opposite directions (figure 9.30). So the net field at P due to the charge at X and Y is as follows.

$$E = \frac{\sigma}{4\pi\epsilon_0}\left(\frac{A_x}{x^2} - \frac{A_y}{y^2}\right), \qquad \frac{A_x}{x^2} = \frac{A_y}{y^2} \qquad \therefore E = 0$$

So the fields due to X and Y cancel each other out exactly. In fact, it can be shown that the field inside a charged conductor of *any* shape is always zero (see chapter 20). This *only* happens because the electric field around a point charge obeys a $1/r^2$ law.

Figure 19.30 The field inside a charged conducting shell is always zero

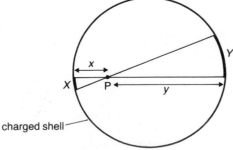

X $\quad$ x $\quad$ P $\quad$ y $\quad$ Y

charged shell

Potential

Equation (19.14) describes the variation of potential around a charged sphere. Notice that it doesn't contain the radius of the sphere, only its total charge. So if you stayed a distance r from the centre of a sphere, there would be no change in your potential if the sphere shrunk down to the size of an electron, provided the total charge on it remained constant. In other words, equation (19.14) describes the variation of potential around a point charge as well as a sphere.

$$V = \frac{q}{4\pi\epsilon_0 r}$$

V is the potential at a point near a single charge (V)

q is the charge (C)

r is the distance of the point from the charge (m)

Let us use this expression to estimate the electrical energy of an electron in a hydrogen atom (figure 19.28). The potential around the proton is given by $V = q/4\pi\epsilon_0 r$, with $q = +1.6\times10^{-19}$ C. If we hold the electron one typical atomic radius away from the proton (0.5×10^{-10} m), then we can calculate the value of the potential at the electron and hence find its energy.

$$V = \frac{q}{4\pi\epsilon_0 r}$$

$$\therefore V = \frac{+1.6\times10^{-19}}{4\pi \times 8.9\times10^{-12} \times 0.5\times10^{-10}} = +29 \text{ V}$$

$$E_e = qV$$

$$\therefore E_e = -1.6\times10^{-19} \times (+29) = -4.6\times10^{-18} \text{ J}$$

The energy of the electron is negative, about -29 eV. You should expect it to be negative as you have to do work on an electron to tear it out of an atom and place it at infinity where E_e is zero. The energy we have just calculated is actually the electrical energy of the whole atom. If you start off by working out the potential at the centre of the atom due to the electron at its edge and then work out the electrical energy of the proton sitting in the middle, you get the same answer, i.e. -29 eV. (To get the total energy of the atom you also need to know something about its kinetic energy, but that is another story altogether!)

Field strength

If the electric potential around a charged sphere is independent of its radius, then so is the electric field strength.

$$E = \frac{q}{4\pi\epsilon_0 r^2}$$

E is the electric field strength at a point (V m^{-1})

q is the charge which creates the field (C)

r is the distance from the charge to the point (m)

The field lines and equipotentials around a single isolated charge are shown in figure 19.29.

Coulomb's Law

Suppose that two small charges q_1 and q_2 are placed a distance r from each other as shown in figure 19.31. The force acting on the charges is given by **Coulomb's Law**.

$$F = qE, \qquad E = \frac{q}{4\pi\epsilon_0 r^2}$$

$$\therefore F = \frac{q_1 q_2}{4\pi\epsilon_0 r^2} \qquad\qquad (19.15)$$

In a sense, equation (19.15) is the end of the road as far as exploring electricity is concerned. It encapsulates everything we know about the electrical interaction between charged particles. The large-scale forces between *any* sets of charged objects can, in principle, be worked out with the help of Coulomb's Law. However, in practice, it is easier to solve such problems by using electric fields or potentials rather than forces.

Verifying Coulomb's Law

Notice how we arrived at Coulomb's Law. We *deduced* it from observations about the variation of potential around charged spheres. Verifying it directly by experiment in a school laboratory is difficult, paradoxically because the electrical force is so strong. As soon as you put a useful amount of charge on an object, it leaks off again!

The standard arrangement of apparatus is shown in figure 19.32. Both balls are made from expanded polystyrene, with a diameter of 10 mm and a mass of 0.10 g. They are coated with aluminium to make them conduct. One of them is fixed to an insulating stand, and the other is suspended from a pair of nylon threads so that it is free to move in a direction parallel to the ruler fastened to the bench underneath. That ruler can be used to measure the deflection of the suspended ball as well as the separation of their centres.

Let's start off by calculating the maximum charge you can put on one of the balls in a standard laboratory environment. If the field strength at the surface of the ball exceeds about 10^6 V m^{-1}, the air around it is likely to ionise and allow the charge to leak away.

$$E = \frac{Q}{4\pi\epsilon_0 r^2}$$

$$\therefore Q = E4\pi\epsilon_0 r^2$$

$$\therefore Q = 10^6 \times 4\pi \times 8.9\times10^{-12} \times (5\times10^{-3})^2 \simeq 3 \text{ nC}$$

Treating it as a capacitor, we can estimate the power supply voltage needed to push this amount of charge onto a ball.

$$V = \frac{Q}{4\pi\epsilon_0 r}$$

$$\therefore V = \frac{3\times10^{-9}}{4\pi \times 8.9\times10^{-12} \times 5\times10^{-3}} \simeq 5 \text{ kV}$$

If both balls have a charge of 3 nC, how big is the repulsive force between them when they are placed with their centres 50 mm apart?

$$F = \frac{q_1 q_2}{4\pi\epsilon_0 r^2}$$

$$\therefore F = \frac{3\times10^{-9} \times 3\times10^{-9}}{4\pi \times 8.9\times10^{-12} \times (50\times10^{-3})^2}$$
$$= 3.2\times10^{-5} \text{ N}$$

How much will this displace the ball on the nylon suspension? Let the tension in the nylon thread be T. Then its angle to the vertical is given by the following formula.

$$F = T\sin\phi, \quad mg = T\cos\phi \quad \therefore F = mg\tan\phi$$

If ϕ is small, then $\phi = x/l$ where x is the displacement of the ball and l is the length of the suspension (50 cm).

$$F = \frac{mgx}{l} \qquad \therefore x = \frac{Fl}{mg}$$

$$\therefore x = \frac{3.2\times10^{-5} \times 0.5}{0.1\times10^{-3} \times 9.81} \simeq 15 \text{ mm}$$

This displacement is measurable, so the experiment is feasible provided that the charge on the balls does not leak away while the measurements are being made. (The charge on each ball can be measured afterwards with a coulomb meter.) The $1/r^2$ dependence of the force can be established by measuring the displacement of the suspended ball for different distances from its centre to the centre of the other ball. However, it should be obvious that the experiment is unlikely to yield a very precise value for ϵ_0: its main objective is to *verify* rather than to make fundamental discoveries.

Van de Graaff generators

A **van de Graaff generator** is a spectacular device which can generate very high voltages by mechanical means. Its use is generally restricted to research laboratories. (High voltages for industry and medicine are usually obtained via transformers, rectifiers and capacitors.) However, a lot of useful physics can be learnt in exploring how a van de Graaff generator works, and its research applications allow the structure of nuclei to be probed.

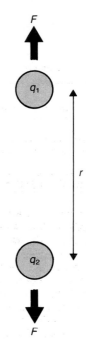

Figure 19.31 Forces between charges

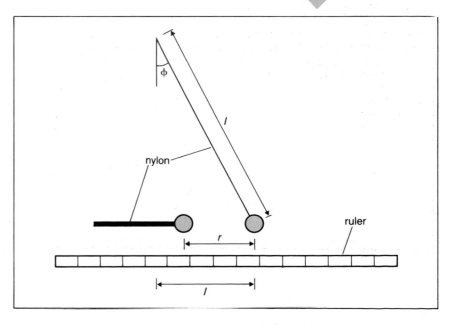

Figure 19.32 Apparatus for verifying Coulomb's Law

Charged spheres

As you can see from figure 19.33, a van de Graaff generator is essentially a hollow conducting sphere (the **dome**) on an insulating stand. A rubber belt carries charge up to it from an earthed conductor below. As the charge builds up on the surface of the dome, the electric field at its surface increases. Breakdown of the air next to the surface of the dome places an upper limit on its voltage. For example, a typical school generator has a dome of diameter 25 cm. You can check for yourself that a breakdown field of 10^6 V m^{-1} limits the voltage of the dome to about 100 kV: this can be increased by either increasing the pressure of the gas around the dome or removing it altogether. Generators which produce 7 MV at a pressure of 27 atmospheres are commonplace in universities.

Charge spraying

Corona discharges at sharp points are used to spray charge onto the belt as it passes over the pulleys. Figure 19.34 will help you to understand how a corona discharge can happen in a low voltage conductor. The two spheres (radius r and R) have been charged and connected by a wire so that they are at the same potential V. (Any difference in potential will cause a flow of charge down the wire until the potentials are the same.) We want to find out which sphere has the largest field strength at its surface.

$$V = \frac{Q}{4\pi\epsilon_0 R} = \frac{q}{4\pi\epsilon_0 r} \quad \therefore \; q = Q \times \frac{r}{R} \quad \textbf{(19.16)}$$

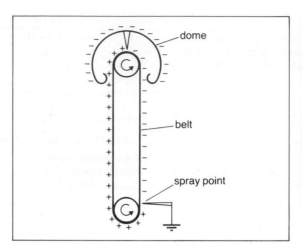

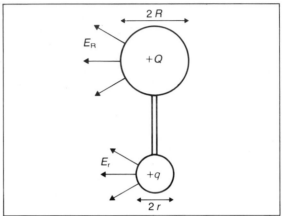

Figure 19.33 A van de Graaff generator

Figure 19.34 Both spheres are at the same potential, but the field at their surfaces is different

Now we can work out the ratio of the fields at the surface.

$$E_r = \frac{q}{4\pi\epsilon_0 r^2}, \quad E_R = \frac{Q}{4\pi\epsilon_0 R^2}$$

$$\therefore E_r = E_R \times \frac{qR^2}{Qr^2} \quad \textbf{(19.17)}$$

If we combine equations (19.16) and (19.17) to eliminate q, we find that the smallest sphere has the largest field strength.

$$E_r \times r = E_R \times R \quad \textbf{(19.18)}$$

So the part of an object which has the smallest radius of curvature is going to have the greatest field strength (and hence charge density) at its surface.

Suppose that the van de Graaff belt is positively charged by friction with its pulleys as it approaches the earthed points (figure 19.35). A negative charge is induced in the points, creating a corona discharge in the air at their tips where the field exceeds 10^6 V m^{-1}. Negative ions created by this discharge are strongly repelled by the points and are therefore sprayed onto the belt, making it negatively charged. The same thing happens when the belt reaches the points inside the sphere. The positive charge induced on the sharp tips of the points sprays positive charge onto the belt, so that the sphere steadily gains electrons. Notice how the electrons which build up on the sphere come from the air near the points rather than from the belt. The charging current in a school van de Graaff machine is approximately 100 nA.

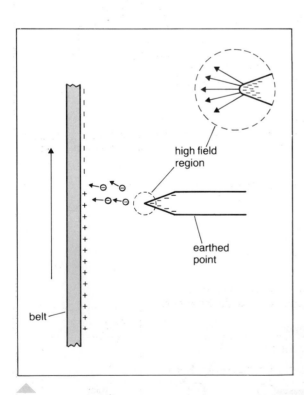

Figure 19.35 Spraying charge from an earthed point onto a moving insulating belt

ACCELERATING NUCLEI   ►► 22

Van de Graaff generators are used to accelerate ions so that their collisions with
stationary atoms can be studied. A **tandem accelerator** for producing high
energy protons is shown in figure 19.36. Negative ions from a low pressure
hydrogen gas discharge are fed into an evacuated tube which runs the length of
the generator. The centre of the generator is held at +7 MV, so the ions have
energies of 7 MeV by the time they reach the centre and shoot through the thin
carbon film. This strips off a couple of electrons from each ion, leaving a proton
which is, of course, positively charged. So it is accelerated down the second
half of the generator, emerging with an energy of 14 MeV.

Machines which produce beams of 14.3 MeV neutrons accelerate deuterium
ions to 100 keV and smash them into a stationary tritium target. The two nuclei
fuse to form a helium nucleus and a high energy neutron which carries away
most of the energy (17.6 Mev) liberated by the mass loss in the reaction. Up to
10^{11} neutrons per second can be generated in this way.

$$^2_1H + ^3_1H \rightarrow ^1_0n + ^4_2He$$

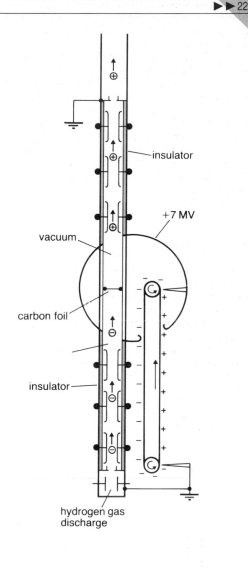

Figure 19.36 A tandem
accelerator for producing
high energy protons

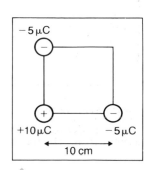

Figure 19.37

OBJECTIVES

After studying this section you should be able to do
the following.

Calculate the field strength and potential around a
charged conducting sphere.

Know that there is no electric field inside a charged
conductor due to the charge on its surface.

Use the formula $C = 4\pi\epsilon_0 r$.

Quote and use the formulae $E = q/4\pi\epsilon_0 r^2$ and
$V = q/4\pi\epsilon_0 r$ for the fields around point charges.

State Coulomb's Law.

Describe an experiment to verify Coulomb's Law.

Explain how a van de Graaff generator works.

Explain why corona discharge occurs at sharp
edges of low voltage conductors.

QUESTIONS

1 A 5.0 cm radius conducting sphere is held at
+ 5.0 kV by a power supply. Calculate the
following quantities:

a the charge on its surface,

b the energy of that charge,

c the field strength at its surface.

d Sketch a graph to show how the field strength
and potential change around and inside the sphere.
Put a scale on the axes.

2 Point charges are placed at three corners of a
square as shown in figure 19.37.

a What is the potential at the fourth corner due to
each of the charges separately?

b What is the total potential at the fourth corner?
How much work would be needed to place a +5 μC
charge on the fourth corner?

c Calculate the field strength at the fourth corner
due to the other three charges — remember the
vector nature of field strength.

d Calculate the total field strength at the fourth corner — quote a size and a direction. (*Hint*: Use vertical and horizontal components.)

e Suppose you wanted to keep a $-8\ \mu C$ charge on the fourth corner. How hard would you have to push it and in what direction?

[3] Pete wants to use the apparatus shown in figure 19.38 to verify Coulomb's Law. Each ball bearing has a diameter of 7.0 mm and is glued onto an insulating perspex rod. The balance (precision ±0.01 g) measures the apparent mass change of one ball as the other is moved towards it. The ruler can be used to measure the separation of the centres of the balls.

a Pete touches the dome of a van de Graaff generator with one of the balls. If the breakdown field strength that day is 3×10^6 V m^{-1}, estimate how much charge the ball picks up.

b Pete then touches the uncharged ball with the charged ball. How much charge does each ball hold now? Does the charge have more or less energy than before?

c How close will Pete have to get the balls before he can detect any force between them? Will the mass of the lower ball appear to increase or decrease?

d Kate reckons that Pete would be better off if he used smaller balls because he would be able to get them closer together. Pete points out that he would be able to get less charge on the balls if they were smaller. What do you think? Would it be better for him to use larger or smaller balls?

[4] At one time, the radius of an electron was estimated by supposing that its mass was a consequence of its electrical energy.

a Write down an expression for the electrical energy of -1.6×10^{-19} C of charge spread evenly over the surface of a sphere of radius r.

b Use the Einstein mass−energy relationship $\Delta E = mc^2$ to estimate r($c = 3\times10^8$ m s^{-1}, $m = 9.1\times10^{-31}$ kg).

[5] The radius of a nucleus is given by the approximate relationship $r = r_0 A^{1/3}$ where $r_0 = 1.2\times10^{-15}$ m and A is the number of particles in the nucleus. Provided that nuclei do not touch, you can assume that the interaction between them is purely electrical.

a An alpha particle is a helium nucleus with two neutrons and two protons. Treating it as a charged conducting sphere, what is its electrical energy?

b Alpha particles from americium-241 have kinetic energies of 5.49 MeV. Suppose that an alpha particle has a head-on collision with an iron nucleus (26 protons, 28 neutrons). Describe how the kinetic energy of the particle changes during the collision. Estimate the momentum and kinetic energy (in MeV) transferred to the iron nucleus in the process — assume an elastic collision.

c How close do the centres of the nuclei get during the collision? Do they touch each other?

[6] The Earth as a whole carries a negative charge, giving a field strength of 120 V m^{-1} at its surface in fine weather.

a If the radius of the Earth is 6.4×10^6 m, estimate how much negative charge it holds.

b Sharp points on the Earth's surface allow its charge to leak into the atmosphere. Explain how they do it.

c Thunderclouds resemble parallel plate capacitors, with positive charge in their top layers and negative charge in their bottom layers (figure 19.39). (They become charged by friction between water droplets and air.) A lightning conductor (a sharp point thrust in the ground) can discharge the lower part of the cloud safely. Explain how it does it.

[7] A school van de Graaff generator is able to create long sparks between its dome (radius 20 cm) and an identical earthed sphere placed nearby. When the closest distance between the sphere surfaces is 50 mm, there is one spark every 3.0 s.

a Assuming that the breakdown field strength for dry air is 3×10^6 V m^{-1}, estimate how much charge is transferred in each spark.

b Estimate the average current in the moving belt.

c How much power, in the absence of friction, does the van de Graaff motor have to provide?

d Estimate the force between the spheres *just* before a spark. Would you be able to feel it?

[8] Factories which have sheets of plastic moving rapidly over rollers often have a series of earthed points placed so that the plastic passes close underneath. Explain to the factory supervisor what these points are for and how they work.

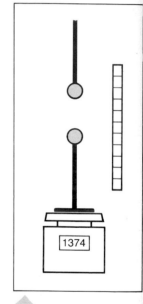

Figure 19.38

Figure 19.39

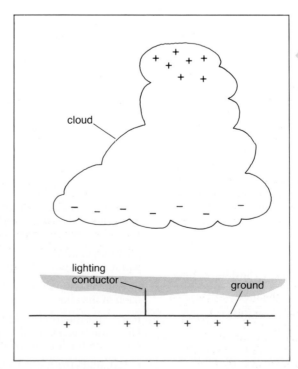

20

G R A V I T Y

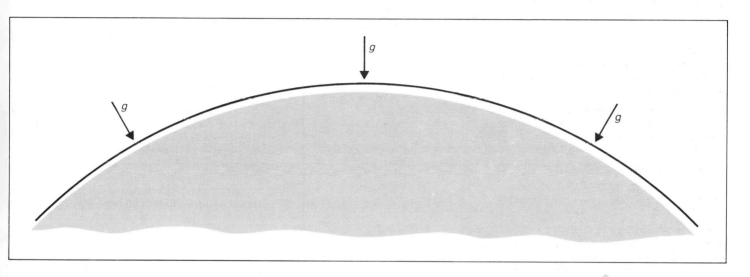

Figure 20.1 The gravitational field of the Earth points towards its centre

It is often claimed that gravity keeps your feet firmly planted on the ground. Yet gravity also keeps hot-air balloons in the sky and ensures that communications satellites keep above the same spot on Earth all the time. Gravity was the first of the four forces in nature to be probed in depth, yet its origins and mechanism are still shrouded in mystery today. This chapter aims to present you with Newton's model of gravity and some evidence which supports it, before initiating you into the physics of satellites and space flight.

UNIVERSAL GRAVITATION

You have a lifetime's practical experience of gravity forces. (The fact that unsupported objects fall downwards is readily grasped by children when they learn how to walk.) However, intuition is a poor substitute for experiment, so we are going to start off by taking you through what can be learnt about gravity in the laboratory. Ultimately, we will have to make measurements of the solar system itself to make really precise tests of any model of gravitation.

Earth-based evidence

The gravitational force on an object is, of course, its weight. By now, the evidence that the weight of an object is proportional to its mass should be overwhelming. So you can think of Earth-bound objects as sitting in a (vector) force field with a strength and direction at every point in space. The **gravitational field strength** g, by analogy with electric field strength E, is the gravity force per kilogram.

$$\mathbf{F} = mg$$

F is the gravitational force on an object (N)

m is the mass of the object (kg)

g is the gravitational field strength ($N\,kg^{-1}$)

Gravity field sensors

A spring balance supporting a 1 kg mass makes a very good gravitational field strength sensor. The extension of its spring tells you the size of the field strength and its angle tells you the direction. A few minutes with such a sensor in a laboratory provides convincing evidence that the local gravity field is uniform. It points downwards (directly away from the sky) and has a strength of $9.81\,N\,kg^{-1}$. Measurements made further afield with sensitive spring balances confirm that **g** always points directly towards the ground (figure 20.1), but that its value does vary slightly from one place to another. This can be partly accounted for by the rotation of the Earth about its axis. There are also small local variations due to the different density of the rocks directly underneath and the slight flattening of the Earth at its poles.

ROTATIONAL CORRECTIONS !

A spring balance measures the force F_B needed to keep the test mass m in static equilibrium. If the Earth was not rotating, the gravity force F_G would be equal and opposite to F_B. However, if that mass is moving with a velocity v in a circle of radius r, then the resultant force of F_B and F_G must be the centripetal force F_C (figure 20.2).

$$F_C = F_G + F_B \qquad (1)$$

The centripetal force must point directly towards the axis of rotation. Since the centripetal force is pretty small anyway, we can get away with just considering its component parallel to F_G and assume that F_B acts directly upwards.

$$\frac{mv^2}{r}\cos\theta = mg - F_B \qquad \therefore F_B = m\left(g - \frac{v^2}{r}\cos\theta\right)$$

$$\therefore g' = g - \frac{v^2}{r}\cos\theta$$

If the Earth is assumed to be spherical with a radius R and an angular velocity ω, we can work out the apparent gravitational field strength g' at angle θ.

$$r = R\cos\theta, \quad v = r\omega \qquad \therefore g' = g - R\omega^2\cos^2\theta \qquad (3)$$

The radius of the earth is 6.4×10^6 m and its angular velocity is $2\pi/(24\times60\times60)$ = 7.3×10^{-5} rad s^{-1}, so $R\omega^2$ is only 3.4×10^{-2}, about 3% of the value of g.

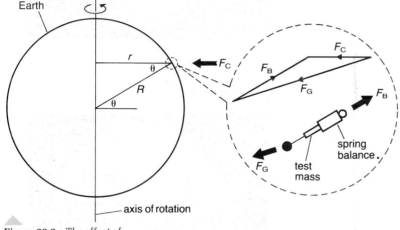

Figure 20.2 The effect of centripetal force on the apparent value of g

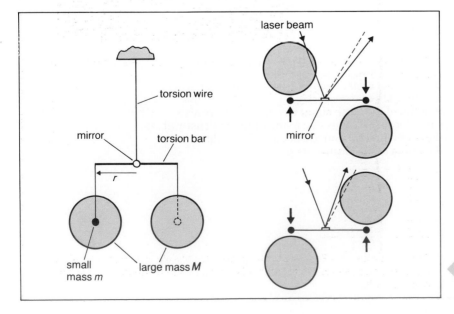

Laboratory experiments

The fact that all objects on the surface of the Earth are pulled towards it is a strong indication that the mass of the Earth itself is the source of the gravity field. The modern apparatus shown in figure 20.3 can be used to investigate the gravity field around a massive sphere: the method was first used by Henry Cavendish in 1798. Two small test masses m are suspended from a thin quartz wire in a draught-proof enclosure. The laser beam reflected off the mirror on the torsion bar falls on a scale so that its deflection can be detected. The deflection θ of the torsion bar is proportional to the couple Γ acting on it.

$$\Gamma = c\theta \qquad \textbf{(20.1)}$$

Two large masses M are placed very near the test masses. The attractive force between the large and small masses applies a couple to the torsion bar, deflecting it slightly. (Typically, the force is only 10^{-10} N!) Then the large masses are swung round through 180° so that they deflect the torsion bar in the opposite direction.

Measurement of the field strength around the large masses requires a knowledge of the torsion constant c. This can be found by displacing the torsion bar from equilibrium and finding the period T of its oscillations. (This can be at least a couple of minutes.)

$$T = 2\pi(I/c)^{\frac{1}{2}} \qquad \textbf{(20.2)}$$

The moment of inertia I of the torsion bar is approximately equal to $2mr^2$ if the test masses are heavy enough.

The experiment is very difficult to do because of the smallness of the field around the large masses. (It is roughly 2×10^{-7} N kg^{-1} at the surface of a lead sphere of diameter 10 cm.) External vibration and air currents inside the apparatus due to temperature gradients can easily swamp the effect being looked for. Nevertheless, it is the best technique yet found for making detailed measurements of the strength of the gravitational field at the surface of a spherical mass. However, it is useless for exploring how the field strength changes as you move away from its source.

The Earth's field

The Cavendish experiment gives convincing proof that there *is* an attraction between two masses. We can use Newton's Laws of Motion to predict how the strength of the gravitational field around an object depends on its mass, but we have to use extra-terrestrial apparatus to find out how it varies with distance! We start with the mass dependence.

Figure 20.3 Apparatus for measuring the gravitational force between pairs of masses

Figure 20.4 The masses exert equal and opposite forces on each other

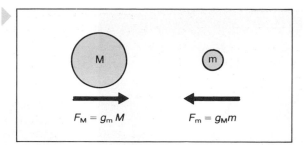

$$F_M = g_m M \qquad F_m = g_M m$$

Mass dependence

Look at figure 20.4. The field around the mass M exerts a force F_m on the mass m placed nearby. Similarly, the field due to the mass m exerts a force F_M on the large mass. If the two masses are an isolated system, then Newton's Third Law can be invoked to say that the two forces must have the same size F and opposite directions.

$$F = F_m = F_M \qquad \text{(20.3)}$$

THE MOON'S ORBIT

The Earth–Moon system (figures 20.5 and 20.6) is a suitable piece of apparatus for investigating gravitational fields. (It was used by Isaac Newton in about 1670 to test his own ideas about gravitation.) The Moon moves around the Earth in a near-circular orbit with a period of 27.29 days (figure 20.7). The distance from the Moon to the Earth can be measured by radar methods. A brief pulse of electromagnetic radiation (microwaves or laser light) is fired at the Moon and the time taken for it to be reflected back to Earth is measured. The delay is about 2 s, giving 3.84×10^8 m for the radius of the Moon's orbit.

Let us guess that the Earth's field strength obeys the following law, where r is the distance from the centre of the Earth and n an unknown number:

$$g = \frac{c}{r^n} \qquad \text{(1)}$$

We already know that the value of g at the Earth's surface (6.37×10^6 m from its centre) is 9.81 N kg^{-1}, so we can get a value for the constant c.

$$g = \frac{c}{r^n} \qquad \therefore \quad 9.81 = \frac{c}{(6.37 \times 10^6)^n}$$

$$\therefore g = 9.81 \times \frac{(6.37 \times 10^6)^n}{r^n} \qquad \text{(2)}$$

If we can find out what g is at the Moon we should have enough data to find n. Suppose that the strength of the Earth's field at the centre of the Moon is g_m: that field provides the centripetal force for the Moon's motion (figure 20.7).

$$F = \frac{mv^2}{r}, \quad F = mg \quad \therefore \quad g_m = \frac{v^2}{r} \qquad \text{(3)}$$

$$v = r\omega, \quad T = \frac{2\pi}{\omega} \quad \therefore \quad \frac{v^2}{r} = \frac{4\pi^2 r}{T^2} \qquad \text{(4)}$$

Combining equations (3) and (4) we can calculate the strength of the Earth's field at the Moon.

$$g_m = \frac{4\pi^2 r}{T^2} \quad \therefore \quad g_m = \frac{4\pi^2 \times 3.84 \times 10^8}{(27.29 \times 24 \times 60 \times 60)^2} = 2.73 \times 10^{-3} \, \text{N kg}^{-1}$$

Figure 20.5 A source of gravitational field . . . .

Figure 20.6 . . . . . and an orbiting test mass in that field

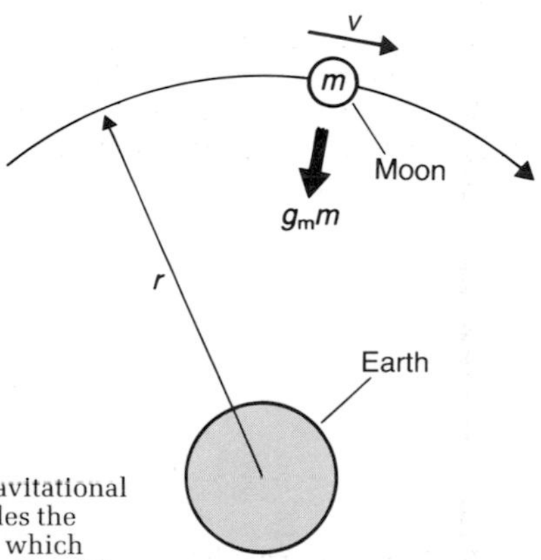

Equation (2) predicts what g_m should be. Table 1 gives values obtained from a number of values of n.

$$g_m = 9.81 \times \left(\frac{6.37 \times 10^6}{3.84 \times 10^8} \right)^n \qquad \text{(5)}$$

Table 1

n	g_m/N kg^{-1}
0.5	1.26×10^{-0}
1.0	1.63×10^{-1}
1.5	2.09×10^{-2}
2.0	2.70×10^{-3}
2.5	3.48×10^{-4}
3.0	4.48×10^{-5}

As you can see, $n = 2$ gives a pretty good fit to the data (within about 1%). So the evidence points to gravity fields obeying an inverse-square law, just like electric fields.

Figure 20.7 Gravitational attraction provides the centripetal force which keep the Moon in its orbit around the Earth

Now think about the strength of the field around each mass due to the other mass.

$$F_m = mg_M, \quad F_M = Mg_m$$

$$\therefore F \propto mM$$

$$\therefore g_m \propto m$$

$$\therefore g_M \propto M \qquad \qquad \textbf{(20.4)}$$

So the strength of the gravitational field around an object ought to be proportional to its mass. This is why objects on the face of the Earth do not appear to be attracted to you by gravitation. If it takes the Earth's 6×10^{24} kg to obtain a field strength of only 10 N kg^{-1}, the field strength around an object whose mass is only 70 kg is likely to be utterly negligible.

Planetary orbits

Of course, establishing a general law with a single experiment is not good scientific practice. So we need to do some other experiments to verify that $g \propto 1/r^2$. The planets (figure 20.8) orbiting around the Sun are the only other large scale masses which we can make measurements on, so we (like Newton) are going to have to use them for our apparatus. Table 20.1 summarises what we know about the motion of some planets from direct measurement. (We have only listed information for planets which have nearly circular orbits.) Can a $1/r^2$ gravitational field predict a relationship between the orbit radius r and the period T?

Table 20.1

Planet	r/m	T/s
Venus	1.08×10^{11}	1.94×10^7
Earth	1.50×10^{11}	3.15×10^7
Mars	2.28×10^{11}	5.93×10^7
Jupiter	7.78×10^{11}	3.74×10^8
Saturn	1.43×10^{12}	9.29×10^8
Uranus	2.87×10^{12}	2.65×10^9

Let's assume that each planet has a circular orbit of radius r around the Sun. The gravitational field strength experienced by a planet is given by the following expression.

$$g = \frac{GM}{r^2} \qquad \qquad \textbf{(20.5)}$$

G is an unknown constant of proportionality and M is the mass of the source of the field, the Sun. If the planet has a mass m, then we can write down an expression for its centripetal force.

$$F = \frac{mv^2}{r}, \quad F = mg \qquad \therefore mg = \frac{mv^2}{r}$$

$$g = \frac{GM}{r^2} \quad \therefore \quad \frac{GM}{r} = v^2 \qquad \qquad \textbf{(20.6)}$$

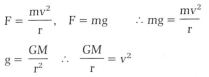

Figure 20.8 Some of the planets in the Solar System

Figure 20.9 Experimental data supporting Kepler's Third Law

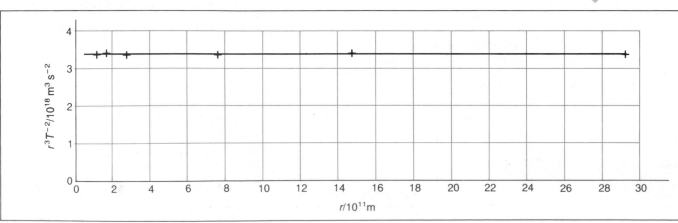

The speed v of the planet is related to its period T and orbit perimeter $2\pi r$.

$$v = \frac{2\pi r}{T} \quad \therefore \frac{GM}{r} = \left(\frac{2\pi r}{T}\right)^2$$

$$\therefore \frac{r^3}{T^2} = \frac{GM}{4\pi^2} \qquad \qquad \textbf{(20.7)}$$

Equation (20.7) is often known as **Kepler's Third Law.** The graph of figure 20.9 shows that data from table 20.1 are in excellent agreement with equation (20.7), and supplies further evidence that there is indeed an inverse square field around a spherical mass. (Why didn't we draw a graph of r^3 against T^2 and put a straight line through the six points?) Furthermore, it can be shown that both circular and elliptical orbits are possible in an inverse-square field. In fact, the assumption of inverse-square fields around spherical masses allows us to account for planetary motion to well within the precision of observations. (The orbits of the two outermost planets, Neptune and Pluto, were deduced from perturbations in the orbits of the other planets well before they were observed directly. The gravity forces from the outermost planets slightly alter the orbits of the other planets.)

Universal gravitation

Having established the basic facts about gravity we can now summarise them precisely with formulae for the field strength and potential around point masses. Furthermore, since the field is proportional to $1/r^2$, we can state some rules for the fields around and inside spherical mass distributions which make the formulae easy to use.

Field strength
The gravitational force between two masses is attractive, so the field always points towards its source (figure 20.11). The convention is to treat the direction *away* from the source as being positive, so g is always going to be negative.

$$g = -\frac{GM}{r^2}$$

g is the strength of the field caused by a point mass ($N\,kg^{-1}$)

G is the gravitational constant ($6.67 \times 10^{-11}\,N\,m^2\,kg^{-2}$)

M is the mass of the field's source (kg)

r is the distance from the source of the field (m)

G is the **Newtonian gravitational constant.** Its value has to be established by experiment, using apparatus similar to that shown in figure 20.3. The best value we have today is only accurate to 0.01%. (The value of ϵ_0 is known to within 0.0001%.)

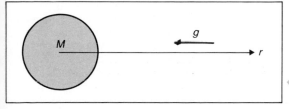

Figure 20.11 Gravitational fields always point towards their source

The Solar System was man's first laboratory. Much of the written information which has come down to us from the ancient civilisations is concerned with recording and predicting the motion of the Sun, Moon and planets. The period of a planet's orbit is relatively easy to measure. You simply watch it move night after night against the background of fixed stars and measure the time taken for it to do one complete cycle. But measuring the radius of its orbit is not so easy, because we have to make our observations from an orbiting platform. Look at figure 20.10. If you assume that both the Earth (E) and the planet (P) have circular orbits, then a series of observations of the angle ϕ between the directions of the planet and the Sun from the Earth can be used to find the ratio of the orbits' radii. Observations of the motion of the planets can therefore be used to establish the radius of their orbit relative to that of the Earth. Radar measurements can then be used to find the radius of the Earth's orbit around the Sun.

Figure 20.10 We observe the planets from a moving platform

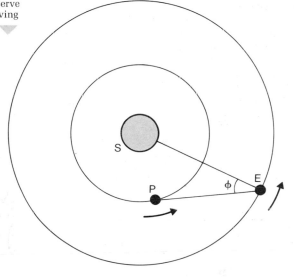

Potential
The gravitational potential V_g around a point mass is related to the field strength by the usual relationship. (The field strength is proportional to the potential gradient.)

$$g = -\frac{dV_g}{dr} \quad \therefore -\frac{GM\,dr}{r^2} = -dV_g$$

$$\therefore \int dV_g = GM \int \frac{dr}{r^2} \qquad \textbf{(20.8)}$$

Equation (20.8) can be integrated with the help of Appendix B and the convention that $V_g = 0$ when $r = \infty$.

$$V_g = -\frac{GM}{r} + c$$

$$\therefore 0 = -\frac{GM}{\infty} + c \quad \therefore c = 0 \qquad \textbf{(20.9)}$$

$$V_g = -\frac{GM}{r}$$

V_g is the gravitational potential due to a point mass ($J\,kg^{-1}$)

M is the mass of the field source (kg)

r is the distance from the point mass (m)

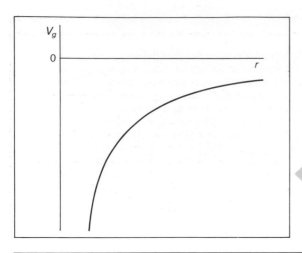

Figure 20.12 shows how the gravitational potential changes around a spherical mass. Notice that it is always negative, because gravitational forces are always attractive.

Figure 20.12 Variation of V_g with r for a small spherical mass

Figure 20.13 Variation of g with r for a spherical mass of uniform density

Spherical sources

The value of g around a spherical distribution of mass (figure 20.13) *only* depends on the mass M and your distance r from the centre of the sphere. Furthermore, if you are inside a massive sphere a distance r from its centre, then the local field strength is *only* due to the mass inside a sphere of radius r. Both of these facts can be explained in terms of the field strength in and around a spherical shell of radius R and mass M (figure 20.14).

$$g = -\frac{GM}{r^2}, \qquad V_g = -\frac{GM}{r} \quad \text{when } r > R$$

$$g = 0, \quad V_g = -\frac{GM}{R} \quad \text{when } r < R \qquad \text{(20.10)}$$

If you consider a solid sphere to be built up from concentric shells, then only the shells between you and the centre are going to contribute to your local field strength. So if a sphere has a radius R and a density ρ, the field strength a distance r from the centre is given by the following pair of equations (see figure 20.15):

$$g = -\frac{4\pi G\rho r}{3} \quad \text{when } r < R$$

$$g = -\frac{4\pi G\rho R^3}{3r^2} \quad \text{when } r > R \qquad \text{(20.11)}$$

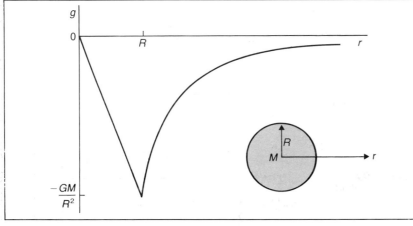

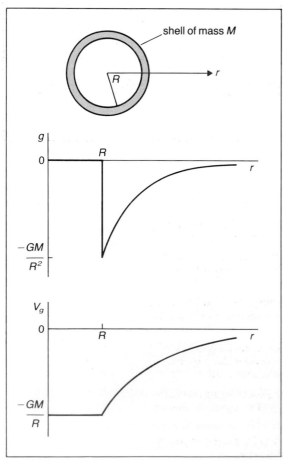

Figure 20.14 The field and potential in and around a spherical shell

Figure 20.15 The field decreases as you move towards the centre of a massive sphere

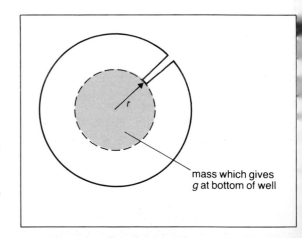

mass which gives g at bottom of well

THE FIFTH FORCE?

Recent experiments indicated that there might be more to gravity than Newton supposed. Measurements of the variation of g at the Earth's surface as a delicate forcemeter was lowered down boreholes or raised up high towers gave results which did not agree exactly with Newton's inverse-square law of gravitation. (The density of the rocks at the Earth's surface can be used to predict how g should vary as you go into the Earth. The fact that the Earth is not a perfect sphere makes the calculation fairly complicated.) The results of the experiments suggested that there is an extra short-range component to gravity (a fifth force), making it stronger than predicted by the inverse-square law when masses are close together. However, there is much controversy about this fifth force and the experimental results are not conclusive. Of course, the success of the inverse square law in modelling planetary motion means that Newton was certainly right about the long-range gravitational interaction between masses.

POTENTIALS AROUND SHELLS

Both electrical and gravitational fields obey an inverse-square law. This has interesting and useful consequences for the fields inside and outside spherical distributions of charge or mass. We are now going to show you how those consequences can be established by integration over a thin spherical shell. The shell shown in figure 20.16 has a surface mass density σ. So the total mass in the shaded ring is given by

$$\Delta m = \sigma \times R\Delta\theta \times 2\pi R\sin\theta = 2\pi\sigma R^2\sin\theta\Delta\theta \qquad (1)$$

All of the mass in that ring is a distance x from the point P. So we can write down its contribution to the potential at P as follows:

$$\Delta V_g = -\frac{G\Delta m}{r} \qquad \therefore \ \Delta V_g = -\frac{G2\pi\sigma R^2\sin\theta\Delta\theta}{x} \qquad (2)$$

We can obtain an expression for x by applying the cosine rule (Appendix B) to the triangle shown in figure 20.16.

$$x^2 = R^2 + r^2 - 2Rr\cos\theta \qquad (3)$$

If we combine equations (2) and (3) and sum the contributions from all the rings in the shell, we end up with the potential at P.

$$\int dV_g = \int_0^\pi -\frac{G2\pi\sigma R^2\sin\theta \ d\theta}{(R^2 + r^2 - 2Rr\cos\theta)^{\frac{1}{2}}} \qquad (4)$$

The integral does not look very inviting, but don't worry about that! Before we use a computer to integrate it, we can tidy it up a bit.

$$\sigma = \frac{M}{4\pi R^2} \qquad \therefore \ V_g = -GM \times \int_0^\pi \frac{\sin\theta \ d\theta}{2(R^2 + r^2 - 2Rr\cos\theta)^{\frac{1}{2}}} \qquad (5)$$

The following program written in BASIC can be used to find the integral for various values of r. We have set $R = 1$, so $r > 1$ gives the potential outside the shell and $r < 1$ gives the potential inside the sphere.

```
10 INPUT R
20 LET I = 0
30 FOR THETA = 0 TO 3.14159 STEP 0.005
40 I = I + SIN(THETA)*0.005/(2*SQR(1 + R*R − 2*R*COS(THETA)))
50 NEXT THETA
60 PRINT I
70 END
```

The graph of figure 20.17 shows how the computed value of the integral depends on r. Outside the shell it is $1/r$ and inside the shell it is 1 (i.e. $1/R$). So equation (5) says the same thing as equation (20.10).

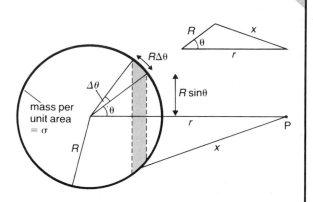

Figure 20.16 Computing the potential due to a thin shell

Figure 20.17 The results of the numerical integration

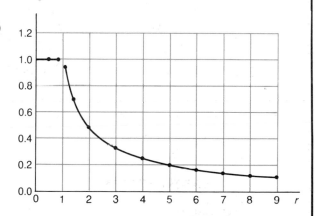

OBJECTIVES

After studying this section you should be able to do the following.

Use the formula $\mathbf{F} = m\mathbf{g}$.

Describe a laboratory experiment to demonstrate the gravitational attraction between two objects.

Quote $g = -GM/r^2$ for the field strength outside a sphere of mass M.

Show that $r^3/T^2 = GM/4\pi^2$ for a planet in circular orbit around a sun of mass M.

Use the formula $V_g = -GM/r$ for the gravitational potential outside a sphere.

Know that the field inside an empty spherical shell is zero.

QUESTIONS

1 The mean radius of the Earth is 6 371 km, and the average value of g at its surface is 9.8 N kg^{-1}.

a Write down an expression for g in terms of the mass of the Earth. Use it to find the mass of the Earth.

b What is the value of g at a height of 300 km above the Earth's surface (typical altitude of a man-made satellite)?

c The mean density of the rocks on the surface of the Earth is 2 600 kg m^{-3}. How does this compare with the mean density of the whole Earth?

d On the assumption that the Earth has a uniform density, calculate the change of g as you go down a 500 m mineshaft.

e In fact, the value of g usually increases as you go further underground. Explain why.

2 Use the data provided in table 20.1 to calculate the mass of the Sun. How big is the gravitational force between the Earth and the Sun? If Mercury orbits the Sun with a period of 0.24 years, what is its distance from the centre of the Sun?

3 Gravity forces are only perceptible on a large scale. So gravity controls the ultimate fate of the universe, but is utterly negligible on a sub-atomic scale. This question should help you see why this is so.

a Two iron spheres of radius 6 m are placed with their centres 100 m apart. Calculate the gravity force pulling them together (ρ = 7 860 kg m^{-3} for iron).

b Calculate what happens to the force if every dimension is increased by a factor of 10^6, so that each sphere is the size of the Earth.

c Calculate the gravity force between a proton and an electron which are 1.0×10^{-10} m apart. How much larger is the electrostatic attraction between the particles?

4 Very sensitive spring balances are used by oil prospectors to detect local variations in g which might signify changes in the rock density deep underground. Suppose that you used a 10 g mass on the end of a spring with a force constant of 5 N m^{-1} and measured changes of its extension with a microscope to within 10 μm — how small a change in g could you detect? What precautions would you have to take in using the apparatus in the field? Would a larger mass and a weaker spring be better or worse in the field?

5 Both electrical and gravitational forces obey an inverse-square law, so it is very tempting to suppose that they are different aspects of just one force. At one time it was proposed that gravity could be accounted for by having the value of ϵ_0 slightly smaller for interactions between particles of different charge than particles of the same charge. So two identical atoms would be attracted to each other.

a Consider two hydrogen atoms (one electron, one proton) separated by a distance r. Calculate the percentage difference of the values for ϵ_0 necessary for this theory to account for gravity.

b Some time later, the existence of neutrons was established. Explain why this killed off the 'different-ϵ_0' theory of gravity.

c Another theory assumes that massive objects continually emit small particles (gravitons) which travel outwards at the speed of light. The rate of emission of particles is proportional to the mass of the object. Any other object which absorbs these particles feels a force towards their source. Explain why this theory gives an inverse-square force law.

d Do you think it matters if all you really know about gravity is a precise formula for the forces between point masses? Isn't the mechanism behind the force also important?

6 Table 20.2 shows how the velocity v of an Apollo spacecraft changed as it coasted directly away from the Earth with its rockets switched off. The total mass of the spacecraft was 34 000 kg; r is its distance from the centre of the Earth.

a Radio waves were used to simultaneously measure the position and velocity of the spacecraft relative to the surface of the Earth. Suggest how.

Table 20.2

r/m	v/m s^{-1}
1.10×10^7	8.41×10^3
5.44×10^7	3.63×10^3
1.70×10^8	1.80×10^3
2.09×10^8	1.53×10^3

b If the total mass of the Earth is 5.98×10^{24} kg, show that any loss of kinetic energy of the spacecraft as it moves away from the Earth is roughly equal to its gain of gravitational energy. Why doesn't the system appear to conserve energy exactly? (There is virtually no friction in space!)

c If the spacecraft continued to coast, how far would it get from the Earth before starting to drift back? (Assume that the Moon has been conveniently moved out of the way.)

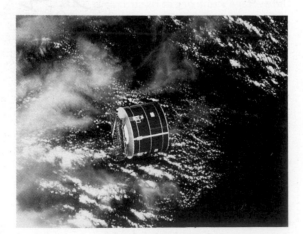

Figure 20.18 A communications satellite

SATELLITES

The economic and social significance of satellites for tomorrow's citizens cannot be underestimated. Apart from their obvious military uses, satellites can be used for world-wide monitoring of resources, pollution and the general health of the planet. Increasingly, satellites are being used for trans-continental communications, involving both television and telephones, making the world a smaller and safer place to live.

Orbits

Two separate classes of orbit are used for satellites. Communications satellites (figure 20.18) are in **geostationary** orbits above the equator so that they stay above the same patch of land surface all the time. Signals from the Earth are beamed up to the satellite via microwaves and then beamed back down again. Survey satellites generally use **polar** orbits, perpendicular to the equator, so that they pass over different patches of land surface on each orbit. It is useful to have the same level of illumination on each pass over a patch of land so that comparisons can be made. The orbit period is therefore an integral fraction of 24 hours, so that the satellite always passes overhead at the same time of day.

Energy of satellites

A satellite in orbit around the Earth has a certain amount of energy, some of which has to be given to it by the rockets which lift it into orbit. Let's work out the energy needed to place a 1 500 kg communications satellite in a circular geostationary orbit. The first step is to find the radius of the orbit by equating the centripetal force (mv^2/r) with the gravitational force.

$$\frac{mv^2}{r} = \frac{GMm}{r^2}, \qquad v = \frac{2\pi r}{T}$$

$$\therefore \frac{r^3}{T^2} = \frac{GM}{4\pi^2} \qquad\qquad (20.12)$$

We can calculate a value for GM from the known value of g at the surface of the Earth, 6.37×10^6 m from its centre.

$$g = \frac{GM}{R^2}$$

$$\therefore GM = gR^2 \quad \therefore GM = 3.98\times10^{14}\ \text{m}^3\ \text{s}^{-2}$$

Plugging this into equation (20.12), we obtain a value for the radius of a geostationary orbit.

$$\frac{r^3}{T^2} = \frac{GM}{4\pi^2} \quad \therefore r^3 = \frac{GMT^2}{4\pi^2}$$

$$T = 24\times60\times60 = 86\ 400\ \text{s} \quad \therefore r = 4.22\times10^7\ \text{m}$$

Now we can calculate the kinetic and potential energy of the satellite in order to find its total energy.

$$E_k = \tfrac{1}{2}mv^2, \qquad \frac{mv^2}{r} = \frac{GMm}{r^2}$$

$$\therefore E_k = \frac{GMm}{2r} \qquad\qquad (20.13)$$

$$\therefore E_t = E_k + E_g = \frac{GMm}{2r} - \frac{GMm}{r} = -\frac{GMm}{2r}$$

$$\therefore E_t = -7.07\times10^9\ \text{J}$$

Of course, the satellite will have some energy when it is sitting on top of its rocket before launching. Its kinetic energy is negligible (you can check this for yourself), so we only need to consider its gravitational energy.

$$E_g = -\frac{GMm}{R} = -9.37\times10^{10}\ \text{J}$$

A single communications satellite may have a lifetime of only 10 years, limited by the amount of fuel it can carry for orientation and orbit corrections. (The on-board circuitry is run by electricity from an array of solar cells.) However, a satellite can provide a long-distance telephone network for a developing country which is quicker and cheaper to implement than a land-based system. Furthermore, a simpler satellite can provide the whole country with TV signals, relaying them over a wide area of the Earth's surface from a single Earth-bound transmitter. The consequences for education and social cohesion in a developing country are obvious.

The most familiar use of a survey satellite is for weather forecasting. A satellite in geostationary orbit can take high resolution TV pictures (figure 20.19) to show cloud formations and continuously transmit them back to Earth for analysis. However, satellites can in fact make images at several wavelengths, ranging from visible to deep infra-red, by using a range of detectors in parallel. The detectors are semiconducting materials which become conductive when light of the appropriate wavelength hits them. There may only be one detector with a mirror scanning the Earth to build up an image or there may be a line of them which build up a picture as the satellite sweeps forward. The recent SPOT commercial survey satellite uses a line of 1728 detectors, giving a resolution of about 30 m on the ground, more than enough for crop detection.

Many features invisible to the human eye become glaringly obvious in the infra-red (see figure 20.20). In particular, the healthiness of crops can be determined from satellite images, so that plans may be made to cope with gluts or shortages at harvest time. Oil pollution from tankers in mid-ocean is easily spotted. The thermal efficiency of housing can be rapidly assessed on a national scale. Satellite information can show how rapidly the globe is being deforested; it can accurately map the advance of deserts and it can provide information about large-scale weather patterns — the list of applications is almost endless.

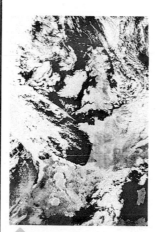

Figure 20.19 A picture of the Earth's surface taken by a weather satellite

Figure 20.20 Landsat image of Mobile, Alabama, USA, showing the large natural harbour around the city

The energy required from the rocket will be the difference between its energy in orbit and its energy on the ground, i.e. 8.66×10^{10} J. To put this in perspective, it is the chemical energy of about 2 tonnes of petrol. The launch vehicle itself will have a mass of about 200 tonnes, most of which will be fuel (figure 20.21). So the cost, in terms of energy alone, of placing a satellite in orbit is high. However, the returns for that expenditure can be valuable beyond measure.

Launch
The trajectory followed by the satellite during lift-off is shown in figure 20.22. The initial part of the flight is vertical to minimise the time spent in the high friction environment of the lower atmosphere. Sometime before the main thrusters switch off and fall back to Earth, the trajectory is curved to give the satellite some horizontal momentum. When the thrusters have been detached, the satellite carries on in free fall. The trajectory is designed so that the highest point in free fall is the required orbit: when it gets there, rockets give the satellite the velocity it needs to stay in orbit. Without that final thrust, the satellite will inevitably fall back into the Earth's atmosphere and burn up. Of course, working out the trajectory of the satellite with the thrusters on or off is going to be tricky because of the decrease in field strength as it gains altitude. Each time a satellite is successfully placed in orbit, Newton's Law of Gravitation has survived a test!

Figure 20.21 The Voyager rocket on its launchpad

Figure 20.22 Trajectory of a satellite during launch

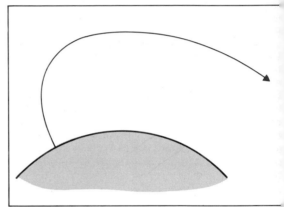

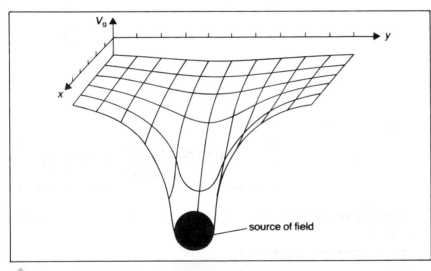

Figure 20.23 A model of the distortion of space around a massive object

Figure 20.24 The maximum altitude of a spacecraft depends on its initial kinetic energy

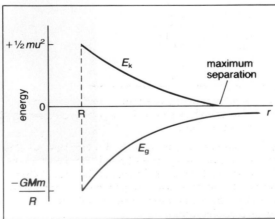

Escaping gravity

Einstein modelled a gravitational field as a distortion of space around a massive object. This is a useful model to have if you are prepared to think only in two spatial dimensions and reserve the third dimension for energy, as shown in figure 20.23. The horizontal surface represents gravitational energy: it is zero at the flat portions. A planet creates a local depression in the energy. Any object wishing to leave the planet completely has to be launched with enough kinetic energy to take it out of the depression onto the flat regions of space where the gravitational field of the planet is negligible.

Escape velocity
Suppose that a spacecraft of mass m is launched from the surface of a planet with a velocity u. How big does u have to be for the spacecraft never to come back? Look at figure 20.24. As the spacecraft moves away, it loses kinetic energy and gains gravitational energy. Provided that it has some kinetic energy left when its gravitational energy becomes zero, the spacecraft will be able to leave and never come back. (This cannot happen for the spacecraft represented in figure 20.24.)

$$\tfrac{1}{2}mu^2 > \frac{GMm}{R} \quad \therefore \ u > (2GM/R)^{\tfrac{1}{2}} \qquad \textbf{(20.15}$$

You can use equation (20.15) to calculate the **escape velocity** for the Earth. It is 1.12×10^4 m s^{-1}.

Black holes

There are strong reasons for supposing that no material object can go faster than the velocity of light 3.0×10^8 m s^{-1}. Figure 20.25 shows how the energy of an electron increases as its velocity increases: other particles follow the same pattern. The theory of relativity predicts that an infinite amount of energy will be needed to get an object of finite mass up to the speed of light. So if the escape velocity of an object exceeds the speed of light, then nothing is going to escape from it. Such objects are known as **black holes**.

You might imagine that black holes ought to be very common. After all, every particle in the universe is attracted to every other particle by gravity so they should eventually clump together in the middle to form one large black hole. However, if one mass falls into the space–time distortion created by another mass, it will have enough energy to climb out again. Only if there is some mechanism for converting some of the kinetic energy into something else (such as a direct collision which generates heat energy) will the two masses get trapped together.

Black holes are difficult to observe because, as their name implies, they emit no light. However, the intense gravitational fields at their surface can accelerate charged particles sufficiently strongly for them to emit X-rays. A number of X-ray sources have been identified by astronomers, and there is much speculation that some of these may indicate the existence of a black hole rotating around a star, sucking plasma from its surface. As for the interior of a black hole, there is much speculation about that too, mainly because we have no way on Earth of duplicating the intense fields which must be present in one.

OBJECTIVES

After studying this section you should be able to do the following.

Calculate the radius of the orbit of a satellite which has a given period of rotation.

Calculate the total energy of a satellite in orbit.

Calculate the escape velocity of a planet.

RETAINING ATMOSPHERES ▶▶ 30

Our atmosphere does not contain hydrogen or helium molecules because they can attain the escape velocity by random collisions with other molecules. The Boltzmann formula can be used to estimate the fraction of molecules which have energy E.

$$n(E) \propto \exp[-E/kT] \qquad (1)$$

Let's use it to compare the probabilities of different molecules reaching escape velocity in a gas at 300 K. For a molecule of mass m to escape from the top of the atmosphere, it must have a certain minimum kinetic energy, i.e. GMm/R. Table 1 shows the values of $\exp[-GMm/RkT]$ for various molecules in the Earth's atmosphere. Notice that it is effectively zero for nitrogen, but lighter molecules stand a finite chance of escaping.

Table 1

Molecule	$\exp[-GMm/RkT]$
hydrogen	1.6×10^{-22}
helium	2.6×10^{-44}
nitrogen	9.5×10^{-305}

The value of g at the surface of the Moon (1.6 m s^{-2}) is not large enough to retain any atmosphere at all. The value of $\exp[-GMm/RkT]$ for a nitrogen molecule at 300 K on the Moon is about 4×10^{-2}, much larger than those in table 1, so the chances of the molecule getting up to escape velocity are quite high.

Figure 20.25 An electron at the speed of light has infinite energy

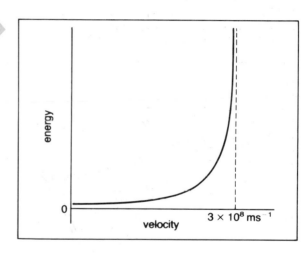

QUESTIONS

1 Table 20.3 contains some information about the Earth–Moon system. The average distance between their centres is 3.84×10^8 m. This question is about the energy changes involved in making a trip from the Earth to the Moon.

Table 20.3

mass of Earth/kg	5.98×10^{24}
mass of Moon/kg	7.36×10^{22}
radius of Earth/m	6.37×10^6
radius of Moon/m	1.72×10^6

a Calculate the gravitational potential at the surface of the Moon due to the Earth.

b What is the *total* potential at the surface of the Moon? (Neglect the effect of the Sun.)

c A spacecraft leaves the surface of the Earth and travels to the surface of the Moon (figure 20.26.) For each of the distances shown in table 20.4, calculate the *total* potential of the spacecraft.

Table 20.4

Distance travelled from Earth/10^8 m
0.0
0.5
1.0
1.5
2.0
2.5
3.0
3.5

d Use your answers to parts (b) and (c) to plot a graph which shows how the potential changes with distance travelled.

e If the spacecraft has a mass of 50 tonnes, what is the minimum energy it will need on take-off to get to the Moon if it coasts the rest of the way? What will its velocity be when it gets to the Moon? Why does the spacecraft have to keep some fuel on board to land on the Moon?

2 A 1.0 tonne survey satellite is placed in a circular polar orbit so that it goes round the Earth 14 times a day. Suppose that it is launched vertically upwards then given a horizontal impulse when it reaches the correct altitude.

a What is the radius of its orbit? What is its altitude (height above the surface of the Earth)?

b How much energy is required to lift the satellite that far above the Earth?

c How much kinetic energy has to be given to the satellite when it reaches the correct altitude?

d It is easily shown that the gravitational energy of a satellite is twice its total energy. Yet a hundred times more fuel is usually used to lift the satellite up to its altitude than is used to give it the kinetic energy necessary to stay in orbit. Why?

3 Satellites in low altitude orbits have their energy reduced by friction with the tenuous atmosphere which exists that far up (figure 20.27).

a What happens to the altitude of a satellite as it loses energy via friction? What is the energy converted to?

b What happens to the speed of the satellite as it loses energy via friction?

c What happens to the size of the friction as the satellite loses energy?

d Use your answers to parts (b) and (c) to explain why taking a spacecraft out of orbit to glide to a safe landing on Earth is a tricky business.

e Estimate the temperature rise of the Space Shuttle when it lands on Earth from a 100 km altitude orbit. The specific heat capacity and melting point of steel are 480 J kg^{-1} K^{-1} and 1813 K respectively. In practice, it doesn't melt. Suggest some ways in which this fate is avoided. (*Hint:* Look at figure 20.28.)

4 a Use the data in table 20.3 to calculate the escape velocity for a spacecraft trying to leave the Moon.

b The mass and radius of the Sun are currently 2.0×10^{30} kg and 7.0×10^8 m respectively. Estimate the minimum energy (in MeV) of a proton at the surface of the Sun which could escape from the Solar System.

c The radius of a black hole is given by the expression $r = GM/c^2$, where c is the speed of light (3.0×10^8 m s^{-1}). What is the radius of a black hole which has the mass of our Sun? What would the field strength at its surface be?

5 In this question you are going to estimate the total gravitational energy of the Sun by assuming that it is a uniform sphere of hydrogen gas.

a Show that the gravitational potential at the centre of a uniform sphere of mass M and radius R is $-3GM/R$. Start off by looking at figure 20.13. Hence write down an approximate formula for the mean gravitational potential inside the sphere.

b If the mass and radius of the Sun are 2.0×10^{30} kg and 7.0×10^8 m respectively, estimate its total gravitational energy.

c The cloud of gas in space out of which the Sun was formed gained kinetic energy as it contracted. If all that kinetic energy became heat energy, estimate the temperature of the cloud when it shrank to the dimensions of the Sun. Assume that the energy of each atom is $3kT/2$.

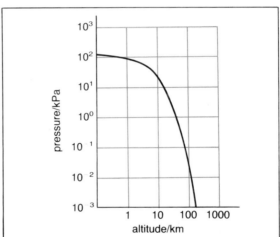

Figure 20.27

Figure 20.26

SUMMARY
FIELD AND POTENTIAL

Atoms can be modelled as arrangements of protons, neutrons and electrons.

Particle	Charge	Mass
proton	$+e$	1.00728
neutron	0	1.00867
electron	$-e$	0.00055

Friction between two different materials can remove electrons from one (leaving it positively charged) and place them on another (leaving it negatively charged).

Metals contain electrons which can flow freely past the array of fixed positive ions. Semi-conductors contain a few free electrons as a consequence of thermal agitation of the atoms. Insulators have no free electrons at all.

A charged object is surrounded by an electric field which exerts forces on other charged objects: $F = qE$. This vector field can be represented with lines whose direction is the force on a positive test charge. The scalar potential field around a charged object is the energy per unit charge placed in the field: $E = -\Delta V/\Delta r$. The potential field can be represented with equipotentials: these are always perpendicular to the field lines. Field lines at the surface of a charged conductor are at right angles to the surface.

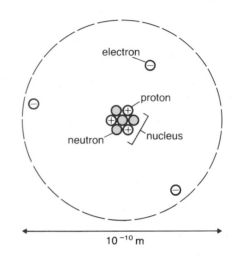

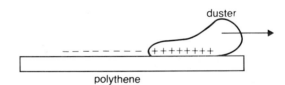

The potential field around a charged object can be measured with a flame probe and an electroscope.

Charged particles (electrons or protons for example) can be accelerated in electric fields. If a particle falls through a p.d. V, the kinetic energy gained equals the electrical energy lost: $\Delta E_k = qV$.

The electric field inside a parallel plate capacitor is uniform if the plate separation is much smaller than their width: $E = V/d$. $C = \epsilon\epsilon_0 A/d$ if the material between the plates has a permittivity ϵ. The electric field around an infinite charged sheet is $\sigma/2\epsilon_0$.

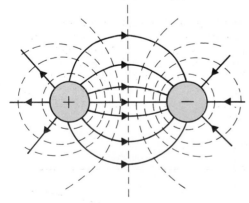

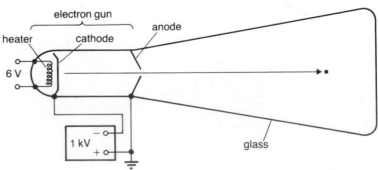

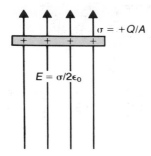

$\sigma = +Q/A$

$E = \sigma/2\epsilon_0$

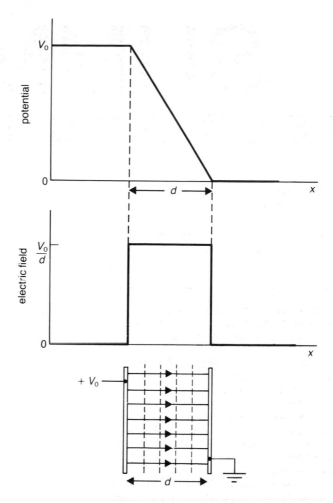

The potential and electric field around a charged sphere are given by $V = q/4\pi\epsilon_0 r$ and $E = q/4\pi\epsilon_0 r^2$. The field inside a static charged conductor is always zero. The capacitance of an isolated sphere is $4\pi\epsilon_0 r$. The force between charged particles is given by Coulomb's Law $F = q_1 q_2/4\pi\epsilon_0 r^2$.

If a gas is subjected to a large enough electric field it will suffer avalanche ionisation. This happens near sharply curved surfaces on conducting objects where the electric field is a maximum. Such corona discharges are used to charge or discharge objects by spraying them with positive or negative ions.

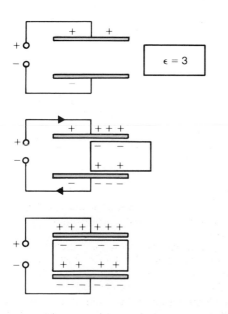

$\epsilon = 3$

The gravitational force between point masses is given by $F = -GMm/r^2$. The gravitational field strength is always attractive: $g = -GM/r^2$, $V_g = -GM/r$ for a point mass or a spherical distribution of mass. The field inside a spherical shell is zero. The force on a test mass in a gravitational field is mg; its gravitational energy is mV_g.

For a satellite in orbit around a massive object, the centripetal force is provided by gravitational attraction: $mv^2/r = GMm/r^2$. The kinetic and gravitational energy of the satellite are given by $\frac{1}{2}mv^2$ and $-GMm/r$ respectively. Kepler's Third Law is $r^3/T^2 = GM/4\pi^2$. The escape velocity for an object trying to leave a planet of mass M and radius R is $(2GM/R)^{\frac{1}{2}}$.

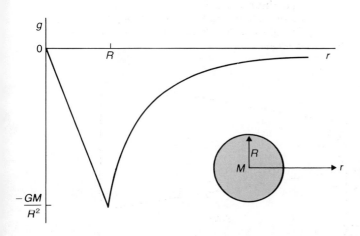

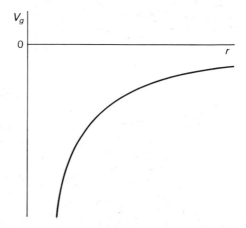

RADIOACTIVITY

21
IONISING EMISSIONS

Radioactivity is a hot topic in physics. Much public concern is, quite rightly, expressed over the dangers of radioactive material and the wisdom of pursuing an energy provision strategy which produces highly toxic radioactive waste. (The photograph overleaf shows Russian Scientists sampling the pollution in the wake of the explosion of a nuclear power station at Chernobyl in 1986). In fact, ever since 6 August 1945 when a small atomic bomb destroyed half the population of Hiroshima, radioactivity has deservedly had a bad public press. Nevertheless, it is not scientific to ignore a branch of physics simply because it has strong military overtones and you find it distasteful: your aversion to it is not going to make it go away. A study of radioactivity has much to tell you about the structure of the nucleus and the forces which moulded the Universe into shape immediately after the Big Bang that heralded its creation. Radioactive phenomena are our window to the sub-atomic world, our way of exploring and testing the fascinating world of quantum mechanics. So this section is not going to apologise for some of the dubious applications of radioactive materials. Instead, it will try to give you a sound working model of radioactivity which you can use to judge for yourself.

DETECTING EMISSIONS

A **radioactive** substance is one which spontaneously emits something which can ionise surrounding materials. These **emissions** from radioactive substances are virtually impossible to detect directly. Although they carry enormous energies by atomic standards (typically several MeV), they have too little energy, charge or mass for direct detection. However, they can be indirectly detected by a wide variety of means. These nearly all use the fact that the emissions create a lot of damage on a microscopic scale in any material they pass through. The emissions ionise the material — most methods of indirect detection rely on measuring the wreckage left in the wake of an ionising emission.

HOW PHOTOGRAPHIC FILM WORKS

Photographic film is designed to detect visible light, but the mechanism by which it does so means that it also detects any ionising emission. As figure 21.1 shows, the plastic base of the film is covered with a film of transparent gelatin which contains a fine suspension of silver bromide crystals. Each crystal is typically about 1 μm across, containing about 10^{10} silver ions. The crystal structure is simple cubic, as shown in figure 21.2: the negative bromine ions sit between the positive silver ions. A charged particle which whizzes through the crystal can tear electrons off the bromine ions, allowing them to neutralise nearby silver ions. As figure 21.3 shows, this causes a local rearrangement of the crystal structure, but this is only temporary — after about a second the silver atom ionises and the electron is free to drift back to a bromine atom. However, if four adjacent silver ions are neutralised, as shown in figure 21.4, the group of atoms is stable. When the film is developed by immersion in suitable chemicals, the stable cluster of silver atoms in the grain acts as a catalyst, resulting in the conversion of the whole grain to an opaque deposit of silver. So the ionisation of just four silver ions causes the deposit of 10^{10} atoms of silver, an amplification of about 10^9!

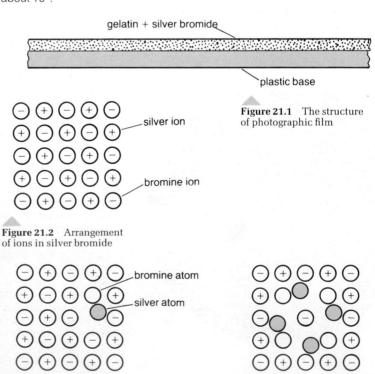

gelatin + silver bromide

plastic base

Figure 21.1 The structure of photographic film

silver ion

bromine ion

Figure 21.2 Arrangement of ions in silver bromide

bromine atom

silver atom

Figure 21.3 When a silver ion is neutralised it is displaced

Figure 21.4 A stable arrangement of four neutral silver atoms

Photographic emulsions

In 1896 Henri Becquerel was the first person to detect the emissions from a radioactive substance. He didn't do it on purpose: he was actually looking for X-ray emissions from rocks which glow in the dark. He placed a sample of a uranium compound on a photographic plate enclosed in black paper and noticed that the plate became fogged, i.e. behaved as if it had been exposed to light. A lesser scientist would have assumed that the plate was faulty and dismissed the observation, but Becquerel didn't. A series of experiments quickly convinced him that something was coming out of his sample which could travel through solid objects. The really important observation was that the activity continued undiminished even when the uranium was completely isolated from external sources of energy, such as light. The emissions from radioactive substances indicated the existence of a hitherto unsuspected source of energy deep inside the atom.

Tracks

Photographic emulsions are widely used as **dosimeters** (figure 21.5). A dosimeter is a device which can hold a record of the intensity of ionising emissions that it, and its wearer, have been exposed to. Each emission leaves a track through the developed emulsion which can be seen under a microscope: the opacity of the developed film is a measure of the total dose of ionising emissions received by the wearer. However, because of its two-dimensional nature, photographic film is generally not a good way of exploring the characteristics of the emissions themselves.

Thick emulsions were much used in the early days of exploring radioactive emissions — the track of a high energy particle (a **cosmic ray**) from outer space is shown in figure 21.6.

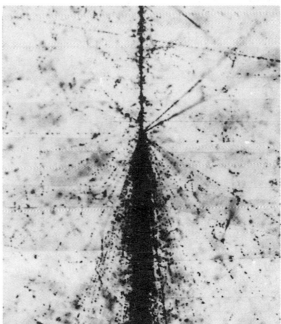

Figure 21.5 A dosimeter: absorbing materials are placed in different places on the film so that the type of ionising emission the wearer is exposed to can be deduced

Figure 21.6 The effect of a single high energy iron nucleus colliding with another nucleus in a photographic emulsion. The cosmic ray, whose energy exceeds 15 000 GeV, enters at the top, leaving a dense trail of silver grains in the developed emulsion. The collision produces a spray of about 850 particles

Cloud chambers

Cloud chambers (and their high-energy equivalent, the **bubble chamber**) offer convincing evidence that the ionisation around radioactive substances is a consequence of something travelling away from them. A cloud chamber photograph is shown in figure 21.7. The **tracks** all seem to emanate from the same source. Each track is a collection of microscopic droplets of water which have formed around the ions created by the emission as it ripped electrons out of the air atoms in its way. The droplets can, in principle, be counted on the photograph, giving a measure of the total energy of the emission. The mean energy delivered to each ion–electron pair is about 35 eV. However, a cloud chamber cannot be used to monitor a radioactive source continuously or measure the rate of its emissions (its **activity**) because of its long recovery time. (For more details read the box on Supersaturation.)

Figure 21.7 Tracks in a cloud chamber formed by alpha particles from a polonium-212 source placed outside the chamber. Notice that one particle has more energy than the rest

SUPERSATURATION ►► 30

Cloud chambers work by setting up a **supersaturated vapour** in the region traversed by the emissions. An **expansion cloud chamber** (figure 21.8) does this by rapidly expanding the wet air in the chamber, suddenly lowering its temperature without disturbing the pattern of ions left in the emission's wake. This encourages the water molecules in the air to form droplets. However, very small droplets cannot form from chance collisions of water molecules without some mechanism to take away surplus energy or encourage them to stick together. Any ions in the air will attract the polar water molecules quite strongly (figure 21.9), forming a centre around which droplets can form. After a short while the droplets will have grown to a visible size and can be photographed. Eventually the droplets become large enough for gravity to pull them to the bottom of the chamber and the tracks disappear. The chamber has to be restored to atmospheric pressure and stray ions removed by an electric field before it can be used again.

Figure 21.8 A cloud chamber

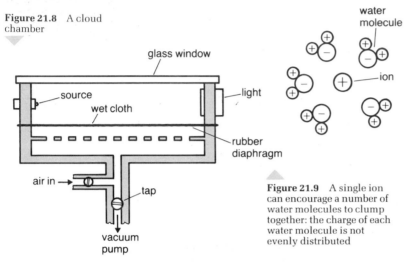

Figure 21.9 A single ion can encourage a number of water molecules to clump together: the charge of each water molecule is not evenly distributed

This supersaturation by depression of the temperature can be easily understood with the help of the Boltzmann formula. If molecules in the air have energy ϵ more than molecules in a drop, then the ratio of molecules in the vapour and liquid phases is given by the following expression:

$$n_{vap} = n_{liq}\exp[-\epsilon/kT]$$

Figure 21.10 The number of molecules in the vapour rises steeply with temperature

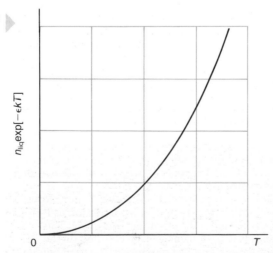

The expression only applies when the liquid and vapour phases have settled to a dynamic equilibrium at temperature T. As you can see from the graph in figure 21.10, a sudden drop in temperature means that a number of molecules in the vapour need to enter the liquid to restore the equilibrium. Thus droplets will immediately form around any ions in the air, removing molecules from the vapour and restoring equilibrium once more.

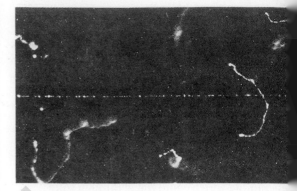

Figure 21.11 Beta particle tracks left in a cloud chamber

Classifying tracks

Cloud chamber tracks fall into three distinct categories, corresponding to three different types of emission. **Alpha particle** (α) sources give rise to dense straight line tracks which have a definite **range** (figure 21.7). **Beta particle** (β) sources give rise to thin wispy tracks which meander around slightly with a much longer range than alpha particles (figure 21.11). Finally, **gamma ray** (γ) sources leave no track directly: a number of tracks like those of beta particles appear in the wake of the gamma ray (see figure 21.12).

Electrical detectors

A number of materials will emit a flash of light (scintillate) when a charged particle whizzes through them. Zinc sulphide **scintillators** were much used by the early investigators of radioactivity because they could be used to measure the **activity** of a source, i.e. the rate at which its emissions are produced. The random distribution of the flashes, both in time and space, as well as their low intensity made counting difficult, but scintillators gave information about emissions which cloud chambers and photographic emulsions could not provide.

Figure 21.12 Two gamma rays passing through a cloud chamber from bottom to top. When the rays pass through a thin lead sheet across the chamber, they are converted into charged particles which leave visible tracks

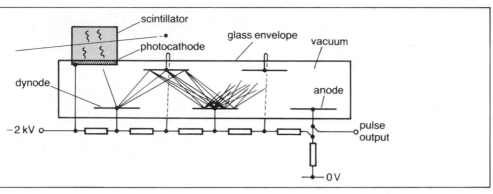

Figure 21.13   A scintillator mounted on a photomultiplier tube

Photomultipliers

The modern equivalent of the zinc sulphide scintillator is the **photomultiplier tube**, shown in figure 21.13. Not only is it more sensitive, but it produces an electrical pulse for each ionising emission it detects, making counting easy. Each flash of light in the scintillator can knock an electron out of the surface of the **photocathode**. This is at a negative voltage so the electron is accelerated towards the first dynode, gaining enough energy to knock several electrons out of it. These are then accelerated towards the next dynode, etc. An avalanche of electrons builds up down the tube, with perhaps 10^6 electrons arriving at the anode 1 ns later. The voltage pulse across the final resistor can be counted by an electronic system. Furthermore, the height of each pulse carries information about the number of ion−electron pairs created in the scintillator by the emission. The number of electrons at the anode is proportional to the light energy reaching the photocathode: in its turn, the light energy released by the scintillator is proportional to the number of ion−electron pairs generated in it. Figure 21.14 shows how the pulse height depends on the energy and type of the ionising emission for a typical scintillating material.

Geiger-Müller tubes

The operation of the Geiger-Müller (GM) tube was described in chapter 18. Like the photomultiplier, it has an electrical pulse output for every ionising emission which gets into it. However, the avalanche process used to amplify the initial ionisation means that all of the output pulses have the same height, not providing any information about the energy of the emission. Furthermore, the dead time of 200 μs limits the maximum count rate to 5 000 s^{-1}. However, the robustness, sensitivity and moderate power supply requirements of the GM tube ensure its widespread use for measuring the activity of radioactive environments.

Solid-state detectors

Each time an ionising emission passes through a suitable semiconductor diode it leaves a trail of holes and electrons in its wake. These can be swept out and collected by a p.d. placed across the semiconductor to generate a pulse which is easily amplified. Since each electron−hole pair has an energy of 2 eV, the size of the pulse can be used to measure the energy which the ionising emission dumps into the semiconductor. Solid-state detectors (figure 21.15) are cheap and robust, but have only a small surface area, so they are less sensitive than GM tubes or scintillators.

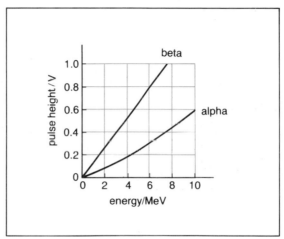

Figure 21.14   The height of the pulse produced by the photomultiplier depends on the nature and energy of the particle detected (in this case by a NaI scintillator)

Classifying emissions

The emissions from naturally occuring (and most synthetic) radioactive substances fall into one of three categories: alpha particles, beta particles or gamma rays. In general, a radioactive substance will emit just one of these three emissions, but sources which emit two or all three of them are not unknown. Each emission has its own collection of characteristics (such as range and energy) which allow it to be distinguished from the other two.

At the turn of the century, intense research into radioactivity established the nature of these three emissions. We are now going to explain the route by which a satisfactory model of each emission was built up, by describing a number of experiments using modern apparatus. Few of these experiments can be satisfactorily performed in a school laboratory, mainly because of the weakness of the radioactive sources available for school use!

Figure 21.15   Solid-state detector

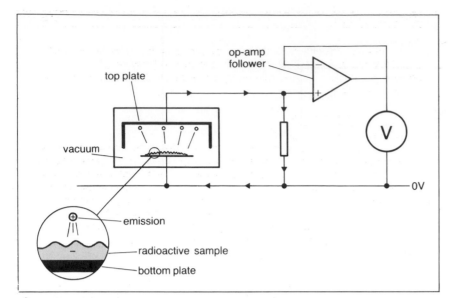

Figure 21.16 Apparatus for determining the charge of an ionising emission

Figure 21.17 Finding the activity of the sample

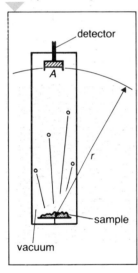

Charge

The apparatus shown in figure 21.16 can be used to determine the sign of the charge carried by each of the emissions. The radioactive source is placed on the bottom plate and the gap between the two plates is evacuated so that no ionisation of the air can take place. As the emissions hit the top plate and are absorbed by it, they transfer their charge to it. So the two plates steadily acquire equal and opposite charges, behaving like a self-charging capacitor. That capacitor is discharged through the resistor, so that there is a steady current in it: the op-amp follower allows the p.d. across the resistor to be measured. That p.d. can be used to estimate the rate at which the radioactive source is emitting charge. For example, suppose that the system settles down with a p.d. of 50 mV across a $10^{11} \, \Omega$ resistor.

$$R = \frac{V}{I} \qquad \therefore I = \frac{V}{R}$$

$$\therefore I = \frac{50 \times 10^{-3}}{1 \times 10^{11}} = 5 \times 10^{-13} \, \text{A}$$

So the source emits 5×10^{-13} coulombs of charge per second.

The next stage is to use a solid-state detector to find the rate at which emissions are being absorbed by the collector. The arrangement is shown in figure 21.17. The activity of the source has to be quite high to get a measurable charging current in figure 21.16, so the apparatus is arranged so that only a fraction of its emissions are picked up by the detector. The source on its plate can only emit over a hemisphere when the source is a distance r from the detector (area A). So only the fraction $A/2\pi r^2$ of its emissions can reach the detector. On the assumption that the detector is 100% efficient, its count rate should allow you to work out the charge carried by each emission.

For example, suppose that the detector has an active area of 1.0×10^{-5} m^2 and is held 5.0 cm from the radioactive source. If it detects 1000 emissions per second, we can estimate the charge carried by each emission as follows. The first step is to calculate the fraction of the emissions picked up by the detector.

Figure 21.18 The deflection of an emission by an electric field can be used to measure the particle's energy

$$\text{activity} \times \frac{A}{2\pi r^2} = \text{count rate}$$

$$\therefore \frac{\text{activity} \times 1 \times 10^{-5}}{2\pi \times (5 \times 10^{-2})^2} = 1 \times 10^3$$

$$\therefore \text{activity} = 1.6 \times 10^6 \, \text{s}^{-1}$$

The activity and emission current can now be used to estimate the charge of each emission.

$$I = \frac{Q}{t} \qquad \therefore 5 \times 10^{-13} = \frac{1.6 \times 10^6 \times q}{1.0}$$

$$\therefore q = 3.1 \times 10^{-19} \, \text{C}$$

The results for the different types of emission are shown in table 21.1

Table 21.1

Emission	Charge/C
alpha	$+3.2 \times 10^{-19}$
beta	-1.6×10^{-19}
gamma	0

So an alpha particle looks as if it contains two protons, a beta particle looks like an electron and a gamma ray has no charge at all.

Energy

Once the charge of alpha and beta particles has been established, their energies can be determined by measuring their deflection in electric fields. Suitable apparatus is shown in figure 21.18: the whole thing is in a vacuum to stop absorption of the emission's energy by air. The source is shielded with lead so that only a thin beam can emerge into the electric field E which is applied at right angles to the beam over a length l. It is easy to show that the deflection φ of a beam of particles with charge q and kinetic energy E_k is given by the following expression. (See question 5 at the end of this section.)

$$\phi = \frac{Eql}{2E_k} \qquad \qquad \text{(21.1}$$

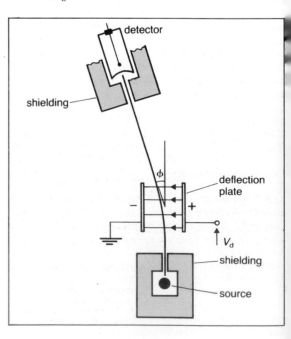

Figure 21.19 Typical energy spectrum for alpha and beta particles

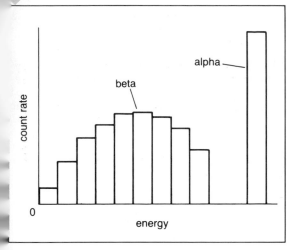

The detector (which could be a GM tube) is surrounded by shielding so that it can only receive emissions which are deflected through a fixed angle φ. The electric field is swept through a range of values by steadily increasing the voltage across the plates, noting the count rate at the detector for each voltage.

Experiments show that all alpha particles from a given source have definite energies, usually only one, but sometimes two or three. The energies are usually a few MeV. For example, americium-241 (a commercial alpha source widely used in domestic smoke detection) emits at 5.49 MeV and 5.44 MeV. On the other hand, beta particles are emitted from a source with a range of energies (figure 21.19): the maximum energy is, however, a characteristic of the source. Beta particles from strontium-90 have maximum energies of 2.27 MeV.

Momentum

The momentum of the charged emissions can be measured by firing them through a magnetic field, as shown in figure 21.22. A thin beam of the emissions (charge q and momentum p) issues from the lead-lined source into a vacuum and hits a magnetic field at right angles to its direction. If the field has a strength B, the charged particle moves in a circle of radius r given by the following expression (from chapter 23).

$$r = \frac{p}{Bq}$$

r is the radius of curvature of the orbit (m)

p is the momentum of the particle (N s)

B is the magnetic field component normal to the orbit (T)

q is the charge of the particle (C)

Figure 21.22 Measuring the momentum of an emission via its deflection by a magnetic field. The field direction is into the plane of the diagram

Gamma rays have no charge so their energy cannot be found by the electrical method described above. In fact, gamma rays are short wavelength electromagnetic radiation, so their energy E is related to their wavelength λ by the Einstein relationship:

$$E = hf, \quad c = f\lambda \qquad \therefore E = \frac{hc}{\lambda}$$

The wavelength of low energy (<1MeV) gamma rays can be measured directly using Bragg diffraction through quartz crystals (figure 21.20): the same method is adopted for measuring the wavelength of X-rays. The deflection θ is very small because the wavelength of the gamma rays ($\approx 10^{-12}$ m) is much smaller than the interatomic spacing (10^{-10} m). The energy of high-energy gamma rays can be found by analysing cloud chamber photographs of **pair production** in magnetic fields. Look at figure 21.21. The gamma ray is converted into an electron and a **positron** on its way through the foil: the curvature of each trajectory gives the momentum of each particle, and hence its energy.

Figure 21.20 Using Bragg diffraction to measure the wavelength of gamma rays

Figure 21.21 The gamma ray enters from the top leaving no track in the chamber. On its way through the lead sheet across the centre of the picture, the gamma ray is converted into a positron and an electron. Tracks for these particles can be seen in the lower half of the picture — they curve in opposite directions as there was a magnetic field going into the plane of the picture

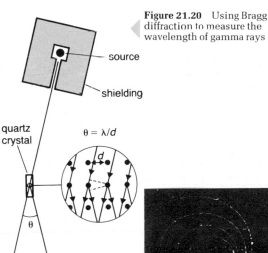

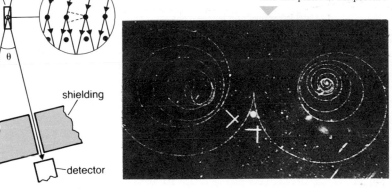

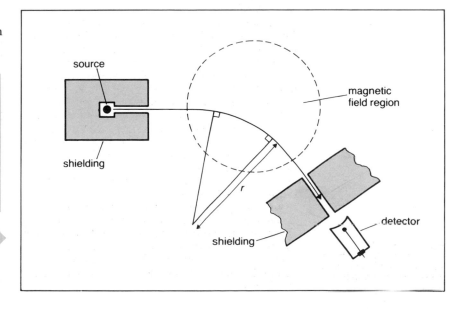

Figure 21.23 A charged particle in a magnetic field. As the particle passes through the lead sheet at the centre it loses momentum as its radius of curvature decreases. The directions of curvature (anticlockwise) and magnetic field (into the photo) give the charge of the particle (positive)

Figure 21.24 Variation of beta particle mass with velocity: notice how the mass appears to go to infinity at the speed of light ($3.00 \times 10^8 \, \text{m s}^{-1}$)

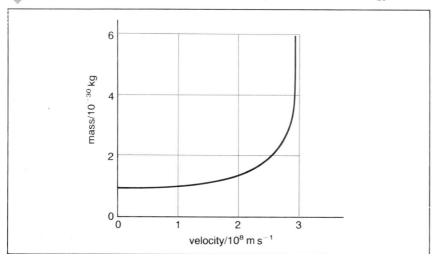

Figure 21.23 shows the effect of a magnetic field on charged particles. (Gamma rays, being uncharged, are completely unaffected by magnetic fields.) Alpha and beta particles are deflected in opposite directions because they have opposite charges. All the alpha particles are deflected by the same amount because they have the same energy and momentum. Beta particles are deflected by a different amount because of the range of energies with which they are emitted.

$$E_k = \tfrac{1}{2}mv^2, \quad p = mv \quad \therefore \; p = (2mE_k)^{\frac{1}{2}} \qquad \textbf{(21.2}$$

The comparatively small deflection of alpha particles indicates that their momentum is much larger than that of the beta particles. In view of the fact that the energy of the two types is comparable ($\approx$MeV), the momentum difference can only arise i the mass of the alpha particles is much greater than that of beta particles.

Mass

The radius of the circular trajectory of alpha and beta particles in a magnetic field can be measured with the help of a cloud chamber (figure 21.23). Since the charge of the particles is known (table 21.1), the radius can be used to measure their maximum momentum. Provided that the maximum energy of each emission has already been determined (figure 21.18), equation (21.2) can be used to find the mass of the particles. It turns out that slow beta particles have the mass of an electron (9.1×10^{-31} kg) and alpha particles have the mass of a helium nucleus (6.6×10^{-27} kg). (Figure 21.24 shows how the measured mass of a beta particle depends on its velocity. The increase at high energies is due to relativistic effects.)

OBJECTIVES

After studying this section you should be able to do the following.

State that the emissions from radioactive substances leave a trail of ions behind them when they pass through matter.

Explain how the ions can be detected with photographic emulsions, scintillators, cloud chambers, solid-state detectors and GM tubes.

Understand the meaning of *activity*.

Know the differences between cloud chamber tracks left by alpha particles, beta particles and gamma rays.

State the relative charge of alpha particles, beta particles and gamma rays.

Describe how the charge of an ionising emission can be measured.

Describe how electric fields can be used to measure the energy of an ionising emission.

Know that alpha particles and gamma rays from a source have definite energies, but that beta particles have a range of energies.

Describe how magnetic fields can be used to measure the momentum of an ionising emission.

Use the formula r = p/Bq.

State the relative masses of alpha and beta particles.

Know that alpha particles are helium nuclei, that beta particles are electrons and that gamma rays are electromagnetic waves.

HELIUM NUCLEI !

In 1909, Rutherford and Royds performed an experiment which clinched the description of alpha particles as helium nuclei. Their apparatus is shown in figure 21.25. Radioactive radon gas generated by the radioactive decay of a sample of radium is compressed into a thin-walled glass chamber by some mercury. The majority of the alpha particles emitted by the radon pass through the thin glass wall into the evacuated space beyond: when they hit its walls they absorb a couple of electrons and become helium atoms. After a few days, when enough helium gas has accumulated in the space, some mercury is used to compress the contents of the evacuated space into a thin discharge tube so that an electric current can be run through it. The discharge emits light which can be studied with a spectroscope: that light contains the characteristic wavelengths of helium.

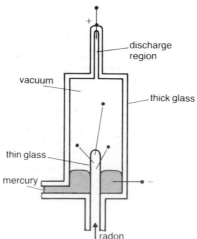

discharge region

vacuum

thick glass

thin glass

mercury

radon

Figure 21.25 Apparatus for showing that alpha particles are helium nuclei

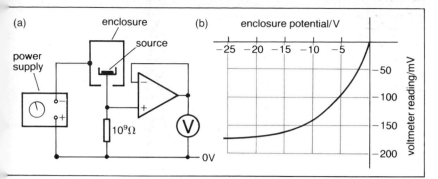

Figure 21.26

1 The apparatus shown in figure 21.26(a) is often used in schools to estimate the energy of alpha particles emitted by a radium source. The source is placed inside a conducting enclosure held at a negative voltage. Positive ions created in the air are swept to the walls and negative ions are swept to the source. The source is connected to ground by a $10^9 \, \Omega$ resistor and the p.d. across it sampled by an op-amp follower.

a The graph of figure 21.26(b) shows how the voltmeter reading depends on the potential of the enclosure walls. Explain its shape.

b Calculate the rate of ionisation of the air inside the enclosure. Assume that each ion carries one electronic charge.

c The alpha particles emitted by the source have an energy of 5.5 MeV. If each ion−electron pair is given an average energy of 35 eV by an alpha particle, estimate the activity (emissions per second) of the source.

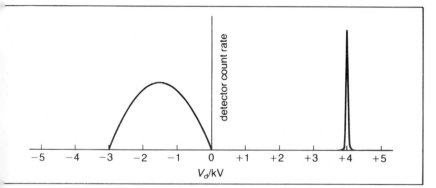

Figure 21.28

Figure 21.29

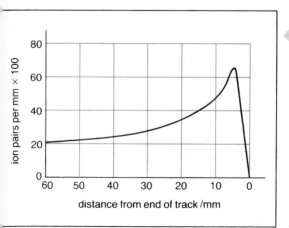

2 A typical school radioactive source has an activity of 5 µCi (microcurie). A source with an activity of one **curie** produces 3.7×10^{10} emissions per second. If a 1 µCi beta source is spread thinly over a small area, estimate the count rate in a GM tube placed 10 cm from it. Assume that the GM tube is 100% efficient with a window of diameter 1.0 cm.

3 Figure 21.27 shows a typical pulse from a solid-state detector when an alpha particle is absorbed by it. Each hole−electron pair created in the detector takes an energy of 3.0 eV from the alpha particle.

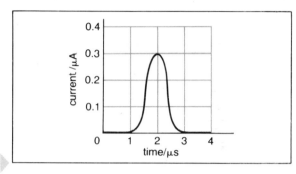

Figure 21.27

a Estimate the number of free electrons generated in the detector.

b If the detector absorbs all of the energy of the alpha particle, estimate its energy in McV.

c Sketch the pulse you would expect to see for a 3.0 MeV alpha particle.

4 The rate at which heat flows out from the centre of the Earth is 60 mW m^{-2}. It is believed that this heat is caused by the radioactive decay of certain elements in the Earth's molten core. If each decay produces an emission with an energy of 2 MeV, estimate the total activity of the Earth's core. If this is also the average activity of the Earth's crust, estimate its specific activity, i.e. activity per kilogram. The mass and radius of the Earth are 5.8×10^{24} kg and 6.4×10^6 m respectively.

5 This question is about the deflection of charged particles by electric fields. The arrangement of apparatus is shown in figure 21.18, with the angle of deflection ϕ fixed at 0.050 radians.

a Show that the angle of deflection is given by $\phi = Eql/2E_k$ for small angles.

b A source which emits 2.0 MeV alpha particles is placed in the apparatus. If the deflecting plates have a length of 10 cm and a separation of 3 mm, calculate the value of V_d which will steer the alpha particles into the detector.

c A different source is placed in the apparatus. The graph of figure 21.28 shows what happens to the detector count rate as V_d is swept from −5 kV to +5 kV. State what facts you can deduce (both qualitative and quantitative) about the emissions coming from the new radioactive source.

6 The graph shown in figure 21.29 shows how many ion pairs are created in each millimetre of air that an alpha particle passes through. (It was obtained by counting the number of droplets along a cloud chamber photograph of an alpha particle track.) The graph is called the Bragg curve, and was widely used in the early days of radioactivity research to measure the energy of alpha particles. (Note the scale of the horizontal axis.)

a Suppose that an alpha particle leaves a 30 mm track in a cloud chamber. Use the graph to estimate how many ion−electron pairs it creates in the process.

b If each ion pair takes a mean energy of 35 eV from the alpha particle, what was its initial energy?

c Estimate the track length of the 5.5 MeV alpha particles emitted by americium-241.

7 Allan plans to detect the deflection of alpha particles by a strong magnetic field. The strongest magnet his school posesses has a strength of 0.2 T over an area of 2 cm × 5 cm. His alpha particles have an energy of 4.8 MeV.

a Calculate the speed of the alpha particles. Do you have to worry about relativistic effects?

b Calculate the radius of curvature of the orbit followed by the particles as they pass through the magnetic field. Estimate the deflection of the alpha particles as they pass through the field.

c Will Allan be able to measure this deflection? Convince him!

d Would he have any difficulty in measuring the deflection of 4.8 MeV beta particles?

ABSORBING EMISSIONS

Ionising emissions are dangerous. When they pass through biological matter they leave a trail of ions in their wake, disrupting molecules and upsetting the delicate chemistry of life. However, that trail of ionisation is also one of the means by which we can reduce the hazardous nature of radioactive substances: dangerous sources can be shielded with appropriate materials which extract energy from emissions. So this section is going to concentrate on the energy loss of ionising emissions as they pass through matter. Each type of emission has its own unique absorption characteristics which can be used to set it apart from the other two. Many applications of radioactive materials exploit the penetrating nature of their emissions: some of these are described at the end of the section. Needless to say, there is also some mention of protective strategies, such as shielding and safe handling procedures.

Range

The **range** of an ionising emission is the distance that it travels through a material before it has lost nearly all of its energy. It can be measured with the apparatus shown in figure 21.30. Various thicknesses of the **absorber** are placed between the source and the detector. The average count rate of the detector is a measure of the fraction of emissions which are transmitted by the absorber. As it travels through matter, an ionising emission loses kinetic energy with each ion−electron pair it creates. The distance that it can travel before it loses all of its kinetic energy depends on its mass and the mechanism by which the ionisation takes place. Thus the range of all three emissions is infinite in a vacuum because there is nothing around to rob them of energy.

Background radiation

The experiment in figure 21.30 looks simple, but there are two complicating factors. The first is the presence of **background radiation**. Even without the source being present, the detector picks up, on

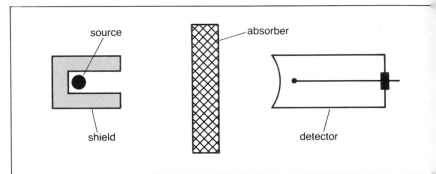

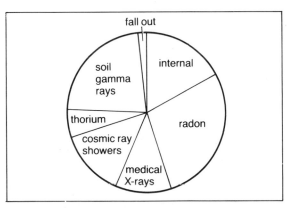

Figure 21.30 Apparatus for measuring the transmission of ionising emissions through solids

Figure 21.31 Different contributions to background radiation

average, about a dozen emissions per minute. (We are assuming it is a standard G-M tube of the type commonly found in schools; the amount of background activity detected depends on the efficiency of the detector and its active volume.) These come from a variety of sources, including building materials, soil, water and the air. The level of natural radioactivity varies widely from place to place, but it is never so low that it cannot be measured. For example, granite rocks are far more radioactive than limestone, so background radiation in Scotland tends to be substantially higher than in England. Soil and rocks contain uranium, a radioactive element which produces radon as a by-product of radioactive decay. This radioactive gas can seep into poorly ventilated buildings through the foundations, raising the level

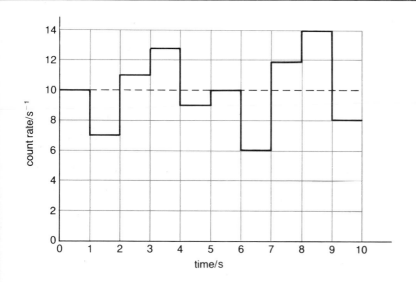

Figure 21.32 The mechanism of a cosmic ray shower. A single high energy gamma ray at the top of the diagram forms an electron–positron pair. In turn, these particles produce other gamma rays, either by electron–positron annihilation or when electrons are deflected by electrons in their path

Figure 21.33 Fluctuations in measured activity can be caused by the limited number of events being sampled

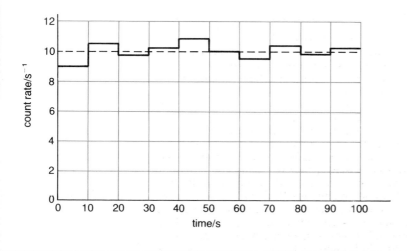

of background radiation. Of course, accidents at nuclear power stations and processing plants can also raise the level of background radiation, but such man-made radiation is still far smaller than the natural activity to which we are subjected all of our lives. The pie chart of figure 21.31 shows estimates of the different sources of background activity which our bodies suffer: the soil gamma ray component is highly dependent on geography, depending on the nature of the underlying rocks.

Cosmic rays are another source of background activity. These extra-terrestrial visitors are high energy atomic nuclei which probably originate from intergalactic space. They are mostly protons and alpha particles in an approximate ratio of 10:1, with a smattering of heavier nuclei. Typically, their energy is 10^{10} eV, but protons with energies of 10^{15} eV have been observed. When these particles collide with an atom in the upper atmosphere they produce high energy gamma rays. The energy of these rays is so large that they readily create an electron–positron pair (figure 21.32). Each of these particles produces a number of lower energy gamma rays as they ricochet off other atoms. In turn, each of those gamma rays may still have enough energy to produce an electron–positron pair, each of which can produce more gamma rays of even lower energy, etc. The end result is a **cosmic ray shower**, a simultaneous burst of gamma rays over a wide area at ground level.

Counting statistics

The second difficulty with using the apparatus of figure 21.30 is the random nature of the events picked up by the detector. The graphs of figure 21.33 show how the count rate varies with time, even though nothing in the apparatus is being changed. The top graph shows the results of counting events over a one second interval. The mean count rate is 10 s^{-1}, but the actual count in any one second can be between 6 s^{-1} and 14 s^{-1}: the variation is about 40% of the mean. The bottom graph shows the results of counting the same events over a 10 s interval. The mean count rate is, of course, still 10 s^{-1}, but the count in any 10 s interval can vary by about 10% of the mean. In general, if you are counting random events in a set time interval, then you can expect the result to differ from the average $<N>$ by up to $<N>^{\frac{1}{2}}$.

$$\Delta N = <N>^{\frac{1}{2}}$$

$$\therefore \frac{\Delta N}{N} = \frac{<N>^{\frac{1}{2}}}{<N>} = <N>^{-\frac{1}{2}} \qquad (21.3)$$

Table 21.2

N	ΔN/N
1	1
100	0.1
10000	0.01

This means that the fractional error in your result can be reduced by making N large. So if you want a percentage error of less than 1%, you need to count at least 10 000 events. Table 21.2 shows how the fractional error depends on the total count.

Alpha particles

Figure 21.34 shows the results of an experiment to find the range of 5.5 MeV alpha particles. The absorber is just air: its thickness is varied by moving the detector away from the source. As you can see, many of the particles get through to the detector if it is less than 40 mm from the source, but none of them get further than 45 mm. (Note the constant background activity picked up for distances over 45 mm from the source.) The range of the alpha particles is 41 mm. It should be intuitively obvious that as the energy of an alpha particle is increased, so is its range (figure 21.35). But how does the range depend on the density of the absorber? In other words, what is the range of alpha particles in materials other than air?

Mass per unit area

Well, the chances of an alpha particle colliding with a nucleus of an atom are so small that it loses most of its energy by colliding with the electrons in matter. Furthermore, for every electron in the solid, there will be one proton and a bit over one neutron. So the electron density of a material will be roughly proportional to its mass density ρ. Suppose that we fling a beam of alpha particles at an absorber with a thickness equal to the range R of the particles. Each electron acts as a target for the projectiles in the beam. For each projectile to lose all of its energy, then it must see a certain number of targets, i.e. it must undergo a certain number of collisions. If the density of the absorber is doubled, then only half the thickness is required to have the same number of targets as before.

$$\rho R = \text{constant} \qquad (21.4)$$

Equation (21.4) predicts that for alpha particles of a particular energy, the product of the range and the density of the absorber should be constant. The quantity ρR is called the **mass per unit area**. In practice, it is not completely independent of the absorber material as you can see from table 21.3. (This is partly because the ratio of protons to neutrons is not the same for light as for heavy atoms.) However, given the vast range of densities covered by the data, the assumption is useful.

Table 21.3

Absorber	ρ/kg m^{-3}	R/m	ρR/kg m^{-2}
air	1.2	4.7×10^{-2}	5.6×10^{-2}
aluminium	2700	2.8×10^{-5}	7.5×10^{-2}
copper	8940	1.3×10^{-5}	11.6×10^{-2}
lead	11350	2.0×10^{-5}	22.8×10^{-2}

For example, suppose that you wanted to find the minimum thickness of polythene which would completely absorb 10 MeV alpha particles. From the graph of figure 21.35, the range of 10 MeV alpha particles in air is 106 mm. Since the densities of air and polythene are 1.22 kg m^{-3} and 960 kg m^{-3} we can use the approximate constancy of ρR to estimate the range in polythene.

$$\rho R = 1.22 \times 106\times10^{-3} = 960 \times R$$

$$\therefore R = \frac{1.22 \times 106\times10^{-3}}{960}$$

$$\therefore R = 1.35\times10^{-4} \text{ m}$$

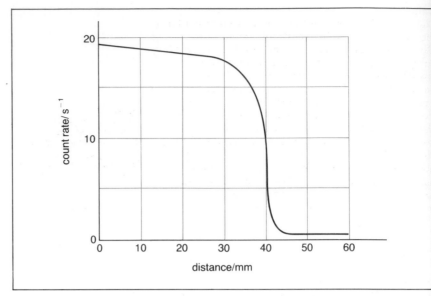

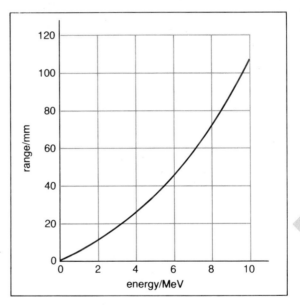

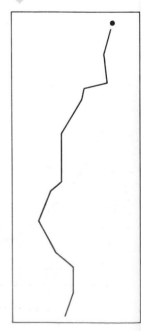

So we expect the range of 10 MeV alpha particles to be about 140 μm in polythene.

Beta particles

In general, the range of beta particles is about a hundred times larger than that of alpha particles of the same energy. This is because of the large difference in mass between the two particles. An alpha particle has about 10 000 times the mass of the electrons it collides with, so momentum conservation means that it will plough straight through absorbers like a bullet through butter. It cannot avoid hitting electrons in its path. However, beta particles have the same mass as the electrons they are colliding with, so they are going to be appreciably deflected with each collision. The passage of a beta particle through matter therefore closely resembles diffusion: this is illustrated in figure 21.36. Furthermore, because the beta particle is relatively easily deflected by its target electron, the probability of an ionising collision which extracts significant energy from the projectile is much reduced.

Figure 21.34 Transmission of alpha particles through different thicknesses of air

Figure 21.35 The range of alpha particles in air depends on their energy

Figure 21.36 Typical path followed by a low energy beta particle travelling through air

Range

Figure 21.37 shows the results of an experiment on the transmission of beta particles through aluminium. As you can see, the number of particles being transmitted is steadily reduced as the absorber thickness is increased. Since beta particles are emitted from a particular source with a range of energies, this is just what you would expect: low energy particles will be more easily absorbed than high energy ones. The range is defined as the thickness of absorber which will absorb *all* of the beta particles. Figure 21.38 shows how the mass per unit area ρR depends on the maximum energy of the beta particles. Let us use it to estimate the range in air of the 2.3 MeV beta particles emitted by strontium-90.

$$\rho R = 12 \text{ kg m}^{-2}, \quad \rho = 1.22 \text{ kg m}^{-3}$$
$$\therefore 12 = 1.22 \times R$$
$$\therefore R = 9.8 \text{ m}$$

Strontium-90 is dangerous to humans because it can get built into our bones. Bone has a density of 1900 kg m^{-3}. You can check for yourself that 2.3 MeV beta particles will easily get through 5 mm of bone.

Figure 21.37
Transmission of beta particles through different thicknesses of aluminium

Figure 21.38 Range of beta particles as a function of energy

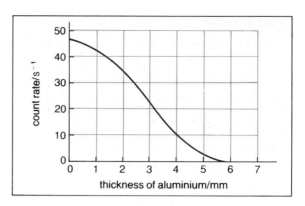

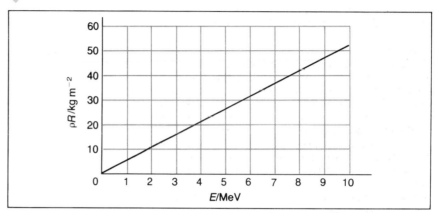

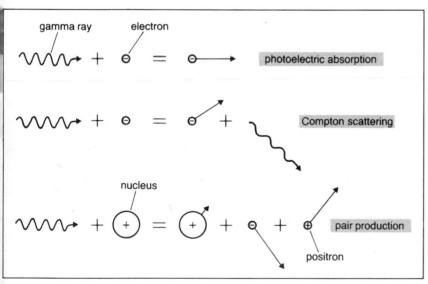
photoelectric absorption

Compton scattering

pair production

positron

Figure 21.39 Different ways in which gamma rays lose energy when they pass through matter

Figure 21.40
Transmission of gamma rays as a function of lead thickness

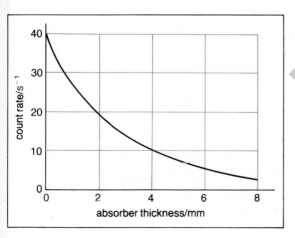

Gamma rays

There are three mechanisms by which gamma rays lose their energy on the way through matter. They are illustrated in figure 21.39. Low energy (<0.5 MeV) gamma rays can be completely absorbed by electrons, effectively producing a beta particle. Moderate energy (<5 MeV) gamma rays can also scatter off electrons, changing direction and losing some energy. Finally, high energy (>1.02 MeV) gamma rays can scatter off a nucleus and be transformed into a positron–electron pair. Note that, unlike alpha and beta particle absorption mechanisms, a single collision is enough to remove a gamma ray completely from a beam. This means that gamma rays have different absorption characteristics — there is no thickness of absorber which will completely remove all of the gamma rays from a beam.

Half-thickness

The graph of figure 21.40 shows how the number of gamma rays transmitted by a lead absorber depends on its thickness. The intensity I of the gamma rays which are not absorbed by a thickness x is given by the following expression.

$$I = I_0\exp[-x/\delta] \tag{21.5}$$

The value of the **absorption length** δ depends on what the absorber is made of and the energy of the gamma rays. In general, δ is small for dense materials and low energy gamma rays. The graph of figure 21.41 shows how the absorption length for lead depends on the energy of the gamma rays.

The **half-thickness** $d_{\frac{1}{2}}$ of a substance is the thickness of material required to remove half of the gamma rays in a beam incident on it. The half-thickness is related to the absorption length, as follows.

$$I = I_0 \exp[-x/\delta]$$

$$\therefore \tfrac{1}{2}I = I_0 \exp[-(x + d_{\frac{1}{2}})/\delta]$$

$$\therefore \tfrac{1}{2}I = I_0 \exp[-x/\delta] \times \exp[-d_{\frac{1}{2}}/\delta]$$

$$\therefore \tfrac{1}{2}I = I \exp[-d_{\frac{1}{2}}/\delta]$$

$$\therefore 2 = \exp[d_{\frac{1}{2}}/\delta]$$

$$\therefore \ln[2] = d_{\frac{1}{2}}/\delta \quad \therefore \boxed{d_{\frac{1}{2}} = 0.69\delta} \qquad (21.6)$$

The half-thickness is a useful concept because it is easy to use in estimating the thickness of shielding required around gamma ray sources. For example, suppose that we wanted to establish how much lead shielding to put around a 5 μCi cobalt-60 gamma ray source. How thick should the shielding be? To start with, it should be obvious from equation (21.5) that an infinite thickness will be needed to get the intensity of gamma rays down to zero. So rather than try to absorb all of the gamma rays, we shall have to be content with reducing their intensity until they pose less of a threat than the natural background radioactivity.

A 5 μCi (microcurie) source will have a total activity of about 2×10^5 s⁻¹. If we use a photomultiplier with a window area of 8×10^{-5} m² to detect the gamma rays at a distance of 10 cm, then we can calculate the count rate C from the detector in the absence of any shielding. Remembering that the gamma rays are emitted from the source in all directions, only a fraction of them will enter the window of the photomultiplier and be detected.

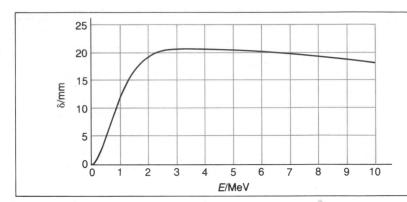

Figure 21.41   Variation of absorption length in lead with gamma ray energy

$$C = \frac{8 \times 10^{-5}}{4\pi \times (10 \times 10^{-2})^2} \times 2 \times 10^5 = 127 \text{ s}^{-1}$$

Background radiation gives a count rate of about 1 s⁻¹ for a typical photomultiplier. You can check for yourself that 127 has to be halved seven times before it becomes approximately 1, so the shielding will have to be at least seven half-thicknesses across. The gamma rays from cobalt-60 have an energy of 1.3 MeV, so their absorption length in lead will be 1.4×10^{-2} m (figure 21.41). The depth x of the shielding must therefore be

$$x = 7 \times (0.69 \times 1.4 \times 10^{-2}) \simeq 7 \text{ cm}$$

Figure 21.42   Stores of radioactive material must be clearly marked

RANDOM ABSORPTION

The exponential dependence of gamma ray transmission on the thickness of the absorber can be explained by making a simple assumption about how gamma rays interact with matter. Suppose that I gamma rays enter a thin slice of absorber per second as shown in figure 21.43. Let's assume that a particular gamma ray is equally likely to be absorbed anywhere in the absorber. This means that the chances of absorption in our slice must be proportional to the thickness of the slice. So we can set the probability that a single ray will interact with the absorber slice equal to $\mu\Delta x$, where μ is a constant. Then the fractional loss of gamma rays from the beam can be calculated as follows:

$$\Delta I = -I \times \mu\Delta x \qquad \therefore \frac{\Delta I}{I} = -\mu\Delta x \qquad (1)$$

If Δx is very small we can replace it with dx and use calculus to solve equation (1). Its solution can be found by consulting the standard integrals in Appendix B.

$$\int \frac{dI}{I} = -\mu \int dx \quad \therefore \ln I = -\mu x + c$$

$$\therefore I = I_0 \exp[-\mu x] \qquad (2)$$

Equation (2) is the same as equation (21.5) if you set $\mu = 1/\delta$.

Figure 21.43   Absorption of gamma rays in a thin slice of matter

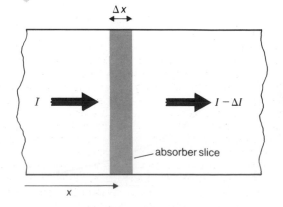

absorber slice

THICKNESS MEASUREMENT

Figure 21.44 shows how beta particles can be used to monitor the thickness of some sheet material as it is produced in a factory. As you can see from figure 21.37, the rate at which beta particles are transmitted by a solid depends on its thickness, so the signal from each detector will depend on the sample of material placed in front of it. Both of the radioactive sources contain the same type of beta emitter, so the detectors only feed out the same signal if the sheet thickness is the same as the reference thickness. (Of course, the reference sheet has to be made out of the same material as the sheet being monitored and the detectors have to be the same distance from the beta sources.) Any difference in the signals is extracted by the difference amplifier to give an error signal.

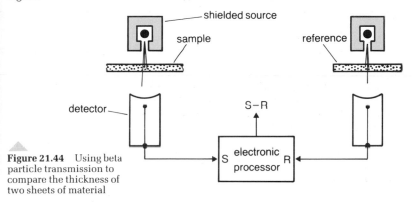

Figure 21.44 Using beta particle transmission to compare the thickness of two sheets of material

The use of two sources and a reference sheet has two advantages. First, the device does not need frequent re-calibration as the activity of the sources diminishes; being identical emitters, both sources will decay at the same rate. Secondly, the reference sheet can be replaced with another sheet of a different thickness, allowing the production of several grades of sheet from the same machine or compensating for changes in the composition of the material. With an appropriate choice of beta particle energy, systems can be built for non-contact measurement of materials ranging from thin tissue paper to 1 mm sheet steel. If gamma ray sources are used, 10 cm thick steel can be monitored.

Figure 21.45 Backscatter gauge

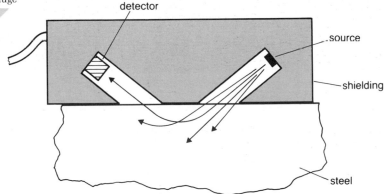

Backscatter gauges

Iron is commonly coated with a thin layer of another metal, such as tin or zinc, to discourage it from rusting. The thickness of such layers can be measured by looking at the intensity of beta particles scattered from them. Look at figure 21.45. The detector shielding prevents beta particles from the source being detected directly. Only those particles which are scattered back off the metal underneath are detected. Of course, many of the particles from the source are absorbed by the metal, but a proportion of them are reflected from atoms in the top layers of the metal with enough energy to emerge and enter the detector. The amount of reflection is dependent on the density of the metal, so the detector signal will change if zinc-plated steel is substituted for unplated steel. If two gauges are used, one can provide a reference signal from unplated steel and the other can produce a signal from the plated steel. The difference of the two is a measure of the thickness of the plating.

Using radioactivity

Radioactivity has a number of useful applications in medicine, research and industry which exploit the penetrating nature of emissions. Its use on the factory floor has been limited by the layman's assumption that radioactive materials are necessarily harmful. So before we describe some of the more elegant applications of radioactive substances, we are going to discuss how they can be safely handled.

Safety

Many people are, quite naturally, uneasy about handling radioactive sources. Unless we receive a fatal dose, we are unlikely to sense the presence of ionising emissions directly. However, detectors of these emissions are very sensitive: a **geiger counter** (a GM tube which produces audible clicks) left on the laboratory bench gives instant reassurance that the occupants of the room are not being subjected to an abnormally large dose of beta particles or gamma rays.

Alpha particles are highly ionising, but have a very short range in solid matter. They are usually completely absorbed by the top (dead) layers of your skin. Furthermore, alpha particles are completely absorbed by clothing and have a range of only a few centimetres in air, so provided that you wear gloves, alpha sources would appear to be perfectly safe. However, if you swallow or breathe in a speck of alpha emitter, then you are in trouble. Your lungs and gut are lined with live cells (unlike your skin) which can be extensively damaged by the highly ionising radiations. For example, a speck of plutonium-239 (an emitter of 5.16 MeV alpha particles) with a mass of only 1×10^{-11} kg will have a total activity of about 20 s^{-1}. This is fairly small when averaged over the whole body, but can create a lot of local damage if the speck is lodged in a lung or distributed in a bone.

Protective clothing and the storage of radioactive materials in clearly marked and amply shielded stores can make a large contribution to safety (figure 21.42). However, the most useful advice to people who handle radioactive sources is to keep their distance. In the absence of absorption by air, the dose received from a source follows an inverse square law with distance, so that doubling your separation from a source lowers your exposure by at least a factor of four. Consider a gamma ray source which has a total activity I_0. A target which has an area A placed a distance r from the source will only receive a fraction of the gamma rays.

$$I = I_0 \times \frac{A}{4\pi r^2} \tag{21.7}$$

So always handle radioactive materials with tongs at arms length and store them well away from places frequented by other people!

OBJECTIVES

After studying this section you should be able to do the following.

Sketch curves which show how the transmission of alpha particles, beta particles and gamma rays depends on the thickness of an absorber.

Explain the differences in absorption characteristics of the three emissions.

Use the rule that $\rho R \simeq$ constant for a particular emission.

State the sources of background radioactivity.

Know that a count of N random events will have an uncertainty of $N^{\frac{1}{2}}$.

Use the formulae $I = I_0 \exp[-x/\delta]$ and $d_{\frac{1}{2}} = 0.69\delta$ to calculate the transmission of gamma rays.

Explain why the intensity of a gamma ray source is proportional to the inverse square of its distance.

Describe and explain precautions to be followed in handling radioactive materials.

QUESTIONS

1 Use the graph of figure 21.35 to estimate the following:

a the range of 2 MeV alpha particles in water (density 1000 kg m^{-3});

b the minimum thickness of paper (density 800 kg m^{-3}) required to completely absorb 8.0 MeV alpha particles;

c the thickness of the mica window of a GM tube which can just about detect 5.0 MeV alpha particles (mica has a density of 2800 kg m^{-3}).

2 The graph of figure 21.46 shows how the count rate of a detector changes when a number of sheets of aluminium foil are inserted in front of a source which emits more than one type of emission. The density of aluminium is 2700 kg m^{-3}.

a Use figure 21.35 to estimate the energy of the alpha particles being emitted by the source. Will your answer be too large or too small? Explain why.

b Helena reckons that the other emission from the source is beta particles. Pat disagrees. Which one of them is right? Describe an experiment you could do to convince them.

3 a Would rubber gloves give protection against beta particles when you handled their source? If the density of rubber is 1100 kg m^{-3}, use figure 21.38 to estimate the maximum energy of beta particles which are completely absorbed by rubber gloves.

b If rubber gloves do not appreciably screen your hands from gamma ray sources, why should you still wear them?

c Estimate the rate at which you intercept gamma rays when an open source of strength 5.0 μCi is left on the bench at the other end of the laboratory. (1.0 Ci is equivalent to an activity of 3.7×10^{10} s^{-1}.) How does this compare with background radioactivity? (The background count for an object with the dimensions of a GM tube is about 0.2 s^{-1}.)

4 A smoke detector which employs an air-filled **ionisation chamber** to detect the emissions from a radioactive source is shown in figure 21.47. Ions generated by the emissions from the source are swept to the electrodes by the p.d. between them. This ionisation current flows through a resistor to generate a voltage proportional to the ionisation current.

a Should the source be an alpha emitter, beta emitter or gamma emitter? Explain your answer.

b When smoke particles enter the chamber, the ionisation current drops. Suggest why.

c The activity of all radioactive sources decreases with time. Explain how a second ionisation chamber could be used to stop this decrease triggering off a false alarm.

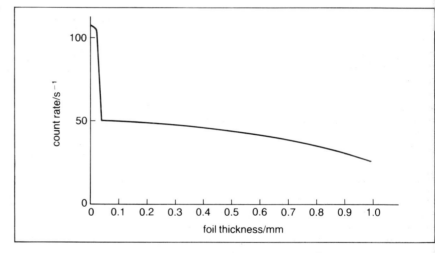

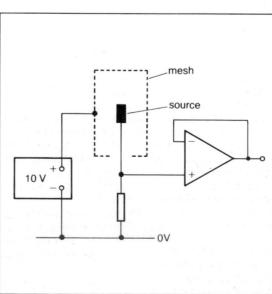

Figure 21.46

Figure 21.47

5 One part in 8000 of potassium is radioactive potassium-40, a long-lived emitter of 1.31 MeV beta particles. The average human body contains about 0.25 kg of potassium, providing it with most of its internal dose of radioactivity.

a If pure potassium-40 has a specific activity of 2.6×10^8 s^{-1} kg^{-1}, calculate the total activity of the human body.

b If the average density of humans is 1000 kg m^{-3}, what is the thickness of human flesh which will completely absorb the emissions from potassium-40? (Use figure 21.38.)

6 a The half-thickness of concrete for high energy gamma rays is about 20 cm, roughly twice as much as that of lead. Why are nuclear power stations shielded with concrete rather than lead?

b Table 21.4 contains the results of an experiment to find the half-thickness of steel for 3 MeV gamma rays. The mean reading of the detector I was noted for different thicknesses x of steel placed in front of the source. If $I = I_0\exp[-x/\delta]$, show that a graph of $\ln I$ against x should be a straight line with a slope of $-1/\delta$. Plot such a graph for the data in table 21.4 and use it to calculate the half-thickness $d_{\frac{1}{2}}$ for steel.

Table 21.4

x/mm	I/s^{-1}
0	1267
1	1233
2	1193
4	1140
8	1010
16	822
32	515

RADIOACTIVE DECAY

Radioactivity is random. The clicks from a geiger counter come at irregular intervals, so that you cannot accurately predict when the next click is going to happen. Furthermore, the activity of all radioactive substances eventually dies down to nothing. These observations can be precisely modelled by assuming that spontancity rules radioactive decay. This section will introduce you to a mathematical model which predicts how the activity of a radioactive source changes with time. A more detailed model of how the nucleus of an atom changes when an ionising emission is produced will be presented in the next chapter.

Random decay

Let us assume that each atom in a radioactive source can only emit one ionising emission. Each **parent** atom produces a single emission, turning into a **daughter** atom in the process (figure 21.48). If the daughter is stable, i.e. cannot produce an emission, then it should be obvious that a source which is initially made of only parents will eventually be transformed into one which is completely made of daughters. Furthermore, the total number of emissions from the source must be equal to the initial number of parents.

Consider a single parent atom. When is it going to decay into its daughter? The irregular nature of the clicks from a geiger counter suggests that the decay is a random process. In other words, the parent has the same chance of decaying at any time, regardless of what the other atoms are doing. If we watch our parent atom patiently, we will be completely unable to predict when it is going to decay. This uncertainty can be modelled with the following piece of algebra:

$$P(\Delta t) = \lambda \Delta t \qquad \text{(21.8)}$$

$P(\Delta t)$ is the probability that the atom will decay during the short time interval Δt. If we double the length of Δt, the chances of the atom decaying should double, so $P(\Delta t)$ must be proportional to Δt.

The constant of proportionality λ is called the **decay constant**: as you will see below, it fixes the rate at which the whole sample of parents turns into daughters.

Exponential drop

Now consider a large number N of parent atoms. Although we cannot say in advance which of those atoms will decay during a short time interval, we can still use equation (21.8) to predict how many (ΔN) of them ought to change into daughters.

$$\Delta N = -P(\Delta t) \times N \qquad \text{(21.9)}$$

(The minus sign indicates that when a parent decays it reduces the number of parents left.) If we use equation (21.8) to eliminate $P(\Delta t)$ from equation (21.9) we obtain an important differential equation.

$$\Delta N = -\lambda \Delta t \times N \quad \therefore \frac{\Delta N}{N} = -\lambda \Delta t \qquad \text{(21.10)}$$

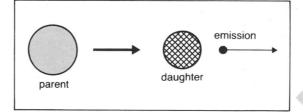

Figure 21.48 A parent atom decays into a daughter atom

We are interested in the number of parents left in the source after a finite amount of time t. So let us sum ΔN over a large number of short time intervals to find the total change.

$$\frac{\Sigma \Delta N}{N} = \Sigma -\lambda \Delta t \qquad \therefore \Sigma \frac{\Delta N}{N} = -\lambda \Sigma \Delta t \qquad \text{(21.11)}$$

If we adopt the standard calculus practice and let Δt shrink to zero, equation (21.11) can be rewritten in terms of integrals which can then be evaluated with the help of Appendix B.

$$\int \frac{dN}{N} = -\lambda \int dt \quad \therefore \ln[N] = -\lambda t + c \qquad \text{(21.12)}$$

The constant c can be found if we assume that the number of parents at $t = 0$ is N_0.

$$\ln[N_0] = 0 + c$$
$$\therefore \ln[N] = -\lambda t + \ln[N_0]$$
$$\therefore \ln[N] - \ln[N_0] = -\lambda t$$
$$\therefore \ln[N/N_0] = -\lambda t$$
$$\therefore N/N_0 = \exp[-\lambda t] \qquad \textbf{(21.13)}$$

$N = N_0\exp[-\lambda t]$

N is the number of parent atoms in the sample

N_0 is the initial number of parent atoms in the sample

λ is the decay constant (s^{-1})

t is the elapsed time (s)

The graph of figure 21.49 shows how N changes with time according to equation (21.13).

Changing activity

Direct confirmation of equation (21.13) is not easy. Precise counting of individual atoms is difficult at the best of times, without the extra complication of ensuring that the daughter atoms are not included in the count. However, each decay of a parent into a daughter produces an ionising emission which can be readily detected. So if we can predict how the activity A of the sample of parents changes with time, we will have something which can be tested by experiment. Our starting point will be equation (21.10).

$$\frac{\Delta N}{N} = -\lambda \Delta t \qquad \therefore \frac{\Delta N}{\Delta t} = -\lambda N \qquad \textbf{(21.14)}$$

The rate of decay of parents is the same as the activity A, i.e. the rate at which emissions are produced.

$$A = \lambda N \qquad \textbf{(21.15)}$$

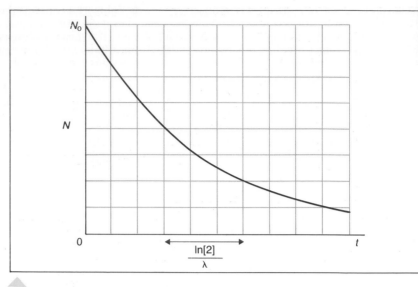

Figure 21.49 $N = N_0\exp[-\lambda t]$

So the activity of the sample is proportional to the number of parent atoms left in it.

$A = \lambda N$

A is the total activity of a radioactive source (s^{-1})

λ is the decay constant of the source (s^{-1})

N is the total number of parent atoms in the source

If we use equation (21.13) to eliminate N from equation (21.15) we obtain a useful expression for the variation of A with time.

$$A = \lambda \times N_0\exp[-\lambda t]$$
$$\therefore A = A_0\exp[-\lambda t] \text{ where } A_0 = \lambda N_0 \qquad \textbf{[21.16]}$$

$A = A_0\exp[-\lambda t]$

A is the activity of the sample (s^{-1})

A_0 is the initial activity of the sample (s^{-1})

λ is the decay constant (s^{-1})

t is the elapsed time (s)

The **becquerel** (Bq) is an alternative unit of activity: 1 Bq corresponds to one decay per second.

Experimental verification

Figure 21.50 illustrates apparatus which is commonly used in schools to verify equation (21.16). A radioactive gas (radon-220) is enclosed in an ionisation chamber. (The gas is a product of the radioactive decay of the solid thorium-232 in a plastic bottle (not drawn). It can be squirted into the ionisation chamber by gently squeezing the bottle.) The outer wall of the chamber is held about 25 V above the central electrode. The current in the chamber creates a p.d. across the 10^{11} Ω resistor which can be measured with the help of the op-amp follower. That current will be proportional to the activity of the radon-220. Each alpha particle it produces will create a certain number of ion–electron pairs in the chamber. Although some of these will recombine as they drift towards the central electrode or wall, the current in the chamber will be proportional to the rate of production of the alpha particles.

Figure 21.50 Apparatus for measuring the half-life of radon-220

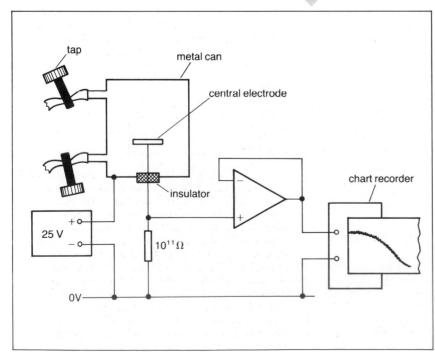

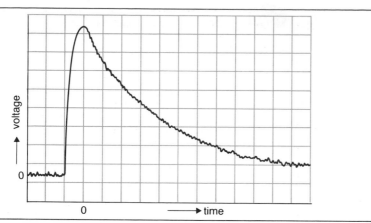

Figure 21.51 Typical chart recorder trace from the apparatus of figure 21.50

The graph of figure 21.51 is a typical chart-recording for the experiment. It shows how the ionisation current changes as time goes on. After the initial surge (corresponding to the introduction of the radon-220), the current looks as if it dies exponentially with time. Note that the curve is not smooth, as predicted by equation (21.16). This is because it is a product of a finite number of random events, giving rise to fluctuations: the equation $A = A_0\exp[-\lambda t]$ predicts how the *mean* activity will change with time. The exponential nature of the curve can be verified by plotting a graph of $\ln[A]$ against t.

$$A = A_0\exp[-\lambda t]$$
$$\therefore \ln[A] = \ln[A_0\exp[-\lambda t]]$$
$$\therefore \ln[A] = \ln[A_0] + \ln[\exp[-\lambda t]]$$
$$\therefore \ln[A] = \ln[A_0] - \lambda t \qquad (21.17)$$

As you can see from figure 21.52, the result is a straight line. The magnitude of the slope gives a value for the decay constant of radon-220: $\lambda = 1.24\times10^{-2}\ \text{s}^{-1}$.

Half-life

The **half-life** $T_{\frac{1}{2}}$ of a radioactive substance is the time taken for its activity to halve. It is related to the decay constant by the following equation (you will be invited to prove it for yourself in the questions at the end of the section.)

$\lambda T_{\frac{1}{2}} = \ln[2]$

λ is the decay constant (s^{-1})

$T_{\frac{1}{2}}$ is the half-life (s)

Figure 21.52 The slope of the $\ln[A]-t$ graph is $-\lambda$

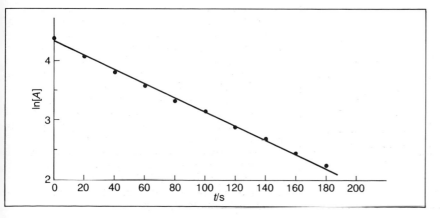

Knowledge of the half-life of a source is useful because it allows you to estimate how rapidly its activity will drop. For example, consider the radon-220 gas investigated in figure 21.50. Its measured decay constant can be used to calculate its half-life.

$$\lambda T_{\frac{1}{2}} = 0.69 \quad \therefore 1.24\times10^{-2} \times T_{\frac{1}{2}} = 0.69$$
$$\therefore T_{\frac{1}{2}} = 56\ \text{s}$$

The half-life of a source is specific to the substance of which it is made. Half-lives of a number of radioactive **isotopes** are listed in table 21.5. Sodium-24 is commonly used as a radioactive tracer for medical work — having a half-life of only fifteen hours means that its activity generally falls below that of the background radiation in a few days. On the other hand, caesium-137 (a component of the fallout from the Chernobyl nuclear power station fire) is going to be detectable for at least the next century. A useful rule of thumb is that the activity of a source drops by an order of magnitude in approximately three half-lives.

Table 21.5

Isotope	Emission	Half-life
sodium-24	γ	15 hours
iodine-131	β	8.1 days
strontium-90	β	28 years
caesium-137	β	30 years
cobalt-60	γ	5.3 years
americium-241	α	458 years
carbon-14	β	5730 years
plutonium-240	α	6580 years
uranium-235	α	7.1×10^{8} years
potassium-40	β	1.3×10^{9} years

Long half-lives

It should be obvious that direct measurement of the half-life of a long-lived isotope is impossible. Instead, it has to be deduced from the activity of a known mass of the isotope with the help of equation (21.15).

$$A = \lambda N, \quad \lambda T_{\frac{1}{2}} = \ln[2] \quad \therefore T_{\frac{1}{2}} = \ln[2]\frac{N}{A} \qquad (21.18)$$

For example, suppose that you wanted to measure the half-life of potassium-40. Naturally occuring potassium contains three isotopes with the concentrations shown in table 21.6 — only the potassium-40 is radioactive.

Table 21.6

Isotope	Percentage
potassium-39	93.22
potassium-40	0.12
potassium-41	6.66

A measured quantity of a potassium compound is placed in a thin layer close to the front of a photomultiplier tube so that half of the beta particles emitted by the potassium-40 are detected (the other half are emitted away from the photomultiplier). For example, suppose that the measured activity of 1.00 g of potassium chloride was 85 s^{-1}. So A, the *total* activity of the sample, should be $2\times85 = 170\ \text{s}^{-1}$, assuming that the detector is 100% efficient. The total number of potassium-40 atoms in the sample can be calculated from the molar mass of potassium chloride (0.074 kg mol^{-1}) and the Avogadro constant ($6.0\times10^{23}\ \text{mol}^{-1}$).

CARBON DATING

Carbon-14 has a half-life of 5730 years. It is continuously produced in the upper atmosphere by cosmic rays. Neutrons which are liberated in a cosmic ray shower can be captured by a nitrogen-14 nucleus to form a very unstable nucleus. This immediately ejects a proton to form a carbon-14 nucleus.

$$^{14}_{7}N + ^{1}_{0}n \rightarrow ^{14}_{6}C + ^{1}_{1}p$$

Most of the carbon in our atmosphere is in the form of carbon dioxide gas, a very small fraction of which is radioactive. The continual steady bombardment of the Earth by cosmic rays maintains a constant proportion of carbon-14 in its atmosphere. An equilibrium concentration is established when the rate of production by cosmic rays is equal to the rate of decay.

During its lifetime a tree is continually absorbing atmospheric carbon dioxide and using it to build long molecules, such as cellulose and lignin. A small proportion of that carbon will be carbon-14. When the tree dies, it no longer interacts with atmospheric carbon dioxide, so the proportion of carbon-14 in its tissues will decrease with time. If A_0 is the activity of a fixed mass of carbon derived from a living tree, then the activity A of the same amount of carbon derived from a sample of wood in a building can be used to date the building.

$$A = A_0\exp[-\lambda t], \quad \lambda T_{\frac{1}{2}} = \ln[2] \quad \therefore A_0/A = \exp[+\lambda t]$$
$$\therefore A_0/A = \exp[\ln[2]\, t/T_{\frac{1}{2}}]$$
$$\therefore \ln[A_0/A] = \ln[2]t/T_{\frac{1}{2}}$$

$T_{\frac{1}{2}} = 5730$ years

$$\therefore t = \frac{5730\,\ln[A_0/A]}{0.693}$$

Unfortunately, the proportion of carbon-14 in living tissue is small and the beta particles it emits have relatively low energy ($\leqslant 0.158$ MeV), so carbon dating is a tricky business. (One gram of contemporary carbon from a living tree only produces 15 beta particles per minute.) Of course, the method assumes that the flux of cosmic rays does not change with time, but independent checks (such as counting the rings of long-lived trees) show that its accuracy is better than ±200 years within the range 600 – 10 000 years.

Figure 21.53 The Turin shroud. The image of a man appears to have been transferred to the linen used to wrap his dead body. This interesting relic was recently dated by three independent laboratories by measuring the proportion of carbon-14 in a few threads taken from a small corner of the cloth. The result was between 1260 and 1390 AD, a good match to the first mention of the shroud in historical documents.

$$N = \frac{1\times10^{-3}}{0.074} \times 6.0\times10^{23} \times \frac{0.12}{100} = 9.73\times10^{18}$$

Now we can use equation (21.18) to calculate a value for $T_{\frac{1}{2}}$.

$$T_{\frac{1}{2}} = \ln[2]\frac{N}{A}$$

$$\therefore T_{\frac{1}{2}} = \frac{0.693 \times 9.73\times10^{18}}{170}$$

$$\therefore T_{\frac{1}{2}} = 4.0\times10^{16}\ s$$

OBJECTIVES

After studying this section you should be able to do the following.

Understand the meaning of *parent* atom and *daughter* atom.

Explain how the concept of random decay leads to the formula $\Delta N/N = -\lambda\Delta t$.

Quote the formula $N = N_0\exp[-\lambda t]$.

Use the formula $A = \lambda N$ to predict the activity of a sample of parent atoms.

Use the formulae $A = A_0\exp[-\lambda t]$ and $\lambda T_{\frac{1}{2}} = \ln[2]$ to predict how the activity of a source changes with time.

Define the half-life of a substance.

Describe how the half-life of short- and long-lived isotopes can be measured.

QUESTIONS

1 The activity of a radioactive isotope is given by the formula $A = A_0\exp[-\lambda t]$ where λ is the decay constant.

a Show that the activity is halved each time that t increases by $\ln[2]/\lambda$.

b How long do you have to wait for the activity to drop by a factor of ten? How many half-lives is this?

c Phosphorous-32 has a half-life of 14.3 days. What is its decay constant? Estimate the activity of a 1.00 g sample of the pure isotope. (The molar mass of phosphorous is 0.031 kg mol^{-1}.)

2 Earl places a gamma ray source in front of a GM tube and uses a data logger to record the count rate from the source over the weekend. His results are shown in table 21.7. When the source is removed, the GM tube records 553 counts in half an hour. Use the data to calculate the half-life of the source.

Table 21.7

Time/hours	0	6	12	18	24	30	36	42	48
Count rate/min^{-1}	289	220	178	133	110	82	68	59	51

3 Carbon from a modern tree has a specific activity of 250 s^{-1} kg^{-1} due to the presence of carbon-14.

a If the half-life of carbon-14 is 5730 years, calculate its decay constant. Hence calculate the number of carbon-14 atoms needed to give an activity of 250 s^{-1}.

b The molar mass of carbon is 0.012 kg mol^{-1}. Calculate the number of carbon atoms in 1.00 kg and hence calculate the percentage of modern carbon which is carbon-14.

c A 0.52 g sample of carbon from an ancient Egyptian sarcophagus had an activity of 5 counts per minute. Estimate the age of the sample.

4 Cobalt-60 is sometimes used as a marker to identify the position of cables and pipes under the surface of the earth. Small wires containing the isotope are placed on top of the pipe before the earth is shovelled over it. The gamma rays from the wire are easily detected with a suitable geiger counter held at the soil surface.

a The half-life of cobalt-60 is 5.26 years. If the registered activity at the surface of the soil is twenty times greater than the background, estimate how long the marker is going to last.

b Suppose that it is important that the marker lasts for at least 200 years. Suggest a suitable initial activity at the surface of the soil if the background count is 0.5 s^{-1}.

5 The half-lives of sodium-21 and sodium-26 are 23 s and 60 s, respectively.

a If two samples are prepared with the the same number of atoms, which one will have the greatest initial activity?

b Calculate the initial ratio of the activities of the two samples.

c Draw two graphs on the same axes to show how the activity of the two samples changes with time.

d Apart from their shape, the two graphs you have drawn have a property in common. Explain what it is.

6 Over 99% of naturally occuring uranium is uranium-238. This decays in a series of steps to produce stable lead-206, emitting a total of eight alpha particles along the way. The half-life of uranium-238 is 4.5×10^9 years; the longest-lived isotope in the chain between uranium-238 and lead-206 has a half life of only 2.5×10^5 years. The helium gas from the alpha particles is trapped in uranium-bearing rock and can be used to estimate its age. The age of the Earth is estimated as 3×10^9 years. Calculate how much helium gas is produced by each gram of uranium in that time.

7 The heat energy produced by the decay of an isotope can be used to generate electricity from a bank of thermocouples (figure 21.54). The power of such sources is limited, but they have the advantage of being able to continue functioning for a long time without any maintenance. They have been used in satellites, heart pacemakers and navigation buoys.

a Would you use an alpha emitter or a gamma emitter as the power source? Could you use a beta emitter?

b Plutonium has been used to power satellites; it emits alpha particles with energy 5.5 MeV. If the energy conversion process is only 10% efficient, calculate the mass of plutonium-238 needed to generate 25 W of electricity. The half-life of the isotope is 86 years and its molar mass is 0.24 kg mol^{-1}.

c Calculate by how much the power output will drop over 15 years.

d If the satellite fails to operate properly when the power drops to below 18 W, estimate its working life.

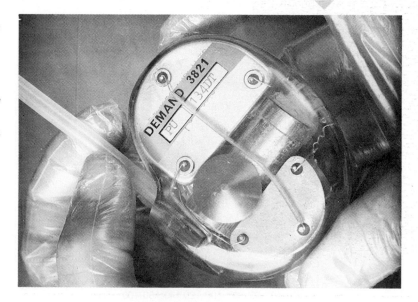

Figure 21.54 A plutonium-powered heart pacemaker

22

THE UNSTABLE NUCLEUS

The discovery of radioactivity at the turn of the century gave physicists a tool with which they could investigate the secrets of the atomic nucleus. Once it was realised that alpha particles were fast moving, heavy, positively charged particles, they ceased to become simply objects for investigation. They became an instrument which could be used to probe inside atomic nuclei and search out the reasons for radioactive decay. This chapter will lead you along the historical path of discovery, describing some landmark experiments which clinched the various aspects of our understanding of nuclear physics. Of course, it appears to be the fate of all discoveries in physics to become man's tools. The nucleus is no exception. Once its basic behaviour was understood, the atomic nucleus was pressed into mankind's service, providing medical radioisotopes, energy and weapons.

THE NUCLEUS

It is well known today that the nucleus of an atom contains all of its positive charge and virtually all of its mass. More precisely, the model of a massive positively charged nucleus at the centre of an atom satisfactorily accounts for its behaviour. The experiment which first forced this model upon the scientific community was performed by Hans Geiger and Ernest Marsden in 1909. They looked at how alpha particles were elastically scattered from a thin gold foil: their results could only be explained if gold atoms contained a small, heavy, positive core.

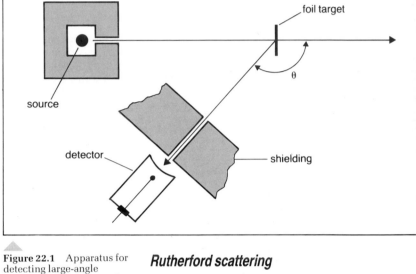

Figure 22.1 Apparatus for detecting large-angle scattering of alpha particles from a foil target

Figure 22.2 Rate of scattering of alpha particles at different angles

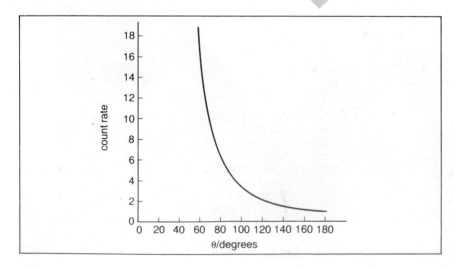

Rutherford scattering

Figure 22.1 shows apparatus which could be used to explore alpha particle scattering from a solid target. The whole thing, of course, has to be in a vacuum to stop the alpha particles losing their energy before or after hitting the target. The lead shielding around the source only lets a narrow well-defined beam of alpha particles emerge towards the target. The detector counts the number of particles deflected off the target (a thin foil) at various angles. (Geiger and Marsden had to use a zinc sulphide scintillator as their detector, not nearly as convenient as a modern solid-state device.)

The graph of figure 22.2 shows typical results of this experiment. The most surprising feature is that any alpha particles are scattered through large angles at all. In fact, about 1 in every 10 000 alpha particles incident on the foil is deflected by an angle of more than 90°. As Ernest Rutherford (who had suggested the experiment to Geiger and Marsden in the first place) said 'It was quite the most incredible event that has ever happened to me in my life. It was almost as if you fired a 15 inch shell at a piece of tissue paper and it came back and hit you.'

In order to appreciate Rutherford's surprise, it helps to understand what physicists knew about alpha particles at the time. Rutherford knew that his alpha particles had an energy of about 4 MeV, were positively charged and had the mass of a helium atom. The Principle of Momentum

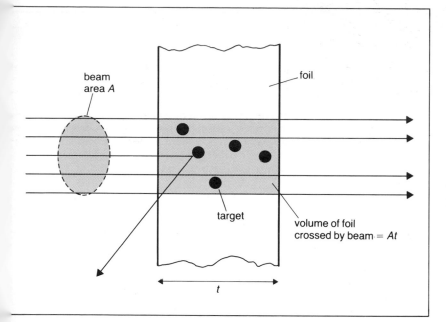

Figure 22.3 Each gold atom provides a target for the alpha particle projectile

The gold foil will present the beam of alpha particle projectiles with a number of targets, as shown in figure 22.3. If the beam has a cross-sectional area A and the thickness of the foil is t, then the number of targets N is easily estimated from the interatomic spacing d_0.

$$N \simeq \frac{At}{d_0{}^3} \qquad \textbf{(22.1)}$$

If each target (nucleus) has a radius r, then it presents an area πr^2 to the projectiles. This area is called the **collision cross-section**. If the projectiles arrive randomly distributed over the area of the beam, then the probability P of one projectile hitting any target is given by

$$P = N \times \frac{\pi r^2}{A} \qquad \therefore \ P = \frac{At}{d_0{}^3} \times \frac{\pi r^2}{A}$$

$$\therefore P = \frac{\pi r^2 t}{d_0{}^3} \qquad \textbf{(22.2)}$$

If we assume that P is very small, then the chance P^2 of one projectile making two collisions is utterly negligible. The gold foil had a thickness of 6×10^{-7} m and the spacing of gold atoms is 2.6×10^{-10} m. Since the observed chance of a large-angle deflection ($>90°$) was 1 in 10^4, $P = 1 \times 10^{-4}$.

$$P = \frac{\pi r^2 t}{d_0{}^3} \qquad \therefore \ 1 \times 10^{-4} = \frac{\pi \ \times \ r^2 \ \times \ 6 \times 10^{-7}}{(2.6 \times 10^{-10})^3}$$

$$\therefore r = 3.0 \times 10^{-14} \text{ m}$$

Notice that the diameter of the nucleus (6×10^{-14} m) appears to be much smaller than the diameter of the whole atom (2.6×10^{-10} m).

Conservation dictates that if a particle is deflected through more than 90°, its mass must be less than the mass of its target. Furthermore, the reflected alpha particles appeared to have lost very little energy during the deflection process. This requires an elastic collision with a target which is much more massive than the projectile. The results can only be explained by assuming that gold atoms contain charged lumps which are much more massive than helium atoms. Since it was known that electrons are easily deflected when they pass through matter (remember the squiggly nature of beta particle tracks in a cloud chamber), the positive charge in an atom must be responsible for deflecting the alpha particles through large angles.

Nuclear dimensions
We can use Geiger and Marsden's results to estimate the size of a gold nucleus. Our model for the interaction between the alpha particle and the nucleus is a very crude one: we shall assume that both act like ball bearings. The nucleus is assumed to be much larger and massive than the alpha particle, and only a hard collision between the two is going to deflect the alpha particle through more than 90°. (Rutherford's model which assumes the correct electrostatic force between the two will be explained later.)

Electrostatic repulsion
Rutherford assumed that all of the positive charge and nearly all of the mass of an atom resided in a very small nucleus. This means that as the alpha particles approach the nucleus they are deflected by electrostatic repulsion. Provided that the nucleus is small enough (or the alpha particles don't have enough energy), then an alpha particle will never actually touch the nucleus on its way past. If we assume that any non-electrostatic forces between the two particles only operate if they touch, then we can write down an expression for the potential energy E_p of the alpha particle when it is a distance r from the centre of the nucleus.

$$E_e = qV, \qquad V = \frac{Q}{4\pi\epsilon_0 r}$$

$$\therefore E_p = \frac{qQ}{4\pi\epsilon_0 r} \qquad \textbf{(22.3)}$$

The behaviour of the alpha particle when it hits the **potential hill** around the nucleus can be modelled with the apparatus shown in figure 22.4. It is a gravitational analogue, with a ball bearing representing the alpha particle. The curved surface is built so that its height above the bench is proportional to $1/r$, where r is the distance from its centre. The ball bearings are rolled down a ramp to give them a fixed amount of kinetic energy. As they move over the curved surface which represents the potential hill around the nucleus, they slow down

Figure 22.4 Using a model of the potential hill around a nucleus

THE SCATTERING FORMULA

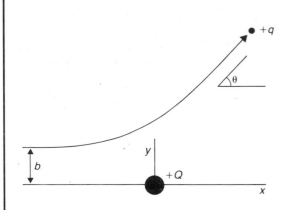

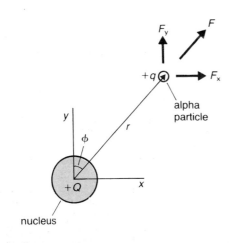

Figure 22.6 Path followed by a single alpha particle when it is deflected by a massive nucleus

Since Rutherford knew about Coulomb's Law, he was able to calculate the trajectory of an alpha particle near a nucleus and make precise predictions about the number of particles he expected to be scattered off the foil at various angles. The excellent match between those predictions and the experiments of Geiger and Marsden meant that physicists were forced to accept that most of the space of an atom appeared to be occupied by electrons. In fact, Rutherford was lucky. Normally Newton's Laws of Motion cannot be used to model the motion of very small particles: quantum mechanics has to be used instead. In this particular case, however, classical mechanics and quantum mechanics (whose existence was only a twinkle in Einstein's eye when Rutherford did his sums) give the same result.

The complete derivation of Rutherford's scattering formula is straightforward but tedious. Look at figure 22.6. The first step is to write down an expression for the force F acting on the projectile when it is a distance r from the target. If the charges of the projectile and the target are $+q$ and $+Q$ respectively, we can use Coulomb's Law.

$$F = \frac{qQ}{4\pi\epsilon_0 r^2} \quad \therefore F_x = F\sin\phi, \quad F_y = F\cos\phi$$

$$\sin\phi = \frac{x}{r}, \quad \cos\phi = \frac{y}{r}, \quad r = (x^2 + y^2)^{\frac{1}{2}}$$

$$\therefore F_x = \frac{qQx}{4\pi\epsilon_0(x^2 + y^2)^{3/2}}, \qquad F_y = \frac{qQy}{4\pi\epsilon_0(x^2 + y^2)^{3/2}} \tag{1}$$

Now Newton's Second Law of Motion can be used to convert equation (1) into expressions for the change in velocity of the projectile in a small time interval Δt.

$$F = \frac{m\Delta v}{\Delta t} \quad \therefore \Delta v_x = \frac{qQx\Delta t}{4\pi\epsilon_0 m(x^2 + y^2)^{3/2}}$$

$$\text{and } \Delta v_y = \frac{qQy\Delta t}{4\pi\epsilon_0 m(x^2 + y^2)^{3/2}} \tag{2}$$

Rutherford had to use calculus to show that equation (2) led to a trajectory which was a hyperbola. It would be a simple matter today to use a computer to calculate the deflection $\theta = \tan^{-1}(v_y/v_x)$ for a projectile with a given initial velocity in the x-direction. It turns out that if the initial value of y is b and the projectile has an energy E, then the deflection is given by the following formula:

$$\tan(\theta/2) = \frac{Qq}{8\pi\epsilon_0 bE} \tag{3}$$

Finally, allowance has to be made for the fact that projectiles can approach the nucleus with a range of values of b and that the foil (thickness t) contains many nuclei spaced a distance d_0 apart. The end result is a formula which predicts the probability $P(\theta)$ that an alpha particle with energy E will be scattered out of the beam at an angle θ and hit a detector of area A at a distance r from the foil.

$$P(\theta) = \frac{A}{r^2} \times \left(\frac{Qq}{4\pi\epsilon_0 E}\right)^2 \times \frac{t}{d_0^3} \times \frac{1}{16\sin^4(\theta/2)} \tag{4}$$

Equation (4) allows a precise prediction of the proportion of alpha particles being scattered off the foil at a particular angle θ, provided that you have values for all of the quantities in it. Rutherford did not have accurate values for Q, q and d_0, but Geiger and Marsden's data agreed well with the $\sin^{-4}(\theta/2)$ prediction of (4), as you can see from figure 22.7.

and then speed up again, emerging in a different direction. Figure 22.5 shows how the trajectory followed depends on the aiming error, i.e. the distance by which the projectile would have missed the target if the hill had not been present.

A little time thinking about this analogue should convince you that the alpha particle will get nearest to the nucleus in a head-on collision. It is a simple matter to calculate this distance of closest approach R for an alpha particle of known energy E_t: all of its kinetic energy will have been converted to potential energy at this point. For example, let us calculate R for a 4.0 MeV alpha particle and a gold nucleus which contains 79 protons. The starting point is equation (22.3).

$$E_t = \frac{qQ}{4\pi\epsilon_0 R}$$

$$\therefore R = \frac{qQ}{4\pi\epsilon_0 E_t}$$

$$\therefore R = \frac{2 \times 79 \times (1.6\times10^{-19})^2}{4\pi \times 8.9\times10^{-12} \times 4\times10^6 \times 1.6\times10^{-19}}$$

$$\therefore R = 5.7\times10^{-14}\text{ m}$$

So, provided that the nucleus is smaller than R, we can be confident that electrostatic repulsion is the only force deflecting the alpha particle on its way past the nucleus.

Probing the nucleus

Figure 22.8 shows how the number of alpha particles $N(\theta)$ scattered from the foil at an angle θ depends on θ if the only force between the alpha particle and the nucleus is electrostatic. Compare it with figure 22.9 which shows the distribution expected if we model the alpha particle and the nucleus as hard spheres: the two graphs have quite different shapes. Only an inverse-square force law between the alpha particle and nucleus gives rise to the distribution shown in figure 22.8. The fact that the experimental data fits the $\sin^{-4}(\theta/2)$ curve is strong evidence that Rutherford's model of the atom is correct.

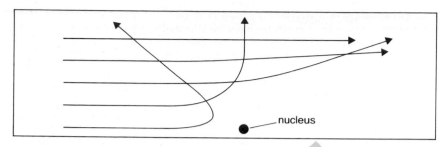

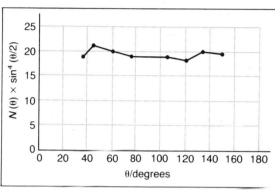

Figure 22.5   Trajectories of alpha particles passing close to a nucleus

Figure 22.7   Some of Geiger and Marsden's data

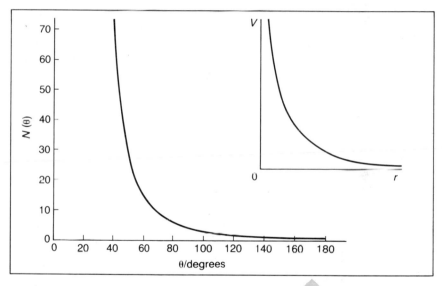

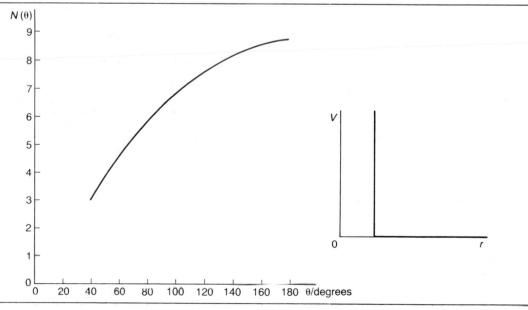

Figure 22.8   Predicted scattering rate at different angles for electrostatic repulsion

Figure 22.9   Predicted scattering rate at different angles for hard spheres

Of course, we only expect data to agree with figure 22.8 if the alpha particles have insufficient energy to actually touch the nucleus. Modern accelerators can generate beams of artificial alpha particles of known energies E_t. Figure 22.10 shows what happens to the distribution $N(\theta)$ as E_t is increased. As you can see, at high energies the distribution no longer matches that predicted by figure 22.8. Instead of flying through a purely electrostatic potential hill, the high energy alpha particles which hit the nucleus head-on 'see' a hill with a deep well at its centre (figure 22.10). If the alpha particle has got enough energy to climb up the hill and drop into the well, it will have 'touched' the nucleus and no longer be subject to just electrostatic forces. The shape of the well can be inferred from the distribution $N(\theta)$ for high values of E_t. It is found that the radius r of the well is given by the following approximate formula, where A is the **nucleon number** or **atomic mass number** of the atom.

$$r \simeq A^{1/3} \times 1.2 \times 10^{-15}$$

r is the radius of the nucleus (m)

A is the nucleon number

Nuclear mass

The Rutherford scattering formula (see box, equation (4)) contains the charge Q of the target nucleus, so a measurement of the number of alpha particles of known energy scattered from a foil of a particular element can be used to calculate the charge of the element's nucleus. This turns out, as you would expect, to be a whole number of electronic charges.

$$Q = Ze$$

Q is the charge of the nucleus

Z is the atomic number of the element

e is the magnitude of the electronic charge

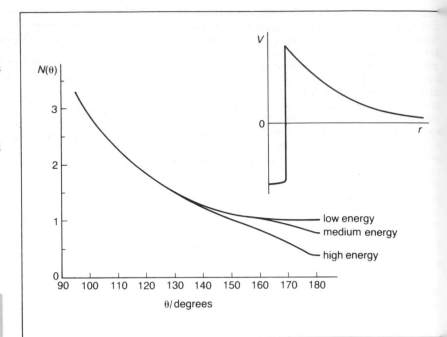

Figure 22.10 At high energies the alpha particle can penetrate the nucleus

The mass of a nucleus is approximately a whole number times the mass of a hydrogen atom. If we assume that a hydrogen nucleus is a single particl (the **proton**), then we can write down an approximate formula for the mass of other nuclei.

$$m \simeq Am_p$$

m is the mass of the nucleus

A is the nucleon number of the nucleus

m_p is the mass of a single proton

The fact that the masses of all nuclei (except, of course, those of hydrogen atoms) are always slightly less than a whole number of proton masse makes radioactive decay possible. So before we attempt to explain why nuclei spit out ionising emissions, you ought to find out how the mass of a single nucleus is precisely measured.

Mass spectrometry
Figure 22.11 shows the arrangement of a **mass spectrometer** of the type invented by Kenneth Bainbridge in 1933: the original machines used photographic plates as ion detectors rather than solid-state devices. The apparatus works as follows.

An electric discharge through a gas of the atoms whose nuclei are to be investigated generates a plasma. Positively charged particles (atoms with one or more electrons stripped from them) leak int the **accelerator region** through a small hole. This region (and the next two) contains a vacuum so that there are few collisions of air molecules with the ions. The ions emerge from the accelerator region with a velocity v which depends on their charge q, mass m and the accelerating potential V.

$$E_e = qV, \quad E_k = \tfrac{1}{2}mv^2 \quad \therefore qV = \tfrac{1}{2}mv^2$$
$$\therefore v = (2qV/m)^{\frac{1}{2}} \quad \textbf{(22.4}$$

Figure 22.11 A mass spectrometer

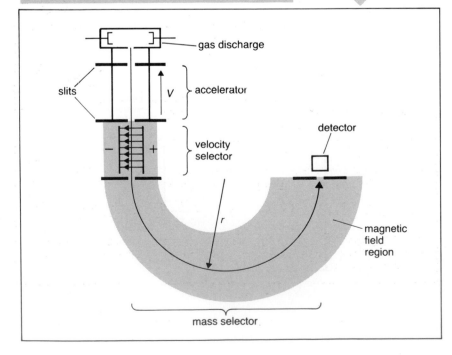

Although we can expect all of the atoms of a particular element to have roughly the same mass, the value of q can be +e, +2e, +3e etc. So when the ions leave the accelerator they enter a **velocity selector**. In this region they are subjected to two forces. They are pushed to the left by an electric field E between the parallel plates: that force is given by qE. The magnetic field B (directed into the plane of the diagram) pushes the ions to the right with a force given by Bqv. Ions are only going to be able to travel through this region into the **mass selector** if the two forces cancel each other out.

$$qE = Bqv \qquad \therefore v = E/B \qquad (22.5)$$

So only ions with velocities given by equation (22.5) will emerge from the velocity selector. Ions with other velocities will hit one or other of the parallel plates and be removed from the beam. The value of E is usually adjusted so that only ions with a charge of +e enter the mass selector.

Once the ions enter the mass selector they travel in a circular trajectory of radius r, with the magnetic force Bqv providing the centripetal force.

$$Bqv = \frac{mv^2}{r} \qquad \therefore m = \frac{Bqr}{v} \qquad (22.6)$$

Since v is known from equation (22.5), we end up with the following formula for the mass of singly charged ions which have trajectories of radius r.

$$m = \frac{B^2 er}{E} \qquad (22.7)$$

For example, suppose that neon is investigated with a magnetic field of 0.25 T and an electric field of 3.0×10^4 V m^{-1}. If the detector is placed 20 cm from the point at which the ions enter the momentum selector, ions will be able to reach it. Assuming that the accelerating potential was such that only singly charged ions made it through the velocity selector, we can calculate their mass.

$$m = \frac{B^2 er}{E}$$

$$\therefore m = \frac{0.25^2 \times 1.60 \times 10^{-19} \times 0.10}{3.0 \times 10^4}$$

$$= 3.3 \times 10^{-26} \text{ kg}$$

If this is compared with the mass of a single proton (measured with the same apparatus using hydrogen), you can convince yourself that neon has a nucleon number of 20. The atomic number of neon is 10: the mass of the nine electrons $(9 \times 9.1 \times 10^{-31} = 8.2 \times 10^{-30}$ kg) can be safely neglected.

Isotopes
In 1920 Francis Aston used a primitive form of mass spectrometer to show that naturally occuring neon contains three **isotopes** each of which has a different nucleon number. His apparatus was capable of measuring the mass of the ions with an accuracy of ±0.1%. Modern values for the mass, nucleon number and abundance of each isotope are given in table 22.1.

Table 22.1

Isotope	Mass/kg	A	Abundance
$^{20}_{10}$Ne	3.315×10^{-26}	20	90.9%
$^{21}_{10}$Ne	3.481×10^{-26}	21	0.3%
$^{22}_{10}$Ne	3.646×10^{-26}	22	8.8%

(Notice the notation used to denote the isotope. The superscript in front of the element symbol is the **mass number** (or **nucleon number**) and the subscript is the **atomic number**.) The discovery of isotopes solved a long-standing puzzle which had defeated chemists for many years. The values for the atomic masses of most elements are very nearly whole numbers times the mass of a hydrogen atom, hence the usefulness of the mass number A. However, some elements did not have values of A which were nearly whole numbers. For example, chlorine has a mass number of about 35.5 — this is because about a quarter of naturally occuring chlorine is the isotope chlorine-37 with the remaining three-quarters being chlorine-35.

Nuclear contents

The fact that the mass of a nucleus is almost a whole number times the mass of a single hydrogen nucleus, makes it tempting to model all nuclei as being collections of protons and electrons. For example, consider the nucleus of magnesium-25 (which accounts for 10% of naturally occuring magnesium). Its atomic number Z is 12, so the nucleus must have a charge of +12e. To get a mass number of 25, the nucleus must therefore contain 25 protons. If we add 13 electrons (total charge −13e) to those protons we end up with something which seems to have the right mass and charge. Unfortunately, the amount of energy required to keep a single electron locked up in a nucleus would raise its mass far above that of a proton, so this model cannot be correct.

ELECTRONS IN NUCLEI ▶▶ 29

The minimum energy that an electron can have when it is forced to stay inside a cubical box of side *l* is given by the following equation:

$$E = \frac{h^2}{8ml^2} \qquad (1)$$

If we set *l* equal to the size of a proton (1.2×10^{-15} m) we can estimate the energy needed to make an electron sit inside a proton.

$$E = \frac{(6.6 \times 10^{-34})^2}{8 \times 9.1 \times 10^{-31} \times (1.2 \times 10^{-15})^2} = 4.2 \times 10^{-8} \text{ J}$$

We can now use the Einstein energy–mass relationship to calculate the extra mass that this energy would give the proton–electron system.

$$\Delta E = \Delta mc^2 \qquad \therefore \Delta m = \frac{\Delta E}{c^2} \qquad \therefore \Delta m = \frac{4.2 \times 10^{-8}}{(3.0 \times 10^8)^2} \approx 5 \times 10^{-25} \text{ kg}$$

This extra mass is about three hundred times larger than the mass of a proton. So it is clearly not possible to hold an electron inside a nucleus without making it unrealistically massive!

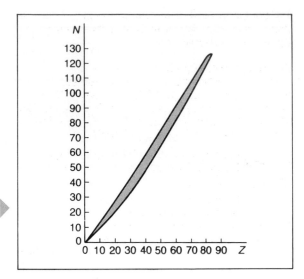

Figure 22.12 The shaded area of the graph encloses all of the stable nuclei

Figure 22.13 Representations of a number of different nuclei

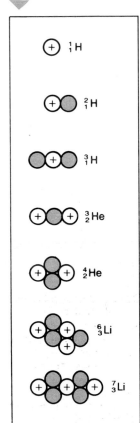

The neutron

The measured charge and mass of atomic nuclei can be modelled by assuming that they are made up of two particles, the proton and the **neutron**. Both have the same size and virtually the same mass, but different charges. Whereas the proton has a charge of $+e$, the neutron has no charge at all. For obvious reasons, both particles are referred to as **nucleons**. With this model, the magnesium-25 nucleus contains 12 protons and 13 neutrons, giving 25 nucleons in all.

The graph of figure 22.12 shows how the neutron number N depends on the atomic (or proton) number for all of the stable isotopes. As you can see, for the light elements (low Z) the number of neutrons is only slightly larger than the number of protons, but for the heavy elements there are roughly three neutrons for every two protons. The nucleons in a nucleus are attracted to each other by the **strong interaction**, a short-range force which only operates over distances of the order of 1.2×10^{-15} m. However, the protons in the nucleus are also subject to electrostatic forces which push them apart from each other. The fact that at least one neutron is necessary to make the two protons of a helium nucleus stick together shows that the strong force on its own is just not large enough to overcome this electrostatic repulsion. On the other hand, helium-4 is the heaviest stable isotope of helium, so there is a limit to the number of neutrons you can push into a nucleus without it falling apart. Figure 22.13 shows how you might model the arrangement of protons and neutrons in the nuclei of some isotopes.

Because they are not charged, neutrons do not interact with electrons. So when a fast neutron travels through matter, it only loses energy via direct collisions with nuclei. Since the chances of such collisions are so small, neutrons are much more difficult to detect than, say, alpha particles. However, when a neutron does hit a nucleus, the interaction can give rise to charged particles or gamma rays: these secondary products are then easily detected. For example, GM tubes filled with boron triflouride are commonly used to make neutron detectors. Fast neutrons (above 1 eV) trigger the boron nucleus into emitting a gamma ray, leaving a stable boron-11 nucleus behind. For slow neutrons (below 1 eV) the neutron is readily absorbed by the nucleus which subsequently disintegrates to emit a 2.79 MeV alpha particle. This **nuclear reaction** can be represented with the following balanced equation: notice how the number of nucleons (the superscripts) and units of positive charge (the subscripts) are conserved in the reaction.

$$^{10}_{5}B + {}^{1}_{0}n \rightarrow {}^{7}_{3}Li + {}^{4}_{2}He$$

OBJECTIVES

After studying this section you should be able to do the following.

Describe the Geiger and Marsden alpha particle scattering experiment.

Explain in qualitative terms how the Rutherford model of a nucleus explains the results of alpha particle scattering experiments.

State a rule for the approximate dimensions of a nucleus of known mass number.

Explain what is represented by the symbols Z and A.

Calculate the distance of closest approach for an alpha particle colliding with a nucleus.

Describe and explain the operation of a mass spectrometer.

Know the meaning of *isotope*, *proton*, *neutron*, and *nucleon*.

Understand the notation $^{A}_{Z}X$ used to represent isotopes

Explain why neutrons are difficult to detect.

Write a balanced equation for a nuclear reaction.

QUESTIONS

1 This question is about scattering alpha particles in a beam from nuclei in a gold foil. The mass number and atomic number of gold are 197 and 79, respectively.

a Use the formula $r \simeq 1.2 \times 10^{-15} A^{1/3}$ to calculate an approximate radius for a gold atom.

b Calculate the maximum energy an alpha particle can have before it risks touching the gold nucleus during a collision. Are protons with the same energy also going to touch the gold nucleus during a collision?

c Explain why the number of alpha particles scattered is expected to be proportional to the thickness of the foil.

d Estimate the kinetic energy given to the nucleus when a 2.0 MeV alpha particle makes a head-on collision with it. (Assume an elastic collision and that the speed of the alpha particle is not changed during the process.)

2 Jane proposes to use the apparatus of figure 22.4 to check that equation (3) (see 'The scattering formula' box) is correct. She is going to measure the

However, this will only happen in practice if enough energy is liberated in the disintegration to carry the alpha particles away from each other. The total energy of the beryllium-8 nucleus will be the rest mass of the lithium-7 nucleus (7.0144 m_u) and the combined rest mass and kinetic energy of the 2 MeV proton (1.0073 m_u and 0.0013 m_u respectively), giving a total of 8.0230 m_u. Each alpha particle has a mass of 4.0015 m_u, so the kinetic energy available for them is 8.0230 − (4.0015) = 0.0200 m_u. Since 1 m_u = 931 MeV, combined kinetic energy of the alpha particles will therefore be 18.6 MeV. Because momentum has to be conserved as well as energy, the two alpha particles will set off in almost opposite directions with an energy of 9.3 MeV each.

Since this process is the one which converts the most mass of the beryllium-8 nucleus into kinetic energy, it is the one which takes place. In fact, the nucleus only hangs together for about 2×10^{-16} s before it disintegrates, leaving the three electrons free to wander off in search of other nuclei.

The apparatus shown in figure 22.17 can be used to verify this prediction. A pair of scintillators on photomultiplier tubes detect alpha particles which are emitted in opposite directions from the lithium target. Electronic circuitry only measures the heights of the pulses from the photomultiplier if they arrive at the same time. The heights of those pulses are the same, equivalent to an energy of about 9.3 MeV.

Photodisintegration

The Einstein mass−energy equation implies that energy can be converted into mass as well as mass into energy. An example of the creation of mass from energy is the photodisintegration of deuterium (hydrogen-2) by gamma rays. The **deuteron** falls apart into a proton and a neutron.

$$^2_1\text{H} + ^0_0\gamma \rightarrow ^1_1\text{p} + ^1_0\text{n}$$

The rest masses of the various particles involved in the reaction are shown in table 22.3: to make matters simple we have chosen to list the masses in MeV as well as m_u. Gamma rays have zero rest mass.

Table 22.3

Particle	Mass/m_u	Mass/MeV
deuteron	2.01355	1875.62
proton	1.00728	938.28
neutron	1.00867	939.58

Now the combined rest mass of a neutron and a proton is 2.24 MeV *greater* than the rest mass of a deuteron. So for the reaction to take place, the energy of the gamma ray must be at least 2.24 MeV. Thus 2.62 MeV gamma rays from a thallium-208 source will leave the proton and neutron to share 2.62 − 2.24 = 0.38 MeV of kinetic energy between them. Since the two products have almost the same mass, they will fly off in opposite directions with almost the same energy as each other.

Spontaneous disintegration

The two nuclear reactions we have studied so far involve the deliberate destruction of an otherwise stable nucleus by injecting a nucleon or a gamma

ray. There are many nuclei which are able to disintegrate spontaneously, converting some of their mass into kinetic energy in the process.

Alpha emission

The isotope uranium-234 is an alpha emitter with a half-life of 2.5×10^5 years. Clearly, if a nucleus can exist for this long without falling apart, it must be fairly stable. However, if you think of the nucleus as a loose bag of 234 nucleons constantly exchanging energy with each other, there is an equal probability of each possible arrangement of nucleons occuring at any instant. Some possibilities are shown in figure 22.18. The diagram at the bottom shows an arrangement whereby an alpha particle has been pinched off from the rest of the nucleus through this random shuffling. If this arrangement results in the alpha particle having enough kinetic energy to escape, then it will do so, providing it is also moving away from the rest of the nucleus. Once the alpha particle has escaped, the process is irreversible: the parent atom has to lose two electrons to become a thorium-230 atom.

$$^{234}_{92}\text{U} \rightarrow ^{230}_{90}\text{Th} + ^4_2\text{He}$$

There are two separate ways in which the alpha particle can be ejected from the parent nucleus as they can have energies of 4.77 MeV or 4.72 MeV. That energy is available because the mass of a uranium-234 nucleus is 4.77 MeV greater than the combined rest masses of a thorium 90 nucleus and an alpha particle.

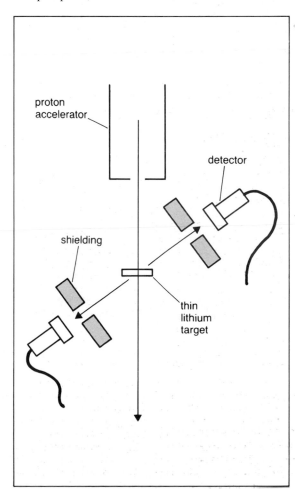

Figure 22.17 Apparatus for verifying the disintegration of lithium

proton accelerator

detector

shielding

thin lithium target

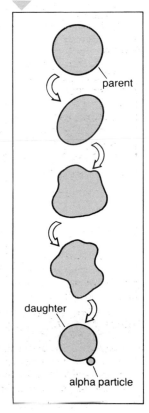

Figure 22.18 The liquid drop model of alpha decay

parent

daughter

alpha particle

TUNNELLING ▶▶ 29

The half-life of an alpha emitter depends on the energy lost by the parent atom in the process. Table 1 lists some data for a number of large nuclei which are alpha emitters.

Table 1

Parent	$T_{\frac{1}{2}}$	E_α/MeV
thorium-232	1.39×10^{10} years	4.05
radium-226	1.62×10^3 years	4.88
thorium-228	1.91 years	5.52
radon-222	3.83 days	5.59
polonium-216	0.16 s	6.89
polonium-212	3.0×10^{-7} s	8.95

As you can see, the half-life decreases rapidly as the alpha particle energy increases. In fact, the half-life $T_{\frac{1}{2}}$ is linked to the alpha particle energy E_α by the following relationship where A and B are constants.

$$T_{\frac{1}{2}} = A\exp[(B/E_\alpha)^{\frac{1}{2}}]$$

This expression was first derived in 1928 using the new science of quantum mechanics. Of course, applying quantum mechanics properly to a system as complex as a nucleus is impossible, so to simplify matters the theory assumed that the alpha particle existed as a separate entity inside the nucleus, bound by the potential well shown in figure 22.19. The well itself is formed from the averaged-out attractive interaction of the alpha particle with the two hundred or so other nucleons milling around it. The potential hill outside the well is formed by the electrostatic repulsion of the alpha particle with the rest of the nucleus. Figure 22.19 shows how the wave function of the alpha particle depends on its energy. Bearing in mind that the amplitude of the wavefunction can be used to calculate the probability of finding the alpha particle at that point, the diagrams show that the chance of finding the particle *outside* the well increases as the particle energy is increased. In a sense, the particle is able to **tunnel** through the walls of the potential well. As the walls get thinner, the particle stands more chance of getting through.

The quantum mechanical picture of alpha decay assumes that probability is built into nature at a fundamental level. The wave function of an alpha particle *only* allows you to calculate the probability of finding it outside the nucleus at any particular instant. There is no way in which nature allows us to predict exactly when the decay will happen. For example, when a thorium-232 nucleus is created it may decay straight away, even though its half-life is roughly that of the age of the Earth!

Figure 22.19
Wave functions for alpha particles bound inside the nucleus

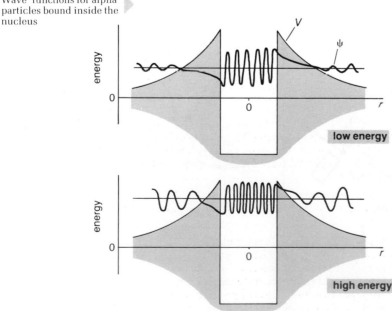

low energy

high energy

Gamma emission

If a uranium-234 nucleus decays by emitting a 4.72 MeV alpha particle, the daughter thorium-90 nucleus will emit a 50 keV gamma ray immediately afterwards. Gamma ray emission is a means whereby nuclei can lose energy without shedding any particles.

$$^{230}_{90}\text{Th} \rightarrow \,^{230}_{90}\text{Th} + \,^{0}_{0}\gamma$$

An alternative process whereby gamma rays are emitted is called **electron capture**. A single electron passing through the nucleus can be annihilated, decreasing the nuclear charge by one unit without altering the number of nucleons. The surplus energy which appears as one of the protons is effectively converted to a neutron is fed out of the nucleus as a gamma ray. For example, the commercially available gamma ray source bismuth 207 emits 570 keV gamma rays by the following reaction.

$$^{207}_{83}\text{Bi} + \,^{0}_{-1}\text{e} \rightarrow \,^{207}_{82}\text{Pb} + \,^{0}_{0}\gamma$$

Beta emission

Neutrons are unstable. A solitary neutron decays by the following process with a half-life of only 11.7 minutes.

$$^{1}_{0}\text{n} \rightarrow \,^{1}_{1}\text{p} + \,^{0}_{-1}\text{e} + \,^{0}_{0}\bar{\nu}$$

(The antineutrino $\bar{\nu}$ is an elusive particle with a tiny rest mass and no charge. It is consequently very difficult to detect.) However, once a neutron forms part of a nucleus, this decay process is suppressed, except in those cases where conversion of a neutron to a proton results in a net conversion of mass to kinetic energy of the beta particle and the antineutrino. For example, strontium-90 (a dangerous isotope because it is readily incorporated into human bones and has a half-life of 28 years) decays as follows:

$$^{90}_{38}\text{Sr} \rightarrow \,^{90}_{39}\text{Y} + \,^{0}_{-1}\text{e} + \,^{0}_{0}\bar{\nu}$$

Although it is tempting to suppose that a single neutron inside the strontium-90 nucleus spontaneously splits into a proton, an electron and an antineutrino, this is not a good model. The transformation only takes place because it is energetically favourable to the nucleus as a whole. This will become clear if you consider the following possible equation for the spontaneous decay of a proton accompanied by the emission of a **positron**, a positively charged electron.

$$^{1}_{1}\text{p} \rightarrow \,^{1}_{0}\text{n} + \,^{0}_{+1}\text{e} + \,^{0}_{0}\nu$$

(The neutrino (ν) has the same mass and charge as the antineutrino.) If you study the contents of table 22.2 you should be able to convince yourself that spontaneous disintegration of an isolated proton is impossible if energy is to be conserved. However, once the proton is part of a nucleus, it can appear to decay this way — provided, of course, that it results in a net conversion of mass to kinetic energy. One example of this is the decay of sodium-22, a radioisotope with a half-life of 2.6 years which emits positrons with a maximum energy of 545 keV.

$$^{22}_{11}\text{Na} \rightarrow \,^{22}_{10}\text{Ne} + \,^{0}_{+1}\text{e} + \,^{0}_{0}\nu$$

Antimatter

Positrons are an example of antimatter, a substance much beloved by science fiction writers! Every fundamental particle has an anti-particle with the same mass but opposite charge: they are routinely created in high energy collisions between charged particles in modern accelerators (figure 22.20). However, it is difficult to preserve anti-particles for very long because they are annihilated when they come into contact with ordinary matter. For example, consider a positron approaching an electron. They have opposite charges, so they will be attracted towards each other. Once they get close enough, they disappear in a puff of two gamma rays!

$$_{+1}^{0}e + _{-1}^{0}e \rightarrow 2_{0}^{0}\gamma$$

Two gamma rays must be emitted to conserve linear and angular momentum: each has an energy of 0.51 MeV, the rest mass of an electron or positron. Beams of high energy (typically 5 GeV each) positrons and electrons are routinely smashed into each other head-on to create exotic short-lived particles for physicists to study.

Figure 22.20 Creating new particles. This photograph shows the tracks of the charged particles created when a high energy proton smashed into a stationary hydrogen nucleus. The proton enters from the bottom. The spiral is an electron knocked out of an atom by the proton: a magnetic field was applied out of the plane of the picture to allow the charge of the particles to be deduced. The proton–proton collision produces seven negative particles, nine positive particles and one neutral one. The latter leaves no track, but its presence is deduced from its subsequent decay into a pair of oppositely charged particles

---

CREATING ISOTOPES

Most artificial isotopes are created by exposing naturally occuring isotopes to a bombardment of neutrons inside a nuclear reactor. Since there is no electrostatic repulsion between a neutron and a nucleus, very slow neutrons can easily penetrate a nucleus and become lodged there. In general, the addition of a neutron to an otherwise stable nucleus creates an unstable isotope which will eventually undergo radioactive decay. For example, naturally occuring sodium-23 becomes sodium-24, a useful medical isotope which is a gamma emitter with a half-life of 15 hours, when exposed to neutrons.

$$_{11}^{23}Na + _{0}^{1}n \rightarrow _{11}^{24}Na$$

Similarly, cobalt-60 can be generated by placing samples of natural cobalt-59 in nuclear reactors. Cobalt-60 is widely used to sterilise medical equipment and food. It is a gamma emitter with a half-life of about 5 years.

OBJECTIVES

After studying this section you should be able to do the following.

Use the equation $\Delta E = \Delta mc^2$.

Understand the meaning of *binding energy* and *atomic mass unit*.

Explain why the mass of a nucleus is less than the total mass of its constituent nucleons.

Predict the energy of the particles emitted during radioactive decay from the masses of the parent and daughter nuclei.

Describe a simple model of alpha decay using the liquid drop model of the nucleus.

Write balanced equations representing alpha, beta and gamma decay.

QUESTIONS

1 The artificial disintegration of a nucleus was first observed by Rutherford in 1919. He bombarded nitrogen gas in a cloud chamber with 7.7 MeV alpha particles from a polonium-214 source. He observed tracks appearing in the cloud chamber which had all the characteristics of being created by high energy protons.

a Use the data of table 22.4 to write down an equation representing the disintegration of nitrogen by alpha particles.

Table 22.4

Atom	Symbol	A	Z	Mass/m_u
nitrogen	N	14	7	14.003074
oxygen	O	17	8	16.999133
helium	He	4	2	4.002603
hydrogen	H	1	1	1.007825

b Show that $\Delta E = \Delta mc^2$ is dimensionally correct. Given that 1 $m_u = 1.6604 \times 10^{-27}$ kg, what is 1 m_u in MeV?

c Use the data of table 22.4 to estimate the energy of the protons emitted during the disintegration of nitrogen. The rest mass of an electron is 0.51 MeV. Why can you neglect the final kinetic energy of the oxygen atom?

d Estimate the minimum energy for the alpha particles which will trigger the disintegration of nitrogen.

2 Uranium-238 has an atomic number of 92. It decays, emitting an alpha particle, to form an unstable short-lived daughter, an isotope of thorium (Th). This subsequently emits a beta particle to become an isotope of protoactinium (Pa). Write down equations representing these two decays (the chemical symbol for uranium is U).

3 Thorium-232 is widely used in schools to generate radon-220, a radioactive gas which is an alpha emitter with a convenient half-life of 55 s. A plastic bottle holds a little thorium powder which decays through a number of intermediate daughters (listed in order in table 22.5). The final daughter is a gas (Rn–220) which can be puffed from the bottle as and when required.

Table 22.5

Element	Symbol	Emission	Half-life
thorium	Th	α	1.4×10^{10} years
radium	Ra	β	6.7 years
actinium	Ac	β	6.1 hours
thorium	Th	α	1.9 years
radium	Ra	α	3.6 days

a Write out a series of equations which represent the various decays between thorium-232 and radon-220; $Z = 90$ for thorium.

b The standard method of displaying this type of **decay chain** is as a graph whose vertical and horizontal axes are A and Z, respectively. Each nucleus in the chain is marked as a blob and an arrowed line with α or β next to it joins the blobs together to show the decay route. Use this method to display the part of the thorium-232 decay chain shown in table 22.5.

4 **a** Use the data listed in table 1 (see the box on 'Tunnelling') to plot a graph of $\ln(T_{\frac{1}{2}})$ against $E_\alpha^{-\frac{1}{2}}$. Draw a best straight line through the points.

b Polonium-214 emits alpha particles with an energy of 7.69 MeV; use your graph to estimate its half-life.

c The half-life of polonium-218 is 3 minutes. Estimate the energy of the alpha particles it emits.

5 One type of commercial source of neutrons uses a thin layer of lithium-7 placed around an americium-241 alpha source. The alpha particles are absorbed by the lithium nuclei which subsequently disintegrate, emitting neutrons with a range of energies.

a Write down an equation which represents the reaction. Use table 22.6 to find the chemical symbols.

b If most of the alpha particles from americium-241 have an energy of 5.5 MeV, calculate the maximum energy expected for the emitted neutrons. (The mass of an electron and a neutron are 0.00055 m_u and 1.00867 m_u, respectively.)

Table 22.6

Atom	Symbol	A	Z	Mass/m_u
lithium	Li	7	3	7.01600
boron	B	10	5	10.01353
helium	He	4	2	4.00260

c Explain why the source emits neutrons with a range of energies rather than just one energy. Estimate the minimum energy of the neutrons emitted.

6 The Super Proton Synchrotron at CERN can simultaneously generate high energy beams of protons and antiprotons. When these particles collide head-on they produce a number of short-lived particles whose properties can be studied (figure 22.20).

a The anti-protons are created in a smaller accelerator by smashing protons into a metal target. If the mass of a proton is 1.67×10^{-27} kg, estimate the minimum proton energy necessary to create a single antiproton in the collision; remember that charge is always conserved.

b In practice, the protons are accelerated to 26 GeV before hitting the target. If the energy-to-mass conversion process is 50% efficient, how many antiprotons can be produced by each proton which collides head-on with a target nucleus?

NUCLEAR POWER

About 20% of the electricity consumed in Britain is generated in nuclear power stations. This is likely to grow in the future as concern over the environmental damage caused by the burning of fossil fuels grows. Although nuclear power is not always the safe, clean technology claimed by the electricity industry, the long-term consequences for the planet of increasing the level of carbon dioxide in the atmosphere may well frighten us into relying more heavily on nuclear power for our electricity needs.

Fission

Uranium ($Z = 92$) has the largest nucleus of all the elements found on Earth. All the elements created artificially which have atomic numbers above 92 have proved to be unstable. Naturally occuring uranium is itself unstable. The abundances and half-lives of the three isotopes are listed in table 22.7.

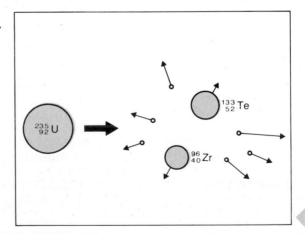

Figure 22.21 Fission of uranium-235

Table 22.7

Isotope	Half-life/years	Abundance/%
uranium-234	2.5×10^5	0.006
uranium-235	7.1×10^8	0.7
uranium-238	4.5×10^9	99.3

All three isotopes are alpha emitters, but they can also decay by **spontaneous fission**. This is illustrated in figure 22.21. The nucleus simply falls apart into two large **fragments** and a few neutrons. If you consult the graph of figure 22.14, it should be obvious that the splitting of a very large nucleus into two smaller fragments is going to result in an increase of the binding energy per nucleon. This means that the total mass of the fragments will be less than the mass of the original nucleus — there must be some conversion of mass to energy. That energy becomes kinetic energy of the two fission fragments and the neutrons. It is almost inevitable that the fission fragments will also be unstable, undergoing radioactive decay (mostly involving the emission of beta particles and gamma rays) once they have been created.

Energy

The graph of figure 22.22 shows the distribution of fragment size produced in the fission of uranium-235. It is a curious and, as yet, unexplained fact that the most likely fission fragments will have mass numbers of 95 and 138 rather than both being 118 as you might expect. Clearly, the amount of mass converted to energy depends on the exact nature of the fission fragments, but an average energy of 206 MeV is released. Table 22.8 shows how that energy is typically shared among the various particles.

Table 22.8

Particle	Energy/MeV
fission fragments	166
neutrons	5
gamma rays	15
beta particles	8
antineutrinos	12

If the fission occurs in solid uranium, then most of the energy of the gamma rays and antineutrinos will leave the system. The kinetic energy of the other particles will eventually be converted to heat energy via collisions with atoms. Since a single uranium atom has a mass of about 4×10^{-25} kg, the heat energy obtained from fission is around 7×10^{13} J kg^{-1}. To put this figure into perspective, let's estimate the mass of fissioning uranium which might provide you with all the electricity you are going to consume in your lifetime, about 10^{12} J. If the energy conversion process has a realistic efficiency of 50%, then about 30 g of fissioned uranium should be sufficient. Compare this with 66 tonnes of coal!

Thermal neutrons

Although spontaneous fission of uranium-235 is a rare event it can be readily triggered by slow neutrons. So, in principle, energy could be extracted from a lump of natural uranium metal by spraying it with a beam of slow neutrons, as shown in figure 22.23. The neutrons are generated by smashing alpha particles into a beryllium target. Most of the kinetic energy of the neutrons is extracted by the **moderator** so that they enter the uranium with energies of well under 0.1 eV. Each of these **thermal neutrons** can then induce the fission of uranium-235 nuclei that they stray into.

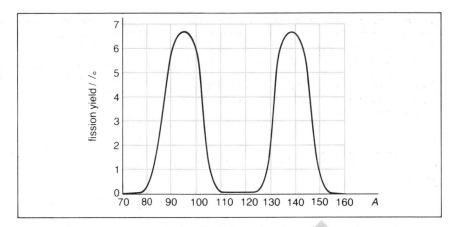

Figure 22.22 Distribution of fission-fragment mass numbers for uranium-235

The presence of the moderator is crucial. Uranium-238, the main constituent of natural uranium, strongly absorbs neutrons with energies between 1 keV and 5 eV. The resulting isotope is unstable, decaying to the relatively stable plutonium-239 in the space of a few days.

$$^{238}_{92}\text{U} + ^{1}_{0}\text{n} \rightarrow ^{239}_{92}\text{U} \rightarrow ^{239}_{93}\text{Np} + ^{0}_{-1}\text{e},$$

$$^{239}_{93}\text{Np} \rightarrow ^{239}_{94}\text{Pu} + ^{0}_{-1}\text{e}$$

So the energy of the neutrons has to be reduced to about 0.05 eV until they are in thermal equilibrium with the atoms around them. This is done via elastic collisions with the nuclei of the moderator. For a head-on collision of a neutron of mass m and speed u with a stationary nucleus of mass M, the final speed v of the neutron is given by the following expression:

$$v = u \times \frac{m - M}{m + M} \qquad (22.8)$$

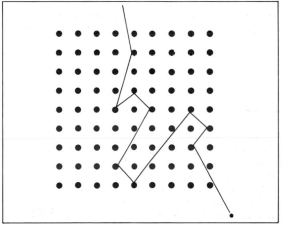

Clearly, if $M = m$, then a single head-on collision will rob the neutron of all its kinetic energy. So water, which contains plenty of hydrogen, would appear to make a good moderator. However, hydrogen is good at capturing neutrons to make deuterium, so ordinary water soaks up the neutrons as well as slowing them down. Carbon-12 does not react strongly with neutrons, so it makes a good moderator: each head-on collision reduces the neutron energy by 28%. Of course, most collisions will be of the glancing type (figure 22.24), so about a hundred of them are required on average to **thermalise** 1 MeV neutrons.

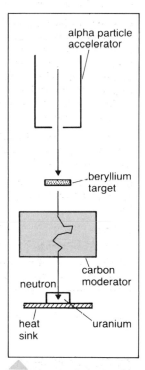

Figure 22.23 Inducing the fission of uranium with a beam of slow neutrons

Figure 22.24 The neutrons do a random walk through the moderator, losing energy via elastic collisions with nuclei of the moderator

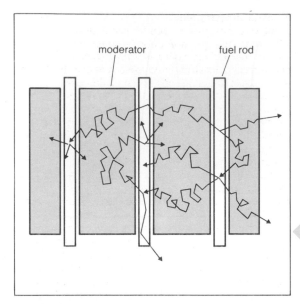

Figure 22.25 The fuel rods are inserted in the moderator

Figure 22.26 Control rods are lowered into the pile to absorb slow neutrons

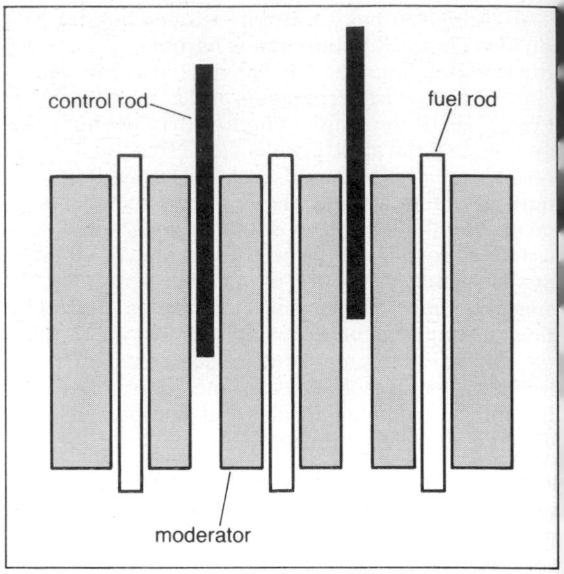

Chain reaction

A glance at the graph of figure 22.12 shows that heavy nuclei have a larger neutron-to-proton ratio than light ones. So the fission process inevitably results in three or four neutrons being sprayed out immediately, with the possibility of another one or two being ejected by the fragments some time later. So the uranium can act as its own neutron source if it is embedded in a suitable moderator to form a **reactor pile** (figure 22.25). Neutrons from a spontaneous fission in one of the **fuel rods** pass into the moderator where they do a random walk, bouncing from nucleus to nucleus, losing energy each time until they are thermalised. Eventually they will stray into another rod and trigger the fission of another uranium-235 nucleus. Those neutrons can, in principle, trigger the fission of yet more uranium-235 nuclei. However, some will stray into a fuel rod before they have been thermalised and be absorbed by uranium-238. Others may be lost from the system altogether, wandering outside the pile. With an appropriate geometry of fuel rods and moderator it is possible to arrange for a self-sustaining **chain reaction** to build up inside the pile: each fission produces, on average, exactly one other fission somewhere else.

Control

Clearly, the maintenance of a steady population of thermal neutrons in a reactor pile is very important. If the number of neutrons is allowed to rise, more fissions will occur, generating yet more neutrons, so that even more fissions will occur until the temperature reaches the melting point of the fuel rods. On the other hand, if the number of neutrons decreases, the chain reaction will eventually grind to a halt and the pile will cease to produce heat energy.

Rods of neutron-absorbing material such as boron or cadmium are used to control the neutron population of a reactor, as shown in figure 22.26. Initially they sit full length in the pile, absorbing thermal neutrons so that the chain reaction cannot build up. They are then gradually pulled up out of the pile so that the neutron population can grow. When the temperature of the pile has reached the required level of about 550 °C, the rods are

subsequently raised or lowered to keep the temperature steady. (The 1% of delayed neutrons produced by each fission allows reactors to have time constants of many minutes.) The insertion of the control rods from above the pile makes the system fail-safe. If there is a power failure of the control system, gravity will pull the rods back into the pile and turn off the chain reaction.

Heat extraction

The advanced gas-cooled reactors currently being built in the UK use high pressure carbon dioxide gas circulating round the pile to extract heat from it. The arrangement is shown in figure 22.27. A heat exchanger transfers heat from the gas to water, which creates steam to run the turbines. The older pressurised water reactor (much used in America) uses water as both the energy extracting medium and moderator: the proportion of uranium-235 in the fuel rods has to be raised to overcome the absorption of neutrons by the water. If **heavy water** (made of hydrogen-2) is used as the moderator, prior enrichment of the fuel is not necessary. This type of pile is very compact and is used for submarines and ships.

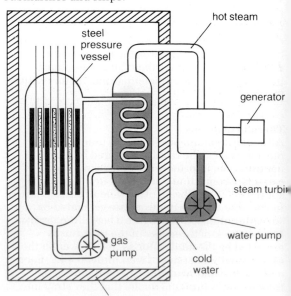

Figure 22.27 The heat exchange system for a gas cooled reactor

Fast reactors

A **thermal reactor** uses thermal neutrons in the pile to induce the fission of uranium-235 in the fuel rods. The much more plentiful uranium-238 in the fuel takes no part in the energy generation process, gradually getting converted to plutonium-239. This man-made material will itself undergo fission, but only if bombarded with fast neutrons. So a reactor pile using plutonium-239 as fuel does not need a moderator to slow down the neutrons. Unfortunately, this reduces the volume of the pile to about 1 m^3, making it much more difficult to extract heat energy from it. (Liquid sodium has been used as the energy transfer medium!) Apart from the attraction of using up plutonium which inevitably builds up as a by-product in thermal reactors, these **fast reactors** offer the attractive possibility of breeding their own fuel. If a blanket of uranium-238 surrounds the plutonium pile, it will absorb fast neutrons to create new fuel. This breeding process could actually produce *more* plutonium in the blanket than is consumed in the pile. Once fossil fuels (like coal and oil) become too expensive or environmentally unacceptable for large-scale generation of electricity, fast breeder reactors will become cost-effective. In the meantime, the uranium-238 from spent fuel rods is stockpiled after the plutonium-239 and the fission fragments have been removed by chemical processing. Given that most of the world's stockpile of plutonium resides in nuclear warheads atop ballistic missiles, the fast breeder reactor may well become the twenty-first century's principal incentive to beat swords into ploughshares by reducing the number of nuclear weapons!

Fusion

Consider the following reaction between two deuterium nuclei. (Deuterium occurs naturally; for every 6 000 atoms of hydrogen-1 in seawater, one is hydrogen-2.)

$$_1^2H + _1^2H \rightarrow _2^3He + _0^1n$$

The mass change in the reaction liberates 3.27 MeV as kinetic energy to be shared between the helium-3 atom and the neutron. This process creates about 8×10^{13} joules of available energy for each kilogram of deuterium. Since deuterium is relatively cheap and plentiful, this method of generating energy is clearly very attractive. However, the problems involved in persuading the reaction to take place in a manageable fashion may turn out to be impossible to overcome.

Figure 22.28 Magnetic fields confine the plasma (the deuterium/tritium fuel) to a narrow ring and heat it to a temperature at which fusion can take place

Figure 22.29 Laser induced fusion. A glass pellet containing a deuterium/tritium mixture is suspended in the middle. The pellet is compressed and heated by laser beams which hit it from all sides

Plasma containment

For two deuterium nuclei to fuse together, the electrostatic repulsion between them has to be overcome. This is easily accomplished with a modern accelerator, firing a beam of fast deuterons into a deuterium target. However, this uses up far more energy than is liberated in the reaction, so it is useless as far as commercial electricity generation is concerned. The alternative is to heat up the deuterium until it forms a plasma, with the nuclei having enough kinetic energy to stand a chance of getting close enough together to fuse.

Research and development of fusion power has followed two paths, neither of which has yet produced a machine which produces more energy than is needed to run it. One approach uses magnetic fields to contain the plasma. As you can see from figure 22.28, the field is arranged so that the plasma is confined to circulate in a volume shaped like a ring doughnut. The second approach (figure 22.29) seals the fuel in small glass pellets and heats them up suddenly by smashing them with a number of laser pulses from all sides. The magnetic containment approach seems more likely to be successful, but progress is very slow and expensive.

Fusion is the method by which our Sun is believed to generate energy. The high pressures and temperatures at its centre were originally created by the gravitational collapse of the hydrogen gas it started from. The protons are fused to form alpha particles in the following three stages.

$$_1^1p + _1^1p \rightarrow _1^2H + _{+1}^0e + _0^0\nu$$

$$_1^2H + _1^1p \rightarrow _2^3He + _0^0\gamma$$

$$_2^3He + _2^3He \rightarrow _2^4He + _1^1p + _1^1p$$

The energy liberated by this reaction prevents further collapse of the Sun. When there is insufficient hydrogen left to keep the reaction going, the subsequent gravitational collapse will allow another cycle of reactions to start up involving the generation of carbon and nitrogen from helium.

There is probably not enough gravitational energy in our Sun to permit carbon nuclei to fuse together to form heavier elements. Stars with greater mass can fuse nuclei of heavy elements, converting mass to energy until their core becomes mostly iron. Iron (Z = 56) has the largest binding energy per nucleon of any element, and is therefore the stablest. It seems likely that stars with a lot of iron in their core eventually become unstable and explode to form supernovae, converting energy to mass as nuclei are fused to make elements with Z > 56.

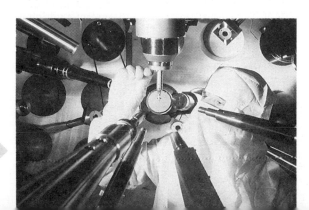

OBJECTIVES

After studying this section you should be able to do the following.

Describe what happens during the fission of a nucleus.

Know that fission converts mass to other forms of energy.

Explain the function and operation of a moderator.

Explain why a chain reaction is possible in a reactor pile.

State the means by which the chain reaction is controlled and energy extracted from the pile.

Describe how mass can be converted to energy by the fusion of light nuclei.

QUESTIONS

1 The CEGB reckons that each of its customers in the UK consumes about 3×10^5 kWh of electricity in their lifetime. 1 kWh is the electrical energy converted by a 1 kW device in an hour.

a Use the data in tables 22.7 and 22.8 to calculate the mass of natural uranium metal needed to provide 3×10^5 kWh of energy in a thermal reactor.

b Use the data of tables 22.9 and 22.10 to calculate the mass of seawater needed to generate 3×10^5 kWh of energy in a fusion reactor; $1\ m_u = 1.66 \times 10^{-27}$ kg.

Table 22.9

Isotope	Mass/m_u	Abundance/%
hydrogen-2	2.0141	0.015
hydrogen-1	1.0078	—
helium-3	3.0160	—
helium-4	4.0026	—
oxygen-16	15.9949	—

Table 22.10

Particle	Mass/m_u
proton	1.0073
neutron	1.0087
electron	0.0005

c One tonne of coal produces 3×10^{10} joules of heat energy. Calculate the mass of coal necessary to generate 3×10^5 kWh of heat energy.

2 Sajel reckons that most of the energy liberated during fission (206 MeV) arises from the electrostatic repulsion of the two fission fragments. 'Just after the neutron has gone into the uranium nucleus, it splits into two smaller nuclei which just don't touch each other. These then rush apart, converting electrical energy to kinetic energy.' Help her argument along with a calculation using the data in table 22.11. Remember that the radius of a nucleus is approximately equal to $1.2 \times 10^{-15} A^{1/3}$ m.

$$^{235}_{92}\text{U} + ^{1}_{0}\text{n} \rightarrow ^{134}_{52}\text{Te} + ^{97}_{40}\text{Zr} + ?^{1}_{0}\text{n}$$

Table 22.11

Isotope	Atomic mass/m_u
uranium-235	235.0439
tellurium-134	134.0913
zirconium-97	97.0890

3 The Sun has a mass of 2.0×10^{30} kg and emits energy from its surface at a total rate of 3.9×10^{26} W. 70% of the material in the Sun is hydrogen, most of the rest being helium.

a Calculate the rate at which the mass of the Sun is decreasing. Estimate how long we will have to wait before all of the hydrogen has been converted to helium. How many years is this?

b If that energy is generated by the process outlined on page 397, estimate the rate at which helium is being produced at its centre. Use the data in table 22.9.

4 This question is about the behaviour of 2.0 MeV neutrons in a carbon moderator. A carbon nucleus has twelve times the mass of a neutron.

a Use equation (22.8) to show that a neutron loses 28% of its energy in a head-on collision with a carbon nucleus.

b Explain why the energy, in MeV, of a neutron after n head-on collisions is $2 \times (0.72)^n$. How many such collisions are needed to reduce the energy below 0.05 eV?

c In practice, the number of collisions needed to thermalise the neutrons is 120. Why is this larger than your answer to part (b)?

SUMMARY
R A D I O A C T I V I T Y

Radioactive substances are the source of emissions which ionise materials through which they pass. The ions left in the wake of ionising emissions can be detected by photographic emulsions, scintillators, cloud chambers, solid-state devices and GM tubes. The activity of a source is the rate at which it produces ionising emissions.

Alpha particles are helium nuclei, with two neutrons and two protons (positive). They produce dense ionisation in straight line tracks with a relatively short range in solids, and a range of a few centimetres in air.

Beta particles are electrons (negative). Their ionisation tracks are less dense than those of alpha particles; the tracks are wiggly. Their range is at least ten times that of alpha particles, a few metres in air.

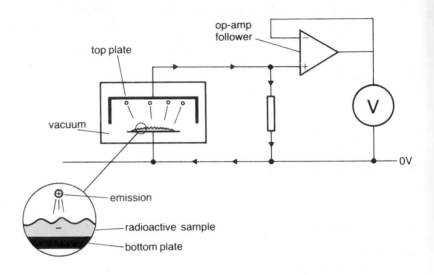

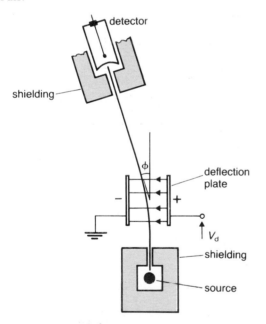

Gamma rays are high energy bursts of electromagnetic radiation (neutral). They ionise matter by a variety of processes, including pair production of electrons and positrons.

Gamma rays are undeflected by electric or magnetic fields. Alpha and beta particles are deflected in opposite directions by electric and magnetic fields. Magnetic field deflection is used to measure their momentum, and electric field deflection measures their energy.

For alpha and beta particles $\rho R \simeq$ constant for particles of a given energy. In general, the range increases with the energy of the particle. Gamma rays have an exponential transmission through matter: their intensity from a point source obeys an inverse square distance law.

The decay of parent nuclei into daughters is a random process: $\Delta N = -\lambda N \Delta t$, $N = N_0 \exp[-\lambda t]$. The activity of a sample is fixed by the decay constant and the number of parent atoms: $A = \lambda N$, $A = A_0 \exp[-\lambda t]$. The activity is halved in one half-life: $\lambda T_{\frac{1}{2}} = \ln[2]$.

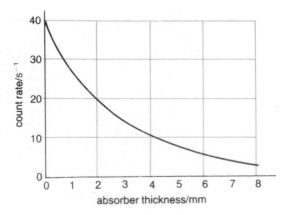

The scattering of alpha particles from thin samples gives strong evidence for the existence of a massive positive nucleus at the centre of an atom (Rutherford scattering). Each nucleus is specified by an atomic number Z and a mass number A. The nucleus contains A particles of which Z are protons: isotopes of an element have the same number of protons but different numbers of neutrons. $r \simeq 1.2 \times 10^{-15} A^{\frac{1}{3}}$

When a nucleus undergoes alpha decay it loses two protons and two neutrons. In beta decay a neutron is converted to a proton, an electron and an anti-neutrino. Gamma decay involves no change of mass or atomic number.

The binding energy of a nucleus can be found by comparing its mass with the mass of its individual protons and neutrons: $\Delta E = \Delta mc^2$. Radioactive decay is means whereby a nucleus can increase its binding energy, converting some of its mass into energy.

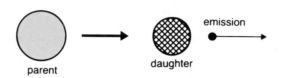

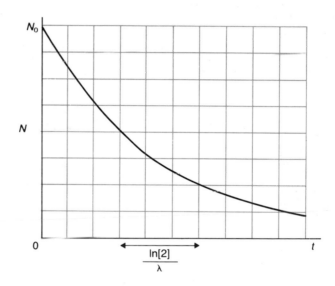

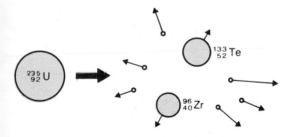

Fission of heavy nuclei can be triggered by the absorption of slow neutrons. If the fast neutrons caused by the fission of uranium-235 are slowed down by elastic collisions with nuclei in a moderator, there is the possibility of a chain reaction which can be controlled by the selective absorption of neutrons.

Energy is liberated when nuclei of light elements are fused together. Hydrogen is fused to form helium in the Sun.

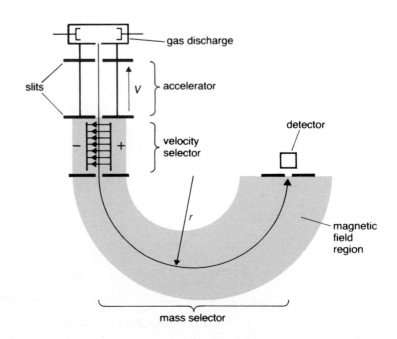

ELECTROMAGNETISM

23

MAGNETIC FIELDS

The Earth's magnetic field was first discovered by the Chinese about 900 years ago. The type of instrument they used is illustrated in figure 23.1. A small sample of a rock called magnetite floats on a block in a dish of water. It is found that the equilibrium orientation of the magnetite is unaffected by rotation or displacement of the dish. The magnetite appears to be reacting with a force field which makes it align along a particular direction. It is now believed that the source of that field is electric currents in the Earth's metallic core.

The modern equivalent of the original magnetic field sensor is the magnetic compass (figure 23.2), an indispensible aid for navigation on land or sea. However, magnetic fields can do much more than just align magnetised materials. Electrical energy can be generated by dragging conductors through magnetic fields, and its efficient transport to where it is needed exploits varying magnetic fields around conductors. So magnetic fields are a vital component of the technology which provides us with our electricity. This chapter is going to introduce you to the generation and detection of magnetic fields. The next two chapters will then show how those fields can be put to the service of mankind.

FIELD STRENGTH

If you have ever used a magnetic compass, the vector nature of the Earth's magnetic field should be obvious. Each place on the Earth's surface has a field direction, conveniently defined as being the direction in which the compass needle points. As you can see from figure 23.3, this leads to the convention that all magnetic compasses point towards the Earth's north polar ice-cap (or away from the south polar ice-cap). But how can you define the strength of the field? Clearly, you could use the strength of the couple acting on the compass needle as a measure of the field strength, but in practice the force that the field exerts on an electric current is used instead.

Currents in fields

You will recall from chapter 10 that the unit of electric current, the ampere, is defined in terms of the attractive forces between two conductors.

A current of one ampere in two straight parallel conductors of infinite length and negligible thickness placed 1 m apart in a vacuum will exert a force of 2×10^{-7} N per metre of conductor.

Figure 23.1 A magnetite compass. The rock is suspended on the surface of some water so that it is free to turn in any direction

This phenomenon can be explored in a school laboratory with the help of a simple **current balance** of the type shown in figure 23.4. A long straight wire runs close and parallel to one side of a metal frame which is balanced on a conducting knife-edge. The attractive force between the frame and the wire can be measured by altering the position of a small counterweight (the **rider**) on the frame to keep it horizontal. For example, suppose that the rider has a mass m and is a distance x from the pivot when there is no current in the frame. When the current is switched on, the value of x has to be increased by Δx to keep the frame balanced horizontally. If we assume that the magnetic force on the frame F only acts on the portion which runs parallel to the wire, we can easily calculate its value with the help of the Principle of Moments.

$$mg \times \Delta x = F \times d \qquad\qquad (23.1)$$

Figure 23.2 A modern navigation compass

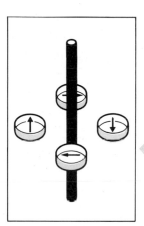

Figure 23.3 The geographical North and South Poles define the axis of rotation of the Earth. As a rough guide, compass needles point towards the North Pole and away from the South Pole

Figure 23.4 A simple current balance. The rider is moved towards or away from the knife edge to balance the magnetic forces between the wire and the frame

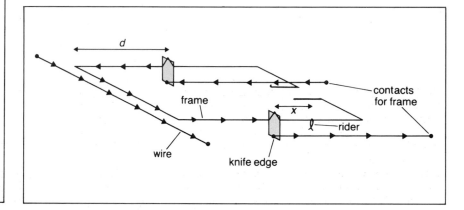

Field lines

The magnetic interaction between the wire and the frame of figure 23.4 is clearly an action-at-a-distance force between two electric currents. The current in the frame interacts with the current in the wire and vice versa. However, it is much more convenient in many situations to think of the wire as being the source of a magnetic field which fills the space around it. Any other current which passes through that field then experiences a force. The existence of the magnetic field around the wire is easily established by exploring the region around it with a small magnetic compass. Figure 23.5 shows the orientations of a number of compass needles placed around the wire. It is tempting to use a **line of force** representation to encapsulate this information, as shown in figure 23.6. The arrows on the **field lines** tell you the direction in which a small compass needle would point if it were placed there. Notice that each field line is a loop, so a single arrow is sufficient to define the direction of the field line anywhere along its length.

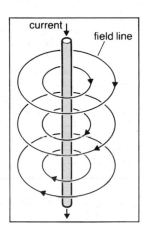

Figure 23.5 Compasses around a current-carrying wire

Figure 23.6 Using field lines to represent the magnetic field around a current in a straight wire

Fleming's Left-Hand Rule

The concentric circles which are used to represent the field around the wire seem to serve the same purpose as the electric field lines often drawn around charged objects. However, the direction of the field lines only tells you which way a compass needle will point. As you can see from figure 23.7, the direction of the force on the frame is at right angles to the direction of the field lines where they cross the current. In fact, to predict the direction of the force, you need to take account of *both* the directions of the field lines and the current. All three are perpendicular to each other. **Fleming's Left-Hand Rule** is a convenient way of remembering the relative directions of the force, field and current: it is illustrated in figure 23.8. The usual mnemonic for remembering which finger represents what quantity runs as follows:
Thumb = Thrust, First = Field and seCond = Current. You can think of those three fingers of your left hand as a particularly useful model of the force on an electric current in a magnetic field.

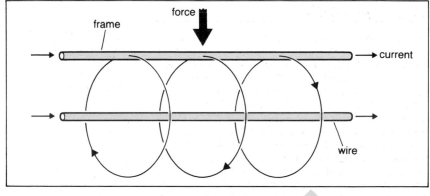

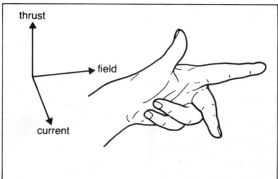

Figure 23.7 The current in the frame interacts with the field of the wire to produce a force

Figure 23.8 Fleming's Left-Hand Rule

Figure 23.9 The component of the field at right angles to the current provides the force

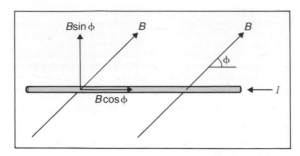

Figure 23.9 The component of the field at right angles to the current provides the force

In figure 23.7, the magnetic field lines are pointing at right angles to the direction of the current in the frame. What happens if the magnetic field is not at right angles to the current ? Look at figure 23.9. If the magnetic field is a true vector field, then we can consider the field B as the sum of two components, one parallel to the wire ($B\cos\phi$) and another perpendicular to it ($B\sin\phi$). The force on the frame arises only from the magnetic field component at right angles to the current. The field component acting parallel to the current produces no force at all.

$F = BIl\sin\phi$

F is the force on the conductor (N)

B is the field strength (T)

I is the current in the conductor (A)

l is the length of the conductor (m)

ϕ is the angle between the field and the current

Field strength

Because of the way in which the ampere is defined, the size of the force on the frame *must* be proportional to the current in it. So, there is little point in trying to verify this with a current balance in the laboratory. However, the current balance can be used to find out how the size of the force depends on the length of the frame. By substituting frames of different length, you can establish that the force F is proportional to the length l of the frame which is parallel to the wire.

$$F \propto Il \quad \therefore F = BIl \qquad (23.2)$$

The constant of proportionality B in equation (23.2) is a convenient way of defining the strength of the magnetic field. The unit of B, the **magnetic field strength**, should be $N\,A^{-1}\,m^{-1}$, but it has been given its own unit, the tesla (T).

Figure 23.10 shows how this definition can be used to measure the field strength at the poles of a horseshoe magnet. The magnet is placed on a digital balance, so that its weight is measured. A loop of wire carrying a known current is inserted into the region in front of one of the poles of the magnet. The forces on the horizontal and vertical arms of the loop are shown in figure 23.10. The force on the horizontal portion of the wire is upwards, causing a downwards reaction force on the magnet itself. Suppose that the apparent mass of the magnet increases by 0.25 g when there is a current of 4.0 A in the wire. If the horizontal portion of the loop is 10 mm long, the field strength B can be calculated as follows.

$$F = mg$$

$$\therefore F = 0.25\times10^{-3} \times 9.81 = 2.45\times10^{-3}\ N$$

$$F = BIl\sin\phi, \quad \phi = 90°$$

$$\therefore B = \frac{F}{Il}$$

$$\therefore B = \frac{2.45\times10^{-3}}{4.0 \times 10\times10^{-3}} = 0.061\ T$$

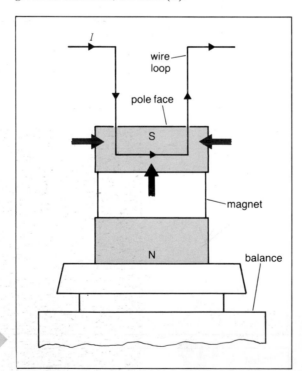

Figure 23.10 Apparatus for measuring the field strength at one pole of a horseshoe magnet

Figure 23.10 Apparatus for measuring the field strength at one pole of a horseshoe magnet

Charged beams

An electric current can, of course, be modelled as a slow drift of charged particles down the length of a conductor. Since any magnetic field component perpendicular to the current causes a force to act on the conductor, it seems reasonable to suppose that the force is really acting on the charge carriers as they move through the field. In other words, a single charged particle with velocity **v** perpendicular to a field **B** should experience a force **F** as shown in figure 23.11.

$F = Bqv$

F is the force on the particle (N)

B is the magnetic field strength (T)

q is the charge of the particle (C)

v is the velocity of the particle ($m\ s^{-1}$)

Figure 23.11 Force on a charge moving through a field

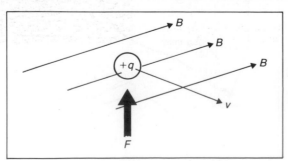

Controlling beams

Magnetic fields are widely used to control beams of charged particles. Figure 23.13 shows the arrangement of coils around the neck of a TV tube. The magnetic field created by the current in those coils deflects the beam of electrons which emerge from the anode so that a picture can be formed on the screen. The direction of the force on the electrons can be deduced from Fleming's Left-Hand Rule, provided you remember that the electron current flows in the opposite direction to conventional current! For example, look at figure 23.14. The electrons in the beam are subjected to a force at right angles to the field lines, so that they travel in a circle. The radius of the circle is easily found by equating the magnetic force to the centripetal force.

$$Bqv = \frac{mv^2}{r} \qquad \therefore \ r = \frac{mv}{Bq} \qquad \textbf{(23.3)}$$

Figure 23.15 shows a **fine beam tube**, a device which allows the trajectory of a beam of electrons to be seen. (The bulb is filled with a low pressure gas of helium atoms. When these are hit by electrons in the beam they emit light. Although these inelastic collisions remove kinetic energy from the beam, the energy loss is not serious.) A uniform magnetic field at right angles to the beam axis makes the beam curve round into a circle.

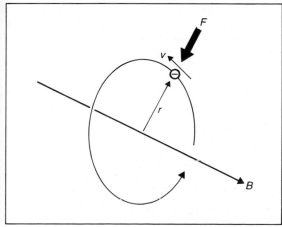

MAGNETIC FORCES !

The magnetic force on a single charged particle can be deduced from the force on a current in a length of wire. Consider the conductor shown in figure 23.12. If we only consider a length *l* sitting in a magnetic field *B* perpendicular to the current, we can write down an expression for the force on all of the mobile charges in that length of the conductor.

$$F = BIl \qquad (1)$$

If the density of mobile charges is *n*, then the current *I* can be related to the drift velocity *v* and their charge *q*.

$$I = nAqv \qquad (2)$$

Now combine equations (1) and (2) to eliminate *I*.

$$F = B(nAqv)l \quad \therefore F = Bqv \times nAl \qquad (3)$$

The total number of mobile charges in the length *l* is equal to *nAl*. So equation (3) says that the force on a single mobile charge is *Bqv*.

Figure 23.12 Charge carriers drifting through a conductor in a magnetic field

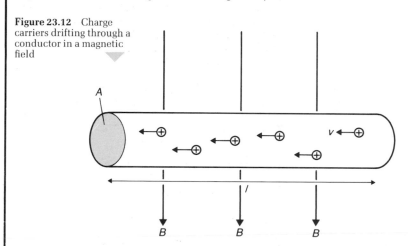

Figure 23.13 The magnetic field coils which control the three electron beams used to paint pictures on the screen of a colour television set

Figure 23.14 The magnetic force keeps the electron moving in a circle

Figure 23.15 A fine beam tube

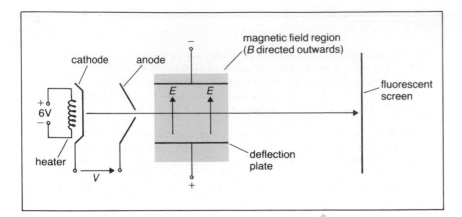

Charge-to-mass ratio

A combination of electric and magnetic fields acting on a beam of charged particles can be used to measure their **charge-to-mass ratio**, q/m. This was the method adopted by Joseph Thomson in 1897 to measure q/m for electrons, an experiment which forced physicists to accept that electrons are a basic constituent of all matter. The arrangement of apparatus is shown in figure 23.16. A beam of electrons emerges from the anode having been accelerated through a potential difference V. If the charge of each electron is e, its velocity v is easily deduced by considering energy conservation.

$$eV = \tfrac{1}{2}mv^2 \quad \therefore v = \left(\frac{2eV}{m}\right)^{\frac{1}{2}} \tag{22.4}$$

The electrons enter a region where they are simultaneously subjected to magnetic and electric fields. The magnetic force pushes the electrons upwards (use Fleming's Left-Hand Rule to convince yourself) and the electric force pushes them downwards. The two fields are adjusted until the two forces cancel each other out, so that the beam is not deflected at all — this can be assessed with the help of the fluorescent screen at the end of the evacuated tube. Since the electric and magnetic forces are equal and opposite, we can obtain another expression for the electron velocity.

$$eE = Bev \quad \therefore v = \frac{E}{B} \tag{22.5}$$

We can combine equations (23.4) and (23.5) to eliminate v and obtain an expression for e/m in terms of measurable quantities.

$$v = \frac{E}{B} = \left(\frac{2eV}{m}\right)^{\frac{1}{2}} \quad \therefore e/m = \frac{E^2}{2VB^2} \tag{22.6}$$

Figure 23.16   Apparatus for measuring the charge-to-mass ratio of electrons: the whole thing has to be in vacuum

Figure 23.17   A collision between an antiproton and a neon nucleus. A large number of short-lived particles emerge from the collision

Thomson found that a beam of negatively charged particles could be extracted from any substance that he used as a cathode. Since the charge-to-mass ratio of the particles in the beam always had the same value, it seemed obvious to conclude that electrons are present in all matter.

Particle accelerators

Electric and magnetic fields are used in modern accelerators to accelerate and deflect beams of charged particles in a research bid to discover more about their internal structure. For example, the gigantic proton–antiproton accelerator at CERN produces collisions in which an energy of 900 GeV is made available to create new particles. A record of such an event is shown in figure 23.17. (All of the particles recorded by the detector are charged so their trajectories are curved in the uniform magnetic field which floods the detection region. The direction of deflection tells you the sign of the particle's charge and the amount of deflection tells you about its momentum.)

CYCLOTRONS

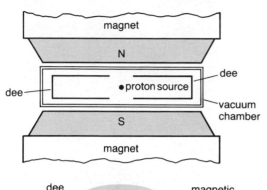

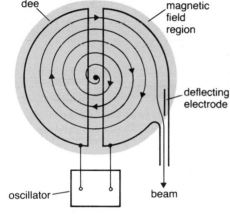

Figure 23.18   A cyclotron

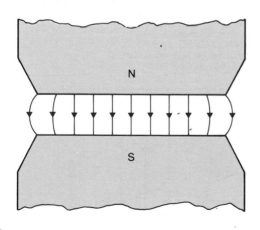

Figure 23.19   The magnetic field between the poles is only uniform away from the edges

The original high energy particle accelerator was built by Ernest Lawrence in 1930. Although the energy of the protons emerging from it was puny by modern standards (only 80 keV), its principles of operation are not much different from those used today. A continuous beam of low energy protons is injected into the centre of a region of uniform magnetic field, as shown in figure 23.18. The field forces the protons to move round in a circle, but it doesn't change their energy. (The force is perpendicular to the velocity, so no work is done on the proton by the field.) A pair of D-shaped conductors (the **dees**) fills the space between the poles of the magnet. The dees are held at different voltages, so as the protons go from one to the other they are accelerated. The trick of accelerating the protons is achieved by alternating the voltage difference between the dees so that each time a proton gets to the gap its energy is increased. That this is possible at all will become clear after some algebra has been introduced. Let us obtain an expression for the time T taken for a proton to travel once round the space between the poles.

$$v = \frac{\Delta x}{\Delta t} \qquad \therefore v = \frac{2\pi r}{T}$$

$$Bqv = \frac{mv^2}{r} \qquad \therefore \frac{Bqr}{m} = v$$

$$\therefore \frac{Bqr}{m} = \frac{2\pi r}{T} \qquad \therefore T = \frac{2\pi m}{Bq} \qquad (1)$$

So if the voltage difference between the dees is reversed once every $T/2$ seconds, some of the protons will always arrive at the gap to be accelerated across it. As those protons gain energy they will follow circular paths progressively further from the centre of the machine but they will always make it round the circle in the same time T (equation (1) does not contain v). Eventually, the protons gain enough energy to emerge from the machine through a gap in one of the dees.

The ultimate limit on the energy attainable by the protons is the size of magnet available. Lawrence built a cyclotron in 1939 which contained a magnet whose poles had a diameter of 1.5 m. We can estimate the maximum energy of the protons produced by this machine as follows. The maximum field strength attainable with a permanent iron magnet is about 1.3 T and it will only be uniform away from the edges of the poles (figure 23.19). So let us assume that the usable field region had a radius of 0.7 m. The energy of protons which are just able to escape this region is easily calculated (the mass of a proton is 6.72×10^{-27} kg). Start by finding their velocity.

$$Bqv = \frac{mv^2}{r} \qquad \therefore v = \frac{Bqr}{m} \qquad (2)$$

$$\therefore v = \frac{1.3 \times 1.6 \times 10^{-19} \times 0.7}{6.7 \times 10^{-27}}$$

$$\therefore v = 2.2 \times 10^7 \text{ m s}^{-1}$$

$$E_k = \tfrac{1}{2}mv^2 \quad \therefore E_k = 0.5 \times 6.7 \times 10^{-27} \times (2.2 \times 10^7)^2$$

$$\therefore E_k = 1.6 \times 10^{-12} \text{ J or 10 MeV}$$

The frequency with which the voltage of the dees had to be alternated can be calculated from equation (1).

$$f = \frac{1}{T}, \qquad T = \frac{2\pi m}{Bq} \qquad \therefore f = \frac{Bq}{2\pi m}$$

$$\therefore f = \frac{1.3 \times 1.6 \times 10^{-19}}{2\pi \times 6.7 \times 10^{-27}} = 5.0 \text{ MHz}$$

So if a 1 kV alternating voltage was applied to the dees, the protons would have circulated around 10 000 times before attaining their maximum energy of 10 MeV, taking about 2 ms to do it.

SYNCHROTRONS

Relativity imposes a ceiling on the energy attainable by protons in a cyclotron. As the velocity of the protons increases so does their mass, according to the following equation.

$$m = \frac{m_0}{(1 - v^2/c^2)^{\frac{1}{2}}}$$

m is the mass of a particle (kg)

m_0 is the rest mass of the particle (kg)

v is the velocity of the particle (m s^{-1})

c is the velocity of light (3.0×10^8 m s^{-1})

So as the protons gain energy they take longer to get round between the dees (see the box on 'Cyclotrons'). Eventually, the motion of the protons is no longer synchronised with the alternation of the voltage between the dees, and no further acceleration is possible. The answer to this problem is obvious: change the frequency of the voltage to compensate as the mass of the protons increases. This is the strategy employed in modern *synchrotrons*. Of course, such a machine will be unable to provide an almost continuous stream of charged particles like a cyclotron does — the particles will have to be accelerated in bunches.

A schematic diagram of a simple proton synchrotron is shown in figure 23.20. The protons whirl around in the high vacuum pipe, constrained to move in a circle by the electromagnets on either side. An alternating voltage is applied between the two conducting sleeves through which the protons move so that they gain energy every time they pass from one to the other. At the same time, the magnetic field strength is increased to keep the protons moving in a circular path of constant radius. As the proton mass increases, the frequency is decreased so that the protons always gain energy when they pass from one tube to another. As with the cyclotron, the maximum energy is limited by the radius of the apparatus. For example, the Super Proton Synchrotron at CERN (figure 23.21) has a radius of about 1 km and is therefore capable of giving bunches of protons up to 400 GeV.

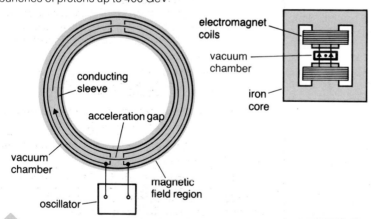

Figure 23.20 A simple synchrotron

Figure 23.21 Some of the bending and focussing magnets of the Super Proton Synchrotron at CERN. The vacuum tube which carries the beam of 270 GeV protons is exposed in the foreground. The whole machine has a diameter of about 2.5 km

Figure 23.22 Using a Hall probe to measure a magnetic field

The Hall Effect

Figure 23.22 shows a **Hall probe** being used to measure the strength of a magnetic field. The probe generates a small voltage whose value is proportional to the component of the field acting perpendicularly to the flat tip. Calibration involves measuring the change in voltage when the probe is inserted into a known magnetic field. Thereafter, the **Hall voltage** can be used to give a quick and accurate measure of the magnetic field strength at the tip of the probe.

Hall voltage

The **Hall effect** occurs when a thin slice of conductor is inserted into a magnetic field as shown in figure 23.23. When there is a current along the length of the slab, a potential difference appears across its width.

Figure 23.23 The p.d. across a thin conducting slice in a magnetic field

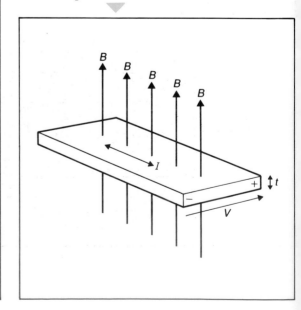

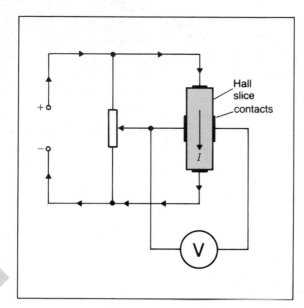

Figure 23.24 Using a potentiometer to provide a zero offset for a Hall slice

$$V = \frac{BI}{nqt}$$

V is the Hall voltage across the slice (V)

B is the field perpendicular to the slice (T)

I is the current in the slice (A)

n is the charge carrier density (m^{-3})

q is the charge of the carriers (C)

t is the thickness of the slice (m)

To get a large Hall voltage it is necessary to use a thin conductor which has a low charge carrier density n. Doped semiconductors can have carrier densities of about 10^{22} m^{-3}, compared with about 10^{28} m^{-3} for metals, so they are usually used to make Hall probes. For example, suppose that an n-type slice of semiconductor is used to make a useful probe. Its sensitivity can be estimated as follows, assuming a current of 5 mA and a thickness of 0.1 mm.

$$V = \frac{BI}{nqt} \qquad \therefore \frac{V}{B} = \frac{I}{nqt}$$

$$\therefore \frac{V}{B} = \frac{5\times10^{-3}}{1\times10^{22} \times 1.6\times10^{-19} \times 1\times10^{-4}}$$

$$\therefore \frac{V}{B} \simeq 30\,\text{mV T}^{-1}$$

In practice, there will be a voltage across the two contacts of figure 23.24 even in zero magnetic field. This is because it is not feasible to place the contacts exactly opposite each other. So the Hall voltage is superimposed on a fraction of the voltage across the slice which drives the charge through it. A potentiometer in parallel with the slice can be used to offset this voltage, allowing a reading of 0 V in a field of 0 T.

THE HALL VOLTAGE FORMULA

Consider the negative charge carriers drifting from left to right through a slice of conductor (figure 23.25). They will be subjected to a magnetic force which will deflect them upwards. So negative charge will accumulate at the top of the slice, leaving a positive charge at its bottom. These charges create a vertical electric field E which will push other charge carriers downwards. Equilibrium is eventually achieved when the vertical magnetic and electric forces are equal and opposite.

$$qE = Bqv, \quad I = nAqv \qquad \therefore E = B \times \frac{I}{nAq}$$

$$E = \frac{V}{d}, \quad A = dt \qquad \therefore \frac{V}{d} = B \times \frac{I}{ndtq}$$

$$\therefore V = \frac{BI}{nqt}$$

Of course, the sign of the Hall voltage depends on the sign of the charge carrier. So a p-type semiconductor has a Hall voltage of opposite sign to that of an n-type semiconductor.

Figure 23.25 Electrons drifting through a conductor in a magnetic field

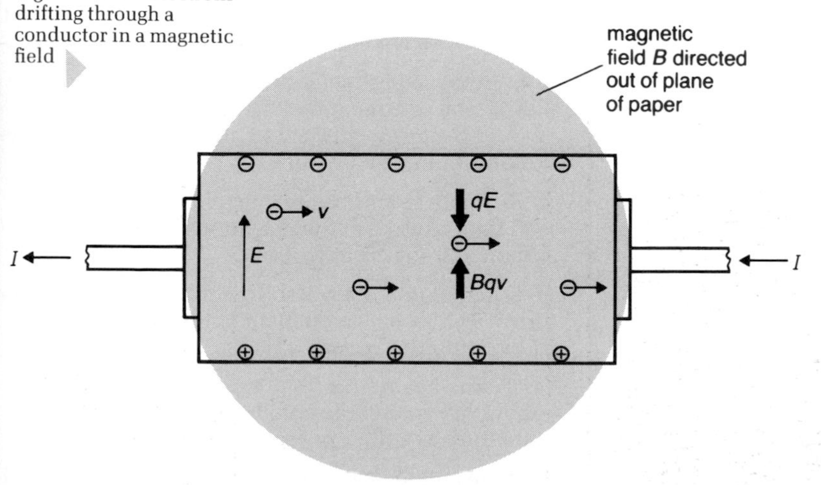

magnetic field B directed out of plane of paper

OBJECTIVES

After studying this section you should be able to do the following.

Know that magnetic forces are action-at-a-distance interactions of electric currents.

State how the direction of a field line is defined.

Use Fleming's Left-Hand Rule to relate the directions of force, field and current.

Explain how magnetic field strength is defined and use the formula $F = BIl\sin\phi$.

Use the formula $F = Bqv$ to find the radius of the circular orbit of a charged particle in a magnetic field.

Describe and explain how q/m can be measured for a particle.

Describe and explain the operation and limits of a cyclotron.

Use the Hall voltage formula $V = BI/nqt$.

QUESTIONS

1 Fiona uses the apparatus shown in figure 23.26 to measure the field strength between the poles of a small magnet. The poles have a diameter of 2.0 cm. The copper bar has a mass of 27 g, a length of 5.0 cm and is suspended by two fine wires of length 30 cm. These wires allow charge to flow along the bar, creating a current in it. Fiona moves the magnet so that the bar always passes through the centre of the field.

a Use the information on figure 23.26 to establish the direction of the field between the magnet poles.

b Table 23.1 contains the data that Fiona obtained with the apparatus: for each value of the current in the bar, she recorded its horizontal position. Use the data to calculate the field strength of the magnet. (*Hint*: $F = W\tan\phi$.)

Table 23.1

Current/A	Position/cm
0.00	10.2
0.50	11.7
1.00	13.1
1.50	14.6
2.00	16.1

2 It is usually stated in elementary textbooks that 'field lines can never cross each other', but only rarely is any justification given. Write out an explanation for the statement.

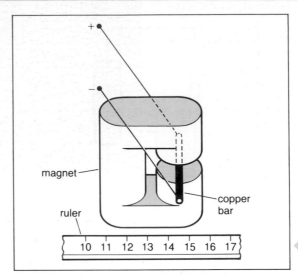

Figure 23.26

Figure 23.27

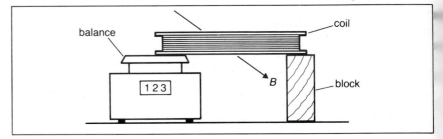

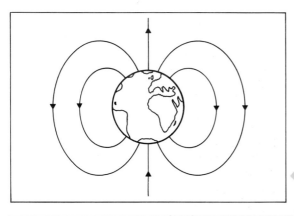

Figure 23.28

Figure 23.29

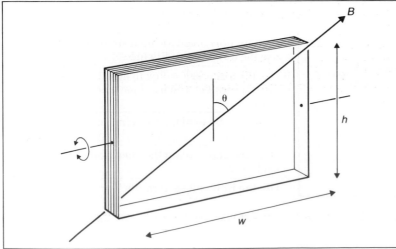

3 The Earth's magnetic field has a strength of 4.4×10^{-5} T in Britain, pointing about 66° below the horizontal. A teacher plans to demonstrate the measurement of this field with the apparatus shown in figure 23.27. A length of wire is wound 50 times around a square former whose sides have a length of 25 cm. One side of the former is supported by a balance which has a precision of ± 0.01 g, the opposite side is supported on a block.

a Draw a diagram to show the direction of the magnetic force on each arm of the coil when there is a current in it. Assume that the current direction is clockwise when the coil is viewed from above.

b Will the experiment measure the vertical or horizontal component of the Earth's field? How should the teacher set about aligning the apparatus for optimum performance?

c Estimate the minimum current necessary in the coil for a reading of the magnetic force to be obtained from the apparatus.

d Comment on the suitability of the apparatus for a precise ($\pm 5\%$) measurement of the Earth's field. How could the apparatus be improved?

4 A fine-beam tube (figure 23.15) is set up in a laboratory so that the coloured streak has the same curvature as a filter paper of diameter 10 cm.

a If the anode–cathode voltage is 250 V, how big is the field strength component perpendicular to the electron beam?

b What would the radius of curvature be if the anode–cathode voltage was doubled?

c Sketch what you would see in the tube if the uniform magnetic field was applied parallel to the electron beam.

d If the field is applied at 45° to the electron beam it follows a spiral path. Explain why.

e The intensity of cosmic rays is greater at the poles than at the equator. It is unreasonable to suppose that the flow of cosmic rays towards the Earth is other than completely symmetrical, so it seems probable that the Earth's magnetic field figure 23.28) is responsible for this shielding. However, a magnetic field is not able to alter the energy of a charged particle which enters it, so how does the shielding work?

5 Figure 23.29 shows a flat rectangular coil pivoted so that it can rotate freely about an axis going through its centre. The coil has n turns of wire and carries a current I. A uniform field B is applied at an angle θ to the plane of the coil.

a Draw a diagram to show the direction of the force on each arm of the coil.

b Show that the couple acting on the coil is given by $\Gamma = BAnI\cos\theta$, where A is the area of the coil.

c The coil is acting like a compass needle. Show how you would attach a pointer to the coil so that it indicated the direction of the field.

d Calculate the maximum couple on a 10 cm diameter coil with 50 turns of wire carrying a current of 100 mA. The coil is pivoted about a horizontal axis in the Earth's field (see question 3 for data).

6 The maximum field obtainable from an electromagnet with an iron core is about 1 T. A new electron–positron accelerator is under construction at CERN which will have a circumference of 27 km.

a Calculate the momentum of the highest energy electrons the ring of magnets will be able to contain.

b The mass m of an electron with velocity v is given by $m = m_0/(1 - v^2/c^2)^{\frac{1}{2}}$, where $m_0 = 9.11 \times 10^{-31}$ kg and $c = 3.00 \times 10^8$ m s^{-1}. Calculate the velocity of the electrons in part (a).

c The total energy E of a particle whose velocity is close to the speed of light is given by the expression $E^2 = p^2c^2 + m_0^2c^4$. Use it to calculate the maximum kinetic energy given to electrons by the accelerator. (Total energy is kinetic energy + rest mass energy.)

d The accelerator will be able to handle bunches of electrons and positrons simultaneously. Why?

7 Figure 23.30 shows a bubble chamber photograph of an electron. The magnetic field is perpendicular to the plane of the photograph.

a Explain why the electron's path is a spiral.

b Which way did the magnetic field point?

c In what ways would the photograph have been different if the particle had been a positron with twice as much energy?

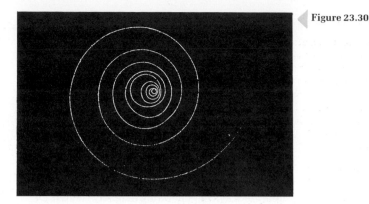

Figure 23.30

8 Mary is doing an investigation to measure the sign of the charge carriers in aluminium. She is using the largest magnet her school possesses (pole pieces 2 cm × 4 cm) and aluminium foil which is 33 μm thick.

a With the help of a diagram, show Mary how to best insert the foil between the poles and how to work out the sign of the charge carriers from the measured Hall voltage.

b Estimate the maximum Hall voltage you could get across a strip of the aluminium foil held between the poles of the permanent magnet ($B = 1.0$ T). Aluminium has a density of 2700 kg m^{-3}, a molar mass of 0.027 kg mol^{-1} and a resistivity of 2.5×10^{-8} Ω m. Typical school power packs can deliver currents of up to 8 A.

c In practice, she gets a Hall voltage of 6 μV when the current is 5.0 A. How many charge carriers are there for each atom in the aluminium?

d Discuss how Mary ought to set about measuring this voltage. What instrument should she use? Will she be able to get the voltmeter probes exactly opposite each other? If not, what should she do to be able to detect the Hall voltage against a background of voltages due to other causes?

9 A number of commercial **flowmeters** use magnetic fields to measure the rate at which a conducting fluid flows down a pipe.

a A uniform magnetic field B is applied perpendicularly to the pipe which has a diameter d. Show that there is a voltage difference $V = Bdv$ across the diameter of a pipe when the fluid has a velocity v.

b The answer to part (a) implies that the voltage difference across the pipe diameter is independent of the resistivity of the fluid flowing down it. So will it work for an insulating fluid like oil? If not, why not?

CREATING FIELDS

Something very obvious has been missed out. In the last section you learnt that magnetic fields are the means by which electric currents interact with each other. Yet we had to invoke the use of a magnet, in the form of a compass, to define the direction of those fields, without actually making it clear what a magnet is. Of course, as you already know, a magnet is a specially treated chunk of iron which experiences forces in magnetic fields. Furthermore, magnets can act as sources of magnetic field in their own right. So are there two separate ways of generating magnetic fields? Or does a magnet behave like a superconductor, containing a current which does not change with time? The answer is even stranger, involving a new property of the electron called **spin**. However, before we try to explain how a permanent magnet can generate a magnetic field, you need to know some more about the fields generated by currents in wires.

Figure 23.31 Direction of the magnetic field around a current in a straight wire

Straight wires

The simplest arrangement for generating a magnetic field from an electric current is illustrated in figure 23.31. A long straight wire carries a current I, generating a field B. A small compass can be used to establish the direction of the field around the wire. The results are summarised in the field lines drawn in figure 23.31, a set of circles concentric with the wire. The direction of the field is linked to the direction of the current: if the latter is reversed, then so is the former. A useful rule for working out the direction of the field from the current is also illustrated in figure 23.31. It is known as the **Right-Hand Grip Rule** (RHG). If you use your right hand to make the universal hitch-hiker sign, your thumb indicates the current direction and your fingers indicate the field direction.

Figure 23.32 Using a Hall probe to investigate the strength of magnetic field near a straight wire

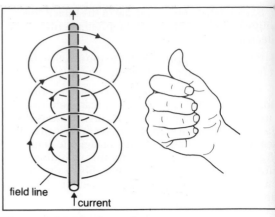

field line   current

The straight wire formula

Although the magnetic field around a long straight wire is small for the sort of currents (<10 A) possible in a school laboratory, it is still possible to use a Hall probe to investigate how the field changes as you move away from the wire. The arrangement of apparatus is shown in figure 23.32(a). An alternating current is maintained in the wire by a signal generator. The consequent alternating magnetic field around it is picked up by the Hall probe. The output will be a small alternating voltage which can be amplified and measured with the help of an oscilloscope. By this means, constant signals from the Earth's field or 50 Hz signals from the mains electricity can be separated from the signal we want to measure. Some results are shown in the graph of figure 23.32(b). As you can see, the field strength appears to be inversely proportional to the distance from the wire.

As we discussed in chapter 10 (page 160), the force between two currents must be proportional to the product of those currents. Since the force on one of the currents is given by the formula $F = BIl$, the field B must be proportional to the other current. So the strength of *any* field is always proportional to the current which creates it.

$$B = 2 \times 10^{-7} \times \frac{I}{r} \qquad (23.7)$$

A value for the constant of proportionality in equation (23.7) is forced upon us by the definition of the ampere: two straight wires 1 m apart must have a force of 2×10^{-7} N acting per metre of their length when they each carry a current of one ampere. In practice, it is much more convenient to define a new fundamental constant μ_0 which fixes the strength of the magnetic interaction.

$$B = \frac{\mu_0 I}{2\pi r}$$

B is the field strength around a long straight wire (T)

μ_0 is the permeability of free space $(4\pi \times 10^{-7} \text{ N A}^{-2})$

I is the current in the wire (A)

r is the distance from the wire (m)

($\mu_0/2\pi$ is, of course, equal to 2×10^{-7}; the use of μ_0 (the **permeability of free space**) makes many other useful formulae simpler.)

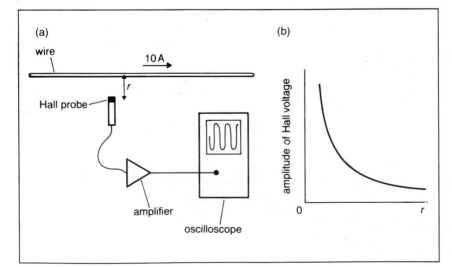

(a)

wire   10 A r

Hall probe

amplifier

oscilloscope

(b)

amplitude of Hall voltage

0   r

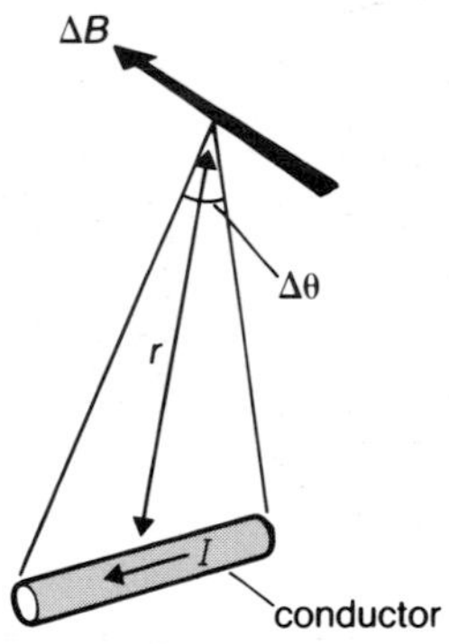

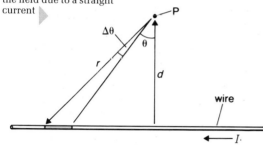

Figure 23.33 The field due to part of a current-carrying conductor

Figure 23.34 Calculating the field due to a straight current

In principle, you can work out the electric field near any charged object by summing together the contributions from each of the charges in it. This is because the field due to a point charge q at a distance r is given by $E = q/4\pi\epsilon_0 r^2$. A similar trick can be performed for magnetic fields. The field ΔB due to a small length of current-carrying conductor which is at a distance r and subtends an angle $\Delta\theta$ is given by the following formula:

$$\Delta B = \frac{\mu_0 I \Delta\theta}{4\pi r} \tag{1}$$

(The direction of the field is given by the RHG rule, as shown in figure 23.33.) This type of formula was first suggested by Biot and Savart in 1820 as a result of investigating the interaction of currents in long wires.

As a check on its accuracy, let us use it to find the field due to an infinitely long wire which carries a current I. Look at figure 23.34. We want to find the total field at P which is a distance d from the wire. Consider the field ΔB at P due to the short length of wire at distance r which subtends an angle $\Delta\theta$.

$$\Delta B = \frac{\mu_0 I \Delta\theta}{4\pi r}, \qquad r = \frac{d}{\cos\theta} \qquad \therefore \; \Delta B = \frac{\mu_0 I}{4\pi d} \times \cos\theta\,\Delta\theta \tag{2}$$

Since all the contributions to the field at P have the same direction (into the plane of the diagram), we only need to integrate equation (2) over the whole length of the wire to obtain the total field at P.

$$B = \frac{\mu_0 I}{4\pi d} \times \int_{-\pi/2}^{+\pi/2} \cos\theta\,d\theta = \frac{\mu_0 I}{4\pi d} \times [\sin\theta]_{-\pi/2}^{+\pi/2}$$

$$\therefore \; B = \frac{\mu_0 I}{4\pi d} \times (1 - (-1)) = \frac{\mu_0 I}{2\pi d} \tag{3}$$

The Biot–Savart formula can be applied to any system of conductors to find the magnetic field they generate. For example, it is very easy to find the field at the centre of a flat circular coil of wire. Suppose that the coil has a radius r and has n turns of wire, each of which carries a current I. A small portion of one coil will contribute a field ΔB at the centre, as shown in figure 23.35. All we have to do is sum these contributions over the whole coil.

$$\Delta B = \frac{\mu_0 I \Delta\theta}{4\pi r} \qquad \therefore \; B = \frac{\mu_0 I}{4\pi r} \times \Sigma\Delta\theta = \frac{\mu_0 I}{4\pi r} \times 2\pi n$$

$$\therefore \; B = \frac{\mu_0 n I}{2r} \tag{4}$$

The integrations can only be performed in simple cases. However, computers can always be used to do the integration by numerical means. For example, figure 23.36 shows the computed field strength and direction in a **Helmholtz coil** arrangement. The two circular coils are mounted one radius apart, giving a large region between them where the field is uniform.

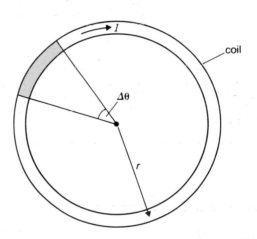

Figure 23.35 Calculating the field at the centre of a circular coil

Figure 23.36 Helmholtz coils. The field is uniform to within 5% in a cylinder of length 0.5r and diameter 0.8r at the centre of the coils

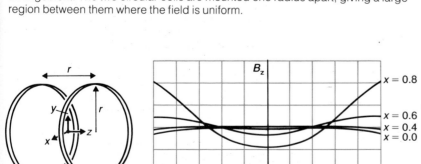

Solenoids

A **solenoid** is a long length of wire wound in spiral fashion around a tube, as shown in figure 23.37. This is a very common arrangement for generating magnetic fields, so knowledge of the field strength around a solenoid is very useful when it comes to understanding and designing real magnetic devices. You will be meeting some of these in subsequent chapters.

Field behaviour

The field in and around a long thin solenoid can be explored with a Hall probe. The results of such explorations are presented in figure 23.38. The field has a number of remarkable properties which have to be explained.

- The field *inside* the solenoid, well away from its ends, is uniform, remaining constant as you move either along its length or along a diameter.
- The field at the end of the solenoid has half the strength of the field inside the solenoid.
- The field *outside* the solenoid is very small, generally pointing in the opposite direction to the field inside the solenoid.
- The strength of the field is proportional to the number of coils of wire per metre of the solenoid.
- Provided that the width of the coil is much smaller than its length, the shape of the solenoid cross-section has no effect on the strength of the field.

$B = \mu_0 NI$

B is the field strength at the centre of the solenoid (T)

N is the number of coils of wire per metre (m^{-1})

I is the current in the coils (A)

Strictly speaking, the formula can only be used for a solenoid whose length is much greater than its diameter. However, it is a useful approximation for solenoids which are too squat to be considered ideal. The direction of the field inside the solenoid can be predicted with a Right-Hand Grip Rule. Look at figure 23.39. If you let your fingers curl round so that they point in the direction of the current in the coil, your thumb points in the direction of the field.

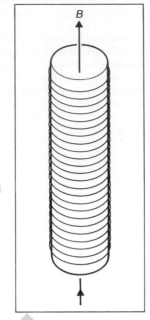

Figure 23.37 The magnetic field inside a solenoid points along its axis

Figure 23.38 Variation of B within a solenoid

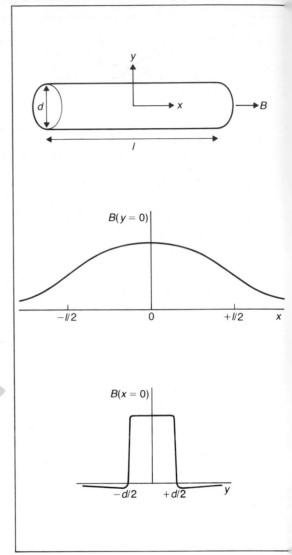

Figure 23.39 The Right-Hand Grip Rule

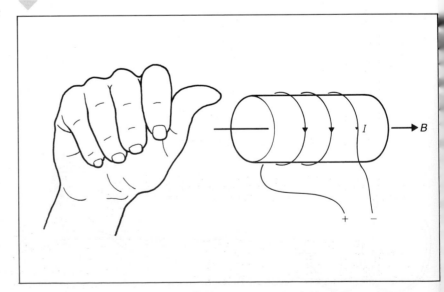

THE SOLENOID FIELD FORMULA

In principle, the Biot–Savart formula can be used to obtain the formula for the field at the centre of a solenoid. A point inside the solenoid is selected and the contributions of the field component along the axis from all the portions of the coils are summed via integration. In practice, a greater insight into magnetic fields is obtained by using a different approach which has the added advantage of involving much simpler algebra!

It can be established by experiment that the field at the centre of a long solenoid is independent of the shape of its cross-section. So we are free to choose the convenient shape shown in figure 23.40. As you can see, the coils have a short height but a large width. So a point on the solenoid axis sees a carpet of long straight wires above and below. The field at that point must therefore be the sum of the fields from each of those wires. We shall start by considering the field due to the wires underneath the point.

The geometry is shown in figure 23.41. The current in the wires which intercept the x-axis is into the page, so that the field B due to the wires in Δx points as shown. We are going to assume that the wires spread to infinity along the x-axis in both directions, so the vertical component of B will be cancelled out by a bunch of wires on the other side of the origin. On the other hand, the horizontal component of *all* the wires will point to the right (convince yourself). So we only need to consider the horizontal component of B. Each wire in the section Δx will provide a horizontal field component δB at P given by the long straight wire formula.

$$B = \frac{\mu_0 I}{2\pi r}, \quad \delta B = B\cos\theta \quad \therefore \delta B = \frac{\mu_0 I \cos\theta}{2\pi r} \qquad (1)$$

If the number of coils per metre is N, then the number of wires in the length Δx is $N\Delta x$. So the horizontal component of the field at P due to the wires at Δx is given by the following expression:

$$\Delta B = N\Delta x \times \delta B \quad \therefore \Delta B = \frac{\mu_0 NI}{2\pi} \times \frac{\Delta x}{r}\cos\theta \qquad (2)$$

If you look at the right-angled triangle in figure 23.41, you should appreciate that Δx is connected to $\Delta\theta$ as follows:

$$\frac{r\Delta\theta}{\Delta x} = \cos\theta \quad \therefore \frac{\Delta x}{r}\cos\theta = \Delta\theta \qquad (3)$$

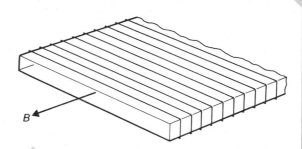

Figure 23.40 A flat solenoid

Figure 23.41 Calculating the field above an infinite carpet of wires

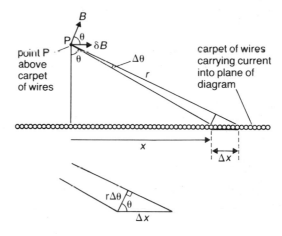

Equations (2) and (3) can now be combined to give a particularly simple and useful expression for the horizontal field due to the wires which subtend an angle $\Delta\theta$ at P.

$$\Delta B = \mu_0 NI \times \frac{\Delta\theta}{2\pi} \qquad (4)$$

If P is effectively at the centre of a carpet of wires which seem to stretch to infinity on either side, then the angle subtended by all the wires will be π.

$$B = \Sigma\Delta B \quad \therefore B = \mu_0 NI \times \frac{\Sigma\Delta\theta}{2\pi}$$

$$\therefore B = \mu_0 NI \times \frac{\pi}{2\pi} \quad \therefore B = \frac{\mu_0 NI}{2} \qquad (5)$$

Equation (5) says that the field on either side of an infinite carpet of long straight wires is independent of the distance from the carpet. The fields are shown in figure 23.42. Notice that they are in opposite directions — the uniformity of the field is shown by the even spacing of the field lines. Figure 23.42 also shows what happens if you place two of these carpets close together with the currents going in opposite directions as they would be in the solenoid of figure 23.40. The fields outside the carpets cancel each other out, and the fields between the carpets add together to give a uniform field $B = \mu_0 NI$.

Of course, this formula should only apply to solenoids which have the shape shown in figure 23.40. However, take a look at figure 23.43. A number of solenoids of square cross-section have been placed side-by-side. They are all the same as each other and carry the same current, so they have the same uniform field along their length. However, that field cannot be due to the currents flowing vertically as these occur in pairs which cancel each other out. So the field in each square solenoid must be equal to the field in the wide solenoid we have been considering.

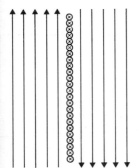

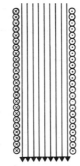

Figure 23.42 The uniform field outside an infinite carpet of wires

Figure 23.43 The field inside a flat solenoid is the same as that inside a square solenoid

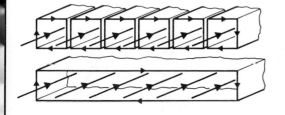

Calibrating ammeters

As an example of the solenoid formula in action, consider the following arrangement for calibrating an ammeter in the laboratory. The apparatus is shown in figure 23.44. A current I flows in the two solenoids, creating a known uniform field B in the small gap between them. The same current flows round a rectangular coil of wire held in the gap by a digital balance: the coil has n turns of wire around it. The current also goes through the ammeter whose reading is to be checked. The vertical force on each horizontal portion of the coil is given by the usual formula.

$$F = BIl, \quad B = \mu_0 NI \quad \therefore F = n \times \mu_0 NlI^2 \quad \textbf{(23.8)}$$

Suppose that each solenoid has 380 turns over a length of 30 cm, giving $N = 380/0.3 = 1.27 \times 10^3$ m^{-1}. The horizontal portion of the coil is 5.00 cm long, and contains 25 turns of wire. If g is 9.81 N kg^{-1}, we can calculate the apparent mass change Δm of the loop as a function of the current.

Figure 23.45 A washing-machine solenoid valve

Figure 23.44 Calibrating an ammeter in the laboratory

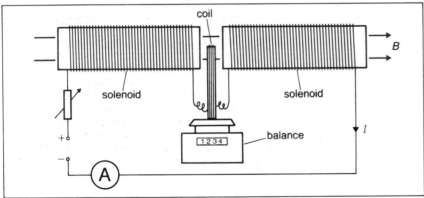

$$F = mg$$

$$\therefore \Delta mg = \mu_0 NnlI^2$$

$$\therefore \Delta m = \frac{\mu_0 Nnl}{g} \times I^2$$

$$\therefore \Delta m = 2.03 \times 10^{-4} \times I^2 \quad \textbf{(23.9)}$$

A standard school digital balance has a precision of $\pm 1 \times 10^{-5}$ kg, so a current of 1.00 A in the apparatus gives $\Delta m = 0.20 \pm 0.01$ g, an accuracy of 5%. Larger currents can be measured more accurately: 5.00 A gives $\Delta m = 5.07 \pm 0.01$ g, an accuracy of 0.2%.

Ferromagnetism

At a very early stage of your science education you discovered that a small group of metals (nickel, cobalt and iron) are strongly affected by magnetic fields. Chunks of these **magnetic materials** will stick to the poles of permanent magnets. Furthermore, you were probably told that permanent magnets were constructed from alloys of magnetic materials. Given the importance of iron in magnetic machines, it is worthwhile spending some time thinking about models which can explain the properties of magnetic materials.

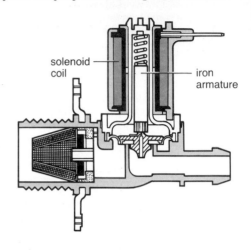

solenoid coil

iron armature

Magnetic moments

A **solenoid valve** is illustrated in figure 23.45; they are widely used in washing machines to control the flow of water. Every time that there is a current in the coil of wire, the slug of iron is tugged into the centre of the solenoid, opening the valve. As soon as the current stops, the spring shoves the slug out of the solenoid and closes the valve. A clue as to why the iron is attracted into the solenoid is shown in figure 23.46; the slug moves into the region where the magnetic field is strongest. (The spacing of the field lines indicates the strength of the field at that point.) This behaviour can be modelled by assuming that each iron atom contains an electric current circulating around in a loop, so that each atom has a **magnetic moment**.

Consider a rectangular loop of wire of area A sitting in a uniform magnetic field B, as shown in

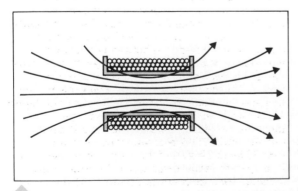

Figure 23.46 Field around a short solenoid

Figure 23.47 Forces on a current-carrying loop in a magnetic field

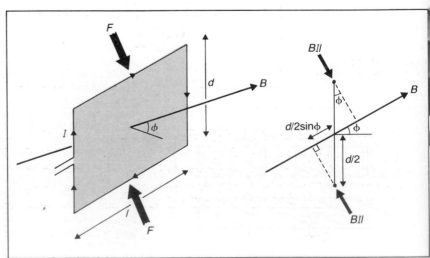

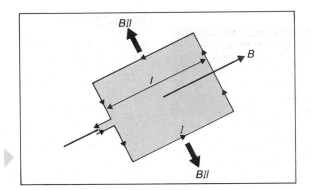

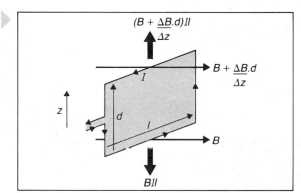

Figure 23.48 The loop will end up with its plane at right angles to the magnetic field

Figure 23.49 There will be a resultant force on a current loop in a magnetic field gradient

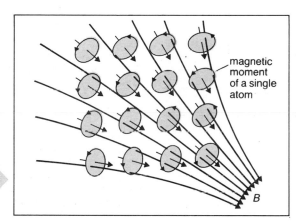

Figure 23.50 Each magnetic moment is aligned by the field and is then tugged towards regions of stronger field

Figure 23.51 Field of a single current loop

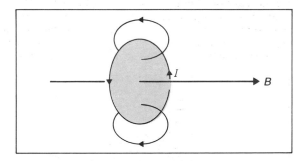

Figure 23.52 Magnetic moments in a permanent magnet

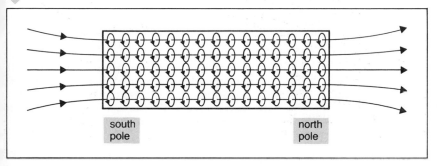

figure 23.47. It carries a current I and the normal to its plane is at an angle ϕ to the field. The forces F on the sides of length l form a couple Γ which twists the loop around an axis at right angles to the field. The size of that couple is easily calculated as follows:

$$\Gamma = F \times d\sin\phi, \; F = BIl \; \therefore \; \Gamma = BIdl\sin\phi \qquad \textbf{(23.10)}$$

The quantity dl is simply the area of the loop. It can be shown that it is only the area of the loop, rather than its shape, which is important in equation (23.10). Furthermore, we can simplify matters further by introducing the **magnetic moment** M of the loop.

$$M = IA$$

M is the magnetic moment of a current loop ($A\,m^2$)

I is the current in the loop (A)

A is the area of the loop (m^2)

$$\Gamma = BIA\sin\phi, \quad M = IA \quad \therefore \; \Gamma = BM\sin\phi \qquad \textbf{(23.11)}$$

Provided that there is some damping mechanism, it should be obvious that the loop will end up as shown in figure 23.48, with the magnetic forces on either end of it being equal and opposite.

Now insert the same loop in a non-uniform magnetic field, as shown in figure 23.49. As before, the loop ends up with its plane perpendicular to the field. However, the top end of the loop is in a stronger field than the bottom end of the loop, so there is a resultant force on it. As you can see, that force pulls the loop towards regions of stronger field.

$$F = M \times \frac{\Delta B}{\Delta z} \qquad \textbf{(23.12)}$$

Let us assume that each atom in a chunk of iron has a magnetic moment which is free to rotate in any direction. When it is placed in a magnetic field, its magnetic moments will align themselves along the field lines and then be tugged in the direction of increasing magnetic field. This is illustrated in figure 23.50: each magnetic moment has been represented by an arrow pointing at right angles to the plane of the current loop.

Permanent magnets

Many atoms have magnetic moments, but once they are bound to each other as ions or molecules in solids these magnetic moments disappear. Only a handful of elements, notably iron, nickel and cobalt, have interactions between their atoms which force them to align their magnetic moments parallel to each other when they are part of a crystal. Since the current loop responsible for the magnetic moment generates a magnetic field (figure 23.51), large-scale alignment of the magnetic moments results in a substantial magnetic field outside the solid. A **permanent magnet** can be formed by forcing all of the magnetic moments to line up in the same direction by inserting it in a solenoid for a short while. Figure 23.52 shows the field lines around a permanent magnet made this way. As you can see, field lines leave one end of the bar (its **north pole**) and enter it at the other end (its **south pole**). Since the magnetic field gradient is large near the poles, they are the places to which magnetic materials are attracted.

Figure 23.53 Domain
boundaries in a nickel
crystal. The sequence from
top to bottom shows how
the domain magnetisation
changes as the applied field
direction is varied from left
through zero to right

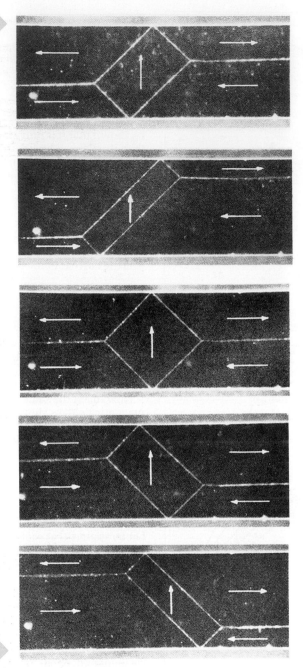

Figure 23.53 Domain
boundaries in a nickel
crystal. The sequence from
top to bottom shows how
the domain magnetisation
changes as the applied field
direction is varied from left
through zero to right

Figure 23.54 Using soft
iron to generate the radial
field around a loudspeaker
coil

Domains

In practice, different parts (**domains**) of the same
crystal can align up in different directions, as
shown in figure 23.53. Evidence for these domains
can be obtained by covering the sample with a
liquid containing tiny scraps of iron. The particles
collect at places where the field gradient outside
the crystal is large, i.e. at the boundaries between
domains. Lines of iron particles can be clearly seen
under a high magnification microscope.

The total field outside the crystal is the sum of
the field from each domain. In the absence of an
external field, each domain will be aligned in a
different direction, giving no net field outside the
crystal. However, if an external field is applied,
some domains will grow and others will shrink,
giving a net alignment of magnetic moments along
the field direction. What happens when the
external field is removed depends on the material
of which the crystal is made. If it is a **soft** magnetic

material, the domain boundaries will quickly
change so that the net alignment disappears. In a
hard magnetic material the domain boundaries
will hardly change when the external field is
removed. So hard magnetic materials make good
permanent magnets.

Field shaping

A combination of soft and hard magnetic materials
is often used to obtain magnetic fields with useful
geometries. For example, look at the magnet
assembly of a loudspeaker shown in figure 23.54. A
coil of wire which is connected to the cone sits in a
radial magnetic field so that the cone is pushed in
or out when there is a current in the coil. Hard
magnetic materials are very difficult to machine
and therefore have to be cast. In the case of this
particular loudspeaker, the permanent magnet is in
the shape of a ring with opposite poles on either
face. Soft iron plates clamped either side of the ring
guide the field lines into the gap to form the desired
radial field for the coil. (As a rule, soft iron
magnetises in such a way as to keep field lines
inside itself.)

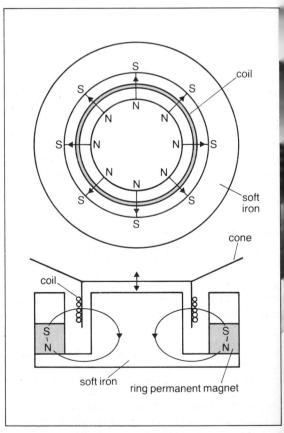

The construction of a moving-coil galvanometer
is another good example of field shaping by soft
iron. Look at figure 23.55. The soft iron core
between the pole pieces distorts the field so that it
is radial and uniform. This is important because it
ensures that the magnetic couple acting on the coil
does not depend on its orientation in the air gap. To
see this, suppose that the coil contains n turns of
wire, each of area A. We can use equation (23.10) to
calculate the couple on the coil when it carries a
current I.

$$\Gamma = nBIA\sin\phi, \quad \phi = \pi/2 \quad \therefore \Gamma = nBAI \quad \textbf{(23.13)}$$

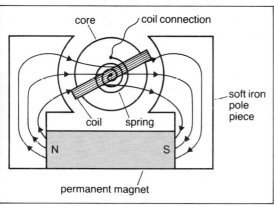

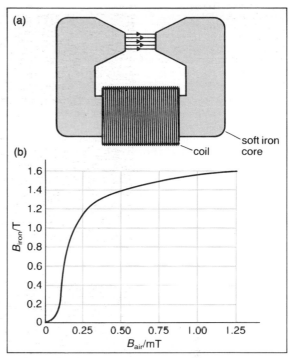

Figure 23.55 Soft iron in a moving-coil galvanometer generates a uniform radial field around the coil

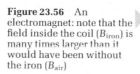

Figure 23.56 An electromagnet: note that the field inside the coil (B_{iron}) is many times larger than it would have been without the iron (B_{air})

Figure 23.57 Variation of μ with external field for pure iron

As you can see from figure 23.55, current enters and leaves the coil via a pair of springs. These obey Hooke's Law, providing a reverse couple which is proportional to the angle of rotation of the coil ϕ. The stiffness of those springs will obviously affect the sensitivity of the meter: a sensitive galvanometer is necessarily fragile because the springs must have a small spring constant c.

$$\Gamma = c\phi = nBAI \quad \therefore \phi = \frac{nBA}{c} \times I \qquad \textbf{(23.14)}$$

You might suppose that a robust galvanometer could be made sensitive by simply adding lots of turns of wire to the coil. However, this simply raises the resistance of the meter, making it less useful. So real meters employ weak springs and strong fields to maintain a high sensitivity with a low resistance.

Electromagnets
An electromagnet is shown in figure 23.56(a). The insulated wire is coiled into a solenoid around a pure iron core, a soft magnetic material. The field generated by the current in the solenoid partially aligns the domains in the iron, creating a much stronger field in the same direction. Field lines emerge from the iron at the poles of the electromagnet, giving a magnetic field in the gap between them. The graph of figure 23.56(b) shows how the field at the poles B_{iron} changes as the current in the solenoid is increased (B_{air} is the field at the centre of the solenoid without the core). The field in the iron saturates at 1.6 T, corresponding to 100% alignment of its domains. Away from saturation, B_{iron} is many hundreds of times larger than B_{air}. Although the graph is not a straight line, it is sometimes useful to make the following approximation.

$$B_{iron} = \mu B_{air} \qquad \textbf{(23.15)}$$

The graph of figure 23.57 shows how the value of μ (the **relative permeability**) changes with B_{iron}: it varies from 250 to 5000. Matters are complicated by the fact that all magnetic materials exhibit **hysteresis**. The graph of figure 23.58 shows how B_{iron} changes when B_{air} is swept from one end of its range to the other and back again—the shape is called a hysteresis loop. Clearly, the magnetic field at the poles of the electromagnet depends on both past and present values of the coil current. In particular, if the current is swept from a large value down to zero, the electromagnet will end up with a permanent magnetic field.

Figure 23.58 Hysteresis loop for an electromagnet made from mild steel

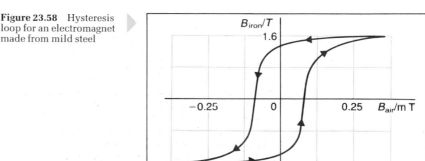

ELECTRON SPIN !

Although it is tempting to suppose that the magnetic moment of individual iron atoms in a permanent magnet is due to the circulation of electrons around the nucleus, it is in fact due to the intrinsic magnetic moment of the electrons themselves. Electrons, in common with many other fundamental particles, have a property known as **spin** which gives them a magnetic moment of 9.27×10^{-24} J T^{-1}. Normally the electrons in atoms interact with each other so that their total spin magnetic moment becomes zero; but if there are an odd number of electrons, there is a residual magnetic moment which can be measured by flinging a beam of the atoms through a magnetic field gradient. However, when the atoms are grouped together in a solid, it is usually energetically favourable for the spins in adjacent atoms to line up in opposite directions to give a net magnetic moment of zero. Only in alloys of iron, cobalt and nickel do the spins of adjacent atoms line up parallel to each other.

OBJECTIVES

After studying this section you should be able to do the following.

Calculate the size and direction of the magnetic field near a long straight wire.

Calculate the size and direction of the magnetic field inside a long thin solenoid.

Describe how the field strength varies in and around a long thin solenoid.

Describe and explain a procedure whereby ammeters may be calibrated by a current balance.

State the elements which are magnetic.

Explain what a magnetic moment is and describe how it behaves in a non-uniform magnetic field.

Know that soft magnetic materials can be used to increase the strength of electromagnets and guide field lines.

Use the domain theory to account for the permanent and temporary magnetisation of magnetic materials.

Describe the different behaviour of a soft and a hard magnetic material.

Know that the poles of a permanent magnet are the places where field lines enter and leave it.

Describe the construction of a moving-coil galvanometer and derive an expression for its sensitivity.

QUESTIONS

1 A teacher proposes to demonstrate the magnetic forces between two wires as follows. A wire 25 cm long will be supported on a balance and another wire of the same length will be slowly lowered towards it from above. Both wires will carry a current of 10 A from a power pack. By means of a calculation, decide whether or not the demonstration will work if the balance has a sensitivity of ±0.01 g. Suggest how the demonstration could be made to work better.

2 A standard solenoid of the type used in school laboratories has 190 turns of wire over a length of 30 cm, with a square cross-section of 50 mm × 50 mm.

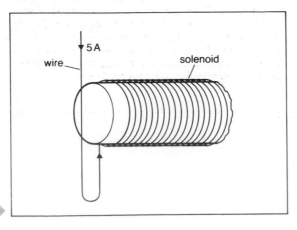

Figure 23.59

a Calculate the field at the centre of the solenoid for a current of 2.0 A in the coils.

b Sketch field lines in and around the coil.

c Suppose that you wanted a field of 3.0×10^{-3} T at the mouth of the solenoid. How big a current would you need in the solenoid?

3 Figure 23.59 shows a length of wire suspended at one end of a solenoid. Both carry the the same current of 5.0 A.

a Which way will the wire be pushed?

b The solenoid has a length of 25 cm and has 700 turns of wire along its length. What is the field at its centre? What is the field at its edge?

c If the solenoid has a radius of 2.5 cm, calculate the magnetic force on the wire. Is the force measurable in a school laboratory?

d Draw a graph to show how the force on the wire depends on the current in the wire and solenoid from −10 A to +10 A.

4 Becky thinks that mice can sense the Earth's magnetic field. To check this she uses a pair of Helmholtz coils (figure 23.36) to cancel out the Earth's magnetic field inside the mouse's cage. Each coil has a radius of 25 cm and contains 300 turns of copper wire. The Earth's field in England has a magnitude of 4.7×10^{-5} T and a direction of 66° below the horizontal.

a By means of a diagram, show how the current must go in the coils to cancel out the Earth's field.

b Calculate the current required if the field at the centre of the two coils is given by $0.72\mu_0 nI/r$.

c Since it is required to have the current maintained over a long time span in the open air, the coil current is to be supplied from a 6 V battery. If copper has a resistivity of 1.56×10^{-8} Ω m, suggest a suitable diameter for the wire used in the coils.

d All of the electrical energy from the battery will be converted to heat in the coils. Suppose that you used wire of twice the diameter that you calculated in part (c). What voltage would you need across the coils to get the same field at their centre? Would the system dissipate heat at a greater or smaller rate than before?

5 A one-turn square coil with sides of length l carries a current I in a uniform magnetic field B, as shown in figure 23.60.

a By considering the forces on each side of the coil, show that the couple on it is given by $\Gamma = BIl^2\sin\phi$.

b Suppose that the field has a gradient of dB/dz at right angles to the field direction. Show that the resultant force on the coil will be MdB/dz when $\phi = 0$.

c A bar magnet can be modelled as a current loop similar to that shown in figure 23.60. Use this model to explain why like poles of bar magnets repel and unlike poles attract each other.

6 The field lines around permanent magnets have been explored in schools since time immemorial by means of iron filings. Explain why filings of soft iron form into lines which track the field lines around a magnet when they are scattered over a sheet of paper placed over the magnet.

7 The **Curie temperature** of a magnetic material is the temperature at which it ceases to have magnetic properties. A soldering iron which exploits this effect is shown in figure 23.61. A slug of magnetic material with a Curie temperature of 180°C is free to move between a heating coil wound on an iron core and the copper top of the heating bit: a weak spring pushes the slug in good thermal contact with the bit.

a Suppose that there was a steady current in the heating coil. Explain how heat energy would get delivered to the bit without its temperature rising above 180°C.

b In practice the current in the heating coil alternates with a frequency of 50 Hz. Explain why the slug is still attracted to the heating coil when it is below 180°C.

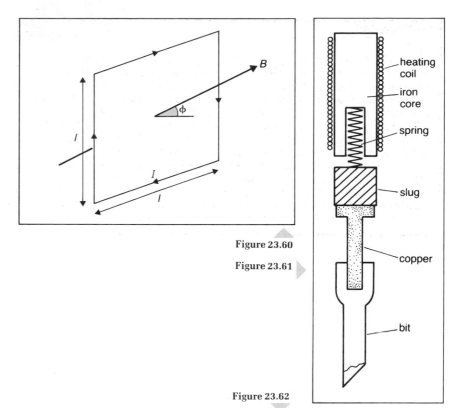

Figure 23.60

Figure 23.61

Figure 23.62

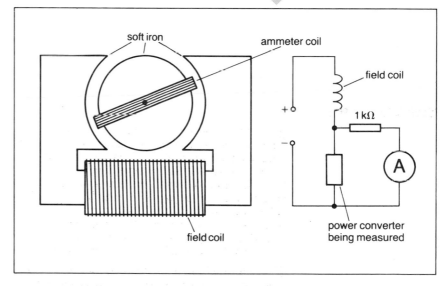

8 Susan has invented a watt-meter — it is illustrated in figure 23.62. 'Its like a moving-coil ammeter, with an electromagnet generating the field. The current in the coil is proportional to the p.d. V across the meter and the field is proportional to the current I going through the meter. So the couple on the coil is proportional to VI.' Comment on her design: it has one major flaw.

24

ELECTROMAGNETIC
INDUCTION

In 1831 Michael Faraday performed an experiment which had far-reaching consequences for electrical technology. His apparatus, shown in figure 24.1, was very simple — just a copper disc suspended between the poles of a permanent magnet. When Faraday rotated the disc he observed that a steady p.d. appeared between the rim and the centre. He had invented a means by which electricity could be generated by moving conductors through magnetic fields. Moreover, Faraday's explanation for the phenomenon which he had discovered involved a fruitful new concept, that of **magnetic flux**.

CHANGING FLUX

Faraday and his contemporaries spent many years trying, in vain, to use magnetic fields to generate electricity. They reasoned that since electric currents could create magnetic fields the reverse process must be possible. However, they concentrated their efforts on static arrangements of magnets and conductors. Unfortunately, it is the *movement* of a conductor through a magnetic field which generates a p.d. across it! This can be proved easily as follows.

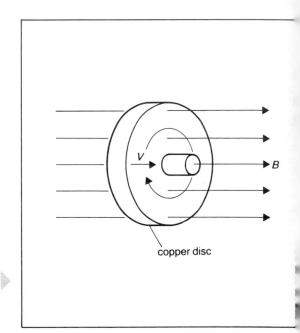

Figure 24.1 When a conducting disc is rotated in a magnetic field a p.d. is induced between the rim and the centre

Figure 24.2 Forces on mobile electrons in a metal swept through a magnetic field

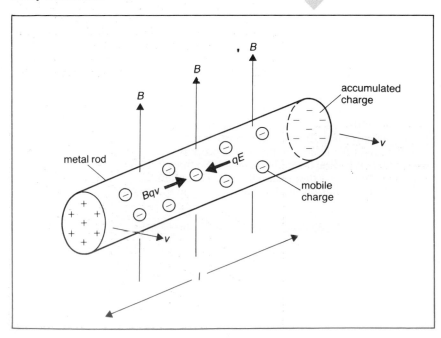

Moving conductors

Consider the situation shown in figure 24.2. A conducting bar of length l is moved at a constant speed v at right angles to a uniform magnetic field of strength B. Each of the charge carriers in the bar will be subjected to a force F_B due to their movement through the field.

$$F_B = Bqv \qquad (24.1$$

So there will be a current along the length of the bar. Charge will drift from one end to the other, setting up an electric field E in it. This field will, in turn, exert a force F_E on all of the charge carriers.

$$F_E = qE \qquad (24.2$$

These two forces act in opposite directions, so positive and negative charges accumulate at either end of the bar until the forces cancel each other out. Thereafter the current in the bar ceases, with a p.d. V across it.

$$F_E = qE, \quad F_B = Bqv \quad \therefore E = BV$$
$$E = \frac{V}{d} \quad \therefore \frac{V}{l} = Bv \quad \therefore V = Blv \qquad (24.3$$

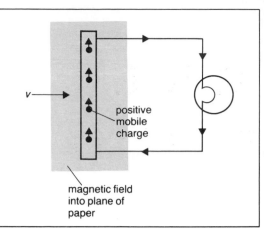

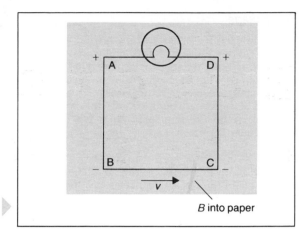

Figure 24.3   Motion of a conductor through a magnetic field can create a current

Figure 24.4   There is no current in a circuit swept through a uniform magnetic field

(The mechanism which sets up this p.d. across the bar is similar to that responsible for the Hall effect.) So the bar looks a bit like a cell whose p.d. is a function of its motion. The p.d. is **induced** in the bar by its movement through the field. If the ends of the bar are connected by another conducting path outside the magnetic field, there will be a current in it. This is shown in figure 24.3. You can use Fleming's Left-Hand Rule to predict which way the charge in the bar is pushed when it is moved through the field. This information can then be used to work out which end of the bar becomes positively charged and hence which way the current goes through the circuit.

$V = Blv$

V is the p.d. induced across the ends of the bar (V)

B is the magnetic field (T)

l is the length of the bar (m)

v is the velocity of the bar (m s^{-1})

Flux

The formula $V = Blv$ can be used to work out the p.d. across a conductor when it is moved through a magnetic field. However, in order to predict how much current will flow as a consequence you have to consider the whole circuit. This will become clear if you consider the thought experiment shown in figure 24.4. A square loop of conductor is pulled through a uniform magnetic field: there is a light bulb in one arm of the loop to indicate any current in it. Two sides of the loop (AB and CD)

will have a p.d. induced in them by their motion. However, the p.d. across the bulb will be zero, so there will be no current in it. If the bulb is to glow, AB and CD must be swept through different strength magnetic fields. For example, if one of the arms is in a region of zero magnetic field (figure 24.5), the bulb will glow when the loop is moved.

In both figures 24.4 and 24.5, the magnetic field could be represented by field lines. For there to be a current in the bulb, it looks as though the total number of field lines going through the loop has to change. Faraday's own model of electromagnetic induction assumes that field lines actually exist as invisible strings and that it is the breaking of these strings by conductors which induces a p.d. across them. The number of field lines threading a flat loop is known as the **flux**, and is defined as follows (refer to figure 24.6).

$\Phi = BA\cos\theta$

Φ is the flux threading the circuit (Wb)

B is the field strength around the circuit (T)

A is the area enclosed by the loop (m^2)

θ is the angle between the normal and the field.

Strictly speaking, the unit of flux ought to be T m^2, but it is such a useful concept that it has its own unit, the weber (Wb). In fact, the flux Φ of a circuit is often more useful than the field strength B. You will therefore come across references to B as the **flux density** of a magnetic field, measured in units of Wb m^{-2}.

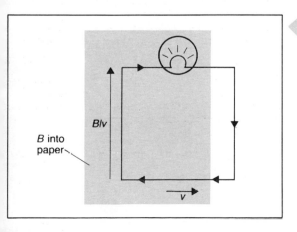

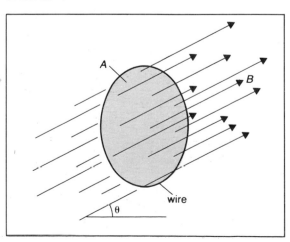

Figure 24.5   As the circuit leaves the region of uniform field there is a current in it

Figure 24.6   The flux of the wire is $BA\cos\theta$

Flux linkage

We are now going to deduce how the p.d. induced in a circuit depends on its flux change with the help of the thought experiment illustrated in figure 24.7. Suppose that the bar is rolled along the frame at a constant velocity v. If the bar is moving through a region of uniform magnetic field, then we can write down the following expression for the p.d. across its ends.

$$V = Blv \qquad (24.4)$$

As the bar moves, the flux of the circuit changes. The area A of the circuit decreases steadily at a rate fixed by the velocity and length of the bar.

$$\Delta A = lv\Delta t \qquad (24.5)$$

If we combine equations (24.4) and (24.5) to eliminate lv, we get an interesting expression for V.

$$V = Blv, \quad \Delta A = lv\Delta t \qquad \therefore lv = \frac{V}{B} = \frac{\Delta A}{\Delta t}$$

$$\therefore V = \frac{B\Delta A}{\Delta t}$$

$$\therefore V = \frac{\Delta(BA)}{\Delta t} = \frac{\Delta\Phi}{\Delta t} \qquad (24.6)$$

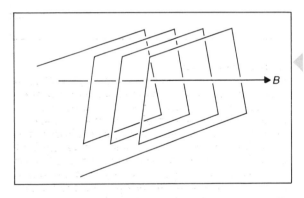

Equation (24.6) says that the p.d. across the bar is the rate at which the flux of the circuit is changing. Since the rest of the frame is not moving through the field, this p.d. is the only one in the circuit and will therefore be registered by the voltmeter. If we assume that it is the change of flux, rather than just area, which is important, then we can use equation (24.6) to work out the p.d. across a coil which has n turns of wire (figure 24.8). The p.d. across each turn of wire will be $\Delta\Phi/\Delta t$, so the p.d. across the whole coil will be n times larger.

$$V = n\frac{d\Phi}{dt}$$

V is the p.d. induced across the ends of a coil (V)

n is the number of turns of wire in the coil

Φ is the flux through each turn of wire (Wb)

The quantity $n\Phi$ is called the **flux linkage** of the coil. So the above formula suggests that the p.d. induced in a coil is simply the rate at which its flux linkage is changing.

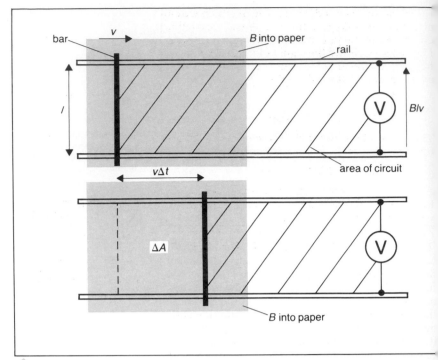

Figure 24.7 The p.d. across the rails is equal to the rate at which the circuit's flux is changing

Figure 24.8 The flux linkage of a coil is the sum of the flux of each turn of wire

Figure 24.9 Investigating the p.d. across a search coil when it is swept between the poles of a permanent horseshoe magnet

Search coils

The apparatus shown in figure 24.9 can be used to verify some of the predictions made above. It consists of a permanent magnet, a data logger and a **search coil**. The last is a small circular coil of copper wire on a non-magnetic frame and handle which can be passed between the poles of the magnet. The graph of figure 24.9 shows a typical signal recorded by the data logger when the search coil is swept between the poles of the magnet at a constant speed. Notice how the signal is positive as the coil approaches the magnet and is negative when it is going away from it, mirroring the sign of dBdt. The area under the positive or negative portion of the graph can be used to measure the field strength of the magnet.

$$V = n\frac{d\Phi}{dt} \quad \therefore Vdt = nd\Phi$$

$$\therefore \Sigma Vdt = n\Sigma d\Phi \qquad (24.7$$

The total flux change $\Delta\Phi$ will be BA, where B is the field strength at the centre of the magnet pole pieces and A is the area of the search coil.

$$\Sigma Vdt = nBA \quad \therefore B = \frac{\Sigma Vdt}{nA} \qquad (24.8$$

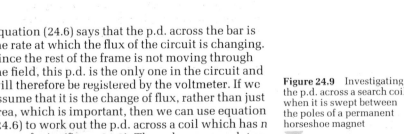

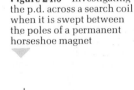

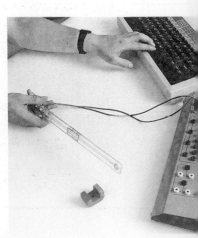

However, this is not the only way in which we can alter the flux linkage of the coil. We can leave the coil between the pole pieces and rotate it instead. Figure 24.10 shows the signal picked up by the logger when the coil is rotated by 180° around an axis perpendicular to the field.

$$\Phi = BA\cos\theta$$

$$\therefore \Delta\Phi = BA\cos(0) - BA\cos(\pi) = 2BA \qquad \textbf{(24.9)}$$

The area under the graph is therefore given by the following expression (see equation (24.7)):

$$\Sigma V dt = n\Delta\Phi \quad \therefore \Sigma V dt = 2nBA \qquad \textbf{(24.10)}$$

Another way of altering the flux linkage of a coil is to alter the number of turns. Suppose that a coil is wound around a bar magnet, as shown in figure 24.11. As the coil is wound, a p.d. is induced in it. The size of that p.d. can be predicted as follows.

$$V = \frac{d}{dt}(n\Phi), \quad \Phi = BA\cos\theta$$

$$\therefore V = BA\,\frac{dn}{dt} \qquad \textbf{(24.11)}$$

So provided that the turns of wire are added at a steady rate, there should be a steady p.d. across the ends of the coil proportional to the flux in the body of the magnet.

Lenz's law

Electromagnetic induction, like everything else in our universe, should obey energy conservation. This idea can be used to predict which way an induced current will go in a circuit. The rule, called **Lenz's Law**, is very simple and can be applied with ease to the most complicated arrangements for changing flux linkage.

> An induced current flows in such a direction as to oppose the change of flux which caused the current to flow in the first place

Before we show you how to apply this rule to useful electromagnetic machines, we shall take you through a thought experiment to convince you of its truth.

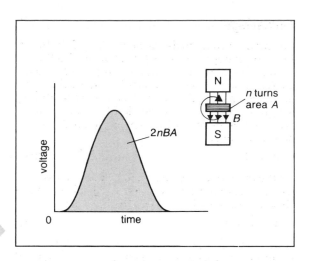

Figure 24.10 The p.d. induced in a search coil when it is rotated through 180° in a uniform field

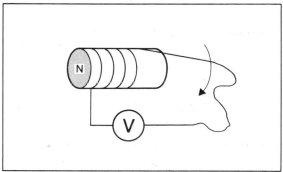

Figure 24.11 Changing the flux linkage of a circuit by wrapping a coil around a magnet

Conserving energy

Of course, you can always use Fleming's Left-Hand Rule to work out the sign of the p.d. induced in a straight conductor when it is swept through a magnetic field. For example, look at figure 24.12. Positive charge carriers will be pushed from left to right along the bar as it is pushed through the field: check for yourself. The resulting current in the bar reacts with the magnetic field (figure 24.13) to give a force F which points in the opposite direction to the velocity v of the bar. So if the bar is set rolling along the frame by a brief push, the induced current will slow the bar down, opposing the mechanism which is changing the flux of the circuit.

Figure 24.12 The current induced in a circuit depends on its resistance

Figure 24.13 The current in the moving bar interacts with the field

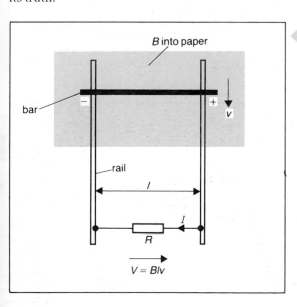

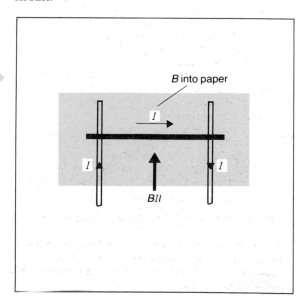

Suppose for a moment that the induced current interacted with the field to give a force which was in the *same* direction as the velocity of the bar. The bar would then accelerate. The increased velocity would, of course, induce a larger p.d. in the bar, increasing the induced current. In turn, this would increase the force accelerating the bar. Clearly, this positive feedback mechanism would make the velocity of the bar increase exponentially without the use of an external energy source. The kinetic energy of the bar would grow, presumably at the expense of the energy in the magnetic field. However, experiments show that the strength of a magnetic field does not appear to change if it is used to induce currents in conductors moved through it. So the device illustrated in figure 24.14 could use a magnetic field to continuously generate light. The axle rolls along the tracks in the magnetic field and the induced p.d. maintains a current in the bulb. Once the axle has been set rolling, it will be accelerated by the interaction of the induced current with the field. Eventually, the induced p.d. should be large enough to light the bulb. Of course, this is a **perpetual motion machine**, a device which defies the Principle of Energy Conservation!

Lenz's Law is obtained by applying the constraints of energy conservation to induced currents. The current in a circuit is a consequence of a change in its flux linkage. If that current results in the conversion of electrical energy, then work has to be done on the system to inject energy into it. So the current interacts with the field in such a way that energy *has* to be put into the system to maintain the flux change.

ENERGY CONVERSIONS

It is instructive to consider the energy conversions which take place when the bar of figure 24.12 is swept through the field. Notice that the size of the force needed to keep the bar moving at a constant speed through the field is a function of the current in the circuit.

$$F = BIl \qquad (1)$$

In turn, the current depends on both the induced p.d. and the resistance R of the circuit.

$$R = \frac{V}{I}, \qquad V = \frac{d\Phi}{dt} = Blv \qquad \therefore I = \frac{Blv}{R} \qquad (2)$$

If all of the resistance is in the resistor, we can calculate the rate at which heat energy appears in it.

$$P = VI \qquad \therefore P_{out} = Blv \times \frac{Blv}{R} = \frac{B^2l^2v^2}{R} \qquad (3)$$

Let us compare this with the power required to keep the bar moving at a constant speed. The force needed is given by equation (1).

$$P = Fv \qquad \therefore P_{in} = BIlv \qquad (4)$$

If we eliminate I from equation (4) with the help of equation (2) we get the following interesting expression:

$$P_{in} = BIlv, \quad I = \frac{Blv}{R} \qquad \therefore P_{in} = \frac{B^2l^2v^2}{R} \qquad (5)$$

If you compare equations (5) and (3) it is obvious that all of the work done moving the bar through the field is converted into heat energy by the resistor. Although the magnetic field is a necessary intermediary in this energy conversion process, its own energy is not affected.

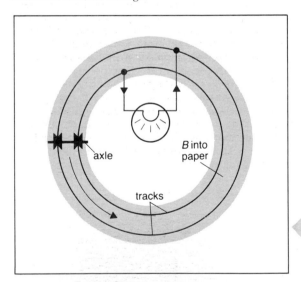

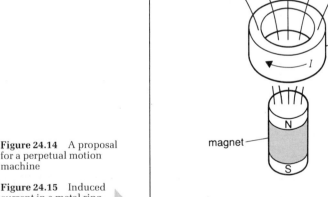

Figure 24.14 A proposal for a perpetual motion machine

Figure 24.15 Induced current in a metal ring dropped onto a magnet

Figure 24.16 The field created by the induced current opposes that of the magnet

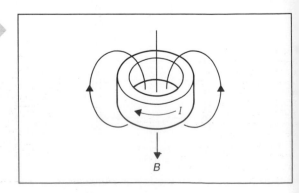

Lenz's Law in action

Suppose that an aluminium ring is dropped on top of a bar magnet as shown in figure 24.15. Which way will the induced current flow round the ring? As it drops, the ring is moving towards a region of greater field strength, so the flux is increasing. Lenz's Law states that the induced current will oppose that increase of flux. Of course, the induced current will create its own magnetic field at the centre of the ring (figure 24.16). If that field opposes the field from the magnet, then the current will be effectively opposing the change of flux. (Use the Right-Hand Grip Rule to convince yourself that the induced current flows as shown in figure 24.16.)

Figure 24.17 A sample of superconductor suspended above a magnet by eddy currents

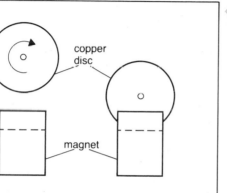

copper disc

magnet

Figure 24.18 Using eddy currents to slow down the rotation of a conducting disc

Figure 24.19 The eddy currents occur where the disc enters and leaves the magnetic field region

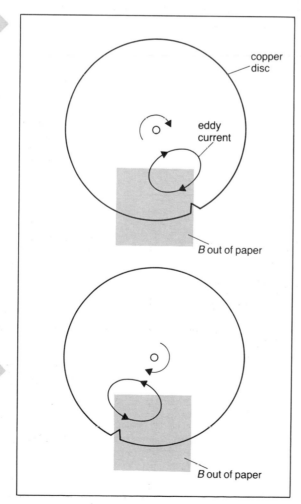

copper disc

eddy current

B out of paper

B out of paper

Figure 24.20 A decelerometer. The shiny aluminium plate is a pendulum which rotates when the whole device is accelerated in the horizontal plane. The aluminium passes between the poles of a strong permanent magnet; eddy currents in the aluminium damp any oscillations of the pendulum

The induced current cannot completely compensate for the change in flux because the ring will have some resistance which will allow the conversion of electrical energy. So the ring has to keep falling in order that gravitational energy can be converted to heat energy by the current in the ring. However, if the ring is made of a super-conducting material with no resistance at all, it will end up suspended in the magnetic field above the magnet (figure 24.17). The initial increase of flux sets up a current in the superconductor. That current interacts with horizontal components of the field to provide an upwards force. No further change of flux is needed to maintain the current, so the superconductor quickly stops falling.

Eddy currents

Figure 24.18 illustrates another example of Lenz's Law in action. A copper disc is set spinning on its axis and lowered into the field between the poles of a permanent magnet. As soon as the disc enters the field it slows down dramatically. Lenz's Law requires that induced currents flow in the disc to try and maintain a constant flux through each portion of it. Consider a single chunk of copper entering the field and leaving it again as shown in figure 24.19. As the chunk enters the magnet, the flux increases and a clockwise current flows in an attempt to get the flux back down to zero. Similarly, as the chunk leaves the magnet a little while later, an anticlockwise current flows in an attempt to keep the flux large. Each of those **eddy currents** interacts with the field to give a braking force on the disc. The size of that force depends on the resistance that the eddy currents experience as they flow in the disc. (The induced p.d. only depends on the rate of flux change, but the current depends on both the p.d. and the resistance.) So a thick disc will experience a larger braking force than a thin one.

Eddy currents are widely used to damp oscillating systems without friction. For example, the accelerometer shown in figure 24.20 uses a magnet to damp the swing of a pendulum when the device is accelerated. (In fact, the device shown is a decelerometer, used for testing the brakes of lorries.)

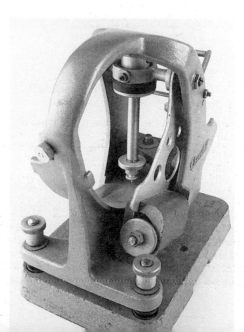

RELAY COILS

An example of the lengths to which an induced current will go to maintain a constant flux in a circuit is illustrated in figure 24.21. A **relay** is an electrical switch controlled by an electromagnet. Each time that there is enough current in the **coil**, the soft iron **armature** is attracted towards the soft iron **core**, rearranging the **contacts**. Relays are widely used to allow small currents from electronic circuits to control much larger currents and voltages. For example, the circuit shown in figure 24.21 has a relay controlling the current in a 60 W motor; a current of only 70 mA in the coil is sufficient to switch the motor on. The **safety diode** has been included in the circuit to protect the driver integrated circuit from destroying itself when it attempts to return the coil current from 70 mA to zero. Suppose that V_{coil} is initially +5 V and that the driver suddenly lowers I_{coil} from 70 mA to 0 mA by lowering V_{out} to 0 V. Lenz's Law requires the coil to try and maintain a constant flux in the core. It can only do this by trying to keep a constant current in the coil. So a **back e.m.f.** appears across the coil, taking V_{coil} below 0 V in an attempt to drag current out of the driver's output. Once V_{coil} gets to −0.7 V there can be a large current in the diode and the back e.m.f. stops falling. However, in the absence of the diode the back e.m.f. would take V_{coil} to a high negative value, probably destroying the driver.

Figure 24.21 Using a relay to interface an electronic circuit to an electric motor

OBJECTIVES

After studying this section you should be able to do the following.

Use the formula $V = Blv$ to predict the p.d. induced in a bar moving through a magnetic field.

Use Fleming's Left-Hand Rule to calculate the sign of the p.d. induced in a bar.

Calculate the flux linkage of a coil of wire.

State that the p.d. induced in a coil is equal to its rate of flux linkage change.

Describe the use of a search coil to measure the strength of a magnetic field.

State Lenz's Law and use it to predict the direction of an induced current.

Explain the braking effect of eddy currents when conducting sheets enter and leave magnetic fields.

QUESTIONS

1 A search coil with 500 turns of average diameter 10 mm is inserted into the region between the poles of a permanent magnet, as shown in figure 24.22. The graph shows how the p.d. across the coil changes with time.

a Explain the shape of the curve. What is the significance of its area?

b Use the graph to estimate the field strength between the pole pieces of the magnet.

c State and explain the sign (if any) of the p.d. across the coil when it is

   i withdrawn from the magnet without any rotation,
   ii rotated through 180° but left between the pole pieces,
   iii rotated through 90° and then withdrawn.

d John notices that the maximum and minimum diameters of the search coil are 12.0 mm and 8.0 mm. He worries about using the average diameter in his answer to part (b). Why? Can you suggest a better way of using the two bits of data?

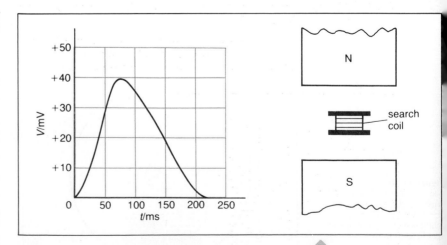

2 A permanent bar magnet is released from rest a short distance above a flat coil of wire, as shown in figure 24.23. It falls freely under the influence of gravity, remaining vertically aligned as it accelerates.

Figure 24.22

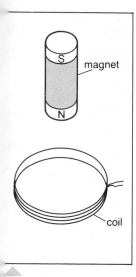

Figure 24.23

Figure 24.24

a Sketch a graph to show how the p.d. induced in the coil changes with time after the magnet has been released. There is no need to put any numbers on the axes. Explain the shape of the graph.

b Describe and explain how your graph would have been different if

   i the magnet had been dropped from a greater height,
   ii the diameter of the coil had been doubled,
   iii the number of turns in the coil had been doubled,
   iv two magnets in line (opposite poles together) had been used,
   v two magnets side-by-side (opposite poles together) had been used.

3 When conductors move through the Earth's magnetic field there is a p.d. induced in them. In each of the examples quoted below, you can assume that the vertical component of the Earth's field is 4.5×10^{-5} T.

a Estimate the p.d. induced between the wing tips of a jumbo jet at cruising speed. Explain why it would be virtually impossible to measure the p.d. in practice.

b Michael Faraday is reputed to have attempted to measure the p.d. induced across the Thames as it flows under Westminster bridge. Estimate the size of the p.d.

c Someone has suggested that British Rail could make use of the p.d. induced in the axles of its trains, tapping off useful current from the rails. Although the p.d. might be small, the current could be quite large because of the low resistances. Is the suggestion sensible?

4 The jumping ring experiment illustrated in figure 24.24 is a classic demonstration of eddy currents and Lenz's Law. When a large alternating current is switched on in the coil, the aluminium ring is pushed up the iron rod and stays halfway up it until the current is switched off again.

a Suppose that the field in the rod grows from zero to a maximum value pointing upwards. Produce a sketch to show the direction of the current induced in the ring.

b Produce another sketch to show the direction of the current in the ring when the field direction changes from upwards to downwards.

c The experiment only works if the rod is iron. It works even better if a bunch of thin iron rods is used instead. Explain why.

d Use Lenz's Law to explain why the ring rises up the rod when the alternating current is switched on: a drawing of the field lines around the coil may help.

e If you increase the thickness of the ring, the induced current should increase. But this also increases the weight of the ring. Will a thin ring rise higher than a thick one?

f By accident, a teacher uses direct current instead of alternating current. Describe and explain what the ring will do when the current is switched on and switched off again.

5 The apparatus shown in figure 24.25 is used to demonstrate the back e.m.f. across a coil when the current in it is suddenly interrupted. The coil has 200 turns of wire wound evenly around a soft iron core of length 10 cm and diameter 4.0 cm. A 6.0 V battery can be connected to the coil via a push switch.

a If $\mu = 500$ for soft iron, estimate the field strength inside the coil when it has a current of 0.5 A in it.

b Calculate the change of flux linkage of the coil when its current drops to zero.

c Suppose that the current in the coil drops steadily from 0.5 A to 0.0 A in 100 μs when the switch is opened. Draw a graph to show how the p.d. across the coil changes with time as the switch is opened — ignore the neon bulb.

d The neon bulb needs 250 V across it before it will glow. What does the neon bulb do when the switch is closed? What happens when the switch is opened?

6 Eddy currents can be used as emergency brakes for vehicles. A disc is attached to the axle and passes between the poles of an electromagnet. When a current is switched on in the electromagnet, eddy currents in the disc slow the vehicle down.

a This type of brake will not bring the vehicle to a halt. Explain why.

b Sketch a design for the electromagnet which will give efficient braking. Does the disc need to be thick or thin? What about its diameter? Suggest a suitable material for the disc.

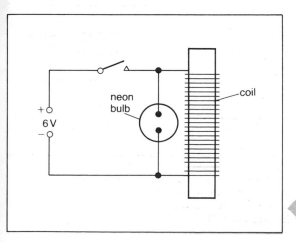

Figure 24.25

Figure 24.26

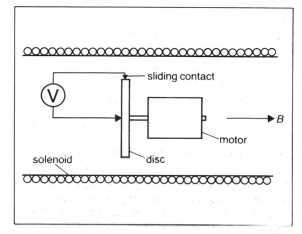

7 The arrangement illustrated in figure 24.26 is used by a student in an attempt to calibrate a voltmeter. An aluminium disc of radius 50 mm is spun round ten times per second by a small electric motor at the centre of a long solenoid.

a If the solenoid has a length of 1.2 m with 2000 turns of wire, calculate the field at the disc when the current in the coil is 5.0 A.

b Consider a disc radius. Calculate the area it sweeps out in 1.0 s. Hence calculate the p.d. between the perimeter and centre of the disc.

c If the disc rotates clockwise when viewed *along* the field direction, is the rim at a higher or lower potential than the axle?

ELECTROMAGNETIC MACHINES

This section is going to introduce you to the physics of electric generators and motors. Real electromagnetic machines are generally very complicated, usually engineered to obtain the maximum efficiency at the expense of simplicity. A full explanation of this very important branch of technology is beyond the scope of this book, so we shall concentrate on the physical principles which constrain the design of useful motors and generators.

Generators

The simplest form of **generator** is illustrated in figure 24.27. It consists of a coil of wire rotated about an axis which is at right angles to a uniform magnetic field. As the coil rotates, its flux linkage is continuously changing, inducing a p.d. across its ends. That p.d. can be transmitted to the outside world via a pair of **slip rings** and **brushes**, two sliding contacts on the shaft which rotates the coil. The current in the coil depends on the circuit connected to the brushes, but it will always flow in such a way that a continuous input of rotational energy is required to generate electrical energy (Lenz's Law).

Alternating voltage

Let us derive an expression for the p.d. induced across the slip rings when the coil is spun at a frequency f. It will help you to understand the important factors in the design of a useful generator. Suppose that the coil has an area A and n turns of wire. The flux linkage at a particular instant is then as follows (consult figure 24.28):

$$\text{flux linkage} - n\Phi = nBA\cos\theta \qquad \textbf{(24.12)}$$

If we adopt the convention that $\theta = 0$ when $t = 0$, then $\theta = \omega t$, where ω is the angular velocity of the coil. Since the coil rotates through 2π radians in every revolution, $\omega = 2\pi f$. Now that we have an expression for the flux linkage we can find out the rate at which it is changing.

$$n\Phi = nBA\cos(\omega t), \qquad V = \frac{\mathrm{d}}{\mathrm{d}t}(n\Phi)$$

$$\therefore V = nBA \times \frac{\mathrm{d}}{\mathrm{d}t}(\cos(\omega t)) \qquad \textbf{(24.13)}$$

The top graph of figure 24.29 shows how the function $\cos(\omega t)$ varies with time. The bottom graph shows how its slope (its rate of change) changes. The peak values for the slope can be estimated by considering the time taken for $\cos(\omega t)$ to get from 1 to 0, i.e. one quarter of a cycle.

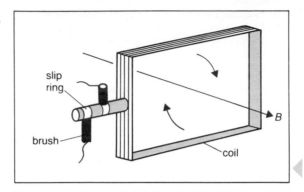

Figure 24.27   A simple generator

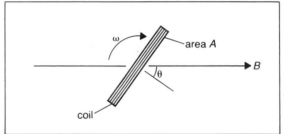

Figure 24.28   The flux linkage changes as the coil rotates

Figure 24.29

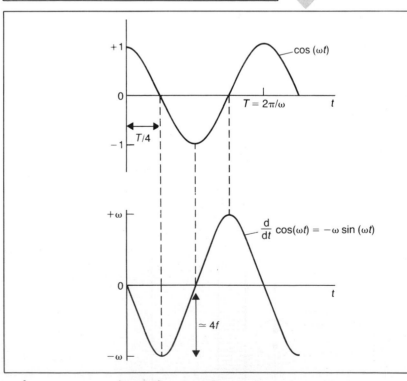

$$\frac{\mathrm{d}}{\mathrm{d}t}(\cos(\omega t))_{\max} \simeq \frac{\Delta\cos(\omega t)}{\Delta t} = \frac{1 - 0}{0.25T}$$

$$f = \frac{1}{T} \qquad \therefore \frac{\mathrm{d}}{\mathrm{d}t}(\cos(\omega t))_{\max} \simeq 4f \qquad \textbf{(24.14)}$$

LARGE GENERATORS

Real generators have their coils wound on a soft iron core to take advantage of the increased field strength that results from placing iron in a magnetic field. As you can see from figure 24.30, the **rotor** has to fit snugly inside the **stator**, with only a small air gap for the flux to get from one to the other. This distorts the shape of the field in which the coil is spinning so that the p.d. is only approximately given by equation (24.16). However, the peak voltage can be many hundreds of times larger than it would have been without the iron core. Of course, the iron will saturate when the field strength gets to about 1.5 T.

Iron is a good conductor of electricity so there will be eddy currents in the rotor as it spins round (figure 24.31). These are obviously a bad thing, diverting rotational energy into heat energy rather than electrical energy. So rotors are constructed from thin layers of iron (**laminations**) with a layer of insulation (usually varnish) between them (figure 24.32). This makes little difference to the flux of the coil but enormously increases the resistance of the path followed by the eddy currents.

Figure 24.31 Eddy currents are induced in the rotor as it spins in the field from the stator

Figure 24.32 This rotor has been made from thin sheets of iron to suppress eddy currents

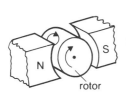

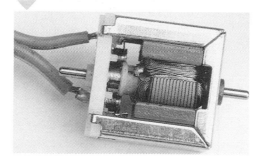

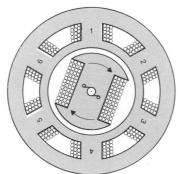

Very large generators used in electricity power stations rotate an electromagnet inside a number of stationary coils as shown in figure 24.33. The relatively small current needed to magnetise the rotor is fed in via a pair of slip rings and the much larger current and induced p.d. is then taken directly from the coils wound on the stator. Three different sets of coils are used to generate voltages which are 120° out of phase with each other. Only four cables are needed to carry the electrical energy away from the generator. Provided that each of the **phases** supplies approximately the same current, the current in the common return line will be relatively small. This allows the return line to be considerably thinner than the other three, with a consequent saving in cost.

Figure 24.33 A three-phase generator

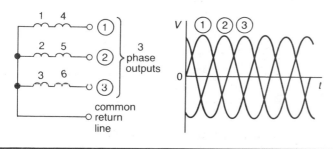

Given the shape of the bottom graph of figure 24.29, it seems reasonable to choose the following approximate expression for the rate of change of flux linkage.

$$\frac{d}{dt}(\cos(\omega t)) \simeq -4f\sin(\omega t)$$

$$\therefore V \simeq nBA \times (-4f\sin(\omega t))$$

$$\therefore V \simeq -4fnBA\sin(\omega t) \qquad (24.15)$$

In fact, calculus can be used to show that the factor of 4 in this approximate expression should be replaced by 2π.

$$\frac{d}{dt}(\cos(\omega t)) = -\omega\sin(\omega t)$$

$$\therefore V = -\omega nBA\sin(\omega t) \qquad (24.16)$$

Equation (24.16) says that to obtain a large induced p.d. the coil must have a large number of turns over a large area, and that it must be spun rapidly in a strong magnetic field. For example, suppose that 100 turns of wire are wound on a square former of side 15 mm and spun in a field of 0.5 T at a rate of 50 revolutions per second — this is similar to a bicycle dynamo. We can use equation (24.16) to calculate the **peak voltage** V_0 induced in the coil.

$$V_0 = \omega nBA, \quad \omega = 2\pi \times 50$$

$$A = (15\times10^{-3})^2 = 2.25\times10^{-4}\,\text{m}^2$$

$$\therefore V_0 = 2\pi \times 50 \times 100 \times 0.5 \times 2.25\times10^{-4}$$

$$\therefore V_0 = 3.5\,\text{V}$$

A similar generator, identical in all respects but scaled up by a factor of 10, would have a peak voltage of 350 V. The values of B, n and ω would remain the same but A would be a hundred times larger.

Figure 24.34 A simple electric motor

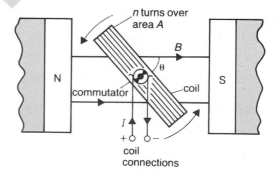

Figure 24.30 Using iron to increase the flux through the coil

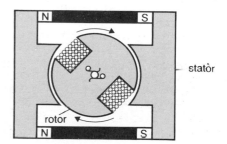

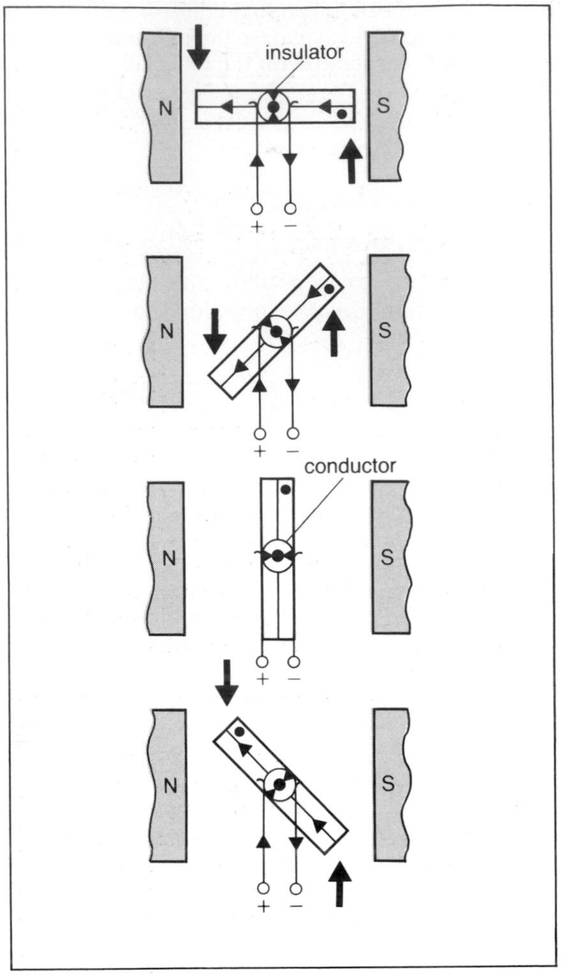

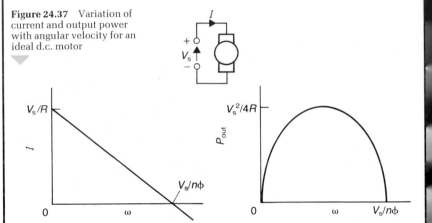

Figure 24.35 The commutator ensures that the couple on the coil acts in the same direction as it spins

Figure 24.36 Using iron to increase the flux through the coil

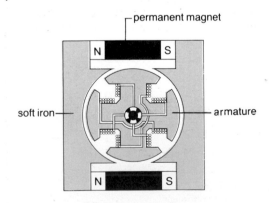

Direct current motors

A direct current (d.c.) electric motor is a device which can convert electrical energy delivered by a continuous p.d. into rotational energy of a shaft. A simple arrangement which can do this is shown in figure 24.34. Current in the coil interacts with the field between the pole pieces of the magnet to produce a continuous anti-clockwise rotation. The couple acting on the coil is given by the following expression.

$$\Gamma = BAnI\cos\theta \qquad (24.17)$$

BACK E.M.F.

The only real difference between the d.c. motor of figure 24.34 and the a.c. generator of figure 24.31 is the commutator. So as the armature spins round, a p.d. is induced in its coils. Since the coils are only connected to the brushes when their planes are parallel to the field, the size of this **back e.m.f.** can be estimated with the help of equation (24.16). (In fact, a d.c. motor makes a respectable generator of continuous current.)

$$V_b \simeq BAn\omega = n\Phi\omega \qquad (1)$$

The graphs of figure 24.37 show how the current and power output of a typical d.c. motor depend on the angular velocity of the shaft. This behaviour is due to the back e.m.f. We can model a real motor connected to a constant p.d. V_s as shown in figure 24.38. The combined resistance of the coils and the internal resistance of the supply is R. If the motor shaft has an angular velocity ω, then we can calculate the current in the circuit.

$$V_s = IR + V_b, \quad V_b = n\Phi\omega \qquad \therefore I = \frac{V_s - n\Phi\omega}{R} \qquad (2)$$

Figure 24.37 Variation of current and output power with angular velocity for an ideal d.c. motor

The power delivered to the armature can also be worked out as follows:

$$P = VI \qquad \therefore P_{out} = V_b I$$

$$\therefore P_{out} = n\Phi\omega \times \frac{(V_s - n\Phi\omega)}{R} \qquad (3)$$

It should be obvious that if $n\Phi\omega$ is less than V_s, then energy will be delivered from the power supply to the armature. If there is no load on the shaft, that energy will increase its angular velocity ω. Eventually $n\Phi\omega$ will become the same as V_s and there will be no further change in ω. In other words, the maximum angular velocity of the motor shaft is given by the following expression.

$$V_s = n\Phi\omega_{max} \qquad \therefore \omega_{max} = \frac{V_s}{n\Phi} \qquad (4)$$

At that maximum speed, the current in the motor will be zero. In practice, some energy will have to be delivered to the shaft to offset the effects of friction, so the current will simply drop to a value which is small compared with V_s/R.

Figure 24.38 The back e.m.f. across the motor affects the current in it

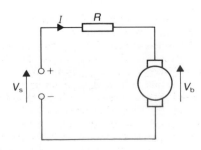

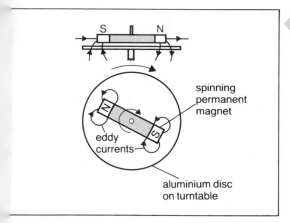

spinning permanent magnet

eddy currents

aluminium disc on turntable

Figure 24.39 Using eddy currents to apply a couple to a metal disc

Figure 24.40 The copper sheet appears to be dragged along by the motion of the field from left to right

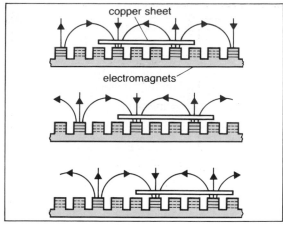

copper sheet

electromagnets

arrangement gives a field pattern which appears to move from left to right along the electromagnets. Any conducting sheet placed in that field will be accelerated to the right until it is moving along with the field. (In practice, the sheet will lag behind the field because of friction.) Furthermore, the eddy currents will also levitate the sheet, holding it out of contact with the electromagnet poles.

As the coil spins under the influence of this couple, the **commutator** ensures that the direction of the current in the coil is reversed after every half a revolution. (This should become clear if you study the sequence of figure 24.35.) However, even though the couple will always act on the coil in the same direction, its size will fall to zero twice in every revolution. A smoother couple can be obtained by using multiple coils, as shown in figure 24.36. The commutator delivers current to each coil in turn when its plane is roughly parallel to the field direction. The result is a more or less steady couple given by the following expression.

$$\Gamma \simeq BAnI = n\Phi I \qquad (24.18)$$

n is, of course, the number of turns in just one of the many coils wound on the **armature**. (As you can see from figure 24.36, each coil is often wound onto the armature in two halves, each at opposite ends of a diameter — this gives room for the shaft at the centre.) The armature itself is constructed of laminated soft iron to maximise the flux and minimise the energy loss by eddy currents.

Induction motors

If you place a conducting sheet in a moving magnetic field, Lenz's Law implies that it will try to move along with the field. If the conductor is able to move along with the same velocity as the field, then it will have managed to minimise the change of flux linkage. This can be verified in the laboratory with the apparatus shown in figure 24.39. As the magnet is spun round next to the aluminium disc, there is a flux change in each portion of the disc as the magnet passes. The eddy currents in the disc interact with the magnetic field, providing a couple which pushes the disc round in the same direction as the magnet.

Linear motors

Induction motors use this principle to convert electrical energy into kinetic energy. A number of electromagnets are fed alternating current in such a way that the magnetic field behaves somewhat like that of a moving bar magnet. Any conducting material placed in that field will experience a force tugging it along the direction in which the field is moving. For example, a simple **linear motor** is shown in figure 24.40. The electromagnets are wired in three groups, each of which is fed current from a different phase of a three-phase supply. As you can see in the sequence of figure 24.40, the

ROTARY MOTORS

Most domestic and industrial induction motors convert electrical energy into rotational energy. The stator generates a rotating magnetic field which passes through a conducting rotor; in order to minimise the flux change through the rotor it spins round with the field. A three-phase induction motor is illustrated in figure 24.41. If a 50 Hz current is used, then the rotor will have a maximum speed of 50 revolutions per second. Note the copper bars inserted in the laminated iron core — the copper carries the induced currents which push the rotor round and the iron ensures a large magnetic field.

Small induction motors have to run off a single-phase alternating voltage. The magnetic field from an electromagnet carrying an alternating current does not appear to move, so would not seem to be suitable for making an induction motor. However, if part of the field is used to induce a large current in a static conductor, the result is a field which does appear to move. This **pole shading** technique is illustrated in figure 24.42. The field due to the eddy currents in the static conductor is 90° out of phase with the field from the pole pieces, so the conducting disc sees a field which appears to move across the electromagnet pole pieces.

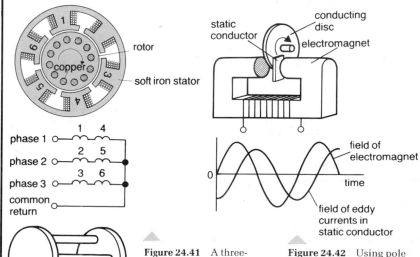

rotor

copper

soft iron stator

phase 1
phase 2
phase 3
common return

static conductor

conducting disc

electromagnet

field of electromagnet

time

field of eddy currents in static conductor

conductors in rotor

Figure 24.41 A three-phase induction motor. The copper bars of the rotor are surrounded by laminated iron

Figure 24.42 Using pole shading to make a simple single-phase induction motor

OBJECTIVES

After studying this section you should be able to do the following.

Describe a simple form of alternating voltage generator and explain how it works.	Use the formula $\Gamma = n\Phi I$.
Use the formula $V = n\Phi\omega\sin(\omega t)$.	Explain the back e.m.f. of a motor.
Explain the need for laminated iron cores in generators.	Use $V_b = n\Phi\omega$ to explain the characteristics of d.c. motors.
Describe a simple form of direct current motor.	Describe and explain the operation of induction motors.

QUESTIONS

[1] A small electric motor has a coil resistance of 2.0 Ω. When it is connected to a 3.0 V supply, the shaft spins with a maximum frequency of 20 Hz. Neglect friction.

a Estimate the flux linkage of the motor's armature coils.

b What is the current in the motor when its shaft is stopped from moving?

c Draw a graph to show how the couple exerted by the motor depends on its frequency of rotation. Put a scale on both axes.

d Draw another graph to show how the power delivered to the motor shaft depends on its frequency of rotation. Use it to estimate the maximum power output of the motor.

e Calculate the efficiency of the motor when it is running at maximum power.

[2] A d.c. motor has a coil resistance R and a flux linkage of $n\Phi$. When the motor is connected to a p.d. V, the shaft has a maximum angular velocity of ω. Neglect friction.

a Suppose that the motor was scaled up by a factor of ten. What would happen to the values of R, $n\Phi$ and ω?

b What would happen to the maximum couple of the motor when it was scaled up by a factor of ten?

c The maximum power output occurs when the angular velocity is $\omega/2$. How does the maximum power change during the scaling up?

[3] Large direct current motors are often made with an electromagnet to supply the magnetic field as shown in figure 24.43. Small motors, like those used in toys and cars, tend to use permanent magnets.

a Suggest why it is not easy to build large motors with permanent magnets.

b The electromagnet (or **field coil**) can be connected in parallel with the armature coil. Describe and explain how the couple exerted by the armature depends on its angular velocity for this connection.

c Explain why the motor described in part (b) can work from an alternating voltage supply as well as a direct voltage supply.

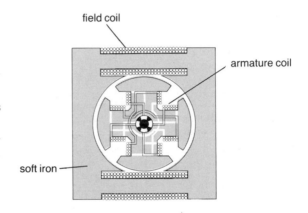

field coil

armature coil

soft iron

Figure 24.43

d An alternative arrangement has the field coil connected in series with the armature coil. The result is a motor whose angular velocity remains roughly constant as more or less energy is extracted from its shaft. Explain why.

[4] A small d.c. motor draws a current of 800 mA from a 1.5 V battery when its shaft is prevented from moving. When its shaft is let go, it spins at a speed of 75 revolutions per second.

a Use the data to calculate the coil resistance and flux linkage.

b What is the current in the motor coil when it is spinning at 25 revolutions per second?

c Calculate the efficiency of the motor when it is spinning at 25 r.p.s.

[5] A simple generator of the type shown in figure 24.27 has 200 turns of wire wound on a coil former of dimensions 50 mm × 100 mm. The field has a strength of 0.5 T.

a Suppose that the coil is spun at a rate of 25 Hz. Calculate the peak voltage induced across the ends of the coil.

b Draw a graph to show how the p.d. across the ends of the coil changes with time.

c The ends of the coil are connected to a 10 Ω resistor. Calculate the peak current in the resistor.

d Estimate the mean power now needed to keep the generator spinning at a constant speed.

] The maximum power output of a commercial generator can be estimated from its dimensions. This question will help you to understand why.

A generator contains n turns of wire on a former of area A. It is spun at frequency f in a magnetic field of strength B. Write down an expression for the peak voltage across the coil. What happens to the peak voltage if every dimension of the generator is doubled?

The internal resistance r of the generator is the resistance of its n turns of wire. What happens to the value of r if every dimension of the generator is doubled?

c In practice, the circuitry run from the generator has a resistance R which is ten times larger than its internal resistance r. Write down an expression for the peak current drawn from the generator by the circuitry.

d What happens to the peak current supplied by the generator when its dimensions are doubled? (R is still $10 \times r$.)

e What happens to the peak output power of the generator when its dimensions are doubled?

INDUCTORS

Permanent magnets are not the only objects which can induce a p.d. in a circuit by changing its flux linkage. *Any* source of changing magnetic field can be used. This includes not only fields due to currents in other circuits (**mutual inductance**) but also the field due to current in the same circuit (**self inductance**). So if the current in one circuit is changed, a p.d. can appear in another circuit. In particular, if one circuit carries an alternating current there is the possibility of an alternating p.d. being induced in another circuit placed nearby. Thus mutual inductance offers the useful possibility of moving electrical energy from one circuit to another via an alternating magnetic field in the space between them.

Mutual induction

Take a look at figure 24.44. The power supply maintains an alternating current I in the **field coil**, so the flux inside the iron core is continuously changing. The **search coil** wound around the core will therefore have a p.d. V induced in it: that p.d. can be studied with the help of an oscilloscope. If we assume that the relative permeability μ of the iron is constant, then we can easily show how V and I are related.

$$V = n \frac{d\Phi}{dt}, \quad \Phi = BA, \quad B = \mu KI$$

$$\therefore V \propto \frac{dI}{dt} \tag{24.19}$$

(The value of K depends on the geometry of the field coil and what fraction of its flux passes through the search coil.)

> $$V = M \frac{dI}{dt}$$
>
> V is the p.d. induced in the secondary circuit (V)
>
> M is the mutual inductance of the two circuits (H)
>
> I is the current in the primary circuit (A)

The unit of **mutual inductance** is the henry (H). In general, the mutual inductance of a pair of circuits depends on their dimensions, shape and the amount of iron looped between them. So before we show you how to estimate the mutual inductance of some real systems, you need to know more about the behaviour of magnetic fields in loops of iron.

Figure 24.44 Apparatus for demonstrating mutual induction

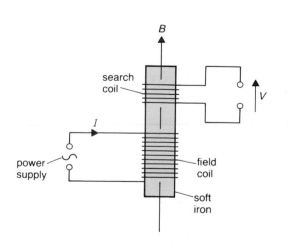

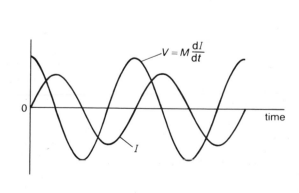

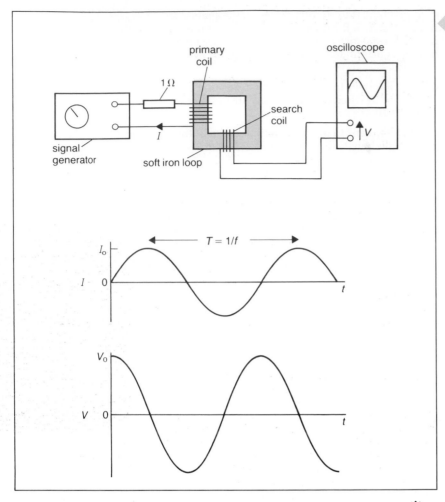

Figure 24.45 Using a
search coil to measure the
flux in a loop of soft iron

Figure 24.46 The flux
inside a soft iron loop is the
same everywhere provided
the field does not get too
large

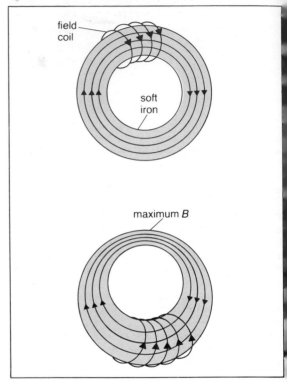

INDUCTION COILS

An **induction coil** is a form of mutual inductor widely used to generate the high voltage sparks needed to ignite the petrol–air mixture in car and motorbike engines. It consists of a pair of coils wound around an iron core, as shown in figure 24.47. When the **contacts** are closed, the 6 V battery maintains a large current in the primary coil. This magnetises the iron core, setting up a large flux inside the secondary coil. As soon as the contacts are opened, this flux rapidly drops to zero, inducing a very large momentary p.d. across the ends of the secondary coil. Of course, Lenz's Law guarantees that as soon as the contacts are opened a large p.d. is also induced across the ends of the primary coil in an attempt to keep the primary current going. Normally this would create a spark across the contacts, reducing the energy available for the spark across the gap of the spark plug. This can be prevented by connecting a capacitor in parallel with the contacts. It allows the current in the primary coil to die down without developing a large p.d. across it.

Figure 24.47 The ignition
system of a motorbike
engine

Flux in iron loops

The apparatus shown in figure 24.45 can be used to measure the field inside an iron loop. An alternating current is fed into the **primary coil**: the peak value I_0 and frequency f of the current can be measured by using the oscilloscope to study the p.d. across the 1 Ω resistor. If the number of turns n of the **search coil** is known, then the peak value voltage V_0 induced in it can be used to estimate the peak flux Φ_0 through it. The flux changes from its maximum value to zero in one quarter of a cycle, i.e. $0.25T$.

$$V = n \frac{d\Phi}{dt} \quad \therefore \ V_0 \simeq \frac{n\Delta\Phi}{\Delta t} = \frac{n\Phi_0}{0.25T}$$

$$f = \frac{1}{T} \quad \therefore \ \Phi_0 \simeq \frac{V_0}{4fn} \qquad \textbf{(24.20)}$$

So the peak flux of the search coil is proportional to the peak voltage of the signal displayed by the oscilloscope.

The first important property of magnetic fields in iron loops can be found by using search coils of different areas. It turns out that the flux of the search coil does not appear to change as its area is changed, so that a coil wound tightly around the iron has the same flux as one which encloses a lot of air as well as the iron. The conclusion is obvious: the magnetic field outside the iron is negligible compared with that inside. This is illustrated in figure 24.46 with the field lines staying inside the iron all the way round the loop.

Secondly, by moving the search coil to different positions, it can be shown that the flux in the iron is the same all the way round the loop. In other words, $\Phi = BA$ remains constant. This means that the field strength B is going to be large at points in the loop where the cross-sectional area A is small. (Of course, there is an upper limit to the value of B, about 1.5 T, at which the iron **saturates**. Once the iron starts to saturate, the flux will no longer be confined to it and there will be a magnetic field in the surrounding air.)

Thirdly, providing that none of the iron saturates, the field strength is given by the ideal solenoid formula.

$$B = \frac{\mu\mu_0 nI}{l} \qquad (24.21)$$

The arrangement of the n turns of wire in the primary coil is not important provided they are all wound in the same sense somewhere along the length l of the loop.

Self induction

If a conductor is wound into a coil, then it will have a flux linkage whenever there is a current in it. So any change of the current will induce a p.d. across the ends of the coil. More precisely, the p.d. will be proportional to the rate of change of flux. The flux itself will be proportional to the current. Therefore the induced p.d. across the ends of *any* conductor will be proportional to the rate at which its current is changing. Devices which are constructed to exploit this effect are called **inductors**. Ideal inductors have no resistance, so the p.d. across them is solely due to the rate at which their current is changing.

$$V = L\frac{dI}{dt}$$

V is the p.d. across the inductor (V)

L is the inductance of the inductor (H)

I is the current in the inductor (A)

Estimating inductance

The arrangement of coils and iron shown in figure 24.48 is often used in school laboratories to demonstrate the properties of inductors. Before we show you how this can be done, it will be useful to estimate the inductance of the arrangement. The coil has 1100 turns of wire wound around one arm of a C-shaped laminated soft iron core. A second identical core is firmly clamped on to make a continuous iron loop of approximate length 0.15 m and cross-sectional area 1.5×10^{-4} m^2. If we assume that μ is 300 for iron, then we can use equation (24.20) to estimate the field strength in the iron when there is a current I in the coil.

$$B = \frac{\mu\mu_0 nI}{l}$$

$$\therefore B = \frac{300 \times 4\pi\times10^{-7} \times 1100 \times I}{0.15}$$

$$\therefore B = 2.7I$$

The next step is to calculate the flux linkage of the coil. Since all of the flux is going to be inside the

iron core, we do not have to worry about the average area of the turns of wire in the coil.

$$n\Phi = BAn$$

$$\therefore n\Phi = 2.7I \times 1.5\times10^{-4} \times 1100 \simeq 0.46I$$

We can now find the inductance of the system by considering the p.d. induced when the current is changed.

$$V = \frac{d}{dt}(n\Phi) \qquad \therefore V = 0.46 \times \frac{dI}{dt}$$

$$V = L\frac{dI}{dt} \qquad \therefore L = 0.46\ H$$

So the inductance is about 0.5 H, provided that the current in the coil is small. A quick glance at figure 23.57 should remind you that the value of μ is a strong function of B, so μ is only going to be 300 for very low field strengths, less than 1×10^{-2} T. Since we have calculated that $B = 2.7I$, this implies that our estimation of 0.5 H will only be remotely true for currents of less than 4 mA! Nevertheless, we can safely assume that the inductance of the system is at least about a henry for currents which do not saturate the iron.

Investigating inductors

The circuit of figure 24.49 can be used to demonstrate the electrical behaviour of a large 6 H inductor. The graph shows how the values of V and I for the inductor change as the switch is opened and closed. The filament lamp and neon bulb are included to give a visual indication of the voltages and currents. Let's go through what happens when the switch is closed and subsequently opened again. (The neon bulb is a discharge tube: there will only be a current in it if the voltage across it exceeds 50 V.)

Figure 24.48 A large inductor

Figure 24.49 Investigating the behaviour of an inductor

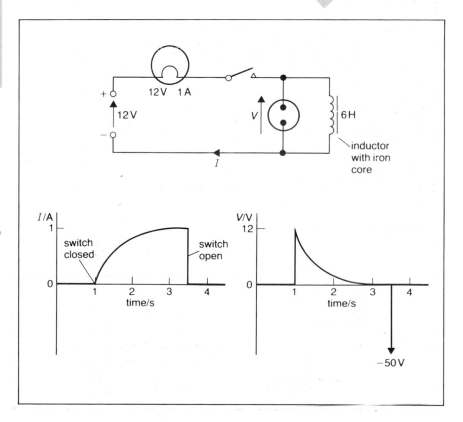

When the switch is closed the p.d. across the inductor quickly shoots up to 12 V, the supply voltage. If we ignore the filament lamp resistance, we can calculate the initial rate at which the current rises.

$$V = L\frac{dI}{dt}, \quad L = 6\,H, \quad V = 12\,V$$

$$\therefore \frac{dI}{dt} = \frac{12}{6} = 2\,A\,s^{-1}$$

Of course, the current cannot continue rising indefinitely. The filament lamp is rated at 12 V, 1 A, placing an upper limit on the current. If the current rises steadily at $2\,A\,s^{-1}$, then it will reach 1 A in 0.5 s, but in practice the rate of change of current will steadily decrease to zero in a few seconds. So when the switch is closed the lamp does not glow immediately, but slowly increases in brightness over a few seconds.

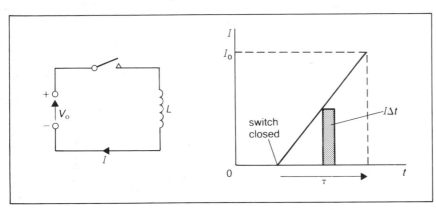

Figure 24.50 How the current in an ideal inductor changes with time when a p.d. is placed across it

Figure 24.51 An RL series circuit

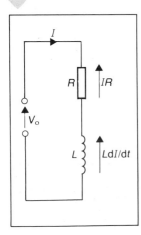

When the switch is subsequently opened, the current drops rapidly to zero. This makes dI/dt a large negative quantity for a brief instant of time, so a large negative p.d. is induced in the coil. This will be clamped to $-50\,V$ by the neon bulb which will emit a short intense flash of light. Suppose that the current dives from 1 A to zero in 5 ms; we can estimate the p.d. across the inductor without the neon bulb as follows:

$$\frac{\Delta I}{\Delta t} = \frac{0-1}{5\times10^{-3}} = -200\,A\,s^{-1}$$

$$V = L\frac{dI}{dt} \quad \therefore V = 5\times(-200) = -1\,kV$$

The energy converted to light in the neon bulb must have been stored in the inductor's magnetic field.

Energy in inductors

We can calculate the magnetic energy stored in an ideal inductor by considering the circuit shown in figure 24.50. When the switch is closed at $t = 0$, the constant p.d. V_0 makes the current I rise steadily from zero to I_0 at time $t = \tau$. Consider a small interval of time Δt and find the energy ΔE delivered to the inductor by the power supply.

$$P = VI, \quad P = \frac{E}{t} \quad \therefore \Delta E = V_0 I \Delta t \qquad \textbf{(24.22)}$$

The total energy delivered to the inductor in time τ is obtained by summing equation (24.22).

$$\Sigma \Delta E = E \qquad \therefore E = \Sigma V_0 I \Delta t$$
$$\therefore E = V_0 \Sigma I \Delta t \qquad \textbf{(24.23)}$$

The current is rising at a steady rate fixed by the values of L and V_0, as shown in the graph of figure 24.50. The quantity $\Sigma I \Delta t$ is just the area under that graph.

$$\Sigma I \Delta t = \tfrac{1}{2}\tau I_0 \qquad \textbf{(24.24)}$$

If we now combine equations (24.23) and (24.24) we obtain an expression for the inductor's energy.

$$E = V_0 \times \tfrac{1}{2}\tau I_0 \qquad \textbf{(24.25)}$$

Finally, we can eliminate τ by considering how the current changes with time.

$$V = L\frac{dI}{dt} \qquad \therefore V_0 = \frac{LI_0}{\tau}$$

$$E = \tfrac{1}{2}V_0 \tau I_0$$

$$\therefore E = \tfrac{1}{2} \times \frac{LI_0}{\tau} \times \tau I_0 \qquad \therefore E = \tfrac{1}{2}LI_0^{\,2} \qquad \textbf{(24.26)}$$

$$E = \tfrac{1}{2}LI^2$$

E is the energy stored in the inductor (J)

L is the inductance of the inductor (H)

I is the current in the inductor (A)

For example, how much energy was dumped into the neon bulb of figure 24.49 when the switch was opened?

$$E = \tfrac{1}{2}LI^2 \quad \therefore E = 0.5 \times 6 \times 1^2 = 3\,J$$

This does not appear to be very much, but consider the short span of time in which it was delivered (5 ms). The average power was 600 W!

Resistor–inductor circuits

Any real inductor is bound to have some resistance R as well as inductance L. So it is important that you are able to accurately predict the behaviour of currents in circuits which contain both resistance and inductance. Although this will involve some calculus, it should present you with no real difficulties as the equations are exactly the same as the ones which cropped up in the work on capacitors (chapter 12).

Approximate solution

Suppose that a resistor R and an inductor L are connected in series with a steady source of p.d. V_0, as shown in figure 24.51. Ultimately we want to write down a piece of algebra which accurately models the current in the circuit at any time. However, it is going to involve a lot of algebra and some calculus, so it will be worthwhile attempting to obtain an approximate model first.

How does the current change with time? Well, it is obviously going to increase from zero to some maximum value. This is roughly modelled in the graph of figure 24.52. When the current is zero we can easily deduce its rate of increase.

$$V = L\frac{dI}{dt} \qquad \therefore \frac{dI}{dt} = \frac{V_0}{L} \qquad \textbf{(24.27)}$$

The maximum current I_0 is fixed by the supply voltage and the resistance R.

$$R = \frac{V}{I} \quad \therefore I_0 = \frac{V_0}{R} \qquad (24.28)$$

Let's assume for the moment that the current rises steadily from zero to I_0 in a time τ. We can then combine equations (24.27) and (24.28) to obtain an expression for τ.

$$\frac{dI}{dt} = \frac{I_0}{\tau}, \quad I_0 = \frac{V_0}{R} \quad \therefore \frac{dI}{dt} = \frac{V_0}{R\tau}$$

$$\frac{dI}{dt} = \frac{V_0}{L} \quad \therefore \frac{V_0}{L} = \frac{V_0}{R\tau}$$

$$\therefore \tau = \frac{L}{R} \qquad (24.29)$$

Notice that the time taken for the current to saturate appears to be independent of the supply voltage V_0. Of course, our answer is only approximate, but it must be dimensionally correct. So we expect the current to change in a time which is proportional to the **time constant** τ.

Exact solution

Look at figure 24.51. At a particular instant of time the p.d. across the inductor is V. Apply Kirchhoff's First Law (see chapter 11) to the circuit to obtain an expression for the current.

$$V_0 = IR + V \quad \therefore I = \frac{V_0 - V}{R} \qquad (24.30)$$

In a short interval of time Δt the current will change from I to $I + \Delta I$, and the p.d. across the inductor will change from V to $V + \Delta V$.

$$I + \Delta I = \frac{V_0 - (V + \Delta V)}{R} \quad \therefore \Delta I = -\frac{\Delta V}{R} \qquad (24.31)$$

Now the change of current can be worked out by considering the p.d. across the inductor.

$$V = L\frac{dI}{dt} \quad \therefore \Delta I = \frac{V}{L}\Delta t \qquad (24.32)$$

If we eliminate ΔI from equations (24.31) and (24.32) we obtain a differential equation which says how the p.d. across the inductor changes with time.

$$\Delta I = \frac{V}{L}\Delta t = -\frac{\Delta V}{R} \quad \therefore \frac{\Delta V}{\Delta t} = -\frac{RV}{L} \qquad (24.33)$$

You have met an equation similar to (24.33) already in connection with the charging and discharging of a capacitor. So rather than set out to solve it all over again, we shall simply quote the solution.

$$V = V_0\exp[-t/\tau] \quad \text{where } \tau = L/R \qquad (24.34)$$

This is shown graphically in figure 24.53: we have assumed that the switch is closed at $t = 0$. The p.d. across the inductor drops exponentially with time, halving every 0.69τ seconds. Our solution can be inserted into equation (24.30) to find out how the current in the circuit changes with time.

$$I = \frac{V_0 - V}{R} \quad \therefore I = \frac{V_0 - V_0\exp[-t/\tau]}{R}$$

$$\therefore I = I_0(1 - \exp[-t/\tau]) \qquad (24.35)$$

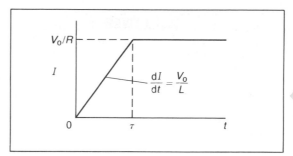

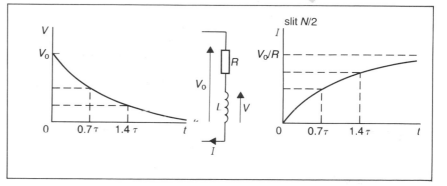

Figure 24.52 Approximate $I-t$ curve for the circuit of figure 24.51

Figure 24.53 Correct $V-t$ and $I-t$ curves for an RL series circuit

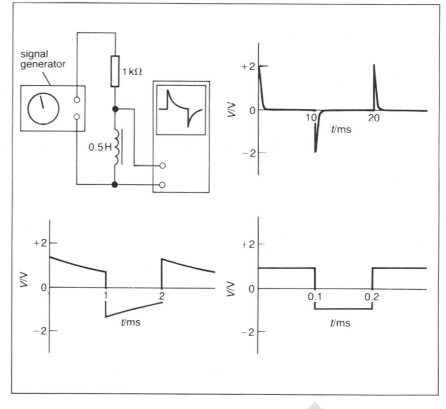

As you can see from figure 24.53, the current rises exponentially from zero to a maximum value fixed by the resistance R and the p.d. V_0 of the power supply.

The apparatus shown in figure 24.54 can be used to verify the truth of equation (24.34). A square wave of amplitude V_0 and frequency f from a signal generator is fed into a resistor in series with an inductor. The oscilloscope displays how the p.d. across the inductor changes with time: a number of traces obtained for different frequencies are shown in figure 24.54. Convince yourself that they are correct.

Figure 24.54 Investigating the waveform across the inductor when a square wave is fed into an RL series circuit

OBJECTIVES

After studying this section you should be able to do the following.

Explain the meaning of *mutual* and *self-induction*.	Estimate the inductance of a coil.
Describe the behaviour of magnetic fields in loops of iron.	Describe and explain the behaviour of the current in a circuit containing an inductor.
Estimate the mutual inductance of two coils.	Calculate the energy stored in an inductor.
Use the formula $V = LdI/dt$.	Obtain and use the formula $I = I_0(1 - \exp[-t/\tau])$.

QUESTIONS

1 An air-cored solenoid commonly found in school laboratories has 190 turns of wire over a length of 0.3 m, each turn having a square cross-section of 50 mm × 50 mm. One of these solenoids has a coil of twenty turns of wire wrapped tightly around its centre to form a mutual inductor.

a Assuming that the solenoid is ideal, obtain an expression for the flux linkage of the coil in terms of the current I in the solenoid. Hence calculate the mutual inductance of the system.

b Suppose that the solenoid was fed an alternating current of amplitude 1.0 A and frequency 1.0 kHz. Sketch a graph to show how the current changes with time. Use your sketch to estimate the maximum value of dI/dt.

c Calculate the amplitude of the alternating voltage across the ends of the coil.

d Describe how you would use an oscilloscope to observe the waveform you drew in part (b).

e State and explain how you would expect the amplitude of the voltage across the coil to change if

   i only the frequency of the current was doubled,
   ii only the coil was moved to the end of the solenoid,
   iii only the number of turns of wire in the solenoid was doubled,
   iv the core of the solenoid was filled with iron.

2 Inductors are commonly used in high frequency circuits as **chokes** — devices which present a high resistance to alternating current.

a Show that the units of self inductance are $V\,s\,A^{-1}$. Hence show that the quantity $\tau = L/R$ has the dimensions of time.

b Suppose that an alternating voltage of frequency f and amplitude V_0 is placed across an inductor L. Sketch a graph to show how the voltage changes with time. Using the same axes, sketch a graph to show how the current in the inductor changes with time.

c Show that the peak current in the coil is approximately equal to $V_0/4f$.

d A resistor R is placed in series with the inductor. Describe and explain what happens to the amplitude of the p.d. across the resistor as the frequency of the alternating voltage is increased from a very low value to a very high value.

3 A 2.0 H inductance is connected in series with a 6.0 Ω resistor, a switch and a 3.0 V supply.

a Calculate the initial rate at which the current changes when the switch is closed.

b What is the value of the current when the switch has been closed for a long time?

c Sketch graphs to show how the p.d. across the inductor and resistor change with time when the switch is closed. Mark values on both axes.

d State and explain how the graphs would be different if

   i the supply voltage had been 6 V,
   ii the resistance had been 3 Ω.

e Explain why a spark appears between the contacts of the switch when it is opened.

4 A teacher demonstrated the properties of inductors with the apparatus shown in figure 24.55. When he switched on the power pack the filament lamp slowly became brighter until it glowed steadily at full brightness. He then took a mallet and used it to knock the iron bar off the iron core, causing the lamp to burn out in spectacular fashion! Explain these observations — the inductor had an inductance of about 10 H and the bulb was rated at 3.5 V, 0.3 A.

5 This question is going to help you find expressions for the energy density of magnetic and electric fields.

a Consider an ideal air-cored solenoid with n turns over a length l, each of which has an area A. Write down an expression for the field at its centre when it carries a current I.

b Assuming the field everywhere inside the solenoid is the same, show that its inductance is given by $L = \mu_0 An^2/l$. Hence show that the energy stored per unit volume (the energy density) inside the solenoid is $B^2/2\mu_0$.

c Estimate the magnetic energy of a small bar magnet.

d By considering an ideal parallel plate capacitor, show that the energy density of an electric field is $\tfrac{1}{2}\epsilon_0 E^2$.

Figure 24.55 ▷

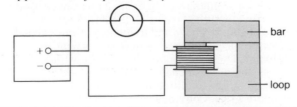

25

ALTERNATING CURRENTS

Alternating currents are definitely more difficult to understand than direct currents. It is therefore quite understandable that the pioneers of commercial electricity in the 1880s chose to generate and distribute *direct* current from power stations. However, only alternating current, thanks to the invention of the transformer, allows efficient transfer of electrical energy over large distances. Furthermore, alternating currents generate radio waves, information carriers which are central to our civilisation. So although a study of alternating currents may be difficult, it will reward you with a better grasp of two fundamental technologies which affect your everyday life.

POWER TRANSMISSION

The problem faced by any commercial producer of electricity is 'How do I get electrical energy from the generator to the consumer, with the minimum of energy loss between the two?' As you can see from figure 25.1, some of the energy fed out by the generator will be dissipated as heat energy in the two conductors which join the generator to the consumer. If the consumer has a resistance R and the two conductors have a resistance r, then it is easily shown (see chapter 12) that the efficiency of energy transfer is given by the following equation.

$$\text{efficiency} = \frac{R \times 100}{R + r} \qquad \textbf{(25.1)}$$

So the solution of the problem appears to be obvious. Make r as small as possible by using low resistivity metals made up into thick cables. However, this is uneconomic when you consider the resistance of a typical consumer. The following calculation will help you to appreciate this.

The situation is illustrated in figure 25.2. A typical power station has an output power of about 1 GW. Suppose that this is shared among ten towns, situated at an average distance of 50 km, so that each town absorbs a power of 100 MW over 100 km of cable. Let us assume that the electricity arrives in the town with a p.d. of 250 V, similar to the domestic mains supply. The current in the two cables is then easily calculated.

$$P = VI \quad \therefore\ 100 \times 10^6 = 250 \times I \quad \therefore\ I = 4 \times 10^5\ \text{A}$$

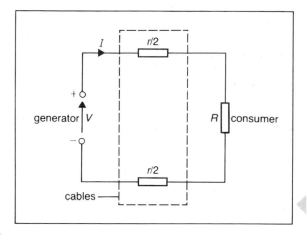

Figure 25.1 Equivalent circuit for a generator delivering electrical energy to a consumer

The effective resistance of the town is therefore $R = V/I = 6.25 \times 10^{-4}\ \Omega$. For an efficiency of 90%, the resistance of the cables must be about ten times smaller than this, i.e. $r = 6.25 \times 10^{-5}\ \Omega$. Assuming that the cables are made from copper, we can now calculate their diameter.

$$R = \frac{\rho l}{A}, \qquad \rho = 1.6 \times 10^{-8}\ \Omega\ \text{m}$$

$$\therefore A = \frac{1.6 \times 10^{-8} \times 100 \times 10^3}{6.25 \times 10^{-5}} = 26\ \text{m}^2$$

The cubes would have to be 5.7 m across! Solid cables of this size would be very expensive to manufacture and install.

Figure 25.2 Connecting the town to the power station by a couple of wires

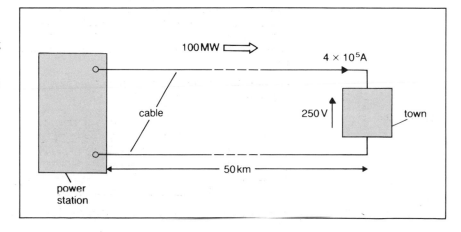

AN EFFICIENT SYSTEM !

$P_{in} \Rightarrow$ generator $\uparrow V_{in}$ | 1:n | I_{in} ... $r/2$ ... I_c $\uparrow V_c$ | n:1 | I_{out} $\uparrow V_{out}$ | R | consumer $\Rightarrow P_{out}$

voltage converter   cables   voltage converter

$\Downarrow$
P_{out}

Figure 25.3 Cutting down the power loss by inserting voltage converters   **Figure 25.4** An overhead transmission line

Figure 25.3 shows an arrangement which can efficiently transmit large amounts of electrical power via relatively cheap cables. It uses a pair of **voltage converters**, devices which can raise or lower the p.d. which is fed into them. (You will find out how to construct an efficient voltage converter on page 445.) Let's obtain an expression for the efficiency, starting with the consumer who has an effective resistance R.

$$P_{out} = V_{out}I_{out} = I_{out}^2 R \qquad (1)$$

The **voltage converter** at the consumer's end of the cable can be assumed to be 100% efficient. Its function is to lower the p.d. across the cables V_c by a factor n to obtain V_{out}.

$$V_c = nV_{out} \qquad (2)$$

Since there is no energy loss in the voltage converter, the current fed out of it must be n times larger than the current fed into it.

$$V_c I_c = P_{out} = V_{out}I_{out} \quad \therefore I_c = \frac{I_{out}}{n}$$

$$P_{loss} = I_c^2 r \quad \therefore P_{loss} = \frac{I_{out}^2 r}{n^2} \qquad (3)$$

Now think about the generator's voltage converter. The power from the generator P_{in} is given by the following expression:

$$P_{in} = P_{out} + P_{loss} \qquad (4)$$

We can write down an expression for the efficiency of the whole system.

$$efficiency = \frac{P_{out}}{P_{in}} \times 100$$

$$\therefore efficiency = \frac{(P_{in} - P_{loss})}{P_{in}} \times 100 \qquad (5)$$

If we assume that $P_{in} \simeq P_{out}$ (in other words, the efficiency is high) and use equations (1) and (3) in (5), we end up with a useful approximate expression for the efficiency.

$$efficiency = (1 - \frac{r}{n^2 R}) \times 100 \qquad (6)$$

This means that for efficient transfer of electrical energy into a resistance R, the resistance of the cables has to satisfy the following condition.

$$r \ll n^2 R \qquad (7)$$

In this country most of the electricity is distributed over long distances at 400 kV, but delivered to the consumer at 240 V. So the voltage converters at either end of the cables have a value of n which is 1667. You can convince yourself that this means the cables can have diameters which are 1667 times less than they would have been without the voltage converters. So in our example illustrated in figure 25.2, the copper cables would only need a diameter of 5.7/1667 ≈ 3 cm for an efficiency of 90%! In practice, power transmission cables are made from aluminium with a steel core, with a total diameter of about 3 cm. Not only is a 3 cm cable cheaper to manufacture than one which is 1667 times larger, it can also be slung from pylons (figure 25.4). Insulation of high voltage cables is difficult and costly if they have to be laid underground. It is far more convenient to have them spaced out from each other in mid-air.

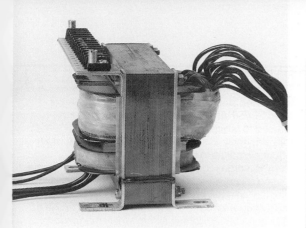

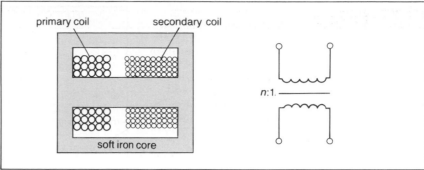

Figure 25.5   Construction of a transformer — the core is made from sheets of iron to suppress eddy currents

High voltage transmission

The secret of transmitting large amounts of electrical energy over long distances is knowing how to reduce the energy lost on the way. Most of it is converted to heat energy by the resistance r of the cables. If the current in the cables is I_c then we can calculate the rate of heat production P_{loss} in them.

$$P = VI, \quad R = \frac{V}{I}$$

$$\therefore P = I^2 R$$

$$\therefore P_{loss} = I_c^2 r \qquad (25.2)$$

As we have shown above, there is a limit to how small we can make r. So efficient power transmission requires low currents in the cables: since $P = VI$, low currents means high voltages.

Transformers

A **transformer** is a mutual inductor specially designed for the efficient exchange of energy between the two coils. It can act as the voltage converter of figure 25.3 — provided that alternating, rather than direct voltages, are used. The construction of a transformer is deceptively simple. As you can see from figure 25.5, it consists of two insulated coils of copper wire wound around a common core of laminated soft iron sheets. The shape of the iron ensures that both coils not only have a large flux through them, but also have the same flux as each other.

Turns ratio

We need to be able to predict the ratio of the voltages across the **primary** and **secondary** coils. Suppose that the primary coil is connected to a source of alternating voltage, as shown in figure 25.6. The consequent alternating current in the primary coil will set up an alternating magnetic field in the iron core. Since both coils are wound around the same loop of iron, they will have the same flux (providing the iron does not saturate anywhere in the loop.) So the alternating flux Φ is going to induce voltages across the ends of *both* coils.

$$V = \frac{n d\Phi}{dt} \quad \therefore \ V_s = n_s \frac{d\Phi}{dt}, \ V_p = n_p \frac{d\Phi}{dt} \quad (25.3)$$

If we eliminate $d\Phi/dt$ from these two equations, we get the expression we are after.

$$\frac{d\Phi}{dt} = \frac{V_s}{n_s} = \frac{V_p}{n_p} \quad \boxed{\therefore \ V_s = \frac{n_s}{n_p} \times V_p} \quad (25.4)$$

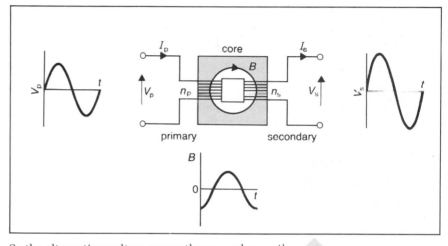

So the alternating voltage across the secondary coil has an amplitude which is n_s/n_p times larger than that of the primary voltage. In other words, it is the **turns ratio** $n = n_s/n_p$ of the two coils which fixes the relative amplitudes of the voltages fed in and out of the transformer. Furthermore, the two voltages are in phase with each other, as shown in figure 25.6 — both waveforms have the same shape.

Figure 25.6   Behaviour of a transformer

Figure 25.7   There is no energy conversion in the coil of an ideal inductor

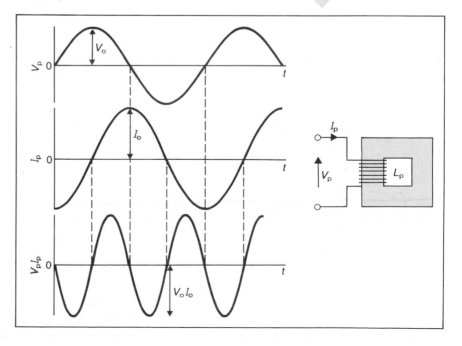

Primary current

Suppose that you need to build a transformer for the national grid with a turns ratio of about 1700. How do you set about deciding how many turns of wire you need in the primary and how large the iron core needs to be? Your starting point is a consideration of the current in the primary coil when no current is drawn from the secondary (figure 25.7). The transformer will behave like an inductor of inductance L_p fixed by the geometry of the primary coil.

$$V = L \frac{dI}{dt} \quad \therefore \quad V_p = L_p \frac{dI_p}{dt} \qquad \textbf{(25.5)}$$

As you can see from figure 25.7, the current I_p will be $\pi/2$ out of phase with the voltage V_p. (Every time that the voltage is zero, the current must not be changing: the maximum and minimum slopes of the current must occur when the voltage has its maximum and minimum values). However, just because there is a current, it does not necessarily follow that any net power is delivered to the primary coil. Look at the bottom graph of figure 25.7. The average power V_pI_p is zero, being negative as often as it is positive. Energy is being continually exchanged between the coil and the power supply but, on average, there appears to be no energy given to the transformer.

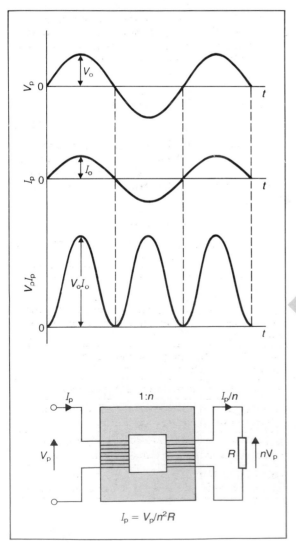

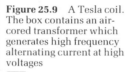

HIGH FREQUENCY TRANSFORMERS

The transformers used to step up and step down the voltage at either end of transmission lines are designed to work efficiently at frequencies of 50 Hz. Transformers are also widely used to process signals at much higher frequencies in audio and radio electronic systems. It is interesting to see what difference increasing the frequency makes to the design of a transformer.

To start with, as the frequency is increased, eddy currents in the core become more of a problem. The increased rate of flux change increases the p.d. induced in the core. Of course, the laminations can be made thinner to keep a high resistance path for the eddy currents, but the favoured solution is to use a **ferrite** core. This is a ceramic material which contains iron, so it is magnetic without being a conductor. Unfortunately, the relative permeability of ferrite is much lower than that of iron. So ferrite cores are only adopted at frequencies of 100 kHz and above.

Provided the two coils are wound on a common former, they will always have the same flux. The iron core is only needed to raise the inductance of the primary coil, reducing the primary current when no current is drawn from the secondary. However, as the frequency of the voltage across an inductor is increased, the current in it goes down anyway. At very high frequencies, like those picked up by TV sets, air-cored transformers are quite efficient!

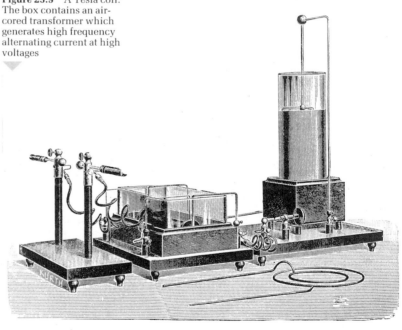

Figure 25.9 A Tesla coil. The box contains an air-cored transformer which generates high frequency alternating current at high voltages

Figure 25.8 The primary current is in phase with the voltage when a resistive load is connected to the secondary

A real transformer will have some resistance in its coils. Any alternating current in the primary coil is going to allow electrical energy to be converted to heat energy, so it is a good idea to keep the current as low as possible. This is done by making the inductance of the primary coil large. This implies lots of turns of wire and/or a large cross-sectional area for each turn, as well as lots of iron inside the coil.

Figure 25.8 illustrates what happens to the primary current when current is drawn from the secondary by a resistive load. If the laminations in the core suppress the eddy currents, we can assume that all of the electrical energy fed into the primary emerges from the secondary. If the turns ratio is n, this means that the primary current I_p must be n times larger than the secondary current I_s. The primary current will be in phase with the primary voltage so that energy is drawn from the power supply (bottom graph of figure 25.8).

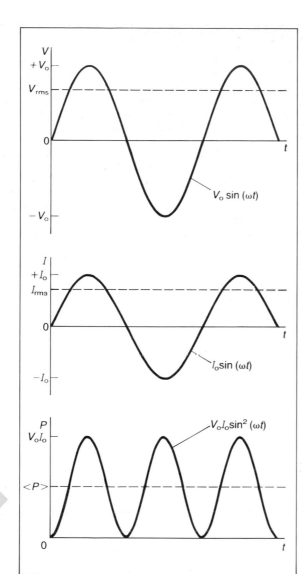

Figure 25.10 The relationship between peak and root-mean-square values

Figure 25.11 Converting a d.c. ammeter into an a.c. one by inserting it into a diode bridge

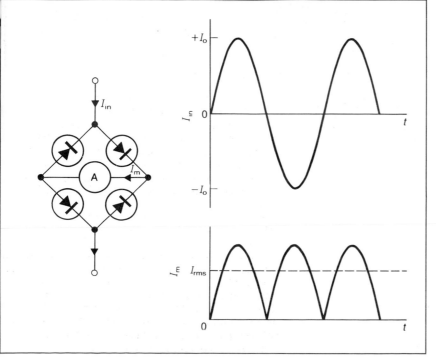

Average power output

Figure 25.10 shows how the p.d. across an alternating voltage supply changes with time. It continuously alternates between a peak positive value $(+V_0)$ and a peak negative value $(-V_0)$, giving an average p.d. of zero. This does not, however, mean that the average energy output of the supply is zero. If a resistor is connected to the supply, then the current in it will change sign every time the p.d. changes sign (figure 25.10). So the average power $<P>$ delivered to the resistor will not be zero.

$$P = VI, \quad V = V_0 \sin(\omega t), \quad I = I_0 \sin(\omega t)$$
$$\therefore <P> = <VI> = V_0 I_0 <\sin^2(\omega t)> \quad \textbf{(25.6)}$$

A glance at the bottom graph of figure 25.10 should convince you that the average value of $\sin^2(\omega t)$ is 0.5. So the average power output of the generator is exactly half the peak power.

$$<P> = \frac{V_0 I_0}{2} \quad \textbf{(25.7)}$$

It is a nuisance to have one formula for the power delivered by a continuous current $(P = VI)$ and another for the power delivered by an alternating current $(<P> = V_0 I_0/2)$. The adoption of **root-mean-square** (r.m.s.) values for specifying the size of an alternating voltage or current gets around this problem. These are defined in such a way that the formula $P = VI$ can be used for both continuous (**direct**) and alternating currents. For a sinusoidal current, the r.m.s. values for current and p.d. can be obtained from the peak values as follows.

$$I_{rms} = \frac{I_0}{\sqrt{2}}, \quad V_{rms} = \frac{V_0}{\sqrt{2}}$$
$$\therefore <P> = V_{rms} I_{rms} \quad \textbf{(25.8)}$$

A.c. ammeters and voltmeters give r.m.s. readings. As you can see from figure 25.11, these meters use a **diode bridge** to convert an alternating voltage or current into one which is always the same sign.

OBJECTIVES

After studying this section you should be able to do the following.

Calculate the efficiency of a low voltage electricity transmission system.

Describe how step-up and step-down transformers can be used to ensure efficient transfer of electricity along cables.

Calculate the efficiency of a high voltage transmission system.

Describe the construction of a transformer.

Explain how a transformer works and how the coil voltages depend on the turns ratio.

Describe and explain the relationship between the primary and secondary currents in a transformer.

State the relationship between peak and root-mean-square values for alternating voltages and currents.

QUESTIONS

1 A teacher uses the apparatus shown in figure 25.12 to illustrate the benefits of high voltage transmission lines to a lower-school class. The two cables have a resistance of 24 Ω each and the bulbs are rated at 12 V, 24 W. The power supply produces 12 V r.m.s. at 50 Hz.

a She starts off by connecting the bulbs as shown in figure 25.12. Estimate the power delivered to each bulb when the power pack is switched on. Explain why they are different.

b She then inserts the two transformers as shown in figure 25.13. When the power supply is switched on, both bulbs glow at apparently full brightness. Explain, in words which her class could understand, why this is so.

c Each transformer has 100 turns of wire in one coil and 2000 turns of wire in the other. What is the r.m.s. p.d. between the cables when the power supply is turned on? What is the r.m.s. current in the cables?

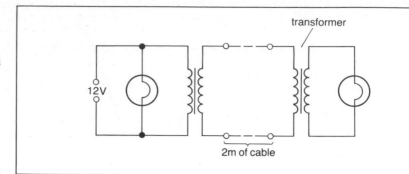

Figure 25.13

Figure 25.12

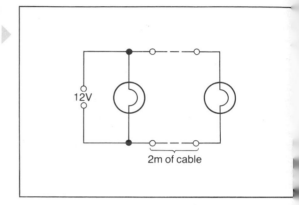

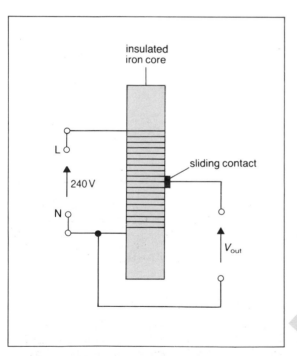

Figure 25.14

Figure 25.15

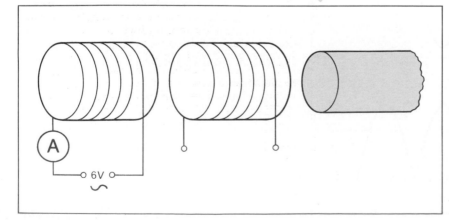

d Estimate the rate at which heat is generated in the cables when they are run at this high voltage.

2 The high voltage electricity grid which delivers electricity from power stations to the consumer in this country runs at 400 kV. Each cable has 54 strands of aluminium wire, each 3.2 mm in diameter, wound on a central core of steel strands.

a What is the function of the steel in the cable?

b If the resistivity of aluminium is 2.5×10^{-8} Ω m, calculate the resistance of 1.0 km of cable.

c Each cable normally carries a current of 650 A. What is the percentage energy loss per kilometre of cable? What will the efficiency of the system be over a distance of 200 km?

d Each of the pylons shown in figure 25.4 carries 25 cables, grouped as six bunches of four and one on the top. (Generators in power stations produce three separate phases of current such that the sum of the currents is always zero.) Estimate the total power being transmitted by the set of pylons.

3 A transformer used to convert the 240 V r.m.s. 50 Hz mains supply into a 9.0 V r.m.s. voltage to run a microcomputer has 180 turns of wire in its secondary coil.

a How many turns does the primary coil have?

b The wires in the secondary coil are much thicker than those in the primary coil. Why?

c If the current in the secondary is 1.5 A r.m.s., what is the current in the primary?

d Draw graphs on the same axes to show how the current and voltage of the secondary change with time. Mark both axes with values.

4 A projector bulb is rated at 12 V, 150 W. If it is run off the 240 V mains supply, suggest a suitable turns ratio for the transformer and a rating for the fuse inserted in the primary circuit.

5 The construction of an **autotransformer** is illustrated in figure 25.14. It can be used to obtain an alternating voltage which has a fraction of the amplitude of the 240 V r.m.s. mains supply. The sliding contact may be moved up and down the coil to vary the amplitude of the output voltage.

a Why is the coil wound on a soft iron former?

b Suppose that the contact is one quarter of the way up the coil. Explain why the output voltage is 60 V r.m.s.

c Suggest how the autotransformer could be wired to obtain voltages *greater* than that of the mains supply.

6 The power rating of a transformer is linked to its size. A transformer designed to handle large powers has to be larger than ones designed to handle small powers. This question will help you to understand why.

a How does the field in the iron core depend on the length of the iron loop, the current in the primary coil and the number of turns of wire in it? What is the upper limit on the field in the iron? What about the flux?

b Explain why the maximum allowable current in the primary coil doubles if every dimension of the transformer is doubled.

c Table 25.1 gives some data for a number of different mains transformers which convert the 240 V mains supply to 12 V. Is the power handling capacity of a transformer proportional to its volume? (You can assume that transformers are cubical in shape with a constant density of 7900 kg m^{-3}.) Estimate the size of a 1 MW transformer.

Table 25.1

Maximum power/W	Mass/kg
50	0.9
100	1.1
250	2.6
500	3.8
1000	8.8

7 Figure 25.15 shows a coil in series with a 6 V r.m.s. supply and an a.c. ammeter. Another identical coil is placed next to it.

a The reading of the ammeter falls from 1.0 A to 0.05 A when a long soft iron bar is inserted through the coils. Explain why.

b The experiment is repeated with a 6 V, 3 W filament lamp connected to the second coil. Describe and explain what will happen to the ammeter reading and the bulb as a soft iron bar is inserted through the two coils.

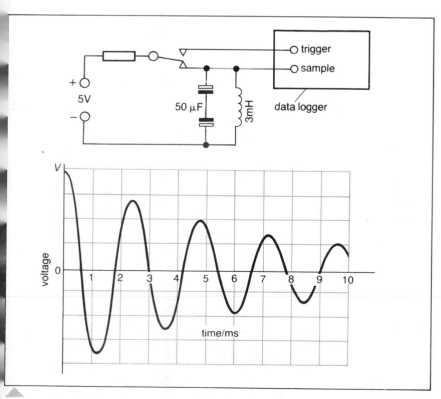

Figure 25.16 Investigating the oscillation of a parallel *LC* circuit

OSCILLATORS AND FILTERS

This section aims to teach you a bit about the production and processing of alternating voltages with the help of inductors and capacitors. You will be introduced to the properties of two important networks: the parallel *LC* circuit will be first because it is the most spectacular.

The parallel LC circuit

Consider the apparatus shown in figure 25.16(a). A 3 mH inductor is connected in parallel to a 50 μF capacitor, with a changeover switch connecting it to a 5 V supply. The data logger starts to sample the voltage across the *LC* circuit when its trigger input is held at 5 V — this happens when the *LC* circuit is disconnected from the power supply. A typical signal recorded by the data logger is shown in the graph of figure 25.16(b). As you can see, the circuit appears to oscillate with a frequency which remains constant as the signal dies down. It looks as if the circuit is performing the electrical equivalent of simple harmonic motion.

Exchanging energy

Why should an inductor in parallel with a capacitor produce a voltage which oscillates? Think about another system which oscillates, a mass on a spring (figure 25.17). That system can have an oscillating displacement because it has two ways of storing energy, i.e. kinetic energy and strain energy.

$$E_k = \tfrac{1}{2}mv^2, \quad E_s = \tfrac{1}{2}kx^2, \quad T = 2\pi(m/k)^{\frac{1}{2}} \qquad \textbf{(25.9)}$$

The mass-spring system can exchange the energy between these two forms, as shown in the graph of figure 25.17, with a period T given by equation (25.9).

Now consider the inductor–capacitor system shown in figure 25.18. It also has two ways of storing energy. Charge moving through the inductor gives energy to a magnetic field and charge stored on the capacitor plates gives energy to an electric field. So it is possible that the energy of the circuit could oscillate between the two forms, somewhat as shown in figure 25.18.

$$E_L = \tfrac{1}{2}LI^2, \quad E_c = \frac{\tfrac{1}{2}Q^2}{C} \qquad \textbf{(25.10)}$$

Take a look at the expressions for energy in equations (25.9) and (25.10). Notice that if we treat the charge Q as being equivalent to the displacement x, then the current I is automatically equivalent to the velocity v (remember $I = dQ/dt$ and $v = dx/dt$). So perhaps L is equivalent to m and $1/C$ is equivalent to k. Therefore the period of oscillation of an LC circuit may be given by the following formula.

$$T = 2\pi(m/k)^{\frac{1}{2}}, \quad m \equiv L, \quad k \equiv 1/C$$

$$\therefore T = 2\pi(LC)^{\frac{1}{2}} \qquad \textbf{(25.11)}$$

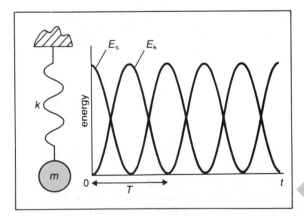

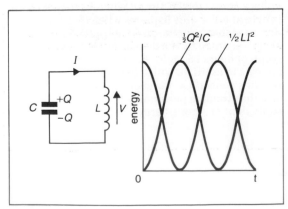

SOLVING THE EQUATIONS

Now that we know what the answer is, we can confidently replace our analogical model with a mathematical one. The symbols we are going to use are defined in figure 25.18. When the charge stored on the top plate of the capacitor is Q, there is a current I in the inductor and a p.d. V across both components. The current is the rate at which the charge on the top plate is decreasing.

$$I = -\frac{dQ}{dt} \qquad (1)$$

Write down the two equations describing the behaviour of each component.

$$C = \frac{Q}{V} \qquad \therefore Q = CV \qquad (2)$$

$$V = L\frac{dI}{dt} \qquad \therefore \frac{dI}{dt} = \frac{V}{L} \qquad (3)$$

Now wrestle with the three equations to eliminate I and Q.

$$Q = CV \qquad \therefore \frac{dQ}{dt} = C\frac{dV}{dt}$$

$$I = -\frac{dQ}{dt} \qquad \therefore I = -C\frac{dV}{dt} \qquad \therefore \frac{dI}{dt} = -C\frac{d^2V}{dt^2}$$

$$\frac{dI}{dt} = \frac{V}{L} \qquad \therefore \frac{V}{L} = -C\frac{d^2V}{dt^2}$$

$$\therefore \frac{d^2V}{dt^2} = -\omega^2 V, \quad \text{where } \omega^2 = 1/LC \qquad (4)$$

Equation (4) is what we are after. It is the SHM differential equation which we solved in chapter 15. We can therefore quote its solution without having to solve it all over again.

$$V = V_0\cos(\omega t), \quad \text{where } \omega = (LC)^{-\frac{1}{2}} \qquad (5)$$

Our analogy with SHM will be reinforced if we write down expressions for the charge and current at different times. You can convince yourself that these are as follows.

$$Q = Q_0\cos(\omega t), \quad \text{where } I = -\omega Q_0\sin(\omega t) \qquad (6)$$

They are the same as the equivalent expressions for the displacement and velocity of a mass on a spring, with Q_0 acting as the amplitude of the oscillation.

Figure 25.17 The energy of a mass on a spring continually alternates between two forms

Figure 25.18 The energy of an LC circuit continually alternates between the capacitor and the inductor

In fact, this prediction matches experimental observations very well. For example, let's predict the period of oscillation of the circuit of figure 25.16.

$$T = 2\pi(LC)^{\frac{1}{2}},$$

$$\therefore T = 2\pi(3\times10^{-3} \times 50\times10^{-6})^{\frac{1}{2}} = 2.4 \text{ ms}$$

As you can see from figure 25.16, this is just what is observed.

$$f = \frac{1}{2\pi(LC)^{\frac{1}{2}}}$$

f is the natural frequency of the circuit (Hz)

L is the inductance of the circuit (H)

C is the capacitance of the circuit (F)

DAMPING

You will have noticed that the signal shown in figure 25.16 is damped. It decreases exponentially with time. The mechanism by which the circuit loses energy is obvious: any resistance will convert electrical energy to heat energy whenever there is a current in it. Let us suppose that the circuit contains resistance R, as shown in figure 25.19. The energy loss ΔE in the short time interval Δt can be worked out as follows.

$$P = I^2R, \quad P = \frac{E}{t} \quad \therefore \Delta E = - <I^2R>\Delta t \qquad (1)$$

If the damping is light, then we can work out the average square current over a whole cycle of oscillation. If you look at figure 25.20 it should be obvious that it will be half the square of the peak current I_0.

$$<I^2R> = <I^2>R \simeq \tfrac{1}{2}I_0^2R \quad \therefore \frac{\Delta E}{\Delta t} = -\tfrac{1}{2}I_0^2R \qquad (2)$$

Now, the total energy of the oscillator is proportional to the square of the peak current.

$$E = \tfrac{1}{2}LI_0^2 \quad \therefore \frac{\Delta E}{\Delta t} = -\frac{E}{\tau}, \quad \text{where } \tau = L/R \qquad (3)$$

You should recognise equation (3) — it is very similar to an equation you met in chapter 12. Its solution is a falling exponential.

$$E = E_0\exp[-t/\tau], \quad E = \tfrac{1}{2}CV^2 \quad \therefore V_0 = A\exp[-t/2\tau] \qquad (4)$$

So the amplitude of the oscillation V_0 should fall exponentially with a time constant equal to $2L/R$. If you want the oscillation to last for a long time, you need to aim for a large inductance and a low resistance.

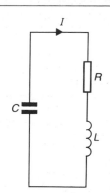

Figure 25.19 A real LC circuit contains some resistance

Figure 25.20

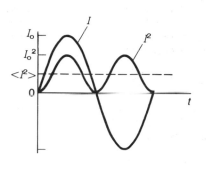

OSCILLATORS

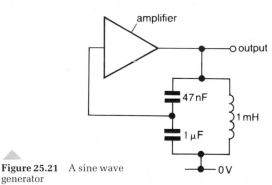

Figure 25.21 A sine wave generator

Figure 25.22 A self-adjusting amplifier suitable for the circuit of figure 25.21

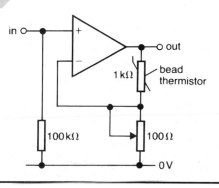

The parallel LC network can be incorporated into amplifiers to make sine wave generators. An example is shown in figure 25.21. The amplifier output is fed into an LC parallel circuit and a small fraction is fed back into the input. The total capacitance of the LC circuit is dominated by the smaller of the two capacitors, i.e. 47 nF (remember $1/C_1 + 1/C_2 = 1/C$). The signal fed back to the input of the amplifier is about twenty times smaller than the signal fed out of the amplifier output, so if the amplifier has a gain of more than twenty the circuit will start to oscillate at the natural frequency of the LC circuit.

$$f = \frac{1}{2\pi(LC)^{\frac{1}{2}}} \quad \therefore f = \frac{1}{2\pi \times (1\times10^{-3} \times 47\times10^{-9})^{\frac{1}{2}}}$$

$$\therefore f = 23\,\text{k Hz}$$

Of course, the amplifier has to be of the non-inverting sort for the oscillation to start. In order for the output waveform to be a pure sine wave, the amplifier has to have some feedback mechanism which makes its gain fall as the average amplitude of the output signal rises. The non-inverting amplifier shown in figure 25.22 incorporates a small **bead thermistor** which will warm up as the oscillation amplitude increases. Its resistance will therefore drop as the amplitude rises, pushing the gain down. An appropriate setting of the variable resistor will ensure a stable oscillation. It is vital that the amplifier has a large gain when the circuit is switched on, otherwise the system will not oscillate at all. A large gain allows the slightest random fluctuation with a frequency of 23 kHz at the amplifier's input to set the system oscillating.

RADIO RECEIVERS

Figure 25.23 A simple medium-wave radio receiver

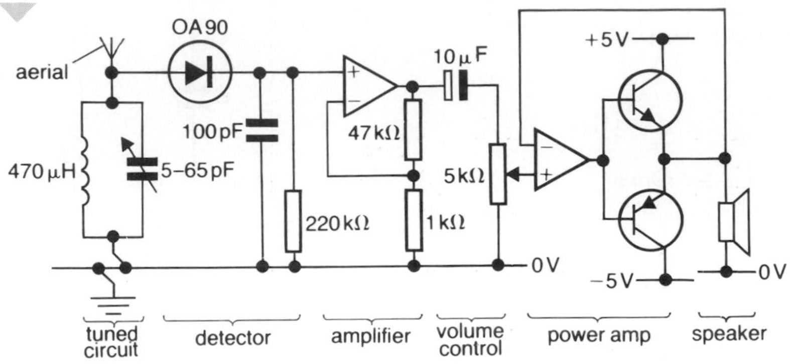

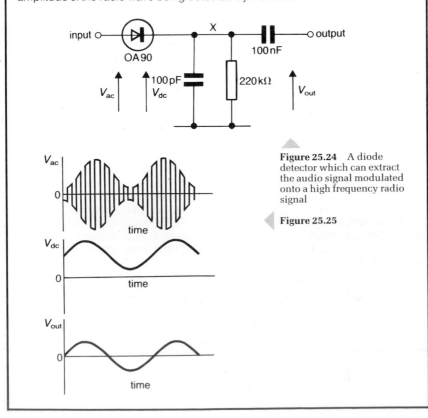

tuned circuit | detector | amplifier | volume control | power amp | speaker

Parallel *LC* networks are widely used in radio receivers to tune into one radio station and exclude the signals from all the others. The circuit diagram of a simple, but effective, radio receiver is shown in figure 25.23: you can clearly see the *LC* network at the left-hand end. The **aerial** is a long length of wire placed so that it intercepts radio waves. As the waves pass by the aerial they set up small alternating currents in it. So any radio wave whose frequency matches the natural frequency of the *LC* circuit will set it oscillating. All the other signals picked up by the aerial will have other frequencies, so they will not affect the tuned circuit. (Think of forced oscillations at frequencies other than the natural frequency of the system.)

Radio broadcasts on the medium wave employ **amplitude modulation** to transmit audio signals. The instantaneous amplitude of the radio wave is proportional to the amplitude of the audio signal, as shown in figure 25.24. So the information is encoded into the amplitude of the radio wave. It is extracted from the output of the *LC* circuit by the **diode detector** circuit: its function is explained in figure 25.25. The diode **rectifies** the signal, charging up the capacitor every time V_{ac} reaches its maximum value. The resistor allows the capacitor to discharge slowly so that V_{dc} can follow any decrease in the amplitude of the radio wave being detected by the aerial.

Figure 25.24 A diode detector which can extract the audio signal modulated onto a high frequency radio signal

Figure 25.25

Filter circuits

A typical filter circuit is shown in figure 25.26. When an alternating voltage V_{in} is fed in from the left, an alternating voltage V_{out} is fed out at the right. The graphs show how the amplitude and phase of the two signals are related. As you can see, signals with frequencies below about 300 Hz are **attenuated**. The circuit is called a **bass cut filter** because it blocks off the lower frequencies and lets through the higher frequencies which make up an audio signal such as speech or music. It does this because the effective resistance of the capacitor is a function of the frequency of the current in it. So in order for you be able to analyse the behaviour of simple filters containing resistors, inductors and capacitors, you first need to understand how the current in each component depends on the frequency of the alternating voltage across it.

Current in capacitors

Consider the circuit shown in figure 25.27. We need an expression for the current in the capacitor when the alternating voltage $V = V_0\cos(\omega t)$ is placed across it. Of course, $\omega = 2\pi f$.

$$C = \frac{Q}{V}, \quad V = V_0\cos(\omega t) \quad \therefore \quad Q = CV_0\cos(\omega t) \quad (25.12)$$

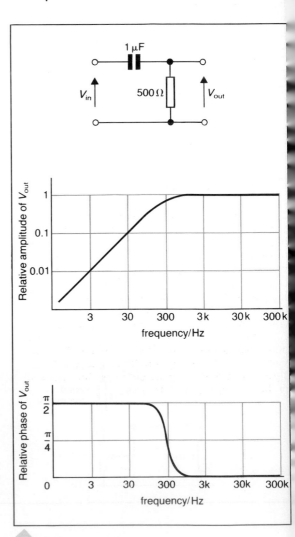

Figure 25.26 A bass cut filter network

So the charge on the top plate of the capacitor will be proportional to the instantaneous voltage across it. The current is the rate at which the charge is changing. Therefore the current will be zero every time that the voltage reaches a maximum or minimum value. This is shown in the graphs of figure 25.27. We can estimate the maximum value of the current by considering the total charge which flows off the top plate in one quarter cycle.

$$I = \frac{\Delta Q}{\Delta t} \quad \therefore \ I_0 \simeq \frac{CV_0}{0.25T} = 4fCV_0 \quad \textbf{(25.13)}$$

A more exact answer can be obtained with the help of calculus (Appendix B).

$$I = \frac{dQ}{dt} \quad \therefore \ \frac{dQ}{dt} = -\omega CV_0\sin(\omega t) = I \quad \textbf{(25.14)}$$

Equation (25.14) says two things. First, the peak current I_0 is related to the peak voltage V_0 by the following expression:

$$I_0 = \omega CV_0 \quad \therefore \ \frac{V_0}{I_0} = \frac{1}{\omega C} \quad \textbf{(25.15)}$$

Secondly, the **phase difference** between the voltage and the current is $\pi/2$. Although this may be evident from a study of figure 25.27, a bit of trigonometry from Appendix B may make it clearer.

$$\cos(\omega t + \phi) = \cos(\omega t)\cos\phi - \sin(\omega t)\sin\phi$$

$$\therefore \cos(\omega t + \pi/2) = \cos(\omega t)\cos(\pi/2) - \sin(\omega t)\sin(\pi/2)$$

$$\cos(\pi/2) = 0, \quad \sin(\pi/2) = 1$$

$$\therefore \cos(\omega t + \pi/2) = -\sin(\omega t) \quad \textbf{(25.16)}$$

So we can write down the relationship between the voltage across a capacitor and the current in it as follows:

$$I = \frac{V_0}{X_c}\cos(\omega t + \pi/2), \quad \text{where } X_c = \frac{1}{2\pi fC} \quad \textbf{(25.17)}$$

The quantity X_C is called the **reactance** of the capacitor; it is measured in ohms. It is very useful because it is similar to resistance. As you can see from equation (25.15), reactance is simply the peak voltage divided by the peak current. (Resistance, of course, is also a voltage divided by a current.) Figure 25.28 shows how the reactance of a capacitor can be measured with the help of a couple of a.c. meters. One meter measures the r.m.s. voltage across the capacitor ($V_0/2^{\frac{1}{2}}$), and the other measures the r.m.s. current in it ($I_0/2^{\frac{1}{2}}$). As you can see from the graph, the reactance of the 1 μF capacitor rises dramatically as the frequency of the a.c. supply is decreased.

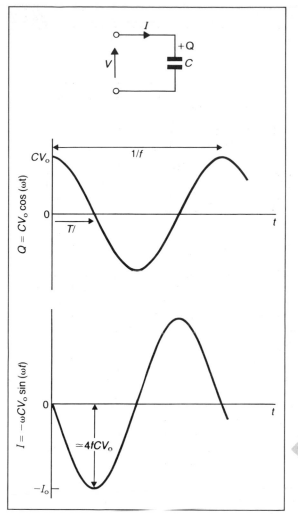

Figure 25.27 The current in the capacitor is $\pi/2$ out of phase with the voltage across it

Figure 25.28 Investigating the variation of reactance of a capacitor with frequency

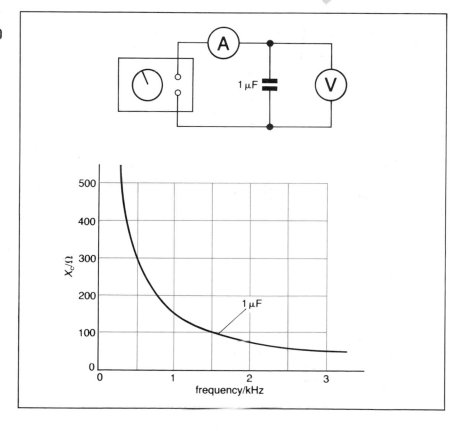

WATTLESS RESISTORS

Figure 25.29 illustrates how a 220 nF capacitor can be used to limit the current through a pair of LEDs connected to the 240 V r.m.s. 50 Hz mains supply. The LEDs are rated at 2 V, 16 mA and indicate that the device is plugged into the mains. The task of the capacitor is to limit the current in the LEDs to a safe level without converting more electrical energy to heat than is absolutely necessary. The first step in understanding how it does this is a calculation of its reactance.

$$X_c = \frac{1}{2\pi fC} \quad \therefore \ X_c = \frac{1}{2\pi \times 50 \times 220\times10^{-9}} \approx 15 \text{ k}\Omega$$

The voltage drop across each LED (2 V) will be negligible compared with the voltage drop across the capacitor. So let's ignore the LEDs altogether and calculate the approximate r.m.s. current in the capacitor.

$$X_c = \frac{V_{rms}}{I_{rms}} \quad \therefore \ 15\times10^3 = \frac{240}{I_{rms}}$$

$$\therefore \ I_{rms} = 16 \text{ mA}$$

Of course, this current will be $\pi/2$ out of phase with the voltage, so the average power delivered to the capacitor will be zero. The graphs of figure 25.29 should help you to see this. On the other hand, each LED will behave like a resistor when it is forward biased, with the voltage in phase with the current. The average power delivered to both LEDs is easily estimated.

$$P = VI \quad \therefore \ P_{LED} \approx 2 \times 16\times10^{-3} = 32 \text{ mW}$$

An alternative way of limiting the current in the LED is to place a resistor in series with it. You can check for yourself that a 15 kΩ resistor will also reduce the r.m.s. current to 16 mA, but that the power delivered to it will be just under 4 W. A capacitor is clearly more efficient than a resistor for limiting the current!

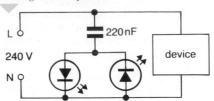

Figure 25.29 Current-limiting with a capacitor

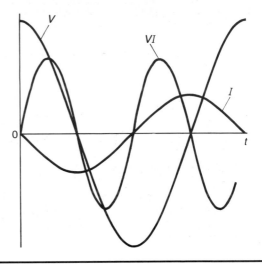

CURRENT IN INDUCTORS

Inductors also have a reactance whose value depends on the frequency of the current in them. The current in an inductor is related to the voltage across it by the following piece of algebra.

$$I = \frac{V_0}{X_L} \cos (\omega t - \pi/2), \quad X_L = 2\pi fL \qquad (1)$$

To see why this is so, consider figure 25.30. If the alternating voltage is represented by $V = V_0\cos(\omega t)$, then we can use calculus to help us find the current.

$$V = L \frac{dI}{dt} \quad \therefore \int V_0\cos(\omega t)dt = \int LdI$$

$$\therefore \frac{V_0}{\omega} \sin(\omega t) = LI \quad \therefore I = \frac{V_0}{\omega L} \sin(\omega t) \qquad (2)$$

If you study equation (25.16), it should be obvious that $\cos(\omega t - \pi/2) = \sin(\omega t)$, so equation (2) is saying the same thing as equation (1).

The graph of figure 25.30 shows how the reactance of an inductor changes with frequency. As the frequency increases, the reactance also increases, cutting down the r.m.s. current if the r.m.s. voltage remains constant. This behaviour complements that of a capacitor nicely — one gets larger as the other becomes smaller.

Figure 25.30 The reactance of an inductor is proportional to the frequency

CROSSOVER NETWORKS

Inductors and capacitors are widely used in high fidelity loudspeaker systems to direct audio signals to the most suitable speaker. As you can see from figure 25.31, a typical system contains two separate speakers. The large one (the **woofer**) is designed to produce the low frequency sounds and the small one (the **tweeter**) is best at making the high frequency sounds. A **crossover network** of inductors and capacitors is often used to direct the alternating voltages from the amplifier to the appropriate speaker. For example, look at the circuit shown in figure 25.32. Each speaker has been approximately modelled by an 8 Ω resistor. The 3 mH inductor ensures that only voltages whose frequencies are below 400 Hz will allow current in the woofer. Similarly, the 50 μF capacitor will only allow currents whose frequencies are above 400 Hz in the tweeter. The graph of figure 25.32 shows how the current in each speaker depends on the frequency of the alternating voltage fed into the network: the voltage is a constant 8 V r.m.s. Note the use of a log–log scale to compress the graph into a manageable space.

Figure 25.31 A loudspeaker system

Figure 25.32 A crossover network

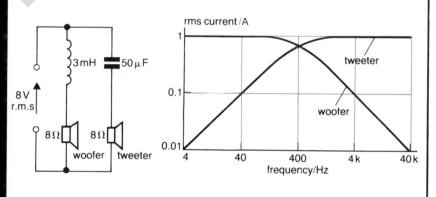

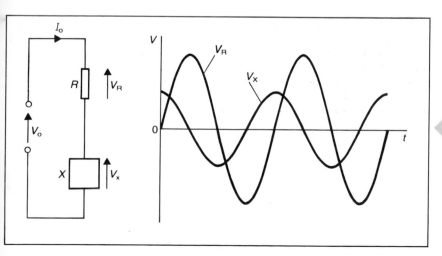

Phasors

A simple filter network is shown in figure 25.33. It consists of a resistor R in series with a reactance X. (The reactance could be a capacitor or an inductor or both in series.) An alternating voltage of known amplitude V_0 and frequency f is placed across the network. How is the current and voltage of each component related to the voltage across the whole circuit? Well, let us think about the current first. Charge in conductors behaves like an incompressible fluid, so the current in both components has to be the same at all times. Similarly, the voltages across the two components at any instant must add up to the total voltage across the circuit (energy conservation). However, the voltage across the reactance is $\pi/2$ out of phase with the current in it, whereas the voltage across the resistor will be in phase with the current. So we must *not* expect the peak voltages across the two components to add up to the peak voltage across the whole network! (Look at the graph of figure 25.33.)

Impedance

The following procedure allows you to calculate anything you want to know about currents and voltages in the network. Take the rules on trust for the moment: we shall attempt to justify them later on. The first step is to calculate the **impedance** Z of the network. This is done with the help of the vector diagram drawn in figure 25.34. Traditionally, the resistance R is drawn as a horizontal vector, with the two reactances X_L and X_C pointing up and down, respectively. The impedance Z is simply the sum of these three vectors.

$$Z = (R^2 + (X_L - X_C)^2)^{\frac{1}{2}}$$

(25.18)

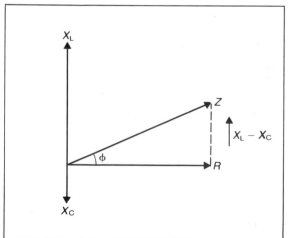

Figure 25.33 The alternating voltages across components in a series circuit do not have to be in phase with each other

Figure 25.34 Vector diagram for computing the impedance of a circuit

Having found the impedance, we can calculate the peak value of the current I_0. (The impedance is the ratio of the applied voltage to the current.)

$$Z = \frac{V}{I} \quad \therefore \ I_0 = \frac{V_0}{Z} \tag{25.19}$$

The phase difference between the current and the voltage can be obtained from figure 25.34. The voltage will be in phase with Z, but the current will be in phase with the resistance R. So the phase angle ϕ by which the current lags behind the voltage is given by the following expression.

$$\tan \phi = \frac{X_L - X_C}{R} \tag{25.20}$$

Now the peak voltages across the individual components can be calculated with the help of the peak current.

$$V_R = I_0 R, \quad V_L = I_0 X_L, \quad V_C = I_0 X_C \tag{25.21}$$

The relative phases of the voltages can be seen from the vector diagram of figure 25.35. Each vector is known as a **phasor**. The total voltage V_0 is the vector sum of all three phasors. The angles between the vectors gives their relative phases. It is standard practice to quote the phase relative to the current — which, of course, will be in phase with V_R. So V_L will lead the current by $\pi/2$ and V_C will lag the current by $\pi/2$.

Phasors in action

Here is an example of the use of impedance and phasors to work out something about a simple filter network. The circuit to be considered is shown in figure 25.36. A 5.0 V r.m.s voltage at 100 Hz is placed across a 2.0 kΩ resistor and a 1.0 μF capacitor in series with each other. What will the a.c. voltmeters read?

Start off by calculating the reactance of the capacitor.

$$X_C = \frac{1}{2\pi f C}$$

$$\therefore X_C = \frac{1}{2\pi \times 100 \times 1\times 10^{-6}} = 1.6 \text{ k}\Omega$$

Then use a vector diagram (figure 25.36) to calculate the impedance of the network.

$$Z = (R^2 + X_C^2)^{\frac{1}{2}} \quad \therefore \ Z = (2.0^2 + 1.6^2)^{\frac{1}{2}} = 2.6 \text{ k}\Omega$$

Now calculate the r.m.s. current in the network.

$$I = \frac{V}{Z} \quad \therefore \ I = \frac{5.0}{2.6\times 10^3} = 1.9 \text{ mA}$$

Finally, calculate the r.m.s. voltage across the two components.

$$V_C = IX_C \ \therefore \ V_C = 1.9\times 10^{-3} \times 1.6\times 10^3 = 3.0 \text{ V}$$

$$V_R = IR \quad \therefore \ V_R = 1.9\times 10^{-3} \times 2.0\times 10^3 = 3.8 \text{ V}$$

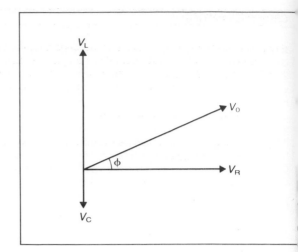

Figure 25.35 Phasor diagram

Figure 25.36 Using phasors to calculate the r.m.s. voltage across the components of an RC network

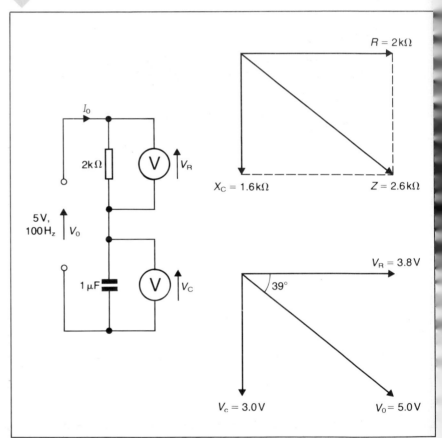

Notice that the sum of the readings across the two voltmeters is greater than the r.m.s. voltage across the whole network. This only appears to be wrong because the meters ignore the relative phases of the two voltages. The phasor diagram of figure 25.36 can be used to predict the relative phase of each voltage. V_C will lag behind V_R by $\pi/2$.

JUSTIFYING PHASORS !

If you want some evidence that the use of phasors and impedance allows you to make predictions about filter networks, then read on. Suppose that the voltage $V = V_0 \cos(\omega t)$ is placed across the network shown in figure 25.37. We want to prove that the current will be given by the following expression.

$$I = \frac{V_0}{Z}\cos(\omega t + \phi), \quad \text{where } \tan\phi = \frac{1}{2\pi RC} \tag{1}$$

The instantaneous voltage across the two components must add up to the total voltage across the network.

$$V_0\cos(\omega t) = IR + \frac{Q}{C} \tag{2}$$

Differentiate equation (2) after shuffling it around.

$$-\omega V_0\sin(\omega t) = R\,\frac{dI}{dt} + \frac{I}{C}$$

$$\therefore -V_0\sin(\omega t) = \frac{R}{\omega}\,\frac{dI}{dt} + IX \tag{3}$$

We need to substitute for I and dI/dt in equation (3). The vector diagram of figure 25.37 will help to simplify the expressions from equation (1) before substitution.

$$\cos(\omega t + \phi) = \cos(\omega t)\cos\phi - \sin(\omega t)\sin\phi$$

$$\therefore I = \frac{V_0}{Z}\cos(\omega t)\,\frac{R}{Z} - \frac{V_0}{Z}\sin(\omega t)\,\frac{X}{Z}$$

$$\therefore I = \frac{V_0}{Z^2}(R\cos(\omega t) - X\sin(\omega t))$$

$$\therefore \frac{dI}{dt} = \frac{V_0}{Z^2}\,\omega(-R\sin(\omega t) - X\cos(\omega t)) \tag{4}$$

Now substitute for I and dI/dt in equation (3).

$$-V_0\sin(\omega t) = -\frac{RV_0}{\omega Z^2}\,\omega(R\sin(\omega t) + X\cos(\omega t))$$

$$+ \frac{XV_0}{Z^2}(R\cos(\omega t) - X\sin(\omega t)) \tag{5}$$

Now equate terms in $\sin(\omega t)$ and $\cos(\omega t)$.

$$-V_0 = -\frac{R^2V_0}{Z^2} - \frac{X^2V_0}{Z^2}$$

$$0 = -\frac{RXV_0}{Z^2} + \frac{RXV_0}{Z^2}$$

Since $Z^2 = R^2 + X^2$ you should have no difficulty in convincing yourself that both of the above equations are true. So the rules for calculating and using impedances must be correct, at least for resistors and capacitors in series.

Figure 25.37

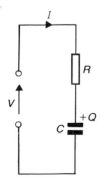
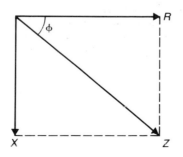

QUESTIONS

1 The simple radio receiver shown in figure 25.23 has a variable capacitor to tune it from one station to another. The capacitance can be changed from 5 pF to 65 pF.

a Calculate the maximum and minimum natural frequencies of the *LC* circuit.

b Suppose that you wanted to pick up stations broadcast on radio frequencies of about 5 MHz. Suggest a suitable value for the inductor in the circuit.

2 The circuit shown in figure 25.38(a) is sometimes used to demonstrate the properties of parallel *LC* circuits. The ammeters indicate the r.m.s. current in various parts of the circuit. The frequency of the alternating voltage is swept from a very low value to a very high value, keeping the r.m.s. voltage at 3.0 V. The graph of figure 25.38(b) shows how the r.m.s. current in the lead from the signal generator depends on the frequency.

a Calculate the individual reactances of the inductor and capacitor at 100 Hz, 1.0 kHz and 10 kHz.

b Explain why the current from the signal generator is large at both high and low frequencies.

c Why does the current from the signal generator drop to zero at 1.0 kHz?

d Draw a pair of graphs, on the same axes, to show how the r.m.s. current in the inductor and capacitor depend on the frequency of the voltage from the signal generator. Mark scales on both axes.

3 You want to use a capacitor to limit the current through a 12 V filament lamp to 50 mA when it is connected to the 240 V r.m.s. 50 Hz mains supply.

a What value of capacitance will have an r.m.s. current of 50 mA in it when it is connected to the mains supply?

b Draw a pair of graphs on the same axes to show how the voltage and current of the capacitor changes with time. Mark scales on both axes.

c What is the peak voltage across the capacitor?

d If the bulb is placed in series with the capacitor, draw a pair of graphs on the same axes to show how the voltage and current in the bulb change with time. Mark scales on both axes.

4 A simple treble cut filter connected to a signal generator is shown in figure 25.39. The circuit is designed to attenuate alternating voltages above about 3 kHz. The r.m.s. voltage from the signal generator is a constant 2.0 V, regardless of the frequency.

a Calculate the reactance of the capacitor at 300 Hz, 3.0 kHz and 30 kHz.

b Hence calculate the impedance of the circuit at each of these frequencies.

c Hence calculate the r.m.s. voltage across the capacitor at each of these frequencies.

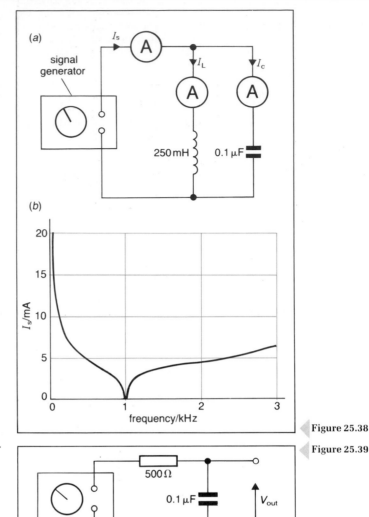

Figure 25.38

Figure 25.39

5 **Suppressors** are often used to protect computers from mains-borne interference. An example of a suppressor circuit is shown in figure 25.40. Any high frequency signals in the mains supply cannot get through to the computer power supply, but the low frequency mains supply gets through unaffected. Explain why.

Figure 25.40

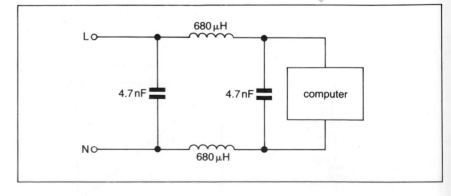

Figure 25.41 ▶

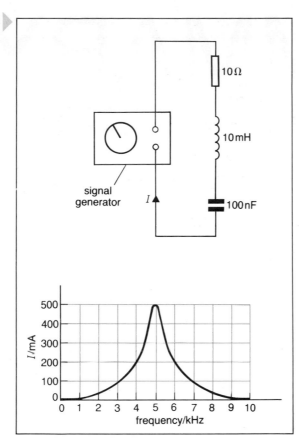

signal generator

I

10Ω

10mH

100nF

6 A circuit which has surprising properties is shown in figure 25.41. A 10 mH inductor, 10 Ω resistor and 100 nF capacitor are connected in series with an alternating voltage supply. The graph shows how the r.m.s. current in the circuit changes as the frequency of the alternating voltage is swept from very low to very high values. The output of the signal generator is a constant 5 V r.m.s.

a Explain why the current is low at very low frequencies. (Which component has the largest reactance? What does the vector diagram for Z look like?) How will its phase be related to the voltage?

b Explain why the current is also low at very high frequencies. How will its phase be related to the voltage?

c Show with the help of a vector diagram that the impedance is 11 Ω when the frequency is 5.0 kHz. What are the values of the reactances of the inductor and capacitor at this frequency?

d Calculate the r.m.s. voltages across the inductor and capacitor when the current in the circuit is a maximum. Sketch what the two signals would look like if displayed simultaneously on a double beam oscilloscope.

SUMMARY
ELECTROMAGNETISM

Magnetic fields are created by moving charges. The direction of a magnetic field is defined as the direction in which it will make a magnetic compass needle point. The force on a current in a field acts perpendicularly to both the current and field directions (Fleming's Left-Hand Rule): $F = BIl\sin\phi$. The force on an isolated moving charge is $F = Bqv$.

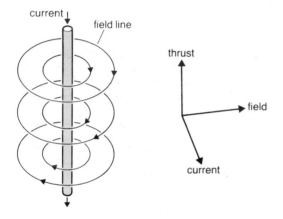

Charged particles moving through magnetic fields travel in spirals or circular orbits: $r = p/Bq$. The Hall voltage is given by $V = BI/nqt$.

The field due to an infinite straight wire is $\mu_0 I/2\pi r$, where $\mu_0 = 4\pi\times10^{-7}$ H m^{-1}, fixed by the definition of the ampere. The field at the centre of a long thin solenoid is $\mu_0 NI$, falling to half this at the ends. The field inside a long solenoid is uniform across its cross-section.

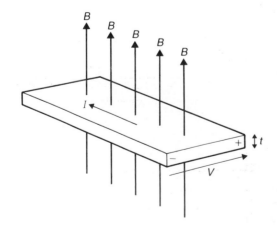

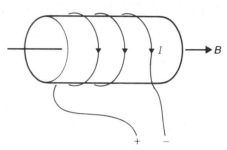

The field strength inside a coil can be greatly increased by winding it around a magnetic material. Such material contains domains where there is local small-scale alignment of the atomic magnetic moments. Domains can be easily realigned in soft magnetic materials, allowing their use to control the path of field lines. Hard magnetic materials have domains which are difficult to align allowing such materials to be surrounded by a permanent magnetic field. North and south poles are regions where field lines leave and enter magnetic materials.

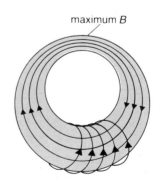

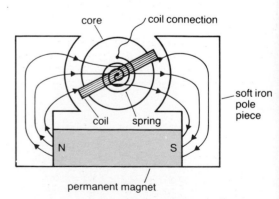

There is an induced p.d. across the ends of a conductor swept through a magnetic field: $V = Blv$. The p.d. induced across the ends of a coil is equal to its rate of change of flux linkage: $V = n\Delta\Phi/\Delta t$, $\Phi = BA$. The direction of a current induced in a conductor acts in a direction which opposes the change of flux which caused the change of flux linkage (Lenz's Law). Magnetic materials which have to move through magnetic fields are laminated to cut eddy currents to a minimum.

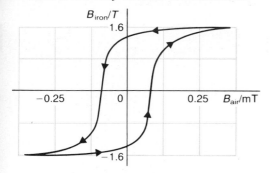

The output p.d. of a coil spun in a magnetic field is given by $V = n\Phi\omega\sin\omega t$. The alternating voltage is usually specified with a frequency and an r.m.s. value: $I_{rms} = I_0/2^{\frac{1}{2}}$. $P_{out} = V_{rms}I_{rms}$. The back e.m.f across a motor is proportional to its speed:
$V = n\Phi\omega$, $\Gamma = n\Phi I$.

Whenever the current in a conductor changes there is a p.d. induced in it due to the change of flux linkage. $n\Phi = LI$, $V = L\Delta I/\Delta t$. An inductor stores magnetic energy: $E = \frac{1}{2}LI^2$. For an inductor in series with a resistor and a steady p.d.
$I = I_0(1 - \exp[-t/\tau])$, $\tau = L/R$.

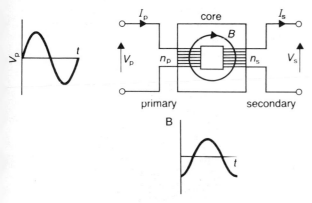

Transformers with laminated iron cores can change the amplitude of alternating voltages with nearly 100% efficiency: nearly all of the energy fed into the primary emerges from the secondary.
$V_p/V_s = n_p/n_s$.

The reactances of capacitors and inductors are given by $X_C = 1/2\pi fC$ and $X_L = 2\pi fL$. There is no conversion of electrical energy when there is alternating current in an ideal inductor or capacitor.

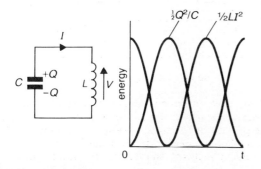

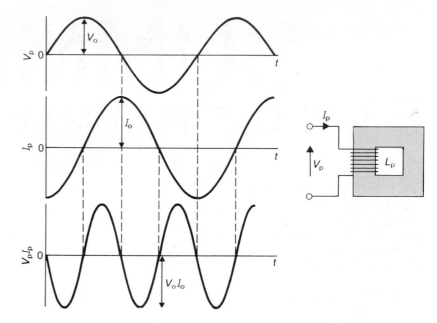

The impedance of a series circuit is given by $Z^2 = R^2 + (X_L - X_C)^2$. The current (r.m.s. or peak) in an a.c. circuit is given by $Z = V/I$: the phase is given by $\tan\phi = (X_L - X_C)/R$. The p.d. across each component is then given by $X = V/I$.

The natural frequency of a parallel LC circuit is $1/2\pi(LC)^{\frac{1}{2}}$; such a circuit has a very large impedance for signals at the natural frequency. The impedance of a series LC circuit is very small for signals which are at the natural frequency.

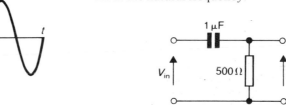

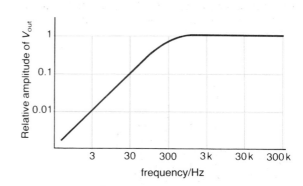

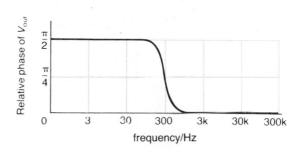

WAVES
IN SPACE

26

ELECTROMAGNETIC WAVES

In 1864 James Maxwell published the results of his researches into electromagnetism. Having encapsulated all that was known about the subject in four equations, Maxwell used them to predict the existence of travelling waves of electric and magnetic fields through empty space. He was also able to prove that the speed of those **electromagnetic waves** should be given by $c = (\mu_0\epsilon_0)^{-\frac{1}{2}}$. Although few people at the time believed that Maxwell was right, partly because of the mathematical nature of his theory (see Table 26.1!), the close coincidence between the values of $(\mu_0\epsilon_0)^{-\frac{1}{2}}$ and the speed of light was intriguing.

Twenty five years later, Heinrich Hertz eventually managed to generate and detect Maxwell's electromagnetic waves and a new era in theoretical physics was born. From then on, fields became more important than their sources or the particles they acted on. With electromagnetic waves, fields stopped being just a convenient abstract link between two objects and acquired an independent existence. Furthermore, that simple formula $c = (\mu_0\epsilon_0)^{-\frac{1}{2}}$ for the speed of electromagnetic waves made Albert Einstein think about how light appears to travel to people who are moving at different speeds. The result was his famous Theory of Relativity.

THE ELECTROMAGNETIC SPECTRUM

Electromagnetic waves have been detected with wavelengths spanning the approximate range of 10^5 m to 10^{-14} m. Table 26.2 shows the names given to waves which lie within this range and summarises their uses. Waves at the extremes of the range (radio waves and gamma rays) have such vastly different properties from each other that it is hard to believe that they are in fact the same phenomenon! All electromagnetic waves share the following characteristics.

- They can travel through a vacuum.
- They have a wave velocity of $(\mu_0\epsilon_0)^{-\frac{1}{2}} = 3.00\times10^8$ m s^{-1}.

Any wave which has these two properties is a member of the **electromagnetic spectrum**. This section is going to show you how a number of different waves with very diverse properties have been shown to belong to this select club. The reasons why electromagnetic waves of vastly different wavelengths have such different absorption characteristics will be unfolded in chapter 29, when you are introduced to quantum mechanics.

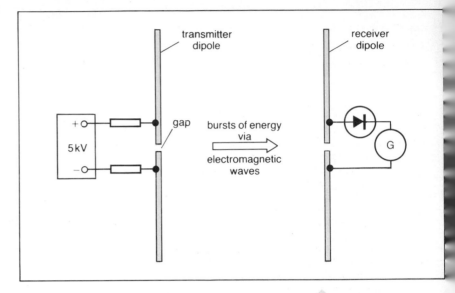

Figure 26.1 A spark transmitter

Table 26.1 Maxwell's equations for free space

$$\frac{dE_x}{dt} + \frac{dE_y}{dt} + \frac{dE_z}{dt} = 0$$

$$\frac{dB_x}{dt} + \frac{dB_y}{dt} + \frac{dB_z}{dt} = 0$$

$$\left(\frac{dE_z}{dy} - \frac{dE_y}{dz}\right)\mathbf{i} + \left(\frac{dE_x}{dz} - \frac{dE_z}{dx}\right)\mathbf{j} + \left(\frac{dE_y}{dx} - \frac{dE_x}{dy}\right)\mathbf{k} = -\mathbf{i}\frac{dB_x}{dt} - \mathbf{j}\frac{dB_y}{dt} - \mathbf{k}\frac{dB_z}{dt}$$

$$\left(\frac{dB_z}{dy} - \frac{dB_y}{dz}\right)\mathbf{i} + \left(\frac{dB_x}{dz} - \frac{dB_z}{dx}\right)\mathbf{j} + \left(\frac{dB_y}{dx} - \frac{dB_x}{dy}\right)\mathbf{k} = -\mu_0\epsilon_0\left(\mathbf{i}\frac{dE_x}{dt} + \mathbf{j}\frac{dE_y}{dt} + \mathbf{k}\frac{dE_z}{dt}\right)$$

Table 26.2

Name	λ/m	f/Hz	Uses
long-wave radio	1×10^4	3×10^4	long-distance communication
medium-wave radio	1×10^3	3×10^5	local AM broadcasting
short-wave radio	1×10^2	3×10^6	CB and amateur radio
VHF	1×10^1	3×10^7	local FM broadcasting
UHF	1×10^0	3×10^8	TV broadcasting
microwaves	1×10^{-1}	3×10^9	telephone links satellite links radar
infra-red	1×10^{-3}	3×10^{11}	heat radiation optical fibre communications
light	7×10^{-7}	4×10^{14}	visual communication
ultra-violet	4×10^{-7}	8×10^{14}	photochemistry
X s	1×10^{-9}	3×10^{17}	medical investigation
gamma rays	1×10^{-11}	3×10^{19}	food sterilisation
	1×10^{-13}	3×10^{21}	

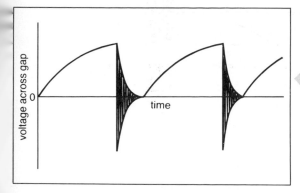

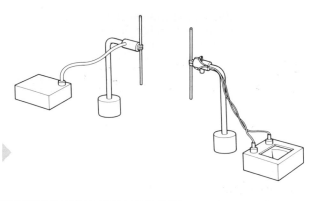

Figure 26.2 The transmitter dipole oscillates briefly each time the electric field in the gap reaches the breakdown strength of air

Figure 26.3 Apparatus for investigating the behaviour of 1 GHz electromagnetic waves

Radio waves

The **spark transmitter** shown in figure 26.1 is similar to the apparatus used by Heinrich Hertz in 1889 to demonstrate the existence of electromagnetic waves. It uses oscillations in a parallel LC network to radiate bursts of electromagnetic waves into the space around. The gap between the two metal rods behaves like a capacitor, charging up from the 5 kV supply via the resistors. Each time the electric field in the gap reaches the breakdown field strength for air, the capacitor is discharged through the gap. However, the rods have a certain inductance, so the voltage between them briefly oscillates with a frequency fixed by the capacitance and inductance (figure 26.2). The waves generated by the alternating currents in the rods (a **dipole aerial**) can be detected by a similar dipole aerial placed nearby. A high frequency diode rectifies the alternating current induced in the receiver aerial so that it can be detected by the galvanometer. The apparatus is a convincing demonstration that an alternating current in one conductor can feed energy into another conductor through the space between them.

Of course, it could be just electromagnetic induction (i.e. the changing flux around the transmitter aerial) which sets up alternating currents in the receiver aerial. However, if the transmitter is acting as a true source of undamped waves then the energy of each wavefront spreads out over the surface of an expanding sphere. So the energy extracted from the wave by a receiver must be proportional to the inverse square of the distance from the transmitter. Spark transmitters of

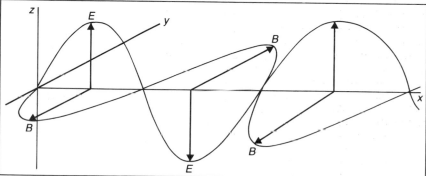

useful power are illegal because their frequency of oscillation is difficult to control. So the properties of radio waves are best explored in the laboratory with a stable high frequency (1 GHz) oscillator connected to a dipole transmitting aerial (figure 26.3). The **power** of the signal picked up by the receiver aerial will, of course be proportional to the square of the galvanometer reading ($P = I^2R$), so the galvanometer reading should be inversely proportional to the distance between the two dipoles.

Waveguides

An electromagnetic wave consists of two separate alternating fields. Figure 26.4 illustrates how these electric and magnetic fields are related. They point at right angles to each other and the direction in which the wave is travelling, oscillating in phase with each other. The amplitudes of the two fields are related to each other by the following formula.

$$B = E/c, \quad c = (\mu_0\epsilon_0)^{-\frac{1}{2}} \tag{26.1}$$

Figure 26.4 The E and B fields of an electromagnetic wave are at right angles to each other

Figure 26.5 An electromagnetic wavefront travelling down a waveguide

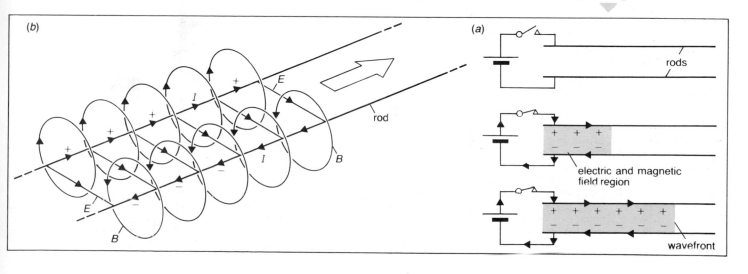

(b)

(a)

rods

electric and magnetic field region

rod

wavefront

In order to understand why the fields behave this way, consider the **waveguide** shown in figure 26.5(a). It consists of a pair of long conducting rods, rather like a parallel plate capacitor, connected to a cell and a switch. When the switch is closed the capacitor starts to charge up. As you can see from the sequence of figure 26.5(b), an electric and magnetic field steadily fills up the gap between the rods. The electric field is due to the equal and opposite charges on the rods and the magnetic field is due to the currents in the rods. It can be shown (see question 5 at the end of this section) that the edge of the field region travels at the speed of light i.e. $(\mu_0 \epsilon_0)^{-\frac{1}{2}}$. Notice that the B and E fields between the rods are at right angles to each other.

Now look at figure 26.6. An alternating voltage is being fed into one end of the waveguide, setting up a wave of alternating magnetic and electric fields travelling down the waveguide. Each time that the voltage from the signal generator changes sign, both the E and B fields change direction, but the energy in the fields travels the same way as before. The wavelength λ of the wave is related to the frequency f of the alternating voltage by the usual formula $c = f\lambda$.

So we can set up a travelling electromagnetic wave in the gap between a pair of conductors. Can we persuade the wave to launch forth into space when it reaches the end of the waveguide? Well, you really need Maxwell's equations to show this properly, but we are going to stick to the argument illustrated in figure 26.7. The E field at the edge of a parallel plate capacitor curls around the edges. So if an alternating E field travels towards the edge of the parallel rods, it can break free to form continuous loops which carry on moving with the velocity of light. A similar thing can happen to the B field. Both fields move through space together at the speed of light, leaving behind the charges and currents which set them up in the first place.

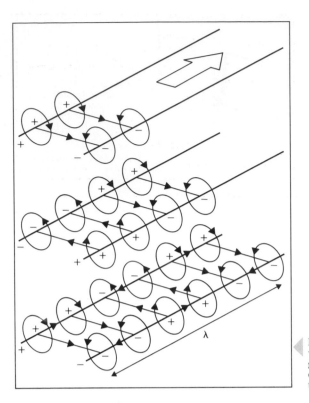

Figure 26.6 An alternating voltage across the rods generates an alternating electromagnetic field which travels along them

Polarisation

Electromagnetic waves are transverse. This means that they can be **polarised**. This is illustrated with the experiment shown in figure 26.8. The power extracted from the wave by the receiver dipole is measured for different orientations. Since the E field from the transmitting dipole is vertical (figure 26.9), it cannot induce any currents in the receiving dipole when it is horizontal. The wave from the transmitter is said to be **vertically polarised**.

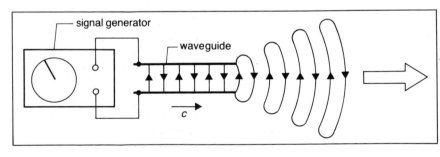

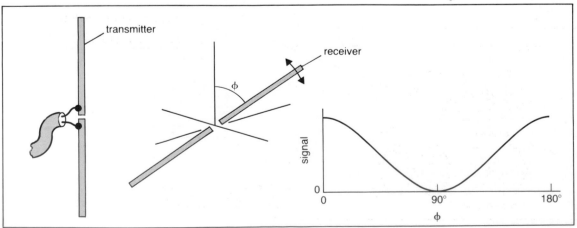

Figure 26.7 How the E field of an electromagnetic wave can break away from the end of the waveguide

Figure 26.8 The signal picked up by the receiver is a maximum when it is parallel to the transmitter

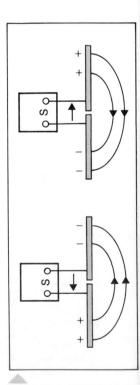

Figure 26.9 The E field of the wave is parallel to the transmitting dipole

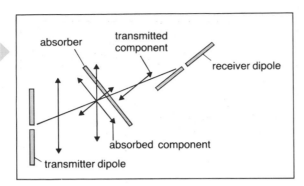

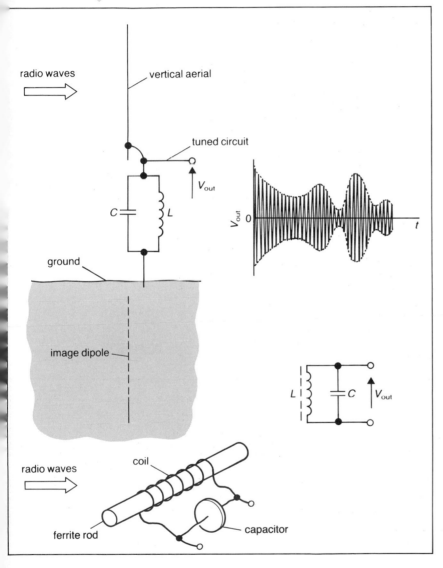

The insertion of a third rod between the transmitter and receiver can alter the polarisation of the wave. Look at figure 26.10. The component of the field parallel to the rod will induce alternating currents in it. If the rod is half a wavelength long, a standing wave of current is set up along its length, converting electrical energy to heat energy. So as the wave passes by the rod it emerges polarised in a direction at right angles to the length of the rod. This new direction of polarisation can be detected by rotating the receiver dipole until it detects a maximum signal.

Radio waves can be detected either through their E field or their B field. For example, stations on the medium wave ($\approx$ 1 MHz) transmit radio waves which are vertically polarised. This means that a vertical conductor (**aerial**) whose bottom end is earthed (figure 26.11) will interact with the oscillating electric field. (The ground below the aerial acts like an electrical mirror, so that the vertical conductor looks like half of a dipole to the incoming radio waves.) Alternatively, a coil wound around a horizontal ferrite rod will interact with the oscillating magnetic field. Figure 26.11 shows how these two types of aerial are incorporated into the parallel LC circuit (the **tuner**) which forms the first stage of a radio receiver.

Wave velocity

The speed of a radio wave can be deduced from separate measurements of its frequency and wavelength. The frequency can be measured electronically, either by displaying the receiver signal on an oscilloscope screen or by feeding it into a counter. Frequencies of up to about 1 GHz can be easily measured this way. The wavelength is measured by getting radio waves to interfere with each other. For example, the wavelength of 1 GHz waves can be found with the arrangement shown in figure 26.12. The transmitting dipole beams a wave towards the flat metal reflector. Two waves arrive at the receiving dipole, one directly from the transmitter, the other from the reflector. The latter is moved until the galvanometer signal is a minimum i.e. the two waves are destructively interfering with each other. The reflector is then moved away from the transmitter until the signal is a minimum once more. The extra path distance introduced for one wave must therefore be one wavelength, i.e. the reflector must have been moved by half a wavelength. Suppose that the reflector is moved 15 cm from one minimum signal to another:

$$c = f\lambda, \lambda = 2\times0.15 \text{ m}, \quad f = 1.0\times10^9 \text{ Hz}$$
$$\therefore c = 1.0\times10^9 \times 0.3 = 3.0\times10^8 \text{ m s}^{-1}$$

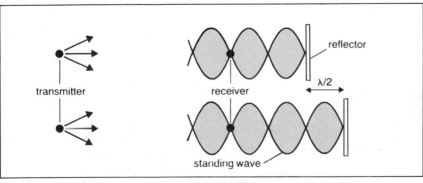

Figure 26.12 Finding the wavelength of a radio wave with the help of standing waves

WIRELESS TELEGRAPHY

In 1901, only 15 years after Hertz had first discovered them, Guglielmo Marconi used radio waves to send messages from England to Newfoundland, a distance of about 3000 km over the Atlantic Ocean. He used a **pulsed carrier** technique to transmit his message in Morse code, switching the radio transmitter on for short and long time intervals to represent the dots and dashes. What is remarkable about Marconi's experiment is that his result, according to the best minds of the day, was impossible! They pointed out that since the Earth is curved, hardly any of the radio waves from the transmitter would reach the receiver (figure 26.13). Marconi used kites to get his aerials raised 150 m above the ground to try and get around this, but what really saved him was the existence of the **ionosphere**. This is a layer of ionised gas trapped in the Earth's upper atmosphere which acts as an efficient reflector for radio waves below 3 MHz. Above 30 MHz, radio waves pass straight through the ionosphere, so these cannot be used for over-the-horizon communications. Television and FM radio broadcasts are therefore local, being beamed out from transmitters at the top of tall towers (figure 26.14) sited at the highest point in the area. High frequency radio waves have short wavelengths, making it possible to build reflectors around receiver dipoles. For efficient reception, each arm of the dipole must have a length of $\lambda/4$. Figure 26.15 shows a **reflector** placed behind a TV receiver dipole and a number of **directors** placed in front of it. The spacing of these components ensures constructive interference of the various reflected waves when they meet at the dipole.

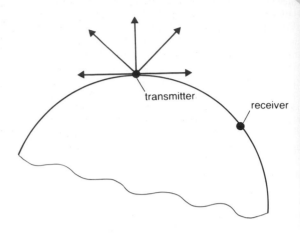

Figure 26.13 A distant receiver cannot pick up radio waves directly from the transmitter

Figure 26.14 The highest television antennae in the world—3255 m above sea level

Figure 26.15 A TV aerial

Microwaves

Microwaves have wavelengths between 10 cm and 1 cm. Consequently, their frequencies range from about 3 GHz to 300 GHz, far above those attainable in conventional electronic circuits. They are generated in devices like the **magnetron** shown in figure 26.16. Bunches of electrons are rapidly swept past cavities so that standing waves can build up inside them. The oscillations inside the cavity modulate the velocity of the electrons, causing them to bunch up even more, providing a positive feedback mechanism which allows the amplitude of the standing waves to increase. Low-power microwaves with wavelengths of 3 cm are usually obtained from Gunn diodes in resonant cavities (figure 26.17), with a waveguide to feed the microwaves out in a particular direction.

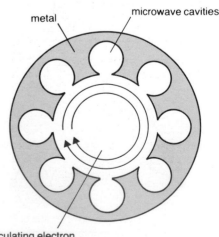

metal

microwave cavities

circulating electron region (vertical magnetic field)

Figure 26.16 A magnetron

Figure 26.17 Low-power microwaves are widely used by supermarkets to detect customers. The transmitter and receiver are in the same housing above the door

Wave properties

The fact that microwaves are generated by electrical means is a strong hint that they might be electromagnetic waves. Their wave nature is easily demonstrated in the laboratory with the apparatus shown in figure 26.19. As the reflector is moved across the line joining the receiver and the transmitter, interference effects are obvious. Note the destructive interference when the reflector is in line with the transmitter and receiver, implying a phase change of $\pi/2$ upon reflection. The insertion of a grid of parallel wires between transmitter and receiver (figure 26.20) shows that the microwaves can be polarised just like radio waves. However, the true test of a member of the electromagnetic spectrum is a measurement of its velocity.

The frequency of a microwave is too high for it to be measured reliably, so its velocity has to be measured by a time-of-flight technique. The shortest time which can be reliably measured in a school laboratory, with the help of an oscilloscope, is about 0.1 µs. Electromagnetic waves travel a distance of 30 m in that time. The arrangement of apparatus shown in figure 26.21(a) could, in principle, be used in school to estimate the speed of microwaves. (In practice, the experiment is illegal because rapid switching of microwaves on and off can interfere with telephone communication systems!) The transmitter is run off a high frequency signal generator so that it emits bursts of microwaves. These are **collimated** by the wax lens and travel towards a **corner-cube reflector**. After reflection they are focused onto the receiver by another wax lens. The aluminium sheet prevents any waves getting straight from the transmitter to the receiver. A double beam oscilloscope is used to compare the signals from the receiver with the signal generator — a typical trace is shown in figure 26.21(b). The time delay between the two falling edges is measured for two different positions of the reflector. A movement of 30 m should result in a 0.2 µs change of time delay.

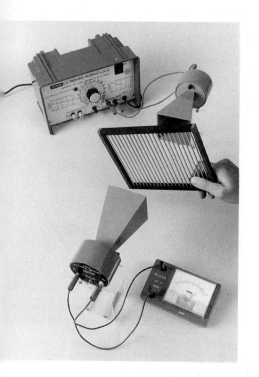

The most familiar domestic application of microwaves is probably their use for cooking food. Microwave ovens (figure 26.18) expose their contents to a flood of 2.45 GHz radio waves. This frequency matches one of the natural frequencies of the water molecule, so the radio waves are absorbed by the water in the food and converted to heat energy. Provided that the food is not wrapped in aluminium foil (an excellent reflector of radio waves), the microwaves penetrate several centimetres into the food, delivering energy into its interior much faster than conduction can. The wave nature of these microwaves is apparent from the methods adopted to avoid standing waves cooking the food unevenly. The dimensions of a typical microwave cooker are of the order of a few wavelengths (λ = 12 cm), so there will definitely be lots of opportunities for destructive interference of the microwaves as they bounce around the cavity. Food which lies at a node will have no heat energy delivered to it by the microwaves. This problem is usually solved by rotating the food inside the cavity, ensuring that no portion of it is at a standing wave node for too long.

Figure 26.18 Microwave oven

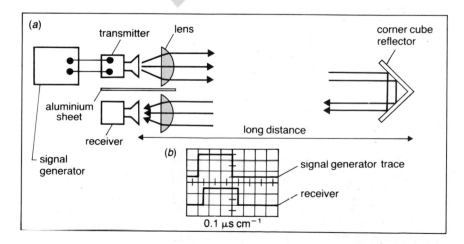

Figure 26.19
Demonstrating the wave nature of microwaves

Figure 26.20 Polarising microwaves

Figure 26.21 Apparatus for measuring the speed of microwaves

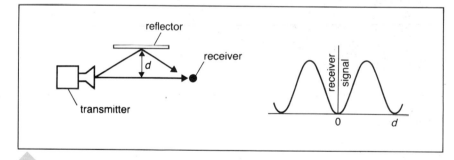

SATELLITE COMMUNICATIONS

Figure 26.22 Satellite transmission station

Figure 26.23 A dipole at the focus of a TV satellite receiver dish

Microwaves are used for satellite communication systems for many reasons. First, they are not affected by the ionosphere and can therefore be used to send signals between a satellite in geostationary orbit and the Earth (figure 26.22). Secondly, their small wavelength (of the order of a centimetre) means that it is feasible to place the transmitting and receiving dipoles in front of parabolic reflecting dishes (figure 26.23). This allows the waves to be sent in a particular direction in a beam which spreads out relatively little as it travels, increasing the intensity of the signal detected by the receiver. Finally, the high frequency of microwaves (about 10 GHz) allows information to be sent at a prodigious rate. To understand this last point, look at figure 26.24. It shows the **frequency spectrum** of a radio wave which is being pulsed on and off f_S times a second. The bandwidth occupied by the components of the frequency spectrum (the **sidebands**) is approximately $10f_S$. If we suppose that a 1 (in electronic terms) is represented by a pulse and a 0 by the lack of a pulse, then a bandwidth of $10f_S$ is needed to transmit $2f_S$ bits of information per second. In other words, if the bit rate is f_B, the bandwidth required is $5f_B$. So if you are prepared to accept a bandwidth of 1 GHz, a single microwave link can transmit information at a rate of 2×10^8 bits per second. The approximate bit rates needed for Morse code, telephone speech and colour television shown in table 1 should put this number into perspective. So a single microwave link can simultaneously handle approximately ten TV channels or 4000 telephone calls!

Information source	Bit rate/Hz
Morse code	5
telephone speech	5×10^4
colour television	2×10^7

Figure 26.24 Frequency spectrum of a radio wave which is being pulsed on and off

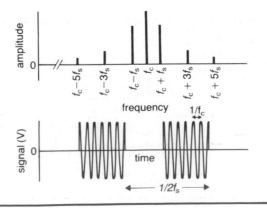

Light

Evidence that light is electromagnetic is hard to come by in everyday experience. Most of our domestic artificial light sources rely on heating strips of metal to white heat. LEDs are the only familiar example of the direct conversion of electrical energy to light. It was therefore regarded as something of a revolution in 1864 when Maxwell proposed that visible light was an electromagnetic wave with a frequency of about 6×10^{14} Hz.

Wedge fringes
Anyone who has noticed the glorious colours of soap bubbles while washing up should be prepared to accept that light is a wave. The bright and dark fringes are even more spectacular when observed in **monochromatic** light from a laser or a sodium lamp (figure 26.25). (Monochromatic light contains waves with just one wavelength rather than a range of them.) The light is partially reflected from both surfaces of the film to give constructive or destructive interference, depending on its thickness.

The arrangement of apparatus shown in figure 26.26 can be used to estimate the wavelength of light. Two sheets of glass are held slightly apart at one end to form a wedge of air. Light from a sodium lamp is then shone on the plates from above. If the air wedge is observed with a microscope, a series of dark and bright fringes can be seen. The lateral separation x of the fringes is given by $2x = \lambda/\theta$, where θ is the angle between the two plates and λ is the wavelength of the light. A similar arrangement which uses a lens on a flat sheet of glass is shown in figure 26.27. The fringes (known as **Newton's Rings**) are very beautiful, especially when white light, containing a mixture of wavelengths, is used.

Figure 26.25 Interference fringes in a thin soap film

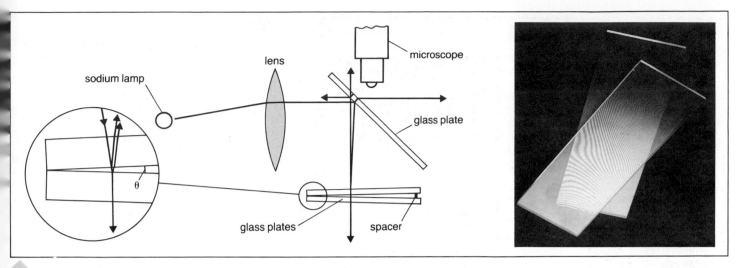

Figure 26.26 Apparatus for viewing wedge fringes—the photograph shows fringes obtained by placing one microscope slide on top of another in sodium light

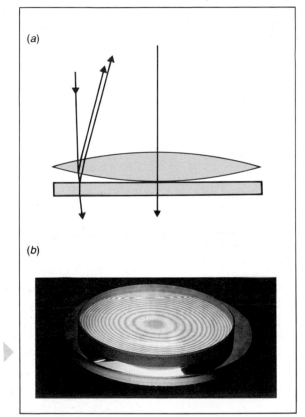

Figure 26.27 An interference pattern caused by two lenses in contact with each other

Figure 26.28 Apparatus for measuring the speed of light

The speed of light

For light to be an electromagnetic wave, it must travel at 3×10^8 m s^{-1}. Verifying this in a school laboratory is not easy. Figure 26.28(a) shows an arrangement of apparatus which, at first glance, looks as if it might do the trick. The laser beam is focused onto the surface of a disc which has a number of slots cut into its perimeter (figure 26.28(b)). As the disc spins round, the beam of light is chopped on and off, so that the portion of the beam reflected off the glass plate to the first photodiode gives rise to a regular train of pulses on the oscilloscope screen. Most of the beam carries on through the glass plate to the corner-cube reflector (a bicycle rear reflector), eventually returning to the second photodiode. The time taken for the round trip between laser and reflector can be measured from the falling edges of the two oscilloscope traces (figure 26.28(c)). (In practice, the oscilloscope has to be triggered off the signal from the first photodiode, so that its falling edge does not actually appear on the screen!)

Let us insert some numbers (see figure 26.28(d)). The shortest time interval we can measure is 1×10^{-7} s. The reflector can be sited 30 m away, giving a time delay of 2×10^{-7} s. For this time delay to be apparent on the oscilloscope screen, the laser beam must be cut off in at least 1×10^{-7} s. The laser can be focussed down to a spot with a diameter of roughly 40 μm, limited by diffraction (see chapter 27).

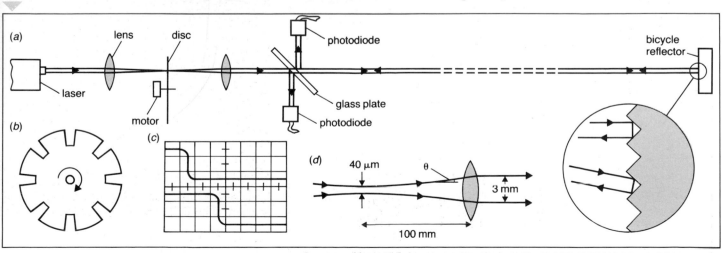

$\theta \simeq \lambda/b$, $\theta = 3/100 = 1.5\times 10^{-2}$ rad, $\lambda = 633$ nm

$\therefore b \simeq 40\ \mu$m

So the perimeter of the disc must be moving at a speed of at least $40\times 10^{-6}/1\times 10^{-7} = 400$ m s^{-1}. If the disc has a radius of 10 cm, this implies a rotational speed of at least 700 revolutions per second! This is about twice as fast as the maximum speed of a small electric motor. So for the experiment to give a precise value for c, the reflector will have to be placed many kilometres from the chopping disc.

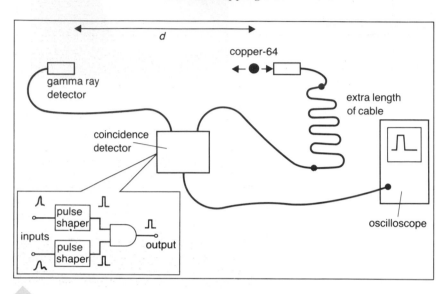

Figure 26.29 Measuring the speed of gamma rays

Figure 26.30 Measuring the speed of pulses down a coaxial cable

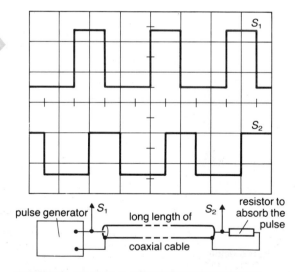

Gamma rays

It is very difficult to demonstrate that gamma rays can be polarised or made to interfere, so their membership of the electromagnetic spectrum is clinched by their velocity. This can be measured with the apparatus shown in figure 26.29. A pair of photomultipliers sample gamma rays which emerge from the copper-64 source in opposite directions. These gamma rays are the result of annihilation of positrons (produced by beta decay in the nucleus) with electrons in the sample. One of the photomultipliers is placed further away from the source, so that there is a time delay between the detection of the gamma rays. A carefully calculated length of coaxial cable is used to connect the other photomultiplier to the **coincidence detector**. This bunch of electronics counts the rate at which pulses arrive simultaneously from both detectors. The extra length of cable is adjusted until the coincidence output is maximised. The whole experiment is then repeated for a number of different distances of the mobile photomultiplier. The speed of electrical pulses down the coaxial cable can, of course, be measured in a separate experiment (figure 26.30) with a pulse generator and an oscilloscope.

OBJECTIVES

After studying this section you should be able to do the following.

State two distinguishing properties common to all electromagnetic waves.

State the names and approximate wavelengths of the principal members of the electromagnetic spectrum.

Understand why a change of electric field is accompanied by a change of magnetic field.

Describe the behaviour of the fields in an electromagnetic wave.

Explain why electromagnetic waves can be polarised.

Describe how the speed of an electromagnetic wave can be measured by a time-of-flight technique.

Describe experiments to show the wave nature of light and radio waves.

Describe how the velocity of gamma rays can be measured.

QUESTIONS

1 The first realistic estimate of the speed of light was made by an astronomer called Roemer in 1676. He observed something odd about the behaviour of one of Jupiter's moons. The moon is eclipsed by Jupiter once every 1.77 days, i.e. passes into Jupiter's shadow. This can be clearly seen with a good telescope. Roemer noticed that when Jupiter was its maximum distance from the Earth, the eclipses were happening 16.5 minutes *later* than when Jupiter was at its nearest point to Earth. Explain why, with the help of a diagram. If the mean radius of the Earth's orbit round the Sun is 1.5×10^{11} m, estimate the velocity of light.

2 Small ships often have the contraption shown in figure 26.31 attached near the top of their masts. It ensures their visibility on other ship's radar screens. Explain how it does it.

3 Polaroid is a synthetic material which completely absorbs light whose electric vector lies perpendicular to a plane in the material (its axis). For this problem, you can assume that light whose electric vector is parallel to the axis is not attenuated at all.

a Polaroid contains long molecules which act like conductors, embedded in an insulating matrix. Are the molecules aligned parallel to the axis or perpendicular to it?

b Light from a filament lamp is randomly polarised. Each wave emitted can have its E field pointing in any direction. By how much does the intensity (power per square metre) of a light beam from a filament lamp fall when a sheet of polaroid is placed in front of it?

c The light going towards the polaroid can have any polarisation. Yet the light emerging from the polaroid is definitely polarised along the polaroid axis. Explain why.

d If a second sheet of polaroid is placed in front of the first, then the intensity of light which gets through is proportional to $\cos^2\phi$, where ϕ is the angle between the axes of the two sheets. By means of a graph, show how the intensity changes when the second polaroid is rotated through 360°. Explain why the graph has the shape it does.

4 The intensity of an electromagnetic wave from a point source is proportional to the inverse square of the distance it has travelled.

a The intensity of sunlight at the surface of the Earth is 1.4 kW m^{-2}. What is the total power output of sunlight from the surface of the Sun? The Earth's orbit radius is 1.45×10^{11} m and the Sun's radius is 6.95×10^{8} m.

b Estimate how far away you can sit from an isolated 100 W bulb and yet be able to read comfortably by it. If the bulb has an efficiency of 8%, estimate the minimum intensity of light necessary for you to be able to read comfortably.

c Table 26.3 lists data for a number of planets. On which of them would you be able to read a book by the light of the Sun? Ignore atmospheric effects.

Table 26.3

Planet	Radius of orbit/m
Saturn	1.4×10^{12}
Uranus	2.9×10^{12}
Neptune	4.5×10^{12}
Pluto	5.9×10^{12}

5 In 1849 Fizeau used the apparatus illustrated in figure 26.32 to measure the speed of light. The wheel had 720 slots cut into its perimeter. The mirror was placed 8.6 km from the wheel which was rotated so that the observer could not see the light source through the slots. This happened when the wheel was rotated at 756 revolutions per minute.

a Explain why the light from the source disappears and then reappears when the wheel's angular velocity is steadily increased from zero.

b Calculate a value for the velocity of light.

c It is possible to make a small electric motor rotate at speeds of 30 000 r.p.m. when it is unloaded. Discuss how you could adapt Fizeau's method for use in a school laboratory using such a motor. Make sure you include a description of how to measure the rotational speed of the motor.

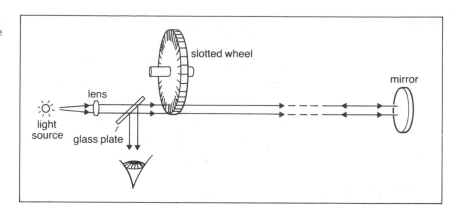

Figure 26.32   Figure 26.31

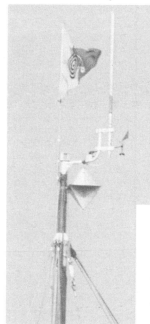

Figure 26.33

6 Table 26.4 contains some data for the experiment shown in figure 26.29. d is the distance of one detector from the copper-64 source and l is the extra length of coaxial cable inserted to achieve coincidence.

Table 26.4

d/m	l/m
2.29	8.23
7.33	11.58
14.88	16.54
34.77	29.97

If the speed of electric pulses down the coaxial cable is 2.00×10^{8} m s^{-1}, use the data of table 26.4 to find the velocity of gamma rays.

7 Figure 26.33 shows the type of radio wave receiver used by Hertz in his original experiments. The wire loop, with its two balls at the end, acts like a parallel LC circuit. If its natural frequency matches the frequency of the radio waves, small sparks cross the gap between the balls.

a Which dimensions of the device affect its capacitance? What about its inductance?

b Hertz would obviously have had to tune his detector to match the frequency of the waves he was transmitting. How would he have to go about this?

c How did Hertz orient his receiver? Does it respond to the E field or the B field of the radio wave?

RELATIVITY

Think about a wave travelling along the surface of the sea at a steady speed. What would it look like if you were in a boat moving with the same velocity? The answer is obvious: the wave would appear to be stationary. This is because the velocity of the wave is *relative* to the velocity of the sea. Now think about a light wave. What would it look like if you could travel alongside it at a speed of 3×10^8 m s^{-1}?

The speed of light

Before you can ask such a question in physics, you must be quite sure that the answer is, in principle, verifiable by experiment. Not a real experiment perhaps, because of the cost, but certainly a thought experiment consistent with the Laws of Physics. So let us think more carefully about how the speed of a light wave might change if we moved along in the same direction. The answer has to be that however fast we move, the light will still appear to be moving with the same speed.

This conclusion appears to be nonsense! Yet consider the expression for the speed of light in space.

$$c = (\mu_0 \epsilon_0)^{-\frac{1}{2}} \qquad \textbf{(26.2)}$$

Both μ_0 and ϵ_0 are fundamental constants. The value of ϵ_0 is obtained by measuring the force between two charged particles, and μ_0 is a consequence of our unit of electric current, the ampere. In principle, scientists in different places could do separate experiments to find the values of μ_0 and ϵ_0 and end up by calculating the same value for c. However, suppose that we put one set of scientists and the equipment they need in a space craft moving at a steady speed away from Earth. Would they get different answers for μ_0 and ϵ_0? Would they calculate a different answer for c? Einstein guessed that they wouldn't, that the speed of light is the same for everybody. Furthermore, he reckoned that the laws of physics and the fundamental constants which go with them are the same all over the Universe, however fast you are moving. These ideas prompted Einstein to suggest the following three postulates for our Universe.

- The speed of light is the same for all observers.
- Observers moving at a constant velocity with respect to each other will be subject to exactly the same laws of physics.
- There is no way that an observer can show that he is not moving at a constant velocity.

(We have already discussed the last postulate in chapter 5, page 57.) The rest of this section will use simple thought experiments to tease out some of the consequences of these postulates. Some of the conclusions will appear outrageous, directly contrary to intuition. Please remember that you have never experienced what it is like to travel at speeds near that of light, so you should expect to be surprised!

PREDICTING c IN WAVEGUIDES !

Figure 26.34 Three different waveguides

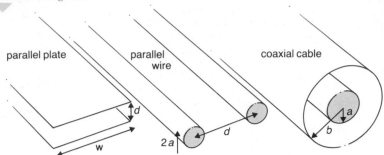

parallel plate

parallel wire

coaxial cable

Consider an electromagnetic wave moving down a waveguide. Any waveguide will do: see figure 26.34 for three examples. Can we show that the wave *has* to move down the waveguide at a velocity $c = (\mu_0 \epsilon_0)^{-\frac{1}{2}}$? Although we could do it mathematically, it is easier to show it with the help of an analogy. Any waveguide has inductance and capacitance spread along its length, so it can be modelled as a long chain of inductors and capacitors (figure 26.35) which will allow a voltage pulse to travel along its length.

You will recall from chapter 25 that the inductor and capacitor in a parallel LC circuit are analogous to the mass and spring in a simple harmonic oscillator. So the voltage pulse travelling down the chain of capacitors and inductors is analogous to a compression pulse travelling down a chain of masses held together by springs (figure 26.35). We can obtain a formula for the speed of that pulse by considering the speed of sound in a solid. After all, a solid can be modelled as a large number of masses and springs. Look at figure 26.35. The spacing of the masses is d_0, with $m = L$ and $k = 1/C$. The speed of compression waves in a material made up of a large number of interconnected masses and springs is given by

$$c = (E/\rho)^{\frac{1}{2}}, \quad E = \frac{k}{d_0}, \quad \rho = \frac{m}{d_0^3} \quad \therefore c^2 = \frac{k d_0^2}{m} \qquad (1)$$

Now replace k and m with their electrical equivalents.

$$k = \frac{1}{C}, \quad m = L \qquad \therefore c^2 = \frac{d_0^2}{LC} \qquad (2)$$

If we rearrange equation (2) using the inductance and capacitance per metre, L^* and C^*, we end up with a very useful expression.

$$c^2 = \frac{d_0^2}{LC}, \quad L^* = \frac{L}{d_0}, \quad C^* = \frac{C}{d_0} \quad \therefore c^2 = \frac{1}{L^* C^*} \qquad (3)$$

Table 1 gives formulae for L^* and C^* for the three waveguides shown in figure 26.34. If each pair is substituted into equation (3), the result is the same each time i.e. $c = (\mu_0 \epsilon_0)^{-\frac{1}{2}}$. Try it for yourself. So it looks as though electromagnetic waves travel at the same speed, regardless of the waveguide used to generate them.

Table 1

Waveguide	L^*	C^*
parallel plate	$\mu_0 d/w$	$\epsilon_0 w/d$
parallel wires	$\mu_0 \ln[d/a]/\pi$	$\pi \epsilon_0 / \ln[d/a]$
coaxial cable	$\mu_0 \ln[b/a]/2\pi$	$2\pi \epsilon_0 / \ln[b/a]$

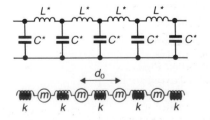

Figure 26.35 The electrical behaviour of a waveguide can be modelled with this network of capacitors and inductors: in turn, the network is analogous to a number of masses connected by springs

Doppler shift

Suppose that we take two students called John and Mary and place them in an inter-galactic science park (figure 26.36). Both are equipped with identical clocks and lasers, and their spacecrafts each have windows so that they can communicate with each other by laser light pulses. They are going to perform a number of experiments to elucidate the consequences of Einstein's ideas. However, before they start properly, they will practise with a couple of simple measurements.

Measuring distance

At one end of the park is a derelict fusion reactor which acts as a distance marker. By firing his laser at it and looking for any Doppler shift of the reflected light, John establishes that he is not moving relative to the marker. He then fires a short pulse of light at the marker and measures how long it takes to return. Suppose that he emits the pulse at time t_1 and it arrives back at time t_2. John can then work out the relative position l_0 of the marker at a particular time t, remembering that the light pulse has to travel to the marker *and* back in a time $t_2 - t_1$.

$$v = \frac{\Delta x}{\Delta t} \quad \therefore \quad l_0 = \frac{c(t_2 - t_1)}{2} \quad \text{at} \quad t = \frac{t_2 + t_1}{2} \quad \textbf{(26.3)}$$

This procedure for measuring distance will become clearer if you study the displacement–time graph of figure 26.37. The vertical displacement axis of x/c has been carefully chosen so that light is represented by a line at 45° to the t–axis. The marker, of course, is not moving relative to John, so its line is horizontal.

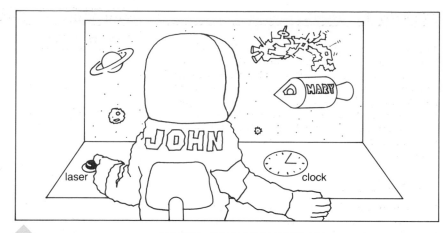

Figure 26.36 The inter-galactic science park

Figure 26.37 Firing a pulse of light at the marker

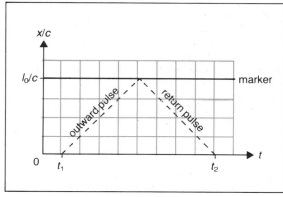

Measuring relative velocity

Now Mary sets off directly towards the marker at a steady speed. At the instant she passes John, a laser pulse is passed between them to synchronise their clocks. So John sets $t = 0$ when Mary's displacement $x = 0$. Figure 26.38 shows how he sets about measuring the speed with which she is moving away. He fires off a laser pulse at time t_1 and waits for it to be reflected off Mary's spacecraft. It arrives back at time t_2. John can now work out how far away Mary was when his laser pulse hit her and hence calculate her relative velocity v. Let the pulse hit Mary at time t' when she is a distance x' from John.

$$v = \frac{x'}{t'}, \qquad x' = \frac{c(t_2 - t_1)}{2}, \qquad t' = \frac{t_2 + t_1}{2}$$

$$\therefore v = \frac{c(t_2 - t_1)}{t_2 + t_1} \qquad \textbf{(26.4)}$$

Of course, Mary could do exactly the same experiment to measure her speed relative to John. She would get exactly the same answer. Different observers moving relative to each other always agree about their relative speed. (We shall come back to this later if you are not convinced.)

The *k*-factor

For the next experiment, Mary travels along the line between John and the marker as before. John emits one pulse per second, as shown in figure 26.39(a). Since light travels at a finite speed and Mary is moving away from John, it should be obvious that Mary sees the pulses arriving at times which are k seconds apart, where $k \geqslant 1$. This is the **Doppler shift**. The pulses emitted by John arrive at Mary stretched by a factor k.

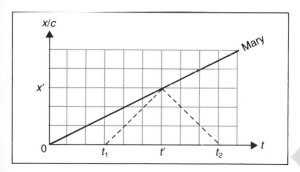

Figure 26.38 Reflecting a pulse off Mary

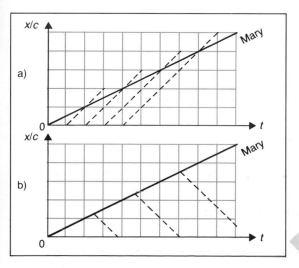

Figure 26.39 John and Mary both emits pulses at intervals of one second

Now suppose that Mary emits pulses towards John at one second intervals (figure 26.39(b)). Those pulses will arrive at John stretched by the *same* factor k. After all, Einstein said that it is only the *relative* motion of the two observers which is important, and John and Mary are agreed that they have the same relative velocity. So if John emits pulses at intervals of 1.0 s and Mary fires back a pulse of light each time she sees one of John's pulses, then John will see pulses arriving at intervals of $k \times k = k^2$ seconds. This experiment is illustrated in figure 26.40. A little geometry applied to this graph gives the following formula for the k−factor.

$$k = \sqrt{\frac{1 + v/c}{1 - v/c}} \qquad (26.5)$$

Frequency shifts

Suppose that Mary emits laser light continuously with a frequency f_0. We can think of this as being a series of clock pulses emitted at intervals of $1/f_0$ seconds. John will receive those pulses stretched by a factor k, arriving at intervals of k/f_0. So the frequency f of the laser beam as measured by John will be given by

$$f = \frac{f_0}{k}$$

$$\therefore f = f_0 \times \sqrt{\frac{1 - v/c}{1 + v/c}} \qquad (26.6)$$

(Provided that v/c is much less than 1, equation (26.6) is virtually the same as the classical Doppler shift formula $\Delta f = -f_0 v/c$.)

As an example, let's calculate the largest frequency shift of laser light you might be able to arrange on Earth. Consider two jet fighters travelling away from each other at about Mach 5, i.e. a relative velocity of 1500 m s^{-1}. If one fighter emits a red laser beam of wavelength 633 nm, what will the colour appear to be to the other fighter? The first step is to calculate v/c and f_0.

$$\frac{v}{c} = \frac{1.5 \times 10^3}{3.0 \times 10^8} = 5 \times 10^{-6},$$

$$f_0 = \frac{c}{\lambda} = \frac{3.00 \times 10^8}{633 \times 10^{-9}} = 4.74 \times 10^{14} \text{ Hz}$$

$$f = f_0 \times \sqrt{\frac{1 - v/c}{1 + v/c}}$$

$$\therefore f = 4.74 \times 10^{14} \times \sqrt{\frac{0.999995}{1.000005}}$$

$$\therefore f = 4.74 \times 10^{14} \times 0.999995$$

The shift in wavelength is therefore going to be far too small to make any difference to the colour of the laser beam! (The shift in frequency can, however, be measured accurately by combining the laser beam from the first jet with light from a similar laser on board the second jet and measuring the beat frequency.)

Time dilation

So far, John and Mary's experiments have produced nothing very startling, just a high velocity correction to the classical Doppler shift formula. The result of their next experiment will certainly give you something to think about!

Figure 26.40 John's pulses arrive back separated by k^2 seconds

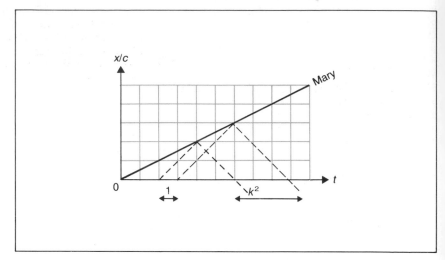

FINDING THE k-FACTOR !

Look at figure 26.41. It shows the $x/c - t$ graph of the light pulse emitted by John 1.0 s after Mary passed him at $x = 0$. The pulse leaves John when his clock reads $t = 1.0$ and returns when it reads $t = k^2$. Consider the triangle DBE. Because it is an isosceles triangle with a right angle at its apex, its height must be half its base i.e. $BC = \frac{1}{2}(k^2 - 1)$. Now consider the right-angled triangle ABC.

$$\tan\theta = \frac{\frac{1}{2}(k^2 - 1)}{1 + \frac{1}{2}(k^2 - 1)} \qquad (1)$$

The angle θ is fixed by Mary's velocity relative to John. Since the displacement axis is x/c, then we can write down another expression for $\tan\theta$.

$$\tan\theta = \frac{x/c}{t}, \quad v = \frac{x}{t} \qquad \therefore \tan\theta = \frac{v}{c} \qquad (2)$$

If you combine equations (1) and (2) to eliminate $\tan\theta$ you eventually end up with equation (26.5).

Figure 26.41

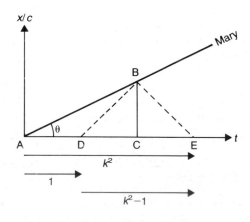

The round trip

Mary travels from John to the marker and back at a constant speed. Along the way she emits pulses of light towards John at intervals of one second. Suppose that Mary takes t_0 seconds to make the round trip. She will emit $t_0/2$ pulses on the way to the marker and another $t_0/2$ on the way back to John (figure 26.42). The first set of pulses will arrive at John stretched by the k-factor, taking a total time t_1 to arrive.

$$t_1 = \frac{t_0}{2} \sqrt{\frac{1 + v/c}{1 - v/c}} \qquad (26.7)$$

The second lot of pulses will arrive compressed by a different k-factor, because Mary is now moving towards John with a velocity v.

$$t_2 = \frac{t_0}{2} \sqrt{\frac{1 - v/c}{1 + v/c}} \qquad (26.8)$$

John's estimate of the time taken for the round trip is therefore given by

$$t = t_1 + t_2 = \frac{t_0}{2}\left(\sqrt{\frac{1 + v/c}{1 - v/c}} + \sqrt{\frac{1 - v/c}{1 + v/c}} \right)$$

$$\therefore t = \frac{t_0(1 + v/c + 1 - v/c)}{2(1 - v/c)^{\frac{1}{2}}(1 + v/c)^{\frac{1}{2}}}$$

$$\therefore t = \frac{t_0}{(1 - v^2/c^2)^{\frac{1}{2}}} \qquad (26.9)$$

Look at equation (26.29) carefully. It says that John's clock has measured a different time for the journey than has Mary's clock. Two identical clocks have been used to measure the time interval between a pair of events (Mary passing John), yet they have come up with different answers! There is only one conclusion. Absolute time does not exist: the measured time interval between two events depends on your velocity.

Slowing down time

Suppose that Mary had used her heartbeats as her clock. (After all, there is nothing in what we have said so far which involves the constructional details of the clock. The only requirement is that it is identical to John's clock.) Then equation (26.9) says that Mary's heart will have made fewer beats than John's during the experiment. Time, however you measure it, goes more slowly in a reference frame which is moving relative to you. This effect is called **time dilation**.

$$t = \frac{t_0}{(1 - v^2/c^2)^{\frac{1}{2}}}$$

t_0 is the time measured by a stationary observer

t is the time measured by a moving observer

v is the relative velocity of the two observers

c is the speed of light in space

Time dilation, however improbable it may seem, has been experimentally observed many times. For example, an atomic clock accompanied the Apollo astronauts on one of their round trips to the moon.

Although the maximum speed attained was only about 2 km s^{-1} ($v^2/c^2 \simeq 4 \times 10^{-11}$), the clock lost a measurable amount of time compared with its twin which was left on Earth. The difference was exactly accounted for by the time dilation equation.

Length contraction

Somewhat shaken by the fact that Mary, his fraternal twin, is now younger than he is, John asks her what she thinks is the distance l between himself and the marker. Mary knows that it took t_0 seconds to make the round trip at a relative velocity v.

$$v = \frac{2l}{t_0} \qquad (26.10)$$

On the other hand, John points out that he thinks she made the round trip of $2l_0$ in t seconds.

$$v = \frac{2l_0}{t} \qquad (26.11)$$

The conclusion is inescapable. If they are to agree on their relative velocity (and they will, because no amount of time dilation is going to affect equation (26.4)), then they must be getting different answers for the distance between John and the marker.

$$\frac{2l}{t_0} = \frac{2l_0}{t}, \qquad t = \frac{t_0}{(1 - v^2/c^2)^{\frac{1}{2}}}$$

$$\therefore l = l_0 (1 - v^2/c^2)^{\frac{1}{2}} \qquad (26.12)$$

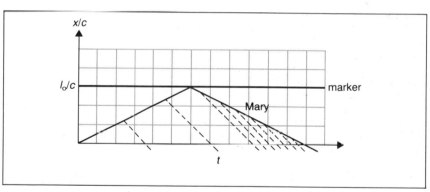

The distance l_0 is called the **proper length** because it is measured by someone (John) moving at the same velocity as the thing being measured. Mary is making the same measurement from a moving platform and consequently gets a smaller answer.

$$l = l_0(1 - v^2/c^2)^{\frac{1}{2}}$$

l is the length measured by the moving observer

l_0 is the length measured by the stationary observer

v is the relative velocity of the observers

c is the speed of light in space

Lateral contraction

Gary and Phil are intrigued by the results of John and Mary's experiments. Any spacecraft moving past them with a relative velocity v should be contracted by a factor $(1 - v^2/c^2)^{\frac{1}{2}}$ in the direction it is moving (figure 26.43). Is there any contraction of the other two dimensions at right angles to the

Figure 26.42 Mary goes on a round trip to the marker and back

Figure 26.43 Length contraction

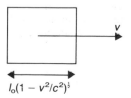
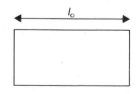

spacecraft's velocity? They decide to investigate with Wanda's help. First of all, Wanda uses a timed laser pulse to measure the diameter of her spacecraft while it is going at velocity v, getting the answer d_0. (This is the proper diameter of the spacecraft as it is measured by a stationary observer: its value will be completely independent of v.) Gary and Phil then position themselves this distance apart in the science park, once again using timed laser pulses to measure the distance. (Another measurement of proper length.) Wanda then flies her spacecraft at velocity v towards Gary and Phil, aiming for the centre of the gap between them. Gary and Phil agree afterwards that an edge of Wanda's spacecraft passed just overhead, so they conclude that there was no lateral contraction.

Gary and Phil's experiment is equivalent to measuring the diameter of Wanda's spacecraft by making her fly through a large sheet of aluminium foil! The diameter of the hole in the foil must be the diameter of the spacecraft, and since that distance can be measured with timed laser pulses by observers standing by the foil, there can be no confusion over its measurement. Of course, the same technique cannot be used to measure the diameter of the spacecraft along the direction of its velocity!

Mass increase

The final experiment is performed by Errol and Celie who are fervent believers of momentum conservation. (Einstein believed in it too.) They decide to use a compressed spring to impart some momentum to a pair of identical balls. The first step is to measure the mass of each ball by measuring its period of oscillation when tethered by a pair of springs. Both of them agree that each ball has a mass m_0. Errol places his ball next to one side of the compressed spring and leaves it there, as shown in figure 26.44. Celie goes to the other end of the science park with her ball and accelerates it to a speed v so that it passes close to the other side of the spring.

Conserving momentum

At the instant that the two balls are in line with the spring, Errol cuts the string restraining it (figure 26.45). Both balls receive the same impulse but in opposite directions, at right angles to Celie's motion. Celie tracks her ball at velocity v, timing how long it takes to move a distance y at right angles to her motion (figure 26.46). She gets the answer t_0 and uses a radio link to give Errol this data. Errol has also done the same experiment on his ball and also obtained the answer t_0. This has to be the case because we could consider Celie to be stationary and Errol to be moving and expect there to be no difference: only their *relative* velocity is important.

Errol calculates the momentum of his ball. It travels a distance y in time t_0.

$$p = mv \quad \therefore p = \frac{m_0 y}{t_0} \qquad (26.13)$$

He was not able to time the other ball over the same distance, but he can use the time dilation equation to convert Celie's timings into the equivalent timing on his own clock.

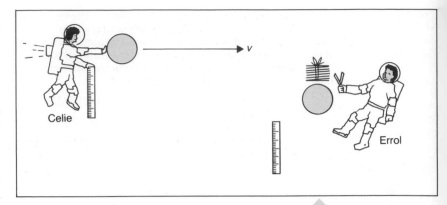

$$t = \frac{t_0}{(1 - v^2/c^2)^{\frac{1}{2}}} \qquad (26.14)$$

So the transverse momentum of Celie's ball, as measured by Errol should be given by

$$p = mv \quad \therefore p = \frac{my}{t_0}(1 - v^2/c^2)^{\frac{1}{2}} \qquad (26.15)$$

where m is the apparent mass of Celie's ball from Errol's viewpoint. (Errol is happy that he and Celie agree on the measurement of the length y, as it is at right angles to her velocity. Length contraction only happens along the direction parallel to the velocity.) If momentum is always conserved, then we can set equations (26.13) and (26.15) equal to each other.

$$p = \frac{my}{t_0}(1 - v^2/c^2)^{\frac{1}{2}} = \frac{m_0 y}{t_0}$$

$$\therefore m = \frac{m_0}{(1 - v^2/c^2)^{\frac{1}{2}}} \qquad (26.16)$$

So Errol is forced to conclude that Celie's ball gained mass while it was being accelerated to its velocity v. Similarly, Celie will think that Errol's ball has gained mass while her own still has its **rest mass** m_0. Mass is a relative, not an absolute, quantity.

$$m = \frac{m_0}{(1 - v^2/c^2)^{\frac{1}{2}}}$$

m is the apparent mass of an object

m_0 is the rest mass of the object

v is the relative velocity of the object and the observer

c is the speed of light in free space

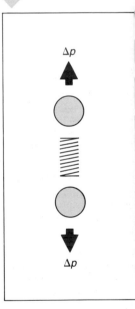

Figure 26.44 The arrangement of apparatus for Errol and Celie's experiment

Figure 26.45 The balls are given equal and opposite impulses by the spring

Figure 26.46 Errol and Celie measure the transverse velocity of the balls

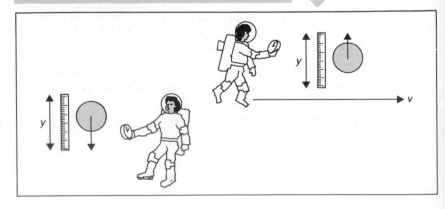

Accelerating electrons

The mass increase of fast electrons has been experimentally verified for speeds up to almost the speed of light. The time taken for an electron trapped in a magnetic field to make one complete orbit was worked out in chapter 23.

$$T = \frac{2\pi m}{Bq} \tag{26.17}$$

The radius of the orbit depends on the momentum of the electron.

$$mv = Bqr \tag{26.18}$$

So if bunches of high speed electrons are forced to orbit around the storage ring of a large accelerator, the orbit time can be used to calculate their mass. The radius of the ring and the orbit time can also be used to calculate their velocity. The result matches Einstein's predictions exactly. CERN is planning to accelerate electrons to energies of 50 GeV in a magnetic storage ring. The rest mass of an electron is only 0.5 MeV, so this is equivalent to increasing the mass of each electron by a factor of 10^5!

OBJECTIVES

After studying this section you should be able to do the following.

Understand why the speed of light is the same for all observers.

Know that an observer cannot prove by experiment that he is not moving.

Explain how electromagnetic waves can be used to make distance and velocity measurements.

Use the time dilation formula.

Use the length contraction formula.

Use the mass increase formula.

Appreciate that momentum is conserved for all observers.

QUESTIONS

1 Estimate your mass increase when you are flying in a jumbo jet at 800 km h^{-1}. If the smallest mass change which can be measured is 1 μg, how fast would you have to move for your mass to increase by this amount.(*Hint:* $(1 + x)^n \simeq 1 + nx$ if x is much smaller than 1.)

2 The nearest star Proxima Centauri is 4.3 light-years away. Suppose that a spacecraft could be accelerated to one third the speed of light to attempt to explore Proxima Centauri before coming back to Earth.

a How long would it take to get the spacecraft up to this speed if it was accelerated at a steady 10 m s^{-2}? (This gives the astronauts an environment where $g = 10$ N kg^{-1}.) Give your answer in years.

b Over what distance, according to Earth, would the spacecraft be able to coast at maximum speed before it had to start decelerating at 10 m s^{-2}?

c Use the time dilation formula to work out how long the astronauts should coast at full speed.

d Estimate the difference in the readings of a clock which made the round trip and an identical clock which stayed on Earth.

3 It has been suggested that an astronaut should be able to travel all the way round our galaxy (the Milky Way) in her own lifetime. If the diameter of the Milky Way is approximately 10^5 light-years, how fast would the astronaut have to move? How long would the people on Earth have to wait for her return?

4 Cosmic rays entering the upper atmosphere create particles called muons which travel downwards with speeds very close to that of light. They readily decay into electrons and neutrinos. Table 26.5 shows how the number of decays of a collection of muons at rest changes with time.

Table 26.5

Time/μs	Activity
0	568
2	229
4	99
6	36
8	6

a Use the data of table 26.5 to find the half-life of a muon.

b Suppose that 600 muons per hour are detected at the top of a mountain which is 2 km above sea level. If the muons are travelling at almost the speed of light, estimate how many should be detected per hour at sea level.

c In practice, the muon detection rate at sea level is 400 per hour. How much time does the 2.0 km journey from mountain top to sea level appear to take from a muon's point of view?

d Use the time dilation formula to calculate the velocity of the muons.

e Can you use the idea of length contraction as an alternative explanation for the results of the experiments?

An image is a ghost! It looks like the real thing, but has no substance that you can grasp. For example, the image of this printed page is an imitation of reality assembled in your brain from information supplied by your eyes. Similarly, the image on a television screen tries to mimic the pattern of light in the television studio. This chapter is going to introduce you to a technology, known as **optics**, which is used for making images with electromagnetic waves. Optics is sometimes regarded as an old-fashioned branch of applied physics — however, the transmission and storage of images is central to the modern entertainment industry and also lies at the heart of many systems which extend and improve our senses.

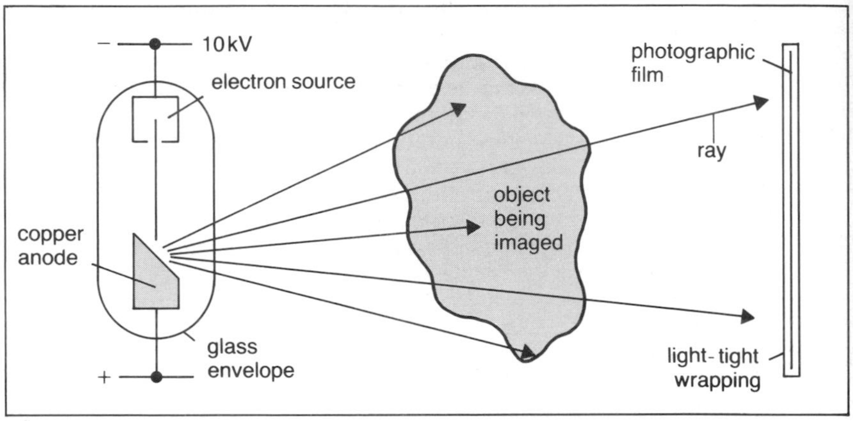

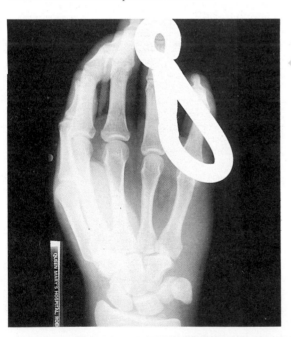

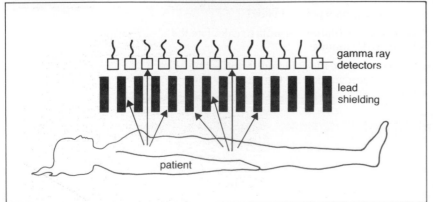

Figure 27.1 Making images with X-rays

Figure 27.2 An X-ray image of a human hand pierced with a metal hook. Notice how the flesh transmits more X-rays than the bone and that the hook is effectively opaque

Figure 27.3 A gamma camera

LENSES

Everybody knows that a lens is a bit of curved glass which can be used to change the direction of beams of light. The best way to appreciate the usefulness of a lens is to begin by studying a few imaging systems which do not use them.

Images without lenses

X-ray radiography is an example of a very simple imaging system, about as simple as you can get. It is illustrated in figure 27.1. It consists of three parts, known as the **wave source**, the **object** and the **image detector**. We will deal with each of these in turn. The wave source emits X-rays from the small point where the 10 keV electron beam hits the copper anode. Those X-rays travel out from the source in straight lines, represented by the **rays** drawn on figure 27.1. The intensity of X-rays which are transmitted by the object depends mainly on its surface density, i.e. length × density along the direction of the X-ray. So the intensity pattern of X-rays which reach the image detector (a photographic emulsion) contains information about the variation of surface density of the object (figure 27.2). It should be obvious that the sharpness of detail in the image depends on both the graininess of the photograph and on the size of the X-ray source.

Gamma ray images

Another equally simple, but very expensive imaging system is shown in figure 27.3. The **gamma camera** forms an image of the gamma ray emissions from a patient who has been injected with a gamma-emitting radioactive tracer. The holes in the lead shielding ensure that only gamma rays from a small portion of the patient's body can

...et to each sensor. Signals from the many sensors ...re recorded and analysed by a computer. The ...sult is an image of the gamma activity of the ...atient, revealing information about the way that ...e tracer is transmitted to and absorbed by their ...ssues. Unlike the X-ray system of figure 27.1, the ...amma camera has to form an image of a ...istributed wave source rather than a point one. ...he multiple-pierced lead shielding ensures that ...ach point on the image detector only receives ...aves from one point on the object. However, it ...hould be obvious that, for a detailed image to be ...uilt up, the gaps in the shielding have to be long ...nd narrow. This means that most of the gamma ...ays emitted by the patient are not detected by the ...ensors. Clearly, there is a trade-off between the ...efinition of the image and its intensity. If you ...vant high definition, you have to put up with a low ...ntensity and be prepared to wait a long time for the ...mage to be built up by the computer.

inhole cameras

...ou have probably played with a pinhole camera ...figure 27.4) at some stage in your school career. ...lthough it is usually regarded as a toy, its ...rinciples of operation are worth your appreciation ...ecause its images can sometimes be superior to ...hose of sophisticated lens cameras. The camera ...ollects light which is scattered off the object, with ...he pinhole ensuring that each point on the ...hotographic film only receives light approaching ...he camera from a particular angle. So the image on ...he film contains information about the intensity of ...ght approaching the pinhole over a range of ...ngles. However, the definition and intensity of ...hat image depends on the size of the pinhole ...figure 27.5). Doubling the diameter of the pinhole ...uadruples the total amount of light getting from ...he object to the film, but it also doubles the ...iameter of the spot on the film representing each ...oint on the object. So a useful pinhole camera ...eeds a long **exposure time** to get enough light ...hrough to the film (figure 27.6).

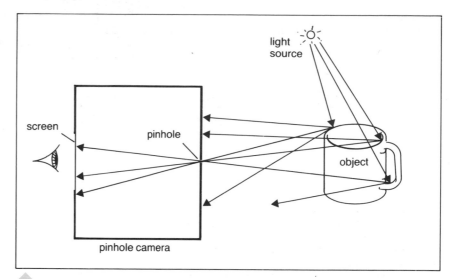

Figure 27.4 A pinhole camera

Figure 27.5 The pinhole has to be small to produce a clear image

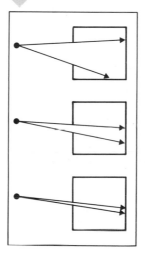

Figure 27.6 A pinhole camera image. Can you explain why the image fades as you move away from its centre? It has to do with the depth of the pinhole

Figure 27.7 A convex lens focusses rays of light from a particular direction to a point in the focal plane

Convex lenses

An ideal **convex lens** is an angle-to-position converter for light. This is illustrated in figure 27.7. Light which approaches any point on the surface of the lens at a particular angle to its **axis** is redirected towards a particular position in the **focal plane** of the lens. So if the lens is used to collect light scattered from a large, distant object and make it fall on a photographic film placed in the focal plane, the result is an image. The amount of light collected by the lens is proportional to its area, so a **lens camera** of the type shown in figure 27.8 can make do with much shorter exposure times than a pinhole camera. There is a price to be paid for this: the image definition is inferior to that of a pinhole camera. However, you need to know a lot more about what a lens does to light before you can understand why the image is imperfect.

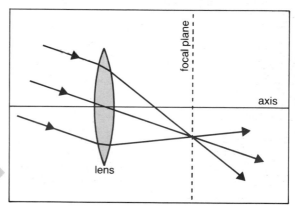

Figure 27.8 A lens camera

Image size

Look at figure 27.9(a) — it illustrates the behaviour of an ideal convex lens. All of the light rays approaching the lens are parallel to the axis. If they are to be **focused** to a single point (the **focal point**) on the axis, then the angle θ by which each ray is deflected must depend on where it hits the lens.

$$\tan \theta = \frac{h}{f} \quad \therefore \quad \theta = \frac{h}{f}, \quad \text{where } \theta < 15° \quad \textbf{(27.1)}$$

(We are going to stick to small-angle approximations for the time being. They are not all that unrealistic for real lens systems.) For a useful convex lens, equation (27.1) applies to *all* rays of light which hit the lens not too far from its centre. Therefore rays which approach the lens at an angle to the axis (figure 27.9(b)) will also be focused to a single point in the focal plane, a distance $f\phi$ above the focal point. So if light from a distant object of height h_o is collected by a lens of focal length f, we can calculate the height h_i of the image in the focal plane (figure 27.10).

$$h_i = f\phi, \quad \phi = \frac{h_0}{u}$$

$$\therefore h_i = h_0 \frac{f}{u} \quad \textbf{(27.2)}$$

The ratio of the image height to the object height is called the **magnifying power** M of the lens.

$$M = \frac{h_i}{h_0} \quad \therefore \quad M = \frac{f}{u} \quad \textbf{(27.3)}$$

Lens formula

Equation (27.3) only works for objects which are sufficiently far away for light rays from one point on their surface to arrive at the lens more or less parallel to each other. What happens if the object is too close for this to be the case? Look at figure 27.11. Each ray from the point object on the axis is focused to a single point (the **image**) somewhere on the other side of the lens, being deflected according to equation (27.1). If we consider a single ray travelling from the object to the image via the lens, then we can obtain a very useful formula relating the positions of the object and image.

$$\theta = \frac{r}{f}, \quad \theta = \theta_u + \theta_v \quad \therefore \quad \theta_u + \theta_v = \frac{r}{f}$$

$$\theta_u = \frac{r}{u}, \quad \theta_v = \frac{r}{v} \quad \therefore \quad \frac{r}{u} + \frac{r}{v} = \frac{r}{f} \quad \textbf{(27.4)}$$

$$\frac{1}{u} + \frac{1}{v} = \frac{1}{f}$$

u is the distance of the object from the lens

v is the distance of the image from the lens

f is the focal length of the lens

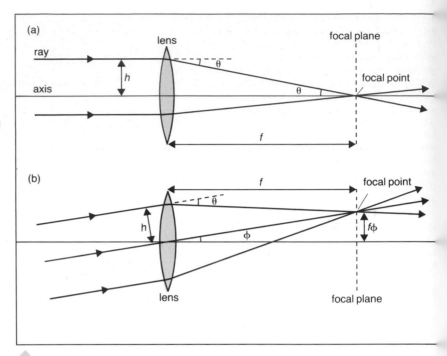

Figure 27.9 The behaviour of an ideal convex lens

Figure 27.10 Forming an image of a distant object

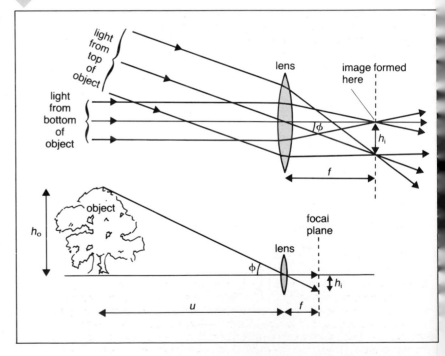

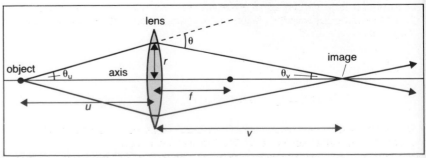

Figure 27.11

t should be obvious that this formula works for mages formed off the axis as well as on it. Figure 27.12 shows how an image of a distributed object is formed by the lens. Rays from a particular point on the object are focused to one point on the image. It should be clear from the diagram why the image is inverted. We can use equation (27.3) to write down a general expression for the magnifying power of the lens.

$$M = \frac{v}{u}$$

M is the magnifying power of the lens

u is the distance of the object from the centre of the lens

v is the distance of the image from the centre of the lens

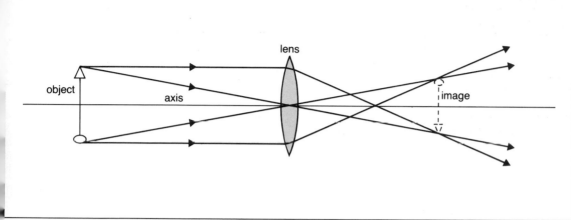

Figure 27.12 Forming a real image

OVERHEAD PROJECTOR

An overhead projector of the type commonly found in classrooms (figure 27.13a) is an excellent example of lens imaging systems in action. The **projection lens** collects light from the object (the transparency), forming an image on the screen. The mirror simply deflects each ray by an angle so that the image will be upright on a vertical screen. If the lens has a focal length of 33 cm, let's estimate how far above the transparency it must be held if the screen is 2.0 m in front of the mirror. (For simplicity, we shall ignore the small distance between the lens and the mirror.)

$$\frac{1}{u} + \frac{1}{v} = \frac{1}{f} \qquad \therefore \frac{1}{u} + \frac{1}{2} = \frac{1}{0.33}$$

$$\therefore \frac{1}{u} = 3 - 0.5 = 2.5$$

$$\therefore u = 40 \text{ cm}$$

How big is the magnifying power of the system?

$$M = \frac{v}{u} \qquad \therefore M = \frac{2.0}{0.4} = 5$$

So the image on the screen will be five times larger than life size.

You will have noticed in figure 27.13(b) that there is a lens underneath the transparency. (A **Fresnel lens** is usually used so that it can be flat and light — you will be introduced to this type of lens later on in this chapter.) Its job is obvious: it collects light from the projector bulb and ensures that it goes through the transparency and projection lens. So the **condenser lens** has to form an image of the projector bulb somewhere near the projection lens. If the bulb is 20 cm below the centre of the condenser lens, we can estimate a suitable focal length for it.

$$\frac{1}{u} + \frac{1}{v} = \frac{1}{f} \qquad \therefore \frac{1}{0.2} + \frac{1}{0.4} = \frac{1}{f}$$

$$\therefore 7.5 = \frac{1}{f} \qquad \therefore f \approx 13 \text{ cm}$$

The curved mirror underneath the bulb ensures that as much light as possible is caught by the condenser lens and directed onto the screen.

Figure 27.13 An overhead projector

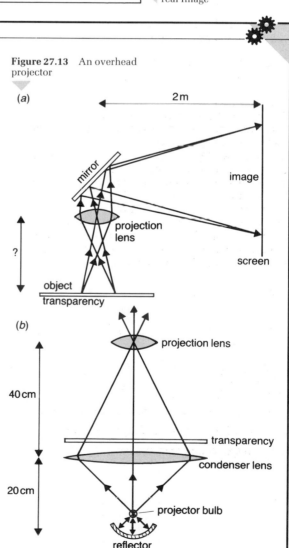

(a)

(b)

Virtual images

Suppose that an object is placed 15 cm in front of a convex lens whose focal length is 20 cm. Where should a screen be placed to catch the image? By how much will the object appear to have been magnified? Let us use the lens formula to answer the first question.

$$\frac{1}{u} + \frac{1}{v} = \frac{1}{f} \quad \therefore \frac{1}{15} + \frac{1}{v} = \frac{1}{20}$$

$$\therefore \frac{1}{v} = \frac{1}{20} - \frac{1}{15} = -0.0167$$

$$\therefore v = -60 \text{ cm}$$

The negative value for v means that the image is formed *behind* the lens rather than in front of it. As you can see from figure 27.14, the object is too close to the lens for the deflection of the rays of light from a point to result in their meeting at a single point on the other side of the lens. On the other hand, all of those rays do appear to come from a single point behind the lens. So if you were looking towards the lens, your eyes would be receiving light which appeared to come from a point somewhere behind the lens. Your brain would therefore locate the image at that point. An image which is caused by rays of light which only appear to come from a point is called a **virtual image.** Quite clearly, there is no way in which it can be seen on a screen, unlike the **real image** of figure 27.12 which can.

The convention whereby virtual images have negative values of v is called **real-is-positive.** Provided that u is always positive, then positive values of v correspond to images on the opposite side of the lens to the object. If v is negative then the image and the object are on the same side of the lens. If in doubt, a quick sketch of some rays from the object which go through the lens should resolve any difficulty about the position of an image!

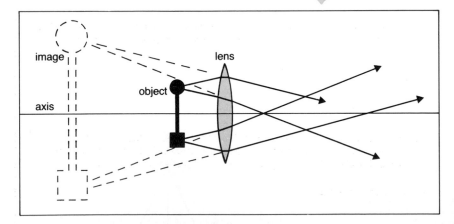

Figure 27.15 shows another aspect of a virtual image. Unlike the real image formed by a convex lens, the virtual image is not inverted. Rays from the top of the object emerge from the lens as if coming from the top of the image. So when you look through a convex lens at an object close to it, you see an upright and magnified image. The magnifying power of this arrangement (known as a magnifying glass) can be calculated from the same formula used for real images. So the magnifying power of the system shown in figure 27.14 is 60/15 = 4.

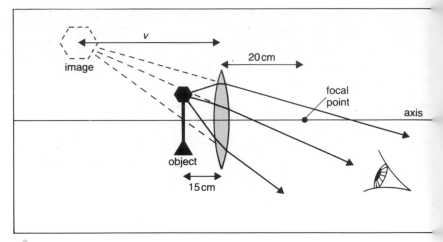

Figure 27.14 An image formed behind the lens

Figure 27.15 A virtual image

Power

Once you have a value for the focal length of a lens you can use the lens formula to calculate where it forms images of objects. However, the strength of a lens is usually quoted in terms of its **power.** This is obtained by taking the reciprocal of its focal length.

$$P = \frac{1}{f}$$

P is the power of the lens (dioptres)

f is the focal length of the lens (metres)

The power of a lens is useful because it allows you to work out the effective focal length of a combination of lenses very easily. The power of a pair of lenses placed next to each other is simply the sum of their individual powers. For example, two 5 dioptre lenses of focal length 0.2 m placed together effectively make a single 10 dioptre lens of focal length 0.1 m.

Refraction

For a convex lens to be useful in imaging systems, it has to deflect light according to equation (27.1). In describing how the image is formed and where it will appear, we have neglected to explain the physics which makes a lens possible in the first place. That physics is called **refraction,** the change of direction of travel of a wave when it crosses from one medium to another.

Changing medium

The speed of light in glass is substantially less than the speed of light in free space. This is because glass, in common with all solids, contains charged particles (electrons and protons) which interact with the electric and magnetic fields of the light wave. The result is a slowing down of the speed from 3.0×10^8 m s^{-1} to about 2.0×10^{-8} m s^{-1}. It is standard practice to present this information about a transparent material as a **refractive index** n.

$$n = \frac{c}{v}$$

n is the refractive index of the material

c is the speed of light in free space

v is the speed of light in the material

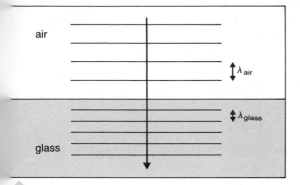

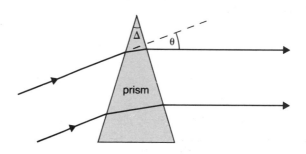

Figure 27.16 The wavelength of light shrinks as it enters a slower medium

Figure 27.17 Refraction

Figure 27.18 Deflection by a thin prism

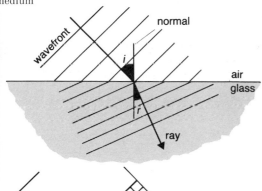

A **prism** is a wedge-shaped piece of transparent material. If the angle Δ at the prism's apex is not too large, then it deviates light through a constant angle θ over a range of small angles of incidence. This is illustrated in figure 27.18.

> $\theta = (n - 1)\Delta$
>
> θ is the angle of deviation of the light
>
> n is the refractive index of the glass
>
> Δ is the angle at the prism's apex

It is a fortunate coincidence that a transparent material whose surface is spherical will deflect light rays according to equation (27.1), i.e. will make a useful lens. (If two surfaces are ground at random against each other with an abrasive substance between them, then both surfaces will end up being spherical.) We are now going to derive an expression for the focal length of a convex lens which has only one spherical surface (figure 27.19). Suppose that a ray approaches the flat face of the lens parallel to the axis and a distance h from it. The surfaces at which the ray enters and leaves the lens look like the surfaces of a prism. We can therefore use the prism formula above to work out the ray deviation θ.

$$\Delta = \frac{h}{R}, \quad \theta = (n-1)\Delta \quad \therefore \theta = (n-1)\frac{h}{R} \tag{1}$$

If you compare this with equation (27.1), you should be able to see how the focal length of the lens is related to its refractive index and radius of curvature.

$$\theta = \frac{h}{f} \quad \therefore \frac{h}{f} = (n-1)\frac{h}{R}$$

$$\therefore \frac{1}{f} = \frac{(n-1)}{R} \tag{2}$$

Equation (2) is a version of the **lensmaker's formula** for plano-convex lenses. It should be clear that to get a short focal length, the lens has to have a sharply curved surface (small R) and be made of a material with a high refractive index.

Convince yourself from the data above that glass has a refractive index of about 1.5. Values for the approximate refractive index of a number of common substances are listed in table 27.1.

Table 27.1

Substance	n
air	1.0003
water	1.33
ethanol	1.36
perspex	1.49
ice	1.31
diamond	2.42
glass	1.51

Now let's think about what happens to a light wave when it travels from air into glass. Look at figure 27.16. As the wave travels across the boundary, its frequency remains unchanged: if f crests approach the glass surface, then f crests must enter the glass. On the other hand, the wavelength λ will have to decrease because $c = f\lambda$.

$$c = f\lambda, \quad n = \frac{c}{v} \quad \therefore n = \frac{\lambda_{air}}{\lambda_{glass}} \tag{27.5}$$

Figure 27.19 Modelling a lens with a thin prism

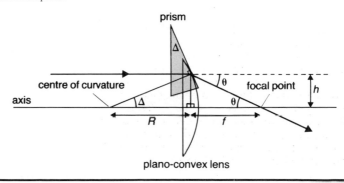

plano-convex lens

(We are assuming that the refractive index of air is exactly one.) If the light enters the glass at a glancing angle (figure 27.17) then it will change direction, i.e. be **refracted**. If you study the wavefronts drawn in figure 27.17, you should be able to convince yourself that the following algebra has to be true.

$$\sin i = \frac{\lambda_{air}}{w}, \quad \sin r = \frac{\lambda_{glass}}{w}, \quad n = \frac{\lambda_{air}}{\lambda_{glass}}$$

$$\therefore \frac{\lambda_{air}}{\lambda_{glass}} = n = \frac{\sin i}{\sin r} \qquad \textbf{(27.6)}$$

Equation (27.6) is known as **Snell's Law**. The angles of incidence and refraction (i and r) are measured between the ray of light and the **normal**, a line drawn perpendicular to the surface of the glass.

> $n_i \sin i = n_r \sin r$
>
> i is the angle of incidence
>
> r is the angle of refraction
>
> n_i is the refractive index of the incident medium
>
> n_r is the refractive index of the refracting medium

Aberration

A spherical lens is only going to form sharp images if the light enters it close to the axis. Light rays which enter the lens a long way from its centre will no longer meet the small-angle criterion used above, so they will not focus down to the same place as the other rays. The result is **spherical aberration**, a smudging out of the image (figure 27.21). One solution is obvious, i.e. only use the centre of the lens, but this does place a limitation on the amount of light the lens can capture. Where the latter is the dominant consideration (like the condenser lens of an overhead projector or the projection lens of a lighthouse (figure 27.22)), a Fresnel lens is used. Have a look at figure 27.23. The surface of the plastic has been moulded into rings. The surface of the rings is tilted at the right angle for light passing through to obey equation (27.1). A conventional spherical lens with the same light-catching ability would not only give aberration, but would be prohibitively bulky and thick, leading to serious transmission losses.

Parallax

Suppose that an object is placed underneath a block of transparent material, as shown in figure 27.24. If the object, which could be a line drawn on a sheet of paper, is viewed from above, it will

---

THE PRISM FORMULA

Figure 27.20 shows a ray of light entering and leaving a prism. We are going to obtain an expression for its deviation, on the assumption that the angle Δ is small. Let's start by considering the ray as it enters the prism.

$$1 \sin i = n \sin r \qquad \therefore i = nr$$

$$\delta = i - r \qquad\qquad \therefore \delta = (n - 1)r \qquad (1)$$

Now consider the ray leaving the prism. Remembering that it is going from glass into air, we obtain an expression for the deflection of the ray on its way out.

$$n \sin i' = 1 \sin r' \qquad \therefore r' = ni'$$

$$\delta' = r' - i' \qquad\qquad \therefore \delta' = (n - 1)i' \qquad (2)$$

The total deflection will be the sum of the two deflections at either face of the prism.

$$\theta = \delta + \delta' \qquad \therefore \theta = (n - 1)(r + i') \qquad (3)$$

Look at the triangle ABC in figure 27.20. The three angles must add up to 180°. Furthermore, the four angles in the quadrilateral ABCD must add up to 360°.

$$r + i' + \alpha = \pi, \quad \Delta + \alpha + \frac{\pi}{2} + \frac{\pi}{2} = 2\pi$$

$$\therefore r + i' = \Delta \qquad (4)$$

Substituting equation (4) into (3) gives us the expression we are after:

$$\theta = (n - 1)\Delta \qquad (5)$$

Figure 27.20   Deviation of a ray passing through a prism

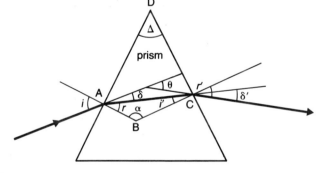

---

appear to be somewhere inside the block. This is because rays of light from the object are refracted as they leave the top surface of the block. If you consider the two rays drawn, which hit the surface at a small angle of incidence i, you can work out the position of the image as follows:

$$n \sin i = 1 \sin r \qquad\qquad \therefore \frac{r}{i} = n \qquad \textbf{(27.6)}$$

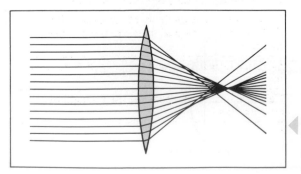

Figure 27.21   Spherical abberation

Figure 27.22   Lighthouse projection lens

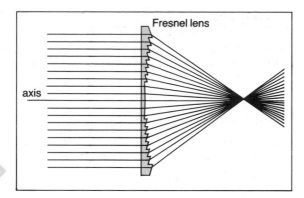

Figure 27.23 A Fresnel lens can be free of spherical abberation

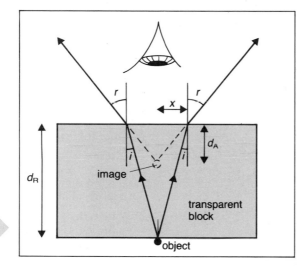

Figure 27.24 Image formed by refraction at the surface of a transparent block

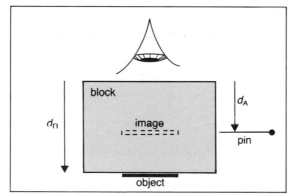

Figure 27.25 Apparatus for measuring the apparent depth of an image

Figure 27.26 Using no-parallax to measure the focal length of a lens

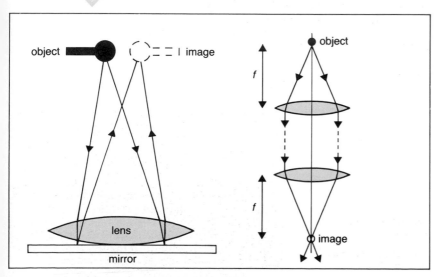

It is convenient to measure the positions of the image and object from the top of the block: these are known as the **apparent** and **real depths**.

$$i = \frac{x}{d_R}, \qquad r = \frac{x}{d_A} \qquad \therefore \frac{r}{i} = n = \frac{d_R}{d_A} \qquad \textbf{(27.7)}$$

The real depth d_R is easily measured with a ruler: it is simply the height of the block. The easiest way of measuring the apparent depth d_A is the method of **no-parallax**. A pin is mounted beside the block as shown in figure 27.25 so that it appears to be in line with the image. If the pin remains in line with the image when your head is moved back and forth, then it must be the same distance from your eyes as the image is. So you simply move the pin up and down the block until this condition of no-parallax is achieved. Then a ruler can be used to measure the distance from the pin to the top of the block.

The no-parallax method can also be used to measure the focal length of a convex lens. One arrangement is shown in figure 27.26. The lens is placed on a flat mirror and the pin is moved up and down until the condition of no-parallax indicates that it is sitting next to its image. It should be obvious from the diagram that this can only happen when the light rays from the point of the pin on the axis emerge from the lens travelling parallel to each other. So, if you forget the existence of the mirror, the image will be formed an infinite distance from the lens.

$$\frac{1}{u} + \frac{1}{v} = \frac{1}{f} \qquad \therefore \frac{1}{u} + \frac{1}{\infty} = \frac{1}{f} \qquad \therefore u = f$$

The mirror will deflect all of the rays by the same angle, so on their way back through the lens they will be focused onto the focal plane.

OBJECTIVES

After studying this section you should be able to do the following.

Describe how X-ray and gamma ray images can be formed.

Describe what a convex lens does to light rays.

Use the lens formula and know its limitations.

Calculate the magnifying power of a lens forming an image.

Describe and explain the difference between real and virtual images.

Calculate the power of a lens from its focal length.

Explain the meaning of *refractive index*.

State Snell's Law and use it to calculate the deflection of a beam of light when it changes medium.

Describe how to measure the refractive index of a material.

Describe how to measure the focal length of a convex lens.

QUESTIONS

1 Figure 27.27 shows a simple camera which has a single lens of focal length 50 mm. Its distance from the film can be adjusted to get the images correctly focused on the film.

a Suppose that the camera is used to photograph a tree which is 10 m high at a distance of 25 m. How far must the lens be placed from the film to give a correctly focused image? How tall will that image be?

b In the foreground of the picture is a child standing 50 cm in front of the camera. Where should the lens be placed for the child's face to be in focus on the photograph? What would the tree look like for this setting?

c The lens can be adjusted from 45 mm to 60 mm in front of the film. Work out the range of distances from the camera lens that objects can be correctly focused onto the film.

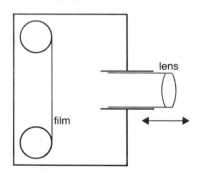

Figure 27.27

figure 27.28

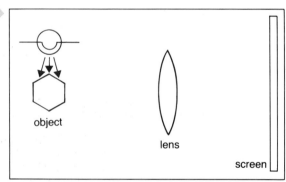

Figure 27.29

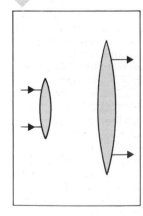

2 Pete uses a 7 dioptre lens to form a real image of a white chess piece on a screen as shown in figure 27.28. The chess piece is 25 mm high and is strongly illuminated from the side.

a Calculate the focal length of the lens.

b He places the object 10 cm in front of the lens, but is unable to form an image on the screen. He reckons that it is because not enough light is being reflected off the object. Is he right? What is his real error?

c Where should Pete place the chess piece if he wants a focused image on a screen which is 50 cm in front of the lens? How big will the image be? What will the image look like?

d What will happen to the image on the screen if the bottom half of the lens is covered with black paint?

3 A lens of focal length f and diameter D is used to form an image of an object which is a distance $2f$ to

the left of the lens. Which of the following statements about the image on the screen are true?

a It is $2f$ to the right of the lens.

b It is smaller than the object.

c It moves to the right when the object is moved to the left.

d It is halved when D is halved.

e Its intensity is doubled when D is doubled.

f It disappears if f is doubled.

4 The device shown in figure 27.29 is a **beam expander**: it can increase the diameter of a laser beam. A parallel-sided beam of diameter 2.0 mm enters from the left and a parallel-sided beam of a different diameter is supposed to leave at the right.

a Copy figure 27.29. By drawing a series of evenly spaced wavefronts on the diagram, show what the beam expander does to the laser beam coming in from the left. Draw a second diagram to show what a number of rays do as they pass between the lenses.

b The small lens has a focal length of 15 mm and is placed 165 mm from the large lens. Suggest a suitable focal length for the large lens.

c What is the diameter of the beam which emerges from the large lens?

d Beam expanders are sometimes placed in front of lasers to decrease the intensity (power per unit area) of the beam. By how much does the expander of figure 27.29 reduce the intensity of the beam? Assume no transmission losses in the lenses.

5 A student uses a magnifying glass to study a plant specimen. He places the lens next to his eye and moves the specimen until he can see it comfortably, i.e. the image is 50 cm behind the lens. If the lens has a focal length of 10 cm, where does he have to place the specimen? How much is it magnified?

6 If you take a straight drinking-straw and place it in a straight-sided glass of water so that it is partly immersed, you will make the following observations. Explain each one.

a When viewed from above, the straw appears to bend where it enters the water.

b When viewed from the side, the straw appears to be broken into two halves.

c When viewed from the side the straw appears to have different diameters inside and outside the water.

7 The refractive index of a material is a function of the frequency of the light passing through it. This can be used to make a **prism spectrometer**, a historical instrument which can separate out the different wavelengths emitted by a light source. Figure 27.30 shows how a **collimating lens** takes light from the slit and feeds it into the prism. A second lens collects the light from the prism and focuses it onto a translucent screen. Table 27.2 contains some data for the refractive index of flint glass at a number of standard wavelengths.

Table 27.2

Colour	λ/nm	n
blue	468	1.641
green	509	1.636
yellow	588	1.627
red	644	1.623

a If the rays of light in the equilateral prism travel parallel to its base, show that the angle of refraction for light entering the prism is 30°. Calculate the angle of incidence for yellow light.

b If white light is fed into the slit, a coloured band is seen on the screen between A and D. What are the colours at A, B, C and D? Explain your answer.

c Explain why the screen is tilted with respect to the focal plane of the second lens. (How does the focal length depend on wavelength?)

8 This question is going to help you appreciate why the total power of a pair of thin lenses placed together is the sum of their individual powers.

a A lens of power 5 dioptres is placed 50 cm from a light bulb. Calculate the distance between the centre of the lens and the image of the bulb.

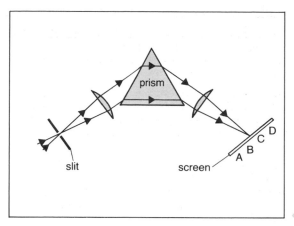

b A 2.5 dioptre lens is placed right next to the 5 dioptre lens. Treat the image of the bulb formed by the 5 dioptre lens as the object of the 2.5 dioptre lens. Calculate the position of the image formed by that lens. (Think carefully about the sign of u.)

c Calculate the power of a single lens which would have the same effect as the two separate lenses placed together.

Figure 27.30

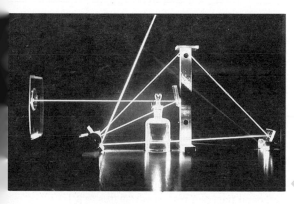

Figure 27.32 Persuading a laser beam to follow a curved path

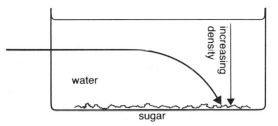

Figure 27.31 Laser light travels in straight lines

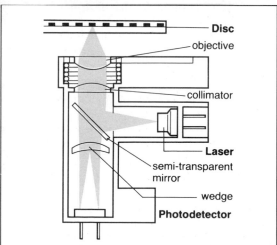

Figure 27.33 The precision optics of a compact disc player

DIFFRACTION

There is little evidence from everyday experience that light is a wave. Most of its apparent behaviour is well modelled by rays which obey Snell's Law and the Law of Reflection. Thus, in the absence of a reflecting surface or a change in refractive index, light travels in straight lines. This is easily verified by squirting a mist of fine droplets in the path of a laser beam (figure 27.31). If you shine the beam into a glass tank of water which has some sugar crystals spread over the bottom, the laser beam certainly doesn't travel in a straight line (figure 27.32). Nevertheless, the ray model can accurately predict this behaviour by considering the refractive index gradient in the sugar solution. The ray model is certainly the best way of describing the way light is processed by complex optical systems such as telescopes and cameras (figure 27.33). However, the ultimate limit on the sharpness of the image formed by such systems is imposed by **diffraction**, a wave phenomenon which cannot be accounted for by the ray model. Whenever the width of a wavefront is limited by an aperture, this introduces a spread of values for direction of the wave. Diffraction makes it impossible for a perfect lens to focus all of the rays from a point object to a single point image.

Slit diffraction

Take a laser beam and shine it on a screen at the opposite end of the laboratory. The result is a small spot a couple of millimetres across. Now place a 0.25 mm vertical slit in front of the beam where it leaves the laser, as shown in figure 27.34. The spot on the screen spreads sideways to become a streak about 25 mm across. As the light travels through the slit it is **diffracted**. Its direction changes so that energy leaves the slit over a range of angles, as shown in the graph of figure 27.34. In order to model this behaviour we shall have to adopt **Huygen's Principle**, a wave description of light.

Huygen's Principle

Figure 27.35 illustrates what happens to water waves when they pass through an aperture. The edge of the wavefront curls round so that the wave emerges from the slit with its energy travelling in a spread of directions. We can explain this with a model first suggested by Christiaan Huygens in about 1660. Each portion of a wavefront acts as the source of a semi-circular wave with the same wavelength as the original wave. All of these **wavelets** from different places along the wavefront then interfere with each other to produce the subsequent wavefronts.

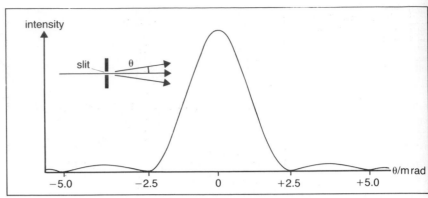

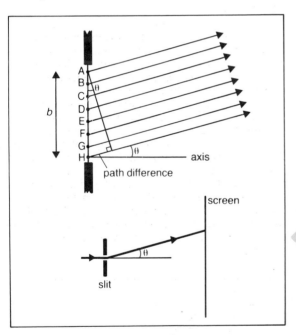

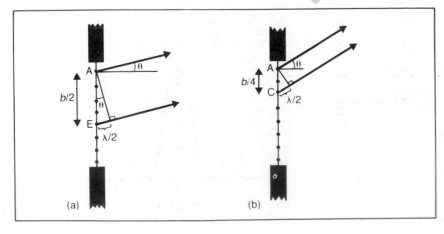

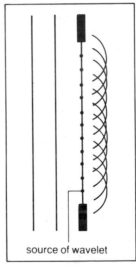

Figure 27.34 Diffraction at a single slit

Figure 27.35 Water waves passing through an aperture

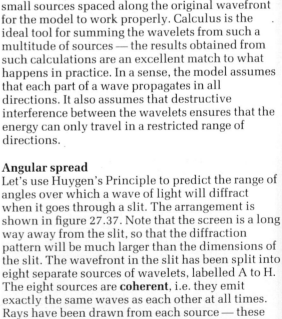

Figure 27.36 Each point on a wavefront acts as the source of a wavelet

Figure 27.37 Rays from a number of sources evenly spaced in a slit: all of the rays will end up at the same place on a distant screen

Figure 27.38 Angles for which no light will reach the screen

For example, consider the straight wavefront in the aperture drawn in figure 27.36. It has been divided into a number of segments, each of which acts as a source of circular wavelets. As you can see, constructive interference gives rise to the subsequent wavefronts. Of course, you have to consider an infinite number of infinitesimally small sources spaced along the original wavefront for the model to work properly. Calculus is the ideal tool for summing the wavelets from such a multitude of sources — the results obtained from such calculations are an excellent match to what happens in practice. In a sense, the model assumes that each part of a wave propagates in all directions. It also assumes that destructive interference between the wavelets ensures that the energy can only travel in a restricted range of directions.

Angular spread

Let's use Huygen's Principle to predict the range of angles over which a wave of light will diffract when it goes through a slit. The arrangement is shown in figure 27.37. Note that the screen is a long way away from the slit, so that the diffraction pattern will be much larger than the dimensions of the slit. The wavefront in the slit has been split into eight separate sources of wavelets, labelled A to H. The eight sources are **coherent**, i.e. they emit exactly the same waves as each other at all times. Rays have been drawn from each source — these show a particular direction along which wavelets can travel to a single spot on the screen. Because the screen is so far away, the rays are drawn parallel to each other, at an angle θ to the axis. Quite clearly, each of the wavelets will have travelled a different distance by the time they reach the screen, so they will not necessarily arrive in phase. For example, the wavelets from A and H will have a path difference of $b\sin\theta$.

Figure 27.39 The amplitude and intensity of the light at the screen as a function of θ

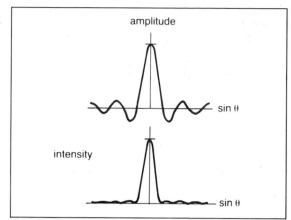

The only way that wavelets from all of the sources can arrive at the screen in phase is for θ to be 0. The wavelets travel the same distance and can therefore constructively interfere to give a large amplitude wave. This is not possible for any other value of θ, so the maximum intensity (amplitude²) occurs on the axis. So as θ increases, the intensity of the light arriving on the screen decreases. We can calculate the angle at which the intensity becomes zero as follows. Look at figure 27.38(a). The wavelets from A and E have a path difference of λ/2 so that they arrive at the screen out of phase and cancel each other out. The same thing happens to the wavelets from all the other pairs of sources (B and F, C and G, D and H), so there is no light on the screen at that particular angle.

$$\frac{b}{2}\sin\theta = \frac{\lambda}{2} \quad \therefore \quad \sin\theta = \frac{\lambda}{b} \qquad (27.8)$$

We can find other angles for which no light reaches the screen. Suppose that the wavelets from A and C destructively interfere when they reach the screen. Then wavelets from all similar pairs of sources (B and D, E and G, F and H) will also destructively interfere. If you study figure 27.38(b), you should be able to convince yourself that this will happen if θ is given by

$$\frac{b}{4}\sin\theta = \frac{\lambda}{2} \quad \therefore \quad \sin\theta = \frac{2\lambda}{b} \qquad (27.9)$$

Now if we had an infinite number of sources along the wavefront in the slit, b would be the width of the slit. So we can generalise equations (27.8) and (27.9) to predict the angles at which no light can emerge from the slit.

$$\sin\theta = \frac{n\lambda}{b}$$

θ is the angle to the axis for which no light emerges

n is the order number, any positive or negative integer

λ is the wavelength of the wave being diffracted (m)

b is the width of the slit (m)

The graphs of figure 27.39 show how the amplitude and intensity of the light on the screen depend on θ. (A negative amplitude means a change of phase for the light wave.) Since our eyes are sensitive to the intensity of the light, the second graph indicates what we see on the screen. Notice that the central maximum is twice as wide as the subsidiary maxima and that very little energy is directed outside the central maximum.

Diffracting microwaves
The apparatus shown in figure 27.40(a) can be used in the laboratory to check the formula we derived above. The microwave source emits electromagnetic waves of wavelength 3.0 cm. These are collimated by the wax lens to form a plane wave which is diffracted by the 6.0 cm slit formed by a pair of metal sheets. A second lens collects waves which leave the slit at a particular angle and focuses them onto the detector. The detector is swept round through a range of angles θ, keeping a fixed distance from the slit all the time. The reading of the galvanometer I can then be plotted as a function of θ: the results are displayed in the graph of figure 27.40(b). Since the galvanometer is measuring the r.m.s. value of the rectified signal from the aerial, the graph shows how the amplitude of the microwaves emitted from the slit changes with angle.

Figure 27.40 Investigating the diffraction of microwaves

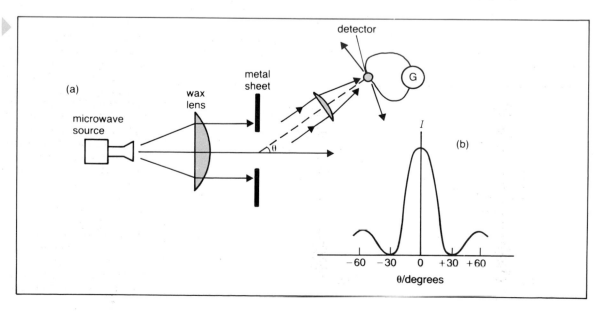

PUBLIC ADDRESS SYSTEM

Figure 27.41 A passive megaphone

Suppose that you wanted to make your voice carry further in one direction. You would probably cup your hands around your mouth. Most people wrongly assume that this reflects sound which would otherwise have gone in the wrong direction. In fact, by increasing the aperture the sound has to travel through, you are ensuring that it diffracts less. A non-electronic megaphone (figure 27.41) exploits the same physics.

Public address systems in large halls use loudspeakers mounted as vertical columns (figure 27.42). Each of the loudspeakers produces identical sound waves, so the whole assembly behaves like a slit source of waves. The waves will diffract sideways over a large range of angles because the wavelength of sound (roughly between 10 m and 10 cm) is larger or equal to the width of the slit. There will be relatively little diffraction in the vertical direction because the height of the source is greater than the wavelength of sounds being produced. The result is an approximately even spread of sound in the horizontal direction, with very little lost to the ceiling or floor.

Figure 27.42 An array of speakers

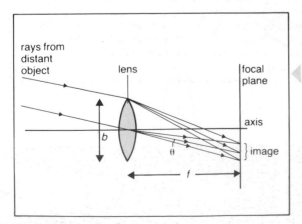

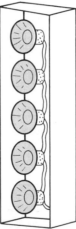

rays from distant object

lens

focal plane

axis

b

θ

} image

f

Figure 27.43 The diffraction pattern of a circular aperture

Figure 27.44 Diffraction of light as it passes through a lens makes point images of distant objects impossible

Circular apertures

Most imaging systems have circular apertures. The diameter of the wavefronts being processed is limited by a mirror or a lens somewhere in the system. Since it is the diffraction caused by this aperture which imposes the ultimate limit on the definition of the image, you need to know how the diffraction depends on the size of the aperture. Figure 27.43 shows the diffraction pattern caused by the passage of light through a circular hole. Notice the black rings around the central maximum where destructive interference takes place. As with the slit diffraction pattern, nearly all of the energy arrives within the central maximum: the peak intensity of the first ring is only 2% of the peak intensity of the whole pattern. The angle θ for total destructive interference of the wavelets from all the sources in the aperture has to be found with the help of calculus.

$$\sin\theta = \frac{1.2\lambda}{b}$$

θ is the angle of the first black ring

λ is the wavelength of the light (m)

b is the diameter of the diffracting aperture (m)

Let's see what this formula has to say about the diffraction of light. Suppose that we have a laser which produces a beam that is 2 mm across. By how much will it diffract if the wavelength is 633 nm?

$$\sin\theta = \frac{1.2\lambda}{b}$$

$$\therefore \sin\theta = \frac{1.2 \times 633 \times 10^{-9}}{2 \times 10^{-3}}$$

$$\therefore \sin\theta = 4 \times 10^{-4} \qquad \therefore \theta = 4 \times 10^{-4} \text{ rad}$$

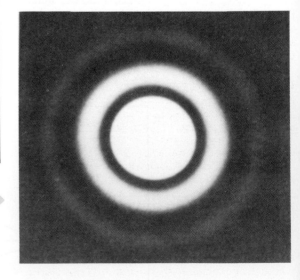

This amount of diffraction allows the diameter of the beam to increase by only 0.8 mm for every metre it travels. So light travels in straight lines like rays because its wavelength is so short: the diffraction is there, but is usually undetectable to the naked eye.

Diffraction in eyes

So if an ideal lens is used to form an image of a distant object, the result will be a disc rather than a point. Look at figure 27.44. Rays can be used to predict where the point image would be in the absence of diffraction. However, the light has to pass through a circular aperture of diameter b, so each ray is spread over an angle 2θ. The result is a disc (ignoring subsidiary maxima) in the focal plane. Its diameter d can be found as follows:

$$\sin\theta = \frac{1.2\lambda}{b} \qquad \therefore 2\theta \simeq \frac{2.4\lambda}{b}$$

$$\frac{d}{f} \simeq 2\theta \qquad \therefore d = 2.4\frac{f\lambda}{b} \qquad \textbf{(27.10)}$$

We have assumed small angles throughout. (This is always a good approximation with real imaging systems.) Let's see what this means in practice. A human eyeball (figure 27.45) has an effective focal length of 20 mm. On a bright day, the **pupil** will have a diameter of about 4 mm. So if the wavelength of light is about 0.5 μm, we can estimate the diameter of the disc on the **retina** formed by a distant point object.

$$d = 2.4\frac{f\lambda}{b}$$

$$\therefore d = \frac{2.4 \times 20\times10^{-3} \times 0.5\times10^{-6}}{4\times10^{-3}}$$

$$\therefore d = 6\times10^{-6}\ \text{m}$$

This is almost exactly the same as the spacing of the light receptors on the central part of the retina. This is hardly surprising, since the receptor spacing has evolved to obtain the maximum spatial information from the light entering the eye.

Rayleigh criterion

If a lens is used to form an image of two distant point sources, then each source will be imaged as a disc in the focal plane. In particular, if the sources are close together the two discs are going to overlap. Since the sources are different, the waves from one source will not be coherent with waves from the other. So there is no possibility of interference between waves from the two sources; their intensities will add together to produce the total intensity. Figure 27.46 illustrates the images formed by point sources when viewed through different apertures. Lord Rayleigh suggested that two point sources could just about be **resolved** if the peak of one intensity distribution lay on top of the first minimum of the other intensity distribution. This is shown in the graph of figure 27.47. In practice, this means that the centres of the discs in the image have to be separated by their diameter. Looking at figure 27.47, it should be evident that for this to happen, the **angular separation** of the two sources must be given by the following formula.

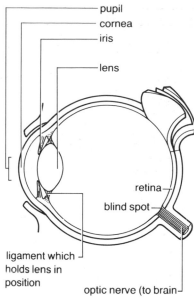

$$\theta = \frac{1.2\lambda}{b}$$

θ is the angular separation of the two point sources

λ is the wavelength of the light (m)

b is the diameter of the aperture (m)

Figure 27.45 A human eyeball

SPY SATELLITES

Many people worry about the ability of spy satellites to snoop on their every action. A quick calculation of the theoretical resolution of a camera in orbit around the Earth should confirm their fears. The cargo bay of the Space Shuttle could not contain an optical instrument of diameter much above 1 m, so let's use that figure as the aperture of a spy satellite camera. For a satellite to have a reasonable lifetime it has to be beyond the frictional clutches of the Earth's atmosphere, with an altitude of at least 100 km. Finally, let's assume that the pictures are taken in short wavelength blue light, i.e. $\lambda = 450$ nm. The resolution of the camera can be estimated from the Rayleigh criterion.

$$\theta = \frac{1.2\lambda}{b} \qquad \therefore \theta = \frac{1.2 \times 450\times10^{-9}}{1.0} = 5.4\times10^{-7}\ \text{rad}$$

Now we can calculate the separation d of two point sources at a distance of 100 km which will be separated by this angle at the satellite.

$$d = 100\times10^3 \times 5.4\times10^{-7} = 5\times10^{-2}\ \text{m}.$$

So a giant spy satellite should be able to resolve details as small as individual people, but be unable (as has been claimed) to read the headlines on the newspapers they are carrying around. Of course, we have only calculated the theoretical limit. The resolution attainable in practice will depend on the turbulence of the atmosphere through which the light has to travel and the adjustment of the camera itself.

Figure 27.46 Images through a microscope with three different apertures. As the aperture is closed down, the images spread out

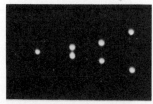 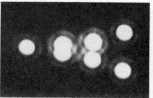 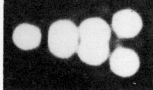

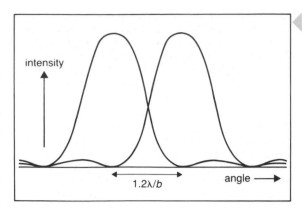

Figure 27.47 Intensity patterns of two sources which can just be resolved according to the Rayleigh criterion

OBJECTIVES

After studying this section you should be able to do the following.

Use Huygen's Principle to explain diffraction.

Understand the meaning of *coherent*.

Derive the single slit diffraction formula.

Sketch graphs to show the variation with angle of amplitude and intensity of waves emerging from a slit.

State the diffraction formula for a circular aperture.

State and use the Rayleigh resolution criterion.

QUESTIONS

1 A student looks at the vertical filament of a light bulb through a fine scratch on a piece of painted glass. The scratch has a width of 0.5 mm.

a A red filter, transmitting light of approximate wavelength 650 nm, is placed in front of the light source. Calculate the angular spread of the diffraction pattern seen by the student. Sketch a graph to show how the perceived intensity of the light changes with angle.

b On the same graph, sketch the variation of intensity if blue light (wavelength 450 nm) is used instead.

c When the student removes the filter she sees a white central maximum with colours at the edges. Explain why she sees colours rather than just black and white.

Figure 27.48

2 The apparatus shown in figure 27.48 is used to verify the circular aperture diffraction formula. Ultrasound of frequency 40 kHz is emitted by a transducer of diameter 15 mm.

a If the velocity of ultrasound in air is 330 m s^{-1}, calculate the range of angles over which the ultrasound is spread.

b A horn is placed on the transducer, increasing its diameter to 50 mm. Calculate the new range of angles over which the ultrasound is transmitted.

3 A loudspeaker which has a diameter of 20 cm is used to play music from a tape recorder. The frequencies of the sounds range from 60 Hz to 6 kHz. The velocity of sound in air under room conditions is 330 m s^{-1}.

a Sketch graphs on the same axes to show the angular distribution of the lowest and highest frequency sounds fed out by the loudspeaker.

b Where do you have to sit to hear a properly balanced sound from the loudspeaker? What happens if you sit elsewhere?

c Hi-fi systems use a small speaker (the tweeter) for the high frequency sounds. Suggest a suitable diameter for the tweeter if the music is to sound balanced wherever you sit in front of the loudspeaker.

4 Melissa rules two black lines on a piece of paper 5 mm apart. John walks backwards until the two lines appear the same as a single line.

a If white light has an average wavelength of 500 nm and the pupil of John's eye has a diameter of 2 mm, estimate how far John can get from the paper before he cannot distinguish the lines apart.

b Will John do better or worse if the whole room is badly lit? (The diameter of the pupil varies in an attempt to keep the total light entering the eye constant.)

5 Why can you hear someone walking down the corridor towards an open classroom door well before you can actually see them walking through it?

Figure 27.49

6 The Jodrell Bank radio telescope has a dish of diameter 77 m. What is its theoretical resolution when receiving radio waves of wavelength 0.21 m? How does this compare with the world's largest refracting telescope at Yerkes Observatory whose lens has a diameter of 100 cm receiving light waves of wavelength 500 nm?

7 A TV broadcasting satellite in geostationary orbit has to be at an altitude of 36 000 km. It receives microwave signals from Earth and broadcasts them back so that they can be received over a wide area of the Earth's surface. The reflecting dishes used for transmitting and receiving can be clearly seen in figure 27.49.

a The diameter of the broadcasting dish is carefully chosen to diffract the microwaves over part of the Earth. If Europe has an effective diameter of 3 000 km (the radius of the Earth is about 6 000 km), suggest a suitable diameter for the broadcasting dish if it is transmitting microwaves of wavelength 5 cm to Europe.

b The transmitting dishes at the ground stations are very much larger than this. Suppose that the ground station dish has a diameter of 25 m and transmits 2 cm microwaves towards the satellite at a power of 1 kW. If the satellite receiving dish has a diameter of 50 cm, estimate the power of the signal it receives from Earth.

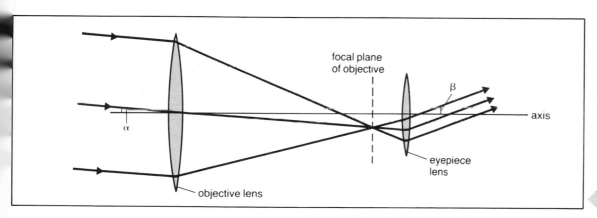

Figure 27.50 A lens telescope

APPLIED OPTICS

This section is going to show you a number of useful optical devices which process electromagnetic waves to form images. We shall start with the oldest (the telescope) and end with the youngest (the endoscope), introducing new ideas and optical techniques along the way as and when required.

Telescopes

A simple lens telescope is shown in figure 27.50. Its function is to make a distant object appear closer. This is accomplished by collecting light from the object at an angle α to the axis and feeding it out to the eye at a larger angle β. The **angular magnification** M of the image is then defined as the ratio of the two angles.

$$M = \frac{\beta}{\alpha} \qquad (27.11)$$

Since the object is a long way away, rays of light from a single point arrive at the **objective** travelling parallel to each other. Therefore they are focused to a single point in the focal plane of the objective (figure 27.50). The **eyepiece** is placed so that the point image is one focal length away from it. As you can see from figure 27.50, this results in a number of rays emerging from the eyepiece at an angle β to the axis. Of course, the image appears upside down, but this is no disadvantage if the telescope is being used to study astronomical objects. Terrestrial telescopes which do not invert the image will be described later on.

We can use figure 27.51 to find out how the magnifying power of the telescope depends on the focal lengths of the objective and eyepiece. Consider the light ray entering the centre of the objective at an angle α to the axis. It will end up a distance h from the axis when it reaches the image point in the focal plane. Let's assume small angles: they are nearly always small in practice.

$$\frac{h}{f_o} = \alpha \qquad (27.12)$$

Now consider a different ray which leaves the image point and goes through the centre of the eyepiece.

$$\frac{h}{f_e} = \beta \qquad \therefore \ \frac{\beta}{\alpha} = \frac{f_o}{f_e} \qquad (27.13)$$

So the angular magnification is simply the ratio of the focal lengths of the two lenses used in the telescope.

Figure 27.51

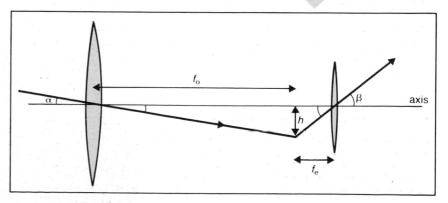

EYERING

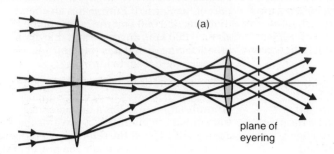

(a)

plane of
eyering

Figure 27.52 All of the
useful light captured by the
objective passes through the
eyering

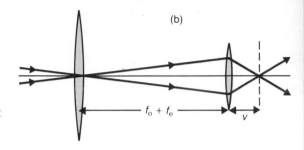

(b)

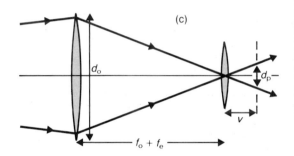

(c)

Where is the best place to put your eye when looking through the telescope? You want to maximise the amount of light getting into your eye, so that the image is bright. You also want to maximise the **field of view**, i.e. the range of angles from the object which you can see. If you look at figure 27.52(a), you should be able to see that light rays from the top and bottom of a distant object which just manage to get through the telescope pass through a ring next to the eyepiece. It is called the **eyering**, because it represents the optimum position of the observer's pupil. As you are about to find out, the fact that all human beings have eyeballs roughly the same size means that the angular magnification of a telescope can usually be estimated from its length.

Let's start off by working out the distance of the eyering from the eyepiece. Figure 27.52(b) shows two of the rays of figure 27.52(a), making it obvious that the eyering position is simply the image of the objective in the eyepiece.

$$\frac{1}{u} + \frac{1}{v} = \frac{1}{f} \qquad \therefore \frac{1}{f_o + f_e} + \frac{1}{v} = \frac{1}{f_e}$$

$$\therefore v = \frac{f_e(f_o + f_e)}{f_o} \qquad (1)$$

Figure 27.52(c) will help you to appreciate how to work out the diameter of the eyering d_p. All of the light entering the objective is supposed to pass through the eyering: the two rays drawn are the ones which pass through the top and bottom of the eyering in figure 27.52(a).

$$\frac{d_p}{v} = \frac{d_0}{f_o + f_e} \qquad \therefore d_p = \frac{vd_0}{f_o + f_e} \qquad (2)$$

If we substitute equation (1) into (2) and make the approximation that the angular magnification is large we end up with the following interesting expression:

$$d_p = \frac{f_e}{f_o}(f_o + f_e) \times \frac{d_o}{f_o + f_e}$$

$$\therefore d_p = d_o \times \frac{f_e}{f_o} \qquad (3)$$

Since the angular magnification is the ratio of the focal lengths, the diameter of the eyering is fixed by the following formula:

$$d_p = \frac{d_o}{M} \qquad \therefore d_o = Md_p \qquad (4)$$

Since the value of d_p is going to be fixed at about 5 mm by the pupil of a human eye, equation (4) says that the angular magnification of a telescope is proportional to the diameter of its objective. In other words, big telescopes magnify more than little ones!

Terrestrial telescopes

One method of making a telescope which does not invert the image is shown in figure 27.53. A **concave** lens has been used as the eyepiece. This diverges the rays from the objective so that they emerge parallel to each other. The lens formula can still be used, provided that we use a negative value for the focal length. Let's work out where the object has to be placed for a concave lens to produce an image at infinity, i.e. one whose rays are parallel to each other.

$$\frac{1}{u} + \frac{1}{v} = \frac{1}{f} \qquad \therefore \frac{1}{u} + \frac{1}{\infty} = -\frac{1}{f_e}$$

$$\therefore u = -f_e \qquad\qquad\qquad (27.14)$$

So if the eyepiece is placed $f_o - f_e$ behind the objective, the telescope will be in normal adjustment. A **Galilean** telescope of this sort is therefore shorter than an astronomical telescope with the same angular magnification. An alternative method of inverting the image is shown in figure 27.54: it is longer than the Galilean type.

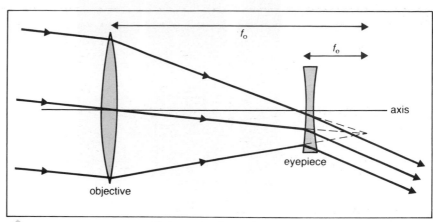

Figure 27.53 A Galilean telescope

Figure 27.54 A terrestrial telescope

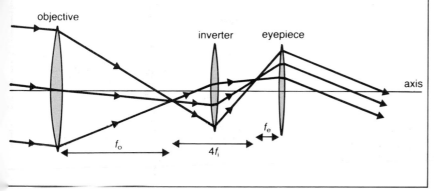

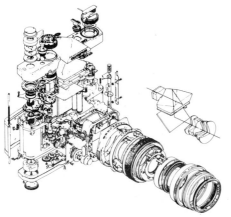

Chromatic aberration

No single lens can have the same focal length for all colours. This is because the refractive index of any material depends on the wavelength of the light going through it. So the image of a black and white object formed by a telescope will have coloured edges. This **chromatic aberration** is a consequence of the different focal length of the lenses for each wavelength. However, it is possible to put lenses of different glasses together to make an optical system whose properties are more or less the same for all colours. An example of this is the **achromatic doublet** shown in figure 27.55. It is for this reason that camera lenses are usually made from several lenses placed in contact with each other (figure 27.56). Other aberrations which would be present in the image if just one lens was used can also be cancelled out if several lenses are used.

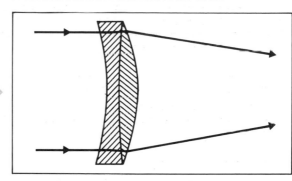

Figure 27.55 An achromatic doublet

Figure 27.56 A modern camera—the insert shows the pieces of glass that make up the compound lens

Figure 27.57 Newtonian telescope

Reflecting telescopes

Reflecting telescopes offer significant advantages over refracting telescopes. They employ a curved mirror as the objective instead of a lens. Not only does this avoid the transmission losses of the glass, but it also completely banishes chromatic aberration. Take a look at figure 27.57: it shows a **Newtonian** telescope. Light coming in from a distant object is focused to a point in front of the eyepiece. The eyepiece then makes an image of that point at infinity, much as it does in a refracting telescope. At first glance, the presence of a small plane mirror in front of the large curved reflector suggests that the image seen through the eyepiece has a hole in the middle of it! However, a little thought should convince you that, like a lens, *any* part of a curved mirror's surface can form the image. The presence of the plane mirror simply cuts down the brightness of that image by preventing some of the incoming light from reaching the eyepiece.

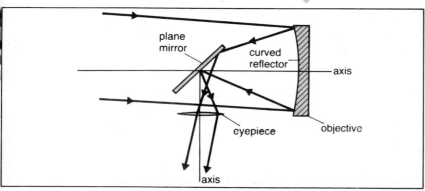

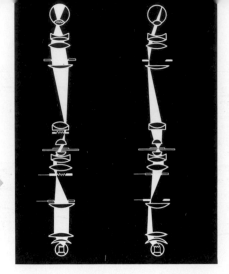

Figure 27.58 Two different ways of showing the passage of light through a microscope—from the lamp at the bottom to an eyeball at the top. Note the use of compound lenses for both the objective and eyepiece

The focal length of a concave mirror is half of its radius of curvature, completely independent of wavelength. If the mirror is parabolic, then even for large angles of incidence it will obey the lens formula with the proviso that for positive values of v you place the image on the *same* side of the mirror as the object. (Look at figure 27.57.) Mirrors can be used to form images at all wavelengths of the electromagnetic spectrum. This is especially useful in the infra-red and X-ray regions where lenses cannot be made.

The light-catching power of a telescope is proportional to the area of its objective, be it a lens or a mirror. So for looking at faint objects such as stars, you need as large an objective as you can get. Large lenses have to be thick at the centre, giving large transmission losses. Furthermore, since they have to be suspended at their edges, distortion due to their own weight becomes a problem. On the other hand, mirrors do not suffer from transmission losses at all and can be supported firmly from behind. So mirrors are used in all the largest telescopes.

Microscopes

As you can see from figure 27.59, a **microscope** is similar in construction to a telescope. The magnification of the object happens in two stages. First of all, the objective makes a magnified real image of the object. Then the eyepiece makes a magnified virtual image of the objective's image. Although it is possible to work out a formula for the magnification of a microscope in terms of the separation of the lenses and their focal lengths, it will be instructive to do a numerical calculation of the magnification instead.

The arrangement of lenses is shown in figure 27.59. Of course, in a real microscope a compound

lens would be used for the objective to reduce aberration to a tolerable level: we have used a single lens here for simplicity. For the final virtual image to be viewed comfortably, it has to be placed at the observer's **near point**. This is the place where objects can be seen when the eye is relaxed — for a normal human eye it is about 25 cm. So we are going to assume that the final image is 25 cm behind the 16 dioptre eyepiece. The lens formula is used to find the position of the image formed by the objective.

$$\frac{1}{u} + \frac{1}{v} = \frac{1}{f}, \qquad P = \frac{1}{f}$$

$$\therefore \frac{1}{u} - \frac{1}{0.25} = 16$$

$$\therefore u = 5 \text{ cm}$$

The eyepiece has therefore given a magnification of $25/5 = 5$. The objective has a power of 50 dioptres and is placed 20 cm from the eyepiece. We can use the lens formula to work out where the object has to be placed in front of the objective.

$$\frac{1}{u} + \frac{1}{v} = \frac{1}{f}, \qquad P = \frac{1}{f}$$

$$\therefore \frac{1}{u} + \frac{1}{0.15} = 50$$

$$\therefore u = 23 \text{ mm}$$

The magnification from the objective is therefore $150/23 = 6.5$. The total magnification of both lenses will be $6.5 \times 5 = 33$. Strong illumination of the object is imperative for high power microscopes. If the object is being enlarged by a particular factor, its brightness will drop by the square of that factor if we ignore transmission losses in the lenses.

Endoscopes

An endoscope is illustrated in figure 27.60. It uses a bundle of **optical fibres** to carry light from deep inside the gut of a human being so that an image can be formed where a doctor can see it. The objective lens forms an image on one surface of the bundle. Light which falls on a particular fibre becomes trapped in it and travels along it until it emerges at the other surface. The eyepiece then forms a magnified image of the pattern of light on the other surface of the bundle of fibres. Provided that the object is well illuminated (usually from another set of optical fibres), the result is a clear but grainy image of the patient's insides.

Figure 27.59 Image formation in a microscope

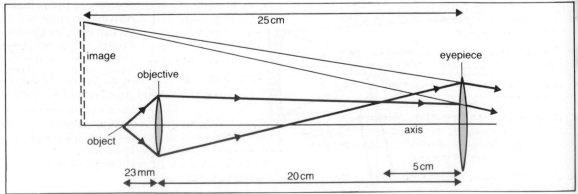

Total internal reflection

Optical fibres can trap light through the phenomenon of **total internal reflection**. This can occur when light tries to leave one medium and enter another medium where it travels faster. For example, look at figure 27.61. The light ray is aimed at the edge of a material of refractive index n. As the angle of incidence increases, there comes a point where the angle of refraction (according to Snell's Law) becomes greater than 90°. This is clearly impossible to achieve, so the light ray is reflected back into the material with no losses. The **critical angle of incidence** c above which refraction out of the material into air is impossible can be calculated from its refractive index.

$$n \sin i = 1 \sin r \quad \therefore n \sin c = 1 \sin 90$$

$$\therefore c = \sin^{-1}(1/n) \quad \text{(27.15)}$$

For example, the critical angle for glass ($n = 1.5$) is about 42°. So light rays in glass which encounter surfaces at angles of incidence of 45° will reflect off them as if they were perfect mirrors (figure 27.62.) Once light has entered an optical fibre it will reflect off the walls (provided the fibre is not bent round too much) until it emerges at the other end. Of course, in travelling through such a long length of glass, absorption is going to be a problem. (Try looking along the length of a piece of window glass!) The glass in the fibre has to be very carefully manufactured to keep such transmission losses to an acceptable level.

Figure 27.60 An endoscope: a bundle of optical fibres carries light from the object to the outside world

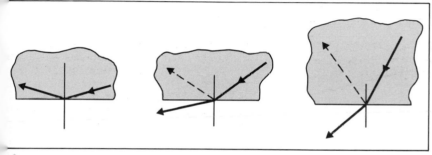

Figure 27.61 Light may not be able to refract out of one medium into another

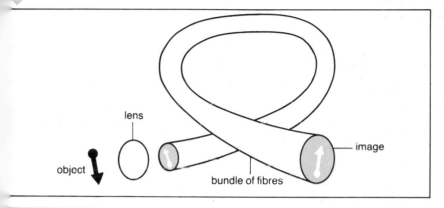

Figure 27.62 Examples of total internal reflection

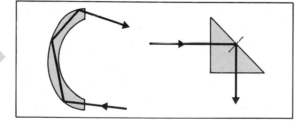

OBJECTIVES

After studying this section you should be able to do the following.

Describe the structure of an astronomical telescope.

Explain how the objective and eyepiece form a magnified image of a distant object.

Calculate the telescope's angular magnification from the focal lengths of its lenses.

Explain the meaning of *eyering*.

Use a concave lens as the eyepiece of a terrestrial telescope.

Apply the lens formula to a concave lens and a concave mirror.

Explain the advantages of reflecting telescopes compared with refracting telescopes.

Describe the structure of a microscope.

Use the lens formula to calculate the overall magnification of a microscope.

Explain why the objective is a compound lens.

Describe the use of bundles of optical fibres for imaging.

Calculate the critical angle of a material and explain its significance for total internal reflection.

QUESTIONS

1 A student proposes to make a telescope out of a pair of lenses with powers of 5 dioptres and 20 dioptres respectively.

a Calculate the focal lengths of the two lenses. Which one should he use as the objective?

b State how far apart the student must place the lenses for normal adjustment of the telescope.

c Draw a diagram to show rays of light passing through the telescope from the top and bottom of a distant object. Indicate where the student should place his eye to see the image.

d What is the value of the telescope's angular magnification?

e With the help of a ray diagram, help the student to design a telescope with the same angular magnification which does not invert the image: mention a suitable value for the focal length of any extra lens you introduce.

2 Large telescopes see further into the universe than small ones can. This problem will help you to see why.

a A small reflecting telescope has a dish of diameter 20 cm. How does the light collected from a single star by the dish compare with that collected by an unaided eye? Assume a pupil diameter of 5 mm.

b The world's largest optical telescope has a dish of diameter 5.0 m. How much more light does it collect than the world's largest refracting telescope which has an objective of diameter 1.0 m?

c If the intensity of light from a star is inversely proportional to the square of its distance, how much further can you see into the universe with the world's largest reflector than with an unaided eye.

d It is claimed that you can see better at night if you use binoculars. Explain why it might work.

3 A microscope is adjusted until the final virtual image is 30 cm behind the eyepiece. The total magnification of the instrument is 120.

a The eyepiece has a focal length of 5 cm. Where does the objective form its image?

b What magnification is produced by the eyepiece?

c The objective has a focal length of 0.5 cm. How far from the eyepiece must it be placed for the microscope to have a total magnification of 120?

4 Figure 27.63 shows a device for sampling the depth of petrol in large underground tanks. Light from an LED is sent down the glass fibre and detected by a photodiode at the other end. Glass has a refractive index of 1.50 and petrol has a refractive index of 1.39.

a Calculate the critical angles for the glass—air and glass—petrol interfaces.

b The glass fibre thread has a diameter of 100 μm. Calculate the minimum radius of curvature to which the thread can be bent in air without the light escaping from it. Do the same for the thread immersed in petrol.

c Explain how the petrol level detector works. Describe how it is used in practice.

5 Figure 27.64 shows a ray of light approaching a curved mirror and travelling parallel to its axis.

a Sketch figure 27.64. Draw the path followed by the ray after reflection. Hence prove that the focal length of a concave mirror is half of its radius of curvature. Assume small angles throughout.

b A shaving mirror has a focal length of 25 cm. If an object is placed 75 cm in front of it, calculate the position and magnification of the image.

c Draw a scale diagram to show three different rays from an off-axis point on the object being focused onto the image.

d In use, the shaving mirror forms an enlarged virtual image about 25 cm behind the mirror. Calculate how close the object has to be to the mirror for this to happen.

6 A combination of lenses known as a **telephoto lens** is shown in figure 27.65. The effective focal length F of the combination can be changed from infinity to a small value by varying the value of d. This is very useful in lens cameras. The powers of the convex and concave lenses are +5D and −20D, respectively.

a Calculate where light from a distant object is focused to by the convex lens. That image will act as the virtual object for the concave lens.

b Suppose that d is 12 cm. Calculate where the concave lens will focus the light from the convex lens. Hence calculate the value of F for the whole combination.

c What value of d will give an effective focal length of infinity?

7 Figure 27.66 is an illustration of Robert Hooke's original microscope. Explain the function of the large globe. Where was the specimen to be studied placed? How was the microscope adjusted to bring the image into focus?

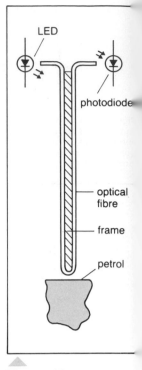

Figure 27.63

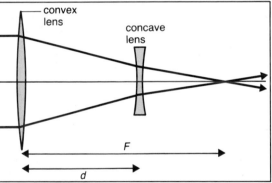

axis

centre of curvature

R

Figure 27.64

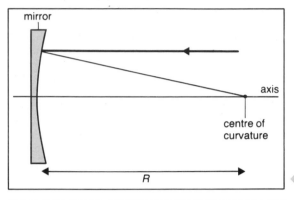

F

d

Figure 27.65

Figure 27.66

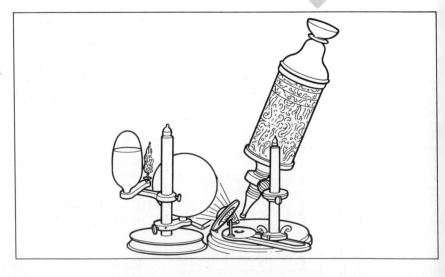

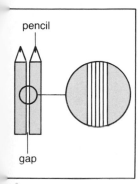

Figure 28.1

Figure 28.2 Young's arrangement to demonstrate double-slit interference with light

Put a pair of pencils together as shown in figure 28.1. Now look at a bright source of light through the small gap between the pencils. The thin black lines that you can see are **interference fringes**, evidence that light is a wave rather than a stream of particles. Interference patterns with light are usually created by persuading a light wave to arrive at a detector by more than one path so that constructive and destructive interference can take place. Such patterns are widely used for the precision measurement of light frequencies, as well as forming the basis of precision measurements of length.

YOUNG'S SLITS

In 1801 Thomas Young performed an experiment which proved, beyond a doubt, that light is a wave. His apparatus is illustrated in figure 28.2. Sunlight passing through a pinhole is allowed to fall on a screen some distance away. Halfway between the screen and pinhole are two more pinholes very close together in the vertical plane. When the light is allowed to get to the screen through both pinholes, the spot is covered with a series of evenly spaced horizontal black lines (**fringes**). These Young's fringes can only be satisfactorily explained by modelling the light as a wave which can simultaneously travel through both pinholes and interfere with itself at the screen.

Figure 28.3 Double-slit interference pattern using laser light

Figure 28.4 The light which passes through each slit acts as a source of circular wavefronts

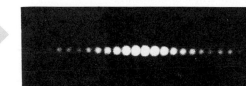

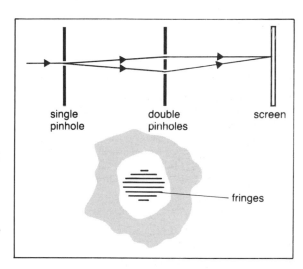

Young's original experiment is very difficult to do. Today, the same demonstration of the wave nature of light is usually done with the help of a laser and a couple of scratches on a piece of carbon-coated glass (figure 28.3). Not only does this provide a narrow beam of light which is much more intense than sunlight, the **coherence** of the waves from a laser makes the experiment very tolerant of alignment errors. By the time you have worked your way through this section, you should not only understand the origin of Young's fringes, but you should also have some appreciation of the difficulties Young faced in getting his demonstration to work.

Two-slit interference

Suppose that a plane wavefront of wavelength λ approaches a pair of slits in an obstacle. At what angles will the wave be able to diffract from the slits and constructively interfere at some distance from them? Look at figure 28.4. The portion of the wavefront which passes through each slit can, according to the Huygen's model, act as a source of circular wavefronts. If we assume that those two sources are **coherent**, (they produce identical waves at the same instant of time) then there is the possibility of interference between the waves where they overlap. Let's suppose that the waves from both slits are allowed to overlap on a screen which is a long way D from the slits.

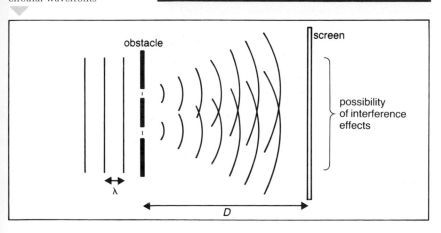

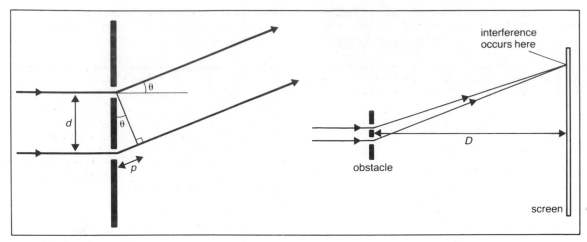

Figure 28.5 Calculating the path difference for rays which interfere with each other at the screen

Figure 28.5 shows rays from the two slits. The waves associated with these rays will overlap and constructively interfere when they get to the screen. If the spacing of the slits d is much smaller than the distance to the screen, then the two rays are effectively parallel, travelling at an angle θ to the axis of the system. For constructive interference, the path difference p must be a whole number of wavelengths.

$$p = n\lambda, \quad \text{where } n = 0, \pm 1, \pm 2, \pm 3 \ldots \quad \textbf{(28.1)}$$

The integer n is called the **order number**. If you look at figure 28.5, it should be clear that p can be calculated from the slit spacing d and the angle θ as follows.

$$\frac{p}{d} = \sin\theta \quad \textbf{(28.2)}$$

If we combine equations (28.1) and (28.2) to eliminate p, we obtain an important expression:

$$n\lambda = d\sin\theta \quad \textbf{(28.3)}$$

In practice, the values of θ for which constructive interference can happen are nearly always small, so we can safely approximate $\sin\theta$ by θ.

> $n\lambda = d\theta$
>
> n is the order number
>
> λ is the wavelength of the wave going through the slits (m)
>
> d is the spacing of the slits (m)
>
> θ is the angle at which constructive interference occurs

For example, how far apart are the bright fringes of a helium–neon laser beam on a screen which is 4.0 m away from a pair of slits 0.5 mm apart? The geometry is shown in figure 28.6. The wavelength of a helium–neon laser is 633 nm. Let's start by working out the angular separation $\Delta\theta$ between adjacent bright fringes on the screen.

$$n\lambda = d\theta \quad \therefore (n+1)\lambda = d(\theta + \Delta\theta)$$

$$\therefore \lambda = d\Delta\theta$$

$$\therefore \Delta\theta = \frac{\lambda}{d} \quad \textbf{(28.4)}$$

Now we can use the small angles approximation to find the fringe spacing x.

$$x = D\Delta\theta \quad \therefore x = \frac{\lambda D}{d}$$

$$\therefore x = \frac{633\times10^{-9} \times 4.0}{0.5\times10^{-3}} = 5.0 \text{ mm}$$

This spacing means that the fringes are visible to the naked eye.

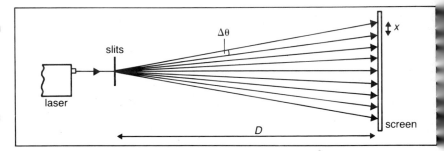

Figure 28.6 Using a laser to generate interference fringes on a screen

The intensity envelope

Interference between the waves passing through the two slits can only occur where they overlap. So, as is evident from figure 28.3, only a limited number of interference fringes will appear on the screen. The light which passes through each slit will be diffracted over a range of angles given by the single-slit diffraction formula.

$$\theta \simeq \frac{\lambda}{b} \quad \textbf{(28.6)}$$

Figure 28.7 shows the intensity pattern on the screen when the light can only get through one slit. If the light gets through both slits, then twice as much light must get to the screen, but spread over the same range of angles as before. Where the waves arrive in phase, the amplitude will be double what it was before, giving four times the intensity. On the other hand, between the bright fringes will be regions of low intensity where destructive interference is occuring. The result is the intensity pattern shown in figure 28.8.

Figure 28.7 The intensity pattern for a single slit

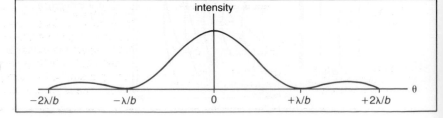

The single-slit diffraction formula can be used to estimate the total number of bright fringes seen when a laser beam is shone through two slits 0.5 mm apart. Suppose that each slit of figure 28.6 is 0.1 mm wide. If we ignore the subsidiary maxima, we can estimate the maximum angle θ_{max} at which the light is diffracted at each slit.

$$\theta \simeq \frac{\lambda}{b} \qquad \therefore \ \theta_{max} \simeq \frac{\lambda}{b} = \frac{633 \times 10^{-9}}{0.1 \times 10^{-3}}$$

$$\therefore \ \theta_{max} \simeq 6.3 \times 10^{-3} \ \text{rad}$$

The angular separation of the bright fringes is somewhat smaller than this. It can be calculated from equation (28.4).

$$\Delta \theta = \frac{\lambda}{d} \qquad \therefore \ \Delta \theta = \frac{633 \times 10^{-9}}{0.5 \times 10^{-3}} = 1.3 \times 10^{-3} \ \text{rad}$$

Bearing in mind that there are fringes on both sides of the axis, there must be about $(2 \times 6.3 \times 10^{-3})/$ $1.3 \times 10^{-3} \simeq 9$ fringes on the screen. Of course, if you want more fringes on the screen, all you have to do is cut down the width of the two slits. The penalty paid for this is a lowering of the intensity of the fringes as you are cutting down the amount of light which gets to the screen.

White light fringes

White light contains a continuous range of wavelengths, covering the approximate range shown in table 28.1. So if you shine white light at the two slits, only a limited number of clear fringes will be seen on the screen. Take a look at figure 28.9. It shows the intensity patterns on the screen for single wavelength (**monochromatic**) sources in the middle of the red, green and blue regions of the spectrum. If all three colours arrive at the screen simultaneously, their intensities will add to produce the pattern shown in figure 28.9. (There is no possibility of a stable interference pattern from light of different wavelengths because they will not be coherent.) All of the waves constructively interfere for $n = 0$, giving a bright white peak; but all the other peaks, if they are visible at all, will be strongly coloured. Three monochromatic waves (as shown in figure 28.9) will be able to combine to form white light peaks at a number of angles other than $\theta = 0$, but light containing a continuous spread of wavelengths between 400 nm and 700 nm will only produce the single peak which appears white.

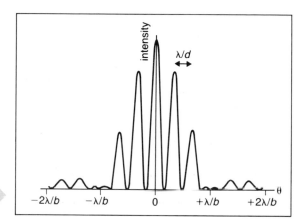

Figure 28.8 The single slit diffraction pattern limits the number of double slit fringes seen on the screen

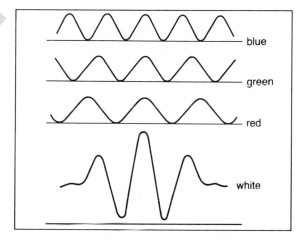

Figure 28.9 The total intensity pattern formed when red, green and blue light are shone simultaneously through a double slit. In practice, the three central maxima are white, with a number of highly coloured maxima on either side

Table 28.1

Colour	λ/nm
blue	400 – 500
green	500 – 610
red	610 – 680

SOURCE WIDTH !

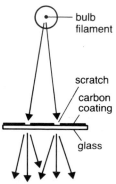

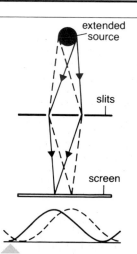

Figure 28.10 Apparatus for demonstrating Young's fringes in the laboratory

Figure 28.11 If the source is too large the fringes can disappear

The classic method of getting students to see Young's fringes in the classroom is illustrated in figure 28.10. They look at the vertical filament of a light bulb through two scratches on a carbon-coated glass slide placed close to their eyes. The distance at which the fringes first become visible depends on the width of the filament emitting the light. This is because there is no **coherence** between waves emitted from different parts of the same filament; the phase difference between the waves does not remain constant. Each wave from the filament will pass through both slits, giving rise to an interference pattern on the retina. However, waves from different places on the filament will produce different interference patterns. This will become clear if you look at figure 28.11. Light from both sides of the extended source forms an interference pattern on the screen. Notice that the $n = 0$ bright fringe for each side of the source occurs at different places on the screen. The lack of coherence between the waves from the two point sources means that their intensity patterns simply add together to give the total pattern on the screen. Of course, if the two sources are too far apart, the fringes become totally smeared out. This will happen when the zero-order bright fringe of one pattern sits on top of the first dark fringe of the other pattern. So for Young's fringes to be visible, the angle subtended by the light source at the slits must be smaller than the angle subtended by the fringes.

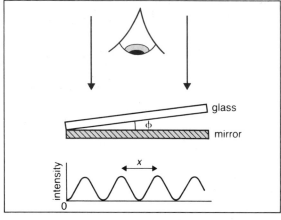

Figure 28.12

Figure 28.13

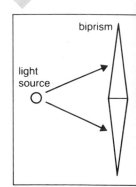

OBJECTIVES

After studying this section you should be able to do the following.

Describe the arrangement of apparatus for the Young's slits experiment.

Derive the fringe formula $n\lambda = d\theta$.

Explain the intensity pattern of the fringes in terms of single-slit diffraction.

Understand the meaning of *monochromatic* and *coherent*.

QUESTIONS

1 Blue monochromatic light of wavelength 450 nm is fed through a pair of slits which are 0.80 mm apart onto a screen which is 2.0 m in front of the slits.

a Calculate the spacing of the bright fringes on the screen.

b Each slit has a width of 0.10 mm. Draw a graph to show the variation of intensity of light on the screen when the light can only pass through one slit. Mark values on the displacement axis.

c Estimate how many fringes of blue light will be seen on the screen.

d Suppose that red light of wavelength 620 nm is used instead of blue light. What will this do to the pattern of fringes seen on the screen?

2 A Young's slits interference pattern is set up on a screen. State, as precisely as you can, what effect each of the following alterations has on the fringe spacing, intensity and number of fringes.

a Doubling the spacing of the slits.

b Doubling the width of each slit.

c Doubling the wavelength of the light.

d Doubling the distance from the slits to the screen.

3 When monochromatic light falls perpendicularly onto the wedge of air between a mirror and a sheet of glass, a set of fringes are formed as shown in figure 28.12. They are called **wedge fringes**.

a Explain, with the help of a ray diagram, how the fringes are formed.

b If x is the distance between the bright fringes and λ is the wavelength of the light, show that the angle ϕ between the mirror and the sheet is given by $\phi = \lambda/2x$.

c Two distance gauges can be compared with the help of wedge fringes. Each gauge is a block with polished ends which are 10 mm square. They are pushed together side by side on a flat surface. A sheet of flat glass is placed over the ends and is illuminated from above with light from a sodium lamp ($\lambda = 588$ nm). If a total of 21 fringes can be seen in the space between the glass and one of the gauges, estimate their difference in length. How could you tell which one was the longer of the two?

4 This question introduces you to two ways of obtaining a Young's slits diffraction pattern without using diffraction.

a Figure 28.13 shows how a **Fresnel biprism** can be used to create two coherent sources of light. Copy the diagram and mark on it the positions of the two sources. Will they be in phase with each other or out of phase?

b An alternative method, called **Lloyd's mirror** is shown in figure 28.14. Copy the diagram and mark on it the position of the virtual source. Explain why it will be out of phase with the real source.

5 A pair of pinholes are placed in front of a point source of monochromatic light so that the light falls on a distant screen.

a If the two pinholes are one on top of the other, sketch the pattern of light seen on the screen.

b A small piece of polarising material is stuck over one pinhole. Another piece of polarising material is placed over the other pinhole with its axis at right angles to the first. Explain why no interference fringes can be seen on the screen.

6 Explain why there is a small bright spot in the centre of the shadow of a circular object placed in front of a point source of light. Describe how you might set about demonstrating the existence of this spot in the laboratory. (This effect was first predicted by Poisson in 1818. When the test was performed and the bright spot was found, the wave theory of light was finally accepted by the scientific establishment.)

Figure 28.14

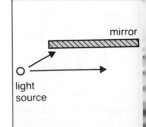

GRATINGS

A **grating** is a device that splits a plane wave into a number of subsidiary waves which can be brought together to form an interference pattern. The two main types of grating are illustrated in figure 28.15. **Transmission gratings** use diffraction through an array of holes or slits to create the subsidiary waves. (Young's slits are a very simple form of transmission grating.) **Reflection gratings** use an array of scattering points or surfaces to generate the subsidiary waves. Anyway, regardless of the means by which the subsidiary waves are created, the interference pattern which results when they are superposed contains information about both the original wave and the grating. So the pattern can be used to explore either the spread of wavelengths present in the original wave or the arrangement of holes/scatterers in the grating.

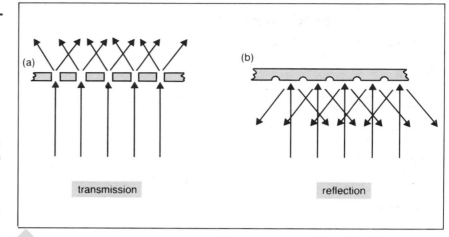

Figure 28.15 Transmission and reflection gratings

Figure 28.16 Wavefronts from three adjacent slits of a transmission grating. The arrows show the directions of constructive interference. You should be able to find the corresponding plane wavefronts by viewing the diagram from the side

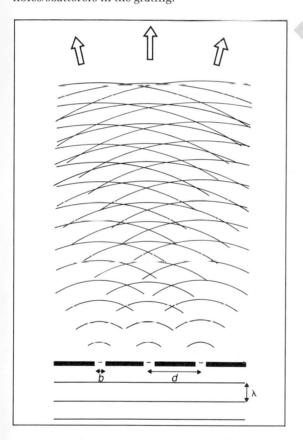

Diffraction gratings

A transmission diffraction grating is illustrated in figure 28.16. It contains a large number of slits of width b separated by a distance d. The plane wave approaching from the bottom is split up into a number of coherent sources when it hits the grating. Each slit emits a wave over a range of angles from $+\theta_m$ to $-\theta_m$, where θ_m is given by the single slit diffraction formula.

$$\sin\theta_m = \frac{\lambda}{b} \qquad \textbf{(28.6)}$$

Since the waves from each slit are coherent they will interfere with each other when superposed on a screen or other detector.

The grating formula

Suppose that a detector collects waves diffracted by the slits of the grating. What is the condition for those waves to constructively interfere? Look at figure 28.17. If the detector is a long way from the grating, then rays which reach the detector from the slits will be effectively parallel, all running at an angle θ to the axis. For *all* the waves to constructively interfere, they must arrive at the detector in phase. If the incident wave approaches the grating parallel to the axis, then complete constructive interference can only happen when each diffracted wave travels a whole number of wavelengths more or less than the wave from the neighbouring slit.

$$p = n\lambda, \quad \text{where } n = 0, \pm1, \pm2, \dots$$
$$p = d\sin\theta \qquad \therefore \; n\lambda = d\sin\theta \qquad \textbf{(28.7)}$$

The similarity of equation (28.7) to the Young's slits bright fringe formula is no coincidence. A Young's slit arrangement is a transmission grating with only two slits. As you will see below, the presence of more than two slits has a profound (and useful) effect on the interference pattern.

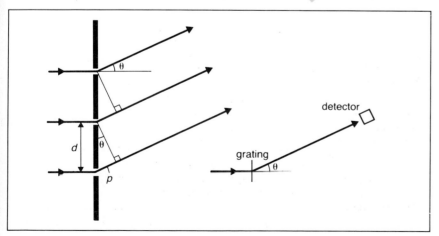

Figure 28.17 Calculating the path difference for wavelets which interfere with each other at the detector

$n\lambda = d\sin\theta$

n is the order number, a positive or negative integer

λ is the wavelength of the wave (m)

d is the spacing between the slits (m)

θ is the angle between intensity maxima and the axis

Spectra

If monochromatic light is directed at the grating parallel to its axis, then constructive interference can occur at several values of θ, provided that they are less than $θ_m$. This is illustrated in figure 28.18. The graph shows how the intensity on the screen depends on the value of θ. As you can see, the maxima are very sharp, with their peaks limited by the intensity pattern for a single slit. (The reasons behind the sharpness of the peaks will be explained below.) So if light containing a mixture of wavelengths is incident on the grating, each wavelength will form its own set of peaks on the screen. The resulting pattern is called the **spectrum** of the light. By measuring the value of θ for each wavelength, its value can be calculated from the known value of d.

For example, suppose that a particular light source (a hydrogen discharge tube) produced the spectrum of lines shown in figure 28.19. The central bright peak corresponds to $n = 0$ and is known as the zero-order spectrum. On either side of it is the first-order spectrum containing four lines (red, green, blue and purple). The second-order spectrum has the same set of lines, but at larger angles. If the grating has 300 slits per millimetre, what are the wavelengths of the four lines in the hydrogen spectrum?

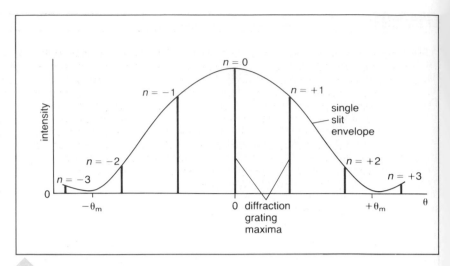

Figure 28.18   Interference pattern for monochromatic light incident on a transmission grating

Start off with the red line in the first-order spectrum. The grating spacing d is $1 \times 10^{-3}/300 = 3.33 \times 10^{-6}$ m and the angle θ is 11.35°. We can therefore use the grating formula to calculate the wavelength of the red line.

$$n\lambda = d\sin\theta \quad \therefore \quad 1 \times \lambda = 3.33 \times 10^{-6} \times \sin(11.35)$$

$$\therefore \lambda = 6.56 \times 10^{-7} \text{ m}$$

So the wavelength of the red line is 656 nm. You can check for yourself that the wavelengths for the other three lines listed in table 28.2 have been correctly calculated from the data of figure 28.19.

Table 28.2

Colour	λ/nm
red	656
green	486
blue	434
purple	410

These four wavelengths constitute the visible part of the emission spectrum of atomic hydrogen. Each chemical element has its own characteristic emission spectrum, containing many lines. Some examples are shown in figure 28.20. By measuring the wavelengths of the lines emitted by a gas discharge, it is possible to deduce the elements in the gas even if they are only present in minute quantities. The pattern of lines in the spectrum of an element contains important clues about the arrangement of electrons within its atoms — we shall be returning to this in chapter 29.

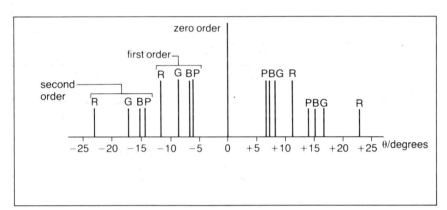

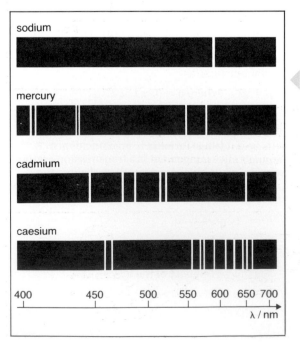

Figure 28.19   Grating transmission pattern for light from a hydrogen atom discharge tube

Figure 28.20   The emission spectra of different elements

RESOLUTION

The sharpness of the maxima produced by a diffraction grating depends on the number of slits N that the light passes through. To see why this is so, consider a grating illuminated with monochromatic light of wavelength λ. The nth order spectrum will contain a single line centred on θ given by $n\lambda = d\sin\theta$ i.e. $\theta \approx n\lambda/d$ for small angles. As you can see from figure 28.21(a), the intensity of the line drops to zero at $\theta \pm \Delta\theta$. We want to find out how to calculate the value of $\Delta\theta$.

Look at figure 28.21(b). Light from the slits labelled 1 and $N/2$ will destructively interfere for the angle $\theta + \Delta\theta$ provided that the path difference is an odd number of half wavelengths. Of course, the light from adjacent slits at angle θ already has a path difference of $n\lambda$, so the path difference for the two slits we are considering will be $Nn\lambda/2 + \lambda/2$ at angle $\theta + \Delta\theta$.

$$\sin(\theta + \Delta\theta) = \frac{((nN/2) + \frac{1}{2})\lambda}{(N/2) \times d} \qquad \therefore \theta + \Delta\theta \simeq \frac{n\lambda}{d} + \frac{\lambda}{Nd} \qquad (1)$$

If light from that pair of slits destructively interferes when it reaches the detector, then so will the light from all the other pairs of slits in the grating which are $Nd/2$ apart. So equations (28.7) and (1) can be used to find an expression for $\Delta\theta$, the effective width of the peak. Assume small angles for simplicity.

$$0 + \Delta\theta = \frac{n\lambda}{d} + \frac{\lambda}{Nd}, \qquad n\lambda = d\theta \qquad \therefore \Delta\theta = \frac{\lambda}{Nd} \qquad (2)$$

The narrower each peak is, the easier it is to distinguish lines with similar wavelengths in a spectrum. For example, suppose that we illuminate 20 mm of the surface of a grating which has 300 lines per mm with yellow light from a sodium lamp (figure 28.22(a)). The total number of slits involved in building the interference pattern will be $20 \times 300 = 6\times10^3$. The two principal lines of the spectrum have wavelengths of 589.0 and 589.6 nm. Will the two lines be resolved?

$$\Delta\theta = \frac{\lambda}{Nd} \qquad \therefore \Delta\theta = \frac{590\times10^{-9}}{6\times10^3 \times 3.33\times10^{-6}} = 3\times10^{-5}\ \text{rad}$$

The two lines have a wavelength difference of 0.4 nm. If they are viewed in first-order, we can estimate their separation $\delta\theta$ in the spectrum.

$$n\lambda = d\theta \qquad \therefore n(\lambda + \Delta\lambda) = d(\theta + \delta\theta)$$

$$\therefore n\Delta\lambda = d\delta\theta$$

$$\therefore \delta\theta = \frac{\Delta\lambda}{d}$$

$$\therefore \delta\theta = \frac{0.4\times10^{-9}}{3.33\times10^{-6}} = 12\times10^{-5}\ \text{rad}$$

The separation of the peaks is therefore about twice their width, so they should be completely resolved (figure 28.22(b)). If only 2 mm of the grating surface had been illuminated, each peak would have been ten times wider and be indistinguishable from the other peak.

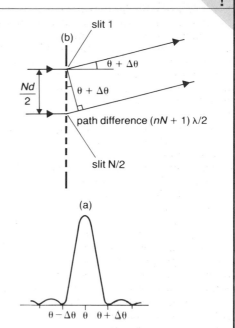

Figure 28.21

Figure 28.22

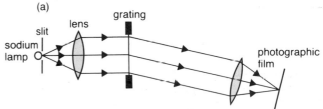

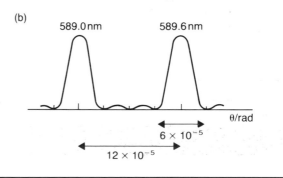

Spectrometers

Figure 28.23 shows how a diffraction grating is used in practice for precision measurements of wavelengths. Light from the source is focused onto a narrow slit by a convex lens. The **collimating lens** takes the light from the slit and makes it into a parallel beam aimed at right angles to the surface of the diffraction grating. A **telescope** collects the light emitted at a particular angle from the grating. It focuses the light down to form an image of the slit which can be seen in the eyepiece. (The use of a telescope avoids the need for a distant detector — the objective takes light from a particular direction and focuses it to a single point in its focal plane.) A pair of **cross-wires** in the eyepiece can be lined up on a particular spectral line by rotating the telescope on its turntable. Any error in getting the grating surface at right angles to the incident beam can be corrected for by measuring the angle through which the telescope has to be swung to get the cross-wires from a line in the $n = +1$ spectrum to the same line in the $n = -1$ spectrum. Half that angle is then θ. A properly aligned instrument with a collimating lens of diameter 25 mm should be capable of resolving lines whose wavelengths differ by only 0.1 nm!

Figure 28.23 A simple grating spectrometer

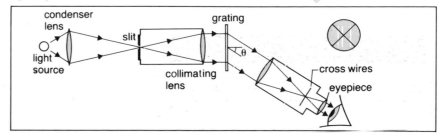

HOLOGRAMS

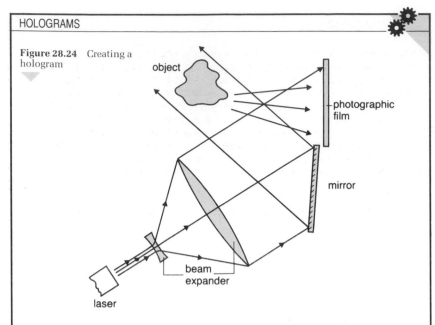

Figure 28.24 Creating a hologram

A hologram is a special diffraction grating designed to create three-dimensional images. When it is illuminated by coherent light, usually from a laser, the diffracted light has all of the characteristics of the light reflected off a real three-dimensional object, giving rise to a very realistic image. Figure 28.24 shows how the hologram can be recorded. Coherent waves from a laser illuminate the object and the photographic film simultaneously. The direct and scattered waves form an interference pattern which is recorded by the photographic film. (A pulse of laser light has to be used, as the slightest movement of the object ruins the hologram completely.) When the film has been developed, it becomes a diffraction grating whose arrangement of clear and opaque surfaces contains *all* of the information (amplitude and phase) present in the waves scattered off the object. (An ordinary photographic negative only stores information about the intensity of the light scattered from the object — the phase information is lost.)

When laser light is correctly shone through the hologram (figure 28.25), the diffracted light is a faithful copy of the original wave scattered from the object. The result is a three-dimensional virtual image which looks just like the original object, including its parallax behaviour. As you move your head around and your eyes collect light from different parts of the hologram, you see a different aspect of the image. In fact, you can cut up the hologram and use each bit to create an image of one aspect of the object!

White light holograms are three-dimensional diffraction gratings. A thick photographic emulsion is used to make the hologram, with the object simultaneously illuminated by pulses from red, green and blue lasers. When the developed hologram is subsequently illuminated with white light from a point source, the arrangement of dark fringes in the emulsion directs each colour in the appropriate direction to create a passable three-dimensional image.

Figure 28.25 Viewing a hologram

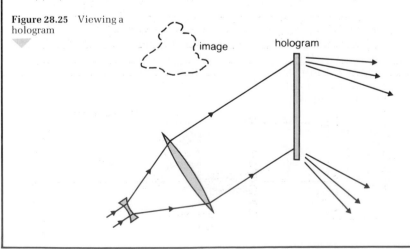

Reflection gratings

Jason von Fraunhofer made the original grating in 1819 by winding fine wire between two screws, but later ruled grooves directly onto glass with a diamond to make a reflection grating. A **reflection grating** is essentially a mirror with a series of lines drawn on its surface (figure 28.26). It looks like a number of parallel reflecting strips separated by grooves. When the grating is illuminated with light waves, the strips act as narrow sources of coherent wavelets, rather like the light transmitted by a transmission grating. The grooves are rough and irregular in cross-section so that waves scattered from them are not coherent and therefore cannot create an interference pattern. The intensity maxima of the reflected light occur for angles θ which obey the usual grating equation.

$$n\lambda = d\sin\theta \qquad (28.8)$$

If you think of the grooves as perfect absorbers of light, then it can be shown that they need to be half the width of the reflecting strips to direct a reasonable amount of light to the first-order maxima.

Reflection gratings offer two advantages over diffraction gratings. First, since they rely on reflection they can be used in regions of the spectrum where transparent materials are hard to find. So reflection gratings can be used to make spectra of ultraviolet and infra-red sources. Secondly, they make more efficient use of the light which is incident on them. A transmission grating only uses about one-third of the light incident on it to make the diffraction pattern, whereas a reflection grating uses at least two-thirds of the light.

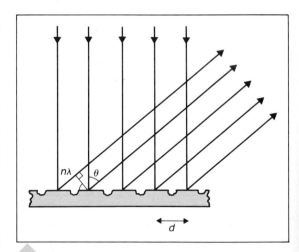

Figure 28.26 A reflection grating

Concave gratings

Since the construction of useful lenses is almost impossible over most of the infra-red and ultraviolet portions of the spectrum, spectrometers designed to operate in these regions use curved mirrors. These pass most of the light on to the grating and the detector, and are free from chromatic aberration. A particularly efficient and versatile arrangement is shown in figure 28.28. The grating has been ruled on the concave mirror surface, so that light from a point source placed at the centre of curvature is focussed somewhere on the **Rowland circle** (named after the man who invented the concave grating). So if the detector is moved along the Rowland circle, it picks up the various order spectra.

X-ray crystallography

X-rays have wavelengths which are between 10^{-8} m and 10^{-11} m. The latter is smaller than the spacing of atoms in a crystal ($\simeq 10^{-10}$ m), so a crystal can act as a grating for X-rays. This was first suggested and attempted by Max von Laue in 1911. He used the arrangement shown in figure 28.29(a). X-rays with a continuous spread of wavelengths are produced by accelerating a beam of electrons into a tungsten anode. The metal tube collimates the X-rays so that they hit the crystal at a well-defined angle. X-rays diffracted by the crystal are detected by a photographic emulsion; an example of the diffraction pattern recorded on the film is shown in figure 28.29(b).

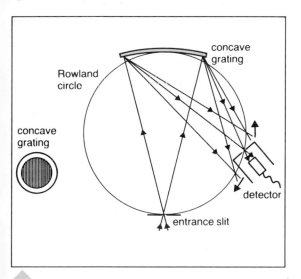

Figure 28.28   A concave reflection grating

Figure 28.29   Diffracting X-rays with a single crystal

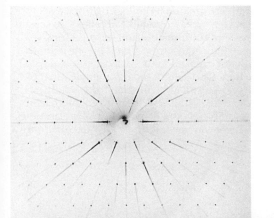

Reflection gratings can be used to measure very short wavelengths if they are used in **grazing incidence** with the light entering almost parallel to the surface of the mirror. Figure 28.27 shows a reflection grating being used in grazing incidence to measure the wavelength of an X-ray source. A set of parallel rays from the source hit the grating running almost parallel to its surface at an angle α. Each strip emits subsidiary waves over a range of angles. Rays which emerge at the same angle α will constructively interfere when superposed at a detector — the path difference introduced by the grating will be zero for this angle, so this direction corresponds to the zero-order spectrum. The first-order spectrum will emerge from the grating at an angle β given by

$$d\cos\alpha - d\cos\beta = \lambda \tag{1}$$

If both α and β are small, we may use the small-angle approximation for cosines.

$$\cos\phi \simeq 1 - \frac{\phi^2}{2} \quad \therefore d(1 - \frac{\alpha^2}{2} - 1 + \frac{\beta^2}{2}) = \lambda$$

$$\therefore \frac{d}{2}(\beta^2 - \alpha^2) = \lambda$$

$$\therefore \frac{d}{2}(\beta - \alpha)(\beta + \alpha) - \lambda \tag{2}$$

We can simplify equation (2) even further if we assume that $\alpha \simeq \beta$.

$$\frac{d}{2}(\beta - \alpha)(2\alpha) = \lambda \quad \therefore \lambda = d\alpha(\beta - \alpha) \tag{3}$$

Reflection gratings in grazing incidence have been used to measure the wavelength of X-rays. This was done for the first time in 1925 for the strongest X-ray line in the spectrum of molybdenum. The metal grating had 50 lines per mm, giving $d = 20$ μm. Metals will only reflect X-rays for very small grazing angles, well under 1°. Typically, the values for α and β are 6.0×10^{-3} and 6.6×10^{-3} radians, giving the following value for the X-ray wavelength:

$$\lambda = 20\times10^{-6} \times 6.0\times10^{-3} \times 0.6\times10^{-3} = 7.2\times10^{-11} \text{ m}$$

Note how short this is: visible light has a wavelength of about 5×10^{-7} m.

Figure 28.27   A reflection grating being used in grazing incidence

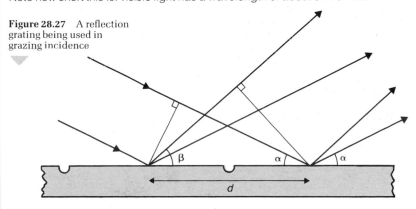

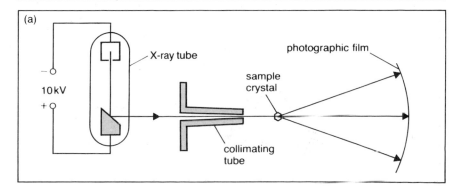

Bragg diffraction

In 1913 Lawrence Bragg explained how the X-ray diffraction pattern could be used to deduce the arrangement of atoms within the crystal. He suggested that a crystal behaves like a three-dimensional reflection grating, with the nucleus of each atom acting as a scattering centre for the X-rays (figure 28.30). The problem is to deduce the angles at which the X-rays from all of these centres will constructively interfere.

Crystals contain regular arrays of atoms. Within a crystal there will always be a number of planes which contain atoms arranged in a regular pattern (figure 28.31). One of these crystal planes for a simple close-packed structure is shown in figure 28.32. A plane wave incident on the atoms in a single crystal plane will be scattered by each atom, but the subsidiary waves can only emerge from the plane in phase with each other in two directions. One of these (the direction of the incident wave) is not very useful. The other (mirror reflection off the plane) is useful. Mirror reflection off the atoms in the plane will *always* ensure that the subsidiary waves can constructively interfere with each other at a distant detector. (This is the reason behind the laws of reflection of waves at flat surfaces. The angle of incidence equals the angle of reflection because it is the only way in which constructive interference of all the wavelets is possible.)

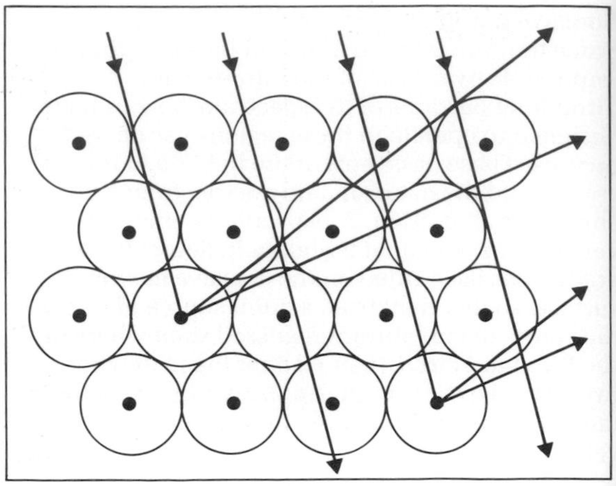

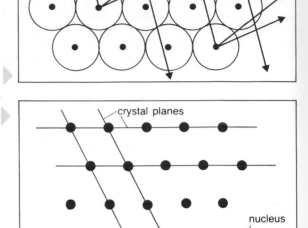

Figure 28.30 The nuclei in a crystal can scatter X-rays

Figure 28.31 Some crystal planes in a hexagonal structure

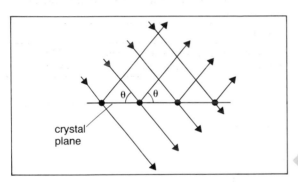

Figure 28.32 Scattering X-rays off a single crystal plane

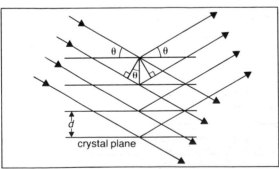

Figure 28.33 Scattering of X-rays from a number of adjacent crystal planes

Figure 28.34 A powder diffraction camera; note the use of a crystal to direct X-rays of a single known wavelength onto the sample

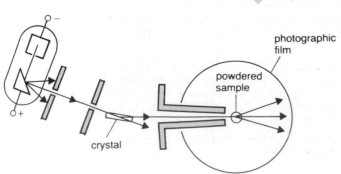

Now consider a number of identical crystal planes stacked one on top each other, as shown in figure 28.33. The spacing between the planes is d and they are at an angle θ to the incident wave. For the waves scattered by atoms in the same plane to be in phase with each other, they have to emerge at an angle θ. However, if the waves scattered off atoms in *different* planes are also to be in phase, then more stringent conditions apply. Look at figure 28.35. The path length between waves reflected off adjacent planes has to be a whole number of wavelengths.

$$2d\sin\theta = n\lambda \qquad \qquad (28.9)$$

Equation (28.9) is the **Bragg Law**. When a beam of X-rays passes through a substance, any of them which encounter crystal planes of spacing d and orientation θ will be deviated from the beam by an angle 2θ provided that their wavelength λ fits the Bragg Law.

Powder diffraction

X-ray diffraction is widely used to study the structure of solids. The usual method is illustrated in figure 28.34. X-rays of a single known wavelength are created by reflecting the waves from a standard X-ray tube off a crystal. The crystal (which may be sodium chloride or something with a similar structure) is cut so that it has its principal crystal planes parallel to its surface. For example, suppose that X-rays deviated by an angle of 20.6° from the main beam are collected from a sodium chloride crystal. What will their wavelength be if the interatomic spacing is 0.282 nm? If we assume that $n = 1$, we can use the Bragg Law to calculate λ.

$$n\lambda = 2d\sin\theta \quad \therefore \lambda = 2 \times 0.282 \times 10^{-9} \times \sin(10.3°)$$
$$\therefore \lambda = 1.00 \times 10^{-10}\,\text{m}$$

Figure 28.35 X-ray diffraction pattern

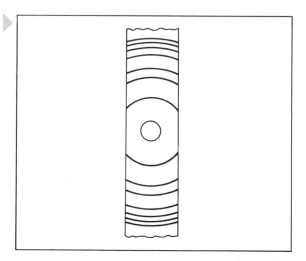

An example is shown in figure 28.35. Of course, once the angle of deflection 2θ and the wavelength λ are known, the crystal plane spacing d can be calculated. The overall structure of the crystal can then be deduced by considering the various values of d obtained for the specimen.

X-ray crystallography is a powerful tool for the exploration of the structure of materials. For example, it was used to deduce the arrangement of atoms in DNA, the famous double-helix molecule in the nucleus of a cell which holds all the instructions for the construction of the next generation of cells.

By restricting the maximum energy of the electrons in the X-ray tube, we can ensure that X-rays of wavelength 0.5×10^{-10} m, corresponding to $n = 2$, are not incident on the crystal (see chapter 29). These monochromatic X-rays fall on a powdered specimen of the substance to be studied. Even though the specimen has been finely ground into a powder, it will consist of a large number of tiny crystals, each with its crystal planes orientated at random. So as the X-rays pass through the specimen they will encounter some crystals with their planes angled so that the Bragg Law can be obeyed. Whenever that happens, part of the X-ray beam is deflected on to a photographic film. The result is a set of narrow rings on the developed film, each one corresponding to a particular value of θ.

OBJECTIVES

After studying this section you should be able to do the following.

Derive the grating formula.

Estimate the number of orders obtainable from a grating by considering the diffraction pattern of a single slit.

Describe how a diffraction grating can be used to form a spectrum of the light from a source.

Know that a hologram is a form of diffraction grating.

Explain why concave gratings are used in infra-red spectrometers.

Derive the Bragg Law.

Explain how X-ray diffraction can be used to deduce the arrangement of atoms in a crystal.

QUESTIONS

1 A diffraction grating has 2750 lines to the centimetre. Light from a helium–neon laser is directed at the grating so that the plane of the grating is at right angles to the beam. A screen is placed 2.0 m in front of the grating to intercept the light diffracted by the grating. Three spots are seen on the screen.

a If the wavelength of the light is 633 nm, calculate the distance on the screen between the spots.

b The central spot is brighter than the other two. Explain why.

c Why can only three spots be seen on the screen? Estimate the width of the slits on the grating.

2 Rowland's original plane reflection grating had 14,000 lines per 2.54 cm of surface. The visible spectrum covers wavelengths between 400 nm and 680 nm. Calculate how many complete visible spectra Rowland would have seen when he shone a beam of white light normally onto his grating. Would there be any overlapping orders, i.e. would the red part of one order spectrum lie on top of the blue part of the next order spectrum?

3 A diffraction grating is illuminated with monochromatic light normally to its surface. Light transmitted by the grating falls on a screen placed some distance away. State and explain the effect of the following changes on the number, intensity, width and spacing of the intensity maxima on the screen:

a Doubling the spacing of the slits on the grating surface.

b Halving the width of each slit.

c Increasing the wavelength of the light.

d Decreasing the width of the beam of light so that less of the grating is illuminated.

4 The angular width $\Delta\theta$ of each intensity peak produced by a diffraction grating is fixed by the width b of the grating. For light of wavelength λ, $\Delta\theta \simeq 2\lambda/b$. This is the same as the angular spread of light passing through a slit of width b.

a Test the above rule by considering a grating with only two slits, i.e. Young's slits. Start by sketching the intensity pattern for the light diffracted by a pair of slits separated by a distance d. Is the width of the peaks approximately equal to λ/d?

b Use the rule to sketch the intensity pattern of the diffraction pattern of a grating with ten slits of spacing d.

c A grating has 400 lines per mm over a width of 20 mm. Light of wavelength 590 nm passes through all of the grating normal to its surface. Calculate the angular separation θ of the three central peaks in the diffraction pattern.

d Use the rule described above to calculate the width $\Delta\theta$ of the peaks.

5 It is claimed that the colours seen on the plumage of some birds, particularly peacocks, are due to interference effects rather than absorption. How could you tell if this was true?

6 This question is about the laws of reflection of light from a mirror. In figure 28.36 we have shown two rays of light reflecting off the surface of a mirror at two points which are a distance x apart.

a What is the general condition on the distance AB − CD for the two rays to be in phase when they reach a distant detector?

b Show that the reflected rays are in phase if $x(\cos\beta - \cos\alpha) = n\lambda$.

c Suppose that $\alpha \neq \beta$. Is it possible for rays which reflect off the mirror for *any* value of x to be in phase?

d Explain why a plane light wave reflected off a very small mirror emerges at a range of angles. Estimate the diameter of mirror which would make this effect visible to the naked eye.

7 Figure 28.37 shows three different crystal planes in a simple cubic structure. You are going to work out the X-ray powder diffraction pattern you would expect to get from such a crystal.

a What are the dots in figure 28.37?

b By means of a scale drawing, or otherwise, find the spacing between the crystal planes. The interatomic spacing of the crystal is 0.25 nm.

c If the crystal is illuminated with X-rays of wavelength 1.0×10^{-10} m, calculate three angles through which the X-rays will be deflected on their way through.

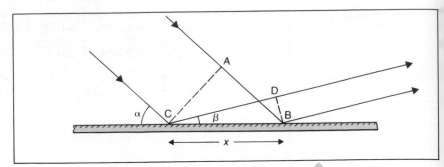

Figure 28.36

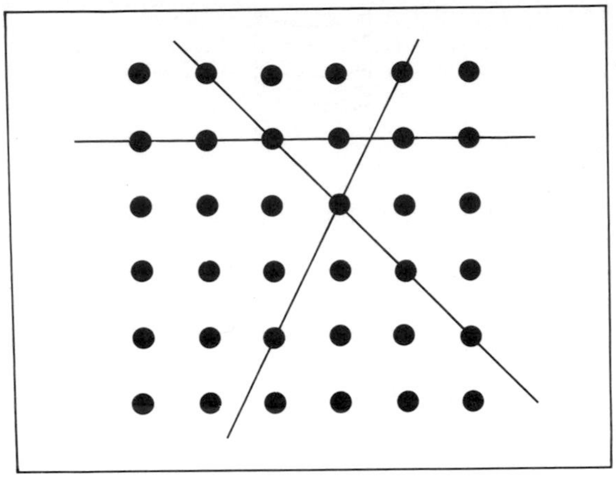

Figure 28.37

d A 20 cm × 4 cm photographic film is placed on the radius of a 10 cm circle centred on the powdered sample. Draw a scale diagram to show the image on the developed film.

e Indicate on your diagram the relative intensity of the lines and dots. Explain your answer.

29

QUANTUM MECHANICS

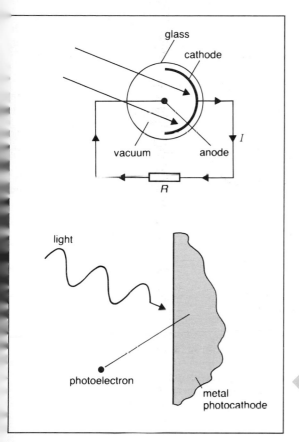

light

photoelectron

metal
photocathode

glass
cathode

vacuum
anode

I

R

Figure 29.1 A photocell

Figure 29.2 Measuring the energy of the photoelectrons

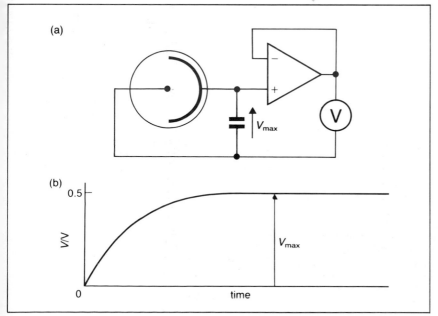

(a)

V_{max}

V

(b)

0.5

V/V

V_{max}

0

time

This chapter deals with the physics of very small things, like neutrons and electrons. On this planet you need a good understanding of the behaviour of pieces of matter which contain at least 10^{20} atoms — with each atom itself containing up to approximately 350 fundamental particles such as neutrons, protons and electrons. Of course, you have never had to manipulate a single electron — but do not be too surprised when you discover that it does not behave in the same way as a speck of dust or a ball-bearing. The behaviour of very small particles is not only odd, it is far odder than you could ever imagine! **Quantum mechanics**, the laws of motion for very small particles, predicts (correctly) some very startling phenomena. This chapter will only be able to scratch the surface of this important field, one of the resounding successes of twentieth-century physics.

PHOTONS

Before 1905, it seemed obvious that waves and particles were different things. Particles were lumps which had mass, shape and charge; whereas waves were travelling vibrations which had frequency, wavelength and polarisation. Thus an electron was a particle and light was a wave. All that changed in 1905 when Albert Einstein published his explanation of a puzzling phenomenon known as the **photoelectric effect**. Thereafter, light could not be modelled purely in terms of waves, but only by a mixture of particle and wave concepts. Einstein's description of light as a particle (the **photon**) guided through space by a wave (the electromagnetic field) shattered the idea of the microscopic world as a scaled-down version of the world we experience directly.

Photoelectric effect

The apparatus needed to demonstrate the photoelectric effect is shown in figure 29.1. Light falls on a flat clean metal surface (the **photocathode**) in a vacuum. The energy is absorbed by mobile electrons on the surface of the metal, giving them enough kinetic energy to enter the vacuum. Electrons ejected from the metal by light this way are called **photoelectrons**. Some of the photoelectrons will be travelling in the right direction to be absorbed by the **anode**. The anode is often a rod so that it intercepts very little of the light. The whole photoelectric cell behaves like a source of p.d. which converts light energy into electrical energy.

One aspect of the behaviour of a photoelectric cell could not be explained by the physics of the day. The energy of the photoelectrons did not depend on the intensity of the light. The intensity could be changed by several orders of magnitude without appearing to alter the energy of the photoelectrons. On the other hand, changing the colour of the light did change the energy of the photoelectrons! Figure 29.2(a) shows how an op-amp follower and capacitor can be used to measure the maximum kinetic energy of the electrons emitted by the photocathode. Each photoelectron which is absorbed by the anode increases the charge on the capacitor plates by e. It must therefore increase the voltage across the plates, increasing the p.d. between anode and cathode. As you can see from the graph of figure 29.2(b), the cathode becomes progressively more positive than the anode as photoelectrons pass from one to the other and the capacitor charges up. When the p.d. across the capacitor is V, we can calculate the kinetic energy change ΔE_k of the photoelectrons on their way from cathode to anode.

$$\Delta E_k = eV \qquad (29.1)$$

Eventually the p.d. between anode and cathode becomes large enough to prevent even the most energetic photoelectron reaching the anode. It loses all of its kinetic energy just before it reaches the anode and returns to the cathode. So when the p.d. reaches V_{max}, the charging current ceases. The value of V_{max} can therefore be used to measure the kinetic energy E_{max} of the most energetic photoelectrons.

$$E_{max} = eV_{max} \qquad (29.2)$$

For example, when blue light (≈ 450 nm) is shone on the potassium cathode of a photocell, the value of V_{max} is typically 0.5 V. So the maximum energy of the photoelectrons is about 0.5 eV.

represents the behaviour of a photocell whose cathode is made from a particular metal. Note how the lines all have the same slope but different intercepts. This can be summarised with the following piece of algebra.

$$E_{max} = hf - \phi \qquad (29.3)$$

The slope of the lines is fixed by the value of h and their intercepts by the value of ϕ. Since all of the lines have the same slope, h is going to be a universal quantity, the same for all metals. It is called **Planck's constant**, and it has the value 6.63×10^{-34} J s. The intercept ϕ is known as the **work function** of the metal.

Einstein suggested that the form of equation (29.3) could be explained by postulating that a light wave of frequency f could only deliver energy to an electron in lumps of exactly hf. (This quantity of energy is often called a **photon**.) Thus when the light illuminates the cathode surface, electrons within it are given an energy hf. If they are near the surface they can leave the metal, provided that hf is greater than the work function ϕ. (The work function is the energy needed to extract a mobile electron from the metal. Some values are listed in table 29.1.) So the kinetic energy of the photoelectrons will be the difference between the energy of a photon and the work function, as stated in equation (29.3).

Table 29.1

Metal	ϕ/eV
potassium	2.2
lead	4.0
zinc	4.3
tungsten	4.6
nickel	5.2

Quantisation

Using the modern jargon, Einstein was suggesting that the photoelectric effect can be explained if the energy of an electromagnetic wave is **quantised**. That is, the energy exchanged with the wave is always nhf where n is an integer.

> $E = hf$
>
> E is the energy of a photon (J)
>
> h is Planck's constant (6.63×10^{-34} J s)
>
> f is the frequency of the wave (Hz)

So the energy delivered by an electromagnetic wave comes in lumps known as **photons**. This applies to both the creation and absorption of electromagnetic waves. Therefore a helium–neon laser which emits red light of wavelength 633 nm does not steadily convert electrical energy into light: it does so in discrete steps, each the size of a photon. We can calculate the size of those steps as follows:

$$E = hf, \quad c = f\lambda$$

$$\therefore E = \frac{hc}{\lambda}$$

$$\therefore E = \frac{6.63 \times 10^{-34} \times 3.00 \times 10^8}{633 \times 10^{-9}}$$

$$\therefore E = 3.14 \times 10^{-19} \text{ J}$$

Figure 29.3 Variation of photoelectron energy with frequency for different metals

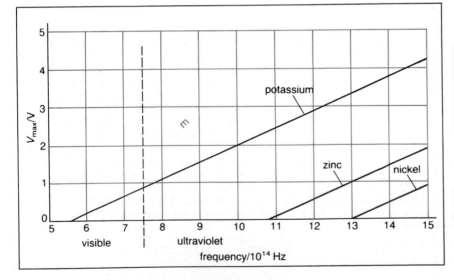

Variation with frequency
The graph of figure 29.3 shows how the value of V_{max} changes with the frequency of the light illuminating the photocathode. (The frequency can be adjusted by using a spectrometer to isolate a known narrow band of wavelengths from the spectrum of a white light source.) Each curve

The power of a school laser is about 0.5 mW. It is interesting to work out how many photons such a laser creates per second. Let that number be n.

$$P = \frac{E}{t}, \quad E = nhf$$

$$\therefore 0.5 \times 10^{-3} = n \times \frac{3.14 \times 10^{-19}}{1.0}$$

$$\therefore n = 1.6 \times 10^{15} \text{ s}^{-1}$$

Photocurrent

Einstein's relationship can be used to predict how the rate of emission of photoelectrons (the **photocurrent**) depends on the intensity of the light incident on the cathode. Since the intensity of a light beam is the rate at which it delivers energy per unit area, it will be proportional to the rate at which photons are absorbed by the metal. So the photocurrent should be proportional to the light intensity. This prediction can be checked in the laboratory with the apparatus shown in figure 29.4. The 12 V power supply ensures that *all* of the photoelectrons are captured by the anode. The consequent current I is measured with the galvanometer. The cathode is illuminated by a light bulb whose filament is a distance r away, so that the light intensity will be proportional to $1/r^2$. A graph of I against $1/r^2$ should be a straight line if the bulb has a small filament and is the only source of light. The filter can be used to illuminate the cathode with a restricted range of wavelengths, but its presence is optional.

Particles or waves

It is tempting to imagine that a laser emits a stream of particle-like photons which rush out at the speed of light, disappearing in a 'puff' of energy when they are absorbed by a photoelectron. This is the particle model of electromagnetic radiation. It explains why photoelectrons have an energy which is independent of the light intensity and why light appears to travel in straight lines. On the other hand, diffraction and interference of light can only be explained with a wave model. Which model is the better one to use?

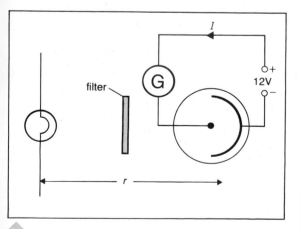

Figure 29.4 Apparatus for verifying that the photocurrent is proportional to the light intensity

---

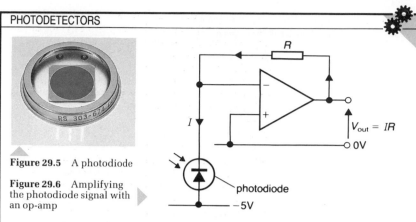

Figure 29.5 A photodiode

Figure 29.6 Amplifying the photodiode signal with an op-amp

$V_{out} = IR$

The photoelectric effect is widely used to convert light signals to electrical signals. The simplest device which does this is a **photodiode**, illustrated in figure 29.5. Light which passes through the junction between the p and n regions of the semiconductor can give photons to electrons, giving them enough energy to break free from an atom and move freely through the crystal. The **quantum efficiency** of a good photodiode can be as high as 0.7, so that 70% of the photons aimed at the photodiode surface create mobile electrons. The circuit shown in figure 29.6 can be used to convert the photocurrent into a measurable voltage: the photodiode is reverse biased so that it only conducts when light is absorbed by it.

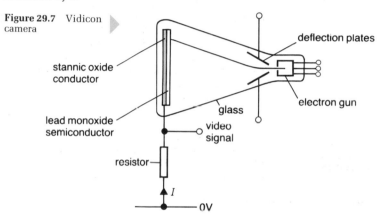

Figure 29.7 Vidicon camera

The **vidicon camera** shown in figure 29.7 also uses the photoelectric effect to detect light, but over a much wider area than a photodiode. It is basically a television camera, emitting a stream of data in electronic form about an image. That image is thrown by a lens system onto a sheet of lead monoxide (a semiconductor) covered with a thin layer of transparent conducting stannic oxide. Wherever light falls on the semiconductor, the photoelectric effect introduces mobile charges so that it becomes a conductor. An electron beam is swept across the back surface of the lead monoxide in a **raster** (figure 29.8), sweeping from left to right with each row being below the last one. The current in the resistor at any instant is then a measure of the number of mobile electrons at the point (**pixel**) being probed by the electron beam. So the output voltage is proportional to the intensity of the light falling on part of the lead monoxide semiconductor. Typically, the screen is divided into 625 rows, each of which contains 833 pixels. Each pixel is scanned by the electron beam 25 times a second.

Figure 29.8 A screen raster

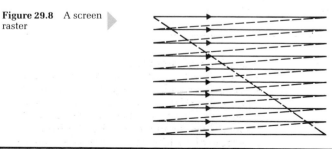

One way round this difficulty is to treat light like a wave some of the time and as a particle for the rest of the time. Thus, when you are thinking about diffraction gratings you think of light as a wave, and when you are thinking about photoelectrons, you think of light as a particle. You may be able to get away with this some of the time, but what do you do when faced with a situation which involves both wave-like *and* particle-like behaviour?

Young's slits revisited

The following thought experiment will help you to grasp the true nature of light. (Similar experiments have been performed, and their results are in excellent agreement with the wave—particle model we are about to introduce.) Figure 29.9 shows a situation where light behaves both like a wave and a particle. It is a Young's slits arrangement with a line of photodetectors instead of a screen. The photodetectors are **avalanche photodiodes**, the solid-state equivalent of the photomultiplier tube. A single photoelectron triggers the release of a large number of mobile electrons so that a large output pulse is obtained. As you can see from figure 29.10, each photodetector is connected to a loudspeaker and a counter, so that photons arriving at its surface can be detected and recorded.

Now suppose that the light source is very feeble. What will happen when you switch it on? You will hear a random series of identical clicks from the speakers as photons enter the detectors, exactly as predicted by the particle model. The average rate at which photons are detected will be steady, but the actual rate will fluctuate randomly from one instant to the next. Initially, photons will appear to be detected at random by the various detectors, but as time goes on it will become apparent that more photons are arriving at some detectors than at others. Eventually the distribution of photons counted by the various detectors looks like the intensity distribution predicted by the wave model for Young's slits (figure 29.11). Certain detectors count no photons at all, being at the places of destructive interference for the waves from each slit. Other detectors at the positions of full constructive interference count lots of photons.

Figure 29.9 Double-slit interference

Figure 29.10 Each photon detected produces an audible click and is recorded by the counter

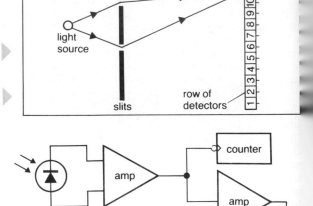

Figure 29.11 The distribution of photons recorded by the array of photodiodes compared with that predicted by the Young's slits formula

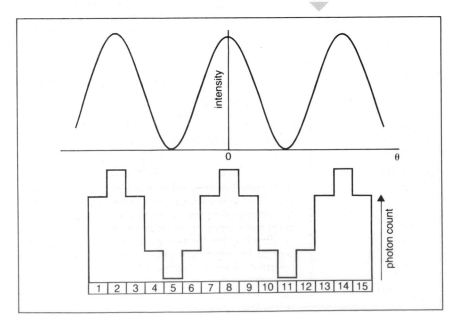

Probability waves

We can model these results as follows. The wave spreading out from the source is used to calculate the amplitude of the wave arriving at each detector. Of course, two waves arrive at each detector, one from each slit, so they are superposed before calculating the amplitude. The square of the amplitude is then used to calculate the intensity of the wave at the detector. The intensity is the *average* rate at which energy is delivered to a unit area of the detector — it tells you the rate at which photons will be delivered to it. The intensity of the wave certainly cannot be used to predict which detector will receive the next photon or exactly when it will arrive. Nobody knows how to do that. All it can do is tell you the *probability* that a photon will arrive at the detector. There is a high probability of photons arriving at detectors where the wave amplitude is large and a correspondingly low probability of their arriving at detectors where the wave amplitude is low.

You may dislike the idea of a physics model which can, at best, only calculate a probability for single events. However, if you think about it, there are other models in physics that only work on a large scale. The behaviour of gases is one example. However, don't fall into the trap of assuming that the wave—particle theory of light is used because it is too complicated to think of the behaviour of a single photon. In principle, it is possible to use Newton's Laws to calculate the trajectory of every particle in a gas once you have enough information about the forces which act between them. This is not the case with photons. Probability is built deep into the model and there is no way round it: nature herself is uncertain about what will happen next as far as small scale events are concerned. The wave—particle model is the best description we have of electromagnetic radiation, coping equally well with radio waves and gamma rays. Whether you like it or not, electromagnetic radiation travels like a wave, but is created and destroyed in lumps, like particles. (In fact, as you will find out in the next section, particles also travel like a wave!)

Energy levels

A typical emission spectrum for an element is shown in figure 29.12. The fact that it consists of a number of discrete wavelengths means that the atoms are only creating photons of certain energies. This suggests that an atom can only have a number of discrete energies, with a photon being created when the atom drops from one **energy level** to another. Look at figure 29.13, the energy–time graph for a particular atom in a discharge tube. The atom starts off in the **ground state**, its state of least energy E_0. Collision with an electron pushes the atom to its first excited state E_1. After a few nanoseconds the atom drops back to the ground state, emitting a photon with a particular wavelength.

$$E = hf, \quad c = f\lambda \quad \therefore E_1 - E_0 = \frac{hc}{\lambda} \qquad \textbf{(29.4)}$$

Hydrogen

As an example, let's work out the energy levels of the hydrogen atom implied by the four lines in its visible spectrum (figure 29.14(a)). Their wavelengths are given in table 29.2.

Figure 29.12 Emission spectrum of hydrogen

Figure 29.13 How the energy of an atom changes when it is pushed out of its ground state and subsequently emits a photon

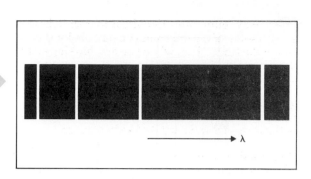

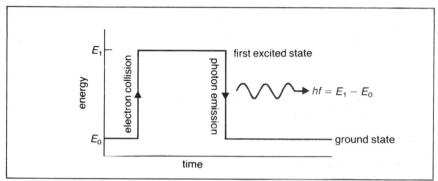

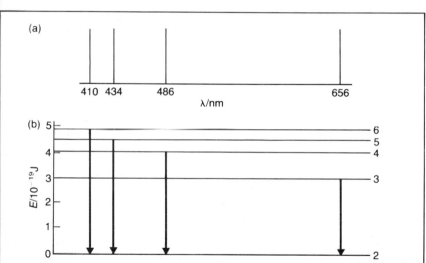

(a)

410 434 486 656

λ/nm

Figure 29.14 The energy levels required to explain the visible spectrum of hydrogen

Figure 29.15 Five transitions not marked in figure 29.14

Figure 29.16 The full energy level diagram for hydrogen

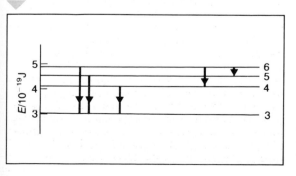

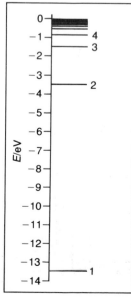

Table 29.2

Colour	λ/nm	f/Hz	E/J
red	656	4.57×10^{14}	3.03×10^{-19}
green	486	6.17×10^{14}	4.09×10^{-19}
blue	434	6.91×10^{14}	4.58×10^{-19}
purple	410	7.32×10^{14}	4.85×10^{-19}

If we assume that all four photons are the result of the atom dropping from one of four excited states to a common ground state level, we can use the photon formula to calculate the separation E between the levels. The five energy levels are illustrated in the **energy level diagram** of figure 29.14(b) which shows the transitions responsible for the four different visible photons. (The numbers used to label the energy levels will become obvious soon.)

If figure 29.14 is correct it implies that at least five other different photons should be emitted by hydrogen atoms. These are shown in figure 29.15. Let's work out the wavelength of the photon emitted when the atom drops from the top energy level to the one beneath it.

$$E = hf$$
$$\therefore 4.85\times10^{-19} - 4.58\times10^{-19} = 6.63\times10^{-34} \times f$$
$$\therefore f = 4.07\times10^{13} \text{ Hz}$$

$$c = f\lambda$$

$$\therefore \lambda = \frac{c}{f} \qquad \therefore \lambda = \frac{3.00\times10^8}{4.07\times10^{13}} = 7.37 \text{ μm}$$

This is in the infra-red region of the spectrum, as are all the other transitions marked in figure 29.15. Spectroscopes employing concave gratings and infra-red sensors have detected all five photons, confirming that the energy level diagram is a good partial description of a hydrogen atom. The complete diagram is shown in figure 29.16. You can check for yourself that transitions which involve the ground state (labelled 1) all emit ultraviolet photons.

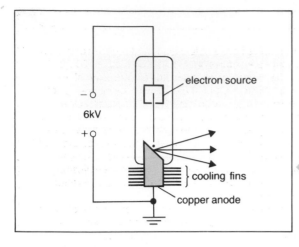

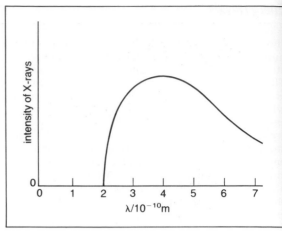

Figure 29.17 An X-ray source

Figure 29.18 The spectrum of X-rays from a copper anode produced by 6.0 keV electrons

Figure 29.19 The effect of increasing the electron energy

X-ray spectra

The spectrum of X-rays emitted from atoms thumped with high speed electrons gives further evidence for the quantisation of energy. Figure 29.17 shows the usual arrangement for generating X-rays. A beam of electrons is accelerated by an electric field, giving energies of up to 25 keV. As the electrons hit the copper anode they lose their kinetic energy, emitting X-rays with a range of wavelengths which can be measured with a crystal spectrometer. The process is not very efficient and a lot of the electron's energy is converted to heat, hence the need for a copper anode and cooling fins to keep the anode cool. Figure 29.18 shows the spectrum obtained when the electron beam energy is 6.0 keV. Note that there is a definite short wavelength limit. This can be predicted with the photon formula as follows. The highest energy photons will be created when a single electron converts all of its kinetic energy into an electromagnetic wave.

$$E = hf \qquad \therefore f = \frac{E}{h}$$

$$\therefore f = \frac{6.0 \times 10^3 \ \times \ 1.6 \times 10^{-19}}{6.63 \times 10^{-34}} = 1.45 \times 10^{18} \text{ Hz}$$

$$c = f\lambda$$

$$\therefore \lambda = \frac{c}{f} = \frac{3.0 \times 10^8}{1.45 \times 10^{18}} = 2.0 \times 10^{-10} \text{ m}$$

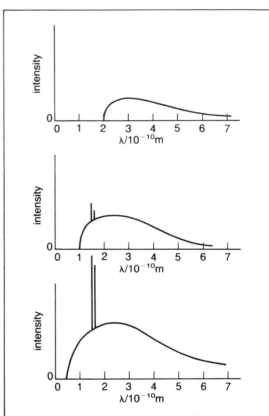

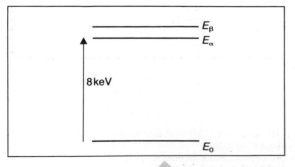

Figure 29.20 Some energy levels for a copper atom

Figure 29.21 Collision of a 10 keV electron with a copper atom and the subsequent emission of a 0.14 nm X-ray photon

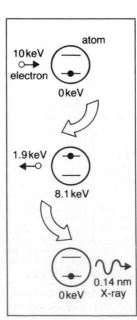

The sequence of figure 29.19 shows what happens as the energy of the electron beam is doubled and then doubled again. The short wavelength limit is halved and then halved again, but a pair of sharp lines also appear in the spectrum at wavelengths of about 1.4×10^{-10} m and 1.6×10^{-10} m. These are due to transitions between energy levels of the copper atom, as shown in figure 29.20. Electrons of energy below 8.0 keV will be unable to move the atom from its ground state to either of the excited states labelled E_α and E_β. On the other hand, electrons of energy above 8.1 keV will be able to push the atoms from their ground state to either of the two excited states. The atom subsequently returns to the ground state, emitting one of two photons on the way. This is illustrated in figure 29.21 — the 10.0 keV electron gives 8.1 keV to the atom during the collision, carrying away the other 1.9 keV. Shortly afterwards, an 8.1 keV X-ray photon is emitted.

GAS LASERS

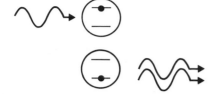

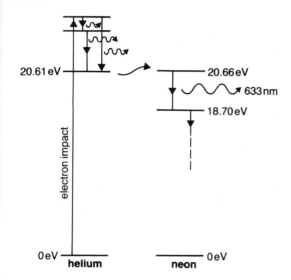

Figure 29.22 Stimulated emission

Figure 29.23 Energy levels of helium and neon atoms involved in the production of 633 nm laser light

Figure 29.24 A gas laser

The term **laser** comes from the words light amplification by stimulated emission of radiation. The process of **stimulated emission** is illustrated in figure 29.22. A photon incident on an atom in its excited state stimulates the emission of an identical photon. (Of course, for this to happen the energy of the incident photon must be an exact match to the energy between the atom's two states.) One photon goes in and two come out travelling in the same direction, with the same polarisation and phase. So if a single photon of the right frequency enters a gas of atoms in an excited state, a large number of identical photons will be created: the gas acts as an amplifier. In practice, atoms in an excited state quickly fall back to the ground state after a few nanoseconds by **spontaneous emission**. The trick of building a laser is to ensure that the atoms are pushed up to their excited state faster than they fall down again.

A helium–neon gas laser uses an electrical discharge in helium to push neon atoms into a suitable excited state for stimulated emission to take place. The energy level diagrams for helium and neon are shown in figure 29.23. Electron–atom collisions push the helium atoms into high energy states which then decay down by the emission of photons of a variety of wavelengths. About 1 in 10^5 of the atoms end up in a **metastable state**, 20.61 eV above the ground state. They cannot get to the ground state by spontaneous emission. However, they can lose their energy through collision with neon atoms, because neon has an excited state which is 20.66 eV above its ground state. (Kinetic energy of the atoms can provide the 0.05 eV difference between the energies of the two atoms.) In this way, a large number of neon atoms can be pushed into this excited state, fast enough for stimulated emission to take place to the level which is 18.70 eV above the ground state.

The practical details of a helium–neon laser are shown in figure 29.24. Curved mirrors at either end of the discharge tube allow photons to pass backwards and forwards through the excited neon atoms. The mirrors need to reflect at least 99% of the photons which hit them, so they are made from transparent multi-layered coatings. Partial reflection of the incident wave off the junctions between the different layers creates a series of wavelets which, if the geometry is correctly matched to the wavelength, will constructively interfere to give a reflected wave. The output of the laser is the 1% of photons which leak through the mirrors.

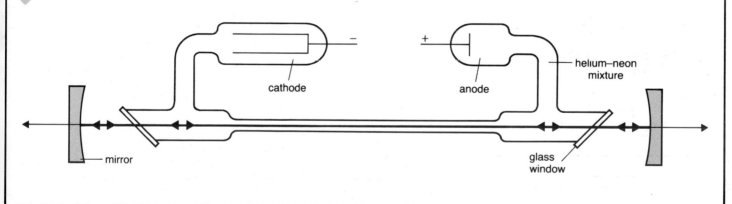

OBJECTIVES

After studying this section you should be able to do the following.

Describe how the maximum energy of photoelectrons can be measured.	Describe the wave–particle model of light.
Understand the meaning of *photon* and *work function*.	State how the intensity of a light source is related to the rate at which it delivers photons.
Use the formula $E = hf$.	Use an energy level diagram to predict the emission spectrum of a system.
Use the photon idea to explain the behaviour of a photoelectric cell.	Describe how X-rays are generated and calculate their low wavelength limit.

QUESTIONS

1 The apparatus shown in figure 29.25 is used to measure Planck's constant in a school laboratory. White light from a filament lamp is passed through a filter so that light of a limited range of frequencies hits the caesium photocathode. The maximum voltages V_{max} to which the capacitor charges for each filter are listed in table 29.3.

Table 29.3

λ/nm	V_{max}/V
390–400	0.75
415–425	0.56
440–450	0.42
465–475	0.29
490–500	0.15

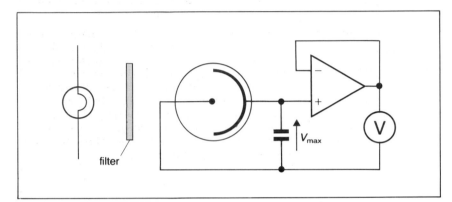

Figure 29.25

a Why should you do the experiment starting with the green filter and working towards the purple one?

b Draw a graph to show how V_{max} depends on the frequency of the radiation incident on the photocathode. (Do you use the average wavelength transmitted by the filter to calculate the frequency?)

c Use your graph to obtain values for Planck's constant and the work function of caesium.

d Your answer for Planck's constant is about 10% smaller than the true value. This is probably because the anode was coated with a layer of caesium, a volatile metal. By considering the photocurrent due to stray light hitting the anode, explain why each value of V_{max} is lower than it should be.

2 A 400 nm filter is used in the apparatus of figure 29.25. The whole apparatus is kept in the dark, so that when the bulb is switched on it is the only light source.

a Sketch a graph to show how the value of V, the p.d. across the capacitor, changes with time when the light bulb is switched on. Explain why it has the shape it does.

b The experiment is repeated with the bulb twice as far away from the photocathode as before. What effect does this have on the initial current charging the capacitor when the bulb is switched on? Sketch on your graph of part (a) how V will change with time.

c Suppose that the experiment of part (a) is repeated with a 500 nm filter. What effect will this have on the rate at which the capacitor charges up?

3 Nikki uses a coulomb meter and a sheet of zinc to demonstrate the photoelectric effect to her friends. The apparatus is shown in figure 29.26.

a Zinc has a work function of 4.3 eV. Calculate the maximum wavelength of light which will cause photoelectrons to be emitted from zinc.

b Nikki charges the sheet to −1.5 V before exposing it to ultraviolet radiation from a mercury discharge lamp. The most intense line in the mercury emission spectrum has a wavelength of 254 nm. Calculate the maximum energy of the photoelectrons emitted from the zinc surface.

c Explain why photoelectrons with a wide range of energies are emitted from the zinc.

d The reading of the coulomb meter eventually rises to +0.04 V and stays there. Nikki thinks this may be due to the relatively low kinetic energy of air molecules which pick up the photoelectrons. Convince her with a calculation. ($\frac{1}{2}m<c^2> = 3kT/2$ for an ideal gas.)

e Dick tries the experiment for himself later, but connects the battery round the wrong way. To his dismay, he finds that the coulomb meter reading stays resolutely at +1.5 V when the zinc is exposed to ultraviolet light. Explain why this happens.

4 Calculate the rate at which each of the sources listed in table 29.4 emit photons.

Table 29.4

Source	λ/m	P/W
X-ray tube	$1×10^{-10}$	10
laser	$6.33×10^{-9}$	$5×10^{-4}$
sun lamp	$2.54×10^{-9}$	50
microwave	0.12	500
radio transmitter	10	5000

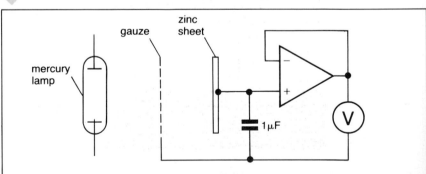

Figure 29.26

5 The energy level diagram of an imaginary element is shown in figure 29.27(a). The atoms can pass from any level to any other by absorbing or emitting photons.

a Calculate the wavelengths of all the photons emitted by a sample of the atoms in a gas discharge. Which of them would be in the visible part of the spectrum?

b Suppose that white light is passed through a sample of the gas and then analysed with a spectrometer as shown in figure 29.27(b). Explain why three sharp black bands appear in the spectrum of the transmitted light and calculate their wavelengths.

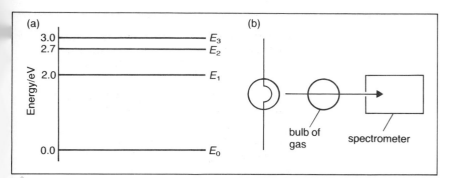

Figure 29.27

6 If you go to discos, you will know that white shirts can **fluoresce** when exposed to ultraviolet light. They emit blue light when the invisible ultraviolet light is switched on.

a Suggest a reason for this phenomenon. (Think about the energies of blue and ultraviolet photons.)

b Why is it impossible to make a substance fluoresce visible light when it is exposed to infra-red light?

7 The **gravitational red shift** is the change of wavelength of an electromagnetic wave as it leaves the gravitational field of a star or planet. The gravitational mass of a photon can be calculated from the mass–energy formula $E = mc^2$.

a Explain why the photon wavelength is increased as it moves away from a star.

b Our Sun has a mass and radius of 2.0×10^{30} kg and 7.0×10^8 m. Calculate the change of gravitational energy of a yellow photon of wavelength 590 nm on its way from the surface of the Sun to deep space.

c How does your answer to part (a) compare with the original energy of the photon? Will the red shift be measurable with a spectrometer?

d Suppose that the Sun shrinks until it has the density of an atomic nucleus, i.e. 2.3×10^{17} kg m^{-3}. (This will happen when it has run out of elements to fuse together and create heat.) Assuming that the Sun's mass remains constant in the process, calculate the gravitational red shift of a 590 nm photon emitted from its new surface.

8 Sahib has suggested that the apparatus shown in figure 29.4 could be used as a light intensity meter to measure the strength of sunlight. Estimate the maximum expected photocurrent for a photocell with a photocathode of radius 5 mm exposed to bright sunlight (intensity 1 0 kW m^{-2}). In practice, the photocurrent is only 5% of the value you have calculated. Suggest two reasons why. Will this invalidate the use of the device as a precision intensity meter?

WAVE MECHANICS

Look at the photograph of figure 29.28. It shows a Young's slits interference pattern. The remarkable thing about the pattern is that it was *not* obtained by firing a beam of electromagnetic radiation at a double slit. A beam of electrons was used instead! Electrons are particles, with a definite rest mass and charge, yet they can obviously interfere with themselves like waves do. To make an interference pattern on the screen, each electron must act like a wave and pass through both slits at once (figure 29.28). The wavelets from each slit can then combine on the screen to give regions of high and low probability of arrival for the electron. Of course, the electron arrives as a 'lump', giving off a flash of light when it hits the screen. The conclusion is inescapable. An electron travels like a wave but arrives in lumps.

Quantum mechanics is a very mathematical model, so we shall only be able to give you a brief taste of it. Unlike relativity, which is based on a small number of statements that can be tested directly by experiment, the basic equations and rules of quantum mechanics have been found by trial and error. This section will not discuss those rules very much. Instead, it will try to give you some idea of how the physics of small particles is different from the physics of your surroundings.

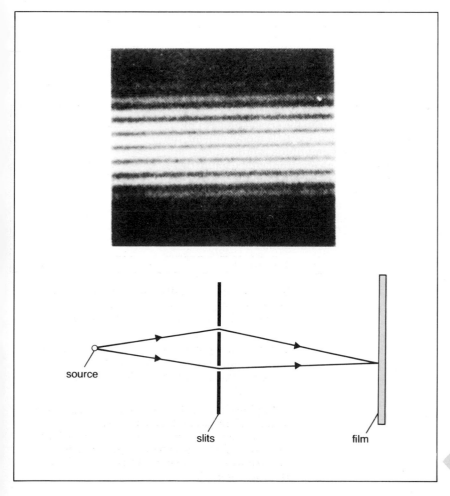

Figure 29.28 Interference fringes obtained by firing electrons through a pair of slits

De Broglie waves

In 1924, Louis de Broglie (pronounced 'broy') stated how the wavelength of a particle could be calculated from its momentum. At the time, there was no evidence at all that particles had other than particle-like behaviour. Einstein's explanation of the photoelectric effect was generally accepted and experiments had shown that X-rays behaved like particles when colliding with electrons, conserving both momentum and energy. The momentum of a photon is given by $p = h/\lambda$; de Broglie suggested that the same formula could be applied to particles.

$$p = \frac{h}{\lambda}$$

p is the momentum of the particle (N s)

h is Planck's constant (6.63×10^{-34} J s)

λ is the wavelength of the particle (m)

Let's use de Broglie's rule to calculate the wavelength of a 1.0 keV electron. Start off by calculating the momentum of the electron.

$$E_k = \tfrac{1}{2}mv^2, \quad p = mv$$

$$\therefore E_k = \frac{p^2}{2m} \tag{29.5}$$

$$\therefore p = (2mE_k)^{\frac{1}{2}}$$

$$\therefore p = (2 \times 9.1 \times 10^{-31} \times 1.0 \times 10^3 \times 1.6 \times 10^{-19})^{\frac{1}{2}}$$

$$\therefore p = 1.7 \times 10^{-23} \text{ N s}$$

Now we can use the de Broglie rule to find the wavelength.

$$p = \frac{h}{\lambda}$$

$$\therefore \lambda = \frac{h}{p}$$

$$\therefore \lambda = \frac{6.63 \times 10^{-34}}{1.7 \times 10^{-23}} = 3.9 \times 10^{-11} \text{ m}$$

The wavelength of a 1.0 keV electron is therefore a bit smaller than the diameter of an atom ($\simeq 10^{-10}$ m). So if 1.0 keV electrons are fired at a crystal they should be diffracted by a substantial angle.

Electron diffraction

The apparatus shown in figure 29.29 can be used to show that a beam of electrons can be diffracted by a powdered specimen. The electrons are accelerated through a p.d. V so that when they hit the specimen they can each be modelled as a plane wave of wavelength λ. We can use equation (29.5) to write down an expression for the wavelength in terms of the accelerating p.d.

$$p = \frac{h}{\lambda}, \quad E = \frac{p^2}{2m}, \quad E = eV$$

$$\therefore \lambda = \frac{h}{(2eVm)^{\frac{1}{2}}} \tag{29.6}$$

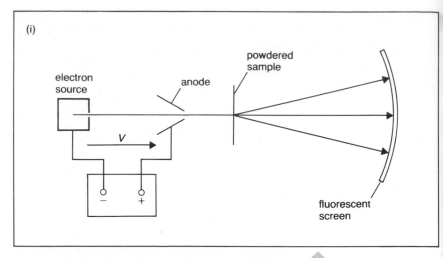

(i)

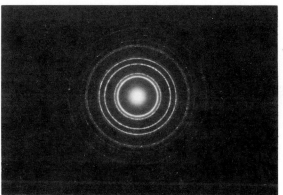

Figure 29.29 Electron diffraction apparatus

Figure 29.30 Diffraction pattern of electrons fired at a thin gold foil: each grain in the foil has a random orientation of its crystal planes, so the pattern consists of concentric circles rather than spots

Any crystals in the specimen which have crystal planes oriented at an angle θ to the electron beam will strongly reflect part of the wave if the Bragg Law is obeyed.

$$\lambda = 2d\sin\theta \qquad \therefore \theta \simeq \frac{\lambda}{2d} \tag{29.7}$$

(d is the spacing between the crystal planes.) By analogy with the wave–particle model of light, the square of the wave's amplitude is proportional to the probability that an electron will be found there. So electrons will be deflected from the beam at a variety of angles 2θ, each one corresponding to reflection by a different set of crystal planes in the specimen. Typically, the spacing of crystal planes is about 2.0×10^{-10} m: we can use this to estimate the deflection of 1.0 keV electrons.

$$\theta = \frac{\lambda}{2d} \quad \therefore \ 2\theta = \frac{2 \times 3.9 \times 10^{-11}}{2 \times 2.0 \times 10^{-10}} \simeq 0.2 \text{ rad}$$

So if the electrons hit a suitably coated screen which is 15 cm away from the specimen, the radius of the bright circle will be $0.2 \times 15 = 3$ cm, easily visible to the naked eye. Figure 29.30 shows the diffraction pattern of electrons transmitted by a thin gold foil. A thin specimen has to be used to get sharp diffraction rings. As electrons pass through a thick specimen they lose energy and their wavelength becomes longer, smudging out the diffraction pattern.

ATOM DIFFRACTION

Wavelike behaviour is not restricted to electrons and other fundamental particles. It is a characteristic of *all* particles. The apparatus shown in figure 29.31 shows how helium atoms can be diffracted off the surface of a lithium fluoride crystal. (Lithium fluoride is an ionic crystal with a simple cubic structure.) A beam of helium atoms of known momentum is generated with the help of a pair of rotating wheels with slots cut in their perimeters. The crystal acts like a reflection grating, with the helium atoms being diffracted by the regular array of ions on its surface. Of course, mirror reflection of the atoms from the crystal will occur anyway, like balls bouncing off a wall. However, constructive interference between waves reflected off adjacent lines of ions (figure 29.31) results in a sideways deflection of the helium atoms by an angle ϕ where $\lambda = d\sin\phi$. A helium atom at room temperature has a momentum of about 10^{-23} N s, corresponding to a wavelength of about 10^{-10} m. If the spacing between adjacent planes of identical ions in the crystal is 5×10^{-10} m, some helium atoms should emerge from the crystal deflected by $\phi \simeq 0.2$ radians.

Figure 29.31 A beam of monoenergetic helium atoms can reflect off the surface of a crystal like waves off a reflection grating

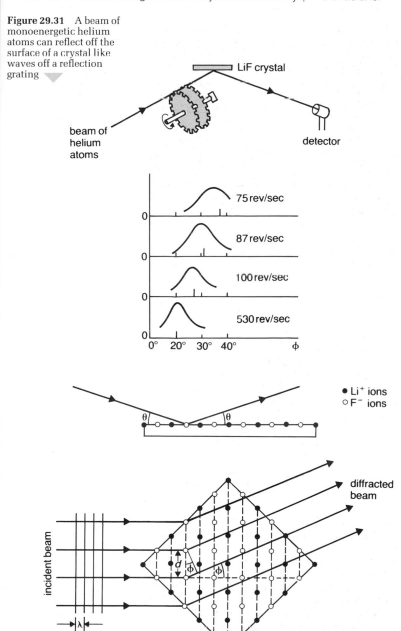

Particles in boxes

In 1925, Erwin Schroedinger discovered the equation for calculating the waves associated with a particle. Here it is for a particle free to move along a line.

$$-\frac{h^2}{8\pi^2 m}\frac{d^2\psi}{dx^2} + V\psi = \frac{ih}{2\pi}\frac{d\psi}{dt}$$

ψ (psi) is the particle's **wavefunction**, the wave whose amplitude squared gives you the probability of finding the particle. The shape of the wavefunction is fixed by the shape of the potential well $V(x)$ in which the particle has been placed. For example, a number of wavefunctions for a parabolic potential well are shown in figure 29.32. There are usually only a limited number of possible wavefunctions for a given potential well, each associated with a particular energy. Although it is a good model for a number of systems, the set of wavefunctions for a parabolic potential well $V = \frac{1}{2}kx^2$ is not easy to find. So we will consider a mathematically simpler but less widely applicable well — that of a particle in a box with strong sides.

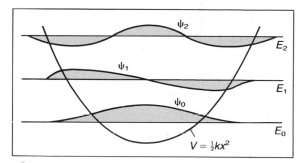

Figure 29.32 Wavefunctions for a parabolic potential well

Figure 29.33 The real and imaginary parts of ψ for a free particle of definite energy (note that $|\psi|^2$ is constant)

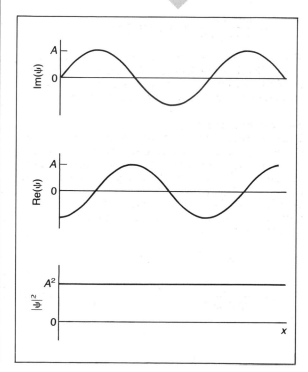

Free particle

If a particle of mass m has no resultant force on it, then its potential V is constant. If you are mathematically minded, you can convince yourself that if V is a number, then $\psi = A\exp[i(\omega t \pm Kx)]$ is a solution of Schroedinger's equation. The wavefunction is therefore a travelling wave whose frequency and wavelength are given by the following expressions.

$$hf = \frac{p^2}{2m} + V, \quad p = \frac{h}{\lambda} \qquad \textbf{(29.8)}$$

The first expression says that the total energy of the particle (kinetic and potential) fixes the frequency of the wave. The second expression is the de Broglie rule linking the momentum of a particle to its wavelength. Figure 29.33 shows what ψ looks like for a particle of definite energy E: the first two graphs show the real and imaginary parts of the wavefunction separately. The fact that the wavefunction has imaginary parts (it contains i, the square root of -1) should tell you that it is not possible to detect it directly. Like electromagnetic waves (which *are* real and detectable), the square modulus of the wavefunction's amplitude $|\psi|^2$ gives you the probability of finding the particle there. So where the wavefunction is zero, the particle will never be found. The most likely places for the particle to be found are where the wavefunction is large. In fact, as you can see from figure 29.33, $|\psi|^2$ is the same everywhere for a free particle, so you are equally likely to find it anywhere.

Energy quantisation

Suppose that you took a particle and placed it in a tube of length l so that it could move freely along the length of the tube, but couldn't get out. What does Schroedinger's equation say about the particle's energy? The potential well for the particle is shown in figure 29.34. $V = 0$ inside the tube and $V = \infty$ outside it. Since the particle is never found outside the tube, ψ must be 0 at $x = 0$ and $x = l$. The wavefunction inside the tube will consist of waves travelling in both directions. The only way in which such waves can maintain a finite amplitude is when they interfere to give a standing wave. This will only happen if a whole number of half-wavelengths fits into the length of the tube. So any real particle placed in the tube can only have certain values for the wavelength of its wavefunction.

$$\frac{n\lambda}{2} = l \qquad \therefore \lambda = \frac{2l}{n} \qquad \textbf{(29.9)}$$

Of course, the wavelength decides the momentum and kinetic energy of the particle.

$$p = \frac{h}{\lambda} \qquad \therefore p = \frac{nh}{2l} \qquad \textbf{(29.10)}$$

$$E = \frac{p^2}{2m} \qquad \therefore E = \frac{n^2h^2}{8ml^2} \qquad \textbf{(29.11)}$$

The energy level diagram and associated wavefunctions for the particle are shown in figure 29.35. (The wavefunctions are real.) There are a number of remarkable things which Schroedinger's equation predicts for the particle.

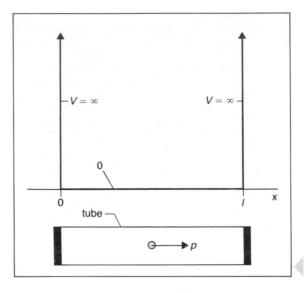

Figure 29.34 Potential well for a particle in a box

- It has one of a number of discrete energies given by equation (29.11).
- The lowest energy of the particle is not zero.
- The spacing of the energy levels is fixed by the length of the tube as well as the mass of the particle.
- There are some places in the well where the particle will never be found.

Let's use equation (29.11) to estimate the ground state energy of an electron in a hydrogen atom. The diameter of a hydrogen atom is about 10^{-10} m. If an electron (mass 9.1×10^{-31} kg) is placed in a tube of length 10^{-10} m, then its lowest energy ($n = 1$) will be roughly the same as that of the electrons in a hydrogen atom.

$$E = \frac{n^2h^2}{8ml^2}$$

$$\therefore E = \frac{1 \times (6.6 \times 10^{-34})^2}{8 \times 9.1 \times 10^{-31} \times (1.0 \times 10^{-10})^2}$$

$$\therefore E \simeq 6 \times 10^{-18} \text{ J or } 37 \text{ eV}$$

This is fairly close to the true value of 14 eV. So the minimum energy of a particle depends on the space it has to move in!

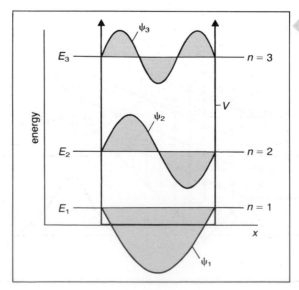

Figure 29.35 Wavefunctions and energy levels for a particle in a box

Moving particles

The wavefunction and **probability distribution** for a particle in the first excited state ($n = 2$) in a tube is shown in figure 29.36. The probability distribution is the square of the wavefunction's amplitude: it gives you the probability of finding the particle at various points in the tube. So you are equally likely to find the particle at either of the peaks of the probability distribution, and you will never find it at the edges or the middle of the tube. Since the wavefunction is a standing wave, the probability distribution does not move left or right. So a particle of definite energy does not appear to move.

Suppose that the particle does not have a definite energy. Figure 29.37 shows the wavefunction for a particle at $t = 0$ whose average energy is between that of the ground and first excited states. It is obtained by adding together the wavefunctions for the $n = 1$ and $n = 2$ states. Since each of those

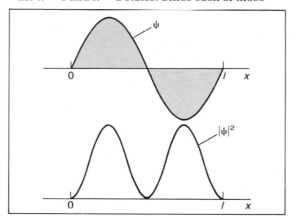

Figure 29.36
Wavefunction and probability distribution for a particle in the first excited state

standing waves has a different frequency, the new wavefunction will produce a probability distribution which changes with time. This is illustrated in the sequence of figure 29.38. Notice how the peak of the distribution sloshes backwards and forwards, implying movement of the particle inside the tube. However, if you measure the energy of the particle rather than its position, you are equally likely to find it in the $n = 1$ state or the $n = 2$ state.

Figure 29.37
Wavefunction for a particle which could be in both ground and first excited states

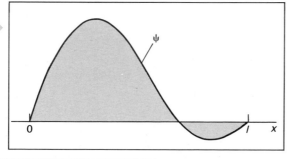

Figure 29.38 The time development of $|\psi|^2$ for a particle whose wavefunction is a mixture of ψ_2 and ψ_1

Atoms

When Schroedinger invented his equation in 1925 he was trying to explain the energy level diagram of atomic hydrogen. In 1885, Johann Balmer published a formula which could be used to calculate the wavelengths of the hydrogen emission spectrum.

$$\frac{1}{\lambda} = R_H \left(\frac{1}{m^2} - \frac{1}{n^2} \right) \tag{29.12}$$

The constant R_H is 1.09×10^7 m^{-1} and m and n are integers, with $n > m$. With the advent of the wave−particle model for light 20 years later, Balmer's equation was used to find an expression for the energy levels E_m and E_n involved in the emission of photons from hydrogen atoms.

$$E = hf, \quad c = f\lambda \quad \therefore \frac{hc}{\lambda} = E_n - E_m \tag{29.13}$$

Comparing equations (29.12) and (29.13), it should be obvious that the energy levels are given by the following formula.

$$E = -\frac{hcR_H}{n^2}, \quad \text{where } n = 1, 2, 3, \ldots \tag{29.14}$$

The energy level diagram is shown in figure 29.16. (The energies are all negative because the electron is bound to the proton — it is convention to have zero energy when the two particles are an infinite distance apart.) Over the next 20 years, many people attempted, with little success, to explain why an electron placed near a proton could only have the energies specified by equation (29.14). Schroedinger was the first person to come up with a theory which fitted the facts exactly. He was able to predict the following formulae for the radius and energy levels of a hydrogen atom.

$$r = n^2 \times \frac{h^2 \epsilon_0}{\pi m e^2}$$

$$E - -\frac{1}{n^2} \times \frac{e^4 m}{8h^2 \epsilon_0{}^2} \tag{29.15}$$

You can check for yourself that the formulae predict that the radius and energy of a hydrogen atom in its ground state ($n = 1$) are 5.31×10^{-11} m and -13.5 eV respectively. Furthermore, equations (29.15) and (29.14) are the same i.e. the theory is a perfect match to experimental data.

Although Schroedinger's equation is resoundingly successful at predicting the properties of hydrogen atoms, it is too complicated to be solved for atoms with two or more electrons. Numerical methods have to be used with the help of large computers to sort out the energy level structure and arrangement of electrons in all atoms other than hydrogen.

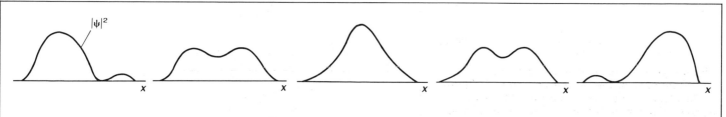

HYDROGEN ATOMS

A hydrogen atom is a single electron bound to a single proton. If we consider the relatively massive proton to be stationary at $r = 0$, then the electron appears to move in a potential well V given by the electrical potential energy formula.

$$V = -\frac{e^2}{4\pi\epsilon_0 r} \tag{1}$$

This well is illustrated in figure 29.39. It is a three-dimensional well — we have only drawn the radial dependence of the potential energy. To insert equation (1) into Schroedinger's equation and find the allowed energy levels is a difficult and tedious business. However, it is possible to come up with the right answers if we make an inspired guess that a particular wavefunction is possible. To make the maths very easy, let's assume that the electron is bound to the proton with a very special probability distribution. The electron can be anywhere on a circle centred on the proton and nowhere else. This means that it has a definite wavelength given by the de Broglie formula.

$$p = \frac{h}{\lambda} \quad \therefore \lambda = \frac{h}{p} \tag{2}$$

Look at figure 29.40. For the wavefunction not to vanish it must form a standing wave around the circle, with a whole number of wavelengths fitting exactly into the perimeter.

$$n\lambda = 2\pi r \quad \therefore \lambda = \frac{2\pi r}{n} \tag{3}$$

We can combine equations (2) and (3) to find out how the momentum of the electron is related to the radius of the circle.

$$\lambda = \frac{2\pi r}{n} = \frac{h}{p} \quad \therefore p = \frac{nh}{2\pi r} \tag{4}$$

So as the electron gets closer to the proton its momentum increases. Of course, this means that its kinetic energy also increases. However, the total energy is the sum of the kinetic and potential energies.

$$E = \frac{p^2}{2m} - \frac{e^2}{4\pi\epsilon_0 r} \quad \therefore E = \frac{n^2 h^2}{8\pi^2 m r^2} - \frac{e^2}{4\pi\epsilon_0 r} \tag{5}$$

This complicated expression can be simplified by defining a pair of constants A and B.

$$E = \frac{A}{r^2} - \frac{B}{r}, \quad A = \frac{n^2 h^2}{8\pi^2 m}, \quad B = \frac{e^2}{4\pi\epsilon_0} \tag{6}$$

The graph of figure 29.41 shows that the total energy E is a minimum at a particular value of r. At any other value of r, the electron can emit a photon and reach a lower energy state. The value of r which has the minimum value of E can be found by looking for the point on the curve which has a gradient of zero.

$$E = \frac{A}{r^2} - \frac{B}{r} \quad \therefore \frac{dE}{dr} = -\frac{2A}{r^3} + \frac{B}{r^2} = 0$$

$$\therefore r = \frac{2A}{B} \tag{7}$$

If we insert the values of A and B from equation (6), we end up with an expression for the equilibrium distance between proton and electron.

$$r = n^2 \times \frac{h^2 \epsilon_0}{\pi m e^2} \tag{8}$$

We can also insert equation (7) into equation (6) to get an expression for the energy of the electron–proton system.

$$E = -\frac{1}{n^2} \times \frac{e^4 m}{8 h^2 \epsilon_0{}^2} \tag{9}$$

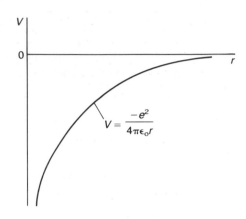

Figure 29.39 Potential well for an electron in a hydrogen atom

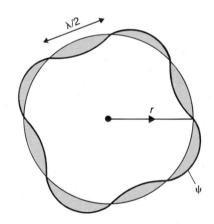

Figure 29.40 Possible wavefunction for an electron in a hydrogen atom

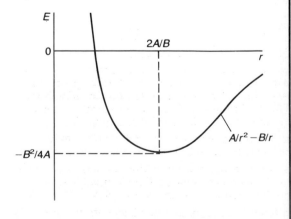

Figure 29.41

OBJECTIVES

After studying this section you should be able to do the following.

Calculate the wavelength of a particle from its momentum.

Explain why particles can be diffracted by crystals.

Sketch wavefunctions for a particle confined in a one-dimensional box.

Calculate the kinetic energy of a particle from its momentum and mass.

Derive an expression for the energy levels of a particle in a box.

State how a probability distribution can be obtained from a wavefunction.

Know that Schroedinger's equation predicts the correct energy levels for a hydrogen atom.

QUESTIONS

1 Calculate the momentum and wavelength of the following particles.

a A 23 keV electron in a colour TV set.

b A typical air molecule at room temperature.

c A 5 MeV alpha particle.

2 The electron diffraction tube of the type shown in figure 29.29 is being used by Jackie to check de Broglie's theory of electron wavelengths. The electrons are fired through a graphite film onto a screen where two rings and a central spot can be seen.

a If each electron is accelerated by a p.d. V, show that its wavelength is predicted to be $\lambda = h/(2eVm)^{\frac{1}{2}}$.

b Jackie measures the inner diameter D of the outer ring for several different accelerating voltages V. Her results are shown in table 29.5. By means of a graph, show that her results are in agreement with de Broglie's theory.

c Why do the rings get brighter as they shrink?

d Each ring on the screen has a sharp inner edge but a diffuse outer edge. Jackie thinks this is because different parts of the graphite have different crystal structures. John reckons it has to do with the electron beam losing energy on its way through the crystal. Nicola says that not all of the electrons in the beam will have the same energy. Which of them is right? Explain why.

Table 29.5

V/kV	D/mm
2.0	88
3.0	70
4.0	63
5.0	54

3 A typical uranium nucleus contains 238 particles. The nucleus can be thought of as a box which traps the particles into a small volume. The minimum kinetic energy of a particle of mass m trapped in a cube of side l is $3h^2/8ml^2$.

a Use the formula $r = A^{1/3} \times 1.2 \times 10^{-15}$ m to estimate the diameter of a uranium nucleus.

b Estimate the minimum kinetic energy of a single nucleon and an alpha particle trapped in the nucleus. Quote your answers in MeV.

c It has been suggested that if a neutron has a wavelength which is twice the diameter of a uranium nucleus, a standing wave will be set up in the nucleus and the neutron will be captured. Calculate the neutron energy required for this to happen.

4 This question is about the wavefunction drawn in figure 29.42. It is for a particle in the potential well V drawn under the wavefunction. The total energy of the particle is E.

a Copy the wavefunction and mark on it the regions where the particle will never be found. Sketch a graph of ψ^2.

b There are places in the well where the particle has negative kinetic energy. Indicate where they are.

c Where is the particle most likely to be found?

d Is it more likely to be found on the left or the right of the central barrier?

e How can you tell from the wavefunction where the particle has its maximum kinetic energy?

f Suppose that you placed the particle into the right-hand side of the well with energy E. Estimate the chances of finding it on the left-hand side of the barrier some time later. (This is called **tunelling**.)

5 Optical microscopes can resolve detail down to about 0.5 µm, the wavelength of visible light.

a Consider a microscope trying to make a magnified image of a small hole of diameter D in an opaque object. Describe what the image looks like when the light shone through the hole has a wavelength of

i D/10,　**ii** D,　　**iii** D×10.

b An electron microscope uses the transmission of electrons through the object to form an image. The resolution is limited by the wavelength of the electrons. What is the accelerating voltage necessary for the electrons to have a wavelength of

i 0.5 µm (the wavelength of light)?　**ii** 0.5 nm?

c Explain why electron microscopes can produce images of much higher magnification than optical microscopes.

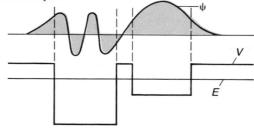

Figure 29.42

SUMMARY
W A V E S   I N   S P A C E

The velocity of electromagnetic (EM) waves is given by $(\mu_0\epsilon_0)^{-\frac{1}{2}} = 3.00\times10^8$ m s^{-1}. The B-field of an EM wave is perpendicular to both the E-field and the direction of propagation. EM waves can be polarised by suitable materials, usually by selective absorption of a component of the E-field.

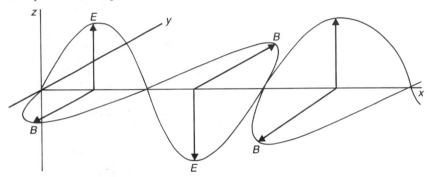

Special relativity states that all observers can only measure their velocity *relative* to other observers and they all agree on the value for the speed of EM waves. A moving clock appears to run slow to an outside observer: $t = t_0/(1 - v^2/c^2)^{\frac{1}{2}}$. A moving object appears to contract along its direction of motion: $l = l_0(1 - v^2/c^2)^{\frac{1}{2}}$. The apparent mass of an object increases as its velocity increases: $m = m_0/(1 - v^2/c^2)^{-\frac{1}{2}}0$.

The refraction of light is given by Snell's Law: $n_i\sin i = n_r\sin r$. Total internal reflection of light occurs when the angle of incidence exceeds the critical angle: $\sin c = n^{-1}$.

The lens formula can be used for rays going through a thin lens close to the centre: $1/u + 1/v = 1/f$. The power of a lens is related to its curvature: $P = 1/f$. The power of a concave lens is negative. The focal length of a mirror is half its radius of curvature, independent of wavelength. Mirrors do not suffer from the transmission losses of lenses so they can be used to form images with a wide range of EM waves.

Waves are diffracted when they pass through slits: $\sin\theta = \lambda/b$ for the first zero of the diffraction pattern. The Rayleigh criterion for the angular resolution of point sources imaged through circular apertures is $\theta \simeq 1.2\lambda/b$.

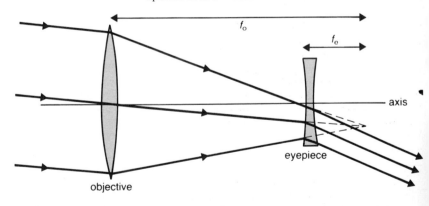

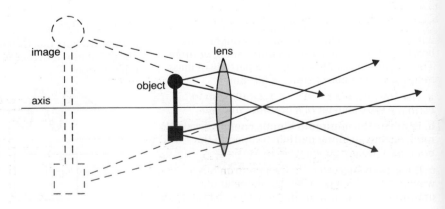

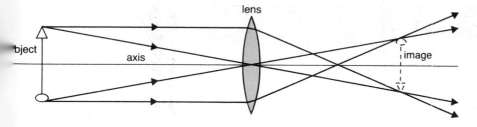

Interference maxima from a transmission or reflection grating meet the condition $n\lambda = d\sin\theta$. The number of maxima is fixed by the single slit diffraction envelope. The angular width of the maxima decreases as the number of slits in the grating increases.

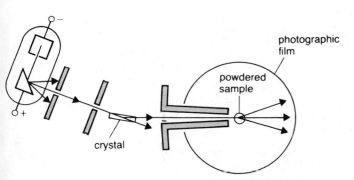

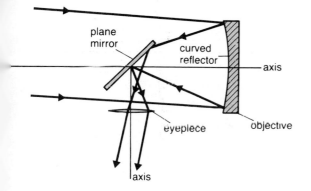

X-rays reflect strongly off crystals if they meet the Bragg Law $n\lambda = 2d\sin\theta$. X-ray diffraction patterns of powdered samples illuminated by monochromatic X-rays can be used to measure the arrangement and spacing of atoms within the sample.

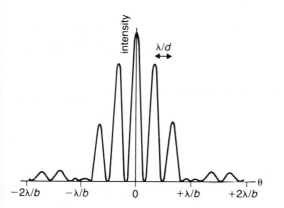

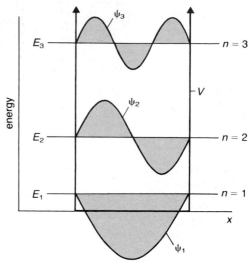

An EM wave of frequency f can only exchange energy with its environment in lumps of size hf (photons). The intensity (amplitude squared) of an EM wave is proportional to the rate at which it can deliver photons. Ultraviolet photons have enough energy to liberate photoelectrons from metals: $E_k \leqslant hf - \phi$. Electrons hitting solids can convert their kinetic energy into X-ray photons.

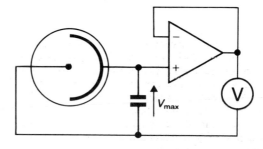

Each particle is associated with a wavefunction whose amplitude at a point can be used to calculate the probability of finding the particle there: $p(x) \propto |\psi(x)|^2$. For a particle in a force-free environment $\lambda = h/p$. Particles bound to a region of space have quantised energy levels: movement between the energy levels can be accomplished by the emission or absorption of photons. The energy of a particle in a one-dimensional box is given by $E = n^2 h^2 / 8ml^2$.

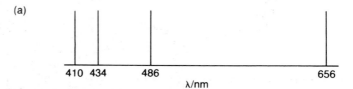

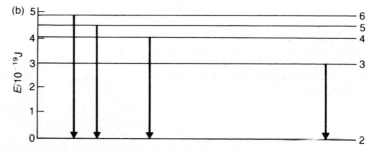

THERMODYNAMICS

30

THERMAL EQUILIBRIUM

Here is a statement which will seem obvious. If two objects at different temperatures are placed in contact with each other they will eventually end up at the same temperature. However, there is nothing in the laws of physics discussed so far in this book which forces the two objects to do this. Provided that they conserve energy, there is no reason why one object should not gain heat energy at the other one's expense. Of course, this never happens in practice. Figure 30.1 shows a simple experiment you could do in the laboratory to verify it. A copper can of hot water is placed in some cold water in an insulated container. As time progresses, the temperature of one lot of water falls and the temperature of the other lot rises until they are in **thermal equilibrium** with each other. The final temperature can be predicted by invoking energy conservation. If the insulation is perfect, the heat energy lost by the hot water is equal to the heat energy gained by the cold water.

There is no extra law needed in physics to state that heat energy *must* flow from a hot body to a cold one. It isn't necessary, because heat is not a fluid. It is energy shared out at random among the atoms of an object. This chapter is going to show you how the random exchange of energy between atoms inevitably leads to thermal equilibrium on a macroscopic scale. The important concept of **entropy** will be introduced along the way, leading to a definition of temperature which is independent of the instrument used to measure it.

SHARING HEAT

Although the conclusions of this section will be universally applicable, most of the initial discussion will be centred on heat energy in an **Einstein solid**. This is an ideal crystal whose atoms have equally spaced energy levels. A single atom in a crystal behaves like a particle sitting at the bottom of the potential well created by its neighbours (figure 30.2). Providing that the amplitude of oscillation is small, that atom will undergo simple harmonic oscillation in three independent directions. The frequency of oscillation will be fixed by the mass of the atom and the shape of the well. Of course, as one atom oscillates it will exert periodic forces on its neighbours, so there will be a continual exchange of energy among the atoms. Therefore we can model the whole crystal as a large number of identical simple harmonic oscillators which are coupled to each other.

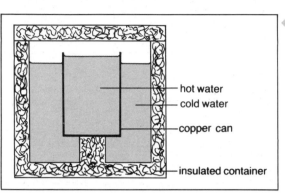

hot water
cold water
copper can
insulated container

Figure 30.1 A system which is not in thermal equilibrium

Figure 30.2 A particle in a parabolic potential well

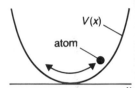

$V(x)$

atom

x

An atom sitting at the bottom of a potential well has a number of allowed energies. They can be found with the help of Schroedinger's equation. If we insert $V = \frac{1}{2}kx^2$ for the potential, we get the following equation to solve:

$$ -\frac{h^2}{8\pi^2 m}\frac{d^2\psi}{dx^2} + \frac{1}{2}kx^2\psi = \frac{ih}{2\pi}\frac{d\psi}{dt} \qquad (1) $$

Unlike most of the equations in quantum mechanics, this one can be solved with the help of calculus, but it is tedious and difficult. So we shall adopt another strategy to find the energy levels for a simple harmonic oscillator. Look at figure 30.3. The charged mass on the end of the spring has a natural frequency f_0. Give the system some energy and it will oscillate. The vertical acceleration of the charge will result in the emission of radio waves which have a frequency f_0. So the oscillator creates photons of energy hf_0. Every time it emits a photon, it drops from one energy level to the one below (figure 30.3): the spacing between the energy levels is hf_0. Initially, when the amplitude of oscillation is large, the rate of production of these photons will be high. The loss of energy damps the oscillator, progressively reducing its amplitude and the rate of photon production. However, since the natural frequency of the oscillator is independent of its amplitude, the size of the photons remains constant. So the spacing between the energy levels should remain constant at hf_0 even when the total energy of the oscillator is very small.

Figure 30.3 Energy levels for a charged mass on a spring

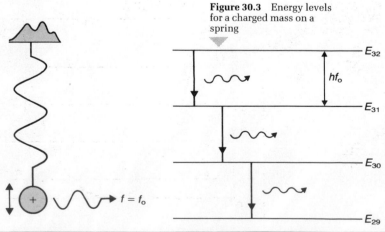

E_{32}

hf_0

E_{31}

E_{30}

$f = f_0$

E_{29}

Quanta and sites

The energy level diagram for a one-dimensional simple harmonic oscillator is shown in figure 30.4. The allowed energies are given by the following formula.

$$E = (n + \tfrac{1}{2})hf_0, \quad \text{where } 2\pi f_0 = (k/m)^{\tfrac{1}{2}} \qquad \textbf{(30.1)}$$

The energy needed to push the oscillator up one energy level is called a **quantum**. Its size ϵ is independent of the total energy E of the oscillator.

> $\epsilon = hf_0$
>
> ϵ is a single quantum (J)
>
> h is Planck's constant (J s)
>
> f_0 is the natural frequency of the oscillator (Hz)

In an **Einstein solid** all of the atoms have the same natural frequency. Each atom can oscillate independently in the x-, y- and z-directions. So if the solid contains N atoms, it has 3N **sites** at which the quanta can be held. If we ignore the **zero-point energy** of $\tfrac{1}{2}hf_0$, then the energy at each site is a whole number of quanta, i.e. $E = n\epsilon$. Because of the coupling between the atoms, the quanta will be able to move around from one site to another, doing a random walk through the solid. (The exchange of quanta between sites is random because we are dealing with events on a very small scale where probabilities are all that the theory of quantum mechanics allows us to calculate.)

Quanta per site

The number of sites in a solid of graspable size is mind-bogglingly huge! Let's estimate the number of sites N in a small copper coin. A typical coin has a radius of 10 mm and a thickness of 1 mm. Knowing the density and molar mass of copper (8.9×10^3 kg m^{-3} and 6.4×10^{-2} kg mol^{-1} respectively) it is an easy matter to calculate the number of atoms in it. Each atom is able to oscillate in three independent directions, so it has three sites.

$$m = \rho V$$

$$\therefore m = 8.9 \times 10^3 \times 1 \times 10^{-3} \times 2\pi \times 10^{-4}$$
$$= 6 \times 10^{-3} \text{ kg}$$

$$\therefore N = 3 \times \frac{m}{6.4 \times 10^{-2}} \times 6 \times 10^{23}$$

$$\therefore N \simeq 2 \times 10^{23}$$

The number of quanta in a coin at room temperature is also very large. It can be estimated by dividing the heat energy of the coin by the energy of a single quantum. The latter can be calculated by considering a single copper atom in the coin. The effective force constant is found from its Young's modulus and interatomic spacing (1.3×10^{11} Pa and 2.6×10^{-10} m).

$$k = E d_0$$

$$\therefore k = 1.3 \times 10^{11} \times 2.6 \times 10^{-10} = 34 \text{ N m}^{-1}$$

Since the mass of a copper atom is 1.1×10^{-25} kg, we can estimate the size of a single quantum.

$$\epsilon = hf_0, \quad 2\pi f_0 = (k/m)^{\tfrac{1}{2}} \quad \therefore \epsilon = \frac{h}{2\pi}(k/m)^{\tfrac{1}{2}}$$

$$\therefore \epsilon = \frac{6.63 \times 10^{-34}}{2\pi} \times \left(\frac{34}{1.1 \times 10^{-25}}\right)^{\tfrac{1}{2}}$$

$$\therefore \epsilon \simeq 2 \times 10^{-21} \text{ J (or 0.01 eV)}$$

If we assume that the specific heat capacity of copper (380 J kg^{-1} K^{-1}) remains constant down to 0 K (it doesn't), then we can estimate the heat energy in the coin at 300 K.

$$\Delta Q = mc\Delta T$$

$$\therefore \Delta Q = 6 \times 10^{-3} \times 380 \times 300 \simeq 700 \text{ J}$$

The number of quanta in the coin will therefore be ($700/2 \times 10^{-21} \simeq 4 \times 10^{23}$, about two for every site. So, on average, each atom will have about six quanta, but the number at any instant will fluctuate from one moment to the next.

Ways and entropy

Consider an Einstein solid which is thermally isolated. Although its total heat energy E remains absolutely constant, the way in which that energy is shared among the sites is continually changing. Since the exchange of quanta between sites is random, it seems reasonable to suppose that each way of sharing the quanta is equally likely to happen if we wait long enough. This idea is central to the rest of the chapter, so before rushing on to meet the concept of entropy, you ought to spend a little time thinking about ways of sharing quanta among sites.

Ways

Figure 30.5 shows how three quanta can be shared among three sites (a single atom). The sites are distinguishable from each other, but the quanta are not. (Each site represents a particular direction for the atom; each quantum is simply a certain amount of energy.) As you can see, there are ten ways of doing it. Each way is equally likely to occur during the random exchange of quanta among the sites. Table 30.1 lists the number of ways W in which the z site can have different numbers of quanta n. Use figure 30.5 to check it for yourself. So if you counted the quanta at the z site at any instant, the most likely answer would be zero! (Intuitively, you would expect it to be one, since there are three quanta shared among three sites.)

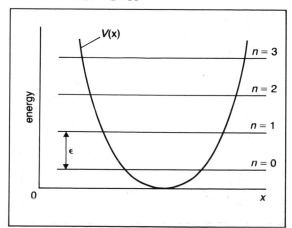

Figure 30.4 Energy level diagram for an atom in an Einstein solid

Table 30.1

n	W
0	4
1	3
2	2
3	1

There are six ways in which two quanta can be shared among three sites, as shown in figure 30.6. If you consider a single site, it should be clear that, once again, the most probable situation is no quanta and the least probable situation is all of the quanta. The number of ways for each energy are listed in table 30.2.

Table 30.2

n	W
0	3
1	2
2	1

Now suppose that we take two atoms and make them one system without letting them interact. One atom has three quanta, the other has two. How many ways can the whole system shuffle its quanta? For each of the ten ways that the first atom can arrange its three quanta, the second atom can have six different arrangements of its two quanta. So the total number of ways is $10 \times 6 = 60$. In general, the total number of ways for a system made of two non-interacting sub-systems is the product of their individual ways.

$W = W_1 W_2$

W is the total number of ways for the whole system

W_1 is the number of ways for the first sub-system

W_2 is the number of ways for the second sub-system

Entropy

The **entropy** of an object is a very convenient measure of the number of ways in which the quanta can be arranged among its sites. It is defined to be proportional to the logarithm of the number of ways so that it is a calculable number.

$S = k\ln[W]$

S is the entropy of the object ($J\,K^{-1}$)

k is Boltzmann's constant ($1.38 \times 10^{-23}\,J\,K^{-1}$)

W is the number of ways for the object

The following example will help you to appreciate why entropy is used instead of ways. Suppose that we have 10^{23} atoms in a solid, each of which has three quanta to arrange among its three sites. From figure 30.5, each atom has ten ways of doing this. If the atoms do not interact with each other (not a very realistic assumption), then the total number of ways will be 10 to the power 10^{23}, i.e. the product of the ways of the individual atoms. This number is far too large for your calculator to handle — try it! However, your calculator *will* be able to cope with the entropy of the system.

$W_t = W^N, \quad S = k\ln[W] \quad \therefore S = k\ln[W^N]$

$$\therefore S = kN\ln[W]$$

$$\therefore S = 1.38 \times 10^{-23} \times 10^{23} \times \ln[10]$$

$$\therefore S = 3.2\,J\,K^{-1}$$

In general, the entropy of a system is calculated from *all* the ways in which the system can arrange itself. For the moment, we will restrict the discussion to the number of ways in which quanta can be shuffled among sites. Contributions to the entropy from ways of arranging the molecules will be dealt with in the next chapter.

Equilibrium

The following thought experiment should help you to understand why objects placed in contact with each other end up at the same temperature. The two objects are shown in figure 30.7, joined so that they can exchange quanta. For simplicity, we will assume that both objects are made of the same material, but they do not have to have the same size. However, the total energy of the system remains constant: there is no way for them to exchange quanta with the rest of the universe.

Changing entropy

Suppose that the two parts of the system have heat energies Q_1 and Q_2. Each part will have a number of quanta which it can arrange among its sites. The number of ways can be used to calculate the entropy of the whole system.

$S = k\ln[W] \quad \therefore S_1 = k\ln[W_1], \quad S_2 = k\ln[W_2]$

$W = W_1 W_2$

$\therefore S = k\ln[W_1 W_2] = k\ln[W_1] + k\ln[W_2]$

$\therefore S = S_1 + S_2$ **(30.2)**

As the two parts exchange quanta at random through the link between them, the total entropy will change. The graph of figure 30.8 shows how you might expect S to depend on the value of Q_1. Each value of Q_1 corresponds to one way of distributing the quanta between the two parts; the entropy of each part is then a measure of the number of ways in which its quanta can be arranged among its sites. The value of S will be quite low when Q_1 is 0 or Q; the more that the quanta are shared out between the two parts, the more ways they can be arranged among the sites.

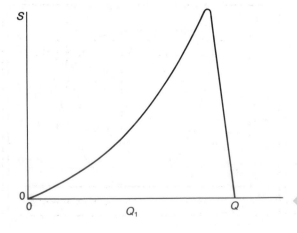

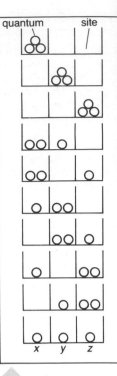

Figure 30.5 Ways of arranging three quanta among three sites

Figure 30.6 Ways of arranging two quanta among three sites

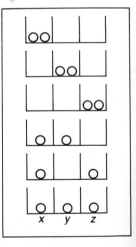

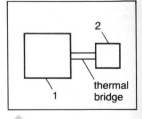

Figure 30.7 Two systems which can exchange quanta via a thermal bridge

Figure 30.8 How the total entropy depends on the heat energy in one part of the system

Figure 30.13

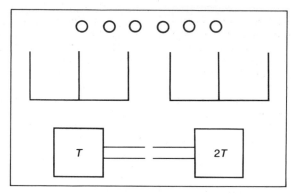

4 Calculate the magnitude and sign of the entropy changes of the objects in italic type.

a A *coin* given 50 J of energy at 250°C in a flame.

b A *chicken* which loses 200 J of energy at −5°C in a refrigerator.

c A 10 kW *immersion heater* in a large amount of water at 50°C, switched on for 1 minute.

5 Two identical objects can be crudely modelled as two sets of two sites, as shown in figure 30.13. The two objects share six quanta between them before they are placed in thermal contact with each other.

a If the initial temperatures of the objects are *T* and 2*T*, how are the quanta shared between them? Assume that *c* is independent of temperature.

b Calculate the initial entropy of each object. Hence calculate the initial entropy of the whole system.

c What would you expect the final temperature of the two objects to be? How many quanta would they share between them when thermal equilibrium had been reached?

d Calculate the final entropy of the system if the objects are separated when thermal equilibrium has been established. Has the total entropy of the system increased?

6 A steam turbine takes steam from a reactor pile at 550°C and uses it to generate electricity. The used steam leaves the turbine at 100°C and is returned to the reactor pile, having converted some of its heat energy to electricity at a rate of 100 MW.

a Assume that the turbine/generator system has an efficiency of 50%. At what rate is heat energy taken from the reactor pile at 550°C? What is the rate at which this decreases the entropy of the pile?

b At what rate does heat energy leave the turbine at 100°C? What is the rate at which this increases the entropy of the pile?

c What is the total rate of change of entropy of the pile?

d Repeat steps (a) to (c) for an efficiency of 60%.

e Explain why the efficiency of the system could never be 60% in practice.

THE BOLTZMANN FACTOR

Ludwig Boltzmann felt that entropy was such an important concept that he asked for the equation $S = k\ln[W]$ to be carved on his tombstone! It was Boltzmann who first showed that chaos at a microscopic level could lead to orderly large scale changes. Most of his work was concerned with the random movement of particles in a gas (the subject of the next chapter), but his ideas also apply to the random shuffling of quanta among sites. This section will show you how Boltzmann used entropy to work out the chances of a single site having a certain number of quanta. The resulting formula, containing the **Boltzmann factor** $\exp[-E/kT]$, has far-reaching consequences for many branches of technology including chemistry, electronics and structural engineering. We will use the Boltzmann formula to model several widely different phenomena so that you can appreciate its versatility.

Fluctuations

Suppose that you have an Einstein solid which is thermally isolated. Its quanta are continually moving from site to site, doing a random walk through the solid. We want to work out how many of the sites are likely to have a certain number of quanta at any moment. This is relatively straightforward if you only have a few sites and quanta. Look at figure 30.14(a). It shows the

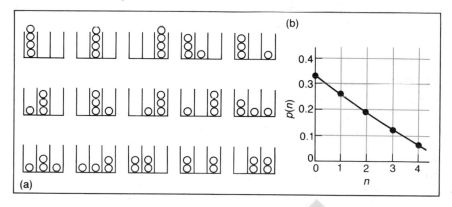

number of ways of sharing four quanta among three sites. If each way is equally likely to occur, then we can use figure 30.14(a) to calculate the probability $p(n)$ of a particular site (the one in the middle) having n quanta at any instant. For example, there are five ways of having no quanta on the middle site. Since the total number of ways is 15, $p(0) = 5/15 = 0.33$. The values for $p(n)$ calculated this way are listed in table 30.4.

Figure 30.14 The probability of finding quanta in a particular site

Table 30.4

n	W	$p(n)$
0	5	0.33
1	4	0.27
2	3	0.20
3	2	0.13
4	1	0.07

LARGE SYSTEMS !

Figure 30.15(a) shows an isolated **system** which has a total energy E. Each quantum has an energy ϵ, so the total number of quanta will be $N = E/\epsilon$. What are the chances $p(n)$ of a small part of the system (the **sub-system**) having n of those quanta? If $W(N - n)$ is the number of ways in which the whole system can arrange all of its quanta, keeping n of them in the sub-system, then each way is equally likely to happen. So if $W(N)$ is the *total* number of ways for the system, we can define $p(n)$ as follows:

$$p(n) = \frac{W(N - n)}{W(N)} \quad \therefore \ln[p(n)] = \ln[W(N - n)] - \ln[W(N)] \tag{1}$$

You will recall that $S = k\ln[W]$. The entropy of the rest of the system $S(N - n)$ depends on its energy as shown in figure 30.15(b). So if we extract n quanta from the system, its entropy will change.

$$S(N - n) \simeq S(N) - \left(n\epsilon \times \frac{\Delta S(N)}{\Delta E}\right) \tag{2}$$

Provided that the sub-system is very much smaller than the whole system, $\Delta S(N)/\Delta E$ will not change as n is changed. In other words, the temperature T of the system does not change.

$$\Delta S = \frac{\Delta Q}{T} \quad \therefore \Delta S(N) = \frac{\Delta E}{T} \tag{3}$$

Now combine equations (2) and (3) to find $S(N - n)$, the entropy of the whole system when n quanta are in the sub-system.

$$S(N - n) = S(N) - \frac{n\epsilon}{T} \tag{4}$$

Finally, combine equations (1) and (4) to get the expression we are after.

$$S(N - n) = k\ln[W(N - n)]$$

$$\therefore S(N) - \frac{n\epsilon}{T} = k\ln[W(N)] + k\ln[p(n)]$$

$$\therefore -\frac{n\epsilon}{kT} = \ln[p(n)]$$

$$\therefore \exp[-n\epsilon/kT] = p(n) \tag{5}$$

So the probability that the sub-system has n quanta is proportional to the **Boltzmann factor** $\exp[-n\epsilon/kT]$. (It is not equal to it, because the sum of all $p(n)$ does not add up to 1. This is because of the way we defined it in equation (1).)

Figure 30.15

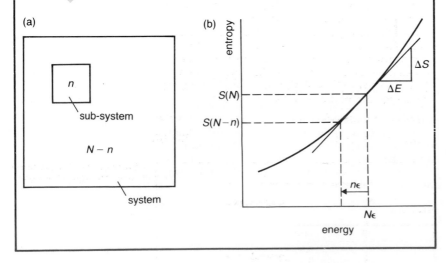

(a)

As you can see from the graph of figure 30.14(b), the most likely number of quanta per site is zero. It is *not* the same as the average number of quanta per site, $<n>$. This can be calculated from the probabilities $p(n)$ as follows:

$$<n> = \Sigma np(n)$$

$$\therefore <n> = (0 \times 0.33) + (1 \times 0.27) + (2 \times 0.20) + (3 \times 0.13) + (4 \times 0.07) = 1.33$$

Of course, this is exactly what you would expect, i.e. 4/3. The above example should help you to grasp why the chance of a particular site having a certain amount of energy decreases as the energy increases, but its conclusions really only apply to a single atom. To derive a result of any real use, we need to consider a more realistic model of a solid with a large number of atoms and quanta.

Energy probability

Suppose that you have a large number of identical objects in contact with each other. If they are in thermal equilibrium then the probability that one of the objects in the whole system has a particular energy is given by the **Boltzmann formula**.

> $p(E) = A\exp[-E/kT]$
>
> $p(E)$ is the probability that the object has energy E
>
> A is a constant
>
> E is the energy of the object (J)
>
> k is Boltzmann's constant $(1.38 \times 10^{-23} \text{ J K}^{-1})$
>
> T is the temperature of the whole system (K)

As an example of the Boltzmann formula in action, consider the atoms in a lump of copper at the boiling point of liquid nitrogen (77 K). Assuming that it is an Einstein solid, the energy levels of each site are 2×10^{-21} J apart (see page 531). Table 30.5 lists the values of $\exp[-n\epsilon/kT]$ for various values of n: you should check them for yourself.

Table 30.5

n	$\exp[-n\epsilon/kT]$
0	1.000
1	0.152
2	0.023
3	0.004

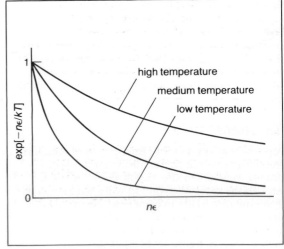

Figure 30.16 The Boltzmann factor for different temperatures

Quite clearly, most of the sites will have no quanta at all. The graph of figure 30.16 shows how $\exp[-n\epsilon/kT]$ depends on $n\epsilon$ for three different temperatures. Notice that as the temperature is raised, there is more chance of a site holding a large number of quanta, but the shape of the distribution does not change, i.e. the most likely number of quanta is always zero.

Applications

The rest of this section is devoted to examples of systems which can be modelled with the help of the Boltzmann formula. The models will be simple, so you should not expect too close a match between theory and experiment. Nevertheless, agreement is usually startlingly good. This is mainly because $\exp[-E/kT]$ changes so rapidly with E and T.

Atmospheric pressure

The graphs of figure 30.17 show how the pressure and temperature of the atmosphere depend on the altitude h. The apparently exponential variation of pressure can be modelled with the help of the Boltzmann formula. For a particular air molecule of mass m to be found at a certain altitude, it must have a gravitational energy of mgh. The probability that it will have this energy is given by

$$p(E) = A\exp[-E/kT], \quad \text{where } E = mgh \quad \textbf{(30.6)}$$

(The kinetic energy can be ignored if we define the total energy of a molecule at ground level as zero. Since the temperature hardly changes with altitude, we can assume that the molecule's average kinetic energy remains constant.) The pressure of a gas is proportional to its density:

$$P = \frac{\rho}{3}<c^2>^{\frac{1}{2}} \quad \therefore P \propto \rho \text{ if } T \text{ is constant} \quad \textbf{(30.7)}$$

Although the temperature is not independent of the altitude, you can see from figure 30.16 that it does not change by very much. So it is a good approximation to say that

$$P \propto p(E) \quad \therefore P = C\exp[-mgh/kT]$$

$$\therefore \ln[P] = \ln[C] - (\frac{mg}{kT} \times h) \quad \textbf{(30.8)}$$

A graph of $\ln[P]$ against h should therefore be a straight line with a slope of $-mg/kT$. This is shown in figure 30.18. Below 10 km, the data are a very good fit to equation (30.8), giving a slope of -1.34×10^{-4} m^{-1}. If we assume that the atmosphere is made of nitrogen molecules (mass 4.67×10^{-26} kg) at an average temperature of $-20°C$, we can predict a value for this slope.

$$\frac{mg}{kT} = \frac{4.67\times10^{-26} \times 9.81}{1.38\times10^{-23} \times (273 - 20)}$$

$$= 1.31\times10^{-4} \text{ m}^{-1}$$

Given the crudity of the model we have used, the agreement is surprisingly good. (The gap between theory and experiment can be narrowed by taking account of the presence of heavier molecules such as oxygen and carbon dioxide in the atmosphere.)

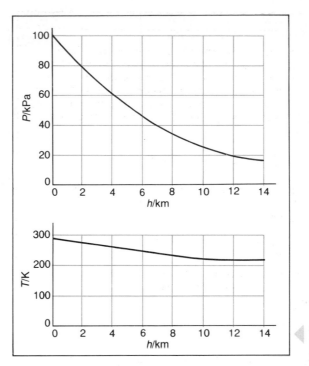

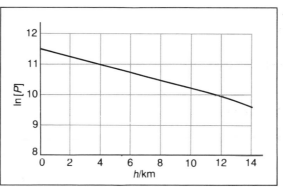

Figure 30.17 Atmospheric pressure and temperature as a function of altitude

Figure 30.18 $\ln[P] = \ln[C] - mgh/kT$

Thermistors

A thermistor is basically a lump of intrinsic semiconductor. At 0 K it is a perfect insulator, but the density of mobile charge carriers rises rapidly with temperature. We can model this by assuming that each charge carrier needs to acquire an energy ϵ before it can move freely through the solid. The energy level diagram for a single charge carrier is shown in figure 30.19 — the particle can either be in the ground state $E = 0$ or in the excited state $E = \epsilon$. The Boltzmann formula can be used to write down the probability of finding a particular charge carrier in each of these states.

$$p(0) = A\exp[-0/kT] = A \quad \textbf{(30.9)}$$

$$p(\epsilon) = A\exp[-\epsilon/kT] \quad \textbf{(30.10)}$$

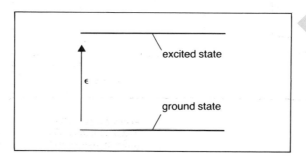

Figure 30.19 Energy levels for electrons in a thermistor

If the charge carrier density is N, equations (30.9) and (30.10) can be used to find the ratio of mobile and fixed charge carriers in unit volume of the thermistor.

$$\frac{n(\epsilon)}{n(0)} = \frac{Np(\epsilon)}{Np(0)} = \frac{A}{A} \exp[-\epsilon/kT]$$

$$\therefore n(\epsilon) = n(0)\exp[-\epsilon/kT] \quad \textbf{(30.11)}$$

If $\epsilon \ll kT$, then most of the charge carriers will be in the ground state, i.e. $n(0) \simeq N$. So the mobile charge carrier density will be equal to $N\exp[-\epsilon/kT]$.

Doubling the number of charge carriers in a resistor is equivalent to placing two of them in parallel, effectively halving the resistance. So the resistance of a thermistor should be inversely proportional to its mobile charge carrier density.

$$R \propto \frac{1}{n(\epsilon)} \quad \therefore R \propto \frac{1}{N\exp[-\epsilon/kT]}$$

$$\therefore R \propto \exp[+\epsilon/kT] \quad \textbf{(30.12)}$$

So a graph of $\ln[R]$ against $1/T$ is predicted to be a straight line with a slope of ϵ/k. Figure 30.20 shows such a graph for a real thermistor. As you can see, the data are a good fit to the prediction over a large range of temperatures.

Vapour pressure

Suppose that you place a liquid in a large evacuated container, as shown in figure 30.21(a). Initially, the more energetic molecules at the surface of the liquid will leave it and enter the vacuum to form a gas. The pressure of that gas will be proportional to its density, so as time goes on the pressure will increase. However, any gas molecules which hit the surface of the liquid will probably enter it and be lost to the gas. Ultimately, a dynamic equilibrium is reached, where the rate at which molecules enter the gas equals the rate at which they leave it. We want to predict the gas pressure at which this equilibrium is achieved.

Let's make two assumptions. First, that a molecule in the gas has an energy ϵ more than a molecule in the liquid. Secondly, that most of the molecules are in the liquid. If we state that a molecule in the liquid has zero energy (we are always free to choose the zero of energy), then the number in the gas n is linked to the number in the liquid N by the Boltzmann formula:

$$n = N\exp[-\epsilon/kT] \quad \textbf{(30.13)}$$

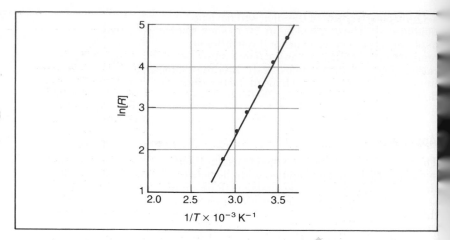

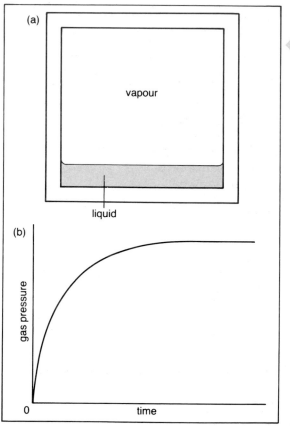

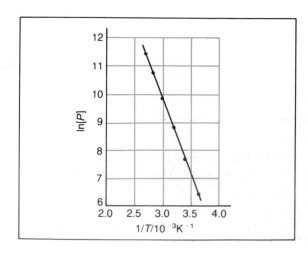

Figure 30.20
$\ln[R] = \ln[R_0] + [\epsilon]/kT$

Figure 30.21 The vapour rapidly comes into dynamic equilibrium with the liquid

Since the gas pressure will be proportional to the number of gas molecules, we can use equation (30.13) to predict how that pressure (the **saturated vapour pressure**) should vary with temperature.

$$P \propto \exp[-\epsilon/kT] \quad \textbf{(30.14)}$$

Figure 30.22
$\ln[P] = \ln[P_0] + \epsilon/kT$

(Of course, the pressure of a gas is also proportional to its temperature. However, a small temperature rise can make a large difference to $\exp[-\epsilon/kT]$, so we can safely ignore the direct temperature dependence.) The value of ϵ can be estimated by considering the **molar latent heat of vaporisation** of the liquid, L_v. This is the energy required to convert one mole of liquid into a gas, so $\epsilon = L_v/6.02 \times 10^{23}$. The graph of figure 30.22 shows how the vapour pressure of water varies with temperature. As you can see, $\ln[P] \propto 1/T$. The slope of the graph is a good match to the value of $-\epsilon/k$ obtained from direct measurement of L_v.

PRESSURE COOKERS

The Boltzmann factor is the reason why domestic pressure cookers can only achieve a modest 20°C rise in the boiling point of water. It is also the reason why that relatively small rise dramatically speeds up the rate at which food cooks. Food in an open pan of water reaches a maximum temperature of about 100°C because that is the temperature at which water boils at atmospheric pressure (100 kPa). Below 100°C, any bubbles of vapour which form at random in the body of the water at 100°C have a vapour pressure of less than 100 kPa (see figure 30.23). They will therefore be collapsed immediately by the larger pressure from the atmosphere. However, at 100°C, the vapour in the bubbles has a pressure equal to that of the atmosphere, so that they can rise to the surface of the water and release the vapour. So when the water is boiling, all of the heat energy fed into it goes to creating water vapour, stopping any further temperature rise of the water. The vapour will not be in direct contact with the source of heat, so its temperature will also be 100°C.

A pressure cooker (figure 30.24) stops the water vapour escaping. So, once the water starts to boil at 100°C the gas pressure above the water starts to rise. This increase in pressure on the water means that it needs to rise above 100°C for bubbles of vapour inside it not to collapse. The water continues to boil, but its temperature rises steadily until the increased pressure inside the cooker opens the valve. This then prevents the pressure from rising any further by letting the vapour escape as fast as it is created. We can estimate the increase of pressure needed to get the cooker to 120°C with the help of the data for water in table 1.

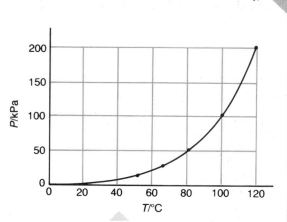

Figure 30.23 The vapour pressure rises very rapidly with temperature

Figure 30.24 A pressure cooker

Table 1

latent heat of vaporisation	2.26×10^6 J kg^{-1}
molar mass of water	0.018 kg mol^{-1}
Avogadro's number	6.02×10^{23} mol^{-1}

The pressure P is proportional to the Boltzmann factor $\exp[-\epsilon/kT]$. Since the pressure is 100 kPa at 373 K, we can estimate the pressure P' at any other temperature T' once we know the value of ϵ.

$$\epsilon \times 6.02 \times 10^{23} = 0.018 \times 2.26 \times 10^6 \quad \therefore \epsilon = 6.8 \times 10^{-20} \text{ J}$$

$$P = A\exp[-\epsilon/kT] \quad \therefore \ln[P] = \ln[A] - \frac{\epsilon}{kT}$$

$$\therefore \ln[P'] = \ln[A] - \frac{\epsilon}{kT'}$$

$$\therefore \ln[P] - \ln[P'] = \frac{\epsilon}{kT'} - \frac{\epsilon}{kT} \tag{1}$$

If we let T' be $373 + 20 = 393$ K, we can use equation (1) to calculate the value of P'

$$\ln[100] - \ln[P'] = \frac{6.8 \times 10^{-20}}{1.38 \times 10^{-23}} \times \left(\frac{1}{393} - \frac{1}{373}\right)$$

$$\therefore \ln[P'] = 5.3$$

$$\therefore P' \simeq 200 \text{ k Pa}$$

So the pressure has to be doubled to raise the temperature by about 5%! However, that temperature rise is enough to double the rate at which potatoes cook. When food is cooked, some of its large molecules are broken into smaller ones which are easier for us to digest. If the molecule needs a certain amount of energy ϵ before it can fall apart, then the rate at which cooking takes place should be proportional to $\exp[-\epsilon/kT]$, rising rapidly with temperature.

Creep

When a solid is subjected to a steady stress, its strain will steadily increase. This is known as **creep**. It happens because atoms in the solid can, by chance, acquire enough energy to escape from their nearest neighbours and move to an adjacent site. If the extra energy needed for this is ϵ, then the probability of an atom getting that energy will be proportional to $\exp[-\epsilon/kT]$. So the rate at which a solid elongates under the influence of a steady stress should also be proportional to $\exp[-\epsilon/kT]$. The creep rate could therefore rise rapidly with temperature. This is important in engineering structures, such as nuclear reactors, which have to operate at high temperatures.

HEAT CAPACITY OF SOLIDS !

The Boltzmann formula can be used to predict the molar heat capacity of solids. Consider an Einstein solid with N sites, each of which can hold quanta of size ϵ. The probability that a particular site has n quanta is given by the Boltzmann formula.

$$p(n) = A\exp[-n\epsilon/kT] \qquad (1)$$

The constant A is the sum of all possible values of $p(n)$. This ensures that $p(n)$ can be used to find the average energy per site $<E>$.

$$<E> = \frac{\Sigma\, p(n)n\epsilon}{\Sigma\, p(n)} \qquad (2)$$

The summations are over all values of n from 0 to ∞. Combining equations (1) and (2) we get a useful expression for the average energy per site.

$$<E> = \frac{\Sigma\, n\epsilon\exp[-n\epsilon/kT]}{\Sigma\, \exp[-n\epsilon/kT]} \qquad (3)$$

If your maths is good enough, you may be able to convince yourself that equation (3) becomes

$$<E> = \frac{\epsilon}{\exp[\epsilon/kT]\, -\, 1} \qquad (4)$$

This result was first obtained by Einstein in 1907. If the temperature is high enough, then $\epsilon \ll kT$ and an approximation from Appendix B can be used.

$$\exp[x] \simeq 1 + x \qquad \therefore <E> \simeq \frac{\epsilon}{1\, +\, \epsilon/kT\, -\, 1} = kT \qquad (5)$$

$<E> = kT$

$<E>$ is the average energy per site (J)

k is Boltzmann's constant (1.38×10^{-23} J K^{-1})

T is the temperature of the solid (K)

So a solid with N atoms, at a high enough temperature, should have a total heat energy Q of $3NkT$ (kT per site). The **molar heat capacity** C of the solid can be found by replacing N with L, Avogadro's number.

$$Q = 3LkT \quad \therefore \Delta Q = 3Lk\Delta T \quad \therefore C = 3Lk \qquad (6)$$

$$\therefore C = 3 \times 6.02\times10^{23} \times 1.38\times10^{-23}$$

$$\therefore C = 24.9 \text{ J mol}^{-1}\text{K}^{-1}$$

The molar heat capacities of a number of metals at room temperature are listed in table 1. Agreement with the theory is moderately good, considering how complex a real solid is. The fact that many solid metals have the same molar heat capacity at high enough temperatures was first recognised by Dulong and Petit in 1819.

Table 1

Metal	$C/\text{J mol}^{-1}\text{K}^{-1}$
aluminium	23.7
copper	24.2
iron	24.2
lead	26.1
tin	26.4

OBJECTIVES

After studying this section you should be able to do the following.

State the Boltzmann formula.

Know that it only applies to systems in thermal equilibrium.

Use the Boltzmann formula to find the number of atoms with a certain energy.

Use the Boltzmann formula to explain the temperature variation of resistance in semiconductors.

Predict the change in vapour pressure of a liquid when its temperature is changed.

State that the average energy per site in an Einstein solid is kT at a high enough temperature.

QUESTIONS

1 The graph of figure 30.25 shows the probability $p(E)$ of a single atom in a solid having a particular energy at temperature T.

a Explain why the area under the curve is 1.00.

b Draw graphs to show how the curve of figure 30.25 would change if the temperature of the solid was

i halved
ii doubled.

c A system has only two energy levels at 0.0 and 5.0×10^{21} J. By calculating $\exp[-E/kT]$ determine the probability of finding the system in each energy level at a temperature of

i 150 K
ii 300 K
iii 600 K.

2 The resistance R of a pure semiconductor is well modelled with the equation $R = R_0\exp[\epsilon/kT]$.

a A particular sample of semiconductor has a resistance which varies with temperature as shown in table 30.6.

Table 30.6

$R/k\Omega$	$T/°C$
41	0
20	20
11	40
6	60

Use a graph of $\ln[R]$ against $1/T$ to find a value for ϵ. Quote your answer in eV.

b Calculate the resistance of the sample at 100°C.

3 Table 30.7 contains some data for the vapour pressure of ethanol at various temperatures.

a Use it to show that $P = P_0\exp[\epsilon/kT]$ and hence estimate the molar latent heat of vaporisation of ethanol.

b The boiling point of ethanol can be used to measure the height above sea level. Atmospheric pressure ($\simeq 100$ kPa) drops by 12 Pa per metre of altitude. How high do you have to go for the boiling point to drop by 1 °C?

Table 30.7

P/kPa	T/K
1	267
2	277
5	291
10	302
20	315
50	335
100	351

4 The viscosity of many fluids varies exponentially with temperature. This can be modelled by treating a liquid as a solid where the atoms have a relatively high probability of getting enough energy to escape from their nearest neighbours. Let that energy be ϵ. The fraction of molecules which can change position in the liquid at any instant will be proportional to $\exp[-\epsilon/kT]$. The viscosity μ is a measure of the mobility of a liquid. Some data for water is given in table 30.8. Use the data to show that $\mu = \mu_0\exp[\epsilon/kT]$. Estimate the energy needed for one water molecule to break free from its neighbours in the liquid.

Table 30.8

Viscosity	T/K
1.77	273
1.00	293
0.65	313
0.47	333
0.36	353

5 Chips are often cooked in vegetable oil at 160°C. Potatoes at 120°C in a pressure cooker take half the time to cook than they do at 100°C. If a chip takes 20 minutes to cook in boiling water, estimate how long it would take in oil at 160°C. State what you are assuming about the cooking process.

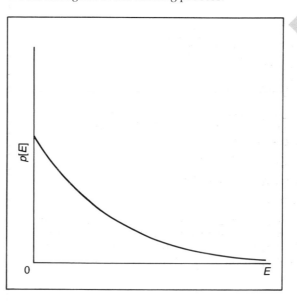

Figure 30.25

$p(E)$

0   E

31
GAS THERMODYNAMICS

The internal combustion engine and the refrigerator are two major tools which affect the standard of living in the Western World. **Heat engines** which run off liquid fuels allow us the freedom of cheap and convenient personal transport. **Heat pumps** which can cool our food make it possible to purchase and store a wide range of fresh foods at any time of the year. Both inventions can be ranked alongside the washing machine and the vacuum cleaner as the great domestic liberators of the twentieth century. The design of most heat engines and pumps exploits the energy transfer involved in compressing and expanding gases. So this chapter will start off by explaining the physics of gas compression. Then it will describe the operation of the petrol engine and domestic refrigerator and explain how the Second Law of Thermodynamics imposes limits on their efficiency. Finally, after a discussion of the links between entropy and disorder, you will find out how living organisms can appear to defy the Second Law of Thermodynamics and you will learn the ultimate fate of the Universe!

WORKING GASES

This section is going to deal mainly with the thermodynamics of ideal gases. For the most part, we are going to model an ideal gas as a fluid which obeys the **Ideal Gas Equation**.

> $PV = nRT$
>
> P is the pressure of the gas (Pa)
>
> V is the volume of the gas (m^3)
>
> n is the number of moles of the gas
>
> R is the ideal gas constant (8.3 J K^{-1})
>
> T is the temperature of the gas (K)

You will also recall from chapter 8 that in an ideal gas the average kinetic energy of a gas molecule is proportional to its temperature.

$$\tfrac{1}{2}m<c^2> = \frac{3kT}{2}, \quad \text{where } R = Lk \qquad \textbf{(31.1)}$$

(L is, of course, Avogadro's number 6.02×10^{23} mol^{-1}.)

In science, there always comes a point where a model fails to totally explain some aspect of the real world. You are about to see why the molar heat capacity of an ideal gas should be 5R/2. In practice, it is often much larger. Not only does this require

new thinking about the structure of molecules, it also needs quantum mechanics and the Boltzmann formula to make a model whose predictions agree with experiment.

Heat capacity

Suppose that you have a known amount of ideal gas in a solid box at temperature T. The total energy E of the gas can be worked out from equation (31.1) if you know how many molecules N it contains.

$$E = N \times \tfrac{1}{2}m<c^2> \qquad \therefore E = \frac{3}{2}NkT \qquad \textbf{(31.2)}$$

So if you have n moles of a gas, you can predict the heat energy ΔQ needed to raise its temperature by ΔT.

$$E = \frac{3}{2}NkT, \quad N = nL, \quad R = Lk$$

$$\therefore E = \frac{3}{2}nRT$$

$$\therefore \Delta E = \frac{3}{2}nR\Delta T = \Delta Q \qquad \textbf{(31.3)}$$

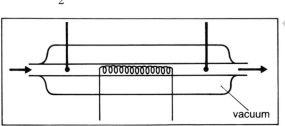

The **molar heat capacity at constant volume**, C_v, is the heat energy needed to change the temperature of one mole of the gas by one kelvin. Its value can be obtained from equation (31.3).

$$\Delta Q = \frac{3}{2}nR\Delta T, \quad \Delta Q = nC_v\Delta T$$

$$\therefore C_v = \frac{3R}{2} \qquad \textbf{(31.4)}$$

C_v is hence expected to be $3R/2 = 12.5$ J mol^{-1} K^{-1} for all gases at all temperatures.

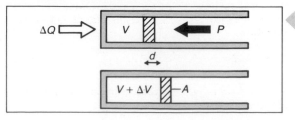

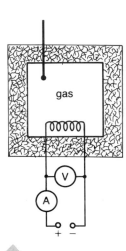

Figure 31.1 Apparatus for measuring the molar heat capacity of a gas at constant volume

Figure 31.2 Apparatus for measuring the heat capacity of gases at constant pressure

Figure 31.3 If a gas expands when heat energy is added to it then it does work

Figure 31.1 shows how you might set about measuring C_v in practice. A known amount of heat energy is delivered to the gas from an electrical heater, and the consequent temperature rise measured with a thermocouple. In practice, this sort of experiment is very difficult to carry out because of the relatively large heat capacity of the box. It is much easier to use a constant flow arrangement, as shown in figure 31.2, where the heat capacity of the container is irrelevant and the heat loss can be accounted for. However, the gas is being allowed to expand at atmospheric pressure as its temperature is raised, so we need to predict the **molar heat capacity at constant pressure**, C_p. We can do this with the help of a thought experiment performed with the apparatus shown in figure 31.3.

Heat capacity at constant pressure

The gas in the cylinder of figure 31.3 will remain at atmospheric pressure if the piston is able to slide freely. As heat energy is given to the gas through the cylinder walls, the gas will expand and do some work pushing the piston to the right. Since energy is conserved, any difference between the heat energy given to the gas and the work done by the gas must be the increase of internal energy of the gas. This is stated formally in the **First Law of Thermodynamics**.

> $\Delta Q = \Delta U + \Delta W$
>
> ΔQ is the heat energy given to the system (J)
>
> ΔU is the increase of internal energy of the system (J)
>
> ΔW is the work done by the system (J)

If we can find expressions for both ΔU and ΔW, we should be able to predict the heat energy ΔQ needed to raise the temperature of a mole of gas by 1 K. The internal energy of a gas can only be the kinetic energy of its molecules. So we can use C_v to find ΔU for a given temperature rise ΔT.

$$\Delta U = nC_v\Delta T \qquad (31.5)$$

(The cylinder contains n moles of gas.) If the piston has area A and moves a distance d, the work done by the gas, assuming a constant pressure P, is given by

$$E = Fd, \quad P = \frac{F}{A} \qquad \therefore \Delta W = PAd$$

$$\Delta V = Ad \qquad \therefore \Delta W = P\Delta V \qquad (31.6)$$

where ΔV is the change of volume of the gas.

> $\Delta W = P\Delta V$
>
> ΔW is the work done by the gas as it expands (J)
>
> P is the pressure of the gas (Pa)
>
> ΔV is the increase in volume of the gas (m^3)

We can get a useful alternative expression for equation (31.6) by considering the Ideal Gas Equation.

$$PV = nRT \quad \therefore \frac{\Delta P}{P} + \frac{\Delta V}{V} = \frac{\Delta T}{T} \qquad (31.7)$$

Since we are not allowing the pressure to change, ΔP must be zero.

Figure 31.4
Representation of a diatomic molecule

$$\frac{\Delta V}{V} = \frac{\Delta T}{T} \quad \therefore PAV = PV \times \frac{\Delta T}{T}$$

$$PV = nRT \quad \therefore P\Delta V = nR\Delta T \qquad (31.8)$$

Now we can insert equations (31.5) and (31.8) into the First Law of Thermodynamics.

$$\Delta Q = \Delta U + \Delta W$$

$$\therefore \Delta Q = nC_v\Delta T + nR\Delta T$$

$$\therefore \Delta Q = n\times(C_v + R)\times\Delta T$$

$$\therefore \Delta Q = nC_p\Delta T, \quad \text{where } C_p = C_v + R \qquad (31.9)$$

Equation (31.9) predicts that the molar heat capacity at constant pressure of any gas, at any temperature or pressure, should be

$$\boxed{C_p = C_v + R}$$

$$\therefore C_p = \frac{3}{2}R + R = \frac{5}{2}R = 20.8\,\text{J mol}^{-1}\,\text{K}^{-1}$$

Some measured values of C_p for a number of selected gases at room temperature and pressure are shown in table 31.1. As you can see, the match between theory and experiment is very impressive.

Table 31.1

Element	$C_p/\text{J mol}^{-1}\,\text{K}^{-1}$
helium	20.8
neon	20.8
argon	20.8
krypton	20.8
xenon	20.8
radon	20.8

Molecular shape

At first glance, the data of table 31.1 appear to represent another great triumph for the kinetic theory of gases. Well, take a look at the data presented in table 31.2. These gases are also at room temperature and pressure. The value 29.2 is exactly $7R/2$! Table 31.1 lists all of the **noble gases**. These are known to be inert, i.e. chemically inactive, so we would expect their gases to be well described by a hard sphere model. Table 31.2, on the other hand, contains **diatomic** molecules. Such a molecule is pictured in figure 31.4: it contains two atoms rigidly joined together. So the experimental evidence suggests that the shape of the molecule dictates the molar heat capacity of the gas. Table 31.3 lists values of C_p for some gases at room temperature whose molecules contain three atoms: they are fairly close to $8R/2 = 33.2\,\text{J mol}^{-1}\,\text{K}^{-1}$.

Table 31.2

Compound	$C_p/\text{J mol}^{-1}\,\text{K}^{-1}$
hydrogen	29.2
oxygen	29.1
nitrogen	29.1
nitrous oxide	29.1
carbon monoxide	29.0

Table 31.3

Compound	$C_p/\text{J mol}^{-1}\,\text{K}^{-1}$
carbon dioxide	37.1
hydrogen sulphide	34.2
water	33.6
ammonia	35.6

EXCITING DEGREES OF FREEDOM !

Figure 31.6 The Boltzmann formula for a system which does not have quantised energy levels

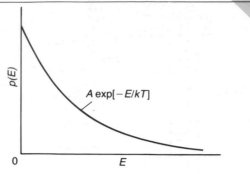

The average energy of a degree of freedom is only $\frac{1}{2}kT$ if the spacing between its energy levels ϵ is much smaller than kT. This is easily shown as follows. The probability that the degree of freedom has an energy E is given by $p(E) = A\exp[-E/kT]$. If the energy levels are very close together, then this distribution looks like the one shown in figure 31.6. The average energy $<E>$ of a degree of freedom is given by the following expression:

$$<E> = \int Ep(E)dE, \quad \text{where } p(E) = A\exp[-E/kT] \tag{1}$$

The value of A must allow all of the values of $p(E)$ to add up to 1.

$$\int p(E)dE = 1 \qquad \therefore A \int \exp[-E/kT]dE = 1 \tag{2}$$

If your maths is good, you can combine equations (1) and (2) to show that $<E> = \frac{1}{2}kT$.

Figure 31.7 shows the probability distribution when the spacing of the energy levels ϵ is similar to kT. The chances of that degree of freedom having an energy of more than zero are very small. So at low temperatures the degrees of freedom which have relatively large energy spacings are not **excited**. For example, look at the graph of figure 31.8. It shows how C_v changes with temperature for oxygen. At low temperatures it appears to have five degrees of freedom but at high temperatures it has seven. The extra two degrees of freedom are due to vibration of the molecule along its axis: one degree is elastic energy, the other is kinetic energy. The fact that they are becoming excited at about 700 K allows us to estimate the separation ϵ between those vibrational energy levels.

$$\epsilon \simeq kT \quad \therefore \epsilon \simeq 1.38 \times 10^{-23} \times 700 = 1 \times 10^{-20} \text{ J}$$

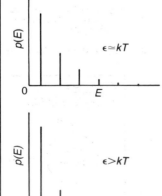

Figure 31.7 The probability distribution for a system with quantised energy levels

Figure 31.8 The variation of C_v with temperature for oxygen

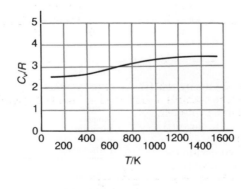

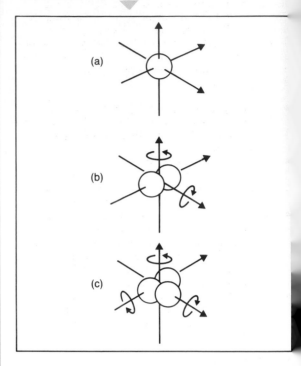

Equipartition

The experimental evidence in the tables above suggests that molecules have other sorts of energy apart from kinetic energy. A triatomic molecule (figure 31.5(c)) can rotate about three independent axes, so there are three ways in which it can have rotational energy. This is similar to the three independent ways in which it can have kinetic energy. These are illustrated in figure 31.5(a). Each way that a molecule can have energy is called a **degree of freedom**. The **Principle of Equipartition** states that each degree of freedom has the same average energy as all the other degrees of freedom. (Although it is of limited use today, this principle proved very useful before quantum mechanics was discovered.)

$<E> = \frac{1}{2}kT$.

$<E>$ is the average energy of a particle per degree of freedom (J)

k is Boltzmann's constant (1.38×10^{-23} J K^{-1})

T is the temperature of the particle's environment (K)

So a triatomic molecule (such as carbon dioxide) will have three rotational degrees of freedom as well as the three translational ones, giving a total of six. The average energy per molecule should therefore be $6 \times \frac{1}{2}kT = 3kT$. Each degree of freedom contributes $\frac{1}{2}R$ to the value of C_v, so C_p should be $6 \times \frac{1}{2}R + R = 8R/2$. The fact that monatomic gases have $C_p = 5R/2$ suggests that they only have the three translational degrees of freedom. They do not appear to rotate. Similarly, diatomic molecules only appear to have the two rotational degrees of freedom illustrated in figure 31.5(b). Rotation about the molecule's axis of symmetry does not appear to happen.

Refrigerators

A refrigerator is a device which transfers heat energy from something cold to something hot. Figure 31.9(a) shows the main parts of a domestic refrigeration system. The **compressor** pumps a fluid around the system in a loop between the cold object and the hot object. Let's start with the vapour in the compressor and see what happens to it on the way round.

- The **compressor** quickly raises the pressure of the vapour so that there is no time for any heat to escape from it. This is called an **adiabatic compression**.
- The vapour passes through a one-way valve into the **condenser** where it gradually turns into a liquid. This requires the liquid to lose energy to the hot object in contact with the condenser.
- The liquid, still at high pressure, passes through a **throttling valve** into the low pressure region of the **evaporator**. As the liquid turns back into a vapour, it has to extract energy from its surroundings. So heat energy is transferred from the cold object to the vapour.
- Finally, the vapour passes through a one-way valve into the compressor to have its pressure and temperature raised by an adiabatic compression.

Indicator diagrams

The cycle of operations is summarised with the P–V graph of figure 31.9(b). This type of graph is known as an **indicator diagram**. The area of the loop is a measure of the energy which has to be put into the system to get the fluid round the cycle. To see this, consider the work done on the fluid by the compressor.

$$\Delta W = P\Delta V \quad \therefore W = \Sigma\, P\Delta V \qquad \textbf{(31.10)}$$

This will be the area under the graph of figure 31.10(a). Since the fluid is shrinking, work is being done on it. On its way through the throttling valve and the evaporator the fluid expands, doing work on the compressor. This is represented by the area under the graph of figure 31.10(b). Clearly, the total work done by the compressor per cycle is the difference between the two areas, i.e. the area enclosed by the loop in figure 31.9(b).

Efficiency

Figure 31.11 shows the energy transfers in and out of a refrigeration system (or **heat pump**). The heat energy Q_c is extracted at temperature T_c from the cold object and heat energy Q_h is given to the hot object at temperature T_h. W is the work put into the heat pump to make the heat transfer happen. The **efficiency** of the system is the heat extracted from the cold object per joule of work done.

$$\text{efficiency} = \frac{Q_c}{W} \qquad \textbf{(31.11)}$$

The Second Law of Thermodynamics can be used to place an upper limit on the efficiency. This is very useful, because it applies to *all* types of heat pump, regardless of their construction. Any heat pump will only work if it increases the total entropy of the Universe in the process. Consider the entropy changes of the hot and cold objects.

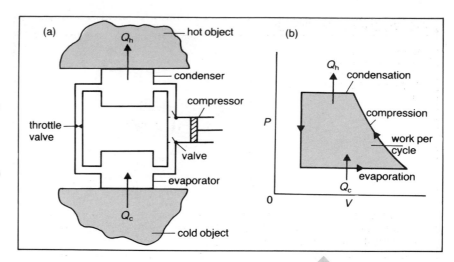

Figure 31.9 Essential details of a refrigerator

$$\Delta S = \frac{\Delta Q}{T}$$

$$\therefore \Delta S_h = +\frac{Q_h}{T_h}, \qquad \Delta S_c = -\frac{Q_c}{T_c} \qquad \textbf{(31.12)}$$

The total entropy change ΔS must be greater than or equal to zero.

$$\Delta S = \Delta S_h + \Delta S_c \geqslant 0$$

$$\therefore \frac{Q_h}{T_h} \geqslant \frac{Q_c}{T_c} \qquad \textbf{(31.13)}$$

The heat pump must also obey the First Law of Thermodynamics, i.e. it must conserve energy. We can use this with equation (31.13) to obtain an expression for the efficiency which only involves temperatures.

$$Q_c + W = Q_h \quad \therefore \text{efficiency} = \frac{Q_c}{Q_h - Q_c} \qquad \textbf{(31.14)}$$

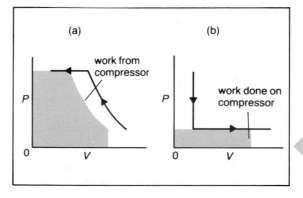

Figure 31.10 Work done during two halves of the whole cycle

Figure 31.11 A heat pump

The efficiency will be a maximum when Q_h is as small as possible. (Look at equation (31.14) and convince yourself.)

$$Q_h \geqslant Q_c \frac{T_h}{T_c}$$

$$\therefore \text{efficiency} \leqslant \frac{Q_c}{Q_c \dfrac{T_h}{T_c} - Q_c}$$

$$\therefore \text{efficiency} \leqslant \frac{T_c}{T_h - T_c} \qquad \textbf{(31.15)}$$

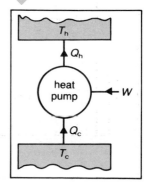

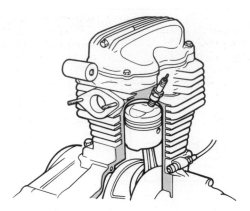

Figure 31.12 An internal combustion engine

The maximum value of the efficiency is set by the temperatures at either end of the heat pump. Note that it gets smaller as the difference between the hot and cold temperatures increases. Let's calculate the maximum efficiency of a domestic refrigerator keeping food at 2°C in a room which is at 20°C.

$$\text{efficiency} = \frac{275}{293 - 275} = 15.3$$

So for every joule of electricity consumed by the compressor, up to 15.3 joules can be extracted from the food and given to the room. In practice, the efficiency will be less than this because of all the processes in the pump which increase the total entropy.

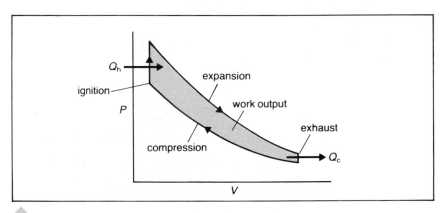

Figure 31.13 Indicator diagram for an ideal petrol engine

Figure 31.14 A heat engine

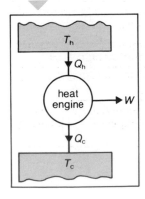

Internal combustion engine

Internal combustion engines are very complicated devices. Taking you through the complete cycle of operations of the engine shown in figure 31.12 is well beyond the scope of this book. So we shall use a simple model of what happens to the air–petrol mixture as it is exploded in the cylinder. The indicator diagram for one cycle of a petrol engine is shown in figure 31.13. The total work done by the engine in that cycle is the area of the loop. Let's start at the point where the cold air–petrol mixture enters the cylinder.

- The gas is drawn into the cylinder at a constant pressure.
- The gas is then adiabatically compressed so that its volume shrinks by a factor of about 8 (the **compression ratio**). Because the compression involves work being done on the gas, its temperature will rise along with its pressure to about 650 K.

- The air–petrol mixture is ignited by a spark. This releases a large amount of heat energy which suddenly raises the temperature of the gas to about 850 K.
- The hot gases then expand adiabatically, doing work on the piston. The work done by the gas is at the expense of its internal energy, so its temperature drops to about 400 K.
- Finally, the cooled gas is vented to the outside world where it delivers surplus heat energy to the surrounding air.

Efficiency

The maximum efficiency of *any* heat engine is set by the Second Law of Thermodynamics. The flow of energy through a **heat engine** is illustrated in figure 31.14. The heat flow from a hot object to a cold object is used to generate a certain amount of work, increasing the total entropy of the Universe in the process. The system is isolated, so it also has to conserve energy.

$$Q_h = Q_c + W \quad \therefore W = Q_h - Q_c \quad \text{(31.16)}$$

The efficiency of the system will be the ratio of the work output to the heat energy input.

$$\text{efficiency} = \frac{W}{Q_h}$$

$$\therefore \text{efficiency} = \frac{Q_h - Q_c}{Q_h} \quad \text{(31.17)}$$

The total entropy of the whole system must increase.

$$\Delta S = \Delta S_c + \Delta S_h \geqslant 0 \quad \text{(31.18)}$$

The entropy of the **hot object** decreases when it loses energy, but the entropy of the **cold object** is increased.

$$\Delta S = \frac{\Delta Q}{T}$$

$$\therefore \Delta S_h = -\frac{Q_h}{T_h}, \qquad \Delta S_c = +\frac{Q_c}{T_c}$$

$$\therefore \Delta S = \frac{Q_c}{T_c} - \frac{Q_h}{T_h}$$

$$\therefore Q_c \geqslant Q_h \frac{T_c}{T_h} \quad \text{(31.19)}$$

If we substitute equation (31.19) into (31.17) we obtain a useful expression for the maximum efficiency. This will happen when Q_c is as small as possible.

$$\text{efficiency} \leqslant \frac{T_h - T_c}{T_h} \quad \text{(31.20)}$$

As an example, let's estimate the maximum efficiency of a petrol engine. The explosion raises the temperature of the gas to 850 K. After doing work on the piston, this gas is released at a temperature of about 400 K. So the heat enters the system at $T_h \simeq 850$ K and leaves it at $T_c \simeq 400$ K. Therefore the maximum efficiency is $(850 - 400)/850 \simeq 0.5$. In practice, the efficiency is about half this, mainly because of the various ways in which a real petrol engine converts kinetic energy to heat energy through friction.

Adiabatic changes

In order to estimate the work done by the gas in one complete cycle, you need to be able to predict how the pressure and temperature of the gas change during an **adiabatic** compression or expansion — one which involves no heat flow. Since no heat energy enters or leaves the gas during an adiabatic change, any work done by it or on it must result in a change of temperature.

$$\Delta Q = \Delta U + \Delta W, \quad \Delta Q = 0$$

$$\therefore \Delta U = - \Delta W \qquad (31.21)$$

Figure 31.15 Isothermal and adiabatic compressions

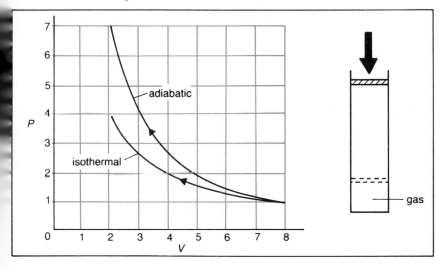

For an **isothermal** change (one at constant temperature) PV = constant. The equivalent expression for an adiabatic change is PV^γ = constant where γ is about 1.4 for air.

> PV^γ = constant
>
> P is the pressure of the gas
>
> V is the volume of the gas
>
> γ is C_p/C_v

Figure 31.15 compares the results of an adiabatic and an isothermal compression of some gas enclosed by a piston and cylinder. The increase in pressure caused by the temperature rise of the gas is clearly shown.

As an example, consider the compression cycle of a petrol engine. Suppose that 400 cm^3 of air–petrol mixture at 290 K is drawn into the cylinder at a pressure of 1 atmosphere. What is its pressure and temperature after its volume is rapidly reduced to 50 cm^3?

$$PV^\gamma = \text{constant}$$

$$\therefore 1 \times 400^{1.4} = P \times 50^{1.4}$$

$$\therefore P = \left(\frac{400}{50}\right)^{1.4} = 18.4 \text{ atmospheres}$$

We can use the Ideal Gas Equation to find the final temperature of the gas.

$$\frac{PV}{T} = \text{constant}$$

$$\therefore \frac{1 \times 400}{290} = \frac{18.4 \times 50}{T}$$

$$\therefore T = 667 \text{ K}$$

ADIABATIC COMPRESSION FORMULA !

Consider one mole of an ideal gas in a cylinder. It expands rapidly, so that there is no time for it to exchange heat with the cylinder walls. The work done on the piston during a small increase in volume ΔV is related to the drop in temperature ΔT.

$$\Delta Q = \Delta U + \Delta W, \quad \Delta Q = 0 \quad \therefore \Delta U = - \Delta W$$

$$\Delta W = P\Delta V, \quad \Delta U = C_v \Delta T \quad \therefore C_v \Delta T = - P\Delta V \qquad (1)$$

Of course, the pressure will drop as well as the temperature. The changes in volume, temperature and pressure are related by the Ideal Gas Equation.

$$PV = RT \qquad \therefore \frac{\Delta P}{P} + \frac{\Delta V}{V} = \frac{\Delta T}{T} \qquad (2)$$

If we combine equations (1) and (2) to eliminate ΔT, we end up with an equation linking the changes in pressure and volume only.

$$\frac{\Delta P}{P} + \frac{\Delta V}{V} = - \frac{P\Delta V}{C_v T}, \qquad PV = RT \qquad \therefore \frac{\Delta P}{P} + \frac{\Delta V}{V}\left(1 + \frac{R}{C_v}\right) = 0$$

$$\therefore \frac{\Delta P}{P} + \frac{\gamma \Delta V}{V} = 0, \quad \text{where} \quad \gamma = \frac{C_v + R}{C_v}$$

$$\therefore PV^\gamma = \text{constant}$$

OBJECTIVES

After studying this section you should be able to do the following.

State that C_v is $3R/2$ for an ideal gas.

State and explain the First Law of Thermodynamics.

Explain the difference between C_p and C_v.

Use the formula $C_p = C_v + R$.

Use the Principle of Equipartition to estimate the molar heat capacity of a real gas.

Describe the operation of a simple refrigerator and calculate its maximum theoretical efficiency.

Describe the operation of a simple heat engine and calculate its maximum theoretical efficiency.

Explain the difference between an isothermal and an adiabatic change of a gas.

Use the formulae PV^γ = constant and $PV = nRT$ to calculate the pressure and temperature changes in an adiabatic compression.

QUESTIONS

1 In order for a room to be comfortable to work in, the air in it should be completely changed twice an hour. Assume that air is a diatomic ideal gas.

Figure 31.16

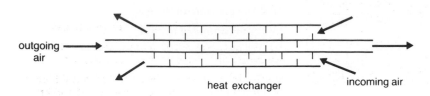

heat exchanger   incoming air

outgoing air

a Using the room you are sitting in at the moment, calculate how many moles of air it contains. Assume a pressure of 100 kPa and a temperature of 20°C.

b Suppose that the air is slowly replaced every half hour with cold air at 0°C from the outside world. Calculate the average power of the heater needed to get that air up to 20°C. (Will the air be heated at constant volume or constant pressure?)

c It is more efficient to use a **heat exchanger** to extract heat from the air as it is expelled and give it to the cold air as it comes into the room. A very simple heat exchanger is shown in figure 31.16. The outgoing gases of part (b) are circulated through the incoming gases via thin-walled pipes and fins so that they come into thermal equilibrium with each other. State the temperature of the gases when they reach thermal equilibrium. Estimate the rate at which heat is transferred between the two gases this way. Calculate the heater power necessary if such a heat exchanger is used.

d Elanit reckons that a series of heat exchangers could heat the incoming air up to almost 20°C in stages, almost eliminating the need for extra heating. Is it possible? Sketch Elanit's design and discuss important features.

2 An ideal gas in a cylinder is compressed so that its final volume is one-fifth of its initial volume. The gas has $\gamma = 1.4$ and its initial temperature and pressure are 290 K and 100 kPa respectively.

a Suppose that the compression is isothermal. What is the final temperature and pressure of the gas?

b What is the final pressure and temperature of the gas if the compression is adiabatic?

c Draw graphs to show how the pressure depends on the volume for both types of compression. Plot both curves with the same axes.

3 The indicator diagram for an imaginary heat engine is shown in figure 31.17.

a Estimate how much work it does in one cycle.

b Is the gas expanding isothermally or adiabatically between A and B? Explain your answer.

c Suggest, with reasons, what is happening to the gas in the heat engine between B and C. Will the gas lose heat energy or gain it between B and C?

d What is happening to the gas between C and A? Will it lose heat energy or gain it?

4 A diesel engine achieves higher efficiencies than a petrol engine because it has a larger compression ratio. This question should help you to see why. Assume ideal gas behaviour throughout, with $\gamma = 1.4$.

a 400 cm³ of air at 27°C is drawn into a cylinder at atmospheric pressure (100 kPa) and compressed adiabatically to a volume of 25 cm³. (This corresponds to a compression ratio of 16.) Calculate the final pressure and temperature of the air.

b Oil is sprayed into the compressed air and ignites immediately. Why does the diesel engine not need a spark plug?

c The explosion raises the temperature of the compressed air by 200 K. What is the pressure and temperature of the air after it has done work on the piston?

d Calculate the maximum efficiency of the engine.

e Repeat the whole question for an engine with a compression ratio of only 8. (You can assume that the fuel still ignites spontaneously when it is sprayed into the hot compressed gas.)

5 A domestic refrigerator can extract about 3×10^6 J of heat per hour from its interior at 1°C and put it into the surroundings at 30°C.

a Calculate the maximum possible efficiency of such a refrigerator.

b If the actual efficiency is half the theoretical value, what is the electrical power needed to keep the refrigerator running?

c Suppose that a refrigerator was used to extract heat from an underground sewer at 5°C and put it into a house at 20°C. If the actual efficiency is half the theoretical maximum value, estimate the electrical power needed for the refrigerator to heat the whole house at a rate of 15 kW. Comment on your answer. Suggest why such domestic heating systems are not yet widely used.

6 The **Third Law of Thermodynamics** effectively states that it is impossible to cool an object below 0 K. One way of proving this is to consider a heat pump trying to cool an object from an initial temperature T to a lower temperature $T - \Delta T$. Show that the heat pump will have an efficiency of zero when $T = 0$.

Figure 31.17

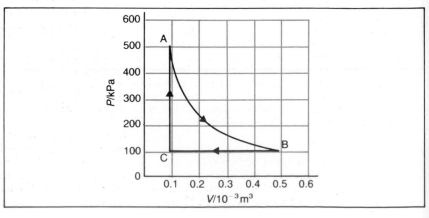

Figure 31.18

7 Compressed air is widely used in industry as a source of energy. Air at room temperature and pressure (290 K and 100 kPa) is typically compressed to 250 kPa and stored in a reservoir (figure 31.18). Some time later, the compressed air can be piped to a piston where it expands back to room pressure, doing work in the process.

a Assume that one mole of air ($\gamma = 1.4$) at room temperature and pressure is adiabatically compressed from 100 kPa to 250 kPa. Calculate its initial and final volume.

b Draw a $P-V$ graph for the air during the compression. Use it to *estimate* the work done on the gas.

c Calculate the final temperature of the gas.

d If the gas cools to room temperature in the reservoir, what does its pressure drop to?

e The gas is now transferred to a piston where it is expanded isothermally to a pressure of 150 kPa. Calculate its final volume. Draw a $P-V$ graph for the gas as it expands and use it to *estimate* the work done by the gas on the piston.

f How does the work done by the piston compare with the work done by the compressor?

g Comment on the efficiency of the system.

DISORDER

You will recall from chapter 30 that the entropy of an Einstein solid can be calculated from the number of ways in which it can arrange its quanta among its sites. However, calculating the entropy of a gas is not so straightforward for two reasons. First, because a gas molecule is like a particle in a box, its energy levels are not evenly spaced (figure 31.19). This means that the quanta exchanged between molecules when they collide are not all the same size. Secondly, a gas has entropy because of the different ways in which its molecules can be arranged. This section will show you how the entropy of a gas can be calculated. It also discusses how the entropy due to disorder in a system can be decreased at the expense of the total entropy of the system.

Arranging molecules

Take a look at figure 31.20. It represents various stages in the spreading of a gas into an otherwise empty container which is thermally isolated. Each stage shows the arrangement of molecules at a later time than the previous stage. As time goes on, the system becomes more **disordered**. To start with, all of the molecules are arranged in a corner of the box. At the end, they are spread at random throughout the whole container. Intuitively, it is obvious which of the pictures represent the initial and final situations. Yet there is nothing in the laws of physics which says that gas molecules in a box cannot clump together spontaneously in one small part of it — it just never happens! The reason why it never happens has to do with the number of ways of arranging particles in a limited volume.

Counting ways

Suppose that we divide the container into v identical cells and scatter N distinguishable particles among them at random. Each cell is large enough for all of the particles to fit into it. There

will be v ways of placing the first particle in the container. For each of those ways there will be v ways of placing the second particle. So there are $v \times v = v^2$ different ways of arranging two particles in the container. It should be obvious that there are v^N ways of arranging N particles in the container.

$$W = v^N$$

W is the number of ways of arranging the particles

v is the number of cells

N is the number of particles

In a gas, collisions between the particles continually rearrange them. Each way of arranging the particles is therefore equally likely to occur at any instant. Let's use this argument to estimate the probability of all the particles in a gas clumping together.

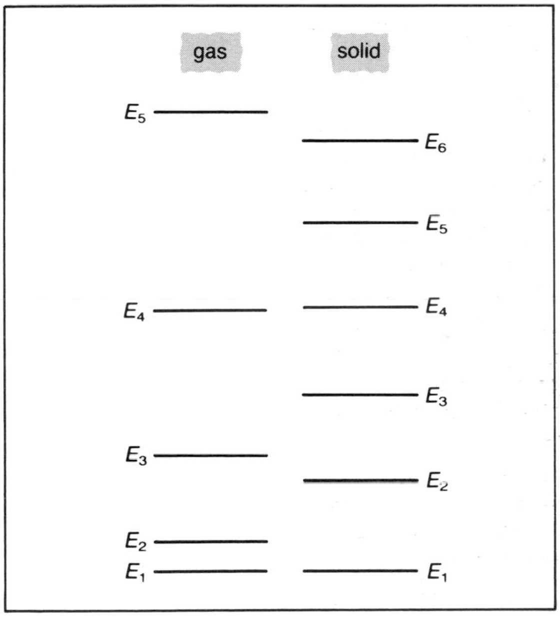

Figure 31.19 Energy levels for atoms in solids and gases

Figure 31.20 Stages in the spreading of a gas in a box

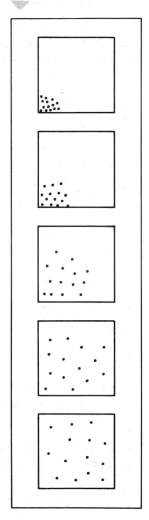

When the particles are clumped together, they are in a single cell. There are v cells, so this can happen in v ways. (Don't worry about the arrangement of particles within the cell.) The probability p of finding all of the particles in a single cell is therefore

$$p = \frac{v}{v^N} \quad \therefore p \simeq v^{-N} \qquad (31.22)$$

(We have assumed that N is much larger than 1.) Let's put some numbers in. One mole of iodine gas has a volume of 2.36×10^{-2} m^3 at room temperature and pressure. The equivalent amount of solid has a volume of 3.48×10^{-5} m^3. Let's take the latter as the size of our cell, giving $v = 2.36 \times 10^{-2}/3.48 \times 10^{-5} \simeq 700$. Since p is likely to be small, we shall have to calculate its logarithm.

$$p = v^{-N} \quad \therefore \ln[p] = -N \ln[v]$$
$$\therefore \ln[p] = -6.02 \times 10^{23} \ln[700]$$
$$\therefore \ln[p] \simeq -4 \times 10^{24}$$
$$\therefore p \simeq 10^{-2\,000\,000\,000\,000\,000\,000\,000\,000}$$

The probability of finding all the particles in a single cell is, to all intents and purposes, zero!

One-way changes

The expansion of a gas into an empty container is a one-way change. In practice, the gas particles end up evenly spread throughout the container. This is simply a consequence of the large number of particles involved. To see why this is so, consider a thought experiment with a gas that contains very few particles. We divide the container into just two cells, as shown in figure 31.21 and place N distinguishable particles in it. Table 31.3 lists the probability of finding all of the particles in the left-hand side of the box if they are shuffled at random from one side to the other. So only if the number of particles is very small is there any real probability that they will shuffle themselves spontaneously into one half of the container. In any real situation where the particles start off in one half of the container, they will eventually spread out to fill the whole container.

Table 31.3

N	2^{-N}
1	0.500000
2	0.250000
4	0.062500
8	0.003906
16	0.000015

Figure 31.22 shows the results of some computer simulations of the situation we have been discussing. Each graph shows how the number of particles in the left-hand half of the box changes with time when the particles are allowed to swap from one side to another at random. All of the particles started in the left-hand side of the box. For small numbers of particles, there is no real pattern, but for large numbers there appears to be an exponential decrease towards a dynamic equilibrium where the particles are evenly shared between the two halves of the box. Random movement of particles on a small scale leads to orderly changes on a large scale.

Entropy

When a gas is placed in a container, each arrangement of its particles is equally likely to occur as time goes on. However, the most likely arrangement will be the one which can be achieved in the greatest number of ways. The entropy of the gas due to the arrangement of its N particles among v cells can therefore be defined as follows:

$$S = k\ln[W], \quad W = v^N \quad \therefore S = Nk\ln[v] \qquad (31.23)$$

So when a gas has reached equilibrium on a large scale, it will have reached the situation which has the maximum entropy. Furthermore, all spontaneous large-scale changes of the gas will increase its entropy, i.e. lead to situations where the particles can be arranged in more ways than before.

Let us work out the change of entropy ΔS which results from an increase of volume ΔV. The number of cells will be proportional to the volume V of the gas.

$$v \propto V \quad \therefore \frac{\Delta v}{v} = \frac{\Delta V}{V} \qquad (31.24)$$

We can use equation (31.23) to find the entropy before and after the expansion.

$$S = Nk\ln[v] \quad \therefore S + \Delta S = Nk\ln[v + \Delta v]$$
$$\therefore \Delta S = Nk\ln[v + \Delta v] - Nk\ln[v]$$
$$\therefore \Delta S = Nk\ln[(v + \Delta v)/v]$$
$$\therefore \Delta S = Nk\ln[1 + \Delta v/v] \qquad (31.25)$$

Finally, equation (31.24) can be used to find the entropy change in terms of the volume change.

$$\Delta S = Nk\ln[1 + \Delta V/V]$$

ΔS is the entropy increase of the gas (J K^{-1})

N is the number of particles in the gas

k is Boltzmann's constant (1.38×10^{-23} J K^{-1})

ΔV is the volume increase of the gas (m^3)

V is the original volume of the gas (m^3)

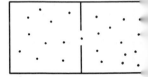

Figure 31.21 Dynamic equilibrium, corresponding to the maximum entropy for the system

Figure 31.22 Results of computer simulations of particles moving at random between two halves of a box

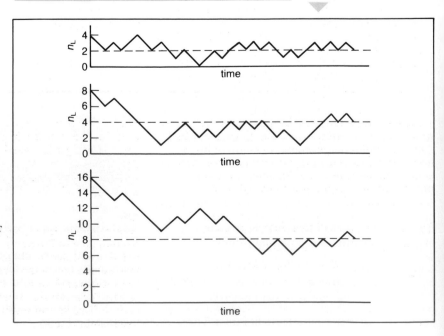

BOILING POINTS

The normal boiling point of water (373 K at 101 kPa) is the temperature at which the entropy increase due to expansion is exactly balanced by the entropy decrease due to latent heat. Consider one mole of water in a cylinder and piston (figure 31.23). Table 1 shows the entropies of the liquid and gas forms of water at 101 kPa and 298 K. We can use this to prove that the liquid will never spontaneously turn into a gas under those conditions.

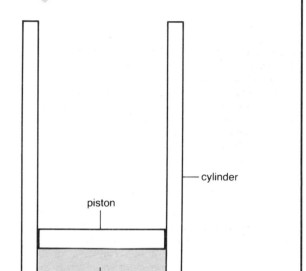

Figure 31.23 A liquid enclosed in a cylinder by a piston

Table 1

State	$S/J \text{ mol}^{-1} \text{ K}^{-1}$	$C_p/J \text{ mol}^{-1} \text{ K}^{-1}$
liquid	69.9	75.3
gas	188.7	33.6

Suppose that the liquid turned into a gas. Its entropy would increase by 188.7 − 69.9 = 118.8 J K^{-1}. However, it would need to take some latent heat from the cylinder at 298 K. The molar latent heat of vaporisation of water is 4.07×10^4 J mol^{-1}, so the entropy change of the cylinder (which has to provide this heat energy) would be −4.07×10^4/298 = −136.6 J K^{-1}. So if the water did spontaneously turn into steam, the system would suffer a net loss of entropy, i.e. +118.8 − 136.6 = −17.8 J K^{-1}. It would therefore not happen.

Suppose that we heat the steam up to 398 K at 101 kPa. There will be two contributions to its entropy increase. The entropy change due to the addition of heat energy can be estimated as follows:

$$\Delta S = \frac{\Delta Q}{T}, \quad \Delta Q = C_p \Delta T \quad \therefore \Delta S \simeq C_p \frac{\Delta T}{T}$$

Assume that T is the average temperature at which heat energy is delivered to the gas.

$$\frac{\Delta Q}{T} \simeq \frac{33.6 \times 100}{348} \simeq 9.7 \text{ J K}^{-1}$$

The other contribution is due to the expansion of the gas.

$$PV = RT \quad \therefore \quad \frac{\Delta V}{V} \simeq \frac{\Delta T}{T}$$

$$\therefore \Delta S = R\ln[1 + \Delta T/T]$$
$$\therefore \Delta S = 8.31\ln[1 + 100/348]$$
$$\therefore \Delta S \simeq 2.1 \text{ J K}^{-1}$$

So the entropy of a mole of steam at 398 K and 101 kPa is about 188.7 + 9.7 + 2.1 = 200.5 J K^{-1}. You can check for yourself that the entropy of a mole of water under the same conditions is 69.9 + 21.6 = 91.5 J K^{-1}.

Now suppose that water at this higher temperature and pressure spontaneously turns into steam. The entropy change of the cylinder due to latent heat is less than before, i.e. −4.07×10^4/398 = −102.3 J K^{-1}. The entropy change due to the expansion is now 200.5 − 91.5 = + 109.0 J K^{-1}. The total entropy change of the whole system is now + 109.0 − 102.3 = +6.7 J K^{-1}. Since this is positive, the water will definitely turn into steam.

For each way in which the gas can arrange its particles, there will be a number of ways in which it can share its energy among those particles. So if the particles can be arranged in W_p ways and the energy can be arranged in W_e ways, the total number of ways W is going to be given by

$$W = W_p W_e \qquad \textbf{(31.26)}$$

The total entropy will therefore be given by

$$S = k\ln[W] \quad \therefore \ S = k\ln[W_p W_e]$$
$$\therefore \ S = k\ln[W_p] + k\ln[W_e]$$
$$\therefore \ S = S_p + S_e \qquad \textbf{(31.27)}$$

The total entropy of a gas is therefore the sum of its individual entropies. In general, the change of entropy of a gas is given by the following formula.

$$\Delta S = \frac{\Delta Q}{T} + Nk\ln[1 + \frac{\Delta V}{V}]$$

Life

At first glance, living organisms appear to defy the Second Law of Thermodynamics. They take in small molecules in a highly disordered state and use them to create the large ordered molecules such as proteins and carbohydrates which are essential to life. For example, consider the reaction between carbon dioxide and water which happens in plants to generate glucose.

$$6CO_2 + 6H_2O \rightarrow C_6H_{12}O_6 + 6O_2$$

This represents a decrease in entropy because the amount of disorder is reduced. The number of molecules at the start of the reaction (12) is much greater than the number at the end (7), corresponding to a loss of entropy. The compensating increase in entropy comes from the light photons which are absorbed by the plant to provide the reaction with the energy it needs. A plant is essentially a heat engine (figure 31.24), taking in heat energy from the Sun at a high temperature and losing some of it at a much lower temperature. The hot object which provides the heat is the surface of the Sun, at about 6000 K. The cold object which accepts the surplus heat energy from the engine is the Earth, at about 300 K. Each time a visible photon of energy 4×10^{-19} J is absorbed by a plant, the entropy loss of the Sun is $4 \times 10^{-19}/6000 = 6.7 \times 10^{-23}$ J K^{-1}. However, if the plant gives all of that heat energy to the Earth at 300 K, its entropy gain is $4 \times 10^{-19}/300 = 1.3 \times 10^{-21}$ J K^{-1}. So the net change in entropy of the solar system is $1.3 \times 10^{-21} - 6.7 \times 10^{-223} = +1.3 \times 10^{-21}$ J K^{-1}. Of course, the plant has to extract some energy from the photons to stick the carbon dioxide and water molecules together to make the glucose molecule, but enough heat energy must be re-radiated at the lower temperature to ensure a net increase in total entropy of the Universe.

Living organisms exploit the fact that the Second Law of Thermodynamics only requires that the *total* entropy of an isolated system must increase as it moves towards equilibrium. Our solar system is a long way from equilibrium. Most of its particles are in a relatively ordered state, clumped together in the Sun or planets, so the entropy of particle arrangement is far smaller than it could be. Similarly, it is also far from being in thermal equilibrium, with heat energy pouring out from its centre at a vast rate. Living things exploit the continual increase of entropy of their surroundings to create small pockets of decreasing entropy, building orderly arrangements of large molecules out of the increasing chaos which surrounds them.

Ultimately, of course, the Universe will achieve thermal equilibrium (maximum entropy) and life will cease.

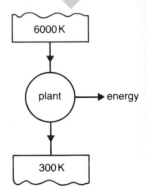

Figure 31.24 A plant cell as a heat engine

OBJECTIVES

After studying this section you should be able to do the following.

Calculate the number of ways that N particles can be arranged among v cells.

Know that small-scale random motion of molecules can result in large-scale one-way motion of a gas.

Know that the entropy of a gas can be changed by changing its internal energy or its volume.

Explain how living organisms appear to defy the Second Law of Thermodynamics.

QUESTIONS

1 For this question you will need a die and six small squares of paper numbered from 1 to 6. Draw a line down the centre of a large sheet of paper and place all six squares on the left-hand side of the line. The paper represents a box and each square represents a molecule in that box.

a Throw the die 25 times. At each throw, pick up the square whose number matches that of the die and move it to the other side of the paper. At the end of each throw, record the number of squares on the left-hand side of the sheet of paper. Plot a graph to show how the number of squares on the left hand side changes with time.

b Calculate the probability of finding all six squares on the left-hand side of the sheet.

c Repeat part (a) with a coin and only two squares of paper.

d Comment on the difference between your answers to parts (a) and (c).

2 The entropy of one mole of butane at 298 K and 101 kPA is 310.1 J K^{-1}. Butane liquefies at 272.5 K. One mole of butane gas is placed in a cylinder and piston similar to the one shown in figure 31.23 and cooled at 101 kPa from 298 K to 272.5 K.

a Calculate the change of volume of one mole of butane as it is cooled. Assume that it behaves like an ideal gas.

b Use $\Delta S = Nk\ln[1 + \Delta V/V]$ to calculate the entropy change of the butane due to the change of volume when it is cooled.

c C_p is 97.4 J mol^{-1} K^{-1} for butane gas. Estimate the entropy change of the butane due to the heat energy extracted from it.

d Estimate the entropy of the butane gas at the end of the cooling process.

e The molar latent heat of vaporisation of butane is 2.40×10^4 J mol^{-1}. If the butane spontaneously turns to a liquid, how much entropy is delivered to the cylinder in the process?

f What is the entropy of liquid butane at its boiling point?

3 The spreading of a gas so that it evenly fills the whole of its container is an example of a one-way process which can be explained with the help of entropy. Another one-way process is the tendency of moving objects to come to a halt because of friction. Explain this one-way process in terms of entropy and the Second Law of Thermodynamics. (Think about the energy conversion brought about by friction.)

Emitters

Once you have a thermopile or bolometer which has been calibrated so that it can be used to measure the intensity of heat radiation (W m^{-2}), you can start to study the characteristics of emitters of heat radiation. Figure 32.10(a) shows how you could explore the variation of intensity with distance from a small emitter. The output of the detector is measured for a number of different distances from the compact white-hot filament of a projector bulb. A suitable straight-line graph (figure 32.10(b)) should convince you that, like all electromagnetic radiation from a point source, heat radiation obeys an inverse square law.

Stefan's Law

Thermopiles and bolometers are not wavelength specific. They absorb all radiation incident on them regardless of whether it is ultraviolet, visible or infra-red. Their output is therefore a measure of the *total* heat radiation they absorb, unlike photodiodes which only respond to a limited range of frequencies. The thermopile of figure 32.10(a) can be used to find out how the total rate of heat radiation from an object depends on its temperature T. A filament lamp acts as the source of radiation. The resistance of the tungsten filament is very nearly proportional to its temperature (figure 32.11), so readings of the p.d. across the lamp and the current in it are taken. It is found that the thermopile reading rises very rapidly as the temperature of the filament is increased. In fact it can be proved that the rate of heat radiation from a black body at temperature T is given by **Stefan's Law**.

$$P = \sigma A T^4$$

P is the rate of heat radiation from a black body (W)

σ is the Stefan-Boltzmann constant (5.67×10^{-8} W m^{-2} K^{-4})

A is the surface area of the black body (m^2)

T is the temperature of the black body (K)

Exactly what a black body is in this context will be explained shortly. In the meantime, as an example of Stefan's Law in action, let's estimate how much current would be needed in a copper wire of length 5 cm and diameter 0.5 mm to make it glow red hot (about 1000 K). The rate of heat radiation can be calculated easily, remembering that the surface of the wire is a cylinder.

Special semiconductor materials have been developed whose resistance varies dramatically with temperature. When incorporated into bolometers they can make very sensitive detectors of chopped infra-red radiation. For example, they are widely used in burglar alarm systems for detecting the infra-red radiation emitted by intruders. Semiconductor diode detectors of infra-red radiation tend to be wavelength dependent. The response of a **photodiode** is shown in figure 32.7: compare this with the response of a thermopile or bolometer which is wavelength independent. This is because photodiodes exploit the photoelectric effect. There is a lower limit to the frequency of a photon which will set an electron free and allow it to drift through the crystal lattice. (Absorption of the wavelengths above 1 μm is responsible for the other limit to the photodiode's response.) Television cameras which use infra-red photoconducting surfaces are extensively used for night vision (figure 32.8) and for showing where heat radiation is escaping from buildings or people (figure 32.9).

Figure 32.7 Current in a photodiode as a function of wavelength

Figure 32.8 A night scene recorded by a camera sensitive to infra-red radiation

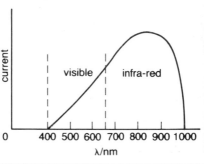

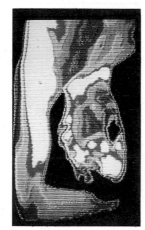

Figure 32.9 Thermograph of a person, showing the hot and cold places

$$P = \sigma A T^4$$

$$\therefore P = 5.67 \times 10^{-8} \times 5.00 \times 10^{-2} \times 2\pi \times 0.25 \times 10^{-3} \times (1000)^4$$

$$\therefore P \simeq 4.5 \text{ W}$$

If this is the only mechanism of heat loss, then it should be equal to $I^2 R$. The resistivity of copper at this temperature is about 7×10^{-8} Ω m.

$$R = \frac{\rho l}{A}$$

$$\therefore R = \frac{7 \times 10^{-8} \times 5 \times 10^{-2}}{\pi \times (0.25 \times 10^{-3})^2} \simeq 0.018 \text{ Ω}$$

$$P = I^2 R$$

$$\therefore 4.5 = I^2 \times 0.018$$

$$\therefore I \simeq 16 \text{ A}$$

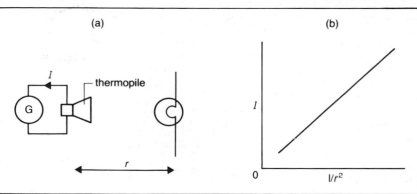

(a)

I

thermopile

G

C

r

(b)

I

0

1/r²

Figure 32.10 Using a thermopile to verify that heat radiation from a bulb is inversely proportional to the square of its distance

Emissivity

It is a peculiar fact of heat radiation that the best absorbers are also the best emitters. The following thought experiment should help you to understand why this is so. Consider the empty cavity shown in figure 32.12(a). Let's suppose that the walls are perfectly absorbing, i.e. do not reflect any of the heat radiation incident on them. The cavity is then a **black body** and obeys Stefan's Law, pumping out heat radiation at a rate of σAT^4. The heat radiation inside the cavity is in thermal equilibrium with the walls, so the rate of emission at the walls must be *exactly* the same as the rate of absorption, i.e. σAT^4.

Now let's place an object inside the cavity, as shown in figure 32.12b. Its surface (of area A') only absorbs a fraction ϵ of the radiation incident on it. So the rate of heat absorption is $\epsilon\sigma A'T^4$. If the object is in thermal equilibrium with the cavity walls, then the rate of heat emission must be equal to the rate of heat absorption. So the rate of heat emission must also be $\epsilon\sigma A'T^4$. The quantity ϵ is known as the **emissivity** of the surface: it is 1 for a perfectly black surface and 0 for a perfectly shiny one.

$P = \epsilon\sigma AT^4$

P is the rate of heat absorption by the object (W)

ϵ is the emissivity of the object's surface

σ is the Stefan-Boltzmann constant $(5.67\times10^{-8}\,\text{W m}^{-2}\,\text{K}^{-4})$

A is the surface area of the object (m²)

T is the temperature of the surroundings (K)

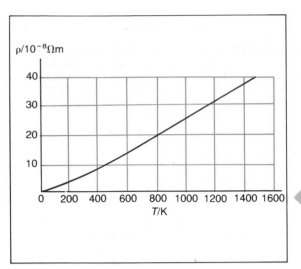

Figure 32.11 Resistivity of tungsten at various temperatures

Figure 32.12 An empty cavity contains black body radiation

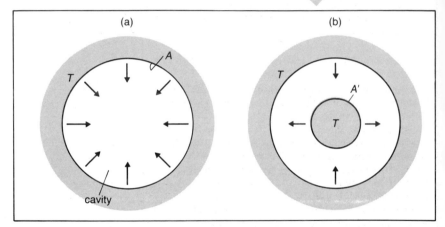

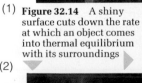

LOSING HEAT

The surface of an object is a crucial factor in fixing how long it takes to come into thermal equilibrium with its surroundings. Suppose that a hot sphere with surface area A and temperature T_h is placed in a cold enclosure whose temperature is T_c. The rate at which the sphere absorbs heat energy P_{in} depends on its emissivity ϵ.

$P_{in} = \epsilon\sigma AT_c^4$ (1)

The rate at which heat energy is lost by the sphere P_{out} is given by a similar expression.

$P_{out} = \epsilon\sigma AT_h^4$ (2)

So the total rate of heat loss of the sphere is given by

$P_{out} - P_{in} = \epsilon\sigma A(T_h^4 - T_c^4)$ (3)

The sphere will cool down most rapidly if its emissivity is 1, maximising the rate at which it exchanges heat energy with its surroundings. However, if its emissivity is small (it is shiny) then it will take a long time to come into thermal equilibrium with the walls. This piece of physics has been exploited for centuries in the design of stoves and kettles (figure 32.13). Stoves are blackened so that they lose their heat rapidly to their surroundings. On the other hand, kettles retain their heat and their contents stay above room temperature for a long time. Figure 32.14 illustrates a number of other applications of shiny surfaces for controlling heat flows. In each case, the surface's job is to slow down the rate at which it comes into thermal equilibrium with its surroundings.

Figure 32.13 A coal- or wood-burning stove radiates much more heat if it has a blackened surface

Figure 32.14 A shiny surface cuts down the rate at which an object comes into thermal equilibrium with its surroundings

WIEN'S LAW

A thermopile and grating spectrometer can be used to explore the spectrum of radiation emitted by a hot object. If the spectrometer is like the one shown in figure 32.1 there are no problems with absorption, particularly if it is evacuated. The results are shown in the graphs of figure 32.15. The area under the curves must be proportional to the total rate of emission of radiation $\epsilon\sigma T^4$, so at each wavelength the intensity of radiation increases rapidly with temperature. The wavelength at which the intensity peaks is given by Wien's Law (pronounced 'veens').

$$\lambda_m T = 2.9\times10^{-3}$$

λ_m is the maximum intensity wavelength (m)

T is the temperature of the emitter (K)

Bearing in mind that visible light has a wavelength of about 0.5 μm, it should be clear from figure 32.15 that an object has to be above 2000 K before an appreciable fraction of its heat radiation lies in the visible range. Wien's Law is very useful for estimating the temperature of very hot objects. For example, the intensity of radiation from the Sun depends on its wavelength: it peaks at 500 nm, in the yellow region of the spectrum. We can use this to calculate the surface temperature of the Sun. (Its interior is much hotter, about 10^8 K.)

$$\lambda_m T = 2.9\times10^{-3} \quad \therefore T = \frac{2.9\times10^{-3}}{500\times10^{-9}} = 5800 \text{ K}$$

The colour of a star can therefore be used to estimate its surface temperature. A star which appears redder than the Sun must have a lower surface temperature. Similarly, stars which have a higher surface temperature than the Sun have a bluish appearance.

Wien's Law can be better appreciated if you think of the electromagnetic radiation inside a cavity, such as the one of figure 32.2. Each standing wave possible in the cavity represents a site at which the system can store energy. (The photons involved with a standing wave of frequency f will have an energy of hf.) So there will be a dynamic equilibrium between thermal energy of the atoms in the cavity walls and heat radiation in the cavity. The Boltzmann formula $\exp[-hf/kT]$ allows us to calculate the probability that a photon of frequency f will be created in the cavity at temperature T. Once hf much larger than kT, the chances of finding radiation come very small. So it is reasonable the photons in the cavity will be proportio of the ow that Wien's Law says that you are most likely to extract p gy $5kT$ from a hole in the side of the cavity.

$$\lambda_m T = 2.9\times10^{-3}, \quad c = f\lambda \quad \therefore f_m = \frac{cT}{2.9\times10^{-3}k}$$

$$E = hf \quad \therefore hf_m = \frac{hc}{2.9\times10^{-3}k} \times kT$$

$$\therefore hf_m \simeq 5kT$$

Figure 32.15 Spectrum of radiation from black bodies at various temperatures

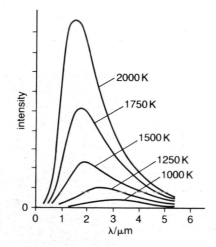

Solar energy

You are now going to find out how the physics of heat radiation can be used to predict the equilibrium temperature of a planet. In particular, we shall be looking at the various factors which are going to result in an overall warming of the Earth's surface in your lifetime. The data of table 32.1 will be used in the calculations which follow.

Table 32.1

radius of the Sun	7.0×10^8 m
radius of the Earth	6.4×10^6 m
Earth–Sun distance	1.5×10^{11} m

The Sun is a black body because the gas at its surface will absorb any radiation incident on it. The temperature of that surface is 5800 K, so we can use Stefan's Law to calculate the total power output of the Sun.

$$P = \sigma A T^4$$

$$\therefore P = 5.67\times10^{-8} \times 4\pi \times (7.0\times10^8)^2 \times (5800)^4$$

$$\therefore P = 4.0\times10^{26} \text{ W}$$

Only some of this energy is going to be intercepted by a planet. If you look at figure 32.16, it should be obvious that a planet of radius r at a distance R from the Sun will absorb the heat radiation which passes through an area πr^2 on the surface of a sphere of radius R.

$$P_{in} = P \times \frac{\pi r^2}{4\pi R^2} \qquad \therefore P_{in} = \frac{Pr^2}{4R^2} \qquad \textbf{(32.1)}$$

The photograph of figure 32.17 is convincing proof that the Earth does not absorb all of the Sun's radiation. So the emissivity ϵ must be less than 1. In fact, it is about 0.65 with most of the reflected heat radiation being bounced off the top of the clouds.

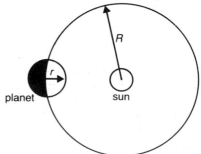

Figure 32.16 A planet intercepts radiation from the Sun over an area of πr^2

Figure 32.17 The Earth. Since this photograph was taken in reflected light the Earth cannot be a black body

THE BIG BANG

In 1965 two radio engineers (Arno Penzias and Robert Wilson) accidentally discovered a radio whisper from outer space which many astronomers believe is the black body radiation left over from the **Big Bang**. The radio waves have an intensity peak at a wavelength of 2 mm, corresponding to a temperature of only 3 K, and arrive at the Earth with the same intensity of about 5 μW m^{-2} from all directions. The Big Bang is the event which heralded the creation of the Universe, a collossal explosion of matter and energy at the start of time. There is a lot of evidence from the red shift of galaxies that they are all rushing apart from each other, i.e. space is expanding. Extrapolating back in time, all the visible matter in the Universe would have been concentrated at one point about 1.5$\times10^{10}$ years ago. When the Universe was created in the Big Bang it was extremely hot, but as it expanded it cooled down. (This is similar to the expansion of a gas. As it expands, its temperature drops.) Initially, a wide variety of mass–energy transformations were possible, including the conversion of protons into neutrons. The minimum temperature needed for a proton gas to create neutrons by random exchange of energy is about 10^{11} K, with black body radiation of wavelength 10^{-14} m — but about 1 s after the start of the Universe it was sufficiently cool for stable helium nuclei to form, leaving about one neutron for every ten protons. You can think of the black body radiation of the Universe as being standing waves inside an ever-increasing cavity, continually being Doppler shifted to longer and longer wavelengths. The Universe now has a diameter of about 10^{27} m and its temperature has dropped to a mere 3 K.

$$P_{in} = \frac{\epsilon P r^2}{4R^2}$$

$$\therefore P_{in} = \epsilon \times \frac{4.0\times10^{26} \times (6.4\times10^6)^2}{4 \times (1.5\times10^{11})^2}$$

$$\therefore P_{in} = \epsilon \times 1.8\times10^{17} \text{ W}$$

This is equivalent to a power of about 1 kW m^{-2} at the equator. The Earth will radiate heat out into space over its whole surface. If we assume a uniform surface temperature T, then Stefan's Law can be used to calculate the rate of heat loss P_{out}.

Figure 32.18

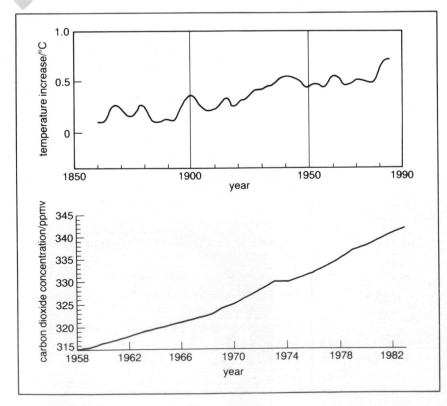

$$P = \epsilon\sigma A T^4$$

$$\therefore P_{out} = \epsilon \times 5.67\times10^{-8} \times 4\pi \times (6.4\times10^6)^2 \times T^4$$

$$\therefore P_{out} = \epsilon \times 2.9\times10^7 \times T^4$$

When thermal equilibrium has been reached, $P_{in} = P_{out}$. So we can predict the value of T at which this will happen.

$$P_{in} = \epsilon \times 1.8\times10^{17} = P_{out} = \epsilon \times 2.9\times10^7 \times T^4$$

$$\therefore T = 280 \text{ K}$$

Given the crudity of our model, the final answer is surprisingly close to the measured value of about 290 K (17°C).

Greenhouse effect

You will have noticed that our estimate for the average temperature of the surface of the Earth does not require a value for its emissivity. However, it does assume that the emissivity is the same for all wavelengths involved in the heat radiation process. This is not true. Apart from reflection by clouds, our atmosphere is almost transparent to radiation in the visible and near infra-red part of the spectrum. However, carbon dioxide and water molecules in the atmosphere strongly absorb the long wavelength infra-red radiation typical of a black body at 300 K ($\lambda \simeq 50$ μm). So heat energy radiated from the Earth's surface is partially absorbed by the atmosphere and re-radiated. This **thermal shield** cuts down the total rate of heat radiation from the Earth, raising its temperature.

This **greenhouse effect** is responsible for the slow rise in temperature of the Earth over the past century as the use of fossil fuels (such as coal and oil) has increased the proportion of carbon dioxide in the atmosphere (figure 32.18). Before life evolved on Earth, it is believed that carbon dioxide was a large fraction of its atmosphere and that today's low concentration of 0.3% is a result of biological activity. Nearly all of the original atmospheric carbon has been locked into the Earth's crust as fossil fuels or carbonaceous rocks (such as chalk and limestone). The effect of a carbon dioxide atmosphere on planetary temperatures is quite drastic. Table 32.2 gives some data for Venus, some of it gleaned from interplanetary probes which have landed on its surface.

Table 32.2

radius	6.1$\times10^6$ m
distance from Sun	1.1$\times10^{11}$ m
surface temperature	750 K

If we ignore the atmosphere, the surface temperature of Venus is predicted to be 325 K (convince yourself). In fact, this is roughly the temperature of the *top* of the atmosphere which is very cloudy. The surface of the planet, under its blanket of carbon dioxide which absorbs and re-radiates long wavelength radiation, is at a very much higher temperature. Conditions were never this extreme on Earth as life could not have evolved without the presence of liquid water. However, when life first appeared in the oceans, the average temperature of the Earth was probably higher than it is today because of the large amount of carbon dioxide in its atmosphere.

Energy conversion

Not all of the heat radiation incident on the Earth from the Sun is re-radiated into space. A small fraction of it is converted into chemical energy by the living organisms which cover its surface. We can estimate that fraction by considering a tree, such as the one shown in figure 32.19. It absorbs light energy and converts it into chemical energy in its trunk, roots and branches. Wood has an energy density of about 10^{10} J m^{-3} (this is energy of combustion). The tree takes about 25 years to grow to full size, producing a trunk of height 20 m and radius 0.25 cm, so the energy stored in it is about 5×10^{10} J. The rate of delivery of heat energy by sunlight is about 1 kW m^{-2}. The leaf canopy is approximately hemispherical with a radius of about 5 m. Leaves are green so they do not absorb all of the sunlight incident on them. If we assume that only 25% of the energy is absorbed, the tree takes in about 10^9 J in a single day or 5×10^{12} J in 25 years. Quite clearly, the tree is only about 1% efficient at converting solar energy into something more useful. Nevertheless, if you assume that half of the Earth's surface (land and sea) can support life, a 1% efficiency means that at least 6×10^{14} J of energy is extracted from sunlight by living organisms in each second.

The current annual fuel consumption of the world is about 3×10^{20} J, doubling every 20 years. This corresponds to a power of 3×10^{13} W. Most of this comes from fossil fuels, compact sources of solar energy laid down in the Earth's crust millions of years ago. To generate the same amount of energy from plants alone would require 5% of the Earth's surface. Of course, fuels like oil are particularly convenient for transport — generating such fuels from plants is possible (sugar cane is fermented to make alcohol for cars in South America) but not at 100% efficiency. Furthermore, the average person needs about 10^7 J of energy via food each day. With a current world population of 5×10^9 people, we need 6×10^{11} J of energy from food every second. (Many people don't get this much.) If we assume a 1% conversion efficiency of plant energy (sometimes called **biomass**) to useful food, perhaps via animals, our food requirements need another 5% of the Earth's surface.

The current global energy balance for the human race is approximately summarised in table 32.3. Remember that no account is made in the table of the other living organisms who share the planet with us.

Table 32.3

total sunlight	10^{17} W
fuel consumption	10^{14} W
food requirements	10^{13} W

There seems to be quite a large surplus of energy, but that is necessary to keep the Earth at a habitable temperature. Once we start to convert a large fraction of the Sun's heat radiation into chemical energy on a long-term basis, then the Earth's temperature will start to fall. Furthermore, the efficiency with which solar energy is converted to more useful forms like food and fuel is usually very low, under 1%. Quite clearly, reliance on photosynthesis alone cannot realistically meet our fuel needs. Of course, we have to rely on photosynthesis for our food energy because plants and animals are the only things which we can digest. Fossil fuels, on the other hand, will not last for ever. This should be clear from table 32.4 which lists the known reserves of energy locked up as coal, oil and gas and the rate at which they are being used up at the moment.

Table 32.4

Fuel	Reserves/J	Annual consumption/J
coal	2×10^{23}	1×10^{20}
oil	5×10^{21}	1×10^{20}
gas	3×10^{21}	6×10^{19}

If you bear in mind that the rate of fuel consumption doubles every 20 years, all the oil will be used up in your lifetime. After that, coal could be converted into liquid fuel but eventually the human race is going to have to adopt a lifestyle which not only matches the limited rate at which solar energy is delivered to its planet, but ensures a stable atmospheric composition so that the average surface temperature remains constant.

OBJECTIVES

After studying this section you should be able to do the following.

Describe an experiment to demonstrate the existence of heat radiation.

Explain what a *black body* is.

Describe the construction of heat radiation detectors.

Use Stefan's Law to calculate the rate of emission of heat radiation from the surface of an object.

Understand the meaning of *emissivity*.

Use Stefan's Law to calculate the rate of absorption of heat radiation by an object.

Estimate the rate at which energy is delivered from a star to a planet.

Explain the greenhouse effect.

Discuss the energy requirements of the human race.

Figure 32.19 A solar energy storage system

QUESTIONS

1 A classic experiment which demonstrates that heat radiation obeys an inverse-square law is illustrated in figure 32.20(a). A thermopile is placed in front of a large tank of boiling water with a blackened flat surface. The aperture on the front of the thermopile limits the angular spread of the heat radiation which can be detected by the device. The graph of figure 32.20(b) shows how the thermopile reading changes as it is moved away from the tank.

a Why is the surface of the tank painted black?

b Suppose that the thermopile collects radiation from an area A of the tank when it is a distance R from it. What happens to A and the thermopile reading if the value of R is halved?

c Does the graph of figure 32.20 support your answer to part (b)? Can you explain any disagreement?

2 The total power output of the Sun is 4.0×10^{26} W. The planet Mercury is, on average, a distance of 5.8×10^{10} m from the centre of the Sun.

a Calculate the intensity of heat radiation arriving at the surface of Mercury. Quote your answer in $W\,m^{-2}$.

b Estimate the temperature of Mercury.

3 A satellite which enters the Earth's shadow is in danger of failing because its temperature drops too low for its electronics to work properly. Assume that a 500 kg satellite is made of steel with a specific heat capacity of $440\,J\,kg^{-1}\,K^{-1}$. It has a cylindrical shape, with height of 1.0 m and a radius of 0.50 m.

a The sides of the cylinder are covered in solar cells which absorb sunlight to generate electricity. Will the emissivity of the cells be 1 or 0? What about the shiny foil which covers the ends of the cylinder?

b If the satellite is at a temperature of 300 K, calculate the rate at which it emits heat radiation.

c Outer space has a temperature of 3 K. At any instant, half of the satellite is exposed to outer space; the other half sees the Earth radiating as a black body at 290 K. Calculate the rate at which the satellite absorbs heat radiation from its surroundings.

d Calculate the rate at which the temperature of the satellite drops when it enters the Earth's shadow.

e If the satellite's electronics stop working below a temperature of 250 K, estimate the maximum safe time that it can spend in the Earth's shadow.

4 A 60 W light bulb contains a thin filament of tungsten at a temperature of 3100 K. The filament is coiled around itself to fit into the bulb (it has an uncoiled length of about 50 cm) and has an emissivity of about 0.4.

a Calculate the effective surface area of the coiled filament. Assume that all of the electrical energy is converted into heat radiation.

b Use Wien's Law to calculate the most intense wavelength emitted by the bulb. In what region of the spectrum is it?

c The filament has a length of 50 cm and a radius of 2×10^{-5} m. If its density and specific heat capacity are $19\,350\,kg\,m^{-3}$ and $142\,J\,kg^{-1}\,K^{-1}$, respectively, estimate the time taken for the filament to cool to dull red (1000 K) when the electric current in it is switched off.

5 Figure 32.21 shows a solar powered car. This question will help you to estimate its maximum power output.

a The rate at which heat radiation arrives at the top of the Earth's atmosphere is $1.4\,kW\,m^{-2}$. If a quarter of this is absorbed by a cloudless atmosphere, what is the rate of delivery of solar energy at the Earth's surface on a good day?

b The car is covered with solar cells. Estimate the area which will intercept the sunlight during the day.

c A good silicon solar cell will deliver a current of 25 mA at a p.d. of 0.5 V for each cm^2 of area in bright sunlight. Calculate the energy conversion efficiency of a solar cell.

d Estimate the power available from the car's solar cells on a bright sunny day. Comment on your answer.

6 This question compares the conversion efficiency of plants with solar cells.

a A $1.0 \times 10^4\,m^2$ field of wheat in this country can produce 5.6×10^{10} J of useful food energy per year. If the average rate of arrival of heat radiation during the day is $500\,W\,m^{-2}$, what is the conversion efficiency of a field of wheat?

b A similar field is carpeted with solar cells which have a conversion efficiency of 10%. What is the *average* power output of the field?

c How large a field would you need to produce the same power as a medium-sized power station, i.e. 1 GW?

d Both methods of converting sunlight to useful energy have hidden energy costs which have to be paid. For example, the field has to be ploughed before the wheat can be grown. What are the hidden energy costs for the solar cell field?

Figure 32.20

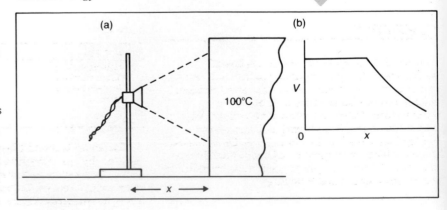

Figure 32.21

7 A student sets up a light bulb at the focal point of a concave mirror at one end of the lab. She places the bulb of a mercury thermometer at the focal point of another concave mirror at the other end of the lab. The two mirrors share the same axis.

a Explain why the temperature of the thermometer rises above room temperature when the bulb is switched on.

b What happens to the temperature rise if the thermometer bulb is coated with black paint?

c The student replaces the light bulb with a block of ice. Explain why the reading of the thermometer goes below room temperature.

Figure 32.22

8 Solar heating panels are sometimes used in the UK to provide domestic hot water from the Sun's heat radiation. An example is shown in figure 32.22. They can heat water from 10°C to 50°C.

a If the maximum rate of arrival of heat radiation is 1.0 kW m^{-2}, estimate the *average* rate of arrival over 24 hours in the UK.

b How should the panels be mounted on a house for maximum efficiency?

c Why is the back of the panel painted black? What is the purpose of the glass sheet on the front of the panel?

d Estimate the volume of hot water used by a typical family in 24 hours.

e If the panels have a conversion efficiency of 50% estimate the area needed to provide a family with all the hot water they need. ($C = 4200$ J kg^{-1} K^{-1} and $\rho = 1000$ kg m^{-3} for water.)

9 When the tungsten filament of a light bulb is very hot, most of its power output is in the form of heat radiation. So the electrical power input VI should equal $\epsilon\sigma AT^4$ if T is high enough. Furthermore, the resistance V/I can be used to measure the temperature T via the graph of figure 32.11. Table 32.5 lists some data for a light bulb. Use the numbers to draw a graph which will show you if the above reasoning gives a correct prediction.

Table 32.5

V/V	I/mA
0.02	3
0.05	9
0.10	16
1.00	51
2.00	69
5.00	122
8.00	150
10.00	169
12.00	190
14.00	212

CONDUCTION

After food, heat energy is your most basic requirement. Forty-one percent of the fuels used in this country have their energy converted into heat to keep our environment at a comfortable temperature. Table 32.6 shows the various ways in which the energy from fuels (coal, gas, oil or nuclear) was used in the UK in 1984. Quite clearly, there is plenty of scope for making more efficient use of our limited supply of fossil fuels by reducing the energy costs of space heating.

Table 32.6

Use of energy	Energy/J
domestic heating	1.45×10^{18}
workplace heating	1.05×10^{18}
public place heating	0.81×10^{18}
transport	1.29×10^{18}
industry	2.66×10^{18}
lighting, etc.	0.81×10^{18}

The Second Law of Thermodynamics is the reason why space heating is expensive in energy terms. As soon as the temperature of an object is raised above that of its surroundings, the total entropy can always be increased if some heat energy is transferred from the object to the rest of the world. So a continual input of energy is necessary to prevent the system from coming into thermal equilibrium. However, the power necessary to maintain a steady temperature difference between two objects depends on the rate at which they can exchange heat energy with each other. The objects need to be **insulated** from each other. This section will show you how to calculate the rate at which heat energy passes through solid objects and discusses some of the tricks which can be used to engineer efficient space heating systems.

Thermal conductivity

Here is an experiment which you have performed many times. Fill a china mug with a hot drink such as tea or coffee and use your hands to monitor the temperature rise of the outside of the mug. It should be obvious that after a while there is a steady flow of heat energy through the walls of the mug from the hot water to your cold hands. This situation is represented in figure 32.23. The arrows show the radial flow of heat energy at right angles to the mug walls. Let's consider the various factors which affect the rate at which heat energy flows through the walls of the mug.

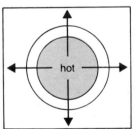

Figure 32.23 Radial heat flow through the walls of a coffee cup

Figure 32.24 The rate of heat flow through a slab is proportional to its area and the temperature gradient

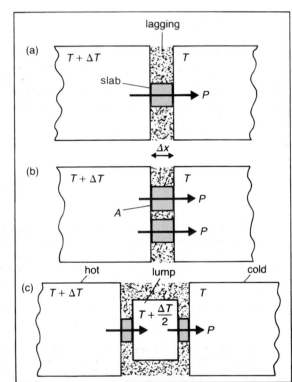

Area and temperature gradient

It will be more convenient to deal with a layout which has linear rather than circular symmetry as shown in figure 32.24(a). The hot object has temperature $T + \Delta T$, the cold one a temperature T. The heat energy flows at right angles to the slab which has a surface area A and thickness Δx. (The lagging is there to minimise heat energy loss from the edges of the slab.) Let the rate of heat energy flow through the slab be P. It should be intuitively obvious from figure 32.24(b) that two slabs between the hot and cold objects allows twice as much heat energy to flow between them.

$$P \propto A \qquad (32.2)$$

The second factor which decides the rate of heat flow is the **temperature gradient** $\Delta T/\Delta x$. Look at the thought experiment illustrated in figure 32.24(c). The slab has been split into two parts, each of thickness $\Delta x/2$. The lump in the middle will remain at a steady temperature of $T + \Delta T/2$ if the rate of heat flow through both parts of the slab is the same. It will then gain heat energy at the same rate as it is losing it. Providing that the lump has no other way of gaining or losing heat energy, then the total heat energy flow from the hot object to the cold object must be the same as in figure 32.24(a). So if the thickness of a slab is halved, the rate of heat flow remains unchanged provided that the temperature change is also halved.

$$P \propto \frac{\Delta T}{\Delta x} \qquad (32.3)$$

We can incorporate equations (32.2) and (32.3) to form an equation which can be used to predict the rate of heat flow between the two faces of an object.

$$P = -kA\frac{\Delta T}{\Delta x}$$

P is the rate of heat flow along a bar (W)

k is the thermal conductivity of the bar (W m^{-1} K^{-1})

A is the cross-sectional area of the bar (m^2)

$\Delta T/\Delta x$ is the temperature gradient along the bar (K m^{-1})

(The minus sign shows that the heat flow is in the direction of decreasing temperature. It is often omitted.) The value of the **thermal conductivity** k depends on the material of which the bar is made. Values for a number of different materials are listed in table 32.7.

Table 32.7

Material	k/W m^{-1} K^{-1}
copper	400
aluminium	200
steel	60
concrete	1.5
glass	1.1
brick	0.7
wood	0.15
paper	0.06

As an example of the use of the thermal conductivity formula, let's use table 32.7 to estimate the rate at which heat energy flows through the concrete foundations of a typical house in the winter (figure 32.25). The interior of the house will be a comfortable 18°C, but the ground underneath might well be at 5°C. Let the floor area be 40 m^2 and the foundation's thickness 25 cm.

$$P = kA\frac{\Delta T}{\Delta x}$$

$$\therefore P = 1.5 \times 40 \times \left(\frac{18 - 5}{0.25}\right) \approx 3 \text{ kW}.$$

In practice, the rate of heat flow is much less than this. Carpets on the floors make a lot of difference. You will be shown how to take account of this later on when you meet the concept of thermal resistance.

Conductors

You may have noticed from table 32.7 that all of the materials with high values of k are metals. This means that the heat flow rates through them tend to be fairly high, even for modest temperature gradients. This can be demonstrated with the apparatus (affectionately known as **Searle's bar**) shown in figure 32.26(a). The solid cylinder of the metal under test is held between a **heat source** (the electric heater) and a **heat sink** (the copper coils carrying cooling water). The thick **lagging** (cotton wool) around the bar forces most of the heat energy to travel along its length, eventually giving rise to a temperature gradient which can be detected by the thermocouples. (Their small size does not interfere with the flow of heat energy in the bar.) The graph of figure 32.26(b) shows that, when everything has settled down, there is a uniform temperature gradient down the length of the bar. The rate of heat flow down the bar can be calculated from the temperature rise of the cooling water and its flow rate. Table 32.8 gives typical results for the experiment with a bar made of brass.

Table 32.8

hot thermocouple temperature	85 °C
cold thermocouple temperature	24 °C
thermocouple separation	98 mm
cold cooling water	12.0 °C
hot cooling water	15.7 °C
cooling water flow rate	290 g min^{-1}
c (water)	4200 J kg^{-1} K^{-1}
diameter of bar	39 mm

The thermal conductivity of the rod can be worked out as follows. Start off by calculating the rate of heat flow from the cooling water data. Consider the heat given to the water in 1 minute.

$$\Delta Q = mc\Delta T$$

$$\therefore \Delta Q = 0.29 \times 4200 \times (15.7 - 12.0)$$

$$\therefore \Delta Q = 4.51 \text{ kJ}$$

The rate of flow of heat down the bar can now be calculated, assuming that it only loses heat to the cooling water.

$$P = \frac{E}{t}$$

$$\therefore P = \frac{4.51 \times 10^3}{60} = 75.1 \text{ W}$$

Finally, we can use the thermal conductivity formula to find k.

$$P = kA \frac{\Delta T}{\Delta x}$$

$$\therefore 75.1 = k \times \pi \times \left(\frac{39 \times 10^{-3}}{2}\right)^2 \times \left(\frac{85 - 24}{98 \times 10^{-3}}\right)$$

$$\therefore k = 101 \text{ W m}^{-1} \text{ K}^{-1}$$

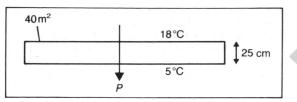

Figure 32.25 Heat flow through a building's foundations

Figure 32.26 Searle's bar

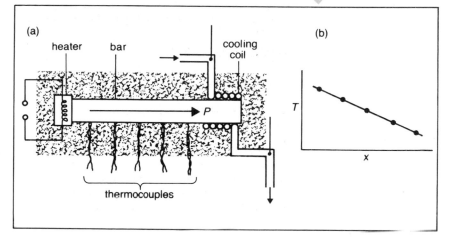

SURFACE EFFECTS

Although metals are excellent conductors of heat, their performance can be severely curtailed by **surface effects** caused by the poor conductors surrounding them. For example, consider a domestic central heating pipe, as shown in figure 32.27. It has a diameter of 16 mm, with walls that are 1 mm thick. If it carries water at 40°C through a room at 20°C, how much heat energy will escape from it per metre of its length? Since the heat flow is going to be radial, we can flatten out the pipe (figure 32.27) and use the thermal conductivity formula.

$$P = kA \frac{\Delta T}{\Delta x} \quad \therefore P = 400 \times (1 \times 2\pi \times 8 \times 10^{-3}) \times \frac{(40 - 20)}{1 \times 10^{-3}}$$

$$\therefore P = 402 \text{ kW}$$

This is obviously an unrealistic answer. If it were true, you would not need radiators in a central heating system! In practice, the rate of heat flow through the pipe walls is restricted by the air outside it. Figure 32.28 shows the typical variation of air temperature on either side of a pane of window glass. Air is a very poor conductor of heat, so a relatively large temperature gradient is required to make heat flow through it at the same rate as it is transmitted through the glass. The same **surface effect** reduces the temperature gradient across the copper walls of the pipe, reducing the rate of heat flow to a mere 20 W.

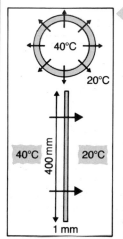

Figure 32.27 Calculating the heat flow through the walls of a central heating pipe

Figure 32.28 Air trapped near the surface of the glass reduces the heat flow through it

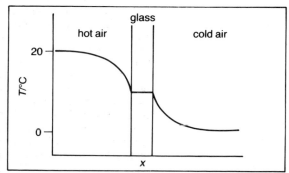

Mobile electrons

Metals are good conductors of heat energy because they contain mobile electrons. These electrons are free to travel throughout the volume of the metal, much as the molecules of a gas are free to move around inside their container. The average velocity of the mobile electrons is about 10^6 m s^{-1}. (Mobile electrons in a metal have to be modelled with quantum mechanics as particles in a box: this is why their average energy is *not kT*.) So the passage of heat energy through a metal is similar to its passage through gases. Heat energy injected at one end of the gas increases the kinetic energy of the molecules at that end. That energy gets transferred down the gas by collisions between its molecules, with each quantum doing a random walk through the container, passing from one molecule to another. If we suppose that, on average, a certain number of collisions are necessary for each quantum to make its way from the hot end of the gas to the cold end, then the rate of heat flow will increase as the average speed of the molecules is increased. We can take this idea over to the mobile electron gas in a metal. The high speed of those electrons ensures that energy injected at one end will quickly arrive at the other end.

Insulators

An **insulator** is a material which is not a good conductor of heat. In general, many commercial insulators exploit the low thermal conductivity of air (0.024 W m^{-1} K^{-1}) by trapping it in pockets so that it cannot be convected away. One of these is illustrated in figure 32.29. Measuring the thermal conductivity of an insulator is tricky because it is difficult to persuade a measurable amount of heat to flow through it. You need to apply a large temperature gradient over a large area, suggesting a disc-shaped sample. The following method, known as **Lee's disc**, can be used in a school laboratory.

The apparatus is shown in figure 32.30(a). Let's assume that you want to measure the thermal conductivity of cardboard. A disc of carboard is firmly sandwiched between a pair of polished brass discs. (Close thermal contact between the sample and the brass is important — smearing the surfaces with grease helps.) The top disc incorporates an electrical heater and the bottom disc can radiate heat to the surroundings. When the system has settled down and the thermometer readings are steady, the temperature gradient across the sample can be measured. (All of the bottom disc, a good conductor, will be at the same temperature.) The temperature of the bottom disc is also noted. The heat flow through the bottom disc has to be measured by a subsidiary experiment. It is heated to a temperature above the one it reached previously and then mounted so that it can radiate freely from all of its surfaces. Its temperature is measured at regular intervals and plotted on a graph similar to the one shown in figure 32.30(b). The rate of change of temperature $\Delta T/\Delta t$ at the brass disc's steady-state temperature can be combined with its mass m and specific heat capacity c to calculate the total rate at which the disc is radiating heat from its bottom surface only.

$$\Delta Q = mc\Delta T \quad \therefore P = \frac{mc}{2}\frac{\Delta T}{\Delta t} \qquad (32.4)$$

Figure 32.29 Insulating materials for reducing heat flow out of buildings

Figure 32.30 Lee's disc

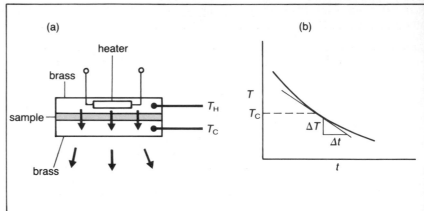

(a)

heater

brass

sample

T_H

T_C

brass

(b)

T

T_C

ΔT

Δt

t

LAGGING

It is common practice to wrap layers of insulating material around hot water systems to cut down the rate of heat loss. This is illustrated in figure 32.31. A copper hot water tank has been wrapped in a 5 cm thick jacket of cotton wool which has a thermal conductivity of 0.03 W m^{-1} K^{-1}. The tank has a surface area of 2.5 m^2 and holds water at 60°C in a house at 20°C. If the copper skin of the tank has a thickness of 2 mm, at what rate will it lose heat energy? The rate of heat flow will be the same in both the copper skin and the lagging. Let the temperature at the inside of the jacket be T. Consider the heat flow through the copper.

$$P = kA \frac{\Delta T}{\Delta x} \quad \therefore P = 400 \times 2.5 \times \frac{(60 - T)}{2 \times 10^{-3}}$$

$$\therefore P = 5 \times 10^5 \times (60 - T) \qquad (1)$$

Now consider the heat flow through the jacket.

$$P = kA \frac{\Delta T}{\Delta x} \quad \therefore P = 0.03 \times 2.5 \times \frac{(T - 20)}{5 \times 10^{-2}}$$

$$\therefore P = 1.5 \times (T - 20) \qquad (2)$$

Combining equations (1) and (2) to eliminate P we can find the value of T. It turns out to be almost 60°C, so that most of the temperature gradient is across the jacket, reducing the rate of heat loss to 60 W.

Figure 32.31 Lagging around a copper hot water tank

$\Delta Q = \Delta U + \Delta W$ (First Law of Thermodynamics). The work done by an expanding gas is $P\Delta V$: $C_P = C_v + R$ for ideal gases. The temperature of a gas does not change when it expands isothermally: for an ideal gas, $PV = nRT$. For adiabatic changes of an ideal gas, no heat energy is exchanged with its surroundings: $PV^\gamma = $ constant, $\gamma = C_P/C_v$.

Heat engines use the flow of heat energy from high temperatures to lower temperatures to do useful work. The total entropy of the engine and its surroundings must increase in the process, limiting the maximum efficiency to $(T_h - T_c)/T_h$. Heat pumps require the input of energy to make heat flow from a low temperature to a higher one: the maximum efficiency is given by $T_c/(T_h - T_c)$. It follows that heat pumps have an efficiency of zero at 0 K, making it impossible to cool objects below this temperature (Third Law of Thermodynamics).

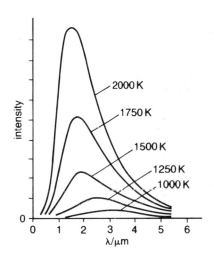

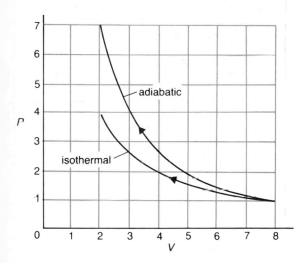

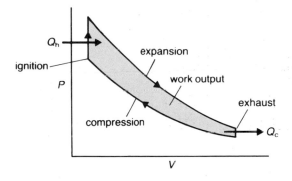

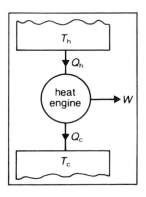

All objects above 0 K emit heat radiation in the form of EM waves, in the infra-red region of the spectrum at room temperature. The rate of emission is given by Stefan's Law; $P = \epsilon\sigma AT^4$. The rate of absorbtion from surroundings at temperature T' is given by $P = \epsilon\sigma AT'^4$. The emissivity ϵ of a surface is the fraction of the incident heat radiation which it absorbs: a black body has an emissivity of 1. The peak wavelength in the emission spectrum of a black body is given by Wien's Law: $\lambda T = 2.9\times10^{-3}$.

Heat energy flows through an object when there is a temperature gradient across it: $P = kA\Delta T/\Delta x$. The thermal resistance of an object is analogous to electrical resistance: $R_T = \Delta x/kA$, $P = \Delta T/R_T$. Thermal resistances can be calculated just like electrical ones for parallel and series connections. P is analogous to I and ΔT is analogous to V. Gases have low values for thermal conductivity because the quanta can only be exchanged between particles when they collide. Metals have high values for thermal conductivity because the quanta can be transported by the mobile electrons.

APPENDIX A
FORMULAE AND SYMBOLS

FORMULAE

The following list allows you to quickly check that you have correctly remembered a particular formula. Most of them are listed in the order in which they appear in the book, grouped together in blocks. Don't be tempted to use an unfamiliar formula to solve a problem before you have consulted the relevant chapter!

Forces

weight	$W = mg$
mass	$m = \rho V$
Hooke's Law	$F = kx$
stress	$\text{stress} = \dfrac{F}{A}$
strain	$\text{strain} = \dfrac{x}{l}$
Young's modulus	$\text{stress} = E \times \text{strain}$
ball-and-spring model	$k = Ed_0$

Momentum

momentum	$p = mv$
velocity	$v = \dfrac{\Delta x}{\Delta t}$
Newton's Second Law of Motion	$F = \dfrac{\Delta p}{\Delta t}$
	$F = ma$
acceleration	$a = \dfrac{\Delta v}{\Delta t}$
VUSAT formulae	$v = u + at$
	$s = ut + \tfrac{1}{2}at^2$
	$v^2 = u^2 + 2as$
fluid friction	$F \simeq \rho A v^2$
components	$p_x = p\cos\theta$
	$p_y = p\sin\theta$
	$p^2 = p_x{}^2 + p_y{}^2$
centripetal force	$F = \dfrac{mv^2}{r}$
angular velocity	$\omega = \dfrac{\Delta \theta}{\Delta t}$
contact friction	$F = \mu R$
couple	$\Gamma = Fd$
moment of inertia	$I = \Sigma mr^2$
angular momentum	$L = I\omega$
angular acceleration	$\Gamma = I\alpha$
	$\Gamma = \dfrac{\Delta L}{\Delta t}$
centre of mass	$MX = \Sigma mx$
moment	$M = Fd$

Energy

total energy	$E = mc^2$
work	$E = Fd$
power	$P = \dfrac{E}{t}$
	$P = Fv$
gravitational energy	$E_g = mgh$
kinetic energy	$E_k = \tfrac{1}{2}mv^2$
strain energy	$E_s = \tfrac{1}{2}kx^2$
rotational energy	$E_r = \tfrac{1}{2}I\omega^2$
potential energy	$F = -\dfrac{\Delta E_p}{\Delta x}$
efficiency	$\text{efficiency} = \dfrac{\text{work output}}{\text{work input}} \times 100$
thermal expansion	$\dfrac{\Delta l}{l} = \alpha \Delta T$
heat energy	$\Delta Q = mc\Delta T$
pressure	$P = \dfrac{F}{A}$
ideal gases	$P = \dfrac{\rho <c^2>}{3}$
	$m<c^2> = 3kT$
	$PV = NkT$
universal gas constant	$R = Lk$
diffusion	$d = n^{\frac{1}{3}}\lambda$
mean free path	$\lambda = \dfrac{V}{N\pi d_0{}^2}$
latent heat	$\Delta E = mL_f$
upthrust	$U = \rho Vg$
pressure	$P = \rho gh$
Bernoulli's theorem	$P + \tfrac{1}{2}\rho v^2 = \text{constant}$
Poiseuille's formula	$\dfrac{\Delta V}{\Delta t} = \dfrac{\pi r^4}{8\mu}\dfrac{\Delta P}{\Delta l}$

Electricity

current	$I = \dfrac{Q}{t}$
	$I = nAqv$
energy	$\Delta E = qV$
power	$P = VI$
	$P = I^2R$
resistance	$R = \dfrac{V}{I}$
	$R = \dfrac{\rho l}{A}$
series resistors	$R = R_1 + R_2$
parallel resistors	$\dfrac{1}{R} = \dfrac{1}{R_1} + \dfrac{1}{R_2}$
potential dividers	$V_{out} = \dfrac{V_{in} \times R_b}{R_t + R_b}$

Wheatstone's bridge	$\dfrac{R}{R_s} = \dfrac{R_1}{R_2}$
capacitance	$C = \dfrac{Q}{V}$
energy in capacitor	$E = \frac{1}{2}CV^2 = \frac{1}{2}Q^2/C = \frac{1}{2}QV$
capacitors in series	$\dfrac{1}{C} = \dfrac{1}{C_1} + \dfrac{1}{C_2}$
time constant	$\tau = RC$
charging current	$I = I_0\exp[-t/\tau]$
	$t = \tau\ln[I_0/I]$
halving-time	$t_{\frac{1}{2}} = 0.69\tau$

Oscillations

energy	$E = \frac{1}{2}kA^2$
period	$T = 2\pi(m/k)^{\frac{1}{2}}$
	$T = 2\pi(l/g)^{\frac{1}{2}}$
frequency	$f = \dfrac{1}{T}$
displacement	$x = A\cos(\omega t),\ \omega = (k/m)^{\frac{1}{2}}$
velocity	$v = -A\omega\sin(\omega t)$
acceleration	$a = -\omega^2 x$
wave equation	$y(x,t) = A\cos(\omega t - Kx),$
	$\omega = 2\pi f,\ K = 2\pi/\lambda$
wave speed	$c = f\lambda$
	$c = (T/\mu)^{\frac{1}{2}}$
	$c = (E/\rho)^{\frac{1}{2}}$
	$c = (\gamma P/\rho)^{\frac{1}{2}}$
Doppler shift, moving source	$\dfrac{\Delta f}{f} = \dfrac{v}{c}$
Doppler shift, moving reflector	$\dfrac{\Delta f}{f} = \dfrac{2v}{c}$
constructive interference	$\Delta r = n\lambda$
standing waves in strings	$\dfrac{n\lambda}{2} = l$

Field and potential

electric field strength	$F = qE$
potential gradient	$E = -\dfrac{\Delta V}{\Delta r}$
parallel plate capacitor	$E = \dfrac{V}{d}$
	$C = \epsilon_0\dfrac{A}{d}$
uniform sheet of charge	$E = \dfrac{\sigma}{2\epsilon_0}$
Stoke's Law	$F = 6\pi\mu rv$
field outside point charge or sphere	$E = \dfrac{Q}{4\pi\epsilon_0 r^2}$
potential outside point charge or sphere	$V = \dfrac{Q}{4\pi\epsilon_0 r}$
	$V = \dfrac{Q}{4\pi\epsilon_0 r}$
capacitance of a sphere	$C = 4\pi\epsilon_0 r$
Coulomb's Law	$F = \dfrac{q_1 q_2}{4\pi\epsilon_0 r^2}$
gravitational field strength	$F = mg$
Kepler's Third Law	$\dfrac{r^3}{T^2} = \dfrac{GM}{4\pi^2}$
field outside point mass or sphere	$g = -\dfrac{GM}{r^2}$
potential outside point mass or sphere	$V_g = -\dfrac{GM}{r}$

Radioactivity

range	$\rho R \simeq$ constant
transmission of gamma rays	$I = I_0\exp[-d/\delta]$
parent atoms	$N = N_0\exp[-\lambda t]$
activity	$A = \lambda N$
half-life	$\lambda T_{\frac{1}{2}} = \ln[2]$
nuclear charge	$Q = Ze$
nuclear mass	$m \simeq Am_p$
nuclear radius	$r \simeq A^{1/3} \times 1.2\times10^{-15}$
Einstein's mass−energy formula	$\Delta E = \Delta mc^2$

Electromagnetism

force on a current	$F = BIl\sin\phi$
force on a charge	$F = Bqv$
Hall voltage	$V = \dfrac{BI}{nqt}$
field around a straight wire	$B = \dfrac{\mu_0 I}{2\pi r}$
field at centre of a solenoid	$B = \mu_0 NI$
magnetic moment	$M = IA$
couple on a coil	$\Gamma = BM\sin\phi$
p.d. across a bar	$V = Blv$
flux	$\Phi = BA\cos\theta$
	$n\Phi = LI$
p.d. across a coil	$V = n\dfrac{d\Phi}{dt}$
inductance	$V = L\dfrac{dI}{dt}$
energy in inductor	$E = \frac{1}{2}LI^2$
current in inductors	$I = I_0(1 - \exp[-t/\tau]),\ \tau = L/R$
transformer	$V_s = \dfrac{n_s}{n_p} \times V_p$
natural frequency of LC circuit	$f = 1/2\pi(LC)^{\frac{1}{2}}$
r.m.s. current	$I_{rms} = \dfrac{I_0}{\sqrt{2}}$
reactance	$X = \dfrac{V}{I}$
reactance of a capacitor	$X_C = \dfrac{1}{2\pi fC}$
reactance of an inductor	$X_L = 2\pi fL$
impedance	$Z = (R^2 + (X_L - X_C)^2)^{\frac{1}{2}}$

Waves in space

speed of electromagnetic waves	$c = (\mu_0\epsilon_0)^{-\frac{1}{2}}$
time dilation	$t = \dfrac{t_0}{(1 - v^2/c^2)^{\frac{1}{2}}}$
length contraction	$l = l_0(1 - v^2/c^2)^{\frac{1}{2}}$
mass increase	$m = \dfrac{m_0}{(1 - v^2/c^2)^{\frac{1}{2}}}$
magnifying power	$M = \dfrac{v}{u}$
lens formula	$\dfrac{1}{u} + \dfrac{1}{v} = \dfrac{1}{f}$
lens power	$P = \dfrac{1}{f}$
refractive index	$n = \dfrac{c}{v}$
Snell's Law	$n_i \sin i = n_r \sin r$
single slit diffraction	$\sin\theta = \dfrac{n\lambda}{b}$

resolution	$\theta = 1.2\dfrac{\lambda}{b}$
Young's slits	$n\lambda \simeq d\theta$
diffraction grating	$n\lambda = d\sin\theta$
Bragg Law	$n\lambda = 2d\sin\theta$
photoelectric effect	$E_k = hf - \phi$
photon energy	$E = hf$
de Broglie wavelength	$\lambda = \dfrac{h}{p}$
energy levels for boxed particles	$E = \dfrac{n^2h^2}{8ml^2}$

energy levels for SHM $\quad E = (n + \tfrac{1}{2})hf_0, \; 2\pi f_0 = (k/m)^{\frac{1}{2}}$

Thermodynamics

ways	$W = W_1W_2$
entropy	$S = k\ln[W]$
	$\Delta S = \dfrac{\Delta Q}{T}$
Boltzmann formula	$p(E) = A\exp[-E/kT]$
First Law of Thermodynamics	$\Delta Q = \Delta U + \Delta W$
work done by a gas	$\Delta W = P\Delta V$
molar heat capacity	$C_p = C_v + R$
equipartition	$<E> = \tfrac{1}{2}kT$
isothermal change	$PV = \text{constant}$
adiabatic change	$PV^\gamma = \text{constant}$
entropy change of a gas	$\Delta S = Nk\ln[1 + \Delta V/V]$
Stefan's Law	$P = \epsilon\sigma AT^4$
Wien's Law	$\lambda_m T = 2.9\times10^{-3}$
thermal conductivity	$P = -kA\dfrac{\Delta T}{\Delta x}$
thermal resistance	$R_t = \dfrac{\Delta T}{P}, \quad R_t = \dfrac{\Delta x}{kA}$

SYMBOLS

a	acceleration (m s^{-2})
A	cross-sectional area (m^2) activity (s^{-1})
b	slit width (m)
B	magnetic field strength (T)
c	speed of light (m s^{-1})
	speed of wave (m s^{-1})
	specific heat capacity (J kg^{-1} K^{-1})
C	capacitance (F)
	molar heat capacity (J mol^{-1} K^{-1})
C_p	heat capacity at constant pressure (J mol^{-1} K^{-1})
C_v	heat capacity at constant volume (J mol^{-1} K^{-1})
d	distance moved by a force (m)
	separation between plates of a capacitor (m)
	grating slit spacing (m)
	diffusion distance (m)
e	electron charge (C)
E	energy (J) total energy (J)
	work done (J)
	electric field strength (N C^{-1})
	Young's modulus (Pa)
E_g	gravitational energy (J)
E_k	kinetic energy (J)
E_p	potential energy (J)
E_r	rotational energy (J)
E_s	strain energy (J)
f	frequency (Hz)
F	force (N)
g	gravitational field strength (N kg^{-1})

G	gravitational constant (N m^2 kg^{-2})
h	Planck's constant (J s) height (m)
I	current (A)
	moment of inertia (kg m^{-2})
k	Boltzmann's constant (J K^{-1})
	force constant (N m^{-1})
	thermal conductivity (W m^{-1} K^{-1})
l	length (m)
L	Avogadro's number, inductance (H)
	angular momentum (kg m^2 s^{-1})
L_f	latent heat of fusion (J kg^{-1})
L_v	latent heat of vaporisation (J kg^{-1})
m	mass (kg)
M	moment (N m)
	mutual inductance (H)
	mass (kg)
n	any positive or negative integer
	number of moles turns of wire
N	number of particles
	turns of wire per metre
p	momentum (N s) probability
P	pressure (Pa) power (W)
q	charge (C)
Q	heat energy (J) charge (C)
r	distance (m) radius (m)
R	electrical resistance (Ω)
	radius (m)
	universal gas constant (J K^{-1} mol^{-1})
R_t	thermal resistance (K W^{-1})
s	displacement (m)
S	entropy (J K^{-1})
t	time (s) thickness (m)
T	period of oscillation (s)
u	initial velocity (m s^{-1})
U	internal energy (J) upthrust (N)
v	final velocity (m s^{-1})
V	volume (m^3) potential (J C^{-1})
	p.d (V)
W	weight (N) work done (J) ways
x_C	reactance (Ω)
x_L	reactance (Ω)
Z	impedance (Ω)
α (alpha)	expansivity (K^{-1})
	angle (rad)
	angular acceleration (rad s^{-2})
γ (gamma)	ratio of principal heat capacities
Γ (gamma)	couple (N m)
ϵ (epsilon)	emissivity
	permittivity
	quantum (J)
ϵ_0	permittivity of free space (F m^{-1})
θ (theta)	angle (rad)
λ (lamda)	wavelength (m)
	decay constant (s^{-1})
μ (mu)	viscosity (N s m^{-2})
	mass per unit length (kg m^{-1})
	relative permeability
μ_0	permeability of free space (T m A^{-1})
ρ (rho)	density (kg m^{-3})
	resistivity (Ω m)
σ (sigma)	Stefan's constant (W m^{-2} K^{-4})
	charge density (C m^{-2})
	electrical conductivity (Ω^{-1} m^{-1})
τ (tau)	time constant (s)
ϕ (phi)	angle (rad)
	work function (J)
Φ (phi)	magnetic flux (Wb)
ω (omega)	angular velocity (rad s^{-1})

APPENDIX B
MATHEMATICS

Maths is inseparable from physics. This is especially true at A-level — you cannot understand or apply physics to any useful extent without involving some mathematics along the way. Indeed, it is frequently claimed that physics is the hardest of the sciences because it is the one which relies so heavily on maths. However, don't be dismayed. Physics treats maths as a tool, as a set of procedures and rules which allow you to apply the basic ideas of physics to new situations. If you have followed a course in maths to GCSE level, you will have come across many of the basic procedures and rules already. This appendix shows you all of the mathematical techniques you will need on your A-level physics course. To help you, each branch of maths is introduced with an explanation of its usefulness to physicists. There is no attempt here to provide rigorous mathematical proofs: we are only interested in helping you to use maths as a means to an end, not as an end in itself.

ALGEBRA

Physics is partly concerned with seeking out the relationship between measurable quantities. For example, Hooke's Law states that the extension of an object is, within limits, proportional to the force applied to it. So when the force is doubled, the extension is also doubled. This can be succinctly and precisely stated with the following **algebraic formula**.

$$F = kx \tag{A.1}$$

The force and extension are represented by the **variables** F and x respectively. F and x can have any value; k is a **constant** whose value is fixed by the object. Equation (A.1) is a coded version of Hooke's Law, using symbols rather than words. Provided that you know the precise meaning of the symbols, the formula makes calculations easy. For example, suppose that you want to find the force which will extend the object by 5.0 mm. If the force constant of the object is $2.0\ \text{kN m}^{-1}$, the calculation goes as follows.

$$k = 2.0 \times 10^3\ \text{N m}^{-1} \qquad F = kx$$
$$x = 5.0 \times 10^{-3}\ \text{m}$$
$$\therefore F = 2.0 \times 10^3 \times 5.0 \times 10^{-3}$$
$$\therefore F = 10\ \text{N}$$

Notice how values for the variables have to be expressed in the standard units of newtons and metres *before* they are put into the formula. This ensures that the value of the unknown variable is also expressed in standard units.

The formula $F = kx$ is a shorthand way of saying 'to calculate the force F you have to multiply the force constant k by the extension x.' Some other aspects of the shorthand used in formulae are listed below. ($\equiv$ means 'equivalent to').

x multiplied by $y \equiv xy$ or yx

x divided by $y \equiv \dfrac{x}{y}$ or x/y

x added to $y \equiv x + y$

x subtracted from $y \equiv y - x$

x squared $\equiv x^2$

square root of $x \equiv x^{\frac{1}{2}}$ or $\sqrt{x}$

reciprocal of $x \equiv \dfrac{1}{x}$ or x^{-1}

Manipulation

Algebra comes into its own in physics when it is used to create new formulae. This can be done with the help of the rules listed below.

if $xy = xz$ then $y = z$

if $y = \dfrac{xz}{x}$ then $y = z$

if $y = zx$ then $\dfrac{y}{z} = x$

if $y = z + x$ then $y - x = z$

if $y = vx + vy$ then $y = v(x + y)$

if $y = (-x)(-z)$ then $y = xz$

if $y = (-x)z$ then $y = -xz$

These rules can be used to adapt standard formulae. For example, suppose that you wanted to calculate the force constant of an object from known values of the force and the extension. You might rearrange the formula as follows before plugging the numbers into it.

$$F = 100\ \text{N} \quad F = kx \quad \therefore \frac{F}{x} = k$$

$$x = 0.25\ \text{m} \qquad \therefore k = \frac{100}{0.25} = 400\ \text{N m}^{-1}$$

The rules really come into their own when you combine two formulae to make a new one. This process is called **elimination of variables**, and is much used in physics to make predictions. For example, you can eliminate v from the standard formulae $E = \frac{1}{2}mv^2$ and $p = mv$ to obtain the new formula $E = p^2/2m$. The starting point is to make v the **subject** of both formulae.

$$E = \tfrac{1}{2}mv^2 \qquad \therefore \frac{E}{\frac{1}{2}m} = v^2$$

$$\therefore \left(\frac{E}{\frac{1}{2}m}\right)^{\frac{1}{2}} = v \tag{A.2}$$

$$p = mv \qquad \therefore \frac{p}{m} = v \tag{A.3}$$

Now we combine equations (A.2) and (A.3) by setting them equal to each other.

$$\frac{p}{m} = v, \quad \left(\frac{E}{\frac{1}{2}m}\right)^{\frac{1}{2}} = v$$

$$\therefore \frac{p}{m} = \left(\frac{E}{\frac{1}{2}m}\right)^{\frac{1}{2}} \tag{A.4}$$

Finally, we shuffle the symbols of equation (A.4) to get the formula we are after.

$$\frac{p}{m} = \left(\frac{E}{\frac{1}{2}m}\right)^{\frac{1}{2}}$$

$$\therefore \frac{p^2}{m^2} = \frac{E}{\frac{1}{2}m}$$

$$\therefore \frac{\frac{1}{2}mp^2}{m^2} = E$$

$$\therefore \frac{\frac{1}{2}p^2}{m} = E$$

$$\therefore E = \frac{p^2}{2m} \tag{A.5}$$

An alternative technique for eliminating a variable is called **substitution**. It is used in the following example where t is being eliminated from $s = ut + \frac{1}{2}at^2$ and $v = u + at$ to make $v^2 - u^2 = 2as$. The first step makes t the subject of the simple formula.

$$v = u + at \quad \therefore v - u = at$$

$$\therefore \frac{v - u}{a} = t \tag{A.6}$$

Equation (A.6) is then substituted for t in the complicated formula

$$s = ut + \tfrac{1}{2}at^2$$

$$\therefore s = u\left(\frac{v - u}{a}\right) + \tfrac{1}{2}a\left(\frac{v - u}{a}\right)^2$$

$$\therefore s = \frac{uv}{a} - \frac{u^2}{a} + \frac{\frac{1}{2}a}{a^2}(v - u)(v - u)$$

$$\therefore s = \frac{uv}{a} - \frac{u^2}{a} + \frac{((v - u)v - (v - u)u)}{2a}$$

$$\therefore s = \frac{1}{a}\left(uv - u^2 + \left(\frac{v^2 - uv - uv + u^2}{2}\right)\right)$$

$$\therefore as = uv - u^2 + \tfrac{1}{2}v^2 - uv + \tfrac{1}{2}u^2$$

$$\therefore as = \tfrac{1}{2}v^2 - \tfrac{1}{2}u^2$$

$$\therefore 2as = v^2 - u^2 \tag{A.7}$$

Small changes

It is very useful to know how one variable in a formula will change when another variable is changed by a small amount. The following rule allows you to do this.

if $y = zx^n$ and $y + \Delta y = z(x + \Delta x)^n$, then

$$\frac{\Delta y}{y} \simeq \frac{n\Delta x}{x}$$

The approximately-equals sign $\simeq$ has been used because the rule is only exactly correct when the fractional change $\Delta y/y$ is very small. The following example should help you to grasp what small means in this context.

The kinetic energy of an object is given by the formula $E = \frac{1}{2}mv^2$. If the velocity v is increased by Δv, by how much does the energy E change?

$$E = \tfrac{1}{2}mv^2 \qquad \therefore \frac{\Delta E}{E} \simeq \frac{2\Delta v}{v}$$

$$\therefore \Delta E \simeq \frac{2E\Delta v}{v} \tag{A.8}$$

Of course, ΔE can be worked out exactly as follows.

$$E = \tfrac{1}{2}mv^2 \quad \therefore E + \Delta E = \tfrac{1}{2}m(v + \Delta v)^2$$

$$\therefore \Delta E = \tfrac{1}{2}m(v + \Delta v)^2 - E \tag{A.9}$$

Table A.1 compares the answers obtained from equations (A.8) and (A.9) for $E = 1$, $m = 2$ and $v = 1$. As you can see, provided that the value of Δv is at least a hundred times smaller than v, there is no significant difference between the answers for ΔE from the two equations.

Table A.1

Δv	$2E\Delta v/v$	$\frac{1}{2}m(v + \Delta v)^2 - E$
0.5	1.00	1.25
0.1	0.20	0.21
0.05	0.1000	0.1025
0.01	0.0200	0.0201
0.005	0.010000	0.010025
0.001	0.002000	0.002001

Binomial theorem

The following approximation is sometimes very useful.

if $y = (1 \pm x)^n$ then $y \simeq 1 \pm nx$ if $x \ll 1$

For example, suppose that you want to find the change in mass of an object when it gets to one-tenth of the speed of light. The formula for the mass m at speed v looks like this.

$$m = m_0(1 - v^2/c^2)^{-\frac{1}{2}}$$

$$\therefore m \simeq m_0(1 - (-\tfrac{1}{2})v^2/c^2)$$

$$\therefore m \simeq m_0 + \tfrac{1}{2}m_0v^2/c^2$$

$$\therefore m - m_0 \simeq 0.005m_0 \text{ for } v/c = 0.1$$

Errors

In general, the value of a variable often depends on the values of more than one other variable. The following rule shows how one variable changes when all of the others are changed by a small amount.

$$\text{if } y = x^n z^m \text{ then } \frac{\Delta y}{y} = \frac{n\Delta x}{x} + \frac{m\Delta z}{z}$$

This is very useful if you want to estimate the error of a quantity which has been calculated from a number of measured quantities. For example, suppose that you calculate the resistance of a length of copper wire from its resistivity, diameter and length. Table A.2 summarises the basic data. The values for the error of each piece of data come from the precision of the measuring instrument or the limited number of decimal places quoted in resistivity tables.

Table A.2

Variable	Symbol	Value	Error
length/mm	l	763	± 1
diameter/mm	d	0.24	± 0.02
resistivity/Ω m	ρ	1.56×10^{-8}	$\pm 0.01 \times 10^{-8}$

The resistance R is calculated with the help of the following formulae.

$$R = \frac{\rho l}{A}, \quad A = \pi r^2, \quad r = \frac{d}{2}$$

$$\therefore R = \frac{4\rho l}{\pi d^2} \qquad \textbf{(A.10)}$$

The fractional change of the resistance $\Delta R/R$ for small changes of the resistivity, diameter and length is therefore given by the following equation.

$$R = \frac{4\rho l}{\pi d^2}$$

$$\therefore \frac{\Delta R}{R} = \frac{\Delta \rho}{\rho} + \frac{\Delta l}{l} - \frac{2\Delta d}{d} \qquad \textbf{(A.11)}$$

The data in table A.2 can be used to calculate the maximum fractional changes of ρ, l and d caused by the measurement errors. These can then be inserted into equation (A.11) to find the maximum fractional change of the resistance. (The sign of the individual changes are chosen to maximise the total change.)

$$\frac{\Delta R}{R} = \frac{\Delta \rho}{\rho} + \frac{\Delta l}{l} - \frac{2\Delta d}{d}$$

$$\therefore \frac{\Delta R}{R} = \frac{0.01}{1.56} + \frac{1}{763} + \left(\frac{2 \times 0.02}{0.24}\right)$$

$$\therefore \frac{\Delta R}{R} = 0.006 + 0.001 + 0.167$$

$$\therefore \frac{\Delta R}{R} = 0.174 \qquad \textbf{(A.12)}$$

Quite clearly, the measurement of diameter is the dominant cause of error. Taking account of all sources of error we can conclude that $\Delta R \approx 0.17R$, i.e. that the percentage error could be up to 17%.

GEOMETRY

Table A.3 lists a number of useful formulae for the surface area A and the volume V of a number of simple shapes.

Table A.3

Shape	A	V
triangle, base b, height h	$\frac{1}{2}bh$	—
rectangle sides h, d	hd	—
circle, radius r	πr^2	—
cube, side l	$6l^2$	l^3
cylinder, height h, radius r	$2\pi rh + 2\pi r^2$	$\pi r^2 h$
sphere, radius r	$4\pi r^2$	$4\pi r^3/3$

Angles

Many of the important quantities in physics are vectors, having a direction as well as a size. So you have to account for the angle at which a quantity is pointing as well as its size. Furthermore, the formulae which model the behaviour of waves involve angles. So it is important that you know the way that angles are defined and the properties of functions such as sines, cosines and tangents.

Radians

In general, angles are measured in **radians** when they appear in the context of physics. Take a look at figure A.1. The size of the angle θ in radians between the two radii is defined by the following piece of algebra.

$$\theta = s/r$$

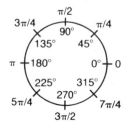

Figure A.1

s is part of the perimeter of the circle ($2\pi r$) so it is easy to convert radians into degrees. (Some values are depicted in figure A.2.) Angles are often used to say how far something has rotated. Positive angles correspond to an anti-clockwise rotation and negative angles correspond to a clockwise rotation.

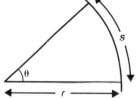

Figure A.2

The pair of circles in figure A.3 make this clear. It should be obvious that any positive angle can also be represented as a negative angle. For example, $+\pi/2 = -3\pi/2$.

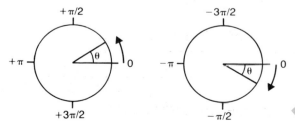

Figure A.3

Triangles

Figure A.4 shows a right-angled triangle. Pythagoras' Theorem links the three sides.

$$o^2 + a^2 = h^2$$

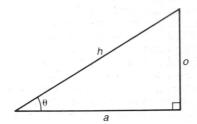

Figure A.4

Three important functions of angles are defined via a right-angled triangle. The sine, cosine and tangent functions are ratios of the opposite (o), adjacent (a) and hypotenuse (h).

$$\sin(\theta) = o/h$$
$$\cos(\theta) = a/h$$
$$\tan(\theta) = o/a$$

Table A.4 lists the values of these functions for a number of different values of θ between $\pi/2$ and 0. For angles outside the range $\pi/2$ and 0 the functions sine, cosine and tangent may be negative. The three circles in figure A.5 shows the sign of each function in the range 0 to 2π.

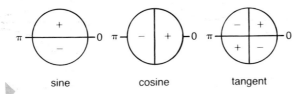

sine   cosine   tangent

Figure A.5

Table A.4

θ/rad	$\sin(\theta)$	$\cos(\theta)$	$\tan(\theta)$
0	0.00	1.00	0
$\pi/4$	0.71	0.71	1
$\pi/2$	1.00	0.00	∞

Angles in physics are measured in radians because of the approximate expressions for sine and cosine functions when the angles are small.

$$\tan(\theta) = \sin(\theta) \simeq \theta$$
$$\cos(\theta) \simeq 1 - \theta^2/2 \text{ if } \theta \text{ is small}$$

These approximations are immensely useful, especially the first one. You can judge for yourself exactly how good an approximation it is by looking at table A.5.

Table A.5

θ/rad	$\sin(\theta)$	$\tan(\theta)$
0.0500	0.0500	0.0500
0.1000	0.0998	0.1003
0.5000	0.4794	0.5463
1.0000	0.8415	1.5574

A number of useful identities involving sine and cosine functions are listed below.

$$\sin(-\theta) = -\sin(\theta)$$
$$\cos(-\theta) = +\cos(\theta)$$
$$\cos^2(\theta) + \sin^2(\theta) = 1$$
$$\cos(\theta + \phi) = \cos(\theta)\cos(\phi) - \sin(\theta)\sin(\phi)$$
$$\cos(\theta - \phi) = \cos(\theta)\cos(\phi) + \sin(\theta)\sin(\phi)$$
$$\cos(\theta) + \cos(\phi) = 2\cos\left(\frac{\theta + \phi}{2}\right)\cos\left(\frac{\theta - \phi}{2}\right)$$
$$\cos(\theta) - \cos(\phi) = -2\sin\left(\frac{\theta + \phi}{2}\right)\sin\left(\frac{\theta - \phi}{2}\right)$$

EXPONENTIALS AND LOGARITHMS

Some of the quantities handled by physics are so small or so large that they are very difficult to deal with. **Logarithms** and **exponentials** are useful techniques for handling very large and very small numbers. It is therefore common practice to present numbers in physics using **exponentials** of ten. For example, Avogadro's number is usually quoted as 6.02×10^{23} rather than 602 000 000 000 000 000 000 000. Similarly, it is not very convenient to write the charge on an electron as $-0.000\ 000\ 000\ 000\ 000\ 000\ 160$ C. -1.60×10^{-19} C is much neater.

The following rules are very useful when exponentials of ten are multiplied or divided by each other.

$$10^m \times 10^n = 10^{m+n}$$
$$10^m \div 10^n = 10^{m-n}$$

For example, suppose that you wanted to calculate how much charge there is in a mole of electrons. You would have to do the sum

$$-1.6 \times 10^{-19} \times 6.02 \times 10^{23}$$
$$= -1.6 \times 6.02 \times 10^{-19} \times 10^{23}$$
$$= -9.63 \times 10^{23-19}$$
$$= -9.63 \times 10^{4}$$

In practice, you would probably use an electronic calculator to do the whole sum for you, but it is important that you be able to make estimates of answers in your head.

Base e

Exponentials of the number 2.7182818 (known as e to mathematicians) are commonly used in physics. The reason for this lies in the following equation, which crops up in many places. It says that the fractional change $\Delta y/y$ of one variable is proportional to another variable t.

$$\frac{\Delta y}{y} = \alpha t \qquad \text{(A.13)}$$

The only formula for y which fits this equation is an exponential of e.

$$y = Ae^{\alpha t} \quad \text{or } y = A\exp[\alpha t] \qquad \text{(A.14)}$$

(A and α are constants.) A number of important properties of exponentials are listed below.

$$\exp[x]\exp[y] = \exp[x + y]$$

$$\frac{\exp[x]}{\exp[y]} = \exp[x - y]$$

$$\exp[x]^n = \exp[nx]$$

$$\frac{1}{\exp[x]} = \exp[-x]$$

$$\exp[x] \simeq 1 + x \text{ if } x \text{ is small}$$

Table A.6 lists some values of exp[x] for various important values of x. Check them with your calculator.

Table A.6

x	exp[x]
$-\infty$	0.00
-1	0.37
0	1.00
$+1$	2.72
$+\infty$	∞

Logarithms

The **natural logarithm** (ln) of a variable x is defined by the following procedure.

$$\text{if } x = \exp[y] \text{ then } y = \ln[x]$$

Logarithms are a useful way of compressing the range covered by a variable. This should be clear from table A.7; although x changes by a factor of 10 000, ln[x] only changes by about 10.

Table A.7

x	ln[x]
10^{-2}	-4.60
10^{-1}	-2.30
10^{0}	0.00
10^{+1}	$+2.30$
10^{+2}	$+4.60$

The important properties of logarithms are listed below.

$$\ln[xy] = \ln[x] + \ln[y]$$

$$\ln[x/y] = \ln[x] - \ln[y]$$

$$\ln[x^n] = n\ln[x]$$

$$\ln[\exp[x]] = x$$

GRAPHS

Graphical representations of algebraic functions are an essential part of the physicist's toolkit. Whereas formulae are precise statements which can be manipulated and combined according to fixed rules, they only come to life for many people when they are translated into a graph. Formulae tell you the value of one variable if you know the values of all the others: a graph, on the other hand, can instantly tell you how one variable changes when another one is changed. So it is important that you are able to recognise and sketch the graphs of the algebraic functions which commonly appear in physics. A number of them are drawn in figure A.6.

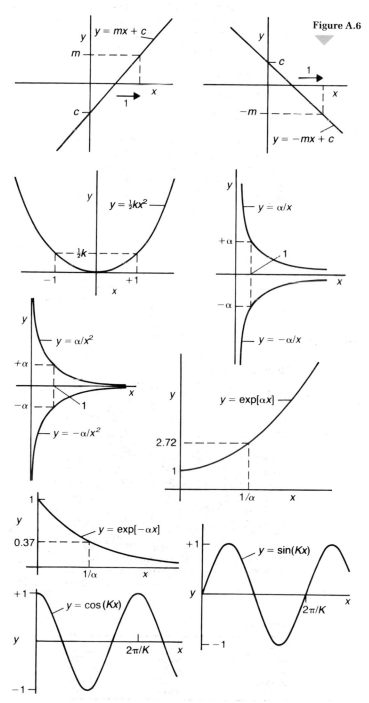

Figure A.6

DIFFERENTIALS

The **gradient** (or **slope**) of an algebraic function $f(t)$ is the rate at which it changes when the variable t is changed. If you look at figure A.7 you will see that if t is changed from t to $t + \Delta t$ then f changes from f to $f + \Delta f$. The gradient is defined as follows.

> gradient $= \Delta f/\Delta t$ if $\Delta t \simeq 0$

Since the value of the gradient depends on the value of t, it will only be well defined when the change of t is extremely small. The **differential** of a function df/dt is a formula for its slope when $\Delta t = 0$. Table A.8 lists the differentials of a number of common functions which appear in this book; α and n are constants.

Figure A.8 ▶

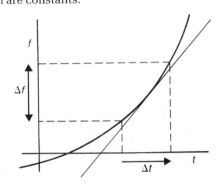

Figure A.7 ▶

Table A.8

Function	Differential
f	df/dt
α	1
αf	$\alpha df/dt$
t^n	nt^{n-1}
$1/t^n$	$-n/t^{n+1}$
$\cos(\alpha t)$	$-\alpha\sin(\alpha t)$
$\sin(\alpha t)$	$\alpha\cos(\alpha t)$
$\exp[\alpha t]$	$\alpha\exp[\alpha t]$

Figure A.9 ▶

INTEGRALS

Physics is very good at exact statements of the forces between very small particles. In order to work out what happens to a real object you often have to add together the forces on all of the particles in it. There is a whole branch of mathematics called **integration** devoted to generating formulae for this sort of summation. Before we introduce you to a table of useful integrals, it may help if you understand their relationship to summations and areas on graphs.

Summations

Suppose that you wish to add n quantities together, each of which has the value α. This can be formally expressed with a summation sign as follows.

$$\Sigma\alpha = n\alpha \qquad (A.15)$$

Here are another couple of useful summations. In the first case, the value of the variable n runs from 1 to n. In the second, n runs from 1 to ∞.

$$\Sigma n = \frac{n}{2}(n+1) \qquad (A.16)$$

$$\Sigma\alpha^{-n} = \alpha/(\alpha - 1), \quad \text{where } \alpha > 1 \qquad (A.17)$$

Areas

In physics, the area under the curve of a graph is often a useful quantity. For example, take a look at figure A.8. The area under the velocity–time $(v-t)$

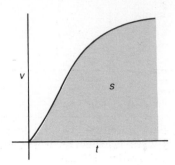

curve is the displacement s of the object. If the t-axis is chopped into small sections of length Δt (figure A.9), then the displacement can be approximately found by summing the areas of the individual rectangles of height v and width Δt:

$$s \simeq \Sigma v\Delta t \qquad (A.18)$$

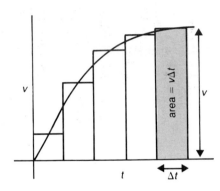

It should be obvious that the smaller the value of Δt, the more accurate the answer will be. In the limit that Δt becomes zero, the summation will return the true value of the displacement. Under these circumstances Δt is replaced with the symbol dt and the summation sign is replaced with an integration sign.

$$s = \int v\,dt \qquad (A.19)$$

If the curve on the graph can be represented by an algebraic function, then it is possible to find a formula for the area underneath it. That formula is known as an **integral.** Table A.9 lists the integrals used in this book; α, c and n are constants.

Table A.9

Function	Integral
f	$\int f\,dt$
αf	$\alpha\int f\,dt$
α	$\alpha t + c$
t^n	$\dfrac{t^{n+1}}{n+1} + c$
$1/t$	$\ln[t] + c$
$\sin(\alpha t)$	$-\dfrac{\cos(\alpha t)}{\alpha} + c$
$\cos(\alpha t)$	$\dfrac{\sin(\alpha t)}{\alpha} + c$
$\exp[\alpha t]$	$\dfrac{\exp[\alpha t]}{\alpha} + c$

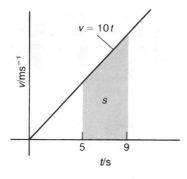

$$s = \int v\,dt \quad \therefore s = \int 10t\,dt$$
$$\therefore s = 10 \int t\,dt$$
$$\therefore s = 10\frac{t^2}{2} + c \qquad \qquad \textbf{(A.20)}$$

We know that $s = 0$ when $t = 5$ s. So we can find the value of the constant c and hence find the value of s at $t = 9$ s.

$$s = 5t^2 + c \qquad \therefore 0 = (5 \times 5^2) + c$$
$$\therefore c = -125 \text{ m}$$
$$s = 5t^2 - 125 \quad \therefore s = (5 \times 9^2) - 125$$
$$\therefore s = 280 \text{ m}$$

Figure A.10

Every integral in table A.9 can have an arbitrary constant c added to it. Its value can be determined by considering the value of t for which you know the area (or integral) will be zero.

For example, suppose that the object has a constant acceleration of 10 m s^{-2} so that $v = 10t$. We want to find the displacement of the object between $t = 5$ s and $t = 9$ s (figure A.10).

APPENDIX C
DIMENSIONS

This appendix lists the dimensions of important quantities. You should be able to use them to work out the dimensions of other quantities from their units. For example, suppose that you wanted to work out the dimensions of electrical resistivity ρ. From appendix A, the unit of resistivity is Ω m. From the table below, the dimensions of resistivity must therefore be $[M\,L^2\,T^{-3}\,A^{-2}] \times [L] = [M\,L^3\,T^{-3}\,A^{-2}]$.

mass	kg	[M]
length	m	[L]
time	s	[T]
current	A	[A]
force	N	$[M\,L\,T^{-2}]$
work, energy	J	$[M\,L^2\,T^{-2}]$
power	W	$[M\,L^2\,T^{-3}]$
pressure	Pa	$[M\,L^{-1}\,T^{-2}]$
frequency	Hz	$[T^{-1}]$
charge	C	$[A\,T]$
voltage	V	$[M\,L^2\,T^{-3}\,A^{-1}]$
resistance	Ω	$[M\,L^2\,T^{-3}\,A^{-2}]$
capacitance	F	$[M^{-1}\,L^{-2}\,T^4\,A^2]$
magnetic field	T	$[M\,T^{-2}\,A^{-1}]$
magnetic flux	Wb	$[M\,L^2\,T^{-2}\,A^{-1}]$
inductance	H	$[M\,L^2\,T^{-2}\,A^{-2}]$

APPENDIX D
CIRCUIT SYMBOLS

cell	LDR
battery	water contacts
low-voltage power supply	switch
separate connecting wires	photodiode
joined connecting wires	microphone
earth connection	filament lamp
resistor	motor
potentiometer	LED
variable resistor (rheostat)	buzzer
constant current source	galvanometer
thermistor	

Symbol	Name	Symbol	Name
	ammeter		NOR gate
	voltmeter		EOR gate
	capacitor		relay
	inductor		reed relay
	transformer		driver
	diode		power amplifier
	AND gate		operational amplifier
	OR gate		flip–flop
	NOT gate		binary counter
	NAND gate		seven segment display

Stacking solids (page 21)

2 (a) 1.6×10^{-4} m.
(b) No.
(c) Yes, assuming precision of ± 0.05 mm.

3 (a)

W/N	c/mm
0.00	0.00
1.25	0.10
2.50	0.15
3.75	0.25
5.00	0.30

(b) $\Delta c/\Delta W = 6.4\times10^{-5}$ m N^{-1}.
(c) $c = KW$, where $K = 6.4\times10^{-5}$ m N^{-1}.

4 (a) Ground floor holds up 39 floors
$\therefore c = 3.9\times10^{-3}$ m.
(b) 2.0×10^{-3} m.
(c) Using equation (2.5), total compression $= 7.8\times10^{-2}$ m.

5 (a) Assume change in length proportional to number of spring balances being supported.
Length $= 0.10 + (n\times0.01)$.
(b) Total length $= 14 + 13 + 12 + 11 + 10 = 60$ cm.

Mass, weight and density (page 26)

1 (a) No change.
(b) Decrease.
(c) Increase.
(d) Decrease.

2 (a)

Weight/N	pd/μV
0	0
177	10
353	19
530	27
706	35
883	43

(b) 590 N.
(c) Put each foot on the scales in turn and add all four readings together.

3 (a) $W = mg$, $m = \rho V$, $V = d^3 \therefore W = \rho g d^3$.
(b) $P = \rho g d$. (c) $d = 0.339$ m.
(e) $\rho = 6.80\times10^3$ kg m^{-3}.

4 (a) Effect of exercise, state of mind or health?
(b) Build two clocks and set them going at different times.

Hooke's Law (page 30)

1 (a)

F/N	x/mm	Elastic limit $\simeq 22$ N ± 1 N.
0.0	0.0	
9.8	1.6	
19.6	3.2	
29.4	4.6	
39.2	5.6	

(b) $k = 6.13\times10^3$ N m^{-1}. (c) 4.09×10^4 N m^{-1}.
(d) 18.3 mm.

2 (a) 1.0×10^4 N m^{-1}. (b) 70 kg.

3 (a) If $g = 10$ N kg^{-1} then $k = 1.25\times10^4$ N m^{-1}.
(b) $x = 0.20$ m. In practice the spring is kept partly compressed when the car is raised.

4 (a) $k = 400$ N m^{-1}.
(b) (i) $x = 2 + 1 = 3$ cm $\therefore k = 267$ N m^{-1}.
(ii) $x = 2/3 + 1 = 1.67$ cm $\therefore k = 479$ N m^{-1}.
(iii) $x = 2 + (2\times1) = 4$ cm $\therefore k = 200$ N m^{-1}.

5 How is a forcemeter really calibrated?

Stress and strain (page 34)

1 (a) 6.0×10^{-4}.
(b) $A = 1.26\times10^{-7}$ m^2 $\therefore$ stress $= 7.80\times10^7$ Pa.
(c) 1.3×10^{11} Pa.

2 (a) 1.72×10^5 Pa.
(b) Strain $= 1.72\times10^{-5}$ $\therefore x = 6.9\times10^{-6}$ m.

3 (a) 5.25×10^{-2} m^2, 5.00×10^{-2} m^2, 5.00×10^{-2} m^2.
(b) X-shaped section, least stress.
(c) Strain $= 9.5\times10^{-5}$ $\therefore x = 9.5\times10^{-4}$ m.

4 (a) $x = \alpha l\Delta T$.
(b) Strain $= x/l$ $\therefore$ stress $= Ex/l$ $\therefore F = ExA/l$.
(c) Stress $= E\alpha\Delta T$. (d) 1.3×10^8 Pa.
(e) $A \simeq 7\times10^{-3}$ m^2 $\therefore F \simeq 6\times10^5$ N.

5 Stress $= F/A$, $F = mg$, $m = \rho V$, $V = hA$
$\therefore$ stress $= \rho hg$.

Stress–strain curves (page 38)

1 (a)

Stress/Pa	Strain
2.41×10^8	1.94×10^{-4}
4.80×10^8	3.89×10^{-4}
7.24×10^8	5.83×10^{-4}
9.64×10^8	1.03×10^{-3}
1.20×10^9	1.81×10^{-3}
1.44×10^9	4.47×10^{-3}

(c) 1.2×10^{11} Pa. (d) Elastic limit $\simeq 3.3\times10^{-4}$.
(e) Stress of 1.3×10^8 Pa gives strain of $\simeq 2.5\times10^{-3}$. Strain decreases by 1.1×10^{-3} (Hooke's Law) when stress removed, leaving deformation of $\simeq 2.5$ mm.

3 A could be concrete, B steel and C nylon.

4 (a) 2.34×10^6 Pa.
(b) $W = mg$, $m = \rho V$, $V = l\pi r^2$ $\therefore W = \rho l\pi r^2 g$
$l' = 4l$, $r' = 4r$ $\therefore W' = 64W = 4.71\times10^4$ N.
(c) 9.37×10^6 Pa. (d) $r = 8$ cm; the bone is $8\times$thicker whereas the whole arm is only $4\times$thicker. There must be an upper limit to size of arm which can have any muscle at all.

5 (a) Length of outer surface $= 2\pi(R + r)$
$\therefore$ strain $= 2\pi r/2\pi R$.
(b) Assuming Hooke's Law, 1.1×10^{-3}.
(c) $r < 1.1\times10^{-4}$ m ($\simeq 0.1$ mm).
(d) Stranded cable is more flexible but more expensive to make.

Forces between atoms (page 45)

1 (a) $N = mL/A$, $m = \rho V$, $V = l^3$ $\therefore$ $N = \rho L l^3/A$.
   (b) $V = N d_0^3$, $V = l^3$ $\therefore$ $N = l^3/d_0^3 = \rho L l^3/A$
   $\therefore d_0 = (A/\rho L)^{1/3}$.
   (c) Assuming a simple cubic structure, calculated values of d_0 range from 2.28×10^{-10} m to 3.12×10^{-10} m.
2 (a) $d_0 = 2.6 \times 10^{-10}$ m
   (b) $k = 4.0$ N m^{-1} $\therefore$ $E = 1.5 \times 10^{10}$ Pa.
3

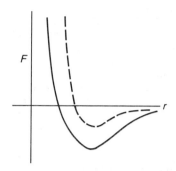

Refining the model (page 51)

2 Grinding would anneal but hammering work hardens.
3 If the teeth have been toughened by quenching, annealing must be avoided at all costs.
4 Think of stress concentration.
7 $Nl/N^{\frac{1}{2}}l = 6$ $\therefore$ $N = 36$.
8

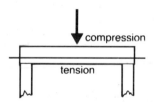

Momentum (page 62)

1 (a) 500 Ns. (b) 1000 Ns. (c) -500 Ns.
   (d) 15 s neglecting mass loss.
2 9.62 km s^{-1} in direction of satellite.
3 (a) $p = mv$, $v = \Delta x/\Delta t$ $\therefore$ $\Delta t = m\Delta x/p$.
4 Set the vehicle moving on an accurately horizontal track; use the photodiodes to measure its velocity at several points along the track.
5 (a) $-mv$. (b) $+mv$. (c) $+2mv$.
   (d) $p = -2mv = Mv'$.
   (e) $M = 50$ kg, $m = 0.5$ kg, $v = 5$ m s^{-1}; relative velocity $= 2 \times 5mv/M = 0.5$ m s^{-1}.
   (f) Movement back and forth but no change of position of centre of mass.
6 (a) True. (b) True. (c) False. (d) False. (e) False.
   (f) True.
7 She is right. However, it is always possible to find out where the momentum went if it appears to be lost by a system.

Force (page 69)

1 (a) $+0.35$ N s. (b) -0.28 N s. (c) $+0.63$ N s.
   (d) -3.15 N.
2 (a) 40 N.

(b)

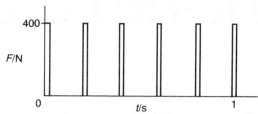

3 (a) 60 mph $= 27.8$ m s^{-1} $\therefore$ $p = 2.78 \times 10^4$ N s.
   (b) 2.78 kN.
4 (a) 2×10^{-3} m^3. (b) $V = \pi r^2 v$ $\therefore$ $v = 25.5$ m s^{-1}.
   (c) 4.07 m s^{-1}. (d) $0.5(25.5 - 4.07) = 10.7$ N s.
   (e) 42.9 N.
5 (a) $m = 2.94 \times 10^4/v$. (b) $V = 2.45 \times 10^4/v$.
   (c) 8.83 m s^{-1}.
6 (a) $v/2$. (b) $2d/v$. (c) $mv^2/2d$. (d)

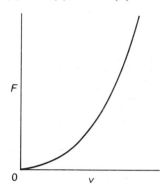

7 (a) 4.7×10^{-2} N s. (b) 0.235 m s^{-1}.

Forced motion (page 76)

1

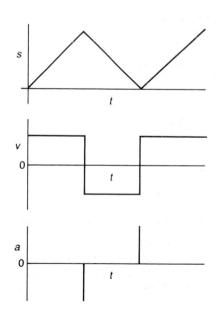

2 (a) 3.33 m s^{-2}. (b) 2.67 kN. (c) 93.8 m.
3 $a = -8.57$ m s^{-2} $\therefore$ $s = 15 + 52.5 = 67.5$ m.
4 (b) $g \approx 7.3$ m s^{-2}.
5 (a) 0.25 s. (b) 19.6 cm.
6

Angle	Range/km	Altitude/km
30°	7.95	1.15
45°	9.16	2.29
60°	7.95	3.44

7 (a) $s \simeq 0.20$ m $\therefore u \simeq 2$ m s^{-1}.
   (b) $m \simeq 75$ kg $\therefore \Delta p = 150$ N s.
   (c) $\simeq 1.25$ m.
8 Human = 57 m s^{-1}. Elephant ($r = 1.0$ m) = 100 m s^{-1}.
   Mouse ($r = 0.025$ m) = 17 m s^{-1}.
9 (a) $70 \times 9.81 = m \times 5$. (b) $m = \rho \times \pi r^2 v$.
10 (a) 6.0 kN. (b) 2.3 s.
11 (a) 4.43 m s^{-1}. (b) $4.43(0.707)^n$. (c) 0.500^n.
   (d) $0.90(0.707)^n$. (e)

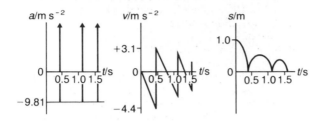

12 (a) 14.3 m s^{-2}. (b) 930 N. (c) 638 N. (d) 1568 N.
   (e) 930 N.
   (f) Mass drops as fuel is ejected from engines.

Momentum vectors (page 82)

1 (a) Satellite = 1.54×10^6 N s, meteorite = 1.00×10^5 N s.
   (b) 1.54×10^6 N s. (c) 6.49×10^{-2} rad.
   (d) 3.05 km s^{-1}.
2 0.65 N.
3 (a) 7.36×10^{-2} N s. (b) 5.89×10^{-3} rad. (c) 17.4 s.
4 (a) 6.53 kN. (b) 6.26 m s^{-1}. (c) 157 m.
5 (a) $\omega = 7.27 \times 10^{-5}$ rad s^{-1} $\therefore v = 3.05$ km s^{-1}.
   (b) 0.22 N kg^{-1}. (c) If $T = 30$ days then $g = 2.1 \times 10^{-3}$ N kg^{-1}.
6 (a) If $m = 70$ kg, $F = 2.37$ N. (b) Your weight.

Cancelling forces (page 88)

1 (a)

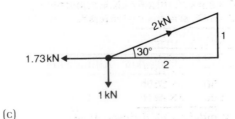

   (b) 1.5 kN. (c) 15 kN.
2 (b) $F = W \sin\theta$, $R = W \cos\theta$.
   (c) $F = 4.9$ N, $R = 8.5$ N, $\mu = 0.58$.
   (d) $W \sin\theta = \mu W \cos\theta \therefore \theta = 30°$.
3 (a) 1.63 kN.
   (c) $F = \mu R$, $R = mg$, $F = ma \therefore a = \mu g$.
4 (a) 1.41 kN. (b) 1 kN.

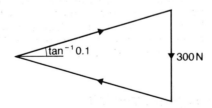

   (c)

(d) Eight.
5 (a) $T\cos\phi = W$, $T\sin\phi = F$.
   (b) 1.18×10^{-2} N.
6 (a) $ma = T\sin\phi$, $T\cos\phi = mg$.
   (b)

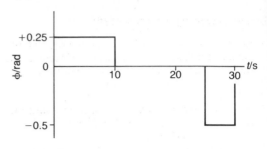

Twisting forces (page 98)

2 (b) Taking moments about connection to wall, $T = 2$ kN.
   (c) 2 kN, 30° to the horizontal into the wall.
3 (a) $90 \times 0.5 = 45 \times mg \therefore m = 0.102$ kg.
   (b) The last row is wrong, reading should be 1.2 N.
4 (a) $Tl\cos30 = 25(l/2)\sin30 \therefore T = 7.22$ kN, 14.4 kN.

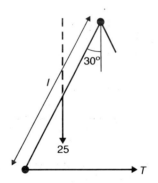

   (b) Less ($T \propto W\tan\theta$).
5

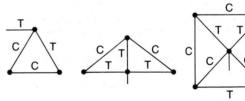

7 (a) Turntable 2.25×10^{-2} kg m^2, disc 4.5×10^{-5} kg m^2.
   (b) 0.252 rad s^{-1} anticlockwise.
9 (a) 1.49×10^{10} kg m^2 s^{-1}. (b) 1.46×10^{-4} rad s^{-1}.
   (c) $661 - 329 = 331$ m s^{-1} to the East.

Energy (page 109)

1 (a) 24.5 J. (b) 12.3 N. (c) 3.13 m s^{-1}. (d) 24.5 J.
2 (a) 1.00 J. (b) 100 N, 0 N, 50 N.
   (c) $a = 1000$ m s^{-2}, $v = 6.32$ m s^{-1}, $E = 1.00$ J.
4 (a) $\simeq 200$ kJ. (b) $\simeq 3$ kJ. (c) $\simeq 3$ J. (d) $\simeq 5$ J.
5 Find out how muscles work!
6 (a) mg, $h_f - h_i$. (b) The same.
7 (a) $\Delta p = m(v - u)$. (b) $F = m(v - u)/t$.
   (c) $(v + u)/2$.
   (d) $(v + u)t/2$. (e) $\frac{1}{2}m(v - u)(v + u) = \frac{1}{2}mv^2 - \frac{1}{2}mu^2$.

9 $a \simeq 3$ m s^{-2}, $m \simeq 1000$ kg $\therefore P \simeq 5$ kW.
10 (a) $E_k = 10$ J, $E_g = 6278$ J.
   (b) Length = 11.3 m $\therefore$ delivery time = 22.6 s
   $\therefore$ power per passenger = 278 W
   $\therefore$ total power = $80 \times 278 + 1200 = 23.4$ kW.

Energy conservation (page 118)

1 (a) $\frac{1}{2}mv^2 = mgh$. (b) 25% – heat energy in ball,
   surface and surrounding air. (c) Air resistance
   converts kinetic energy into heat energy.
2 $\simeq 28(1 \times 0.5 \times 10^{-2}) = 0.14$ J.
3 (d) mu^2.
4 (a) $d' = d$ to conserve energy and momentum.
   (b) $l^2 = d^2 + (l-h)^2 \therefore 2hl = d^2 + h^2 \simeq d^2$.
   (c) $d' \ll d$. (d) $d' \gg d$.
6 (a) For an incline of θ, $P = cAv^3 + mgv\sin\theta$; if P
   is fixed then v must decrease as θ is increased.
   (b) For a cube of side l and density ρ, $P = cl^2v^3$
   $+ \rho l^3 gv\sin\theta$. On the flat, $P \simeq cl^2v^3$. Up a steep
   slope $P \simeq \rho l^3 gv\sin\theta$ . . .
8 (a) 1.10×10^6 J. (b) 6.3×10^6 J. (c) 17.4%.
9 (a) $\simeq 22(0.5 \times 0.5 \times 10^{-3}) = 5.5$ mJ.
   (b)

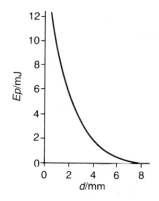

10 $E_k = 7.6 \times 10^{-15}$ J, $v = 1.29 \times 10^8$ m s^{-1} (too close
   to c for it to be relied on).

Heat energy (page 127)

1 (a) 0.04 mV K^{-1} $\therefore (0.64 + 0.80)/0.04 = 36°$C.
   (b) Assuming a linear relationship between
   voltage and temperature +8.48 mV at +232°C
   and − 9.20 mV at − 210°C.
   (c) Small heat capacity, robust, allows remote
   sensing.
2 (b) 420 K. (c) Pt resistance agrees best with gas
   thermometer.
3 (a) $P = E/t$, $E = Fd$, $v = d/t \therefore P = Fv$.
   (b) $p = 736$ W $\therefore \Delta Q = 6.62 \times 10^6$ J.
   (c) 5520 J kg^{-1} K^{-1}.
4 (a) $mc\Delta T = mgh \therefore h = 43$ m. (b) 0.08 K.
5 (a) 0.024 kg s^{-1}. (b) 2.92 hours.
6 (a) 81 W.
   (b) $m = 65$ kg, $\Delta Q = 7.8 \times 10^5$ J, $P = 2 \times 81 =$
   162 W $\therefore t = 1.4$ hours.
   (c) $m = 4^3 \times 65$ kg, $P = 162 \times 4^2 = 2.59$ kW.
   (d) $t = 5.3$ hours.
   (e) $m = 0.1^3 \times 65$ kg, $P = 162 \times 0.1^2$
   $\therefore t = 0.13$ hours.
7 (a) $E = Fd$, $d = 2\pi r \times 100$.
   $\therefore c = 416$ J kg^{-1} K^{-1}.
   (b) $\Delta T/\Delta t = -1.5 \times 10^{-3}$ K s^{-1},
   $c - 405$ J kg^{-1} K^{-1}.
8(d) $VI - V'I' = (m - m')c\Delta T$
   $\therefore c = 4182$ J kg^{-1} K^{-1}.

The Ideal Gas Equation (page 134)

1 (a) $m = 1.0 \times 10^{-15}$ kg, $<c^2>^{\frac{1}{2}} = 3.5 \times 10^{-3}$ m s^{-1}.
   (c) Slows down.
2 (a) $m = 5.6 \times 10^{18}$ kg $\therefore 1.2 \times 10^{44}$ particles.
   (b) $m = 6 \times 10^{-4}$ kg $\therefore 1.2 \times 10^{22}$ particles.
   (c) 1 in 10^{22} was in Caesar's lungs
   $\therefore$ 1 per lungful.
   (d) No.
3 (a) 1.09×10^{24}.
   (b) Each balloon needs 8.37×10^{23} molecules,
   1.89×10^{26} molecules available in cylinder
   $\therefore$ 226 balloons filled.
   (c) 626 K.
4 (a) $V = 1767$ m^3, $m = 1815$ kg
   $\therefore \rho = 1.03$ kg m^{-3}.
   (b) Bottom end is open, so air inside bottom of
   balloon must be at atmospheric pressure.
   (There will be a relatively small pressure
   gradient inside the balloon to keep it inflated.)
   (c) $PV = NkT \therefore \rho = mN/V = P/kT$
   $\therefore \rho \propto T^{-1}$, $T = 330$ K.
5 Bulb volume = 5.24×10^{-7} m^3, stem volume =
   4.08×10^{-7} m^3, $V \propto T$ at constant P
   $\therefore V = 2.34 \times 10^{-9}T \therefore \Delta T = \pm 1.3$ K,
   temperature range approximately 225 K to
   395 K. Would need recalibrating every time
   atmospheric pressure changed!
7

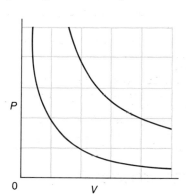

8 Each molecule in the gas gains momentum at a
   rate mg. If the total momentum of the gas does
   not change with time, each molecule must
   transfer downwards momentum of mg to the
   box in each second. $F = \Delta p/\Delta t$ . . .

Diffusion of gases (page 139)

1 (a) Vertical motion: $0 = v\sin\theta - \frac{1}{2}gt^2$, horizontal
   motion: $d = v\cos\theta$, θ small $\therefore v^2 = gd/2\theta$ . . .
   (b) 1.09×10^{-4} m, $\Delta s \simeq 5 \times 10^{-5}$ m (0.05 mm).
   (c) 2.5×10^{10}.
   (d) $\lambda = V/N\pi d_0^2 \therefore V/N = 8 \times 10^{-19}$ m^3,
   $P = 5 \times 10^{-3}$ Pa.
2 $m = 1.33 \times 10^{-25}$ kg $\therefore <c^2>^{\frac{1}{2}} \simeq 300$ m s^{-1}
   $\therefore n = 1.3 \times 10^5/\lambda$, $d = n^{\frac{1}{2}}\lambda \therefore \lambda = 7.9 \times 10^{-8}$ m,
   $V/N = 3.9 \times 10^{-26}$ m$^3 \therefore d_0 = 3.9 \times 10^{10}$ m.
3 (a) $d = n^{\frac{1}{2}}\lambda$, $n = ct/\lambda \therefore d = (ct\lambda)^{\frac{1}{2}}$.
   (b)

d/mm	t/s
0.5	5×10^{-3}
5	5×10^{-1}
50	$5 \times 10^{+1}$
500	$5 \times 10^{+3}$

   (c) $t \propto md_0^2 \therefore CO_2$ diffuses slower.

Atoms in liquids (page 143)

1 (a) Yes. (c) 19.5 kJ mol^{-1}.
(d) 0.110 kg mol^{-1} (cadmium).
2 (a) $\Delta T/\Delta t = 8.33\times10^{-2}$ K s^{-1} $\therefore P = 48.3$ W.
(b) 1.74×10^5 J kg^{-1}.
3 (b) $<c^2>^{\frac{1}{2}} \simeq 500$ m s^{-1}, $\lambda \simeq 5\times10^{-10}$ m
$\therefore n = 1\times10^{12}$.

(c)

t/s	d/mm
1	0.5
60	4
3600	30

Behaviour of fluids (page 149)

1 (a) 4.18 g. (b) Pressure inside is greater than
outside $\therefore$ balance reads more than 5.43 g.
(c) 12.5 mm.
2 Six mariners; legs in the water may allow the
seventh on the raft.
3 Both wrong if all the guests float as total
upthrust is unchanged. Bricks sink so upthrust
is decreased and level drops.
4 (a) 6.76 m.
(b) Assuming energy conservation
$m = 37.7$ kg, 30 s.
5 (a) 18.7 kPa.
(c) $\Delta\rho/\rho = -\Delta V/V$, $\Delta V/V = 1.81\times10^{-4}\Delta T$
$\therefore P = 133367(1 - 0.00018T')$ if T' in °C.
6 $\Delta P = \frac{1}{2}\rho v^2 \therefore v \simeq 8$ m s^{-1}.
7 (a) Power $\propto$ rate of combustion $\propto$ rate of air
supply $\propto$ pressure difference between chimney
and outside $\propto$ chimney height.
(b) Bernoulli's Theorem? Downwind.
9 (a) 2.35×10^3 Pa m^{-1}. (b) 1.00×10^{-3} N s m^{-2}.
(c) (i) 1.06 cm^3. (ii) 8.5 cm^3. (iii) 34 cm^3.
(iv) 11.4 cm^3.

Charge (page 164)

1 (a)

Metal	n/m^{-3}	A/m^2	v/m s^{-1}
copper	8.48×10^{28}	2.46×10^{-7}	5.99×10^{-5}
nickel	9.13×10^{28}	1.77×10^{-8}	7.74×10^{-4}
tin	3.70×10^{28}	2.09×10^{-6}	1.62×10^{-5}

(b) By analogy with fluid flow down pipes you
might expect that the wire with the fastest
moving electrons will convert the most
electrical energy into heat. In fact, you can't tell
from the information provided; suppose that
the nickel was cooled until it became a
superconductor!
2 (a) 3.2×10^3 C, 2.0×10^{22} electrons.
(b) $\simeq 3.3$ kJ.
3 (a) Conductors = roads, carriers = lorries,
output transducer = supermarket,
cell = warehouse.
(b) Charge = trailer, potential = cornflakes per
lorry, output power = rate of sale of cornflakes
at supermarket.
(c) Lorry counter.
(d) Switch acts like traffic lights. Road is
jammed full of lorries, so red traffic lights stop
them all. All lorries before supermarket are full
of cornflakes $\therefore$ can deliver as soon as lights
turn green.
4 (a) 10.4 A $\therefore$ 13 A fuse. (b) $I = 0.2$ A $\therefore$ 3 A fuse.
(c) $I = 4.2$ A $\therefore$ 5 A fuse.

5 (a) -2500 V. (b) 4.00×10^{-16} J. (c) Kinetic
energy $\rightarrow$ light and heat energy.
(d) 3.13×10^{16} s^{-1}, 12.5 W.
(e) $v = 2.96\times10^7$ m s^{-1} $\therefore F = 0.845$ μN.

Resistance (page 171)

1 (a) In series with 99.9 kΩ. (b) In parallel with
10.0 mΩ.
2 (a) $P = VI$, $R = V/I \therefore P = I^2R$.
(b) $l = 40$ m $\therefore R = 0.25$ Ω. (c) 113 W. (d) 98.5%.
3 (a) $P = VI$, $R = V/I \therefore P = V^2/R$.
(b) 7.07 V. (c) 4.00 Ω.
4 (a) $\Delta V = (V/l)\Delta x$, $\Delta x = <v>\tau$, $\Delta E = -q\Delta V \dots$
(c) Equate KE gained with lost electrical energy
(d) $R = 2ml/nA\tau q^2$, $R = \rho l/A \dots$
(e) $n = 8.48\times10^{28}$ m^{-3} $\therefore \tau = 5.38\times10^{-14}$ s.
5 (a) 1, 2.5 Ω. (b) 2, 1.5 V, 5 Ω. (c) 4, 15 Ω.
(d) 3, resistance increases with increasing
power.
6 (a)

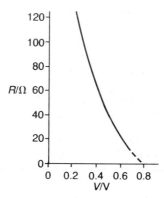

(b) When p.d. $\simeq 0.8$ V, current through diode is
effectively infinite. Maximum meter current
and power $\simeq 30$ mA, 23 mW.

Power circuits (page 180)

1 (a) 1.9 V, 670 Ω.
(b) Guess 1.9 V for a single LED. Gives $I =$
26 mA through 120 Ω resistor. Curve is so steep
at this current that p.d. hardly varies when
LEDs connected in parallel. So 2 LEDs = 13 mA
each ($\simeq 25$ mW), 7 LEDs $\simeq 4$ mA each ($\simeq 8$ mW).
2 (a) 2.8 Ω, 70 W. (b) 0.2 A. (c) 30 Ω, 6.5 W.
3 $I \simeq 0.42$ A $\therefore$ 12V, 5 W.
4 (a) $I = 44$ mA through both components, buzzer
= 4.2 V, bulb = 1.8 V.
(b) 6.0 V across both components, 100 mA in
both.
5 (a) 15 Ω. (b) 22.5 Ω.
(c).

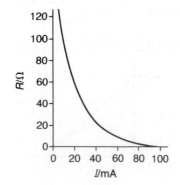

(d) ≈ 1.5 kΩ.

6 (a) 99 μA, 9.9 V. (b) 9.36×10^{-3} A, 10 mA fsd, resistance < 10 Ω to get most of 10 V across resistor.

7

	emf/V	ir/Ω	I/A	P/W
(i)	6.0	3.2	1.875	5.625
(ii)	3.0	0.8	3.75	5.625
(iii)	1.5	0.2	7.50	5.625

8 (i) 91.0 μA, 2.91 V $\therefore$ 32.0 kΩ.
   (ii) 62.5 μA, 3.00 V $\therefore$ 48.0 kΩ.

Sensor circuits (page 188)

1 (a) 6.0 V $\rightarrow$ 1.88 V. (b) 3.0 V $\rightarrow$ 0.0 V.
   (c) 1.5 V $\rightarrow$ 0.0 V.
2 Use the 100 kΩ voltmeter in the figure.

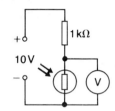

3 Meter resistance = 20 kΩ $\therefore$ resistor = 980 kΩ.
4 2.0 kΩ.
5 (a) p.d. across R_s = p.d. across R_2 ...
   (b) 70.5 Ω. (c) $R = \rho l/A$, if A is constant then $R \propto l$.
6 As R_t cools its resistance will decrease, raising the potential at Y. The potential at X remains unchanged. Use a motor car/bike to calibrate?

Charge storage (page 197)

1 (c) $Q \approx 1.2\times10^{-3}$ C, $V = 1.50$ V $\therefore$ $C \approx 800$ μF.
2 (a) $I = \Delta Q/\Delta t$, $\Delta t = 1/f$ ...
   (b) $Q = 1.46\times10^{-7}$ C, $C = 2.52\times10^{-8}$ F.
3 (a) 1.20×10^{-4} A. (b) 2.03 ms.

4

	C/μF	V/V	E/mJ
(i)	25	40	20
(ii)	100	20	20
(iii)	400	10	20

5 Chris is right. Charge on each capacitor is $\frac{1}{2}Q$ $\therefore$ final energy = $2\times((\frac{1}{2}Q)^2/2C) = Q^2/4C$. (Initial energy = $Q^2/2C$). If energy cannot be converted to heat via resistance it will be used to create a pulse of electromagnetic waves instead.
6 Remember that charge is conserved when the second switch is pressed.
7 (a) 41.3 J, energy density = 1.49×10^6 J m^{-3} (petrol is 3.36×10^{10} J m^{-3}).
   (b) $Q = CV \therefore \Delta Q = C\Delta V$, $I = \Delta Q/\Delta t$ ...
   (c) 1.24×10^4 s ($3\frac{1}{2}$ hours).

Time constants (page 204)

1 (a)

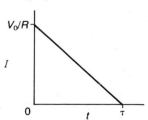

(b) $Q = \frac{1}{2} \times V_0/R \times \tau$, $C = Q/V$ ...
(c) $<I> = 3V_0/4R$, $\Delta Q = <I>t_{\frac{1}{2}}$ ...
2 (a) LT^{-1}, LT^{-2}, MLT^{-2}, $ML^{-1}T^{-2}$, ML^{-3}.
3 (a) $F = ma$, $a = \Delta v/\Delta t$, $F = T - Mg$ ...
   (b) 47 m s^{-1}.
   (c) $v = 378$ m s^{-1}, $s = 10.4$ km.
4 (a) 90 μA.

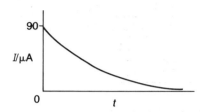

(b) $I_0 = 90$ μA, $I = 25$ μA $\therefore$ $C = 9.37\times10^{-4}$ F.

5

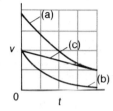

6 (a) +5 V (b) similar to figure in question 4(a).
   (c) $t = RC\ln[5/1.7] = 11.2$ s. (d) 3.08 V.
   (e)

7 (a) $I = 51.5$ μA, $I_0 = 152$ μA $\therefore$ $t = 16.8$ s.

Electronic systems (page 215)

1 (a) Resistance < 10 kΩ $\therefore$ > 1 W m^{-2}.
   (b) Bulb comes on and stays on.
   (c) Swap resistor and LDR around.
2 (a) Motor spins when thermistor gets hot.
   (b) Resistor gets hot when LDR is in the dark.
   (c) Bulb glows when the switch is not pressed.

Logic gates (page 221)

1

A	B	C	Q
0	0	1	1
0	1	1	1
1	0	0	0
1	1	0	1

D	E	F	R
0	0	1	0
0	1	1	1
1	0	0	0
1	1	0	0

G	H	I	J	K	S
0	0	1	1	1	0
0	1	1	0	1	0
1	0	0	1	1	0
1	1	0	0	0	1

2

C	S	I	U	D
0	0	1	0	0
0	1	1	0	1
1	0	0	0	0
1	1	0	1	0

When C is 1, signals at S appear at U. When C is 0 signals at S appear at D. The C input is used to direct streams of pulses coming into S out through either D or U.

3 (a)

C	B	A	L	S
0	0	0	1	0
0	0	1	1	0
0	1	0	1	0
0	1	1	1	1
1	0	0	1	1
1	0	1	0	1
1	1	0	0	1
1	1	1	0	1

(b) Press B and A or just C.
(c) LED glows, buzzer makes a noise.
4 The LEDs display the number of switches (0, 1 or 2) that are being pressed.
5 NOT, AND, OR.

Latches, counters and timers (page 231)

1 C is the barrier switch, D and E start, A or B stop.
2 (a) Rising.

(b)

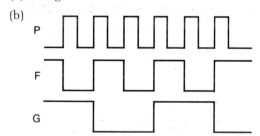

(c)

pulse	G	F
0	1	1
1	1	0
2	0	1
3	0	0
4	1	1
5	1	0
6	0	1

3

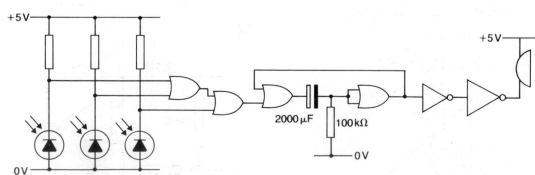

4

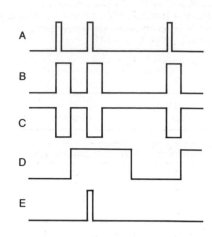

5 (a) P = D, Q = A.
  (b) P = E, Q = F.
  (c) P = C, Q = B.
6 (a) $\tau = 10$ s $\therefore t = 7$ s.
  (b)

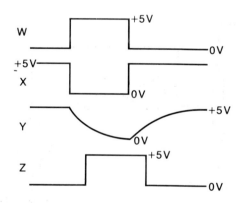

(c) $RC = 1.4$ s $\therefore 100$ μF, 14 kΩ.

Comparators (page 239)

1 (a) 2.94 V ∴ $R = 1.43$ kΩ, i.e. 55°C.
   (b) Buzzer initially off; comes on suddenly
   when temperature drops below 55°C.

2 (a) 2.00 V, 2.80 V, 3.46 V, 4.00 V.

(b)

Number	Minimum voltage/V
1	2.00
2	2.80
3	3.46
4	4.00

(c)

Number	Minimum power
1	4
2	8
3	12
4	16

(d) Faster, more robust, easier to read, draws
less current, much less precise, probably
cheaper to construct.

3 (a)

Output/V		V_D/V	
+4.0	+3.4	+4.0	+4.5
−4.0	0.0	−0.6	+0.5
	a	b	c

4 (a) +0.67 V. (b) just above +0.67 V.
   (c) −0.67 V.
   (d) Just below −0.67 V.

5

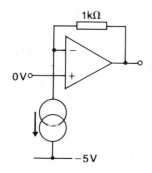

Amplifiers (page 247)

1 (i) −10, −2.5 V (ii) +5, −0.5 V (iii) −0.1, +0.5 V
   (iv) +4, +0.8 V (v) −50, +0.5 V
   (vi) +22.4, −2.24 V

2 (b) +1 → +101

3 (a) $I = 30$ nA ∴ $P = 9.00 \times 10^{-10}$ W.
   (b) $V = 1.39$ V ∴ $P = 9.71 \times 10^{-5}$ W.
   (c) 1.08×10^5, from the power supply.

4 (a)

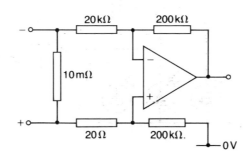

(b)

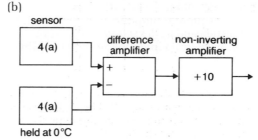

6 (a) $V_{out} = A(V_+ - V_-)$, $V_- = IR - 5$,
   $V_{out} \leqslant +4$ V, $A = 2 \times 10^5$.
   (c) $I = 5$ mA $= I_0 \exp[eV_{out}/kT]$
   ∴ V_{out}/T = constant.
   (d)

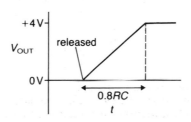

7 Use a difference amplifier with resistors ≃
   100 kΩ followed by an inverting amplifier of
   gain 500.

8 (i) 2 V, 33 Hz (ii) 2 V, 333 Hz (iii) 10 V, 25 Hz
   (iv) 0.75 V, 167 Hz

9 10 ms cm⁻¹, 1 V cm⁻¹.

Analogue-to-digital conversion (page 252)

1 (a) X = 1.00 V, Y = 2.00 V, Z = 3.00 V.

(b)

B	A	V_{in}/V
0	0	→ 1
0	1	1 → 2
1	1	2 → 3
1	0	3 → 4

2 (a) (Similar to oscilloscope input.)

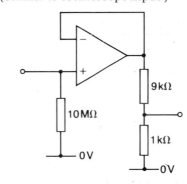

(b)

3 (a) 5 kΩ, 20 kΩ, 40 kΩ. (b) 1.6 kΩ.
4 Use a summing amplifier with four 10 kΩ input resistors and a 2.5 kΩ feedback resistor, followed by an inverting amplifier of gain −1.
5

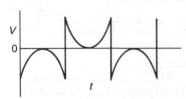

Simple harmonic motion (page 264)

1 (b) 15.8 N m^{-1}. (c) 35.4 s, 17.7 s, 35.4 s.
2 (a) $\Delta U = \rho Agx$. (b) $F = ma$, $F = -g\rho Ax$ ...
   (c) Damping too great for many cycles to be observed. (d) $\simeq 5$ s.
3 (a) Yes (if she is always in contact with the trampoline).
   (b) No. (c) No. (d) Yes.
4 (a) Doesn't matter. (b) $ma = -2kx \therefore T = 1.22$ s.
   (c) No effect.
   (d) Strain energy $= 2 \times \frac{1}{2} \times kx^2 = 0.20$ J
   $\therefore v = 0.52$ m s^{-1}.

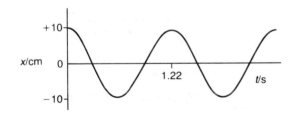

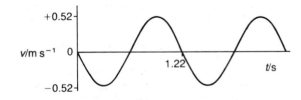

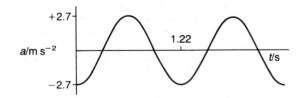

5 If one side depressed by x, $\Delta P = 2\rho gx$;
   $F = ma = \Delta PA$, $m = lA\rho$ where l is length of liquid $\rightarrow f = (2g/l)^{\frac{1}{2}}/2\pi$.
6 (a) 40 cm, 0.20 kg, 1.27 s.
   (b) $E = mgx^2/2l = 2.45x^2$.

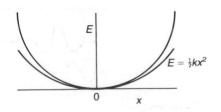

(c) Spring constant increases, but because the bob travels in two dimensions, the increased distance means that the period of large amplitude oscillations is $> 2\pi(l/g)^{\frac{1}{2}}$.
7 (a) 3.98 m, not a point mass on the end of a string.
   (b) Invar; has the lowest expansivity giving smallest variation of period with changing temperature.
   (c) Extra mass changes distance of centre of mass from pivot. Creep will extend the pendulum over the years, so an increased number of pennies over the years will keep the centre of mass the same distance from the pivot.
8 (a) $E = \frac{1}{2}c\theta^2$, $c = 9.88$ μJ deg^{-2}. (b) 33.6 mJ.
   (c) $\Delta\theta/\theta = $ constant $= 60/180 = 1/3 \therefore -180°$, $+120°$, $-80°$, $+53°$, $-35°$.
9 (a) 4.5×10^{-26} kg, 18 N m^{-1}. (b) 3.2×10^{12} Hz.
   (c) 2.1×10^{-11} m.
   (d) $\frac{1}{2}k(0.15d_0)^2 = 1.38\times10^{-23}T_m$, $k = Ed_0$
   $\therefore Ed_0^3 \propto T_m$; plot a graph of Ed_0^3 against T_m and put a straight line through the points and the origin.

Displacement–time curves (page 269)

1

t/s	x/m	v/ms^{-1}
0	0	0
2	14	18
4	60	28
6	120	32
8	185	33
10	251	33

2 (a) $x = 5.00\times10^{-2}\cos(8.66t)$,
   $v = -0.433\sin(8.66t)$, $a = 3.75\cos(8.66t)$.
   (b) 0.726 s. (c) 0.433 m s^{-1}.
3 $E_k = \frac{1}{2}mv^2$, $E = E_p + E_k$, $\omega^2 = k/m$ ...
4 Try $x = At^n$ (think of a VUSAT formula!)
5 (a) $x = r\cos\theta$, $\theta = \omega t \therefore x = r\cos(\omega t)$.
   (b) 42.3 r.p.m.
   (c) Both will have the same friction force so both will lose energy at the same rate. The one with the largest energy will therefore suffer the least damping, so choose the more massive one.
6 (a) Equilibrium extension $= 0.0491$ m $=$ amplitude of oscillation.
   (b)

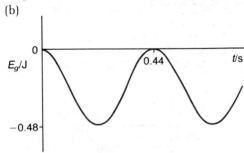

(c) $E_k = \frac{1}{2}mv^2$, $E = \frac{1}{2}kA^2 \therefore A = 35.4$ mm.

Forced oscillations (page 277)

1 (a) Large mass to reduce effects of damping and keep a constant amplitude periodic force applied to the blade.
   (b) $T = 2.0$ s $\therefore l = 0.99$ m.
   (c) $m = 50$ g, $T = 2$ s $\therefore k = 0.49$ N m^{-1}
   $\therefore m = 170$ g.

(d)

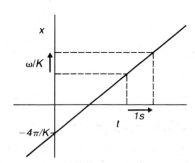

2 (a) $k = 4.91 \times 10^4$ N m^{-1}, $f = 1.1$ Hz. (b) 18 m.
   (c) $m \approx 10$ kg, $k \approx 1.25 \times 10^4$ N m^{-1} for each
   wheel assembly $\therefore f \approx 6$ Hz and $s \approx 3.6$ m.
   (d) Damped. (e) $T = 2\pi(m/k)^{\frac{1}{2}}$.
3 (a) Low mass gives low friction ($F = \mu W$).
   (b) Small k (large compliance) means small
   forces on groove edges when needle is moved
   back and forth.
   (c) Resonant frequency $(k/4\pi^2m)^{\frac{1}{2}}$ must be
   >16 kHz or <16 Hz; choose $f = 1$ Hz
   $\therefore$ compliance ≈ 10 m N^{-1}.
4 Anything which damps vibrations from the
   helicopter.
5 (a) No external force $\therefore$ no momentum change
   $\therefore m\Delta x/\Delta t + M\Delta X/\Delta t = $ constant, compatible
   with $mx + MX = 0$.
   (b) $F = k(X - x)$, $a = -\omega^2 x$, $F = ma$ . . .
   (d) $f = (k/4\pi^2\mu)^{\frac{1}{2}} \therefore f^2 \propto \mu^{-1} \therefore$ plot a graph of f^2
   against μ^{-1} and see if it is a straight line
   through the origin.
6 (a) $F = kx$, $F = ma$ . . . (b) Oscillates in SHM;
   $T = 2\pi(m/k)^{\frac{1}{2}} = 1.0$ s, initial velocity $= 2$ m s^{-1}
   at $x = 0$, $\therefore A = 0.32$ m.
   (d) $T = 0.89$ s $\therefore$ stable after ≈ 1s if critically
   damped, $\Delta x = m\Delta a/k \therefore \Delta a = \pm 1.3$ m s^{-2}.

Transverse waves (page 263)

1 (a) 0.167 m. (b) Six cycles in length 1.00 m.
   (c) As for (b) but displaced to the right by
   0.50 m.
2 (a) 2 cm, 4.5 cm s^{-1}, 3 cm, 1.5 Hz.
   (b) Frequency unaffected by tension
   $\therefore$ 1.5 cycles of displacement at any one point
   during one second.
3 (a) ft. (b) $ft\lambda = ct \therefore c = f\lambda$. (c) 0.30 m,
   5.1×10^5 cycles.
4 (b) $E = \frac{1}{2}mv^2$, $v = A\omega$, $m = \mu\Delta x$ . . .
   (d) $P = E/t$, $f = 1/t$ . . .
5 (a) $x = (\omega/K)t - 4\pi/K$. (b) $\Delta x/\Delta t = \omega/K$.

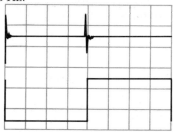

(c) $x = A\cos(\omega t + Kx)$.
6 (a) Concentric circles of relative radius 86, 117,
   149, 180 and 211, assuming dibber creates a
   trough before a crest.

(b)

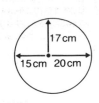

(c) 9.42 rad s^{-1}.
(d) (i) Ripples slowly move towards source.
(ii) Slowly move away from source.
(iii) Twice as many ripples, but not moving.
7 (b) $c = 2$ m s^{-1}, $\lambda = 1$ m $\therefore f = 2$ Hz.
   (c) $c = 2$ m s^{-1}, $\lambda = 3$ m $\therefore f = 0.67$ Hz.
   (d) $c = 3$ m s^{-1}, $\lambda = 2$ m $\therefore f = 1.5$ Hz.
   (e) $c = 1$ m s^{-1}, $\lambda = 2$ m $\therefore f = 0.5$ Hz.

Longitudinal waves (page 291)

1 (a) $\Delta x = 51$ cm, $\Delta t = 1.5$ ms $\therefore c = 340$ m s^{-1}.
   (b) Each change of current in the speaker sets it
   oscillating in damped SHM.
   (c) 333 Hz.

2 (a) 2.67 ms. (b) 200 pulses in 2.67×10^{-3} s
   $\therefore$ 74.9 kHz.
   (d) $\pm 5\lambda \therefore \pm 1.5$ mm.
3 (a) 0.92 m. (b) 0.69 m $\therefore 1.2 \times 10^{-4}$ s. (c) 39 cm.
4 (a) 667 Hz. (b) $\Delta t = 0.4$ ms $\therefore c = 1.3 \times 10^3$ m s^{-1}.
   (c) 2.67 kHz.
   (d) $\Delta c/c = -\frac{1}{2}\Delta\rho/\rho$, $\Delta\rho/\rho = -\Delta V/V = 3\alpha\Delta T$
   $\therefore \Delta c = 0.06$ m s^{-1} K^{-1}.
5 (b) $A \to A \times 10^{-3} \therefore r \to r \times 10^3 = 10$ km.
   (c) Assume $A = 10^5$ Pa at $r = 1$ m, distance =
   10^7 m, about halfway round the Earth.
   Damping, reflections and the curvature of the
   Earth's surface have all been ignored.
   (d) High frequencies are heavily damped
   $\therefore$ distant thunder is a low frequency rumble.
   High frequencies are heard first from local
   thunder, so there must be some dependence of
   c on f for sound waves in air.

Superposition (page 300)

1 (a) 0.25 m s^{-1}.
   (b)

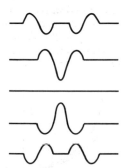

(c) Kinetic energy?

2 (a) $A = 20$ mm, $\omega = 1.05 \times 10^3$ rad s^{-1}, $\phi = \pi/2$.
(b) (ignoring phase shifts.)

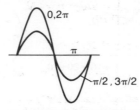

(c) Twice that of original wave.
(d) $A + B$, $A - B$, average energy $= A^2 + B^2$.
3 (a) $\Delta f \simeq 50$ Hz. (b) 0.021 m s^{-1}.
(c)

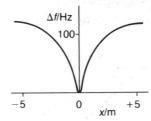

4 $\Delta f \simeq 10$ Hz between 0 and 70 mph.
5 (a) Moving away between 5.3×10^7 and 3.3×10^7 m s^{-1}.
(b) Moving towards between 5.0×10^7 and 1.0×10^8 m s^{-1}.
(c) 5.3×10^7 m s^{-1} away.
(d) $v \simeq 5 \times 10^7$ m s^{-1} $\therefore T = 1.26$ s, $g = 2.5 \times 10^8$ N kg^{-1} !
Ship will appear green all the time from the moon's surface.
6 (a) Both waves arrive in phase having travelled the least distance.
(b) 60 mV and 40 mV. (c) $\Delta r = 1.98$ cm $\therefore \lambda = 3.96$ cm.
(d) 100 mV, 20 mV.
7 (a) $\lambda = 300$ m $\therefore \Delta r = 150$ m, $r = 2h/\cos 45°$, $\therefore \Delta h = 53$ m.
(b) 0.12 m s^{-1}. (c) Katrina is right.

Reflecting waves (page 309)

1 (a)

n	λ/mm
1	99
2	59
3	42
4	33
5	27

(b)

n	λ/mm
1	80
2	48
3	34
4	27
5	22

$\therefore \lambda = 27$ mm.
2 (a) $n\lambda/2 = l$, $c = f\lambda$, $c = (T/\mu)^{\frac{1}{2}}$ $\therefore f = (n^2 T/4\mu l^2)^{\frac{1}{2}}$.
(b) (i) $f \to 2f$ (ii) $f \to 0.707f$ (iii) $f \to 0.707f$.
(c) Increased friction with the air as the transverse velocity of the wire is increased.
4 $\simeq 340$ Hz, 680 Hz and 1020 Hz.
5 (a) 47.1 m s^{-1}.
(b) 25 Hz, 50 Hz, 75 Hz.
(c) New wire will be stiffer increasing c, but it will also be heavier decreasing c. In practice,

fundamental frequency increases.
6 (a) $T = \mu f^2/4l^2$.
(b) μ is not independent of tension.
(c) $l = 0.7$ m $\therefore \mu = 7.14 \times 10^{-2}$ kg m^{-1} $\therefore c = 26.5$ m s^{-1} $\therefore f = 99$ Hz.
7 (a) $\simeq 340$ m s^{-1}, 640 m s^{-1}.
(b) $\simeq$ Doubled.
(c) Woodwind will have a shift of $+7$ Hz due to the increased value for c in air ($c = (\gamma RT/M)^{\frac{1}{2}}$). Stringed instruments will have a much smaller shift of either sign depending on the relative expansivity of the string and its frame.

Electric forces (page 321)

1 (a)

Plate	V/kV	Q/nC
left	+5	+50
right	0	−50

(c)

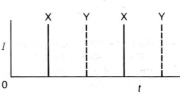

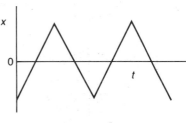

(d) (i) decrease (ii) increase (iii) decrease.
3 (a) Surplus of electrons?
(b) Redistribution of electrons.
(c) Same as before.
4 (a) $A = 3.14 \times 10^{-10}$ m^2 $\therefore R = 1.91 \times 10^{16}$ Ω.
(b) Assuming constant current $= 7.85 \times 10^{-13}$ A, $t = 5096$ s.
(c) 0.017 s.
5 Excess electrons on the polythene surface cannot move to places where the metal has atom-to-atom contact with the polythene. So although the polythene polarises the foil, it cannot discharge it.
6 (a) $R \propto n^{-1}$? (b) Light from sources other than the bulb.

Fields (page 328)

1 (a)

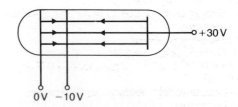

(c) (i) 1 kV m^{-1} (ii) 1 kV m^{-1}.

(d)

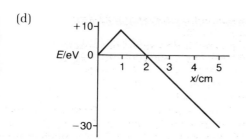

2 (a) Positive charge, magnitude unknown.
(b) 1.15×10^3 N C^{-1} from the right-hand sphere.
3 (a) 5000 V (area under the curve).
(b) 2.5 mJ if no change in charge distribution on the sphere.

4

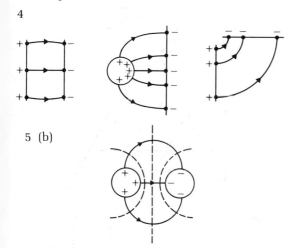

5 (b)

(c) From the work done taking the charged strip away from the isolated spheres.
(d) Work must be done separating the spheres, $E = \frac{1}{2}QV \therefore V$ increases.
6 (a) Near the needle; positive ions will move away from the needle and drift towards the attractor.
(b) The powder picks up positive ions and sweeps them up the tube.
(c) Each time a positive ion is blown up the tube by the air stream, a negative charge is left on the attractor. The air stream has to do work separating these charges, giving them electrical energy.
7 Field polarises the foil; resultant couple is zero when foil lies parallel to field, but it can point in either direction.

Charged sheets (page 336)

1 (a) 3.0 kV. (b) 30 kV. (c) Replace plug with a parallel plate capacitor of spacing 6 mm.
2 (a) $l = 32$ m, reduces to only 16 m when rolled into a cylinder.
(b) 480 pF.
3 (a) $C \to \frac{1}{2}C \therefore V \to 2V$.
(b) Energy doubles due to work done pulling plates apart.
(c) Remains constant.
(d) C changes from 8.14×10^{-7} F m^{-2} to 8.85×10^{-10} F m$^{-2} \therefore V$ goes from $+9$ V to $+8.3$ kV.
4 (a) Constant. (b) Constant. (c) Decreases.
(e) Decreases.
5 Non-uniform field will exert a force as well as polarise the ruler.

6 (a) Opposite charges on the plates attract each other.
(b) $F = qE$, $E = V/d$, $q = CV$ ...
$\therefore \Delta mg = A\epsilon_0(V/d)^2$.
(c) 5 mm.
7 (a) See chapter 5. (c) No.
8 (a) 28 pF.
(b) Increases; $\Delta C/C = -\Delta d/d \therefore \Delta C = +0.28$ pF.
(c) $\tau = 28$ ms.
(d) $T = 1$ ms, giving virtually no time for charge to get on or off the plates; $\Delta V/V = -\Delta C/C$
$\therefore \Delta V = 100$ mV.

Charged spheres (page 343)

1 (a) 2.78×10^{-8} C. (b) 6.95×10^{-5} J.
(c) 1×10^5 N C^{-1}.
(d)

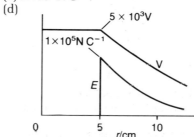

2 (a) -450 kV, $+636$ kV, -450 kV.
(b) -263 kV, -1.32 J.
(c) 4.50×10^6 N C^{-1} to the left, 4.50×10^6 N C^{-1} downwards, 4.50×10^6 N C^{-1} away from 10 μC charge.
(d) 1.86×10^6 N C^{-1} towards 10 μC charge.
(e) 14.9 N towards 10 μC charge.
3 (a) 4.09 nC (b) 2.05 nC each, half the energy is lost.
(c) 19.6 mm, increase.
(d) $F \propto r^4 \therefore$ double radius of ball increases force by 16.
4 (a) $E_e = 1.15 \times 10^{-28}/r$.
(b) $\Delta E = 8.20 \times 10^{-14}$ J $\therefore r = 1.40 \times 10^{-15}$ m.
5 (a) 2.42×10^{-13} J
(b) $p \simeq 2.16 \times 10^{-19}$ N s, $E_k \simeq 2.59 \times 10^{-13}$ J.
(c) 1.36×10^{-14} m (when nuclei touch their centres are 6.4×10^{-15} m apart).
6 (a) 5.47×10^5 C. (b) Corona discharge.
7 (a) E 22.5 cm from centre $= 1.5 \times 10^6$ V m^{-1} for each sphere $\therefore Q = 8.4$ μC. (b) 2.8 μA.
(c) maximum voltage is 380 kV
$\therefore$ mean power $\simeq 0.5$ W.
(d) $\simeq 5$ N.

Universal gravitation (page 351)

1 (a) 5.97×10^{24} kg. (b) 8.95 N kg^{-1}.
(c) 5.53×10^3 kg m^{-3}.
(d) $\Delta g/g = \Delta r/r \therefore \Delta g = -7.7 \times 10^{-4}$ N kg^{-1}.
(e) See part (c).
2 From Kepler's Third Law $M = 2.00 \times 10^{30}$ kg, $F = 3.54 \times 10^{27}$ N, $r = 5.79 \times 10^{10}$ m.
3 (a) $m = 7.11 \times 10^6$ kg $\therefore F = 3.37 \times 10^{-1}$ N.
(b) 3.37×10^{23} N (c) 1.01×10^{-47} N, 2.30×10^{-8} N.
4 $mg = kx \therefore \Delta g = 5 \times 10^{-13}$ N kg^{-1}; $\Delta g = k\Delta x/m$
$\therefore$ go for large m and small k to maximise sensitivity.
5 (a) $Gm^2/r^2 = 2e^2/4\pi\epsilon_0 r^2 - 2e^2/4\pi(\epsilon_0 + \Delta\epsilon_0)r^2$
$\therefore \Delta\epsilon_0/\epsilon_0 = 4 \times 10^{-37}$.
(b) If atoms contain neutrons, their mass is not

proportional to the number of charges they contain.

(c) Of P particles emitted per second, only $P \times \pi r^2/4\pi R^2$ will be intercepted by a test mass of radius r at distance R.

(d) Only if it allows prediction of phenomena not already dealt with by the formula.

6 (a) Time-of-flight for pulses reflected from spacecraft for distance, Doppler shift of radio emissions for velocity.

(b)

r/m	E_g/J	E_k/J
1.10×10^7	-1.23×10^{12}	$+1.20 \times 10^{12}$
5.44×10^7	-2.49×10^{11}	$+2.24 \times 10^{11}$
1.70×10^8	-7.98×10^{10}	$+5.51 \times 10^{10}$
2.09×10^8	-6.49×10^9	$+3.98 \times 10^{10}$

The field of the Moon has been ignored.

(c) At $r = 5.42 \times 10^8$ m, $E_k = 0$.

Satellites (page 355)

1 (a) -1.04×10^6 J kg^{-1}. (b) -3.89×10^6 J kg^{-1}.

(b)

d/10^8 m	V_g/10^6 J kg^{-1}
0.0	-62.60
0.5	-7.09
1.0	-3.77
1.5	-2.57
2.0	-1.96
2.5	-1.60
3.0	-1.36
3.5	-1.30

(c) 3.07×10^{12} J, 1.30×10^{11} J, 2.28×10^3 m s^{-1}.

2 (a) $r = 7.27 \times 10^6$ m, $h = 902$ km.

(b) $\Delta E_g = 7.75 \times 10^9$ J.

(c) $v = 7.40 \times 10^3$ m s^{-1} $\therefore$ $E_k = 2.74 \times 10^{10}$ J.

3 (a) Decreases, heat energy.

(b) Increases ($v = 2\pi(GM/4\pi^2 r)^{\frac{1}{2}}$).

(c) Increases (due to increased speed and density).

(e) $\Delta V_g = 9.8 \times 10^5$ J kg^{-1}, $E_k = 3.1 \times 10^7$ J kg^{-1} $\therefore$ $\Delta T = 6.57 \times 10^4$ K. The outer surface is coated with an insulating material which allows the heat to be radiated and convected away before it can be conducted into the spacecraft and destroy it.

4 (a) 2.39×10^3 m s^{-1}. (b) 2 keV.

(c) 1.48×10^3 m, 6.1×10^{13} N kg^{-1}.

5 (a) $\simeq -2GM/R$. (b) -7.6×10^{41} J. (c) $\simeq 3 \times 10^7$ K.

Detecting emissions (page 369)

1 (a) High enclosure potential ensures that all ions reach the walls before they recombine.

(b) $I = 1.8 \times 10^{-10}$ A $\equiv 1.1 \times 10^9$ electrons s^{-1}.

(c) $\simeq 7 \times 10^3$ s^{-1}.

2 23 s^{-1}.

3 (a) Area $\simeq 3 \times 10^{-13}$ C $\equiv 1.9 \times 10^6$ electrons $\therefore$ $E = 5.6$ MeV.

(c) Same width, half the area.

4 $n = 9.65 \times 10^{25}$ s^{-1}, activity $\simeq 17$ s^{-1} kg^{-1}.

5 (a) See chapter 5. (b) 3.00 kV.

(c) Positive particle with energy 2.67 MeV, negative particles with energy ranging from 0 to 1.00 MeV.

6 (a) 1.3×10^5. (b) 4.6 MeV.

(c) 1.57×10^5 ion pairs, $\therefore$ 8 squares $\therefore$ $\simeq 40$ mm.

7 (a) 1.52×10^7 m s^{-1}.

(b) $r = 1.59$ m $\therefore$ $\Phi \simeq 0.05/1.59 = 3 \times 10^{-2}$ rad.

Absorbing emissions (page 376)

1 (a) 1.2×10^{-5} m. (b) 0.11 m. (c) 15 μm.

2 (a) 0.03 mm in aluminium $\therefore$ 70 mm in air $\therefore$ $\simeq 8$ MeV.

(b) Probably β; try applying a magnetic field.

3 (a) $R \simeq 1$ mm $\therefore$ 200 keV.

(b) Stop you picking up radioactive dust from sources.

(c) $A \simeq 0.5$ m^2, $d \simeq 5$ m $\therefore$ 300 s^{-1}; GM tube with area of 8×10^{-5} m^2 would detect 5×10^{-2} s^{-1} $\therefore$ much less than background.

4 (a) All ions need to be produced inside chamber $\therefore$ short-range alphas should be used.

(b) Particles pick up the ions, slowing down the rate at which they drift to the electrodes and increasing their chances of recombining by random collision.

(c) See figure 21.44.

5 (a) Activity $= 8.13 \times 10^3$ s^{-1}. (b) 6 mm.

6 (a) Lead creeps very badly under its own weight, so it would need a concrete box to hold it upright anyway. Concrete is a far superior structural material; it needs much reinforcing with steel because the interior of a nuclear reactor is at a high pressure.

(b) $\delta = 35$ mm $\therefore$ $d_{\frac{1}{2}} = 25$ mm.

Radioactive decay (page 381)

1 (a) $A = A_0 \exp[-\lambda/(\ln[2]/\lambda)] = 0.5 A_0$?

(b) $\ln[0.1] = -\lambda t$, $\lambda t_{\frac{1}{2}} = \ln[2]$ $\therefore$ $t = 3.33 t_{\frac{1}{2}}$.

(c) $\lambda = 5.61 \times 10^{-7}$ s^{-1}, $N = 1.94 \times 10^{22}$ $\therefore$ $A = 1.09 \times 10^{16}$ s^{-1}.

2 Background $\simeq 18$ min^{-1}; plot $\ln A$ against t, slope $= -4.38 \times 10^{-2}$ hr^{-1} $\therefore$ $t_{\frac{1}{2}} = 15.8$ hours.

3 $\lambda = 3.84 \times 10^{-12}$ s^{-1} $\therefore$ 6.52×10^{13} atoms.

(b) 5.02×10^{25} atoms kg^{-1} $\therefore$ 1.30×10^{-14}% carbon-14.

(c) $A = 160$ s^{-1} kg^{-1} $\therefore$ $t = 3700$ years.

4 (a) 23 years. (b) 1.37×10^{11} s^{-1}.

5 (a) sodium-21. (b) $1 : 2.61$.

(d) Both have the same area under the curve = initial number of parent atoms.

6 $N_0 = 2.53 \times 10^{21}$, $\lambda = 4.88 \times 10^{-18}$ s^{-1} $\therefore$ $\Delta N = 9.36 \times 10^{20}$ $\therefore$ 7.5×10^{21} atoms of helium ($\simeq 300$ cm^3 at room temperature and pressure).

7 (a) Short-range alphas so that all their energy is dumped in a small volume. Beta's could be used.

(b) $A = 2.84 \times 10^{14}$ s^{-1} $\therefore$ $m = 0.443$ kg.

(c) 20.4 W. (d) 1.28×10^9 s ($\simeq 40$ years).

The nucleus (page 388)

1 (a) 7.0×10^{-15} m.

(b) 32.5 MeV, protons definitely penetrate.

(d) $p \simeq 2 \times 6.54 \times 10^{-20}$ N s $\therefore$ $E_k \simeq 163$ keV.

2 The balls can have rotational energy.

3 (a) 6.67×10^4 m s^{-1}, $m = 4.04 \times 10^{-26}$ kg $\therefore$ $V = 562$ V.

(b) $r = 56$ mm $\therefore$ 112 mm.

(c) $\Delta r/r = \Delta p/p$ $\therefore$ $\Delta r \simeq 4$ mm.

4 6.2×10^{15} atoms per second $\therefore$ $\simeq 3$ hours per mg.

5 (a) $^9_4\text{Be} + ^4_2\text{He} \rightarrow ^{12}_6\text{C} + ^1_0\text{n}$

(b) Maximum energy only transferred in a head-on collision, alphas lose energy on their way to the target; $v = 3.3 \times 10^7$ m s^{-1}.

(c) 4.68×10^6 m s^{-1}.

(d) 1.9×10^{-27} kg, just about.

Nuclear transformations (page 393)

1 (a) $^{14}_{7}N + ^{4}_{2}He \rightarrow ^{1}_{1}H + ^{17}_{8}O$
(b) $[ML^2T^{-2}] = [M] \times [LT^{-1}]^2$?
(c) $\Delta m = 18.005677 - 18.006598 \equiv 1.2$ MeV
(electrons balance if atomic masses taken
throughout) $\therefore$ proton energy $= 6.5$ MeV;
oxygen nucleus much more massive than
proton so only gains $\simeq 0.4$ MeV ($\simeq 6\%$ of proton
energy).
(d) $E = 2e7e/4\pi\epsilon_0 d$, $d = 5 \times 10^{-15}$ m
$\therefore E \simeq 4$ MeV.

2 $^{238}_{92}U \rightarrow ^{4}_{2}He + ^{234}_{90}Th$
$^{234}_{90}Th \rightarrow ^{0}_{-1}e + ^{234}_{91}Pa$

3 (a) Final daughter is Rn-220 ($Z = 86$).

4 (b) 9×10^{-4} s. (c) 6 MeV.

5 (b) Mass gain $= 3.6 \times 10^{-3}$ m_u
$\therefore$ neutron energy $= 2.1$ MeV.
(c) Loss of alpha's energy by collision,
minimum energy $= 0$ MeV.

6 (a) 1.88 GeV to create a single proton–
antiproton pair.
(b) Six (in practice, many other exotic particles
are created as well, so six antiprotons from a
single collision is a rare event).

Nuclear power (page 398)

1 (a) 2.86×10^{-11} J per fission
$\therefore 5.4 \times 10^{24}$ atoms $= 2.1$ kg.
(b) 5.23×10^{-13} J per fusion $\therefore 1.38 \times 10^{28}$
molecules of $H_2O = 411$ kg ($\simeq 0.5$ m^3!).
(c) 36 tonnes.

2 Model as two charged spheres of radius
6.1×10^{-15} m and 5.5×10^{-15} m which are
touching.
$\therefore E_e = 52e40e/4\pi\epsilon_0 \times 1.16 \times 10^{-14} =$
258 MeV.

3 4.3×10^9 kg s^{-1}, percentage mass loss when four
protons become one helium nucleus $= 7 \times 10^{-5}$
$\therefore 2 \times 10^{16}$ s or $\simeq 1$ Gyr
4 protons $\rightarrow$ 1 helium + 2 positrons,
$\therefore 3.8 \times 10^{-12}$ J per helium atom,
$\therefore 1.0 \times 10^{38}$ atoms s^{-1}.

4 (a) $v^2 = 0.72u^2$. (b) 54.
(c) Less energy is lost by a neutron in a glancing
collision.

Field strength (page 412)

1 (a) Downwards.

(b)

I/A	F/mN
0.5	13.2
1.0	25.6
1.5	39.0
2.0	52.4

$F/I = 2.61 \times 10^{-2}$ N A^{-1} $\therefore B = 1.31$ T.

2 Which way will a compass needle point when
it is placed at a point where field lines cross?

3 (a)

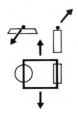

(b) Horizontal; align block and balance along a
N–S axis.
(c) $B = 1.79 \times 10^{-5}$ T $\therefore I = 0.438$ A.
(d) $I \simeq 8.8$ A for $\Delta m = 0.20$ g $\therefore$ feasible, but
only measures the horizontal component of B.

4 (a) $v = 9.37 \times 10^6$ m s^{-1}, $p = 8.54 \times 10^{-24}$ N s,
$B = 1.07 \times 10^{-3}$ T.
(b) 7.07 cm. (c) Straight line. (e) Particles
incident on the equator spiral around the field
lines and get trapped . . .

5 (d) 6.7×10^{-6} N m.

6 (a) $r = 4.30 \times 10^3$ m $\therefore p = 6.88 \times 10^{-16}$ N s.
(b) Guess $v = 3.00 \times 10^8$ m s^{-1}
$\therefore m = 2.29 \times 10^{-24}$ kg $\therefore v \simeq c$.
(c) 1.3×10^{12} eV.
(d) They go round the ring in opposite
directions; collisions can be avoided by pulsing
the particles rather than having a steady stream
all round the ring.

7 (a) The electron loses energy as it creates ions,
so its momentum decreases as time goes on.
(b) Into the plane of the diagram.
(c) Spiral will have four times the initial radius
and will curve in the other direction.

8 (b) $n = 6 \times 10^{28}$ m^{-3} $\therefore V = 25$ μV.
(c) 2.6 electrons.

Creating fields (page 422)

1 $\Delta m = 0.01$ g for a separation of 5 cm, maximum
reading $\simeq 0.1$ g.

2 (a) 1.59 mT. (b) Look at figure 23.46. (c) 7.54 A.

3 (a) To the right. (b) 17.6 mT, 8.80 mT.
(c) 2.2 mN – just about measurable.

4 (b) 43 mA.
(c) $R = 140 \Omega$, $l = 471$ m $\therefore d = 2.6 \times 10^{-4}$ m.
(d) $R \rightarrow R/4$ $\therefore 1.5$ V, $P \rightarrow P/4$.

8 The presence of iron means that B is not
proportional to I.

Changing flux (page 430)

1 (a) Area $=$ change of flux linkage.
(b) Area $\simeq 4.0 \times 10^{-3}$ Wb, $A = 7.85 \times 10^{-5}$ m^2
$\therefore B = 0.10$ T.
(c) All negative.
(d) Use the average area (equivalent to using
$r = 10.2$ mm).

2 (a)

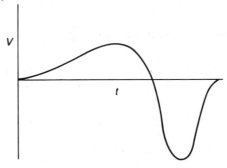

(b) (i) same shape and area but shorter time
(ii) no change
(iii) area doubled but no change of timescale
(iv) no change
(v) no signal at all.

3 (a) $\simeq 0.5$ V. (b) $\simeq 5$ mV. (c) Any power drawn
from the rails would result in a slowing down
of the trains!

4 (a)

(b) Current changes direction.

(c) Eddy currents? (d) Field lines straying from the rod (see figure) interact with the ring to give a vertical force. As the ring rises up the rod the flux becomes weaker so the ring eventually reaches static equilibrium.

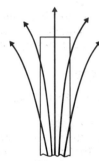

(e) Weight and current are both doubled $\therefore$ no effect.

(f) Jump up and fall down immediately, both times.

5 (a) 0.63 T. (b) 0.158 Wb. (c) 1.583 kV (ignoring the neon bulb).

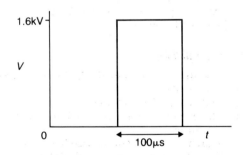

(d) (i) nothing (ii) flashes briefly.

6 (a) Braking force is a consequence of movement of disc through field . . .

(b) Thick, copper, large diameter.

7(a) 10.5 mT. (b) 7.85×10^{-2} m^2, 824 μV.

(c) Higher.

Electromagnetic machines (page 436)

1 (a) $n\Phi = 24$ mWb, $\omega = 126$ rad s^{-1}. (b) 1.5 A.

(c) 3.6×10^{-2} N m.

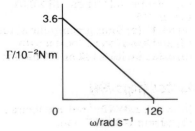

(d)

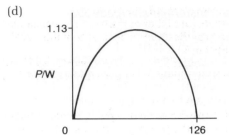

(e) 50%.

2 (a) $R \to R/10$, $\Phi \to 100\Phi$ $\therefore$ $\omega \to \omega/100$.

(b) $I \to 10I$ $\therefore$ $\Gamma \to 1000\Gamma$. (c) $P \to 10P$.

3 (a) Large permanent magnets stick to lumps of steel.

(b) Constant field $\therefore$ couple decreases as angular velocity increases.

(c) If angular velocity is decreased, field current rises, increasing the couple on the armature . . .

4 (a) $R = 1.88$ Ω, $n\Phi = 3.18$ mWb. (b) 532 mA.

(c) 33%.

5 (a) 0.500 Wb, 157 rad s^{-1} $\therefore$ 78.5 V.

(b)

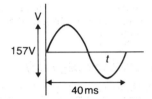

(c) 7.85 A. (d) 308 W.

6 (a) $V \to 4V$. (b) $r \to r/2$. (c) $I = BAN2\pi f/11r$.

(d) $I \to 8I$. (e) $P \to 32P$.

Inductors (page 442)

1 (a) 3.98×10^{-5} H. (b) 6.28×10^3 A s^{-1}.

(c) 0.250 V.

(d) Place a 1.0 Ω resistor in series with the coil and use the oscilloscope to study the p.d. across it (1 V A^{-1}).

(e) (i) doubled (ii) halved (iii) doubled (iv) increased, provided primary current unchanged.

2 (a) $V = LdI/dt$ . . . (b) See figure 24.45.

(d) p.d. falls to zero as f goes from zero to infinity.

3 (a) 1.5 A s^{-1}. (b) 0.5 A.

(c)

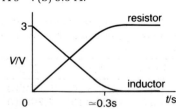

(d) (i) peak voltage doubles, timescale unchanged

(ii) peak voltage unchanged, timescale doubled

(e) dI/dt very large $\therefore$ p.d. across inductor large.

5 (a) $B = \mu_0 nI/l$ (b) $n\Phi = LI$, $E = \frac{1}{2}LI^2$ . . .

(c) $E = V/d$, $C = \epsilon_0 A/d$, $E_e = \frac{1}{2}CV^2$ . . .

Power transmission (page 448)

1 (a) 24 W, $\simeq$ 0.3 W. (c) 240 V, 0.100 A.

(d) 0.48 W.

2 (a) Strength. (b) 0.058 Ω km^{-1}.

(c) $9.4 \times 10^{-7}\%$. (d) 6.24 GW.

3 (a) 4800. (b) higher current $\therefore$ less resistance to keep heat dissipation at an acceptable level.
(c) 56.3 mA.
(d) Computer behaves like a resistor so V and I will be in phase with peak values of 12.7 V and 2.12 A.

4 $I = 0.625$ A $\therefore$ 3 A fuse.

5 (a) Ensure the same flux everywhere along the coil, keep the primary current small when secondary current is zero.
(c)

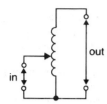

6 (a) $B = \mu_0 nI/l$, $B < 1$ T $\therefore$ $\Phi < A$.
(b) $l \to 2l$, $\therefore$ $I \to 2I$.
(c) Yes (draw a graph), about 1 m across.

7 (a) Increase inductance, $V = LdI/dt \ldots$
(b) System behaves like a transformer, bulb lights up, ammeter reading drops from 1.0 A to a bit below 0.5 A.

Oscillators and filters (page 458)

1 (a) 3.3 MHz to 910 kHz. (b) 40 pF, 25 μH.

2 (a)

f/kHz	X_c/Ω	X_L/Ω
0.1	1.6×10^4	1.6×10^2
1.0	1.6×10^3	1.6×10^3
10	1.6×10^2	1.6×10^4

(d)

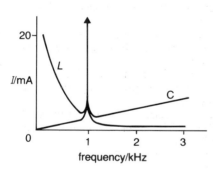

3 (a) $C = 0.66$ μF. (b) See figure 25.29. (c) 339 V.
(d) In phase, peak values 71 mA, 17 V, period 20 ms.

4

f/kHz	X_c/Ω	Z/Ω	V_{out}/V
0.3	5.31×10^3	5.33×10^3	1.99
3.0	5.31×10^2	7.29×10^3	1.46
30	5.31×10^1	5.03×10^2	0.21

6 (a) Large impedance because of the capacitor.
(b) Large impedance because of the inductor.
(c) $X_L = 314$ Ω, $X_C = 318$ Ω $\therefore$ $Z = 11$ Ω.
(d) $I = 0.45$ A $\therefore$ $V_L = 143$ V, $V_C = 145$ V out of phase with each other.

The electromagnetic spectrum (page 472)

1 3.03×10^8 m s^{-1}.

2 Corner cube reflector for efficient reflection of radar waves emanating from other boats.

3 (a) Perpendicular.
(c)

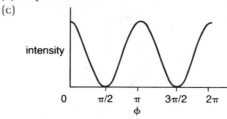

4 (a) $P = 6.1 \times 10^7$ W m^{-2} at surface
$\therefore$ $P = 3.7 \times 10^{26}$ W.
(b) ≈ 2.5 m $\therefore$ ≈ 0.1 W m^{-2}.
(c) All of them.

5 (b) $\Delta t = 1.10 \times 10^{-4}$ s, $\Delta x = 3.44 \times 10^4$ m
$\therefore$ $c = 3.13 \times 10^8$ m s^{-1}

6 2.99×10^8 m s^{-1}.

7 (a) Radius of the balls and their separation; radius of the loop.
(b) Adjust the spacing between the balls.
(c) Plane of coil parallel to direction of the wave to maximise the flux through the loop.

Relativity (page 479)

1 $m_0 = 75$ kg, $\Delta m \approx 2 \times 10^{-9}$ kg,
$v = 1.5 \times 10^3$ m s^{-1}.

2 (a) 1.0×10^7 s.
(b) 5.0×10^{14} m during acceleration, 4.3 light years $= 4.07 \times 10^{16}$ m $\therefore$ coast for 3.97×10^{16} m.
(c) Earth time $= 3.97 \times 10^8$ s
$\therefore$ astronaut time $= 3.74 \times 10^8$ s.
(d) $\approx 4.6 \times 10^7$ s (≈ 1.5 years in a trip of 27 years).

3 $v \approx 3 \times 10^8$ m s^{-1} $\therefore$ galaxy must appear to be 30 light years around $\therefore$ Earth time $= 30\,000$ years.

4 (a) $\lambda = 0.47$ μs^{-1}, $t_{\frac{1}{2}} = 1.5$ μs.
(b) $\Delta t = 6.7$ μs $\therefore$ $N = 26$. (c) 0.86 μs.
(d) $v = 0.99c$. (e) Yes.

Lenses (page 488)

1 (a) $v = 50.1$ mm, 2.0 cm. (b) 55.6 mm, blurred.
(c) ∞ to 0.30 m.

2 (a) 14.3 cm. (b) Virtual image.
(c) 20 cm behind the lens, 62.55 mm high, upside down.
(d) Half as bright but otherwise the same.

3 (a) True. (b) False. (c) False. (d) False.
(e) False. (f) True.

4 (a)

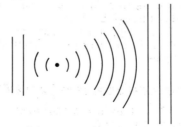

(b) 150 mm. (c) 20 mm. (d) $\times 0.01$.

5 8.3 cm $\times 6$.

7 (a) 54.4°. (b) Blue, green, yellow, red.
(d) Red has a longer focal length.

8 (a) 0.333 m. (b) 0.182 m, 7.5 dioptres.

Diffraction (page 494)

1 (a) $\theta = \pm 1.3 \times 10^{-3}$ rad, see figure 27.34.
(b) $\Delta\theta = \pm 0.9 \times 10^{-3}$ rad.

2 (a) $\lambda = 8.25 \times 10^{-3}$ m $\therefore \theta = \pm 41°$. (b) $\pm 11°$.

3 (a)

θ	f/Hz	λ/m	$\sin\theta$
–	60	5.5	35
20°	6000	0.055	0.35

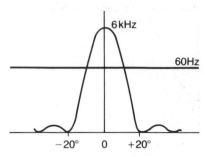

(b) Straight in front. (c) $\simeq 5$ cm.

4 (a) 10 m. (b) Eye has better resolving power in dark provided there is enough light to form a clear image.

5 Think of diffracting light ($\lambda = 500$ nm) and sound ($\lambda = 0.5$ m) by an aperture of width 0.5 m.

6 3.3×10^{-3} rad, 6.0×10^{-6} rad.

7 (a) 0.8 m across. (b) $\theta \simeq 1 \times 10^{-3}$ rad $\therefore$ energy arrives at satellite spread over an area $\simeq 1 \times 10^9$ m^2 $\therefore$ received power is $\simeq 0.2$ μW.

Applied optics (page 499)

1 (a) Objective 20 cm, eyepiece 5 cm. (b) 25 cm. (c) See figure 27.52. (d) 4. (e) See figure 27.54, $f \simeq 5$ cm.

2 (a) 1600:1. (b) 36 times more. (c) $\simeq 1000$ times further.
(d) $\simeq 100$ times more light gets into your eyes.

3 (a) 4.29 cm. (b) 7.0.
(c) $v = 9.1$ cm $\therefore$ separation $= 13.3$ cm.

4 (a) 42° ($n = 1.50$), 68° ($n = 1.08$).
(b) $(r + d)\sin c = r$ $\therefore$ 0.20 mm for air, 1.33 mm for petrol.

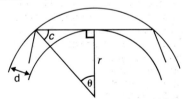

(c) Lower the curved section towards the petrol; as soon as the fibre is immersed no more light gets from the LED to the photodiode.

5 (b) 37.5 cm, $\times 0.5$. (c)

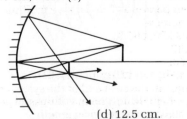

(d) 12.5 cm.

6 (a) 20 cm. (b) $F = 15.1$ cm. (c) 25 cm.

Young's slits (page 504)

1 (a) 1.13 mm. (b) Spread over 18 mm. (c) Fifteen (d) Fifteen fringes spread over 25 mm.

	Spacing	Intensity	Number
(a)	$\times\frac{1}{2}$	$\times 1$	$\times 2$
(b)	$\times 1$	$\times 4$	$\times\frac{1}{2}$
(c)	$\times 2$	?	$\times 1$
(d)	$\times 2$	$\times\frac{1}{4}$	$\times 1$

3 (c) 6.2 μm; use white light and look for the fringes where the glass touches the gauge.

4 (a) In phase. (b) Out of phase.

5 (a) See figure 28.2.

Gratings (page 511)

1 (a) 0.35 m. (b) Single slit diffraction? (c) $\simeq 1.5$ μm.

2

n	λ/nm	θ
1	400	13°
1	680	22°
2	400	26°
2	680	49°
3	400	42°

3

	Number	Intensity	Width	Spacing
(a)	$\times 2$	$\times\frac{1}{4}$	$\times 1$	$\times\frac{1}{2}$
(b)	$\times 2$	$\times\frac{1}{4}$	$\times 1$	$\times 1$
(c)	0	?	+	+
(d)	0	–	+	0

4 (c) 0.238 rad. (d) 30 μrad.

6 (a) $AB - CD = n\lambda$, $n = 0, \pm 1, \pm 2 \ldots$
(c) Only possible if $\alpha = \beta$. (d) $\simeq 5$ μm across.

7 (a) Nuclei. (b) 0.25 nm, 0.18 nm, 0.11 nm.
(c) 23°, 32°, 54°. (d) The figure here includes a line with $n = 2$; the central spot is brightest, planes with greatest density of atoms give the most intense rings.

Photons (page 520)

1 (a) The capacitor will take a long time to discharge.
(b) Use the lowest wavelength.
(c) $\Delta V/\Delta f = 3.78 \times 10^{-15}$ V Hz^{-1}, $h = 6.05 \times 10^{-34}$ J s, $\phi = 2.38$ eV (using correct value for h).

3 (a) $\lambda = 290$ nm. (b) 9.51×10^{-20} J or 0.59 eV.
(c) Energy loss by collision with zinc atoms.
(d) Average KE of air molecule $\simeq 0.04$ eV $\ldots$
(e) Negative ions do not have enough energy to escape the sheet.

4 5.0×10^{15}, 1.6×10^{13}, 6.4×10^{17}, 3.0×10^{26}, 2.5×10^{29}.

5 (a) Infra-red:- 4.14 μm, 1.78 μm, 1.24 μm;
visible:- 621 nm, 460 nm, 414 nm.
(b) Photons at 622 nm, 460 nm and 414 nm can
be absorbed by atoms in ground state and
re-radiated in all directions, i.e. those photons
can be scattered from the beam of white light by
the atoms.

7 (a) Energy conservation; increase of
gravitational energy results in a decrease of
electromagnetic energy ∴ frequency decreases
on way out from star.
(b) $m = 3.75 \times 10^{-36}$ kg ∴ $\Delta E_g = 7.15 \times 10^{-25}$ J.
(c) $hf = 3.37 \times 10^{-19}$ J ∴ $\Delta\lambda/\lambda \simeq 2 \times 10^{-6}$!
(d) $r = 1.3 \times 10^4$ m ∴ $\Delta\lambda \simeq 70$ nm.

8 $hf \simeq 4 \times 10^{-19}$ J, $n = 2.0 \times 10^{17}$ s^{-1} ∴ $I \simeq 30$ mA;
not all of the photons absorbed result in a
photoelectron, some photons may be less than
the work function.

Wave mechanics (page 527)

1

	E_k/J	p/N s	λ/m
(a)	3.7×10^{-15}	8.2×10^{-23}	8.1×10^{-12}
(b)	6.0×10^{-21}	2.7×10^{-23}	2.5×10^{-11}
(c)	8.0×10^{-13}	1.0×10^{-19}	6.4×10^{-15}

2 (b) $\lambda = 2d\sin\theta$, $\lambda \propto V^{-\frac{1}{2}}$, $\sin\theta \propto D$ ∴ $D \propto V^{-\frac{1}{2}}$.
(c) John is right.

3 (a) 1.5×10^{-14} m.
(b) nucleon 2.7 MeV, alpha particle 0.7 MeV.
(c) $\simeq 1$ MeV.

4 (a) Never found where $\psi = 0$.
(b) Where $E < V$.
(c) At the maximum value of ψ^2.
(d) On the right (greatest area under ψ^2).
(e) Smallest wavelength on left
∴ greatest momentum . . .
(f) By comparing areas, roughly 1 in 10.

5 (a) (i) small spot with diffraction rings
(ii) and (iii) no edge to the spot at all.
(b) 6 μV, 6 V.

Sharing heat (page 536)

1 See figure 30.14

2 (a)

n	W	S/J K^{-1}
1	2	9.6×10^{-24}
2	3	1.5×10^{-23}
3	4	1.9×10^{-23}

(b)

n	W	S/J K^{-1}
1	3	1.5×10^{-23}
2	6	2.5×10^{-23}
3	10	3.2×10^{-23}

3 (a) 4.5 kJ.
(b) $m = 4.5 \times 10^{-26}$ kg, $d_0 = 2.6 \times 10^{-10}$ m,
∴ $k = 18$ N m^{-1}
∴ $f = 3.2 \times 10^{12}$ Hz.
(c) 2.1×10^{-21} J.
(d) 2.1×10^{24} quanta among 1.8×10^{24} sites,
roughly 1 quantum per site.

4 (a) 9.6×10^{-2} J K^{-1}. (b) -0.75 J K^{-1}. (c) 0 J K^{-1}.

5 (a) 2:4. (b) 3.74×10^{-23} J K^{-1}. (c) $1.5T$, three
quanta each.
(d) 3.83×10^{-23} J K^{-1}.

6 (a) 200 MW, 2.43×10^5 J K^{-1}.
(b) 100 MW, 2.68×10^5 J K^{-1}.

(c) $+2.5 \times 10^4$ J K^{-1}.
(d) -2.4×10^4 J K^{-1}.
(e) Total entropy change must be positive.

The Boltzmann factor (page 543)

1 (a) Sum of all the probabilities must be 1.
(b)

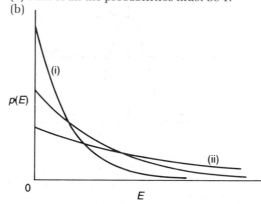

(c)

T/K	Ground state	Excited state
150	0.92	0.08
300	0.77	0.23
600	0.65	0.35

2 (a) $\epsilon = 4.0 \times 10^{-20}$ J or 0.25 eV.
(b) 2.4 kΩ.

3 (a) $\epsilon = 7.08 \times 10^{-20}$ J ∴ $L_v = 4.26 \times 10^4$ J mol^{-1}.
(b) $P = 2.225 \times 10^8 \exp[-5.13 \times 10^3/T]$ kPa
∴ 340 m per K

4 $\epsilon = 2.7 \times 10^{-20}$ J.

5 Cooking rate $\propto \exp[-\epsilon/kT]$ ∴ time $\propto \exp[\epsilon/kT]$
∴ $t = 2.47 \times 10^{-5}\exp[5072/T]$ minutes
∴ 3 minutes at 160°C.

Working gases (page 550)

1 (a) $\simeq 30$ m^3, 41 mol m^{-3} ∴ 1200 mol.
(b) Constant pressure $C_p = 29$ J mol^{-1} K^{-1}
∴ $P \simeq 400$ W.
(c) Assume both settle to 10°C ∴ need 200 W.
(d) Each section would need careful insulation
from the other sections, but heat flow always
involves some increase of entropy, so a perfect
system is impossible.

2 (a) 290 K, 500 kPa.
(b) 952 kPa, 552 K.
(c) See figure 31.15.

3 (a) 40 J. (b) $PV = $ constant ∴ isothermal.
(c) Losing heat and possibly liquefying.
(d) Being heated at constant volume.

4 (a) 4850 kPa, 909 K.
(b) Temperature is well above ignition
temperature.
(c) 122 kPa, 366 K.
(d) 0.67.
(e) 0.56.

5 (a) 9.4. (b) 177 W. (c) 1.6 kW. (d) Good value for
money, but the cold end of the system must be
in an adequate flow so that it doesn't get colder
when heat is extracted from it.

6 If pump extracts heat from object at T to another
at $T + \Delta T$, maximum efficiency $= T/\Delta T \to 0$ as
$T \to 0$.

7 (a) 2.41×10^{-2} m^3, 1.25×10^{-2} m^3.
(b) 2.0 kJ. (c) 376 K. (d) 193 kPa.
(e) 1.61×10^{-2} m^3, 617 J. (f) 31%.

Disorder (page 554)

2 (a) $V = 2.45 \times 10^{-2}$ m^3, $\Delta V = 0.21 \times 10^{-2}$ m^3.
(b) $\Delta S = -0.74$ J K^{-1}. (c) -8.71 J K^{-1}.
(d) 300.7 J K^{-1}. (e) $+88.1$ J K^{-1}. (f) 221.6 J K^{-1}.

Radiation (page 562)

1 (a) Increase radiation rate. (b) $A \rightarrow A/4$. (c) Yes.
2 (a) 9.46 kW m^{-2}. (b) 452 K.
3 (a) 1, 0. (b) 1.44 kW. (c) 0.63 kW.
(d) 3.68×10^{-3} K s^{-1}. (e) $\simeq 4$ hours.
4 (a) 2.86×10^{-5} m^2. (b) $\lambda = 935$ nm, infra-red.
(c) $m = 1.2 \times 10^{-5}$ kg $\therefore$ 1.7×10^{-3} J K^{-1}; P drops
rapidly with temperature, so best to work out
cooling time in stages.

P/W	T/K	Δt/ms
52	3000	
25	2500	16
10	2000	34
3.3	1500	85
	1000	260

$\therefore$ cooling time $\simeq 0.5$ s

5 (a) 1.05 kW m^{-2}. (b) 5 m^2. (c) 125 W m^{-2}, 12%.
(d) $\simeq 600$ W.
6 (a) $\simeq 0.1\%$. (b) 0.25 MW. (c) 4×10^7 m^2 (6.3 km
square).
(d) Making the cells, keeping them clean.

7 (a) Temperature rises until the rate of emission
equals the rate of absorption from the light bulb
via the mirrors.
(b) No change; increased emission balanced out
by increased absorption if ϵ is independent of λ.
(c) Ice is lower than room temperature so it is a
net absorber of heat radiation . . .
8 (a) 250 W. (b) At right angles to midday sun.
(c) Absorb heat radiation, discourage re-
radiation.
(d) Bathful $\simeq 0.5$ m^3 $\therefore$ 10 m^2 (1 kW output).

Conduction (page 568)

1 (a) 2.96×10^{-3} K W^{-1}, 8.33×10^{-3} K W^{-1}.
(b) 1.33 kW. (c) 9°C.
2 (a) 1.14×10^{-3} K W^{-1}, 13.2 kW.
(b) 34.7×10^{-3} K W^{-1}.
(c) 418 W. (d) 0.5 °C, 12.75 °C.
(e) Insulating layer on the outside gets swept
away, reducing the thermal resistance.
3 (a) $A = 7.85$ m^2, $R_T = 0.159$ K W^{-1}, $P = 409$ W.
(b) $m = 1.57 \times 10^3$ kg $\therefore$ $t = 1.61 \times 10^5$ s
(45 hours).
(c) Temperature drops four times faster than
before.
(d) The mouse.
5 (b) Resistivity increases with temperature so
conductivity should decrease.
6 6 W m^{-1} K^{-1}.

I N D E X

FUNDAMENTAL CONSTANTS

permittivity of free space	$\epsilon_0 = 8.85 \times 10^{-12}\,\text{F m}^{-1}$
permeability of free space	$\mu_0 = 4\pi \times 10^{-7}\,\text{T m A}^{-1}$
gravitational constant	$G = 6.67 \times 10^{-11}\,\text{N m}^2\,\text{kg}^{-2}$
speed of light in free space	$c = 3.00 \times 10^{8}\,\text{m s}^{-1}$
Planck's constant	$h = 6.63 \times 10^{-34}\,\text{J s}$
Boltzmann's constant	$k = 1.38 \times 10^{-23}\,\text{J K}^{-1}$
Avogadro's constant	$L = 6.02 \times 10^{23}\,\text{mol}^{-1}$
Stefan's constant	$\sigma = 5.67 \times 10^{-8}\,\text{W m}^{-2}\,\text{K}^{-4}$
universal gas constant	$R = 8.31\,\text{J K}^{-1}\,\text{mol}^{-1}$
electronic charge	$e = 1.60 \times 10^{-19}\,\text{C}$
electron rest mass	$m_e = 9.11 \times 10^{-31}\,\text{kg}$
proton rest mass	$m_p = 1.67 \times 10^{-27}\,\text{kg}$

$1\,\text{cm} = 0.01\,\text{m}$
$1\,\text{eV} = 1.60 \times 10^{-19}\,\text{J}$
$1\,m_u = 1.66 \times 10^{-27}\,\text{kg or } 934\,\text{MeV}$
$1\,\text{year} = 3.15 \times 10^{7}\,\text{s}$
$1\,\text{kWh} = 3.60\,\text{MJ}$
$0°\text{C} = 273\,\text{K}$

Prefix	Symbol	Factor
terra-	T-	$\times 10^{+12}$
giga-	G-	$\times 10^{+9}$
mega-	M-	$\times 10^{+6}$
kilo-	k-	$\times 10^{+3}$
milli-	m-	$\times 10^{-3}$
micro-	μ-	$\times 10^{-6}$
nano-	n-	$\times 10^{-9}$
pico-	p-	$\times 10^{-12}$